MARSHALL'S
PHYSIOLOGY OF REPRODUCTION

MARSHALL'S
PHYSIOLOGY OF
REPRODUCTION

EDITED BY

A. S. PARKES, C.B.E., M.A., D.Sc., Sc.D., F.R.S.
National Institute for Medical Research, London

VOLUME I: PART TWO

LONGMANS

LONGMANS, GREEN AND CO LTD
6 & 7 CLIFFORD STREET, LONDON WI
605–611 LONSDALE STREET, MELBOURNE CI
443 LOCKHART ROAD, HONG KONG
ACCRA, AUCKLAND, IBADAN
KINGSTON (JAMAICA), KUALA LUMPUR
LAHORE, NAIROBI, SALISBURY (RHODESIA)
LONGMANS SOUTHERN AFRICA (PTY) LTD
THIBAULT HOUSE, THIBAULT SQUARE, CAPE TOWN
LONGMANS, GREEN AND CO INC
119 WEST 40TH STREET, NEW YORK 18
LONGMANS, GREEN AND CO
20 CRANFIELD ROAD, TORONTO 16
ORIENT LONGMANS PRIVATE LTD
CALCUTTA, BOMBAY, MADRAS
DELHI, HYDERABAD, DACCA

First Edition, 1910

Second and Revised Edition, 1922

Third Edition, 1960

PRINTED IN GREAT BRITAIN BY
SPOTTISWOODE, BALLANTYNE AND CO LIMITED
LONDON AND COLCHESTER

EDITOR'S NOTE TO VOLUME I, PART TWO

In the Editor's note to Volume I, Part 1, it was stated that the Third Edition of the *Physiology of Reproduction* would be completed by the publication of Volume I, Part 2. This hope has not been realised, and the present volume deals only with events in the male, with the biology and biochemistry of spermatozoa, with fertilisation, and with the endocrinology of reproduction in birds and lower Vertebrates. It has proved necessary to devote a further volume to the endocrinology of mammalian reproduction; this will be published as Volume III within the next year and so complete the work.

It is sad to record that yet another contributor to the Third Edition has not lived to see his work published; Dr. Arthur Walton died suddenly in Cambridge on February 5th, 1959. Fortunately for Marshall's *Physiology of Reproduction*, he had helped to correct the page proofs of the chapters with which he was concerned, so that the book has had the full benefit of his collaboration. But his extensive knowledge, and ripe judgement, and above all his kindly helpfulness, will be sadly missed by all workers in the field.

The preliminary matter to Volume II and Volume I, Part 1, included the Editor's Preface to the Third Edition and a biographical note on Marshall. These have been omitted from the present volume but the latter has been replaced by material of a similar kind. The first draft of Chapter 13 was written by Marshall before his death, and in the course of the recent rewriting by Professor Amoroso the original manuscript of three of the figure legends came to light. This provides not only a good example of Marshall's highly characteristic handwriting but also an indication of his interest in bird behaviour. The manuscript is reproduced on page vi as a further memento of the creator and original author of this book.

A.S.P.

UNIVERSITY OF CAMBRIDGE.

Telephone 2485—2 lines

SCHOOL OF AGRICULTURE,
CAMBRIDGE.

....19

Figures for Chap XIII "P.J.R".

(*Diomedia exulans*).

I. Wandering Albatross. Male faces camera
and spreads wings before female with back to
camera and upraised wings till (I am
sending for this photograph as well as for the
following two. Dr Harrison Matthews by
whom they were taken in the island of
South Georgia.)

√2. Black-browed Albatross (*Diomedia
melanophrys*). Sexes indistinguishable. bird
on the nest is bowing head, the other
begging attention to it.

3. Sooty Albatross (*Phoebetria palpebrata*)
Male with uplifted head calling and displaying
to female who was on a ledge above just
out of the picture. (Elephant seal just on the
beach in background.)

vi

LIST OF CONTRIBUTORS

TO THE THIRD EDITION, VOLUME I, PART TWO

C. R. Austin, D.SC., *National Institute for Medical Research, London.*

E. C. Amoroso, M.D., F.R.S., *Royal Veterinary College, London.*

M. W. H. Bishop, M.A., PH.D., *Royal Veterinary College, London.*

J. M. Dodd, B.SC., PH.D., *Gatty Marine Laboratory, St. Andrews.*

A. J. Marshall, D.SC., *St. Bartholomew's Medical College, London.*

A. S. Parkes, C.B.E., SC.D., F.R.S., *National Institute for Medical Research, London.*

The late Dr. F. H. Marshall, C.B.E., F.R.S., *Cambridge.*

The late Dr. Arthur Walton, *Cambridge.*

ACKNOWLEDGMENTS

CONTRIBUTORS have again been much assisted by permission to reproduce illustrations from a large number of original papers, monographs and treatises. The source of such illustrations is indicated in each case and the contributors wish to offer their best thanks to the respective authors, editors and publishers.

Contributors wish to make personal acknowledgments as follows:

Chapter 7.   To Dr. J. R. G. Birfield, Mr. J. Smiles, Mr. M. R. Young and Dr. J. L. Hancock, who supplied original photographs.

Chapter 9.   To Lord Rothschild (Fig. 9.1), Dr. J. F. D. Frazer (Fig. 9.3); Dr. C. Polge (Fig. 9.5), Dr. R. G. Edwards (Fig. 9.20), Dr. Wade Fox (Fig. 9.25), Dr. Ruth Deanesly (Fig. 9.27), Dr. W. A. Wimsatt (Fig. 9.28), and Dr. C. R. Austin (Fig. 9.33), who provided histological material, or photographic negatives or prints for the illustrations listed; and to Dr. J. Edwards, Dr. A. T. Cowie, Mr. F. T. Day, Mrs. Clare Harvey, Dr. A. U. Smith, Dr. J. H. S. Blaxter, Dr. C. G. Butler, Dr. H. G. Vevers, Professor E. C. Amoroso, Mr. W. N. Harris, and Dr. C. Polge, who assisted in various ways with the preparation of the manuscript.

Chapter 11.   To Mr. P. J. Evennett (Fig. 11.1), Prof. J. Z. Young (Fig. 11.2), Dr. D. B. Carlisle (Fig. 11.5), Dr. O. H. Robertson (Figs. 11.13, 11.15, 11.23), Dr. A. J. Marshall and Dr. B. Lofts (Fig. 11.14), Mr. K. M. Ferguson (Fig. 11.18), Dr. T. Kerr (Fig. 11.19), Prof. J. H. Vivien (Figs. 11.20, 11.21, 11.22), Prof. Kitty Ponse (Figs. 11.25, 11.26, 11.27), Dr. J. C. van de Kamer (Fig. 11.31), Dr. C. Y. Chang and Prof. E. Witschi (Fig. 11. 35), Dr. C. Y. Chang (Figs. 11.37, 11.38, 11.40), Dr. A. P. Blair (Fig. 11.39), Prof. R. R. Humphrey (Fig. 11.41), Prof. L. Gallien (Fig. 11.42), Prof. E. Witschi (Fig. 11.43), Dr. A. Wright (Figs. 11.45, 11.46), Prof. T. R. Forbes (Figs. 11.48, 11.49, 11.51, 11.52, 11.53), and Prof. L. T. Evans (Fig. 11.50), who provided histological material or photographic prints for the illustrations listed.

Chapter 12.   To Dr. A. W. Greenwood (Figs. 12.3, 12.6, 12.10, 12.45), Dr. E. Wolff (Fig. 12.27), and Dr. S. J. Folley and Mr. G. K. Benson (Fig. 12.47), who provided histological material or photographic prints for the illustrations listed.

Chapter 13. To Dr. L. Harrison Matthews (Figs. *13*.4, *13*.5, *13*.6) and Mr. L. Taylor Page (Figs. *13*.1, *13*.2), for prints of original photographs, and to Prof. G. W. Harris for reading the manuscript.

The Editor offers his best thanks to Dr. T. Mann, F.R.S., who read the page proofs of Chapter 8, and to Miss S. Carswell, B.Sc., and Miss M. P. G. Moylan for most valuable assistance. The indexes were prepared, and much checking done, by Mr. W. J. Bishop.

CONTENTS

CHAPTER 7

BY MARCUS W. H. BISHOP AND ARTHUR WALTON

CONTENTS

CONTENTS

CHAPTER 8

BY ARTHUR WALTON

CHAPTER 9

BY A. S. PARKES

CONTENTS

XV

CHAPTER 9A

BY MARCUS W. H. BISHOP AND ARTHUR WALTON

CONTENTS
CHAPTER 10
BY C. R. AUSTIN AND ARTHUR WALTON

CHAPTER 11

BY J. M. DODD

CHAPTER 12

BY A. S. PARKES AND A. J. MARSHALL

CHAPTER 13

BY E. C. AMOROSO AND F. H. A. MARSHALL

EXTERNAL FACTORS IN SEXUAL PERIODICITY . 707

CHAPTER 7

SPERMATOGENESIS AND THE STRUCTURE OF MAMMALIAN SPERMATOZOA

By Marcus W. H. Bishop and Arthur Walton

I. Introduction

Spermatozoa, the reproductive cells of the male, were first observed as far back as 1677 when Johan Ham, a medical student at Leiden, brought them to the notice of the distinguished Dutch microscopist Antony van Leeuwenhoek.

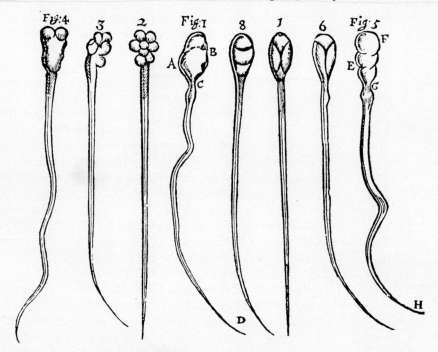

Fig. 7.1—The first published drawings of spermatozoa. (1–4) rabbit spermatozoa; (5–8) dog spermatozoa. (Leeuwenhoek, 1679.)

Leeuwenhoek then examined the spermatozoa of various animals and communicated his observations and drawings to the Royal Society (Leeuwenhoek, 1679). This discovery led to a controversy that lasted for almost 200 years. The " animalculists ", Leeuwenhoek among them, advanced the theory of " *generation ex animalculi* " and believed that spermatozoa were the seeds from which future embryos developed. The " ovists ", on the other hand, tenaciously held to the

earlier doctrine of "*generation ex ovo*" and either denied the existence of spermatozoa altogether or dismissed them as parasites, adventitious infusoria, inert
corpuscles, the results of putrefaction or chemical action, or specialised bodies the
function of which was merely to stir the semen or to arouse sexual desire in the
male.

Although a convinced ovist, Spallanzani deserves the greatest credit for his
early experimental approach to the subject, since he demonstrated quite conclu-

Fig. 7.2 — Human
spermatozoon as
conceived by Hart-
soeker (1694),
showing an ho-
munculus within
the head. The
spermatozoon tail
was thought to
contain the umbili-
cal cord.

sively, by means of artificial insemination, that full fertilising capacity resided in the semen of the male. He attributed
this capacity, however, not to the spermatozoa, which in some
experiments he thought he had excluded by filtration, but
to a chemical influence of the seminal fluid on the egg
(Spallanzani, 1780). Prévost and Dumas (1824) showed
that Spallanzani's deductions were faulty. In their view the
fertilising capacity of semen lay in the spermatozoa and they
brought evidence to show that these were not adventitious
organisms but a characteristic product of the sexually potent
male. Subsequently, Peltier (1835, 1838), Dujardin (1837)
and others proposed that spermatozoa were the product of
the testis and this paved the way for Kölliker's (1841) conclusive demonstration that spermatozoa arise by proliferation
and differentiation from the testis tissue. Penetration of
the spermatozoon into the egg was then described in greater
or less detail by Barry (1843), Nelson (1851), Newport (1851,
1853), Bischoff (1854), Meissner (1855) and others. The egg
(Gegenbauer, 1861) and the spermatozoon (Schweigger-
Seidel, 1865 ; La Valette St. George, 1865) became recognised as single cells, each with a nucleus and cytoplasm,
but the concept of the equivalence of these gametes in the
fertilisation process was not forthcoming until publication
of the works of Van Beneden (1875), O. Hertwig (1876) and
Fol (1879). Van Beneden's (1883) discovery that the conjugating nuclei from the spermatozoon and the egg each
contain half the number of chromosomes of the somatic
cells of the body, and that fertilisation results in the zygote
receiving an equal number from each parent, laid the basis
for the chromosome theory of inheritance. By 1890 the
true nature of the gametes and fertilisation was understood
in principle and also in some detail (*see* Boveri, 1891).

The microscopes available to Leeuwenhoek and other
early workers were primitive by modern standards, and in consequence the early
pictures of spermatozoa are rather crude, though often remarkably good in view
of the equipment used (Fig. 7.1). Sometimes observations were strongly
influenced by prevailing philosophical notions and some observers reported the
presence of alimentary tracts and other organs, and even of complete diminutive
embryos, in spermatozoa (Fig. 7.2). Towards the end of the 19th century the
development of the microscope progressed rapidly and increasingly accurate
descriptions of spermatozoon morphology were given by Donné (1845),

Schweigger-Seidel (1865), Leydig (1883), Brunn (1884), Jensen (1887), Ballowitz (1888) and Benda (1903) among others. This phase of research culminated in the remarkable studies of Retzius (1902, 1906, 1909 ; Fig. 7.3) which Hughes (1957) has described as " the apex of the possibilities of the light microscope."

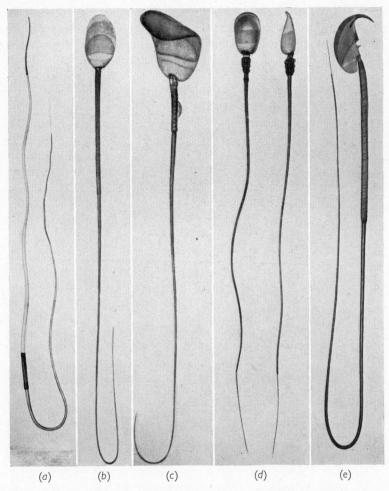

Fig. 7.3a, b, c, d, e—Drawings of spermatozoa from Retzius (1906, 1909). (a) Australian spiny ant-eater (*Tachyglossus aculeatus*). (b) European mole (*Talpa europaea*). (c) Red squirrel (*Sciurus vulgaris*). (d) Pilot whale (*Globicephalus malaena*)—plan and profile views. (e) House mouse (*Mus musculus*).

During the present century, knowledge of the nature of the spermatozoon has grown rapidly through development of new kinds of microscopy (polarising, ultra-violet, electron, phase-contrast, interference-contrast and fluorescence), of histochemistry and of physical and chemical analytical techniques. In consequence, so great a volume of literature has accumulated that a comprehensive review of all previous work is beyond the scope of a single chapter. Further, the wealth of accumulated literature inevitably contains many differences of opinion that are not always easy to resolve. Perhaps the greatest difficulty in the reviewer's path, however, arises from the complexity and ambiguity of the terminology that has been used by various workers. In the ensuing account, an attempt is made to simplify the nomenclature and to use each term in an unequivocal manner. It should be constantly borne in mind, however, that the terms adopted here are not necessarily used in the same sense by all other workers.

Accounts of the early history of the spermatozoon and its role in fertilisation are given in the works of F. R. Lillie (1919), Punnett (1928), Cole (1930), Needham (1931), Meyer (1939) and Nordenskiold (1929). Hughes (1955, 1957) has recently described the development of the microscopy of spermatozoa.

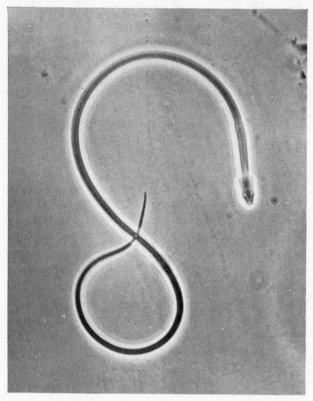

Fig. 7.4—Spermatozoon of the long-nosed bandicoot (*Perameles nasuta*) by phase-contrast microscopy. (C. R. Austin, original.)

II. The Structure of the Spermatozoon

The mammalian spermatozoon is a small highly condensed cell in which cell sap and nuclear sap are virtually absent. It consists of two major parts, the head and the tail (Figs. 7.3 and 7.4). The principal component of the head is the nucleus. This is covered anteriorly by a characteristic cap-like structure, the acrosome, and posteriorly by a cytoplasmic sheath, the post-nuclear cap (Fig. 7.6). The tail is a long flagellum that is differentiated into four regions, the neck, the mid-piece, the main-piece and the end-piece. A small bead of cytoplasm, the cytoplasmic droplet, is sometimes found attached to the mid-piece (Fig. 7.5).

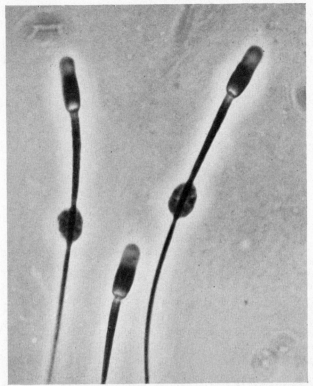

Fig. 7.5—Epididymal spermatozoa of the greater horse-shoe bat (*Rhinolophus ferrum-equinum*) with cytoplasmic droplets at the distal end of the mid-piece. (Phase-contrast, × 2,000.)

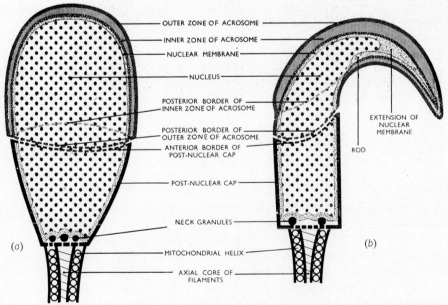

Fig. 7.6a, b—Diagrammatic representation of the probable structure of the heads of (a) bull and (b) golden hamster spermatozoa. (Modified from Bishop and Austin, 1957.)

The size of the mammalian spermatozoon varies somewhat between species and recorded lengths range from 41 to 250 μ (see Table I). There are no reliable estimates of its volume but consideration of the dimensions of the bull spermatozoon suggests that the volume is about 30 cu.μ. This is only about one twenty-thousandth of the volume of the bovine egg. The dry weight of the bull spermatozoon (dried at 105° C.) is about $16 \cdot 5 \times 10^{-12}$ g. (Bhargava, Bishop and Work,

TABLE I

SIZES OF SPERMATOZOA

Species	Approximate lenght (μ)				Source
	Head	Mid-piece	Main-piece	Total	
House mouse (*Mus musculus*)	8·3	21	95	125	Friend (1936)
Harvest mouse (*Micromys minutus*)	5·7	13	45	64	,, ,,
Long-tailed field mouse (*Apodemus sylvaticus*)	9·8	24	100	133	,, ,,
De Winton's field mouse (*Apodemus flavicollis*)	8·8	23	93	125	,, ,,
White rat (*Rattus norvegicus*)	11·7	(67)	110	189	,, ,,
Brown rat (*Rattus norvegicus*)	12·1	(67)	110	190	,, ,,
Black rat (*Rattus rattus*)	10·8	(65)	90	166	,, ,,
Musk rat (*Ondatra zibethica*)	5·4	16	48	68	,, ,,
Bank vole (*Evotomys glareolus*)	6·9	20	59	87	,, ,,
Short-tailed field mouse (*Microtus hirtus*)	7·6	30	80	117	,, ,,
Field vole (*Microtus agrestis*)	6·9	27	(70)	104	Austin (1957)
Cotton rat (*Sigmodon hispidus*)	7·0	19	60	87	Bishop (original)
Chinese hamster (*Cricetulus griseus*)	—	—	—	250	,, ,,
Rabbit (*Oryctolagus cuniculus*)	8·4	8	38	55	,, ,,
Sperm whale (*Physeter catodon*)	4·9	—	—	41	Asdell (1946)
Fox (*Vulpes fulva*)	8·0	—	—	60	,, ,,
Indian elephant (*Elephas maximus*)	8·3	—	—	50	,, ,,
Boar (*Sus scrofa*)	8·5	10	30	49	Hancock (1957)
Ram (*Ovis aries*)	8·2	14	40–45	—	Randall and Friedlaender (1950)
Man (*Homo sapiens*)	4·6	—	—	53	Lane-Roberts, *et al.* (1939)

Values in parenthesis have been obtained by difference.

1959) of which about half is contributed by the tail. The dry weight of the head of the ram spermatozoon, determined interferometrically, is about $7 \cdot 2 \times 10^{-12}$ g. (Davies, Wilkins, Chayen and LaCour, 1954). The specific gravity of the bull spermatozoon is said to range from $1 \cdot 240$ to $1 \cdot 334$ (Lindahl and Kihlström, 1952), but this may be an overestimate since the upper limit exceeds the specific gravity of dried protein (though not that of dried nucleic acid). The refractive index of the human spermatozoon suggests that about half the cell is dry matter (Barer, Ross and Thaczyk, 1953) : by contrast, water constitutes 80 to 90 per cent of most other mammalian cells.

The Nucleus

The nucleus is a more or less flattened structure composed of densely packed chromatin consisting of deoxyribonucleic acid (DNA) conjugated with basic nuclear protein of a histone- or protamine-like character (*see* Section III). In addition, there may be a small amount of non-basic protein. The chromatin appears to be slightly denser in the posterior end of the nucleus (Friend, 1936), but is otherwise homogeneously distributed. In man, however, the nucleus often contains one or more irregular " vacuoles " that are free of chromatin (Fig. 7.15).

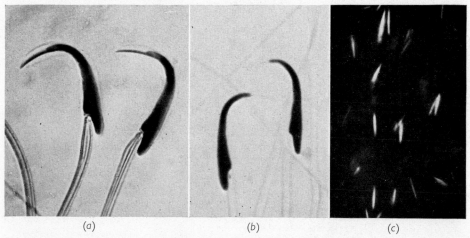

(a)   (b)   (c)

Fig. 7.7a, b, c—Micrographs illustrating the nature of the spermatozoon nucleus. (*a*) Heads of rat spermatozoa by ultraviolet microscopy, showing strong absorption in the nucleus ($\times$ 2,000). (Photographed by M. R. Young). (*b*) Heads of rat spermatozoa stained with Feulgen reagent, showing the characteristic reaction for deoxyribonucleic acid in the nucleus. (*c*) Heads of bull spermatozoa seen in profile by polarised light, showing strong birefringence in the nucleus. (Photographed by M. R. Young.)

Strong birefringence in the nucleus suggests that the nucleoprotein is arranged in a highly orientated, crystal-like manner (Schmidt, 1937 ; Randall and Friedlaender, 1950 ; Fig. 7.7c). Even electron microscopy of very thin sections (0·02 μ) has failed to reveal the presence of discrete chromosomes (*see* Figs. 7.11 and 7.12), and it is probable that these are packed as extended chromonemata. The nucleus is enclosed in a thick nuclear membrane that can be clearly seen by electron microscopy (*see* Fig. 7.11). It is remarkably elastic (Moench and Holt, 1929) and very difficult to disintegrate by physical means.

The nucleus stains intensely with basic nuclear dyes, such as haematoxylin ; gives characteristic reactions for DNA with Feulgen reagent (Melampy, Cavazos and Porter, 1952 ; Daoust and Clermont, 1955 ; Fig. 7.7b), methyl green (Leuchtenberger and Schrader, 1950), and acridine orange (Bishop and Smiles, 1957a, 1958 ; Bishop and Austin, 1957) ; is Gram-positive (Melampy *et al.*, 1952) ; and strongly absorbs ultra-violet radiation (White, Leslie and Davidson, 1953 ; Bishop and Austin, 1957 ; Figs. 7.7a and 7.20). It is resistant to the action of deoxyribonuclease (Daoust and Clermont, 1955), but readily soluble in strong sodium hydroxide (Austin and Bishop, 1958b ; Fig. 7.9).

The Acrosome

The term acrosome appears to have been introduced by Lenhossek (1898) to describe two unrelated structures, the inner zone of the pro-acrosome in the spermatid (*see* p. 56) and the perforatorium in the mature spermatozoon (*see* p. 10).

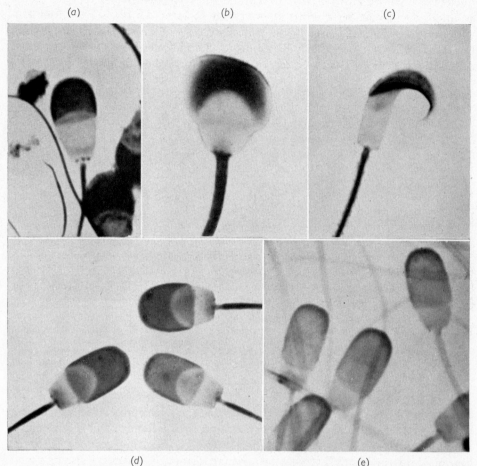

(a)   *(b)*   *(c)*

(d)   *(e)*

Fig. 7.8 a, b, c, d, e—Heads of spermatozoa stained to demonstrate the acrosome. (*a*) Bull, stained with Giemsa (× 2,400) (from Hancock, 1952). (*b*) Guinea-pig, stained with Giemsa (× 2,000).   (*c*) Golden hamster, stained with Giemsa (× 2,900) (from Bishop and Austin, 1957). (*d*) Boar, stained with Giemsa (× 2,800) (from Hancock, 1957).   (*e*) Boar, stained with PAS (× 2,800) (J. L. Hancock, original).

It is here used in the sense adopted by Bowen (1924), Wilson (1925), Baker (1931), Gresson (1948, 1951), Hancock (1952, 1957), Melampy, Cavazos and Porter (1952) and Bishop and Austin (1957) among others, and is believed to be synonymous with acrosomic system (Leblond and Clermont, 1952), kopfkappe (Ballowitz, 1891a, b ; Retzius, 1906, 1909), perforatorium (Waldeyer, 1906 ; Duesberg, 1908b), galea capitis (Blom, 1945, 1950 ; Bretschneider, 1949 ; Rollinson, 1951), capuchon céphalique (Popa and Marza, 1931), spermiocalyptrotheca (Papanicolau and

Stockard, 1918), cytoplasmic cap (Rao and Berry, 1949), head cap (Friend, 1936), and spermatic veil (Williams and Savage, 1925).

The acrosome arises from a secretion product of the Golgi apparatus (*see* p. 56) and in the mature spermatozoon varies greatly in size and shape between species. It is relatively unstable and readily shows degenerative changes on the death of the cell (Hancock, 1952 ; Austin and Bishop, 1958b ; Fig. 7.25). These changes lead to complete removal of the acrosome from the head, and have often mislead investigators in their interpretation of normal structure.

Some workers have described the acrosome as a single structure : others have considered it to consist of two distinct parts, though the evidence given in support of this has not always been valid (*see* Hancock, 1952). Recent work suggests that, in a sense, both points of view are correct. Thus, whereas Hancock (1957a), Hancock and Trevan (1957) and Bishop and Austin (1957) have described the acrosome as consisting of an outer cap overlying an inner one, Burgos and Fawcett (1955) and Fawcett and Burgos (1956b) have produced impressive evidence showing that the inner cap probably lies *within* rather than *beneath* the outer cap. It seems therefore that the acrosome is a unit composed of inner and outer components, referred to as the inner and outer zones (Austin and Bishop, 1958b ; Fig. 7.6). The inner zone appears to be thicker than the outer, especially at the leading edge of the head. The two zones have similar staining properties.

The acrosome reacts characteristically with Giemsa's stain at pH 7·0 (Hancock, 1952), often displaying a segment of lighter colour, the equatorial segment, posteriorly (Fig. 7.8). This segment, which can also often be demonstrated by other techniques, is considered to represent the region in which the outer zone of the acrosome overlaps the inner one (Hancock, 1957 ; Hancock and Trevan, 1957 ; Bishop and Austin, 1957 ; Fig. 7.6). The nature of the Giemsa-reactive material is unknown : it evidently is not very labile.

During spermateliosis (*see* p. 51) the developing acrosome gives a strong positive reaction with the periodic acid-Schiff (PAS) technique of McManus (1946) and Hotchkiss (1948), but the intensity of this reaction decreases as spermatozoa approach their mature form, until in some species it is barely detectable or apparently absent (Leblond and Clermont, 1952 ; Clermont and Leblond, 1955). Since, however, the PAS-reactive material of the acrosome is highly labile (Leblond and Clermont, 1952) and since the intensity of reaction depends upon the fixatives used and upon other conditions of preparation (Clermont and Leblond, 1955 ; Hancock, 1957a), little importance can be attached to reports of negative findings. The negative results of Friedlaender and Fraser (1952) with ram spermatozoa, for example, can be explained by the fact that they washed their material in distilled water before staining. A distinct positive PAS reaction has been observed in the acrosome of ejaculated spermatozoa of the bull (Leuchtenberger and Schrader, 1950 ; Schrader and Leuchtenberger, 1951 ; Melampy, Cavazos and Porter, 1952 ; Hancock, 1952) and the boar (Hancock, 1957a ; Fig. 7.8e), and in epididymal spermatozoa of the Virginian deer (Wislocki, 1949) and the guinea-pig (Clermont, Glegg and Leblond, 1955). It seems probable, therefore, that PAS-reactive material is a typical component of the mammalian acrosome (as also in the spermatozoa of some insects—Schrader and Leuchtenberger, 1951) although the amount of this material present in the mature spermatozoon does appear to vary greatly between species.

B*

According to Hotchkiss (1948) the PAS test is specific for carbohydrates containing 1, 2-glycol and α-amino alcohol groups, and the reactive material of the acrosome is therefore presumed to be polysaccharide, possibly in the form of mucopolysaccharide or mucoprotein.   It is not starch, glycogen or hyaluronic acid : it may well be hyaluronidase, a labile PAS-reactive enzyme that is known to be present in mammalian spermatozoa (Leuchtenberger and Schrader, 1950).   An attempt to characterise this material further has been made by Clermont, Glegg and Leblond, (1955).   These workers extracted guinea-pig spermatozoa with 0·1 N sodium hydroxide, a procedure shown to remove PAS-reactive material from the acrosomes, and identified the monosaccharides galactose, mannose, and fucose, together with a considerable amount of hexosamine, in their hydrolysed " acrosome extract."

When fresh living spermatozoa of a number of mammalian species are treated with acridine orange and subjected to ultra-violet radiation, the acrosome fluoresces bright red and the nucleus bright apple-green (Bishop and Smiles, 1957a ; 1958 ; Bishop and Austin, 1957).   Where the acrosome overlaps the nucleus, the resultant additive colour is yellow or yellow-green depending on the extent to which the two primary colours are mixed.   This method of differentiating the acrosome has proved successful with spermatozoa of the bull, the rabbit, the greater horse-shoe bat, the hedgehog and eight species of rodent, but not with spermatozoa of man. The material responsible for the red fluorescence is evidently highly labile, for it is readily lost when spermatozoa are extensively washed, dried, or stored *in vitro* at room temperature.   Its distribution and lability suggest that it may well be the same as the PAS-reactive material of the acrosome.   Under some conditions, red fluorescence with acridine orange usually indicates the presence of ribonucleic acid (RNA) (Armstrong, 1956 ; Bertalanffy and Bickis, 1956), but it is very unlikely that the acrosome contains appreciable amounts of RNA for it does not stain with pyronine (Daoust and Clermont, 1955) and in the mature cell shows negligible absorption of ultra-violet radiation (*see* Fig. 7.20).   Furthermore, chemical analysis of mature spermatozoa shows that they are remarkable for their lack of RNA (*see* p. 21).

The Perforatorium

The term perforatorium, though often used synonymously with acrosome, is here employed, in the sense adopted by Odor and Blandau, by Leblond and co-workers, and by Austin and Bishop, to describe a distinctive structure at the apex of the head of rat and golden hamster spermatozoa (Blandau, 1951 ; Odor and Blandau, 1951 ; Blandau and Odor, 1952 ; Leblond and Clermont, 1952a, b ; Clermont, Einberg, Leblond and Wagner, 1955 ; Austin and Bishop, 1958b, c). It lies between the acrosome and the nucleus and appears to arise as a modification of the nuclear membrane.   It is considered to be distinct from the acrosome both in origin and composition.   A thickened refractile region of the perforatorium, referred to as the rod by Friend (1936) and by Austin and Sapsford (1951), has long been known in the rat (Jensen, 1887 ; Niessing, 1897 ; Lenhossek, 1898 ; Duesberg, 1908b ; Retzius, 1909) and has also been portrayed in mice of the genera *Mus* and *Apodemus* (Retzius, 1909 ; Friend, 1936) and in the golden hamster, Chinese hamster and cotton rat (Bishop and Austin, 1957 ; Austin and Bishop, 1958b ; Fig. 7.9).

The nature of the perforatorium and its distinction from the acrosome have been subjects of much confusion, but there now seems little doubt that the interpretation of Clermont, Einberg, Leblond and Wagner (1955) is the logical one. According to these workers, the perforatorium in the rat spermatozoon is a rigid refringent structure with three prongs, one dorsal and two latero-ventral, which are connected by a membrane. The perforatorium fits tightly over the apex of the nucleus in such a way that the prongs are continued over the nuclear surface. Posteriorly, the prongs become progressively less pronounced and are eventually indistinguishable from the nuclear membrane. Anteriorly, the perforatorium extends well beyond the apex of the nucleus and is here triangular in cross-section. Histochemically the perforatorium appears to be identical with the nuclear membrane, but quite different from the acrosome. It shows moderate acidophilia and stains

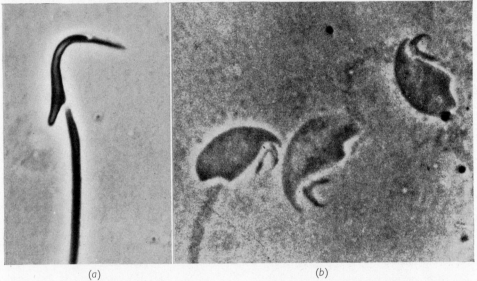

(a)   (b)

Fig. 7.9a, b—Heads of (a) rat and (b) mouse spermatozoa after partial digestion in sodium hydroxide solution, showing the part of the perforatorium referred to as the rod.

strongly with iron haematoxylin. It does not stain with PAS or Feulgen reagents, and unlike the acrosome is remarkably resistant to alkaline hydrolysis.

Blandau (1951) described the perforatorium of the rat spermatozoon as a pronged structure of high optical density that fits over, and extends well beyond, the anterior end of the nucleus. Austin and Sapsford (1952) observed that the "rod" was resistant to alkaline hydrolysis and their photographs also show the perforatorium as a pronged structure fitting over the apex of the nucleus. They did not clearly distinguish the perforatorium from the acrosome and were misled by a clear region at the anterior end of the rat spermatozoon which they considered to be a vesicle. The work of Clermont et al (1955) shows that this clear region is in fact part of the perforatorium and is not in the form of a vesicle.

Definite evidence for the existence of a perforatorium has so far been obtained only in the spermatozoa of certain Murine and Cricetine rodents, but Austin and Bishop (1958a) believe that the homologous structure is probably present in less conspicuous form, as a region of modified nuclear membrane beneath the acrosome, in all mammalian spermatozoa. Support for this conclusion is provided by the appearance of the nuclear membrane of the boar spermatozoon shown in Fig. 7.11a and by studies on the differentiation of spermatozoa of man and the cat (*see* p. 61).

The Post-nuclear Cap

In many species the post-nuclear cap can be readily impregnated with silver (Fig. 7.10) but its nature is obscure. Electron micrographs of sections of bull,

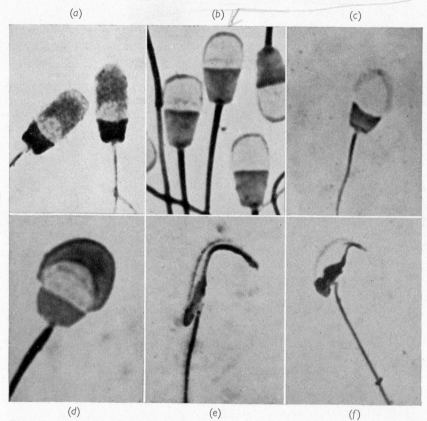

Fig. 7.10a, b, c, d, e, f—Heads of spermatozoa impregnated with silver to show the post-nuclear cap. (*a*) Boar (J. L. Hancock, original). (*b*) Bull. (*c*) Rabbit. (*d*) Guinea-pig (from Bishop and Austin, 1957). (*e*) Albino rat. (*f*) House mouse.

boar and ram spermatozoa show the post-nuclear cap as a distinct, probably double-layered, structure (Figs. 7.11 and 7.12) but in man it is less clear (Ånberg, 1957). It is much more resistant to distortion than the acrosome and seldom lifts from the nucleus. The common boundary of the acrosome with the post-nuclear cap is known as the nuclear ring. It can often be seen as a distinct girdle across the middle of the head (Fig. 7.23a).

The Tail Filaments

An axial core of discrete filaments runs from the neck throughout the length of the tail. These filaments were known to Ballowitz (1888) and other early workers, but their number and disposition have only recently been revealed by electron microscopy (Challice, 1952, 1953 ; Bradfield, 1953, 1955, 1956). These studies show that the filaments are arranged in the form of a central pair surrounded by two concentric rings of nine filaments each (Fig. 7.17). The outer ring has a filament on the same radius as that occupied by each filament of the inner ring.

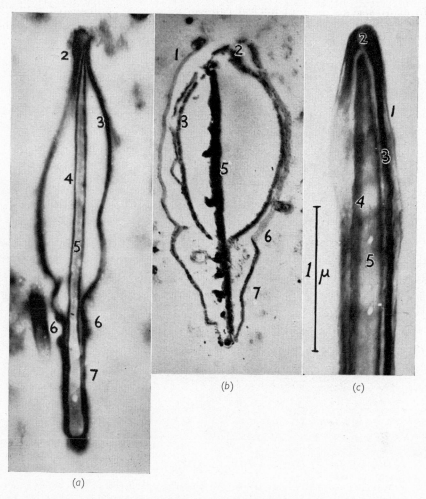

Fig. 7.11a, b, c—Electron micrographs of longitudinal sections of spermatozoon heads, showing (1) the cell membrane; (2) and (3) the acrosome; (4) the nuclear membrane; (5) the nucleus; (6) the nuclear ring; (7) the post-nuclear cap (J. R. G. Bradfield, original). (a) Boar (× 13,000). (b) Bull. (c) Ram (× 38,000).

The filaments all appear to pass straight along the tail and are not twisted about its axis. They are bound together by an inter-filament matrix of unknown nature. The central pair of filaments differ in their solubility characteristics from the remaining filaments and are evidently of different chemical composition.

The arrangement of the filaments is most clearly shown in the mid-piece region of the tail (Fig. 7.13a and b). Here the two central filaments and the nine filaments of the inner ring are each about 180 Å in diameter. Those of the outer ring are thicker.   Three of these (an adjacent pair on one side of the ring and one on the diametrically opposite side) are each about 1,000 Å thick and the remaining six are each about 700 Å thick ; they appear to be built up of numerous subfibrils with a diameter of about 75 Å.   The line joining the central pair of filaments is at right angles to the diameter on which the unpaired thick filament of the outer ring lies (Fig. 7.17a ; Bradfield, 1955).   There is also evidence that each of the three thickest filaments may arise from lateral fusion of a tangential pair of filaments (Challice, 1953).

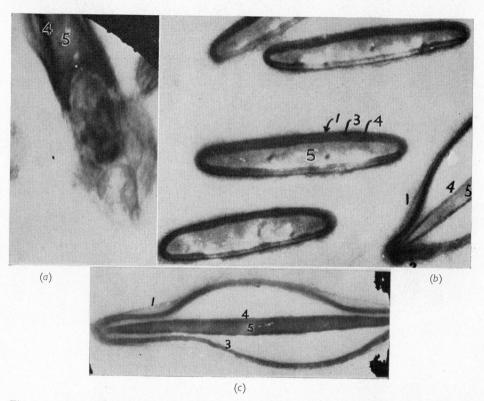

Fig. 7.12a, b, c—Electron micrographs of sections of spermatozoon heads, showing (1) the cell membrane, (3) the post-nuclear cap in (b) and the acrosome in (c), (4) the nuclear membrane and (5) the nucleus.
(a) Longitudinal section through the base of the head and part of the neck of a ram spermatozoon (J. R. G. Bradfield, original).   (b) Three transverse sections through heads of boar spermatozoa in the region of the post-nuclear cap (J. R. G. Bradfield, original).   (c) Oblique section through the head of a boar spermatozoon in the region of the acrosome (from Bradfield, 1956).

The number and arrangement of the filaments is maintained in the main-piece, but here the filaments of the outer ring become reduced in thickness to about the same diameter as that of the remaining filaments and each filament of the outer ring becomes closely applied to its radial partner of the inner ring.   This leads to the appearance of a single ring of nine filaments, each member of which is two filaments on a common radius (Bradfield, 1955).
Ånberg (1957) believes that each filament of the inner ring consists of a tangential doublet and that there are interconnections between each of these nine

doublets and the central pair of filaments. He also states that the filaments of the outer ring are not all of the same length and do not extend throughout the entire length of the tail. Further, the characteristic arrangement of the filaments is lost in the end-piece. Rothschild (1958) agrees with Ånberg that the inner ring consists of nine pairs of filaments. Nelson (1958) has obtained histochemical evidence that adenosinetriphosphatase is localised along the nine filaments of the outer ring.

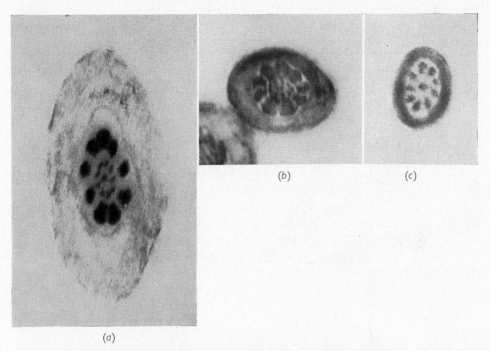

(b)   (c)

(a)

Fig. 7.13a, b, c—Electron micrographs of transverse sections of spermatozoon tails. (a) Mid-piece of ram spermatozoon (from Bradfield, 1955). (b) Mid-piece of boar spermatozoon (J. R. G. Bradfield, original). (c) Main-piece of boar spermatozoon (J. R. G. Bradfield, original).

The Neck

The neck is the short (about 1 μ) anterior end of the tail that connects the tail with the head. Its structure is complex and poorly understood. The point of its insertion on the head is often slightly abaxial.

The neck originates in a basal body that is partly embedded in the base of the head (Fig. 7.12a). It is a composite structure that is presumably the homologue of the basal apparatus or blepharoblast of other flagella and cilia. By some techniques it appears to contain three "granules" (Fig. 7.8a), but by others only two are visible (Fig. 7.16a) (see also Retzius, 1909; Friend, 1936). This suggests that two of the granules differ in their properties from the third. The central granule is probably of centriolar origin and appears to correspond to the anterior distal centriole of Grigg and Hodge (1949) and Hodge (1949), the proximal centriole of Burgos and Fawcett (1955) and the head centriole of Ånberg (1957). Electron micrographs show this "centriole" as a cylindrical or spherical body with a thick

heterogeneous osmiophil wall (often seen as a ring of opaque dots) and a centre
of very low density (Burgos and Fawcett, 1955 ; Ånberg, 1957 ; Fig. 7.35). In
addition, Ånberg has described a circular disc, called the basal plate, that is situated
between the " centriole " and the nucleus and is orientated across the main axis

(a)   (b)

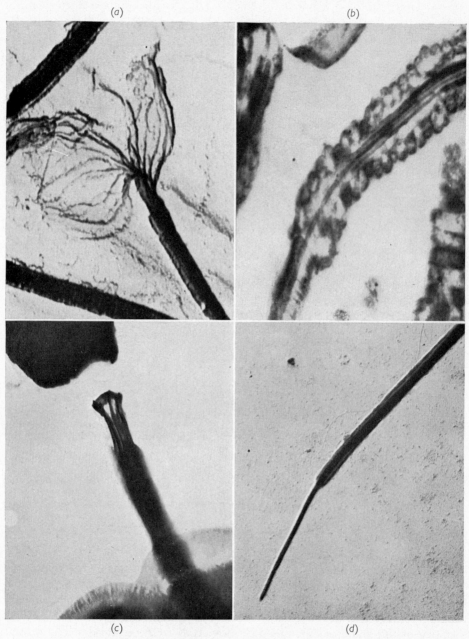

(c)   (d)

Fig. 7.14a, b, c, d—Electron micrographs of spermatozoon tails.   (a) A broken main-piece of a
bull spermatozoon with the axial filaments splayed (J. R. G. Bradfield, original).   (b) Longitudinal section of part of the mid-piece and main-piece of a ram spermatozoon, showing the
mitochondria and axial filaments (J. R. G. Bradfield, original).   (c) The neck of a boar
spermatozoon (from Hancock, 1957).   (d) The end-piece of a boar spermatozoon (from
Hancock, 1957).

of the tail. It consists of homogeneous material of high density and is bounded by a membrane. It may also be of centriolar origin and may correspond to the proximal centriole of Grigg and Hodge (1949) and Hodge (1949). In spermatozoa of the golden hamster, two neck granules can be displaced from the base of the

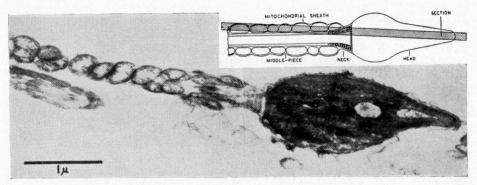

Fig. 7.15—Electron micrograph of a longitudinal section through the head, neck and mid-piece of a human spermatozoon (× 21,000). The diagram shows the approximate plane of section (from Rothschild, 1958).

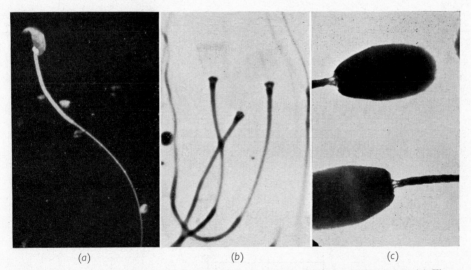

(a)   (b)   (c)

Fig. 7.16a, b, c—Micrographs of spermatozoa illustrating the structure of the neck. (a) Fluorescence micrograph of a mouse spermatozoon treated with rhodamin 6 G. Two brightly fluorescent granules can be seen in the base of the head (from Bishop and Austin, 1957). (b) Bull spermatozoa impregnated with silver. The spermatozoon heads and the mitochondria of the mid-piece are unstained. (c) Electron micrograph of ram spermatozoa showing the appearance of three bundles of fibres in the neck (J. R. G. Bradfield, original).

head by compression (Bishop, unpublished observation): these may correspond to the accessory bodies described by Gatenby and Beams (1935) and Gresson and Zlotnik (1948) (*see* p. 63).

In the posterior part of the neck, the tail filaments exhibit a series of granular thickenings which impart a segmented or banded appearance to the neck (Hodge, 1949; Schultz-Larsen and Hammen, 1956; Ånberg, 1957; Fig. 7.15).

Immediately distal to their insertion on the basal body, the filaments appear to be gathered into three bundles (Randall and Friedlaender, 1950 ; Hancock, 1957 ; Figs. 7.14c and 7.16c).

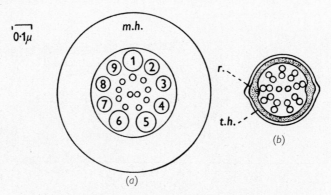

Fig. 7.17a, b—Diagrammatic representation of transverse sections of (a) the mid-piece, and (b) the main-piece. In (a) the filaments of the outer ring are numbered. (m.h. = mitochondrial helix. t.h. = tail helix. r. = rib.) (From Bradfield, 1955.)

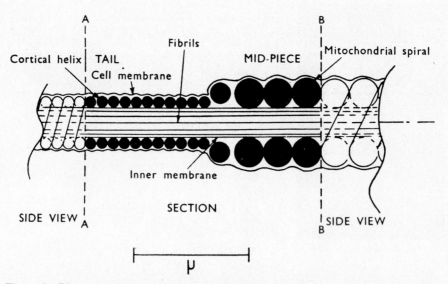

Fig. 7.18—Diagrammatic representation of a longitudinal section through part of the mid-piece and main-piece. (From Challice, 1952.)

The Mid-piece

The mid-piece is the anterior thickened region of the tail that extends from the neck to the posterior distal centriole or Jensen's ring. Here the tail filaments are surrounded by a double helix of mitochondria, sometimes called the spireme, each strand of which is about 0·2 µ thick (Figs. 7.17a and 7.18 ; Challice, 1952 ; Bradfield, 1955). In longitudinal sections of the mid-piece, the mitochondria appear as a series of alveoli of irregular size and shape, each with an osmiophil outer covering and a central space of low density (Fig. 7.14b). Ånberg (1957) believes that the mitochondria of human spermatozoa do not actually coalesce into continuous, helically wound strands, but are merely elongated and arranged in a helical fashion.   The mitochondria of the mid-piece evidently do not contain the elaborate double-membrane structure that is generally characteristic of these organellae in other cells (Bradfield, 1955 ; Yasuzumi, 1956 ; Ånberg, 1957). The mid-piece is sudanophil and is selectively stained by Baker's (1946) acid haematin stain for phospholipids (Wislocki, 1950).   Zittle and O'Dell (1941b) state that the dry weight of the mid-piece of the bull spermatozoon is about 16 per cent of the dry weight of the cell.

The Main-piece

The main-piece is the longest part of the tail.   In this region, mitochondria are absent and the axial filaments are bounded by a tough protein sheath which takes the form of an irregular helix with strands about 250 Å thick.   The strands are thickened at opposite points on the diameter defined by the central pair of filaments (Fig. 7.17b)   These thickenings together form small ribs or fins down either side of the tail (Bradfield, 1955), giving the tail a somewhat flattened cross-section which can sometimes be detected with the light microscope (Dott, 1953). The helix is composed of extremely resistant material with rather curious solubility properties.   It is little affected by normal acetic acid or normal hydrochloric acid, but can be completely dissolved with $N/20$ sodium hydroxide.   It can be digested with trypsin and pepsin (Bradfield, 1955).

The dry weight of the main-piece of the bull spermatozoon is said to be about 33 per cent of the total dry weight of the cell (Zittle and O'Dell, 1941b).

The End-piece

The tail ends in a short (2–10 μ) distal end-piece in which the tail filaments are bounded by a membrane, but not by the helical protein sheath that characterises the main-piece (Fig. 7.14d).

The Cytoplasmic Droplet

The cytoplasmic droplet is a feature of spermatozoa from the epididymis that was known to many early investigators, such as Retzius (1909).   It may also be found on a varying proportion of ejaculated spermatozoa, but usually the droplet becomes detached at the time of ejaculation and may often be found floating freely in the semen.   After gentle centrifugation the droplets tend to collect at the top of the seminal plasma.   In most animals, the droplet has a typical size and shape but in man it is more variable.

Most authors regard the cytoplasmic droplet as a remnant of spermatid cyto-plasm and this suggests that it may contain small amounts of important cytoplasmic constituents, such as Golgi material and RNA.   Gatenby and Woodger (1921) claim to have identified Golgi material within it.   It is PAS-reactive (Hancock, 1952), contains argentophil granules (Gresson and Zlotnik, 1945) and, in man, sometimes contains granules that fluoresce red after treatment with acridine orange (Bishop and Smiles, 1958). Gatenby and Collery (1943) and Collery (1944) claim that two beads are present on guinea-pig and dog spermatozoa, but the significance of this observation is not clear.

Other names for the cytoplasmic droplet include the protoplasmic bead (Gresson, 1950), the kinoplastic droplet (Merton, 1939), the equilibrateur (Popa and Marza, 1931) and the acidophile body (Williams and Savage, 1925).

The Surface Membrane

The entire spermatozoon appears to be covered by a continuous membrane derived from the cell membrane of the spermatid (Figs. 7.11 and 7.12). The agglutinating properties of spermatozoa, however, suggest that the surface membrane of the spermatozoon head differs in its composition from that of the tail. From what is known of cell surfaces in general it is probable that the spermatozoon membrane is composed of a lipid-protein complex. Feulgen and Rossenbeck (1924) obtained histochemical evidence for acetal phospholipids in spermatozoon membranes and Dallam and Thomas (1952) have shown that phospholipids can be easily removed from spermatozoa by washing in saline.

III. The Chemical Composition of the Spermatozoon

Since the pioneer observations of Miescher, Kossel and other nineteenth-century investigators, a large body of literature has accumulated on the chemical composition of spermatozoa (*see* Mann, 1954). Much of this work, however, is concerned with the spermatozoa of fish and invertebrates, and knowledge of the chemistry of mammalian spermatozoa remains far from complete.

Nucleic Acids and Nucleotides

Both histochemical and chemical methods show that the deoxyribonucleic acid (DNA) of the mammalian spermatozoon is entirely confined to the nucleus. The only findings contrary to this opinion, those of Zittle and O'Dell (1941b), probably resulted from contamination.

Measurements of the DNA content of mammalian spermatozoa are summarised in Table II. In this table, the methods of estimation have been classified into two groups : those designated 'cytological' involve optical measurements on individual cells and those designated ' chemical ' involve chemical analyses on large numbers of cells. The excellent agreement that can be obtained between these two types of measurement has been demonstrated by Leuchtenberger, Vendrely and Vendrely (1951). Table II shows that the nuclei of mammalian spermatozoa each contain about 3×10^{-12} g. of DNA. This is about 40 per cent of the dry weight of the nucleus, or 20 per cent of the dry weight of the cell, and approximately half the DNA content of the nuclei of normal mammalian somatic cells.

The purine (guanine and adenine) and pyrimidine (thymine, cytosine and methylcytosine) bases of the DNA of bull and ram spermatozoa have been examined by Wyatt (1951). He found that the molar ratios of adenine : guanine : cytosine : thymine : methylcytosine were $1 \cdot 15 : 0 \cdot 89 : 0 \cdot 83 : 1 \cdot 09 : 0 \cdot 052$ in the DNA of bull spermatozoa and $1 \cdot 15 : 0 \cdot 88 : 0 \cdot 84 : 1 \cdot 09 : 0 \cdot 039$ in the DNA of ram spermatozoa. It is notable that the ratios between the four major bases are almost identical in the two kinds of DNA and that the ratios of guanine : cytosine and adenine : thymine are very close to unity. The purine : pyrimidine ratio was slightly higher in the DNA of bull spermatozoa than in the DNA of calf thymus and ox spleen, and Wyatt suggests that this may have been caused by pre-treatment of the spermatozoa with papain. The proportion of methylcytosine

TABLE II

THE COMPOSITION OF SPERMATOZOON NUCLEI

Source	Animal	Method	$\times 10^{-12}$ (g.)			
			DNA	Protein	Arginine	Dry weight
Zittle and O'Dell (1941b)	Bull	Chemical	4·5	—	—	—
Vendrely and Vendrely (1948)	,,	,,	3·3	—	—	—
Mirsky and Ris (1949)	,,	,,	2·82	—	—	—
,, ,, (1951)	Man	,,	2·72	—	—	—
Davidson, Leslie and White (1951)	,,	,,	3·14	—	—	—
Walker and Yates (1952)	Bull	Cytological	3·9	—	—	—
,, ,, ,,	Ram	,,	2·9	—	—	—
,, ,, ,,	Rabbit	,,	3·1	—	—	—
Leuchtenberger, Leuchtenberger, Vendrely and Vendrely (1952)	Bull	,,	2·8	14·0	—	—
,, ,, ,,	,,	Chemical	3·3	—	—	—
Vendrely and Vendrely (1953)	,,	Cytological	3·2	—	2·16	—
White, Leslie and Davidson (1953)	Man	Chemical	3·14	—	—	—
Leuchtenberger, Murmanis, Murmanis, Ito and Weir (1956)	Bull	Cytological	3·04	4·06	2·07	7·1
Leuchtenberger, Leuchtenberger, Schrader and Weir (1956)	Man	,,	2·46	—	—	—
Bhargava, Bishop and Work (1959)	Bull	Chemical	3·3	—	—	—

was identical in the three kinds of bovine DNA and appeared to be a species specific characteristic. Wyatt also examined the phosphorus content of DNA from bull and ram spermatozoa and found that about 90 per cent of this could be accounted for by the purine and pyrimidine bases.

The ribonucleic acid (RNA) content of mammalian spermatozoa has been examined by several groups of workers. Vendrely and Vendrely (1948), who estimated RNA as RNA-phosphorus by the method of Schmidt and Thannhauser (1945) and Schneider (1945), concluded that bull spermatozoa each contain $0 \cdot 2 \times 10^{-12}$ g. RNA. It is now known, however, that the method used by Vendrely and Vendrely does not exclude acid-insoluble phosphorus compounds that originate from sources other than RNA (Mauritzen, Roy and Stedman, 1952 ; White, Leslie and Davidson, 1953) and in consequence estimates of RNA so obtained are too high. A similar criticism may well apply to the observations of Leuchtenberger, Leuchten-berger,Vendrely and Vendrely (1952), who state that the nuclei of bull spermatozoa each contain $0 \cdot 1 \times 10^{-12}$ g. RNA but do not divulge their method of analysis. (The protein content of spermatozoon nuclei given in this paper is also much higher than that determined by other workers.) Subsequent investigators, using other methods of analysis, have shown that the spermatozoon is remarkable for its virtual lack of RNA. Thus Dr. R. Markham (personal communication) was unable to obtain uridylic acid from ram spermatozoa ; White, Leslie and Davidson (1953) could find only traces of RNA (by electrophoresis of nucleotides, estimation of uracil and histochemical studies) in human spermatozoa ; Daoust and Clermont (1955) were evidently unable to detect RNA (histochemically) in fully formed rat spermatozoa ; Bhargava (1957) and Bhargava, Bishop and Work (1959) found only traces of RNA (estimated as ribose by the orsinol method) in the heads of bull spermatozoa and none in the tails, and Mauritzen, Roy and Stedman (1952) obtained only traces of RNA (estimated as furfural) from the spermatozoon heads of three species of fish (cod, herring and salmon). The small amounts of RNA reported in these studies, if significant at all, could easily arise from contamination with cells other than spermatozoa. On the other hand, the limitations of the methods used, combined with the small amounts of material usually available for analysis and the large amount of DNA present, do not permit the conclusion that RNA is entirely lacking from spermatozoa. Bhargava, Bishop and Work (1959), however, conclude that the RNA content of bull spermatozoa does not amount to more than 1 per cent of the DNA content, and may well be substantially less.

The free nucleotide content of bull spermatozoa is remarkably high (about $0 \cdot 12$ per cent of dry weight) and appears to be almost entirely located in the tail (Bhargava, Bishop and Work, 1959). A large part of this free nucleotide probably consists of adenosine phosphates and phosphopyridine nucleotides (*see* Chapter 9A).

Proteins and Amino Acids

Protein comprises over half the dry weight of the mammalian spermatozoon. This protein mainly consists of the basic nuclear protein that is conjugated with the DNA, alkali-soluble but acid-insoluble lipid-protein complexes and resistant keratin-like protein. In addition there are, of course, a large number of enzymes.

Sarkar, Luecke and Duncan (1947) examined the nitrogen and amino-acid composition of bull spermatozoa. They found that eleven amino acids composed 65 per cent of the dried ash-free and lipid-free residues, of which $25 \cdot 5$ per cent was arginine. The total nitrogen content was $17 \cdot 6$ per cent. In a similar study, Porter, Shankman and Melampy (1951) found that seventeen amino acids composed $69 \cdot 5$ per cent of the dry ash-free and lipid-free residues of which $15 \cdot 4$ per cent was arginine. The nitrogen content was $16 \cdot 7$ per cent.

The high arginine content of mammalian spermatozoa is, of course, attributable to the large amount of nuclear protein present. This protein appears to be inter-mediate in character between histone and protamine. It is usually described as protamine-like, but details of its composition are not available. Dallam and Thomas (1953) examined the nuclear proteins of bull, ram and dog spermatozoa. They considered them to be histone-like and to contain about 27 per cent of argi-nine. Leuchtenberger, Murmanis, Murmanis, Ito and Weir (1956), however, give the arginine content of the nuclear protein of bull spermatozoa as 50 per cent, and this high value is supported by the work of Sarkar et al. (1947) and of Vendrely and Vendrely (1953). The DNA : arginine ratio in the nucleoprotein of bull spermatozoa is only about 1·48 : 1·0 (Vendrely and Vendrely, 1953 ; Knobloch and Vendrely, 1956 ; Leuchtenberger, Murmanis, Murmanis, Ito and Weir, 1956), a value that is less than one-third of that in normal nuclei of bovine somatic cells. In this the bull resembles the domestic fowl, the trout and the pike, but not the carp and tench. It is well known, however, that the nucleoproteins of mam-malian spermatozoa differ in several respects, particularly in their solubility charac-teristics, from those of fish and invertebrate spermatozoa. This was first pointed out by Miescher (1897) and Mathews (1897) and has since been confirmed by other workers (Steudal, 1926 ; Pollister and Mirsky, 1946 ; Dallam and Thomas, 1953 ; Mayer, 1955).

The lipoprotein fraction of bull and boar spermatozoa is said to account for over 40 per cent of the dry weight of the cell (Mayer, 1955 ; Mayer, Madera-Orsini and Berry, 1957). In the bull, this fraction contained about 14 per cent nitrogen, 0·8 per cent phosphorus and 30 per cent lipids. Phospholipid, choles-terol, glucosamine and glucuronic acid were shown to be present. The protein component contained 14·6 per cent nitrogen and 0·5 per cent phosphorus (Mayer et al., 1957). Dallam and Thomas (1953) also found considerable amounts of cholesterol-containing lipoprotein in the heads of bull and dog spermatozoa.

Zittle and O'Dell (1941a, b, c) found that the high sulphur content of bull spermatozoa (1·6 per cent of dry lipid-free material) is entirely accounted for by the amino acids cystine, cysteine and methionine. They suggest that the cystine is associated with a keratin-like protein and provide observations on the actions of specific solvents in support of this. Mayer et al. (1957) also obtained a keratin-like protein from bull spermatozoa and Green (1940a) obtained a resistant protein containing 11·4 per cent of cystine, which he believed to be associated with the spermatozoon " membrane," from ram spermatozoa.

The protein-bound metals of mammalian spermatozoa include iron, mainly in the form of cytochrome, copper and zinc (Mann, 1954).

The enzymes of mammalian spermatozoa evidently include those of the Embden-Meyerhof glycolytic system, the cytochrome system and the Krebs' tricarboxylic-acid cycle (see Chapter 9A). Hyaluronidase is present in considerable amount (Werthessen, Berman, Greenburg and Gargill, 1945 ; Joël and Eichen-berger, 1945 ; Kurzrok, Leonard and Conrad, 1946 ; Swyer, 1947a, b; Jacquet, Plessis and Cassou, 1951) but catalase is notably absent (Blom and Christensen, 1944, 1947 ; Tosic and Walton, 1950 ; Mann, 1954). Hyaluronidase is believed to be located in the acrosome (see p. 10). Nelson (1954, 1955) states that adeno-sinetriphosphatase, succinic dehydrogenase and cytochrome oxidase are almost entirely restricted to the tail. Engelgardt and Burnasheva (1957) also found that adenosinetriphosphatase activity is localized in the spermatozoon tail.

The only study of the free amino-acid content of spermatozoa is that of Bhar-gava, Bishop and Work (1959). These workers found that bull spermatozoa, in contrast to other kinds of mammalian cell, contain only traces of free amino acids.

Lipids

It has long been known that mammalian spermatozoa contain a considerable amount of lipid material and the probable presence of lipid in the surface membrane and mitochondria of the spermatozoon has already been alluded to (*see* p. 20). Kölliker (1856) found that over 12 per cent of the dry weight of epididymal bull spermatozoa was ether-extractable and Miescher (1878), who performed the first analysis of this lipid, believed that about half of it consisted of lecithin. Zittle and O'Dell (1941b) concluded that 13 per cent of the dry weight of epididymal bull spermatozoa was lipid and that the tails contained much more lipid than the heads. They believed that much of this lipid was associated with the " sheath " of the spermatozoon tail. Lovern *et al.* found that 7 to 9 per cent of freeze-dried ram spermatozoa was extractable with a mixture of chloroform and methanol and that 55–60 per cent of this material was aldehydogenic lipid, possibly plasmalogen (acetal phospholipid). Choline was the predominating base in the aldehydogenic lipids and ethanolamine also occurred. The chloroform-methanol extract also contained free cholesterol (about 8 per cent), a sphingomyelin-like substance (about 5·5 per cent), hydrocarbons (about 2 per cent) and other unidentified lipids and non-lipids, but, contrary to Miescher's belief, there was no evidence for the presence of lecithin (Lovern, Olley, Hartree and Mann, 1957). As noted above, Mayer and his associates believe that much of the lipid of mammalian spermatozoa is associated in lipid-protein complexes containing considerable amounts of phospholipid and cholesterol.

The probable presence of plasmalogen in the tails of human spermatozoa was first demonstrated histochemically by Feulgen and Rossenbeck (1924). Later, Boguth (1952) showed that about two-thirds of the plasmalogen content of bull semen was associated with the spermatozoa.

Carbohydrates

Mammalian spermatozoa contain little carbohydrate and the absence of gly-cogen and reducing sugar is notable. The presence of PAS-reactive polysac-charide in the acrosome, and its possible association with hyaluronidase, has already been described (*see* p. 10).

IV. Comparative Aspects of Spermatozoon Structure

In the preceding sections, the general structure and composition of the mam-malian spermatozoon have been considered in some detail with only passing reference to variations that occur between different kinds of spermatozoa. The sizes, shapes and other properties of mammalian spermatozoa are, however, variable within certain limits and the present section is concerned with variations that occur between species, between individuals within species and within indi-viduals, and that are considered to be distinct from the inherent variability found

in any population of organisms.   It also includes a brief discussion of artefacts
that have in the past added confusion to studies of spermatozoon structure.

Differences Between Species

The spermatozoa of placental mammals are all constructed on a common basic
pattern and differences between species, genera, families and orders are all concerned with relatively minor variations of size, shape and proportion.   Differences
between genera are much greater than those within genera, but differences between
congeneric species are none the less quite characteristic.   It seems possible,
indeed, to identify a species merely by examining its spermatozoa.

The most striking differences between different kinds of mammalian spermatozoa involve the shape of the head (*see* Retzius, 1909; Bishop and Austin, 1957;
Figs. 7.19 and 7.20).   In most instances the head is roughly oval and more
or less bilaterally symmetrical in plan view, although the insertion of the tail
is often slightly abaxial.   The head is usually very considerably flattened, and, in
the bull, is only about half a micron thick.   In man, however, it is thick at the base
and pear-shaped in sagittal section.   In many rodents the head is asymmetrical
and hooked ;   in the harvest mouse (*Micromys*) and musk rat (*Ondatra*), on the
other hand, it is asymmetrical but without a hook (Friend, 1936) and in the guinea-
pig it is broad and symmetrical in plan view, but spoon-shaped in profile (Baker,
1931).

The overall absolute size of mammalian spermatozoa, though characteristic for
each species, does not vary greatly between species, (*see* Table I) and is quite
unrelated to the body size of the animal concerned.   Thus the largest mammalian
spermatozoon known is that of a small rodent, the Chinese hamster, and the smallest
recorded is that of the sperm whale.   The relative sizes of the major parts of the
spermatozoon, vary between species.   Thus, the projected area of the spermatozoon head is nearly five times larger in the guinea-pig than in man, although the
overall length of the guinea-pig spermatozoon is only about twice that of the human.
The acrosome is very large in the guinea-pig, very small in man and intermediate
in size in most other species.   The perforatorium is prominent only in certain
Murine and Cricetine rodents.   The proportions of the mid-piece and end-piece
relative to the rest of the tail also vary considerably.   In the rat the length of the
mid-piece constitutes about 40 per cent of the total length of the tail, whereas in
man this proportion is only about 10 per cent.

Differences in spermatozoon morphology between marsupial and placental
mammals are rather greater than those within these sub-classes, but again these
variations seem to be concerned with matters of detail rather than of basic design.
The spermatozoon head in marsupials appears to pivot freely at the point of insertion of the tail (*see* Retzius, 1906, 1909).   It is often deeply invaginated along its
posterior margin (Fig. 7.19b), but is sometimes more rod-like in form (Fig. 7.19a).
Information on the structure of monotreme spermatozoa is unfortunately
scanty, but superficially these spermatozoa resemble those of birds and reptiles
more closely than those of other mammals.   The head is long, narrow and vermiform (Fig. 7.3a).

The differences between different kinds of mammalian spermatozoa provide
interesting examples of the fundamental specificity of living things.   These

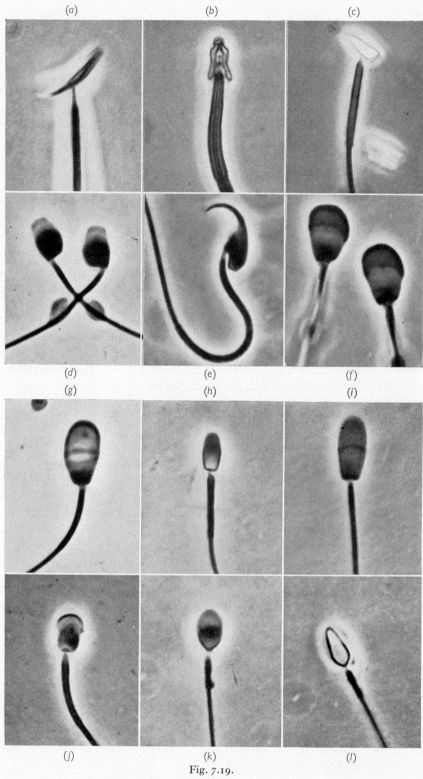

Fig. 7.19.

differences are not related to any obvious physiological requirement and probably they are not of adaptive significance.   In each species the spermatozoa appear to be equally complex and effective.   Except within genera, the differences exhibited are remarkably independent of phylogenetic affinity and no distinct evolutionary trends are apparent.   Ultimately, of course, the basis of these differences is genetic and Friend (1936) has suggested that they arise as secondary expressions of genes that are primarily concerned with characteristics of the soma.   These genes must exert their influence during spermatogenesis, either indirectly through the soma or directly through the spermatogenetic cells.   The possibility that the genotype of the haploid spermatid may be active in shaping the phenotype of the spermatozoon is raised in the succeeding sub-section.

Differences within Species and within Individual Males

There is evidence that the specificity of spermatozoa extends to differences between males within a species and even to differences between spermatozoa of individual males.   The differences considered in this context are of course differences of what may be regarded as normal structure.   Differences associated with abnormal structure are considered separately below (*see* p. 32).

Friend (1936) found small, but apparently significant differences in spermatozoon head length between males of the house mouse (*Mus musculus*) and Braden (1956, 1959) has described differences in the shape of the spermatozoon head that are associated with strain differences in the same species.   The observations of Hancock (1957a) suggest that the heads of boar spermatozoa are more asymmetrical in some males than in others, and differences in the antigenic properties of spermatozoa between males are known in man and the bull (*see* p. 32).   Further, Beatty (1956) has found that the melanizing ability of spermatozoa from " black " rabbits is greater than that of spermatozoa from " white " rabbits.   Thus, spermatozoa from black males become blackened over the region of the post-nuclear cap and mid-piece when incubated with dopa (dihydroxyphenylalanine), whereas those from white males remain unstained.   This difference appears to be associated with the melanizing enzyme dopa oxidase, and to be determined by specific genes at the albino locus.

The evidence for specific differences, as distinct from normal biological variation, between spermatozoa within individual males is at present rather slight, but none the less highly suggestive.   The casual examination of semen samples often suggests that such differences exist, and claims to have demonstrated them between male-determining and female-determining spermatozoa are discussed separately in the next sub-section.   Further evidence is provided by Beatty's (1956) observation that semen from a heterozygous " black-white " rabbit contained spermatozoa of two kinds—those with and those without melanizing ability.   This observation, which requires confirmation, is of exceptional interest since it implies

---

Fig. 7.19a, b, c, d, e, f, g, h, i, j, k, l—Phase-contrast micrographs of the heads of living spermatozoa, illustrating the diversity of form among different species.   (Magnification about × 2,000.) (*a*) Tiger cat (*Dasyurops maculatus*).   (*b*) Long-nosed bandicoot (*Perameles nasuta*).   (*c*) Opossum (*Trichosurus vulpecula*).   (*d*) Hedgehog (*Erinaceus europeus*).   (*e*) Barbary striped mouse (*Lemniscomys barbarus*).   (*f*) Ferret (*Mustela furo*).   (*g*) Rabbit (*Oryctolagus cuniculus*). (*h*) Cat (*Felis catus*).   (*i*) Goat (*Capra hircus*).   (*j*) Greater bush baby (*Galago crassicordatus*). (*k*) Man—plan view.   (*l*) Man—profile view.

that the phenotype of the spermatozoon is in part determined by the specific genetic constitution of the haploid spermatid from which it arises as distinct from the diploid genotype of the parent animal.   Additional support for this is provided by Gullbring's (1957) evidence for the segregation of blood group antigens between spermatozoon genotypes in man.   If spermatozoon characteristics are in fact to any extent determined by segregated genes there arise interesting possibilities for the natural or experimental selection of spermatozoon phenotypes for fertilisation (*see* Bishop, 1960).

Differences between X- and Y-Spermatozoa

In mammals, the male is the heterogametic sex and the spermatozoa are differentiated into female-determining and male-determining gametes by the presence of either the X- or the Y-chromosome respectively (*see* Chapter 22).   For convenience, these two kinds of spermatozoa will be referred to as X-spermatozoa and Y-spermatozoa.

Several workers have tried to distinguish between X- and Y-spermatozoa on the assumption that the unequal size of the sex chromosomes will be reflected in unequal size in the spermatozoon head or nucleus.   It was argued that since the X-chromosome is larger than the Y-chromosome, the nuclei of X-spermatozoa should be correspondingly larger than those of Y-spermatozoa and that this dimorphism should be evident as a bimodal distribution of head or nuclear sizes in each population of spermatozoa.   (Actually, early workers believed that there was only one kind of sex chromosome in mammals, corresponding to the X-chromosome, and that this was present in female-determining spermatozoa and totally lacking in male-determining ones).   Bimodal distributions of this kind have in fact been reported in spermatozoa of several species of insect (Faust, 1913 ; Zeleny and Faust, 1915 b; Zeleny and Senay, 1915), the boar, stallion and bull (Wodsedalek 1913, 1914, 1920), the ram, dog and bull (Zeleny and Faust, 1914, 1915) the rat, mouse and man (Parkes, 1923) and the rabbit and boar (Lush, 1925).   Later workers, however, found no significant evidence for a bimodal distribution of head sizes in spermatozoa of the bull (Williams and Savage, 1925 ; Savage, Williams and Fowler, 1927 ; Lagerlöf, 1934 ; Heberer, 1937) and of the boar and man (Moench and Holt, 1929).   Theoretically, the differences in head or nuclear volume that would be expected from disparity in size between the differential segments of the X- and Y-chromosomes are very small and the possibility of detecting them by simple linear measurements against a background of normal biological variation and experimental error seems very remote.   In view of this and the lack of agreement between workers, it appears that the observed bimodal distributions of spermatozoon size were either fortuitous or determined by factors unconnected with the sex chromosomes.   Differences in head size can easily arise from post-mortem changes in the acrosome and unless precautions are taken to eliminate such effects a bimodal distribution of head size may merely reflect differences between

Fig. 7.20a, b, c, d, e, f, g, h, i—Ultra-violet micrographs (2,750 Å) of the heads of living spermatozoa, illustrating the diversity of form among different species.   (Magnification about × 2,000. Photographed by M. R. Young and J. Smiles.)   (*a*) Cotton rat (*Sigmodon hispidus*). (*b*) Chinese hamster (*Cricetulus griseus*).   (*c*) Golden hamster (*Mesocricetus auratus*).   (*d*) House mouse (*Mus musculus*).   (*e*) Libyan jird (*Meriones libycus*).   (*f*) Field vole (*Microtus agrestis*). (*g*) Guinea pig (*Cavia porcellus*).   (*h*) Greater horse-shoe bat (*Rhinolophus ferrum-equinum*). (*i*) Bull (*Bos taurus*).

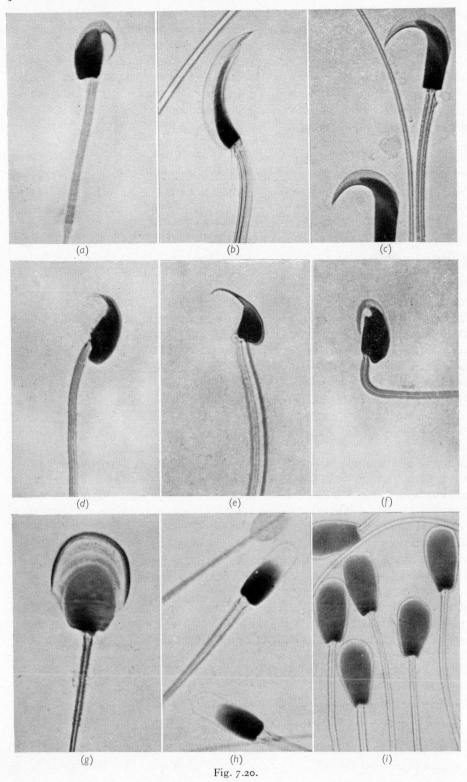

(a) (b) (c)

(d) (e) (f)

(g) (h) (i)

Fig. 7.20.

spermatozoa that show post-mortem changes and those that do not. Measurement of nuclear size might be less susceptible to this kind of error, but the general criticism relating to the smallness of the expected variation still applies. Recently published distribution curves for various nuclear characteristics (diameter, projected area, dry mass, arginine content and DNA content) in the spermatozoa of fertile men and of fertile bulls give no clear indication of bimodality, though suggestions of bimodality were sometimes encountered in spermatozoa from infertile males (Leuchtenberger, Schrader, Weir and Gentile, 1953 ; Leuchtenberger, Weir, Schrader and Murmanis, 1955 ; Leuchtenberger, Murmanis, Murmanis, Ito and Weir, 1956 ; Leuchtenberger, Weir, Schrader and Leuchtenberger, 1956 ; Leuchtenberger, Leuchtenberger, Schrader and Weir, 1956). Lush (1925) and Lovelock (1959) were unable to exploit size or density differences between X- and Y-spermatozoa of the rabbit by differential centrifugation. Lindahl (1956, 1958) believes that X- and Y-spermatozoa of the bull can be separated in a counter-streaming centrifuge, but the results obtained so far are equivocal.

In addition to differences in the mass or volume of chromatin between X- and Y-spermatozoa, it is conceivable that these two kinds of spermatozoa differ in characteristics determined by their differing genotypes. Support for this idea is implicit in the claims that X- and Y-spermatozoa of the rabbit differ in the net electric charge that they carry (Koltzoff and Schröder, 1933 ; Schröder, 1934, 1936a, b, 1937, 1940a, b, 1941a, b, 1956 ; Gordon, 1957). According to these reports, X-spermatozoa are negatively charged at neutral pH, whereas Y-spermatozoa are positively charged and, under certain specified conditions, the two kinds can be separated electrophoretically. Schröder attributes the difference in charge to differences in protein and states that the proteins of anode-migrating (X-) spermatozoa have a lower mean isoelectric point than those of cathode-migrating (Y-) spermatozoa, but the pH at which spermatozoa are said to be separable by electrophoresis is rather high for this explanation to be applicable. Schröder also claims that extracts of anode-migrating spermatozoa possess oestrogenic activity and extracts of cathode-migrating ones possess androgenic activity (Schröder, 1940b). The charge difference, however, is said to be not always well developed and is not shown, for example, in the spermatozoa of young unmated males nor in spermatozoa that have aged in the male reproductive tract (Schröder, 1936). The observations of Gordon (1957) provide support for many of Schröder's claims. Other workers, however, have failed to confirm the alleged difference in charge between X- and Y-spermatozoa (Mahovka and Schegaloff, 1935 ; Mahovka, 1936 ; Siljander, 1936 ; Pilz, 1952 ; Kordts, 1952) although some have succeeded in separating spermatozoa into two classes by Schröder's method (Kordts, 1952 ; Lewin, 1956). For the present it seems best to regard the case as non-proven (see also Bishop, 1960).

The results of attempts to influence the sex ratio at conception are discussed in more detail in Chapter 9.

Antigenic Specificity of Spermatozoa

The antigenic properties of spermatozoa were first investigated by Landsteiner (1899) who showed that the activity of bull spermatozoa after injection into the peritoneal cavity of guinea-pigs was greatly reduced if the recipients had previously been treated with a course of parenteral injections of bull spermatozoa.

Several workers, using *in vitro* methods of testing, subsequently demonstrated the presence in blood sera of antibodies that immobilise spermatozoa after animals had been immunised against their own spermatozoa or against the spermatozoa of other animals of the same or a different species. (Metalnikoff, 1900 ; Metchnikoff, 1900a, b, 1905; Moxter, 1900; Landsteiner, 1901; Weichardt, 1901; Kennedy, 1924; Walsh, 1925; Mudd and Mudd, 1929). Smith (1949a), however, rightly points out that such findings must be interpreted with caution since normal fresh blood sera often exert a toxic effect on spermatozoa (Metalnikoff, 1900; Weichart, 1901; Walsh, 1925; Chang, 1947).

The agglutination of spermatozoa by antisera has also been studied on a number of occasions (Metchnikoff, 1900a ; Weichardt, 1901 ; Henle, Henle and Chambers, 1938 ; Snell and Poucher, 1943 ; Snell, 1944 ; Smith, 1949a, b). There can be no doubt about the general validity of the results obtained, but again caution must be exercised in interpreting experiments of this kind owing to the ease with which spermatozoa can be agglutinated by non-specific agents (Milovanov, 1934 ; Kato, 1936 ; Henle, Henle and Chambers, 1938 ; Chang, 1947 ; Smith, 1949a, b). Weichardt (1901) also prepared anti-agglutinating sera. Wilson (1954) has reported the spontaneous occurrence of spermatozoon agglutinins in the blood serum and seminal plasma of two sterile men.

The complement-fixation test has also been used to study the production and specificity of antibodies to spermatozoa (Landsteiner and van der Scheer, 1927 ; Henle, 1938 ; Henle, Henle and Chambers, 1938 ; Henle, Henle, Church and Foster, 1940; Parsons and Hyde, 1940), and Mudd and Mudd (1929) studied changes in the electrophoretic mobility of spermatozoa brought about by the absorption of antibodies. Pernot (1956) characterised antigenic fractions of guinea-pig spermatozoa by electrophoresis and by precipitation reactions in agar gels.

From the results obtained by these various methods of study, it is clear that mammalian spermatozoa contain a number of antigenic substances. Some of these are species specific, while others, to varying extent, may be found in the spermatozoa of other species (Mudd and Mudd, 1929 ; Henle, 1938 ; Henle, Henle and Chambers, 1938 ; Smith, 1949b). Henle found strong antigenic resemblances between the spermatozoa of bull, sheep and deer, and between the spermatozoa of rat and mouse and a weaker resemblance between the spermatozoa of man and bull. Smith observed a strong antigenic similarity between the spermatozoa of rabbit, guinea-pig, rat and mouse (Fig. 7.21), a weaker relationship between these spermatozoa and those of the ferret and dog, and none at all with those of the bull and goat. Smith also found that the homologous reaction, but not the heterologous reaction, was abolished by the absorption of antisera with intact homologous spermatozoa, and that both homologous and heterologous reactions were abolished by absorption with disintegrated homologous spermatozoa. Absorption with disintegrated heterologous spermatozoa did not completely abolish the homologous reaction. These results suggest that antigens superficially located on the spermatozoa of one species may be more deeply seated in the spermatozoa of other species. Henle, Henle and Chambers (1938) demonstrated in bull spermatozoa three species-specific antigens, three cross-reacting antigens and antigenic differences between the spermatozoon head and tail. Snell (1944) observed antigenic differences between the spermatozoa of different strains of mice. Major blood-group antigens, appropriate to the blood group of the parent male, have been detected on spermatozoa of man and bull (Landsteiner and Levine, 1926 ; Yamakami, 1926 ; Docton, Ferguson, Lazear and Ely, 1952 ; Gullbring, 1957), but in general spermatozoon antigens display a high degree of tissue specificity (Landsteiner and van der Scheer, 1927). Gullbring also made the important observation, which requires confirmation, that the spermatozoa of men of blood group AB are of two kinds, those possessing the A antigen and those

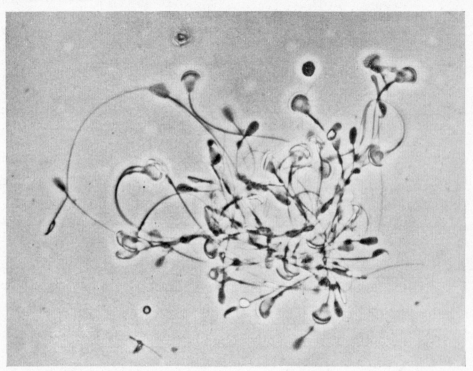

Fig. 7.21—Agglutination of rabbit, mouse, and guinea-pig spermatozoa after 5 minutes in a 1 in 10 dilution of an immune serum prepared in goats against rabbit serum. (From Smith, 1949a.) (*Proc. Roy. Soc., B*, 1949, **136**, 46.)

possessing the B antigen. Schröder (1956) claims to have demonstrated antigenic differences between X- and Y-spermatozoa.

Some possible physiological consequences of the antigenic diversity of spermatozoa are discussed on p. 42.

Abnormal Spermatozoa

Samples of semen usually contain a varying proportion of spermatozoa that clearly depart from the morphological pattern typical of the species, and that may be regarded as abnormal (Fig. 7.22). Such spermatozoa are generally considered to be functionally impaired, and in some instances there is clear evidence that this is so. Their incidence is usually low in males of normal fertility and is often much higher in males of subnormal fertility.   It tends to be higher in man than in other species.   The deviations from normal structure take many forms and affect all parts of the spermatozoon.   They have been extensively studied in man and the bull because of their practical importance in these species (*man* : Cary,

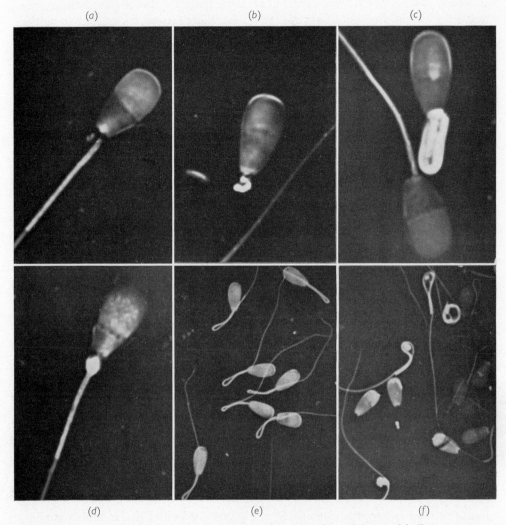

Fig. 7.22a, b, c, d, e, f—Micrographs of nigrosin-eosin preparations of abnormal bull spermatozoa. (a to d, × 2,000); e to f, × 900.) (From Bishop, Cambpell, Hancock and Walton, 1954.) (*a*) Spermatozoon with abaxial tail and a rudiment of a second tail.   (*b*) Spermatozoon with a rudimentary tail.   (*c*) Spermatozoon with a malformed tail.   (*d*) Spermatozoon with a vacuolated head and a cytoplasmic droplet attached to the neck.   (*e*) Spermatozoa with looped tails. (*f*) Decapitate spermatozoa.

1930 ; Moench and Holt, 1931, 1932, 1933 ; Moench, 1936 ; Hotchkiss, Brunner and Grenley, 1938 ; Pollak and Joel, 1939 ; Weisman, 1941 ; Harvey and Jackson, 1945 ; MacLeod and Heim, 1945 ; Williams, 1947 ; Falk and Kaufman, 1950 ; Page and Houlding, 1951 ; MacLeod and Gold, 1951 ;—*bull* : Williams and Savage, 1925 ; Lagerlöf, 1934 ; Herman and Swanson, 1941 ; Lasley and Bogart, 1943 ; Teunissen, 1946 ; Hancock, 1949, 1952, 1953 ; Hancock and

Rollinson, 1949 ; Blom, 1950a, b ; Rollinson, 1951 ; Brochart and Montrose, 1951 ; Bishop, Campbell, Hancock and Walton, 1954).

There is some disagreement between workers on the significance of the various forms of spermatozoon abnormality that have been recorded, and on the manner in which they should be classified. The most generally useful classification, developed from the studies of Lagerlöf (1934) and Blom (1950a, b), appears to be the division of abnormalities into primary and secondary classes. Primary forms are those with malformations that clearly arise from defects of spermateliosis. They include spermatozoa with giant heads, dwarf heads, mis-shapen heads, double heads, abnormal nuclei, abnormal acrosomes, abnormal tails and multiple tails (Figs. 7.22 ; 7.23). Various kinds of primary abnormality often occur together,

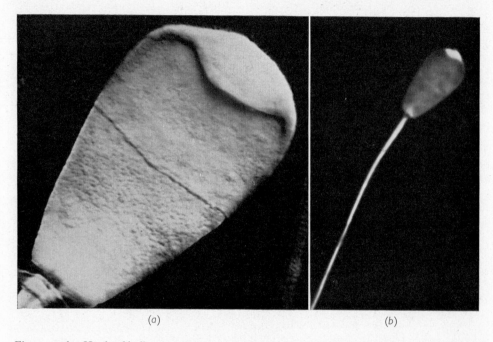

(a)   (b)

Fig. 7.23a, b—Heads of bull spermatozoa with an hereditary defect of the acrosome. (a) Electron micrograph (× 9,000) (from Hancock, 1953). (b) Nigrosin-eosin preparation (× 2,000) (from Bishop, Campbell, Hancock and Walton, 1954).

but sometimes one type predominates and in certain sterile Friesian bulls virtually all the spermatozoa have been shown to possess abnormal acrosomes (Hancock, 1949, 1952, 1953 ; Fig. 7.23). The presence of " vacuoles " in the nuclei of human spermatozoa is usually not considered to be an abnormal feature. The class of secondary abnormalities consists of spermatozoa that appear to have been normally differentiated and have subsequently become deformed while passing through the male reproductive tract. They include decapitate spermatozoa, spermatozoa with looped tails and spermatozoa that have died in the male reproductive tract and show degenerative post-mortem changes. Decapitate spermatozoa are those with complete or incipient separation of the head from the tail at the neck (Fig. 7.22f). This condition affects all the spermatozoa in certain sterile Guernsey bulls (Hancock and Rollinson, 1949 ; Hancock, 1952, 1955). In such instances, a high proportion of the decapitate tails are often alive and actively motile, but most of the heads are judged to be dead by their staining reactions (Bhargava, Bishop and Work, 1959). Spermatozoa with looped tails exhibit a characteristic flexure of the tail at the distal end of the mid-piece, which often encloses a retained cytoplasmic droplet, and which causes the head to be carried backwards as the spermatozoon swims along (Fig. 7.22e). The aetiology and significance of this condition are not known but its incidence can be greatly influenced by treatments *in vitro* (*see* p. 38). The flexure is often seen on the tails of decapitate spermatozoa where it may create the illusion of a head (Fig. 7.22f). The degenerative changes associated with dead spermatozoa are discussed separately in the succeeding sub-section.

Spermatozoa that retain cytoplasmic droplets are also grouped into the class of secondary abnormalities by Blom (1950b) but the justification for this seems doubtful. Except in man, spermatozoa with droplets attached to the neck are rare in ejaculated semen and in most instances seem to accompany primary defects (Fig. 7.22d). Those with droplets attached to the distal end of the mid-piece are usually considered to be slightly immature but not abnormal. Such droplets are a common feature of spermatozoa taken from the epididymis and do not appear to be associated with any functional impairment. In man, the droplet or remnants of it often persists on the neck of the spermatozoon, but this is usually considered to be of no clinical significance.

The development of new methods of quantitative microscopy has recently led to the discovery of a new type of spermatozoon abnormality that is associated with low fertility in man and the bull. Superficially, these spermatozoa appear to have been normally formed but they contain abnormal and highly variable amounts of DNA and arginine in their nuclei (Leuchtenberger, Schrader, Weir and Gentile, 1953 ; Leuchtenberger, Weir, Schrader and Murmanis, 1955 ; Leuchtenberger, Weir, Schrader and Leuchtenberger, 1956 ; Leuchtenberger, Murmanis, Murmanis, Ito and Weir, 1956).

Observations on the development of abnormal spermatozoa are discussed on p. 79).

Differences between Living and Dead Spermatozoa

The incidence of dead spermatozoa is usually about 15 per cent in freshly ejaculated semen samples but may be much higher in males of low fertility. It steadily increases with time after collection and may be greatly influenced by apparently mild treatments *in vitro*. Williams and Savage (1925) and Lagerlöf (1934) observed that spermatozoa that were dead before fixation tended to stain more heavily than those that were alive. Lasley, Easley and McKenzie (1942), however, were the first to devise and use a convenient and reliable staining technique for distinguishing living spermatozoa from dead ones. They based their method upon the observation that dead spermatozoa can be easily supravitally stained with eosin, whereas living spermatozoa remain unstained (Fig. 7.24). The differentiation was made more distinctive by the use of opal blue to provide a stained background. The high affinity that dead spermatozoa have for eosin appears to be attributable to increase in the permeability of the cell membrane at the time of death. The change in staining behaviour is known to be rapid. Many workers have since modified the original technique and have adapted it for use with different kinds of spermatozoa (ram, bull, boar, stallion, buffalo, rabbit and man), and under different *in vitro* conditions (Easley, Mayer and Bogart, 1942 ; Lasley, Easley and Bogart, 1942 ; Lasley and Bogart, 1943, 1944 ; Lasley and Mayer, 1944 ; Emik and Sidwell, 1947 ; Madden, Herman and Berousek, 1947 ; Mayer, Squiers, Bogart and Oloufa, 1951 ; Schaffer and Almquist, 1948, 1949; Stone, Johnstone and Mixner, 1940 ; Blom, 1950c ; Williams and Pollak, 1950; Lasley, 1951 ; Swanson and Bearden, 1951 ; Hancock, 1951 ; Ortavant, Dupont, Pauthe and Roussel, 1952 ; Bonnadonna and Olgiati, 1953 ; Brochart, 1953 ;

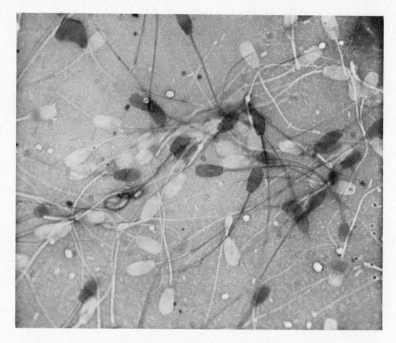

Fig. 7.24—Bull spermatozoa supravitally stained with eosin and opal blue to differentiate between living and dead spermatozoa. The dead spermatozoa are clearly stained, the living ones remain unstained. (From Lasley and Bogart, 1943.)

Campbell, Hancock and Rothschild, 1953 ; Bishop, Campbell, Hancock and Walton, 1954 ; Rao, 1956 ; Dott, 1956 ; Campbell, Dott and Glover, 1956 ; Beatty, 1957). Blom (1950c) and Hancock (1951) substituted nigrosin for the opal

---

Fig. 7.25a to t—Phase-contrast micrographs illustrating degenerative changes in, and loss of, the acrosome (× 2,000). (*a*) Normal golden hamster spermatozoon. (*b*) Golden hamster spermatozoon with raised acrosome. (*c*) Golden hamster spermatozoon with acrosome almost detached. (*d*) Normal Chinese hamster spermatozoon. (*e*) Chinese hamster spermatozoon with acrosome almost detached. (*f*) Chinese hamster spermatozoon without acrosome. (*g*) Normal Libyan jird spermatozoon. (*h*) Libyan jird spermatozoon without acrosome. (*i*) Normal field vole spermatozoon. (*j*) Field vole spermatozoon without acrosome. (*k*) Normal mouse spermatozoon. (*l*) Mouse spermatozoon with raised acrosome. (*m*) Normal cotton rat spermatozoon. (*n*) Cotton rat spermatozoon without acrosome. (*o*) Normal guinea-pig spermatozoon. (*p*) Guinea-pig spermatozoon without acrosome. (*q*) Normal greater horse-shoe bat spermatozoon. (*r*) Greater horse-shoe bat spermatozoon without acrosome. (*s*) Normal bull spermatozoon. (*t*) Bull spermatozoon with raised acrosome. (a, d, g, i, m from Bishop and Austin, 1957; e, h, j, n, p, t, from Austin and Bishop, 1958b).

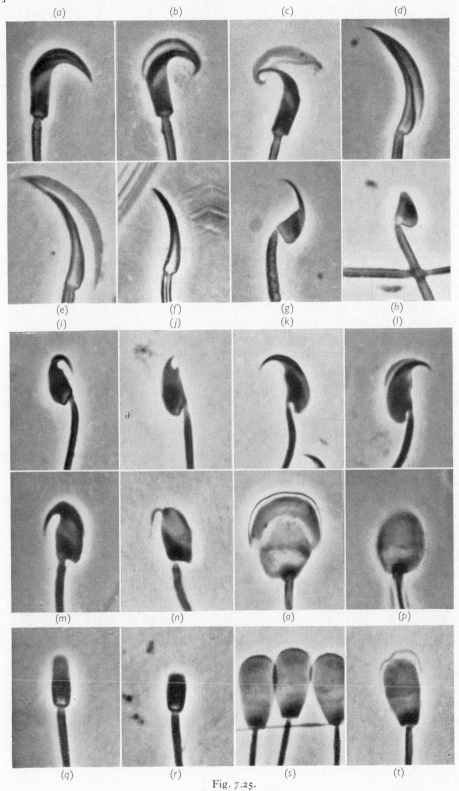

Fig. 7.25.

blue and this has been used by most subsequent workers ; fast green (Mayer *et al.*, 1951), analine blue (Schaffer and Almquist, 1948) and other dyes (Rao, 1956, 1957) have also been used for the same purpose.   Other workers have employed various primary stains in place of eosin ; these include congo red (Emmens, 1947), revector soluble blue (Crook and Mandl, 1947 ; Crook, Irvin and Mandl, 1949), erythrosin and rose bengal (Mayer *et al.*, 1951) and brom-phenol blue (Bonnadonna, 1953 ; Bonnadonna and Olgiati, 1953).   Recently, Bishop and Smiles (1957b) have developed a fluorescence technique for identifying dead spermatozoa using very low concentrations of primulin as a fluorochrome.

The changes that occur in the physiological properties of the cell membrane at the death of the spermatozoon are also associated with the leakage of cellular components from the cell (Mann, 1955), with an increased tendency of spermatozoa to agglutinate (Hancock and Shaw, 1955) and with an increased tendency of the cell to stick to glass surfaces (Bangham and Hancock, 1955).   Bangham and Hancock found that, when suspensions of bull spermatozoa in isomotic sodium-chloride solution were passed through a filter of fine glass beads, only living spermatozoa appeared in the filtrate.   The dead ones remained attached to the filter.

The development of techniques for distinguishing living from dead spermatozoa has led to a better understanding of the degenerative morphological changes that follow the death of the cell and have frequently misled investigators in their interpretation of normal structure.   The most important of these is the post-mortem modification and loss of the acrosome (Hancock, 1952, 1957a; Beatty, 1957; Austin and Bishop, 1958b).   This rapidly follows the death of the cell and may greatly alter the morphology of the spermatozoon head (Figs. 7.25).   The histochemical properties of the acrosome are also affected.   Subsequently, other more easily recognisable changes, such as decapitation and general disintegration, may develop.   Post-mortem degeneration of the spermatozoon may occur *in vivo* —Blom (1945), for example, has described spontaneous detachment of the acrosome in bulls after long periods of sexual rest—and is extremely easily induced *in vitro*.

Preparation Artefacts

In general, the mammalian spermatozoon is remarkably resistant to distortion and disintegration and this has tended to encourage negligence of precautions against preparation artefacts.   Such artefacts do, in fact, occur and must be recognised before valid conclusions can be made about normal structure.   The need for such precautions obviously increases with the increasing resolution of microscope techniques.

The most frequent morphological changes induced in spermatozoa by manipulation *in vitro* involve distortion of the acrosome (Baker, 1931 ; Friend, 1936 ; Hancock, 1952), bending and coiling of the tail (Walton, 1947 ; Salisbury, Willett and Seligman, 1942 ; Pursley and Herman, 1950 ; Bishop, Campbell, Hancock and Walton, 1954) and decapitation (Mercier and Salisbury, 1947).   They may be induced by such agencies as cold shock, osmotic shock, toxic substances and histo-logical reagents.   They not only affect the structure of normal spermatozoa but may also mask abnormalities in abnormal ones (Hancock, 1953).   Sometimes virtually all the spermatozoa in a sample may be affected by distortion in a particular manner. The susceptibility to distortion varies between species and also between males within a species (Bishop *et al.*, 1954 ; Austin and Bishop, 1958b).

V. Functional Aspects of Spermatozoon Structure

The function of the spermatozoon is to initiate development of the egg and to supply the paternal genetic material, and perhaps other important or essential components, to the new embryo. In order to achieve this, the spermatozoon must, of course, first reach and enter the egg. With so exacting a task to perform, it is not surprising that the spermatozoon has evolved into a highly specialised cell and the uniqueness of its structure can be best appreciated in relation to its peculiar functional requirements. In this connection, it is convenient to distinguish the characteristics that are mainly concerned with the independent motile existence of the spermatozoon from those that are more specifically concerned with fertilisation itself.

The Mechanism for Motility

Motility is an almost universal characteristic of male gametes and undoubtedly facilitates the meeting of the spermatozoon with the egg. Although in many mammals the ascent of spermatozoa within the female reproductive tract to the site of fertilisation appears to be brought about largely by movements of the female tract (*see* Chapter 8), there can be little doubt that spermatozoon motility plays an important role in the final meeting of the gametes and in the actual penetration of the egg. It has in fact been shown that the fertility of spermatozoa can be correlated with their motility (Bishop, Campbell, Hancock and Walton, 1954 ; Bishop and Hancock, 1955 ; Bishop, 1955a, b ; Chapter 9A).

The tail is, of course, the propulsive unit of the spermatozoon that pushes the cell along by the propagation of waves of bending (probably two-dimensional) which pass distally along its length and exert pressure on the surrounding medium. The propagation of these waves appears to be an inherent property of the tail, which must contain all the apparatus necessary for motility, since tails that have been separated from heads can be fully motile.

The possible mechanism by which the tail produces its characteristic movement has been discussed by Bradfield (1955). By virtue of their size and position, the outer fibres of the axial core of filaments are thought to be the main contractile elements of the tail and to be capable of propagating localised contractions along their length. The helical protein sheath, together with the inter-fibre matrix, probably provide the skeletal material against which the contractile fibres can work. The inner fibres may be specialised for the rapid conduction of " impulses," probably arising rhythmically in the basal body of the neck, which co-ordinate the localised contractions in the outer fibres. It may be noted, however, that a simpler model than that suggested by Bradfield could be advanced if the fibres were twisted about the axis of the tail, instead of running straight as is at present believed, and if the waves of bending were three dimensional.

There is no evidence of contractile apparatus in the mitochondria and it is likely that they are concerned solely with the provision of energy. Indeed, in view of the known localisation of oxidative enzyme systems within mitochondria, and the role of these organellae in the synthesis of high-energy phosphate compounds, the mid-piece may be regarded as the main power-house of the spermatozoon.   It is possible, however, that glycolytic enzymes are distributed throughout the inter-fibre matrix.   The superficial location of the mitochondria, and the large surface area of the tail as a whole, will greatly facilitate the transfer of metabolites between the tail and the external environment.   There is little cytological evidence of endogenous sources of energy within the tail, though such sources do exist and phospholipid may be used for this purpose to a limited extent.   The metabolic processes by which the spermatozoon obtains energy are discussed in Chapter 9A.

Aspects of the mechanics, hydrodynamics and thermodynamics of the motility of spermatozoa and other small flagellate organisms have been discussed by Taylor (1951, 1952), Hancock (1953), Rothschild (1953), Gray (1955, 1958), Gray and Hancock (1955) Tibbs (1957) and Rikmenspoel, and information on flagella movement in general is given by Gray (1928, 1931).   The calculations of Rothschild and of Tibbs suggest that the chemical energy available is greatly in excess of the requirements for motility.

The main function of the tail is clearly concerned with the requirements of the spermatozoon during its independent phase of existence, but since the tail normally (but not invariably) enters the egg during the course of fertilisation (*see* Chapter 10) it is not impossible that parts of it, such as centriolar structures or mitochondria, may play some role in the development of the embryo.   There is, however, no evidence that this is so.

The Mechanism for Penetrating the Egg

The universal occurrence of the acrosome on the leading surface of the spermatozoon has for many years suggested that the acrosome plays a vital role in enabling the spermatozoon to penetrate into the egg.   Many early workers believed that the acrosome had the function of mechanically piercing the egg-membranes, but this hypothesis has been long since rejected in favour of the view that some enzymatic mechanism was involved.   Bowen (1924) further suggested that enzymes from the acrosome might be responsible for the activation of the egg.   Recently, however, Austin and Bishop (1958a, c) observed that the acrosome is lost from the spermatozoon head before entry into the zona pellucida of the egg.   They suggest that penetration of the zona pellucida is brought about with the aid of an enzyme carried by the perforatorium and that the function of the acrosome is to carry the hyaluronidase that assists the penetration of the matrix of the cumulus oophorus. Entry into the cytoplasm of the egg, on the other hand, appears to occur by active ingestion of the spermatozoon by the surface of the vitellus.   The properties of the spermatozoon that make it acceptable to the vitellus and that are responsible for activating the egg to further development are not known, but these too may be associated with the perforatorium, for during the early stages of fertilisation part of this structure can be clearly recognised within the cytoplasm of rat and hamster eggs (*see* Chapter 10).

Although the acrosome does not appear to be involved in the actual penetration of the egg, it undoubtedly plays an important role in fertilisation, and this is emphasised by the observations of Teunissen (1946) and Hancock (1949, 1953) that morphological deformity of the acrosome is associated with sterility in the bull.

The Genetic Material

The major and perhaps only function of the chromatin of the nucleus of the mature spermatozoon is to supply the egg with the paternal genetic material. It is currently believed that the genetic material is the DNA and that the genetic information is in some way coded and stored within the DNA molecules by the sequential arrangement of the purine and pyrimidine bases along the deoxyribose-phosphate chain (*see* McElroy and Bentley Glass, 1957). Since the function of the nucleus is concerned with the future embryo rather than with the spermatozoon itself, the unique crystal-like structure of the nucleus may be seen as a convenient means of storing the genetic material in a compact and stable form during the biologically inactive period of its existence. Thus, the spermatozoon nucleus appears to be *in sensu strictu* a " resting nucleus."

The apparent inactivity of the nucleus together with the lack of cytoplasmic nucleic acid suggest that the mature spermatozoon contains very little genetic information that can influence its own metabolism. This condition is doubtless associated with the fact that the spermatozoon does not grow or divide. It suggests that the ability of the spermatozoon to repair the damage of wear and tear is severely restricted (though there is some evidence that limited anabolic metabolism may occur—*see* Chapter 9A) and that, even when unlimited exogenous energy sources are available, senescence changes are likely to overcome the cell rather rapidly. Under these circumstances, the life-span of the spermatozoon will be short when metabolism is active and will be longest when metabolism is reduced to a level just sufficient to maintain the integrity of the cell against losses caused by diffusion and other physical processes. Such a state may be approached in the epididymis (*see* Section X) and *in vitro* at very low temperatures (*see* Chapter 9A).

It may be noted parenthetically that the success of the fertilised egg will depend, among other things, upon the quality of the genetic information supplied by the spermatozoon, and it is likely that many instances of abortive development are attributable to fertilisation with spermatozoa that carry faulty or incomplete information (Bishop, 1955a). Support for this idea is provided by the observations that abnormal DNA content in spermatozoa is associated with infertility in man and the bull (*see* p. 35), and that genetic damage caused by X-irradiation of spermatozoa (*see* Chapter 9) or of the testis (*see* p. 93) is associated with embryonic death after apparently normal fertilisation. Again, inherent differences between species in the nature and arrangement of the genetic material probably underlie the failure of development that has been observed after interspecific fertilisation in anurans (G. Hertwig, 1913) and lagomorphs (Chang and McDonough, 1955 ; Adams, 1957).

The Function of the Cytoplasmic Droplet

The characteristic size and shape of the cytoplasmic droplet, together with its invariable presence on spermatozoa when they leave the testis (*see* p. 54) and its orderly migration along the mid-piece during passage through the epididymis

c*

(*see* p. 95) indicate that the droplet is not merely a casual remnant of unwanted material. Its loss from the spermatozoon at the time of ejaculation, however, implies that the function of the droplet is mainly concerned with the physiology of the spermatozoon while within the male reproductive tract. This suggests that the droplet may be involved in the developmental changes that occur in spermatozoa within the epididymis, or in the maintenance of the cell in a quiescent state and for a very much longer period than can be achieved at a similar temperature outside the epididymis. There is certainly no evidence to support the belief of Popa and Marza (1931) that the droplet is essential for the co-ordination of spermatozoon motility.

Serological Considerations

Owing to antigenic diversity between individual animals, spermatozoa within the female genital tract may, to varying degree, be regarded as foreign bodies. Since it is a characteristic of adult organisms that foreign material can be recognised and rejected, antigenetic incompatibility between spermatozoa and recipient females may prejudice the chances of fertilisation. Such a mechanism may underlie the observed failure of many interspecific matings and may even explain instances of infertility within a species (Bishop, 1955a; Austin and Bishop, 1957; Ryle, 1957). The attachment of the spermatozoon to the egg, a normal preliminary to fertilisation, may also be brought about by an antigen-antibody type of reaction (*see* Chapter 10) and here again highly specific mechanisms for acceptance or rejection are possible.

VI. The Cytology of Spermatogenesis

Spermatozoa arise within the tubules of the testis from the spermatogonia, or spermatozoon mother-cells, by a complex process of cell division and differentiation, during which the nucleus is reduced to the haploid condition and both nuclear and cytoplasmic components of the cell are extensively reorganised. These events may be divided into three phases—(1) the divisions of the spermatogonia and their development to spermatocytes, (2) the meiotic divisions of the spermatocytes to form spermatids, and (3) the metamorphosis of the spermatids to spermatozoa. Phases (1) and (2) are often grouped together under the term spermatocytogenesis and phase (3) is called spermateliosis or spermiogenesis. The spermatogonia are believed to originate from the primordial germ-cells that arise early in the embryo and migrate to the genital ridges, though the evidence for this is not completely conclusive (*see* Chapter 5). New spermatogonia are formed from existing ones and the process of spermatogenesis thereby repeats itself indefinitely. The study of spermatogenesis is, of course, of special importance for the light that it sheds on the role of the spermatozoon in fertilisation and heredity. An excellent review of most of the early work on this subject has been provided by Wilson (1925).

The Germinal Epithelium

Before proceeding to a detailed description of the events of mammalian spermatogenesis it is convenient to describe briefly the nature of the cells that make up the germinal epithelium of the normal male.   These are the spermatogonia, the spermatocytes, the spermatids and the Sertoli cells.   Together they form a closely packed, multi-layered community of cells situated on the basement membrane of the testis tubule, with the youngest spermatogenic cells on the membrane and successively older spermatogenic cells in successive layers toward the lumen of the tubule.   The detailed composition of the cell population in any section of tubule varies with time in a cyclic manner (*see* Section VII).

For information on the cytology of the germinal epithelium additional to that given below, reference should be made to the works of Gatenby and Beams (1935), Gresson and Zlotnik (1945), Tobias (1956), Fawcett and Burgos (1956a) and Fawcett and Ito (1958).

The spermatogonia

The spermatogonia are relatively few in number and are situated on or near the basement membrane of the testis tubule.   They may be classified into three types : type-A, type-B and intermediate-type.   The type-A cells are the largest and most primitive ; they have a pale, ovoid nucleus in which the chromatin is mainly distributed as fine " dust-like " granules.   They are the dust-like spermatogonia of Regaud (1901).   The type-B cells are the smallest, and have a dark, spherical nucleus with coarse chromatin masses.   They are the " crust-like " spermatogonia of Regaud.   The intermediate-type cells are intermediate in form between types A and B and are sometimes not readily distinguishable from type-A cells.

The spermatocytes

There are two kinds of spermatocytes, primary spermatocytes and secondary spermatocytes.   Primary spermatocytes are much more numerous than spermatogonia, and two generations of these cells may exist together.   The early primary spermatocytes are morphologically similar to the type-B spermatogonia.   They quickly increase in size, however, and their large spherical nuclei are usually seen in the prophase of the first meiotic division.   The secondary spermatocytes are smaller than the primary spermatocytes and have smaller nuclei.   Their period of existence is short and in consequence they are much less frequently seen than are primary spermatocytes (*see* Table IV, p. 67).

The spermatids

The spermatids are more numerous than any other kind of cell in the germinal epithelium and are situated nearest to the lumen of the tubule.   The early spermatids are relatively small spherical cells, each with a small spherical nucleus containing a nucleolus.   The cytoplasm contains a prominent Golgi apparatus, composed of an inner medulla, or idiosome, and an outer argentophil cortex ; a pair of centrioles in close apposition that stain strongly with iron haematoxylin ; an irregular basophil body, the chromatoid body ; scattered mitochondria and an extensive endoplasmic reticulum.   Subsequently, the shape of the spermatid is modified towards that of the spermatozoon (*see* p. 51).   Often two generations of spermatids are seen together in the same section of testis tubule (*see* Section VII).

An interesting and apparently normal feature of early spermatids is the frequent occurrence of narrow intercellular cytoplasmic bridges that connect spermatids in pairs or in groups of four (Burgos and Fawcett, 1955; Fawcett and Burgos, 1956b; Fig. 7.26). Multinucleate spermatids have also been observed in many species (*see* p. 80).

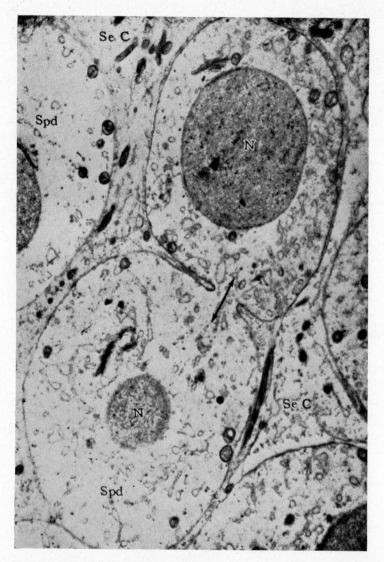

Fig. 7.26—Electron micrograph of a section of two human spermatids joined by an intercellular protoplasmic bridge (at arrow). The spermatids are completely surrounded by Sertoli cytoplasm (Spd = spermatid; N = nucleus; SeC = Sertoli cytoplasm). (From Fawcett and Burgos, 1956b.)

The Sertoli cells

Although not spermatogenic cells, the Sertoli cells are a characteristic component of the germinal epithelium. They were first described by Sertoli (1865) and are sometimes known as sustentacular cells, nurse cells, foot cells, or branched cells. The Sertoli-cell nuclei are clearly distinct from those of the spermatogenic cells : they are the largest nuclei of the germinal epithelium, situated on or near the basement membrane, vesicular, often oval in shape and have a characteristic nucleolus with satellite bodies. The nuclear membrane is often wrinkled, with folds extending deeply into the nucleus. The Sertoli nuclei can be classified into two types, horizontal nuclei and perpendicular nuclei : the horizontal nuclei are flat or oval in shape with the long axis of the nucleus parallel to the basement membrane and the perpendicular nuclei are oval or pyramidal with the long axis perpendicular to the basement membrane. The horizontal type nuclei are the most frequent (Leblond and Clermont, 1952a; *see* p. 72).

The cytoplasm of the Sertoli cell is very irregular in shape. It extends between the younger spermatogenic cells in long, radial, pillar-like processes which are often branched, and which expand to embrace the developing spermatids. It contains numerous inclusions in the form of granules, droplets, wavy fibrils and crystalloids. The cell boundaries are usually indistinct and there exists a widespread opinion that the Sertoli cells form a syncytium. Sapsford (1957, 1958), however, has shown that discrete, often very irregularly shaped, Sertoli cells can be separated from the rest of the germinal epithelium of the adult rat by mild digestion with trypsin. Most of these cells are clearly single, although some are joined by thin strands of cytoplasm. Deep invaginations which accommodate the developing spermatids can be clearly seen. Sapsford has also shown that in the newborn rat the Sertoli cells exist as small, discrete, spherical cells. Elftman (1950) also believes that the Sertoli system is composed of individual cells.

An interesting feature of the Sertoli cells is that they have rarely, if ever, been seen in division.

Division of the Spermatogonia

The manner in which the spermatogonia develop to spermatocytes and also renew themselves is, of course, fundamental to the whole process of spermatogenesis. It is best known in the rat, mouse and golden hamster.

According to Clermont and Leblond (1953), the development of each generation of spermatogenic cells in the rat starts with two successive mitotic divisions of type-A spermatogonia to give further cells of the same type. Three of each four daughter cells so produced then divide to form intermediate-type spermatogonia, while, for reasons unknown, the fourth daughter cell remains dormant. The intermediate-type spermatogonia then divide to produce type-B spermatogonia, and these in turn divide to produce the primary spermatocytes. Shortly afterwards the succeeding generation of spermatogenic cells starts its development by division of the type-A spermatogonia that segregated as dormant cells after the second division. These cells are called the stem-cells. Each stem-cell in turn gives rise to a new stem-cell after the second division and 24 spermatocytes after the fifth division in the manner just described. All divisions are mitotic.

An almost identical sequence of events to that outlined above for the rat has been reported by Clermont (1954) for the golden hamster (*see* Fig. 7.27) and by Oakberg (1956b) for the mouse. In other species, however, the sequence is evidently slightly different, for only three spermatogonial divisions are reported in the guinea-pig (Cleland, 1951) and the monkey (Clermont and Leblond, 1953), but as many as seven or eight in man (Roosen-Runge, 1952). In the ram, each stem cell is said to give rise to 16 primary spermatocytes (Ortavant, 1954a). In each instance, however, stem-cells are segregated in each generation and these form the parent cells of the succeeding generation. In this way the germinal epithelium is maintained.

The recent observations on the periodic segregation of the stem cells confirm the views of Duesberg (1908), Roosen-Runge and Giesel (1950) and Cleland (1951). They dispose of the beliefs that spermatogonia divide unequally so that each division produces a primary spermatocyte and another spermatogonium (Rolshoven, 1941, 1951) and that new spermatogonia arise by transformation of neighbouring cells, such as Sertoli cells.

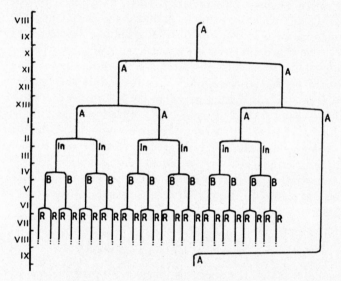

Fig. 7.27—Diagrammatic representation of the pattern of division and differentiation of the spermatogonia of the golden hamster. (A = A-type spermatogonia; In = intermediate-type spermatogonia; B = B-type spermatogonia; R = early primary spermatocyte. The Roman numerals at the left indicates stages of the spermatogenic cycle.) (From Clermont, 1954.)

Division of the Spermatocytes

After a "resting period" of several hours, the early primary spermatocytes suddenly transform into rounded cells which undergo meiosis. This is a special type of cell division during which the nucleus divides twice but the chromosomes divide only once. As a result, the normal diploid number of chromosomes is reduced by half. Each primary spermatocyte gives rise to two secondary spermatocytes and thence to four haploid spermatids.

Outline of meiosis

The prophase of the first meiotic division is long and the successive stages are referred to as leptotene, zygotene, pachytene, diplotene and diakinesis. In leptotene, the chromosomes resemble long threads. During zygotene, homologous chromosomes, one maternal and one paternal, come together in pairs or bivalents and become closely applied throughout their length. The chromosomes shorten and, halfway through pachytene, each divides longitudinally into two chromatids although the centromere of each chromosome remains undivided. Towards the end of pachytene, crossover points or chiasmata are formed between the chromatids in each bivalent. These arise when two of the four chromatids break at

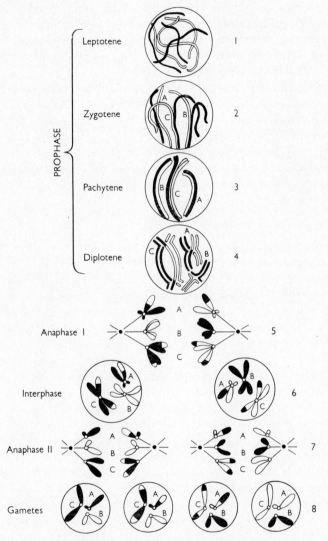

Fig. 7.28—Diagrammatic representation of the stages of meiosis in a nucleus with three pairs of chromosomes (A, B, C). (From De Robertis, Nowinski and Saez, 1954.)

exactly the same level and rejoin diagonally to produce the configuration of an X. In this way, genetic material is transferred between chromatids of homologous chromosomes. At the beginning of diplotene, the paired chromosomes start to separate, but remain held together at the chiasmata. The chromosomes continue to shorten and thicken and, at the end of diakinesis, the nuclear membrane disappears. During metaphase of the first meiotic division, the spindle is formed and each chromosome becomes attached to the spindle by its centromere. At anaphase, the two centromeres of each bivalent move to opposite, randomly chosen poles of the spindle, and each carries with it its attached chromosome. The homologous chromosomes are thus separated and pass to randomly selected daughter-cells, or secondary spermatocytes. It should be noted, however, that these chromosomes are not the same as those that come together at zygotene on account of the interchange of material that occurs between maternal and paternal homologues during pachytene. Furthermore, each chromosome now consists of two chromatids joined by a centromere. During telophase, the nuclear membrane is reconstituted, but the chromosomes remain relatively condensed and quickly enter the second meiotic division. This resembles a normal mitosis, except that the chromosomes are present in the haploid number. At anaphase, the centromeres divide and the chromatids of each pair separate and pass to different daughter cells, or spermatids. Each chromatid may now be regarded as a chromosome. A diagrammatic representation of meiosis is shown in Fig. 7.28. For further details, reference should be made to the works of White (1942, 1954) and De Robertis, Nowinski and Saez (1954).

Segregation of the sex chromosomes

In mammals, the male is the heterogametic sex (see Chapter 22 ; White, 1954 ; Matthey and van Brink, 1957) and an important consequence of meiosis during spermatogenesis is the separation of the X- and Y-chromosomes into separate spermatids and thence into separate spermatozoa. During the prophase of the first meiotic division, the X- and Y-chromosomes pair together over part of their length, the pairing segment, which is homologous in both chromosomes. In addition to the pairing segment, each of these chromosomes has a differential segment (see Figure 7.29). The differential segments carry the genes primarily responsible for sexual differentiation ; they are of unequal length, are not homologous and do not pair. Chiasmata regularly occur in the pairing segments but cannot do so in the differential segments. In marsupials, the centromeres of the sex chromosomes are situated in the differential segments and the X- and Y-differential segments are invariably separated at the anaphase of the first meiotic division. This is referred to as " pre-reduction " (see Figure 7.29). In eutherian mammals, however, the centromeres appear to be generally located in the pairing segments. Under these conditions, a chiasma between the centrioles and the differential segments will delay the separation of the X- and Y-differential segments until the anaphase of the second meiotic division. This is referred to as " post-reduction." The available evidence (see White, 1954) suggests that pre-reduction is much commoner than post-reduction and is invariably found in the bull, boar, ram, stallion, goat and several species of rodent, insectivore, bat and carnivore. Post-reduction does definitely occur, however, and has been reliably reported as the normal method of segregation of the X- and Y-chromosomes in several species of mouse of the genus *Apodemus*. Several workers have claimed that both pre- and post-reduction co-exist in the same species ; White (1954) and Matthey (1957) believe that the evidence for this is inconclusive, but Slizynski (1954) gives evidence supporting the existence of both pre- and post-reduction in the house mouse.

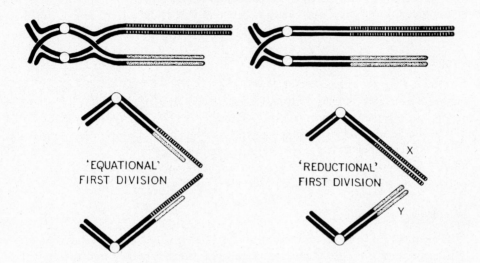

Fig. 7.29—Diagram illustrating the structure of the sex chromosomes (top) and the difference between "post-reduction" (left) and "pre-reduction" (right). (From White, 1954.)

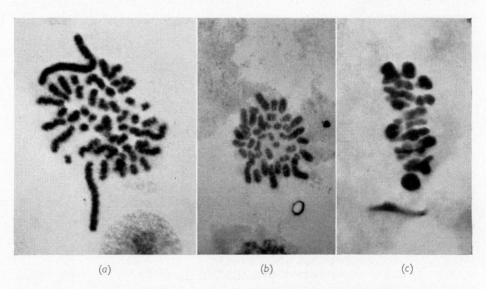

Fig. 7.30a, b, c—Micrographs of chromosome groups in testis-squash preparations fixed in acetocarmine. (a) Polar view of spermatogonial metaphase in the field vole. The X-chromosome (top) and the Y-chromosome (bottom) are clearly shown; (Ultra-violet microscopy, 2,750 Å, × 2,350 (from Austin, 1957). (b) Polar view of spermatogonial metaphase in the albino rat (C. R. Austin, original). (c) Equatorial view of metaphase of first meiotic division in the albino rat. The nucleus of a spermatozoon is shown beneath the chromosomes (C. R. Austin, original).

The end result of pre- and post-reduction is the same : both processes provide a means for ensuring that two of the spermatids resulting from each meiosis carry the X-chromosome and two carry the Y-chromosome.   If X- and Y-spermatids are equally viable and if no cell divisions intervene before spermateliosis, an equal number of female-determining (X) and male-determining (Y) spermatozoa will be produced, and if these are equally competent to reach and fertilise eggs a primary sex ratio of unity will result (*see* Chapter 22).

Synthesis of DNA

During late interphase, the DNA content of the nucleus of the primary sper-matocyte increases to the tetraploid amount in a similar manner to that which occurs in other cells before mitosis.   There is no subsequent synthesis of DNA during the development of the spermatogenic cells.   At the first meiotic division, each secondary spermatocyte receives a diploid amount of DNA and at the second meiotic division each spermatid receives a haploid amount of DNA (Swift, 1950 ; Leuchtenberger, Leuchtenberger, Schrader and Weir, 1956).

Significance of meiosis

The meiotic divisions undergone by the spermatocytes correspond to those that occur during the development of the egg (*see* Chapters 5 and 10), though in oogenesis only one functional gamete is produced at each meiosis and there can be no segregation of sex chromosomes since the female is the homogametic sex. At fertilisation, the syngamy of two haploid gametes restores the normal diploid condition of the nucleus.   Meiosis is therefore the antithesis of fertilisation : the two processes together provide the means whereby new combinations of genetic material arise with each succeeding generation, while the total amount of this material remains constant.

Division of the Spermatids

It is generally accepted that the spermatids do not divide, but Hertwig (1933) and Roosen-Runge (1952) believe that the spermatids of man ordinarily divide once before differentiating into spermatozoa.   The frequent occurrence of multi-nucleate spermatids in many species also suggests that spermatids may be capable of division, although other explanations are possible.   From general considerations, the division of spermatids as a normal feature of spermatogenesis seems unlikely and the subject requires reinvestigation.

Spermateliosis

The spermatid develops into the definitive spermatozoon by a remarkable process of differentiation known as spermateliosis.   Spermateliosis in mammals has been studied by many workers (Table III) and its general cytological features are now fairly well understood.   There remains, however, a great deal of uncer-tainty about many of the detailed aspects of the process and nothing is known of the mechanism whereby spermateliosis is controlled.

Outline of spermateliosis

At first, the spermatids do not differ very greatly in appearance from the spermatocytes, but extensive changes quickly take place. These have been classified into four main-phases, the Golgi-phase, the cap-phase, the acrosome-phase and the maturation-phase, by Leblond and Clermont (1952a, b) and Clermont and Leblond (1955). This classification is illustrated in Figs. 7.31 and 7.32.

TABLE III

PRINCIPAL RECENT INVESTIGATORS OF SPERMATELIOSIS IN MAMMALS

Species	Investigator
House mouse (*Mus*)	Gresson (1942, 1950), Challice (1953), Oakberg (1956a)
Rat (*Rattus*)	Gresson and Zlotnik (1945), Gresson (1950), Austin and Sapsford (1951), Leblond and Clermont (1952a and b), Watson (1952), Daoust and Clermont (1955), Dhillon (1955), Clermont (1956), Yasuzumi (1956)
Guinea- pig (*Cavia*)	Gatenby and Woodger (1921), Gatenby and Wigoder (1929), Leblond and Clermont (1952b), Sharma, Chaudhuri and Sattee (1953)
Golden hamster (*Mesocricetus*)	Gresson and Zlotnik (1945), Leblond and Clermont (1952b), Challice (1953), Clermont (1954)
Rabbit (*Oryctolagus*)	Gresson and Zlotnik (1945)
Cat (*Felis*)	Gresson and Zlotnik (1945), Burgos and Fawcett (1955)
Dog (*Canis*)	Gresson and Zlotnik (1945)
Bull (*Bos*)	Gresson and Zlotnik (1948), Melampy, Cavazos and Duncan (1955), Hancock and Trevan (1957)
Ram (*Ovis*)	Gresson and Zlotnik (1945), Clermont and Leblond (1955), Melampy *et al.* (1955)
Boar (*Sus*)	Gresson and Zlotnik (1945), Melampy *et al.* (1955)
Kangaroo (*Macropus*)	Binder (1927)
Opossum (*Didelphis*)	Duesberg (1920)
Monkey	Clermont and Leblond (1955)
Man (*Homo*)	Gatenby and Beams (1935), Clermont and Leblond (1955), Ånberg (1957), Fawcett and Burgos (1956b)
Reviews	Wilson (1925), Gresson (1951, 1957), Nath (1956)

During the Golgi-phase, a number (usually one to four) of small granules, the proacrosomic granules, arise in the medulla of the Golgi apparatus. These granules are strongly PAS-reactive in contrast to the Golgi medulla which stains only weakly with the PAS-technique. By some techniques, the granules appear homogeneous, but by others it is clear that they each consist of an inner and outer zone that are often referred to as the granule and the vacuole or vesicle respectively. The proacrosomic granules fuse to form the proacrosome which also consists of an inner and outer zone.   The proacrosome, with the attached Golgi apparatus, now comes to lie on the nuclear membrane at what is hereafter referred to as the anterior pole of the nucleus.   Meanwhile, a fine filament, the rudiment of the tail, emerges from one of the centrioles, hereafter called the distal centriole.   This filament

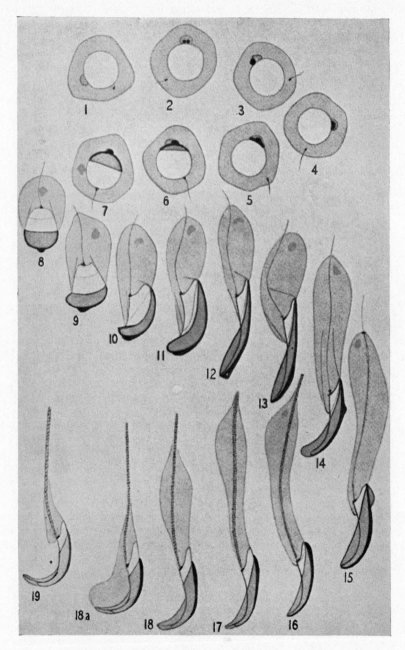

Fig. 7.31—Diagrammatic representation of the stages of spermateliosis in the rat, as seen in preparations stained with PAS reagent and iron haematoxylin. (1–3, Golgi-phase; 4–7, cap-phase; 8–14, acrosome-phase; 15–19, maturation-phase.) (From Leblond and Clermont, 1952a.)

soon extends beyond the main body of the cell, but even before this occurs it exhibits vigorous undulating movements that appear to originate from the centriole (Austin and Sapsford, 1952).

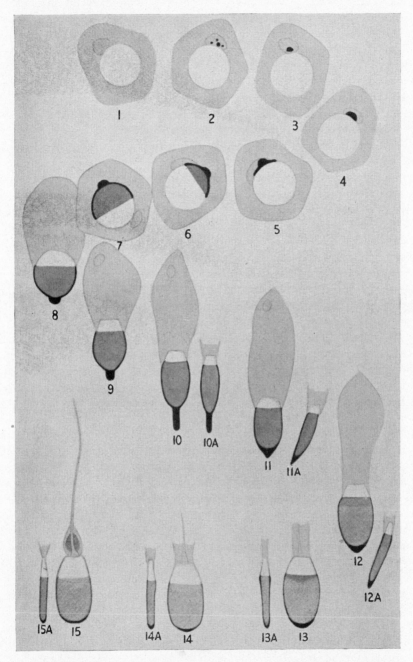

Fig. 7.32—Diagrammatic representation of the stages of spermateliosis in the ram, as seen in preparations stained with PAS reagent. (1–3, Golgi-phase; 4–7, cap-phase; 8–12, acrosome-phase; 13–15, maturation-phase.) (From Clermont and Leblond, 1955.) (By permission of the publisher from Fig. 1, Clermont, Y., & Leblond, C. P., *Amer. J. Anat.*, 1955, **96**, 233.)

During the cap-phase of spermateliosis, the Golgi apparatus becomes detached from the proacrosome and moves toward the posterior part of the cell. The proacrosome then flattens itself on the nuclear membrane and the outer zone of the proacrosome grows to form a cap over the anterior part of the nucleus. The two centrioles, with the tail filament attached to the distal one, move towards the nucleus and the inner or proximal centriole becomes attached to the nuclear membrane at its posterior pole. The chromatoid body appears to float freely in the cell cytoplasm.

During the acrosome-phase of differentiation, the spermatid becomes orientated with the anterior pole of the nucleus towards the basement membrane of the testis tubule and pronounced changes occur in its shape. The cell elongates and the cytoplasm moves posteriorly until the proacrosome and the anterior part of the nucleus protrude well beyond the bounds of the cytoplasm. The nucleus becomes highly condensed and homogeneous, increases its affinity for basic dyes and begins to assume the shape characteristic of the mature spermatozoon. The inner zone of the proacrosome now spreads over the anterior part of the nuclear surface within the cap earlier formed by the outer zone of the proacrosome. The anterior part of the nucleus thus becomes covered by a cap which consists of inner and outer zones. This cap is the acrosome : it develops slowly toward its mature size and shape while still retaining its strong PAS-reactivity. Meanwhile, during the early stages of the acrosome-phase of spermateliosis a tubular structure, the manchette or Schwanzmanchette, becomes visible. It arises on the nuclear membrane in the form of a circumferential collar at the site of the future posterior boundary of the acrosome and the anterior boundary of the post-nuclear cap. The manchette extends posteriorly as a tube that loosely surrounds the posterior part of the nucleus and the anterior part of the developing tail. Between the manchette and the nucleus, an argentophil structure appears in the region of the nuclear ring and extends posteriorly to form a covering to the posterior part of the nucleus. This is the post-nuclear cap. The bulk of the spermatid cytoplasm continues to migrate posteriorly and collects along the anterior region of the tail. As this occurs, the manchette appears to fuse with the cell membrane. The tail filament grows longer and thicker and the chromatoid body comes to envelop the filament near its origin on the distal centriole. The distal centriole gives rise to a ring-shaped structure, the ring centriole, which surrounds the tail filament. The Golgi apparatus floats freely in the posterior part of the cytoplasm. Meanwhile the spermatids become embedded in the Sertoli cytoplasm and appear to migrate towards the Sertoli nuclei (Elftman, 1950).

The developing spermatid now bears considerable resemblance to the mature spermatozoon and during the maturation-phase of development the transformation is completed. The ring centriole moves distally along the developing tail until it comes to occupy a position that marks the posterior limit of the future mid-piece. The ring centriole now becomes known as Jensen's ring. The mitochondria assume a compact spherical form and dispose themselves in a regular manner around the tail in the region between the neck and Jensen's ring. Subsequently, they appear to coalesce into a double helix around the axial filaments. The manchette appears to contribute to the post-nuclear cap and to the outer covering of the mid-piece. The residual cytoplasm condenses along the mid-piece and is gradually eliminated from the cell until only a small bead, the cytoplasmic droplet, remains attached to the neck. The transformation of the spermatid is almost complete : it is released into the lumen of the testis tubule and is now called an early spermatozoon. The early spermatozoa are passed into the epididymis where they develop to functional maturity (*see* p. 95).

Condensation of the nucleus

The spermatid nucleus is at first relatively large, vesicular and lightly staining. It contains one or more rather indistinct pyroninophilic nucleoli. The nuclear membrane appears to be devoid of pore-like openings such as are often found in other kinds of nuclei.

The changes in the distribution of DNA in the nucleus of the developing rat spermatid have been studied by Daoust and Clermont (1955) by means of the Feulgen technique (Feulgen and Rossenbeck, 1924 ; Swift, 1950). These workers find that the nuclei of young spermatids contain fine granules of Feulgen-positive material (DNA), among which are dispersed several larger granules. Towards the end of the cap phase of spermateliosis the DNA appears to disperse into finer granules which accumulate at the two poles of the nucleus and leave a lightly stained equatorial zone in between. Faintly stained nucleoli are still distinguishable : later they appear to disperse. As the nucleus elongates during the acrosome-phase, the Feulgen-positive material becomes more evenly distributed, but small " vacuoles " of unstained material remain. Gradually the staining reaction to the Feulgen reagent becomes more intense. The vacuoles of non-staining material at first become more distinct but subsequently disappear. By the end of the acrosome-phase of spermateliosis, the entire nucleus appears homogeneous and is filled with material that is intensely Feulgen-positive (*see* Fig. 7.38). The chromatin is now very condensed and is resistant to the action of deoxyribonuclease. During the maturation-phase, there is no further apparent change in the distribution and staining properties of the nuclear material.

It is evident from these observations that the DNA of the spermatid nucleus undergoes extensive rearrangement during spermateliosis. These changes, however, are not associated with changes in the total amount of DNA present, for this appears to remain constant after the second meiotic division (Swift, 1950 ; Leuchtenberger, Leuchtenberger, Schrader and Weir, 1956). It is also of interest to note that the nucleus appears to condense as a whole and not into distinctive chromosomes.

The process of nuclear condensation during metamorphosis of the human spermatid has been studied by Fawcett and Burgos (1956b) with the electron microscope. They found that the nuclear material of the early spermatid is composed of closely-packed fine granules (about 100 Å in diameter) of rather low density, with interspersed coarser granules of greater density. The nucleolus was inconspicuous and indefinite in outline. As the nucleus elongates, the fine granules are replaced by coarser granules with markedly increased osmiophilia. As differentiation continues, the coarse granules become more closely packed, but in some nuclei clear irregularly shaped areas, or " vacuoles," remain. Towards the end of spermateliosis, the coarse dense granules (300–400 Å in diameter) coalesce into a smooth homogeneous mass which displays only moderate osmiophilia. Concurrently with these changes in fine structure, there is a steady reduction in the size of the nucleus and a change in the shape of its sagittal section from obtuse to acuminate. These observations confirm and extend similar ones previously made on cat spermatids (Burgos and Fawcett, 1955), excepting that in the cat spermatids there were no persistent " vacuoles " in the nucleus.

Burgos and Fawcett point out that the observed fluctuations of osmiophilia in the nuclear material during spermateliosis are reminiscent of earlier observations of Oliver (1913) on fluctuations in the intensity of staining with iron haematoxylin. In the rat, Leblond and Clermont (1952a, b) found that the affinity of the spermatid nucleus for basic dyes increased progressively during the second half of the acrosome-phase of spermateliosis and reached its maximum at the end of that phase. During the maturation-phase, there is a decrease in basophilia accompanied by an increase in reactivity to the Sakaguchi test for arginine (Lison, 1955). Vendrely, Knobloch and Vendrely (1957) believe that the transformation of histone to protamine in the spermatid nucleus occurs very late in spermateliosis.

The Golgi apparatus and the development of the acrosome

The Golgi apparatus of the early spermatid is a prominent rounded structure, situated near the nucleus, and composed of two distinct zones, the cortex and the medulla. The medulla is often referred to as the idiosome or the archoplasm. The precise nature of the Golgi apparatus has been the subject of a good deal of controversy (see Gresson, 1950, 1957 ; Nath, 1956, 1957), and even the validity of its name is in doubt (Baker, 1955). Many workers have expressed the belief that the cortex is composed of discrete bodies, the dictyosomes, which are variously described as rods, plates, filaments or granules, surrounding or embedded in the medulla (Rau and Brambell, 1925 ; Bell, 1929 ; Gresson, 1942 ; Gresson and Zlotnik, 1945, 1948 ; Sharma, Chandhuri and Sattee, 1953 ; Nath, 1956, 1957). Gatenby and Woodger (1921) state that the cortex appears as a system of curved plates or rods in osmium preparations, but stains either homogeneously or as a reticulum in silver preparations. Studies with the electron microscope, however, show that the spermatid Golgi apparatus consists of a cortex of closely approximated parallel membranes, which limit thin flattened vesicles, and a medulla of small vacuoles (Burgos and Fawcett, 1955; Fawcett, and Burgos 1956b; Clermont, 1956a ; Dalton and Felix, 1957). It is clear, therefore, that the prevalent concept of the dictyosomes as discrete granular elements is no longer tenable.

The association of the Golgi apparatus with the formation of the acrosome was appreciated by many early workers and Bowen (1924) propounded the modern view that the acrosome is essentially a secretion product of the Golgi apparatus. Burgos and Fawcett (1955) believe that the lamellar vesicles of the cortex give rise to the vacuoles of the medulla and that certain of these enlarge and form the proacrosomic granules. These granules increase in size and then fuse to form the proacrosome. The granules and the proacrosome each consist of an inner zone and an outer zone that are often referred to as the granule or bead and the vacuole or vesicle, respectively (Mèves, 1899; Duesberg, 1908b; Bowen, 1922; Gresson and Zlotnik, 1945 ; Oettlé, 1948 ; Gresson, 1950 ; Watson, 1952 ; Burgos and Fawcett, 1955). By some techniques, however, the proacrosomic granules and the proacrosome appear homogeneous and this at first led Leblond and Clermont (1952a) to the conclusion that the outer zone, or vacuole, was an artefact. Later, these workers described the proacrosome as consisting of distinct inner and outer zones (Clermont and Leblond, 1955) and it is clear that these zones correspond to the granule and vacuole of most other workers. Some investigators, however, have described an additional vacuole enclosing the proacrosome : this almost certainly arises from degenerative changes *in vitro* or shrinkage during fixation. It has sometimes been confused with the outer zone of the proacrosome and has led to the suggestion that this too may be an artefact. There is, in fact, no doubt that the two zones of the proacrosome are real and that each contributes in a specific manner to the formation of the acrosome. Both zones are PAS-reactive (Leblond and Clermont, 1952a; Clermont and Leblond, 1955) and both fluoresce red in ultraviolet radiation after treatment with acridine orange (Bishop and Smiles, 1958). In general, however, the inner zone stains more strongly than the outer : it is also more opaque to ultraviolet radiation (Fig. 7.36) and to electrons (Burgos and Fawcett, 1955; Fawcett and Burgos, 1956b; Figs. 7.33, 7.34 and 7.35). With Masson's trichrome stain the inner zone is coloured red and the outer zone green (Clermont and Leblond, 1955). With iron haematoxylin the inner zone stains black and the outer zone yellow (Leblond and Clermont, 1952a). Clermont and Leblond conclude that the proacrosome is probably made up of two different kinds of PAS-reactive material—possibly a basic mucopolysaccharide in the inner zone and an acidic or neutral polysaccharide in the outer zone. The proacrosome is bounded by a distinct membrane (Burgos and Fawcett, 1955).

After its disposition on the nuclear membrane, the proacrosome continues to grow, apparently by coalescence with small vacuoles that arise within the closely applied Golgi apparatus, and both the inner and outer zones increase in size. As this happens, the rounded contour of the nucleus becomes flattened beneath the proacrosome (Fig. 7.34a). When the proacrosome reaches its greatest size, the Golgi apparatus migrates towards the posterior end of the cell. Shortly afterwards, the outer zone of the proacrosome appears to collapse over the anterior pole of the nucleus, as if by loss of fluid, and the nucleus resumes its rounded contour. In this way, the proacrosome comes to form a cap over the anterior pole of the nucleus. The cap spreads posteriorly until more than half the nuclear surface is covered. Its membrane remains continuous and encloses the entire structure including the inner zone of the proacrosome which meanwhile remains unchanged at the apex of the nucleus (Fig. 7.34b). After the developing cap has reached its posterior limit, the inner zone begins to flatten and it too spreads posteriorly over the nucleus but apparently within the confines of the outer zone (Burgos and Fawcett, 1955 ; Fawcett and Burgos, 1956b). In this way, as originally suggested by Duesberg (1908), both zones of the proacrosome contribute to the structure of the acrosome. As development continues, the two zones become less distinct.

During the maturation-phase of spermateliosis, the developing acrosome becomes progressively less reactive to the PAS-test and in man PAS-reactivity appears to be almost entirely lost (Leblond and Clermont, 1952a, b ; Clermont and Leblond, 1955). As pointed out earlier, however, the degree of staining obtained with the PAS-test is greatly dependent upon the technique used, and negative findings must be cautiously interpreted. Oakberg (1956a) does not appear to have noticed any appreciable decrease in PAS-reactivity in the developing acrosome of the mouse.

The preliminary observations of Cleland (1956) suggest that acrosome formation in marsupials is essentially similar to that observed in placental mammals.

After formation of the proacrosome, the Golgi apparatus, which at this stage is often called the Golgi remnant, migrates to the posterior end of the developing

(a)

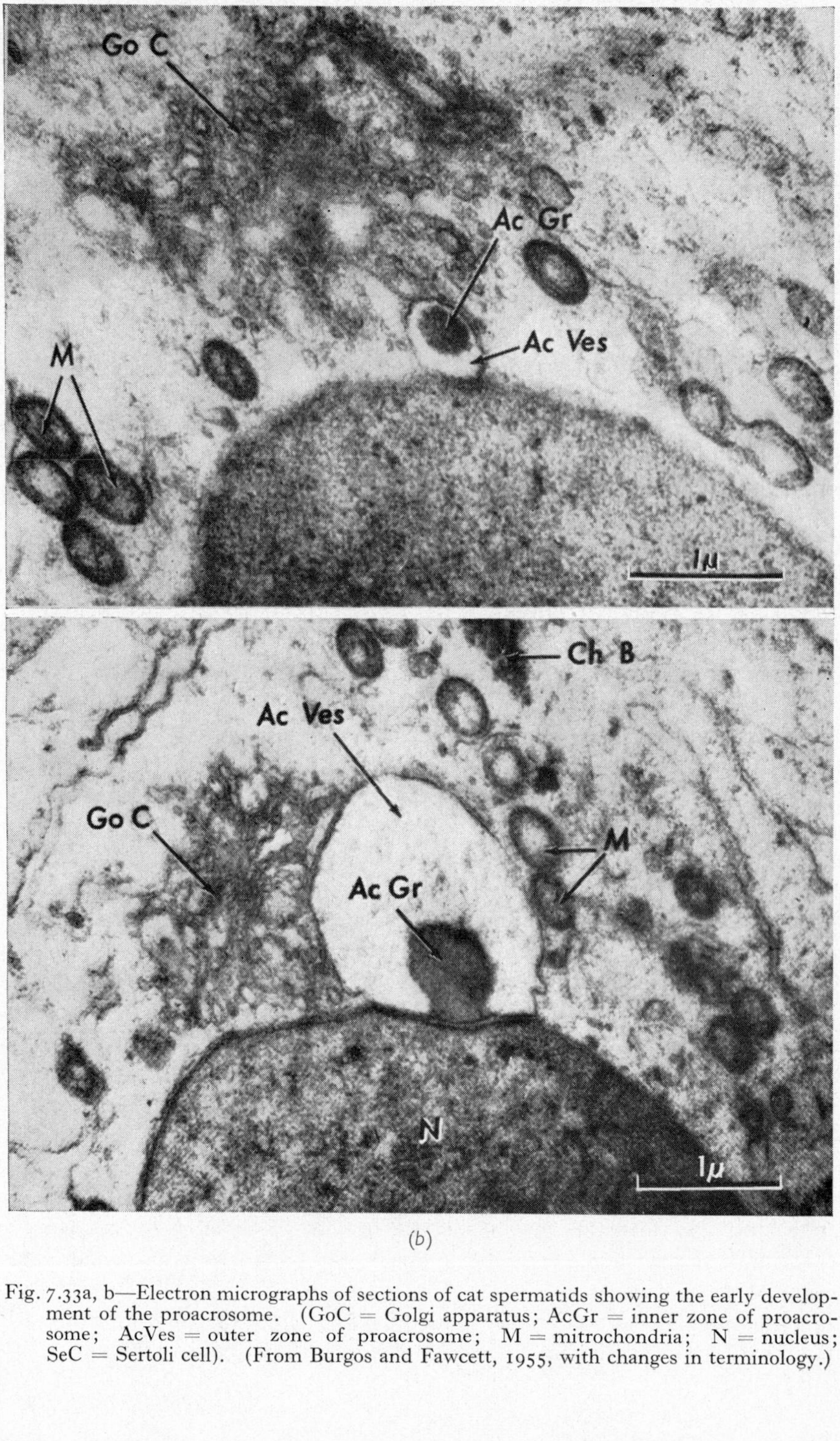

(b)

Fig. 7.33a, b—Electron micrographs of sections of cat spermatids showing the early development of the proacrosome. (GoC = Golgi apparatus; AcGr = inner zone of proacrosome; AcVes = outer zone of proacrosome; M = mitrochondria; N = nucleus;
SeC = Sertoli cell). (From Burgos and Fawcett, 1955, with changes in terminology.)

spermatid. It loses its ordered concentric organisation and plays no further obvious role in spermateliosis. Eventually it is mainly shed from the cell with

(*a*)

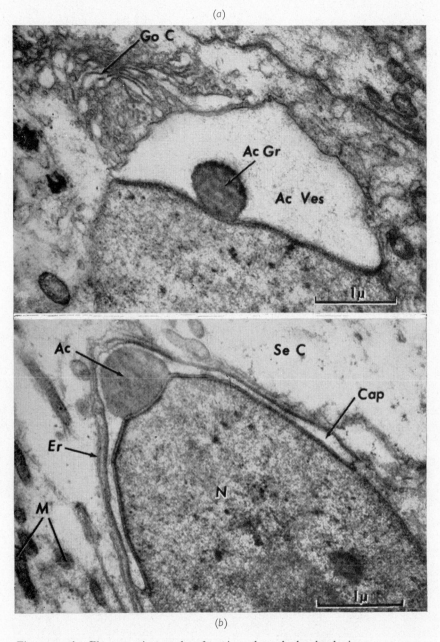

(*b*)

Fig. 7.34a, b—Electron micrographs of sections through the developing proacrosome of cat spermatids. Labels as in Fig. 7.33. (From Burgos and Fawcett, 1955.)

the residual cytoplasm. Some workers, however, claim that a small portion of the Golgi apparatus buds off from the main mass and comes to lie within the cytoplasmic droplet (Gatenby and Woodger, 1921 ; Gatenby and Wigoder, 1929 ;

Gresson and Zlotnik, 1945 ; Gresson, 1950).   Gresson (1950) also believes that Golgi material may take part in the formation of the neck.

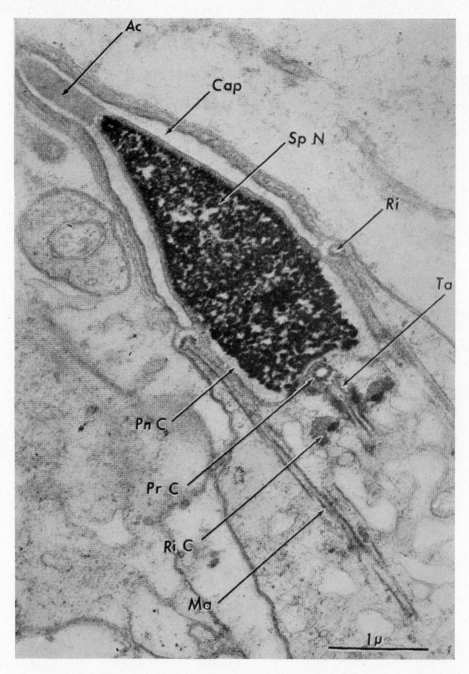

Fig. 7.35—Electron micrograph of a longitudinal section of a late spermatid of the cat. (SpN = spermatid nucleus; Ac = inner zone of proacrosome; Cap = outer zone of proacrosome; Ri = nuclear ring; Ma = manchette; PnC = (?) post-nuclear cap; PrC = " cen-triole; " RiC = ring centriole; Ta = tail filaments.) (From Burgos and Fawcett, 1955, with changes in terminology.)

Development of the perforatorium

During the maturation-phase of spermateliosis in the rat, mouse and golden hamster, the acrosome is displaced forward in relation to the nucleus by the development of the perforatorium. This appears to arise as a thickening and extension of the anterior part of the nuclear membrane (Leblond and Clermont, 1952a, b). It is first visible as a small protrusion at the apex of the nucleus and gradually extends beneath the acrosome until it becomes a prominent feature of the mature spermatozoon (*see* p. 10). It is neither PAS- nor Feulgen-reactive and its origin and properties show that it is distinct from the acrosome. It was not recognised as a distinct structure in the developing spermatozoa of the rat and golden hamster by Gresson and Zlotnik (1945).

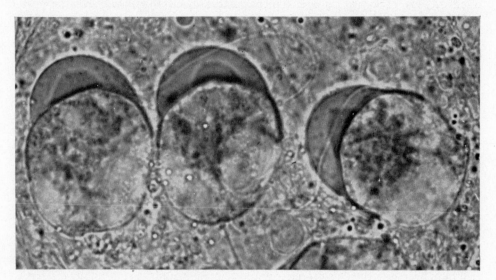

Fig. 7.36—Ultraviolet micrographs (2,750 Å) of nuclei and developing proacrosomes of guinea-pig spermatids (× 3,300). (J. Smiles, original.)

Although the perforatorium has only been definitely recognised in the spermatozoa of certain Murine and Cricetine rodents, there are indications that it may exist in less well developed form in other kinds of mammalian spermatozoa. Thus, electron micrographs of sections of cat and human spermatids do show distinct changes in the nuclear membrane where it is overlain by the acrosome (Burgos and Fawcett, 1955; Fawcett and Burgos, 1956b). These changes appear to involve a thickening of the membrane together with the deposition of a layer of dense, osmiophil, granular material on its inner surface. Ånberg (1957) states that the nuclear membrane of the human spermatid is more conspicuous where it is covered by the acrosome than elsewhere.

Development of the post-nuclear cap

The development of the post-nuclear cap was first studied by Gatenby and Wigoder (1929). According to these workers, the post-nuclear cap of the guinea-pig originates from argentophil granules, the post-nuclear granules, that are present in the cytoplasm of the early spermatid and subsequently coalesce on the surface of the posterior part of the nucleus.   Their figures suggest that this coalescence first occurs in the region of the nuclear ring and subsequently spreads posteriorly. Gatenby and Beams (1935), however, express the belief that the development of the post-nuclear cap in human spermatids starts at the posterior end of the nucleus and spreads anteriorly.   Later, Zlotnik (1943) described the deposition of argentophil granules in the region of the nuclear ring in spermatids of the dog and cat and the subsequent spread of argentophil material posteriorly over the nuclear surface.   These observations were extended by Gresson and Zlotnik (1945) who conclude that the post-nuclear cap is mainly formed by the spread of argentophil material from the nuclear ring, but that the posterior end of the cap is formed from a second argentophil ring, the posterior ring, situated at the posterior end of the nucleus.   Hancock (1957a) and Hancock and Trevan (1957) state that the post-nuclear cap of the boar and bull develops as an argentophil band along the border of the acrosome which extends posteriorly until it covers the entire posterior pole of the nucleus.   They also observed a posterior ring which was no longer distinguishable when the development of the post-nuclear cap was complete.

The centrioles and the tail filaments

The twin centrioles of the early spermatid evidently arise by division of a single centriole during telophase of the second meiotic division (Tobias, 1956).   The division products remain in close apposition and the primitive tail filament can be seen to emerge from one of them while they are still free within the spermatid cytoplasm (Wilson, 1925 ; Austin and Sapsford, 1951).   Wilson (1925) states that the filament is formed from the distal centriole, which he considers to be the blepharoplast, but Gatenby and Beams (1935) and Tobias (1956) believe that the filament originates jointly from both centrioles.   After their migration to the posterior pole of the nucleus, the development of the centrioles is obscured by the complexity of the region of the developing neck and it is reasonably certain that many structures that have been described as products of the centrioles are in fact of totally different origin.   The fate of the proximal centriole is particularly uncertain owing to its nearness to the nucleus and to the fact that staining techniques for the centrioles tend also to stain the nucleus heavily.   Claims that the proximal centriole sometimes divides can probably be discounted (*see* Gatenby and Beams, 1935 ; Gresson and Zlotnik, 1945).   The distal centriole increases in size and becomes relatively conspicuous as a disc-shaped body.   Eventually it gives rise to the ring centriole that encircles the axial filaments and migrates to the position that marks the future posterior limit of the mid-piece.   It then becomes inconspicuous.   Wilson (1925), reviewing the work of earlier investigators, considers that the distal centriole divides to form the ring centriole and a smaller body which remains close to the proximal centriole and forms part of the centriolar apparatus of the neck.   Gatenby and Beams (1935) and Gresson and Zlotnik (1945), however, believe that the distal centriole develops into the ring centriole without division.

The manchette

The nature and function of the manchette (Lenhossek, 1898) are obscure. Many early workers regarded it as a tubular outgrowth of the nuclear membrane (Kölliker, 1899 ; Schoenfeld, 1900 ; Mollé, 1906, 1910).   Others have described it as a system of fine filaments of cytoplasmic origin (Mèves, 1899 ; Oliver, 1913) and the correctness of this view is supported by recent studies with the electron microscope (Watson, 1952 ; Burgos and Fawcett, 1955 ; Fig. 7.35). Burgos and Fawcett have shown that the manchette is made up of fine, tubular filaments. These filaments arise from a distinct ring-like structure, of unknown origin, that girdles the nucleus at the level of the posterior margin of the acrosome and appears to correspond to the argentophil nuclear ring of Zlotnik (1943) and Gresson and Zlotnik (1945). The fully formed manchette encloses the posterior part of the nucleus and the anterior part of the developing tail, including the centrioles, the chromatoid body and most of the mitochondria. As the development of the spermatid continues and the bulk of the cytoplasm moves posteriorly and is discarded, the manchette appears to fuse with the cell membrane and becomes no longer distinguishable. This suggests that the manchette contributes to the covering sheath of the posterior part of the nucleus, the neck and the mid-piece (Gresson and Zlotnik, 1945 ; Gresson, 1950). Lenhossek (1898) and Oliver (1913) also suggested that the manchette took part in the formation of the mid-piece, but this was denied by Gatenby and Beams (1935).

The chromatoid body

Since its early recognition by von Brunn (1876), Brown (1885) and Benda (1891), the chromatoid body or chromatoider Körper has been studied by many workers (*see* Wilson, 1925 ; Tobias, 1956) but it is far from certain that all the structures described under this name are of the same nature. It evidently arises in the cytoplasm of the primary spermatocyte, divides and is passed to the spermatids, but the mode of its origin is unknown (Wilson, 1925 ; Tobias, 1956). Tobias believes that the early spermatids of the gerbil each contain two small chromatoid bodies which subsequently increase in size and coalesce to form a single rounded body with a deeply staining cortex and a lightly staining core. Leblond and Clermont (1952b) describe it as an irregular basophil body that stains intensely with iron haematoxylin, and Burgos and Fawcett (1955) describe it as an irregular mass of osmiophil granular material. Daoust and Clermont (1955) state that it is pyroninophil and contains RNA. It stains vividly with Newton's crystal violet and is Feulgen-negative (Tobias, 1956).

During the acrosome phase of spermateliosis the chromatoid body migrates to the neck region of the spermatid (Duesberg, 1908b ; Leblond and Clermont, 1952 ; Tobias, 1956), but its fate is uncertain. Many early workers expressed the belief that it does not give rise to any of the formed elements of the spermatozoon and is eliminated from the spermatid with the residual cytoplasm (Wilson, 1925). Most probably it contributes to the structure of the neck, and this view is supported by Tobias who believes that part of the chromatoid body forms a discrete rod-like body in the neck and part coalesces with the ring centriole.

The accessory body

Gresson and Zlotnik (1945) have given the name accessory body to certain argentophil structures of variable size that are present in the cytoplasm of spermatocytes and spermatids and are believed to be of Golgi origin. Each spermatid is said to receive at least one of these bodies which often appears to be formed of two closely applied spherical structures. During spermateliosis, an accessory body migrates to the vicinity of the centrioles and ultimately give rise to a characteristic granular structure in the neck of the spermatozoon. Gresson and Zlotnik suggest that the accessory body may later give rise to Golgi material in the mature spermatozoon, and that it is homologous with the accessory body of Gatenby and Beams (1935) and with the chromatoid body of many other workers. The equivalence of the accessory body to the chromatoid body is, however, by no means certain and is not accepted by Tobias (1956).

The mitochrondia

In some species, the mitochondria of the early spermatids are uniformly scattered throughout the cytoplasm; in others, they tend to congregate around the periphery of the cell, and in others again, they tend to gather around the nucleus or the Golgi apparatus (Gresson and Zlotnik, 1945, 1948 ; Sharma, Chaudhuri and Sattee, 1953 ; Burgos and Fawcett, 1955 ; Yasuzumi, 1956 ; Ånberg, 1957). They are rounded bodies in which the internal membranes are less extensive and less orderly in arrangement than in the mitochondria of somatic cells and spermatogonia. The centre of each mitochondrion is often devoid of membranes and occupied by a matrix of relatively low density. As the spermatid develops, the mitochondria cluster around the mid-piece region of the tail filaments within the manchette. Gradually they become arranged in a double helix around the tail filaments between the neck and Jensen's ring. They now contain even fewer internal membranes than previously and each is bounded by a thick, osmiophil triple-layered membrane. They become elongate and horseshoe-shaped and begin to condense around the tail filaments. As this happens, the mitochondria of each helix appear to coalesce into a continuous strand, but the evidence that actual fusion occurs is still equivocal. Not all the mitochondria of the spermatid take part in the formation of the mid-piece : some are eliminated with the residual cytoplasm (Gresson, 1950 ; Bell, 1953 ; Challice, 1953 ; Burgos and Fawcett, 1955; Yasuzumi, 1956; Ånberg, 1957; Nath, 1957).

The cytoplasmic RNA

The cytoplasm of the early spermatid contains widely scattered, small particles of ribonucleoprotein, which are apparently not associated with the membranes of the endoplasmic reticulum as they are in most other cells (Burgos and Fawcett, 1955). During the acrosome-phase of spermateliosis, these particles aggregate into coarser granules and gather at the posterior end of the cell. During the maturation-phase, the RNA material collects into still larger granules, which are eventually released from the spermatid. Some appear to disintegrate rapidly, others are taken up by the germinal epithelium (Daled, 1951 ; Daoust and Clermont, 1955; Clermont, 1956b ; Fig. 7.39). The fate of the RNA of the chromatoid body is unknown.

Formation of the cytoplasmic droplet

Most investigators are agreed that the cytoplasmic droplet which invests the neck of the early spermatozoon is derived from the spermatid cytoplasm, but the manner of its formation is unknown. Merton (1939), however, regards the droplet as a secretion of the Sertoli cell. Several workers state that the droplet contains

Golgi material (Gatenby and Woodger, 1921 ; Gatenby and Wigoder, 1929 ; Gresson and Zlotnik, 1954 ; Gresson, 1950 ; Sharma, Chaudhuri and Sattee, 1953). Its structure has not been examined with the electron microscope. It displays little absorption of ultraviolet radiation (Fig. 7.20h).

The spermatid membrane

As the cytoplasm of the developing spermatid moves posteriorly, the surface membrane comes into close contact with the developing acrosome and can be clearly seen in electron micrographs. Later the membrane appears to invest the posterior region of the head and the mid-piece also. Its relationship to the main-piece of the tail and to the cytoplasmic droplet, and the mechanism whereby the residual cytoplasm is eliminated, are unknown.

Release of Spermatozoa from the Testis

During the final stages of their development the spermatids become deeply embedded in pockets in the Sertoli cells, but the Sertoli-cell membrane remains intact throughout (Burgos and Fawcett, 1955). The mechanism whereby the early spermatozoa are released from the germinal epithelium is unknown : it may conceivably involve diffusion of hyaluronidase from the acrosome. The released spermatozoa appear to be rapidly transported from the testis to the epididymis, for they are rarely seen lying free within the testis tubules.

The Function of the Sertoli Cells

The Sertoli cells clearly play an indispensable role in the development of the spermatogenic cells, but as yet there is no clear understanding of their function. Many workers have suggested that the Sertoli cells are responsible for the main-tenance of the differentiating spermatids and Elftman (1950) points out that the establishment of the intimate association between spermatids and Sertoli cyto-plasm is accompanied by a marked acceleration of spermatid development. Saps-ford (1957) suggests that the maintenance function of the Sertoli cells extends to all the spermatogenic cells of the adult and even to the primordial germ cells of the embryo. Cleland (1951) believes that the Sertoli cells also play an important role in co-ordinating the development of the spermatogenic cells (see p. 73). Certainly the shape and disposition of the Sertoli cells suggest that they would be well suited to function in both maintenance and co-ordinating capacities. Roosen-Runge (1951b) suggests that the Sertoli cells may also have a contractile function. He observed slow undulating movements in the tubules of the rat and dog, and points out that the fibrillae of the Sertoli cells are the only tubule elements that appear capable of contraction.

VII. Dynamic Aspects of Spermatogenesis

A notable feature of spermatogenesis that has long been appreciated is the orderly fashion in which the process takes place. Thus, within any section of testis tubule the various stages of development of the spermatogenic cells are not arranged at random, but exist in well defined cell associations in which the development of any one generation of cells is synchronised and closely integrated with the development of the other generations present.   The various cell associations succeed each other in a regular manner in time and the sequence repeats itself cyclically and indefinitely.   At any given time, however, different tubules are synchronised at different stages of the cycle.   As a result, sections through the testis reveal orderly groups of cells within each tubule, but distinct differences between the cell associations of different tubules.   Longitudinal sections of any tubule also show that the nature of the cell association tends to change gradually along the axis of each tubule.

The Spermatogenic Cycle

The series of changes that occur in a given area of the germinal epithelium between two successive appearances of the same cell association is called the spermatogenic cycle (von Ebner, 1888 ; Regaud, 1901) or the cycle of the seminiferous epithelium (Leblond and Clermont, 1952a, b).   The cycle is divided into stages on the basis of the characteristics of the successive cell associations.   The significance of the cycle, and of the cell associations that constitute its stages, is best appreciated by considering the development of the progeny of a single stem-cell (i.e. a generation of spermatogenic cells).   The ensuing account is based on the observations of Leblond and Clermont on the rat (Leblond and Clermont, 1952a, b; Clermont and Leblond, 1953 ; Clermont and Perey, 1957b), but closely similar descriptions have been given for the golden hamster (Clermont, 1954) and for the mouse (Oakberg, 1956a).

Leblond and Clermont divided the spermatogenic cycle of the rat into fourteen stages, which are designated by the Roman numerals I to XIV.   The development of a new generation of spermatogenic cells starts in stage IX with the division of the stem-cell to produce new type-A spermatogonia.   These divide in stage XII to form more type-A spermatogonia, most of which divide in stage I of the next cycle to form intermediate-type spermatogonia.   These in turn divide in stage IV to produce type-B spermatogonia and in stage VI the type-B spermatogonia divide and give rise to resting primary spermatocytes.   This completes the five mitotic divisions of the spermatogonia (see p. 45).   Following a period of growth which lasts through stages VII and VIII, the primary spermatocytes enter the long meiotic prophase (see p. 46).   Leptotene extends through stages IX to XII, zygotene through stages XIII and XIV, pachytene through stages I to XII of the next (third) cycle and diplotene through stage XIII.   At stage XIV of the third cycle, the first meiotic division is completed and the secondary spermatocytes are formed.   These quickly divide to give rise to the spermatids, and at the beginning of the fourth cycle the spermatids start the long series of morphological changes that constitute spermateliosis (see p. 51).   The first fourteen stages of spermateliosis (designated by Arabic numerals) are used to characterise the fourteen stages (or cell associations) of the spermatogenic cycle (designated by Roman numerals).   The Golgi-phase of spermateliosis (stages 1 to 3 of spermateliosis) extends through stages I to III of the spermatogenic cycle ; the cap-phase (stages 4 to 7) extends through stages IV to VII, and the acrosome-phase (stages 8 to 14) extends through stages VIII to XIV.   Finally, the maturation-phase of spermateliosis (stages 15 to 19) extends through stages I to VIII of the fifth cycle.   Thus, the development of each generation of spermatogenic cells from stem-cell spermatogonia to early spermatozoa extends from the middle of the first cycle to the middle of the fifth cycle and occupies four complete cycles (*see* Table IV).

TABLE IV

THE SPERMATOGENIC CYCLE

Type of spermatogenic cell	Stages of the spermatogenic cycle													
	VIII	IX	X	XI	XII	XIII	XIV	I	II	III	IV	V	VI	VII
Spermatogonia :														
Stem-cell	I	o	o	o	I	I	I	I	I	I	I	I	I	I
Other Type-A	o	2	2	2	3	3	3	o	o	o	o	o	o	o
Intermediate	o	o	o	o	o	o	o	6	6	6	o	o	o	o
Type-B	o	o	o	o	o	o	o	o	o	o	12	12	o	o
Primary Spermato-cytes :														
" Resting "	24	o	o	o	o	o	o	o	o	o	o	o	24	24
Leptotene	o	24	24	24	24	o	o	o	o	o	o	o	o	o
Zygotene	o	o	o	o	o	24	24	o	o	o	o	o	o	o
Pachytene	24	24	24	24	24			24	24	24	24	24	24	24
Diplotene, Diaki-nesis, and Metaphase	o	o	o	o	o	24	o	o	o	o	o	o	o	o
Secondary Sperma-tocytes :	o	o	o	o	o	o	48	o	o	o	o	o	o	o
Spermatids :														
Golgi-phase	o	o	o	o	o	o	o	96	96	96	o	o	o	o
Cap-phase	o	o	o	o	o	o	o	o	o	o	96	96	96	96
Acrosome-phase	96	96	96	96	96	96	96	o	o	o	o	o	o	o
Maturation-phase	96	o	o	o	o	o	o	96	96	96	96	96	96	96

Theoretical relative distribution of types of spermatogenic cell—assuming no losses—throughout the stages of the spermatogenic cycle in the rat. Four generations of spermatogenic cells are present at any given time—these are indicated by the four sets of horizontal and vertical lines : double vertical lines indicate cell division. The figures in the vertical columns represent the relative numbers of various types of spermatogenic cell at each stage of the cycle.

The minority of type-A spermatogonia that do not divide at stage I of the cycle form the new stem-cells. They remain dormant until stage IX when they divide to start the development of the next generation of spermatogenic cells. In this way, a new generation arises in each cycle.

The Stages of the Cycle

Since the development of any one generation of spermatogenic cells occupies four complete spermatogenic cycles, and since a new generation arises in each cycle, four generations of cells can be found in any section of normal testis tubule at the

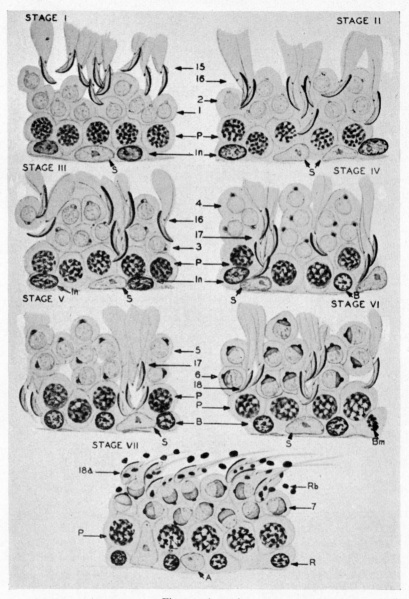

Fig. 7.37 (part 1).

Fig. 7.37—Diagrammatic representation of the stages of the spermatogenic cycle of the rat as seen in preparations stained with PAS reagent and iron haematoxylin. (Arabic numerals refer to spermatids at different stages of spermateliosis; A = A-type spermatogonium; B = B-type spermatogonium; Bm = mitosis of spermatogonium; R = resting spermatocyte; L = leptotene spermatocyte; Z = zygotene spermatocyte; F = pachytene spermatocyte; Di =

same time. Type-A spermatogonia, which include the stem-cells, are always present. Intermediate-type spermatogonia are present during stages II, III, and IV, and type-B spermatogonia during stages IV, V, and VI. Two generations of spermatocytes are present during stages VII to XIII inclusive and two generations of spermatids during stages I to VIII inclusive. The cell associations that form

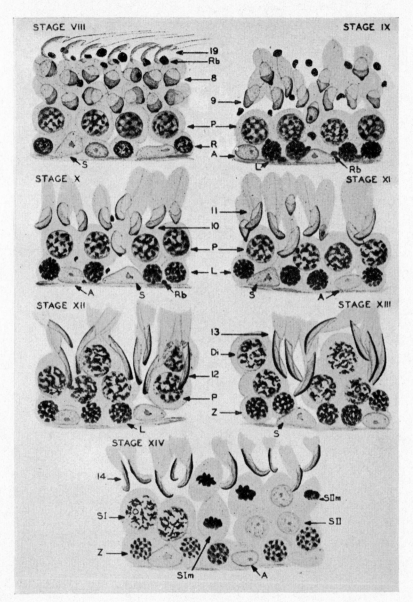

Fig. 7.37 (part 2).

diplotene spermatocyte; SI = primary spermatocyte; SIm = primary spermatocyte in metaphase; SII = secondary spermatocyte; SIIm = secondary spermatocyte in metaphase; S = Sertoli nucleus; Rb = residual body.) (From Daoust and Clermont, 1955.) (By permission of the publisher from Figs. 1–14, Daoust, R., & Clermont, Y., *Amer. J. Anat.*, 1955, **96**, 260.)

the stages of the cycle are illustrated in Figs. 7.37, 7.38 and 7.39 and the theoretical relative numbers of the various types of spermatogenic cell present at each stage of the cycle are shown in Table IV.

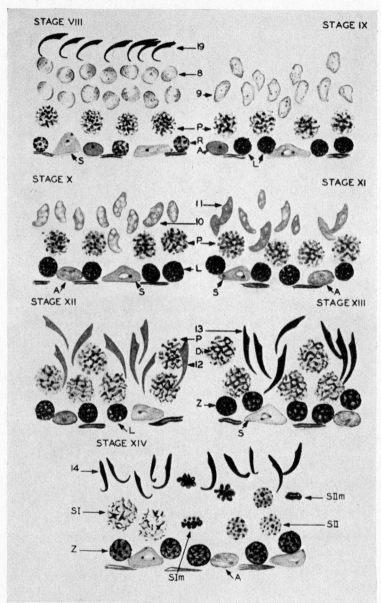

Fig. 7.38—Diagrammatic representation of stages VIII to XIV of the spermatogenic cycle of the rat as seen in preparations stained with Feulgen reagent to show the distribution of DNA. (Labels as in Fig. 7.37.) (From Daoust and Clermont, 1955.) (By permission of the publisher from Figs. 22–28, Daoust, R., & Clermont, Y., *Amer. J. Anat.*, 1955, **96**, 265.)

Leblond and Clermont (1952a, b), and subsequently Oakberg (1956a), have classified the stages of the cycle on the basis of the appearance of the spermatids, or of the younger generation of spermatids when two generations are present. This method was adopted because the stages of spermateliosis provide convenient landmarks by which the stages of the cycle can be defined. Other workers (Table V) have divided the cycle into varying numbers of stages and have defined

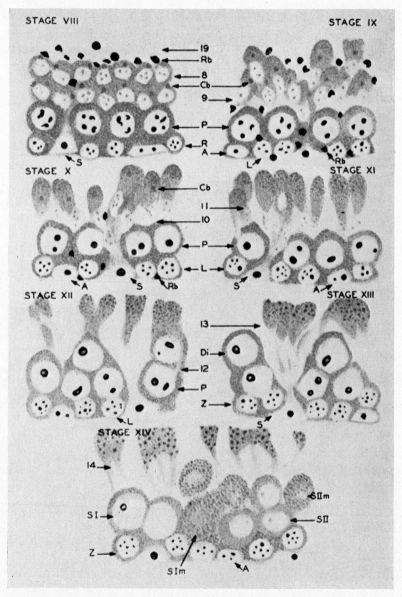

Fig. 7.39—Diagrammatic representation of stages VIII to XIV of the spermatogenic cycle of the rat as seen in preparations stained to show the distribution of RNA. (Labels as in Fig. 7.37.) (From Daoust and Clermont, 1955.) (By permission of the publisher from Figs. 36–42, Daoust, R., & Clermont, Y., *Amer. J. Anat.*, 1955, **96**, 269.)

the stages rather differently. Several, for example Roosen-Runge and Giesel (1950), have started the cycle with the division of the stem-cell to start the new generation of spermatogenic cells. This system is more logical than that of

Leblond and Clermont, but is technically less convenient.   Some comparisons of
the various systems of classification adopted are given by Moree (1947), Leblond
and Clermont (1952a) and Tobias (1956).

From the observations of investigators listed in Table V it is clear that the
spermatogenic cycle is broadly similar in all species that have been examined.
There are, however, differences between species, particularly in respect of the
number and timing of the spermatogonial divisions.   In man, for example, there
appear to be more than five spermatogonial divisions and these do not occur with
the regularity that is observed in the rat.   In consequence, the cycle is less well

TABLE V

INVESTIGATORS OF THE SPERMATOGENIC CYCLE

Species	Investigator
House mouse (*Mus*)	Benda (1887), Schoenfeldt (1902), Curtis (1918), Oakberg (1956a)
Deer mouse (*Peromyscus*)	Moree (1947)
Field mouse (*Apodemus*)	Benda (1887)
Rat (*Rattus*)	Brown (1885), Benda (1887), Von Ebner (1888), Lenhossek (1898), Regaud (1900, 1901), Schoenfeldt (1902), Hoof (1912), Roosen-Runge and Giesel (1950), Roosen-Runge (1952), Leblond and Clermont (1952), Clermont and Leblond (1953), Daoust and Clermont (1955), Clermont and Perey (1957b)
Guinea-pig (*Cavia*)	Schoenfeldt (1902), Benda (1887), Cleland (1951)
Golden hamster (*Mesocricetus*)	Clermont (1954)
Gerbil (*Tatera*)	Tobias (1956)
Rabbit (*Oryctolagus*)	Benda (1887), Curtis (1918)
Cat (*Felis*)	Schoenfeldt (1902)
Dog (*Canis*)	Roosen-Runge (1952)
Bull (*Bos*) and Ram (*Ovis*)	Benda (1887), Schoenfeldt (1902)
Kangaroo (*Macropus*)	Binder (1927)
Man (*Homo*)	Schoenfeldt (1902), Ebner (1902), Roosen-Runge (1952)

regulated, from three to five generations of spermatogenic cells may be observed
together, and it appears that the descendants of any one stem-cell do not necessarily
all complete their development at the same time.   Tubules may also be found
without active spermatogenesis (von Ebner, 1902 ; Roosen-Runge, 1952).   Again,
only three generations of spermatogenic cells are sometimes present in the boar
(Roosen-Runge, 1952).

Cyclic Changes in the Sertoli Cells

According to Leblond and Clermont (1952a) the horizontal type of Sertoli
nucleus always occurs more frequently than the perpendicular type, but during

the first half of the spermatogenic cycle an increasing number of horizontal-type nuclei becomes transformed to the perpendicular type.   In stage VIII of the cycle, the perpendicular-type nuclei reach their highest incidence (about 40 per cent), but they suddenly revert to the horizontal form when the newly formed spermatozoa are released from the germinal epithelium.   Only about 40 per cent of the Sertoli nuclei undergo this transformation in each cycle.   The changes of nuclear shape are not associated with changes in the distribution of DNA (Daoust and Clermont, 1955).   The release of spermatozoa into the lumen of the tubule is also associated with an extensive reorganisation of the Sertoli cytoplasm to embrace the succeeding generation of spermatids (Elftman, 1950).   In the mouse, Leblond and Clermont (1952b) observed cyclic changes in the number, size and distribution of PAS-reactive granules within the Sertoli cytoplasm.

An interesting feature of the adult Sertoli nuclei is that they are never seen in division (Clermont and Leblond, 1953).

The Spermatogenic Wave

Benda (1887) and Von Ebner (1888) were the first to point out that the stages of the spermatogenic cycle not only succeed each other in time, but also in space along the axis of the tubule.   This longitudinal progression of cell associations (or stages of the spermatogenic cycle) is known as the spermatogenic wave.   Regaud (1900) believed that the progression was actually helical.   Von Ebner (1902) found that the length of the wave varied from 25 to 38 mm. with an average of 32 mm. Roosen-Runge and Giesel (1950) also found great variations in this parameter and estimated the average length as only 5·6 mm.

It now seems very unlikely that the spermatogenic wave is as regular as was once believed, for considerable irregularities have been reported in the mouse (Curtis, 1918 ; Federley, 1919), the rabbit (Curtis, 1918), the guinea-pig (Cleland, 1951), and man (Roosen-Runge, 1952).   In some instances, the wave seems to be almost non-existent and in others its direction of progression becomes reversed. It is much less distinct in pubescent and discontinuously active testes than in testes that have been continuously active for some time (Cleland, 1951).

Co-ordination of the Spermatogenic Cycle and Wave

Little is known of the interesting problem of how the spermatogenic cycle is co-ordinated.   Cleland (1951) believes that the synchronisation of development that is shown both within and between generations of spermatogenic cells in each cell association may be controlled by intercellular influences that are mediated through the Sertoli cells.   The pace-makers in this system would most likely be the developing spermatids.   In support of his argument, Cleland points out that synchronous development is often a characteristic of cells that are in close association, especially when protoplasmic contact exists, but that biological variation between cells becomes manifest and synchronisation is lost when the cells become separated.   The processes of differentiation in each generation of spermatogenic cells are presumably determined by the inherent genetical properties of the cells concerned.

The succession of stages of the spermatogenic cycle along the axis of the tubule (i.e. the spermatogenic wave) suggests the propagation of a controlling influence

D*

along the tubule.   There is, however, no direct evidence in support of this concept, and the observed irregularities in the spermatogenic wave argue against it.   Cleland believes that differences in cell associations along each tubule probably arise from slight differences in the time required to complete each cycle in different parts of the tubule.   This could easily be caused by local differences in the supply of nutrients or hormones, including locally produced male sex hormone.   Differences in cell associations produced in this way would be self-perpetuating and would accumulate with time.   Intercellular influences would, however, tend to ensure that differences between adjacent cell associations were slight and the gradual changes that are characteristic of the spermatogenic wave would be produced.   It seems, therefore, that the co-ordination of development within both the cycle and the wave can be largely accounted for in terms of inherent properties of the cell associations.

Finally, it may be noted that there is no obvious biological advantage in a well regulated pattern of spermatogenesis so long as large numbers of spermatogenic cells are always developing.

Diurnal Cycle

Bullough (1948) has reported that the rate of cell division in the testis of the mouse does not display a distinct diurnal rhythm, although diurnal cycles of mitotic activity were observed in other tissues.   Clermont and Leblond (1953) believe this is true for the rat also.

Time Relations

The development of a generation of spermatogenic cells from stem-cell spermatogonia to early spermatozoa occupies four spermatogenic cycles.   This interval will be referred to as the duration of spermatogenesis.   Approximately one cycle is required for the development of type-A spermatogonia to early primary spermatocytes, one and a half cycles for the development of early spermatocytes to secondary spermatocytes, and one and a half cycles for the development of the spermatids to early spermatozoa.   The time interval for each cycle will be referred to as the duration of the cycle.   The interval between successive generations of spermatogenic cells, the generation interval, is equal to the duration of the cycle.

Theoretically, the relative duration of each stage of the spermatogenic cycle will be directly related to the relative frequency with which each stage occurs. Using this principle, Leblond and Clermont (1952b) determined the relative duration of each stage of the cycle in the testes of six adult rats.   Their results, which showed close agreement between animals, are summarised in Table VI. Similar studies have been made by Roosen-Runge and Giesel (1950) and Oakberg (1956b) in the rat and mouse, respectively, but a comparison of results between workers is difficult since each has used a different system to classify the stages of the cycle.

Determination of the absolute duration of spermatogenesis, or of any part of it, is more difficult.   Two convenient methods of approach are determination of the time required for generations of spermatogenic cells to disappear (or reappear) in the testis tubules after acute radiation damage (*see* p. 91), and determination of the time required for the formation of spermatozoa with radio-active nuclei after systemic administration of radio-active precursors of nucleoprotein.

TABLE VI

THE RELATIVE DURATION OF STAGES OF THE SPERMATOGENIC CYCLE IN THE RAT.   (From data by Leblond and Clermont, 1952b)

Stage of cycle	I	II	III	IV	V	VI	VII	VIII	IX	X	XI	XII	XIII	XIV
Relative duration (%)	12	8	2	4·5	5	9	22	7	2·5	2·5	2·5	11	6	5

TABLE VII

THE TIME SPENT IN EACH STAGE OF DEVELOPMENT AND THE TIME REQUIRED TO DEVELOP TO EARLY SPERMATOZOA FOR SPERMATOGENIC CELLS OF THE MOUSE.   (Data from Oakberg, 1957b)

Stage of development of spermatogenic cell	Duration of stage of development (hours)	Time required to develop to early spermatozoa (days)	
		Minimum	Maximum
Spermatogonia :			
Type-A	Always present	33·5	35·5
Intermediate	27·3	28·8	30·0
Type-B	29·4	27·6	28·8
Primary Spermatocytes :			
Resting	31·0	26·3	27·6
Leptotene	31·2	25·0	26·3
Zygotene	37·5	23·4	25·0
Pachytene	175·3	16·1	23·4
Diplotene	21·4	15·2	16·1
Diakinesis and Metaphase	10·4	14·8	15·2
Secondary Spermatocytes	10·4	14·4	14·8
Spermatids	229·2	0·0	14·4

By the first of these methods, the duration of spermatogenesis in the rat and mouse has been estimated as 26 to 28 days (Hertwig, 1938 ; Shaver and Mason, 1950 ; Fogg and Cowing, 1951 ; Shaver, 1953a, b), but since intermediate-type and type-B spermatogonia are very sensitive to radiation damage and are easily destroyed (Oakberg, 1955a, b) it is likely that these estimates actually represent the time taken for early primary spermatocytes to develop into early spermatozoa (Oakberg, 1956).   This is only three-quarters of the complete duration of spermatogenesis, and if corrected on the basis of this assumption the estimates become 34 to 37 days.   Schaefer (1939) and Oakberg (1956) made allowance for radiation damage to spermatogonia and estimated the duration of spermatogenesis in the mouse as 30 to 31 days and 34·5 days, respectively.   Oakberg based his measurements not only on the progressive disappearance of generations of spermatogenic cells from the tubules, but also on their reappearance.   His estimates of the duration of the cycle by these two methods were 8·6 and 8·7 days, respectively.   He also made a careful study of the time intervals occupied by each of stage development (*see* Table VII) (Oakberg, 1956, 1957b).

Results obtained with the isotope-incorporation method have suggested a duration of spermatogenesis of 26 days, or rather less, in the mouse (Howard and Pelc, 1950 ; Glücksmann, Howard and Pelc, 1955 ; Sirlin and Edwards, 1955, 1957a ; Pelc and Howard, 1956), but again these estimates probably represent only three-quarters of the total time because active DNA synthesis takes place in early primary spermatocytes (Swift, 1950).   When the results obtained by isotope incorporation are suitably adjusted, they are in good agreement with those obtained by Oakberg (Sirlin and Edwards, 1957b), but they do seem to suggest a slightly shorter duration of spermatogenesis.   Ortavant (1954b, 1956a) allowed for the effect of isotope incorporation into early primary spermatocytes and reported 40 days as the duration of spermatogenesis in the ram.

It should be pointed out that methods of study involving either acute radiation damage or the incorporation of radio-active isotopes are open to the criticism that the normal duration of spermatogenesis may be seriously influenced by radiation damage.   Oakberg (1956b, 1957b), however, believes that such effects in his own material are negligible and similar opinions are held by other workers (Eschenbrenner and Miller, 1950; Sirlin and Edwards, 1957b).   Other references to the incorporation of radioactive isotopes into spermatogenic cells include Pelc (1957), Dawson (1958a, b), and Edwards and Sirlin (1958).

From studies on the initiation of the spermatogenic cycle in young rats, Clermont and Perey (1957a) concluded that the duration of spermatogenesis was about 40 days in the rat.

VIII. Spontaneous Anomalies of Spermatogenesis

In the two preceding sections, we have discussed the processes of division and development of the spermatogenic cells.   From this account, it can be seen that each stem-cell spermatogonium in the rat or mouse will, if all its descendent cells divide and develop normally, ultimately give rise to 96 spermatozoa.   In reality, however, the number of spermatozoa that arise from each stem-cell is considerably reduced by spontaneous losses of spermatogenic cells at various stages of development.   These losses appear to be a usual feature of spermatogenesis.   Much greater losses occur spontaneously in abnormal instances and these may reduce the number of spermatozoa produced to a very low level or even prevent their formation altogether.   In such cases, the germinal epithelium exhibits a serious deficiency of spermatogenic cells and is described as hypoplastic. In addition, abnormal spermateliosis occurs to a small extent in normal testes and is a prominent feature in some abnormal ones. In some instances, it appears to be associated with abnormal spermatocytogenesis, but in others there is no suggestion of such a relationship.

Normal Loss of Spermatogenic Cells

The occurrence of necrotic spermatogenic cells in apparently normal germinal epithelia of the rat and mouse has been studied by Roosen-Runge (1955) and Oakberg (1956), respectively. In some stages of the spermatogenic cycle, Oakberg found that almost 2·5 per cent of the type-A spermatogonia were necrotic and there was evidence that cell death was associated with cell division. Necrosis in intermediate and type-B spermatogonia was much less frequent. Losses during meiosis, however, reduced the number of spermatids formed to only 87 per cent of the number expected from the number of primary spermatocytes present. There was also some degeneration of early spermatids. In the rat, Roosen-Runge observed that losses during meiosis amounted to 22 per cent of the number of spermatids expected.

The causes of the spontaneous loss of spermatogenic cells are obscure, but it is evident that factors associated with mitotic and meiotic division are largely involved. Oakberg suggests that spontaneous degeneration may represent a selection against the more serious chromosomal aberrations, and possibly even genic changes, that arise during cell multiplication and growth. It is possible that losses that occur after the first meiotic division may act selectively against specific cell genotypes and so affect the distribution of genotypes among spermatozoa. Selective losses of this kind could, for example, alter the proportion of X- and Y-spermatozoa produced and so influence the sex ratio of progeny. Weir (1955) bred mice that had been selected for high and low blood pH and observed divergencies in the sex ratio of offspring which were associated with the blood pH of the sire and McWhirter (1956) reviews evidence suggesting that a similar effect may occur in other species (*see also* Bishop, 1960).

Hypoplasia of the Germinal Epithelium

Spontaneously occurring hypoplasia of the germinal epithelium is a frequent lesion associated with infertility and sterility in laboratory and domestic animals and in man. In many instances there are clear indications that the condition is inherited and in some it is known to be associated with a general reduction of body pigmentation. The degree of hypoplasia varies, both between and within individuals, from slight defects of the germinal epithelium to complete absence of spermatogenic cells.

In Swedish highland cattle, hypoplasia of the testis is associated with white coat colour and is evidently caused by a recessive autosomal gene with incomplete penetrance. The degree of hypoplasia (and of infertility) varies considerably and sometimes only one testis, usually the left, is affected. The spermatocytes often show degenerative changes and giant multinucleate cells are frequently seen in the lumina of the testis tubules. Spermatozoa may be entirely absent and when present are often abnormal. The interstitial tissue of the testis and the sexual behaviour of the bulls concerned appear to be normal. The volume of semen produced is often greater than the average, but the concentration of spermatozoa is usually very low. The fertility of females is also affected by the same gene (Lagerlöf, 1938, 1950, 1951, 1957 ; Eriksson, 1938, 1943, 1950). Defective germinal epithelium has also been reported in dwarf Hereford bulls (Lindley, 1951).

Among other kinds of domestic animal, hypoplasia of the testis appears to occur fairly frequently in rams (Gunn, Sanders and Granger, 1942), boars (Holst, 1949) and goats (Richter, 1936), and is universal in mules and hinnies. In the mule, division of the spermatogonia proceeds regularly, but meiosis does not progress beyond early prophase and the primary spermatocytes degenerate. The interstitial tissue of the testis is well developed and sexual behaviour appears normal (Wodsedalek, 1916 ; Makino, 1955). The female is occasionally fertile. Other mammalian hybrids in which the males are believed to be invariably sterile include donkey × zebra, horse × zebra, bison × domestic cattle, bison × yak, domestic cattle × yak, zebu × yak, bactrian camel × dromedary, lion × tiger, *Peromyscus nasutus* × *P. truei* and *Cavia fulgida* × *C. porcellus* (see Gray, 1954). In some of these, for example the yak × zebu hybrid, there is evidence of early and complete failure of spermatogenesis (Zawadowsky, 1931), but spermatogenesis is said to be normal in the bactrian camel × dromedary hybrid (Gray, 1954). White (1954) states that many instances of hybrid sterility probably depend on mechanical and physiological impediments to the pairing of maternal and paternal chromosomes at meiosis. In general, the heterozygous sex is more severely affected than the homozygous sex.

Several examples of spontaneous testicular hypoplasia are known in laboratory rodents. Thus, degeneration and loss of spermatogenic cells, associated with a high incidence of abnormal spermateliosis, has been observed in mice with certain mutations at the locus of T, the factor for dominant short tail. Males of the t^0/t^1 genotype are sexually active but completely sterile : females are fertile (Bryson 1944). More extensive hypoplasia is shown in mice with mutations at the W-locus. Here the condition is associated with reduction of body pigmentation and with anaemia. Mating behaviour is normal and both sexes are affected (Coulombre and Russell, 1954). In male African mice (*Mastomys natalensis*) selected for pale grey coat colour, spermatogenesis does not proceed beyond the primary spermatocytes. Sexual behaviour is normal and pale grey females are not affected (Menzies, 1957). Complete aspermatogenesis with a germinal epithelium consisting of Sertoli cells only has been observed in certain rats of the Long-Evans strain. The general condition and sexual behaviour of the animals was normal (Smelser, 1935). Varying degrees of testicular hypoplasia, ranging from near normality to complete absence of spermatogenic cells and accompanied by varying degrees of fertility, have been reported in chocolate-coated pink-eyed guinea-pigs. The most frequent stage of spermatogenic arrest appeared to be the primary spermatocyte, but arrest of spermateliosis was also common. The animals were in good health and had normal libido and accessory glands. The females were not affected (Jakway and Young, 1958). A somewhat similar condition accompanies infertility in pale-coated ruby-eyed golden hamsters. Here, however, the males mature late and experience a brief period of fertility at puberty which is quickly followed by sterility. The spermatogenic epithelium is markedly hypoplastic. Ruby-eyed females are fertile (Bruce, 1958).

In man, testicular hypoplasia has been studied by many investigators. One condition, Klinefelter's syndrome (Klinefelter, Rifenstein and Albright, 1942), is of especial interest since many of the affected individuals, although phenotypically male, appear to be of female genotype. In such cases, the testes contain few seminiferous tubules and the germinal epithelium is often represented by Sertoli cells only. Spermatogonia and spermatocytes may be present, however, and in a few instances the production of limited numbers of spermatozoa has been observed. The interstitial tissue is hyperplastic (Bunge and Bradbury, 1956 ; Grumbach, Blanc and Engle, 1957 ; Witschi, Nelson and Segal, 1957 ; Ferguson-Smith, Lennox, Mack and Stewart, 1957 ; Ferguson-Smith, 1958 ; Ferguson-Smith and Munro, 1958). The diagnosis of female genetic sex in Klinefelter's syndrome is based on the presence of sex chromatin in interphase nuclei (Barr and Bertram, 1949 ; Graham and Barr, 1952 ; Moore, Graham and Barr, 1953 ; Moore and Barr, 1954; Barr, 1955, 1956; Lennox, 1956; Plunkett and Barr, 1956; Nelson, 1956; Bradbury, Bunge and Boccabella, 1956).

Abnormal Meiosis

According to Knudsen (1954a) disturbance of meiosis in the bull is first indicated by vacuolation in the cytoplasm of the primary spermatocyte. This is followerd by degenerative changes in the centrosomes and spindle which lead to disorganisation of the first meiotic division or to pyknosis or lysis of the chromosomes. With more severe disturbances no spindle is formed and the chromosomes may undergo the first meiotic division within a persistent nuclear membrane. Such cells do not develop further and are shed from the epithelium. Lesser disturbances of meiosis may lead to the formation of spermatozoa with faulty genetic material. Thus Melander and Knudsen (1953) observed that bivalents with chiasmata near the centromeres have difficulty in co-ordination and in some instances appear to pass undivided to one of the daughter nuclei. Later, Knudsen (1954b) obtained evidence that intrachromosomal aberrations arising from inversion and translocation also interfere with the distribution of chromosomes to the daughter nuclei. Conditions of this kind may lead to the production of spermatozoa with a faulty chromosome complement, such as would account for the variations of DNA content that have been observed by Leuchtenberger and her associates in spermatozoa from infertile men and bulls (*see* p. 35).

Abnormal Spermateliosis

There are relatively few accounts of abnormal spermateliosis.

Rajasekarasetty (1954) studied the development of abnormal spermatozoa in semi-sterile mice with certain mutations at the T-locus. In these animals, abnormal spermateliosis is first apparent as a deficient spreading of the proacrosome over the anterior pole of the nucleus. Later, the nucleus develops abnormally and the resulting spermatozoon head is greatly deformed. Spermatocytogenesis and the development of the spermatozoon tail were apparently normal. In view of the hereditary nature of the infertility in Rajasekarasetty's animals, it is interesting that the development of abnormal spermatozoa appeared to be localised in certain regions of the seminiferous tubules. Bryson (1944) studied abnormal spermato-genesis in mice with other mutations at the T-locus and observed abnormal sper-matozoa similar to those described by Rajasekarasetty. Here, however, abnormal spermateliosis was accompanied by marked abnormalities of spermatocytogenesis. Both abnormal spermatozoa and those that appeared to be morphologically normal were quite sterile.

Harvey (1955) studied the genesis of certain types of abnormal spermatozoa in semi-sterile men. She believes that certain types of nuclear abnormality are associated with abnormal meiosis, that spermatozoa with large heads develop from undivided secondary spermatocytes and that spermatozoa with very small heads may develop from fragmented primary spermatocytes. Again, there was a tendency for abnormal development to be restricted to particular regions of the testis tubule. Harvey suggests that the cause of the abnormality is likely to be environmental rather than genetic but in view of Rajasekarasetty's findings the validity of this conclusion seems doubtful.

Hancock and Trevan (1957) describe spermateliosis in Friesian bulls with a specific genetically-determined form of sterility associated with abnormal struc-ture of the acrosome. Here the outer zone of the proacrosome appears to develop normally, but the inner zone remains in the form of a bead at the apex of the nucleus. All other aspects of spermateliosis in these bulls are apparently normal. The condition is clearly hereditary and appears to be transmitted by an autosomal sex-limited recessive gene (Donald and Hancock, 1953).

Formation of Decapitate Spermatozoa

Hancock (1955) studied the formation of decapitate spermatozoa (*see* p. 34) in two sterile bulls of the Guernsey breed. In these bulls, decapitation occurred almost entirely during the passage of spermatozoa through the caput epididymis and appeared to be associated with the migration of the cytoplasmic droplet from the neck of the spermatozoon to the distal end of the mid-piece (*see* p. 95). In the proximal part of the caput epididymis, most of the spermatozoa were intact, but, in the distal part, 99 per cent were decapitate. In a similar sterile Guernsey bull, however, Bishop (unpublished observations) observed that the majority of spermatozoa were decapitate before leaving the testis. The condition appears to be inherited.

Decapitation of spermatozoa also occurs in bulls of other breeds in association with inflammatory conditions in the reproductive tract (Lagerlöf, 1934). It can be induced in the bull (Lagerlöf, 1934 ; Blom, 1950), ram (Phillips and McKenzie, 1934 ; Gunn, Sanders and Granger, 1942), boar (Holst, 1949) and rabbit (Chang, 1943) by treatments that raise or lower the temperature of the testis and the appear-ance of numerous decapitate spermatozoa in the ejaculate is often an early sign of disturbed testicular function.

Multinucleate Spermatids

Small numbers of multinucleate spermatids appear to be a common feature of apparently normal germinal epithelia in laboratory rodents (Bishop—unpublished observations) but their origin and fate are obscure. In such cells, the nucleus together with the characteristic cytoplasmic components of the spermatid (such as the Golgi apparatus, proacrosome, centrioles and chromatoid body) may be replicated a few or many times and be normal in appearance. All are bounded by a single cell membrane (Fig. 7.40). Large numbers of multinucleate cells are a common feature of testes with degenerate germinal epithelia, or of testes exposed to conditions that disturb spermatogenesis, but it is not certain that they are always spermatids. In instances of disturbed spermatogenesis the multinucleate cells are shed from the germinal epithelium.

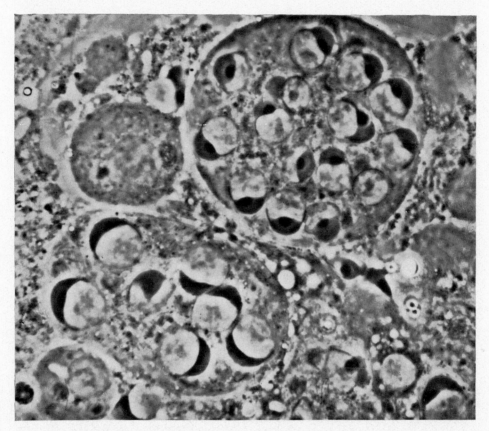

Fig. 7.40.—Phase-contrast micrograph of two multinucleate spermatids, one with eight nuclei and one with sixteen, in the guinea-pig. Note the differences in size between the nuclei of the two spermatids. (J. Smiles, original.)

IX. ENVIRONMENTAL AND EXPERIMENTAL FACTORS AFFECTING SPERMATOGENESIS

The production of spermatozoa starts at the time of puberty and gradually increases up to sexual maturity. In old age, general debility and the cumulative effects of various traumata may occasion a marked decrease or even cessation of spermatogenic activity, but abundant spermatozoa have often been found in the testes and excurrent ducts of men in extreme old age (Hotchkiss, 1945).

Spermatogenesis is known to be affected by a variety of environmental agencies and experimental treatments, some of which are considered in the present Section.

In general, the spermatogenic cells appear to become increasingly sensitive to noxious agents as they develop.   Thus spermatids appear to be the most sensitive and spermatogonia the least.   Sertoli cells are the most resistant of all the elements of the germinal epithelium.   Lagerlöf (1934) and Knudsen (1954a), however, believe that the primary spermatocytes are usually the first of the spermatogenic cells to react to unfavourable conditions.   Meiosis is certainly one of the most critical phases of spermatogenesis, but the first and most pronounced result of spermatogenic damage is generally arrest of spermateliosis with exfoliation of spermatids and the appearance of round multinucleate cells.   Reaction to the effects of X-irradiation provides an exception to the general rule, for under these conditions the most sensitive cells are the B-type spermatogonia.   It should also be noted that injury to the germinal epithelium is often not uniformly distributed throughout the testis—some tubules may show extensive damage while others appear to be essentially normal.

Season and Climate

In many species, spermatogenic activity is seasonal and may be in complete abeyance during the non-breeding season (*see* Bissonnette, 1936; Asdell, 1946; Chapters 4 and 13).   Resumption of activity is usually preceded by a great increase in the size of the testis and of the accessory glands and is probably controlled through the gonadotrophic activity of the anterior pituitary.   In man and domestic animals, seasonal variation is much less apparent (*see* Anderson, 1945a).

Since nutrition and climatic factors such as temperature and humidity all vary with season and may affect the general health and normal functioning of the body, it is not easy to determine which environmental factors primarily control seasonal breeding habits and which are merely of secondary importance.   There is reason to believe, however, that change in the length of daylight is the main variable involved in many instances.   Response to the seasonal stimulus varies in accordance with the reproductive pattern of each species.   It determines the time of mating in such a way that young are born at the season most favourable for their development (Marshall, 1942).

In Suffolk and Romney sheep maintained at Cambridge, England, Walton (1947) observed that the output of spermatozoa began to diminish in the middle of December and reached about half its former level by April.   This was accompanied by an increase in the proportion of abnormal spermatozoa and a decline in libido.   During the following August or September, both the production of spermatozoa and the expression of libido returned to the levels characteristic of the breeding season.   The changes were more pronounced in some rams than in others. They could not be accounted for by variations of temperature or nutrition, and the observations of Yeates (1949) show that they are probably mainly determined by changes in the ratio of light to darkness.   McKenzie and Berliner (1937) observed seasonal degenerative changes in the semen of Hampshire and Shropshire rams in Missouri (U.S.A.).   The changes were less obvious in the Hampshire rams, and may have been in large part conditioned by high summer temperatures.   Berliner and Warbritton (1937) and Bogart and Mayer (1946) attribute summer sterility in rams to an adverse effect of temperature on thyroid activity, but their evidence does not exclude the possibility that light was also involved.   The observations of

Gunn (1936, 1951) and Gunn, Sanders and Granger (1942) illustrate the importance of high temperature and deficient nutrition in seasonal variations of reproductive activity in rams in Australia.   Other investigators of seasonal activity in the
ram include Berliner and Warbritton (1937), Green (1940b), Chang (1941), Phillips,
Fraps and Frank (1945), Starke (1949), Hafez, Badreldin and Darwish (1955),
Ortavant (1956b) and Ortavant and Thibault (1956).

There is little evidence of a true breeding season in the bull although variations
caused by climatic factors do occur (Andersen, 1945a, b ; Mercier and Salisbury,
1947a, b ; Dordick, 1949).

Additional light during the winter stimulates spermatogenesis in the sexually
quiescent ferret.   This effect is augmented by pregnancy-urine extract, which is
ineffective by itself (Allanson, Rowlands and Parkes, 1934 ; Bissonnette, 1935).
In the sexually quiescent hedgehog (*Erinaceus europaeus*), spermatogenesis is
stimulated by increased light, by warmth and by pregnancy-urine extract alone
(Allanson and Deanesly, 1934).   In the thirteen-lined ground squirrel (*Citellus
tridecemlineatus*), seasonal variations in spermatogenesis appear to be unaffected
by light and mainly controlled by temperature.   Animals maintained at 4° C
(40° F) showed no seasonal variations (Wells and Zalesky, 1940).   Again, neither
light nor temperature appear to be important factors in controlling spermatogenesis
in the nocturnal and fossorial Indian gerbille (*Tatera indica cuvierii*) (Prasad,
1956).

Scrotal Function

In most mammals, the onset of spermatogenesis is preceded by the descent of
the testis from its original position in the abdominal cavity, through the inguinal
canal, into the scrotum.   In many species, the descent takes place at an early age
and is permanent.   In others (most rodents, insectivores and bats), the testes
descend into the scrotum at the beginning of the breeding season and are withdrawn into the abdominal cavity at the end of the season.   The mechanism by
which this takes place is still a matter for conjecture, but is evidently under endocrine control.   In monotremes, edentates, cetaceans and proboscideans, the testis
remains permanently within the abdomen (*see* Asdell, 1946; Chapter 4).

In mammals with scrotal testes, the environment provided for the testis by the
scrotum is essential for normal spermatogenesis.   Testes that fail to descend in the
usual manner do not produce spermatozoa and experimental transfer of testes
from the scrotum to the abdominal cavity leads to a rapid degeneration and exfoliation of the germinal epithelium until little more than Sertoli cells remain.   If the
degenerative changes are not too severe, spermatogenesis is gradually restored
when the testis is returned to the scrotum (Griffiths, 1893; Sand, 1921; Moore,
1922, 1926a, 1932; Jeffries, 1931; Asdell and Salisbury, 1941a; Knudsen, 1954a;
Payne, 1955, 1956).

The temperature within the scrotum is a few degrees below that of the abdomen
(Moore and Quick, 1924a; Harrenstein, 1928) and Crew (1922) suggested that lack
of spermatogenesis in the abdomen might be caused by the higher temperature at
this site.   Crew's theory was supported by observations that the application of
heat to the normal scrotum induces rapid degeneration of the germinal epithelium
(Moore, 1922, 1924b, 1951 ; Moore and Oslund, 1924 ; Fukui, 1923a, b ; Young,

1927, 1929 ; Cunningham and Osborn, 1929 ; Heller, 1929 ; Phillips and Mac-Kenzie, 1934 ; Williams and Cunningham, 1940). The effect was the greater the higher the temperature used. Even a slight rise in temperature, such as is produced by placing insulating material around the scrotum, is sufficient to bring about the complete cessation of spermatogenesis in about two weeks (Moore and Oslund, 1924 ; Lagerlöf, 1934 ; Phillips and MacKenzie, 1934 ; Gunn, Sanders and Granger, 1942 ; Glover, 1955). The importance of elevated temperature is further illustrated by the fact that spermatogenesis in testis grafts in mammals proceeds to the formation of spermatozoa only when the graft is located in situations, such as the scrotal wall and anterior chamber of the eye, that have temperatures below that of deep body temperature (Moore, 1951). Moore (1924) suggested that degeneration of the germinal epithelium in the cryptorchid or heated testis might be caused by lack of oxygen, or accumulation of carbon dioxide, resulting from vascular stagnation. Harrison (1956) also believes that locally induced vascular phenomena are involved, and Barron (1933) attributes a similar cause to degenerative changes in the testis that follow section of the spermatic nerve. Harrison and Oettlé (1950) and Oettlé and Harrison (1952) found that occlusion of the blood supply to the testis had disastrous effects on spermatogenesis at normal environmental temperatures. Occlusion for 20 to 30 min. resulted in severe damage to spermatids and spermatocytes. After one hour all spermatogenic cells were destroyed, but Sertoli cells remained ; after 2 hours there was complete necrosis of the seminiferous tubules.

Cooling the testis or scrotum is evidently much less damaging to spermatogenesis than warming. Chang (1943) found that the application of ice to the scrotum of the rabbit induced decapitation of spermatozoa in the epididymis, but did not greatly affect the germinal epithelium. MacDonald and Harrison (1954a, b) observed that immersion of the exposed testicle of the rat in a cooling bath for 1 hour at $+ 2°$ C had little effect on spermatogenesis, but similar treatment at $- 5°$ C resulted in almost complete destruction of the spermatogenic epithelium. At $- 8°$ C, the seminiferous tubules were almost completely destroyed. When the intact scrotum was cooled in the same way, there was very little damage to spermatogenesis at $- 4°$ C and some spermatogonia survived exposure at $- 10°$ C. Similar results have been obtained with the guinea-pig (Harris and Harrison, 1955). Payne (1955) observed necrosis of seminiferous tubules in mice after brief (30 secs.) local cooling of the scrotum with solid carbon dioxide.

The scrotum not only provides for the testis an environment that has a lower temperature than that of the abdomen, but also exerts a temperature regulating function. Crew (1922) noted that the scrotum contracted when cold and relaxed when warm, thus bringing the testis closer to or further from the warmth of the body. These changes appear to be brought about by the tunica dartos (Phillips and MacKenzie, 1934). Further, the close association of the testicular artery with the pampiniform plexus of veins facilitates pre-cooling and pre-heating of the arterial blood supplying the testis (Harrison and Weiner, 1949). Failure of the thermo-regulatory function of the testis is the probable cause of the disorders of spermatogenesis that are known to accompany varicosity of scrotal veins. It may be noted, however, that although the importance of the scrotum can be readily demonstrated in those mammals that possess it, no satisfactory theory has yet been advanced to explain why the scrotum should not be necessary in all mammals.

In birds the testes are abdominal and the body temperature is even higher than in mammals. Ehrenberg, Ehrenstein and Hedgram (1957) have suggested that the significance of the scrotum may be associated with a significant reduction in the rate of spontaneous mutations in spermatogenic cells by reduction in temperature.

Ambient Temperature

In temperate regions, the thermo-regulatory mechanism of the body, including that of the scrotum, can cope with changes of environmental temperature, and this may also be true for indigenous animals in tropical and subtropical areas. On the other hand, animals imported into the tropics and subtropics often prove to have inadequate means of temperature regulation and in such instances there is evidence that high environmental temperatures, especially when associated with high humidity, exert a seriously adverse effect on spermatogenesis (McKenzie and Berliner, 1937 ; Gunn, Sanders and Granger, 1942 ; Andersen, 1945a; Bogart and Meyer, 1946). In such cases it is, of course, difficult to distinguish between the direct effect of temperature on the testis and the indirect effects arising from injury to the health of the animal as a whole.

Bonsma (1940) noted that the body temperature and scrotal temperature of exotic breeds of cattle in South Africa often rose to very high levels, while Afrikander breeds possessed an effective temperature-regulating mechanism. He also observed that the scrotal skin of the Afrikander breeds was much thicker than that of the exotic breeds and that, when environmental temperatures rose especially high, the scrotum contracted and drew the testes close to the body, thereby ensuring that their temperature would not be greater than that of the body. In this case, the scrotum evidently performs its regulatory function of controlling a rise of temperature by contracting instead of relaxing. The effects of high ambient temperatures are certainly much less severe than the effects of local application of heat to the scrotum. Thus, Harrison and Harris (1956) observed no infertility or testicular damage in rats maintained for prolonged periods at near body temperature (98° F). Gunn, Sanders and Granger (1942), however, obtained a rapid degeneration of spermatogenesis in Merino rams kept in an artificial hot (near 100° F) but dry atmosphere. Maule and Knapp (1950) observed that the subjection of rams to high atmospheric temperatures leads to increased testicular temperature.

There is no evidence that spermatogenesis is adversely affected by low environmental temperatures, and mice, for example, breed successfully in cold stores at temperatures between − 3° and − 21° C (Laurie, 1946 ; Barnett and Manly, 1954, 1956 ; Barnett, 1956).

Hyperthermia

Since regulation of the temperature of the testis depends not only upon the proper functioning of the scrotal mechanism, but also upon the thermo-regulation of the body as a whole, it is not surprising that spermatogenesis is affected when homeothermy fails. MacLeod and Hotchkiss (1941) observed that a brief period (up to 3 hours) of artificially induced hyperthermia, during which body temperature was raised to about 41° C, resulted in a pronounced decrease in the production

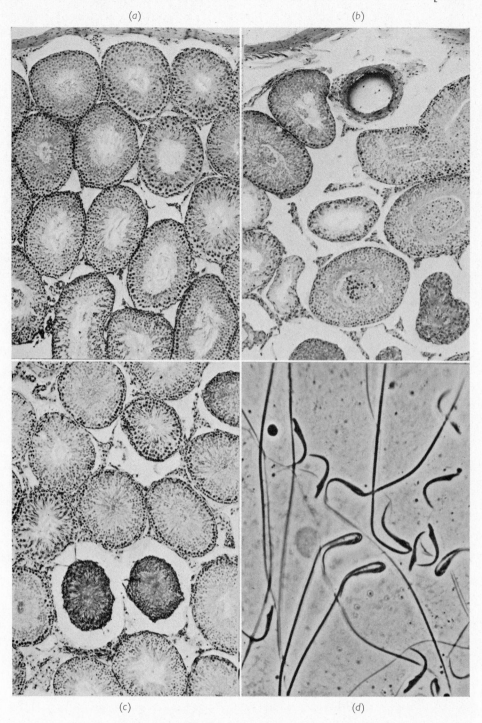

(a)   (b)

(c)   (d)

Fig. 7.41a, b, c, d—(a) Section of testis from a normal rat (× 60).   (b) Section of testis from a rat killed 7 days after reanimation from severe hypothermia (× 60).   (c) Section of testis from a fertile rat killed 8 weeks after reanimation from severe hypothermia (× 60).   (d) Epididymal spermatozoa from a rat killed 5 days after reanimation from severe hypothermia (× 960). (From Goldzveig and Smith, 1956.)

of spermatozoa by young healthy men.   It is also known that spermatogenesis is seriously impaired during the febrile conditions associated with pneumonia and chickenpox (Mills, 1919 ; MacLeod, 1951), and available evidence suggests that the raised body temperature is the major cause of the testicular damage.   Similar observations have been made on rams suffering from fever associated with blowfly strike (Gunn, Sanders and Granger, 1942).   Harrison and Harris (1956), however, found no evidence of infertility or testicular injury in surviving rats and mice that had been exposed for short periods (2 to 40 hours) to temperatures high enough (102° F to 116° F) to kill many of the treated animals.

Hypothermia

Goldzveig and Smith (1956) found that moderate hypothermia (body temperature reduced to between 16° and 20° C) accompanied by acute anoxia and hypercapnia had a brief adverse effect on the breeding performance of male rats. The treatment resulted in slight oedema of the testis with some exfoliation of the spermatogenic epithelium.   Spermatids were destroyed in tubules in the centre of the testis, but in the periphery of the testis the germinal epithelium remained normal in appearance.   In rats subjected to severe hypothermia (body temperature reduced to near 0° C) with complete arrest of the blood circulation for at least 1 hour, damage to spermatogenic cells was more severe, but mainly restricted to spermatids and to spermatozoa within the epididymis.   Injury was again greatest in the centre of the testis and in some tubules of this region the germinal epithelium was reduced to spermatogonia and Sertoli cells.   In most animals, recovery was well advanced within eight weeks of treatment (see Fig. 7.41).

High Altitude and Hypoxaemia

High altitude is known to affect testicular function and fertility.   According to the Foundation Charter of Lima, the capital of Peru was transferred in 1535 from Jauja (11,500 ft. above sea level) to Lima (sea level) because horses, pigs and fowls did not reproduce in Jauja.   Calancha (1639) states that no child was born and reared to Spanish settlers in the mountain city of Potosi, Bolivia, until 53 years after the foundation of the city (see Monge, 1943, 1947, 1948 ; Stickney and Liere, 1953 ; Goldzveig and Smith, 1956).   Monge and Mori Charez (1942) found that male cats and rabbits became azoospermic when transferred to Morococha, 14,000 ft. above sea level in the Andes, and that the germinal epithelium contained only spermatogonia and Sertoli cells.   Moore and Price (1948), however, found that reproduction in four species of laboratory rodents was normal when they were maintained for 60 days at an altitude of 14,260 ft. in Colorado.   Exposure to low atmospheric pressure at ordinary temperature in a low pressure chamber leads to degenerative changes in the testis and other organs of the rat (Dohan, 1942 ; Gordon, Tornetta, D'Angelo and Charipper, 1943 ; Dalton, Jones, Peters and Mitchell, 1945 ; Altland, 1949; Altland and Allen, 1952) and to the production of semen of poor quality in the rabbit (Walton and Uruski, 1946).   These effects appear to be largely attributable to hypoxaemia.   Campbell (1935), Williams and Smith (1935) and Patterson, Smith and Pickett (1938) observed loss of fertility in animals in which hypoxaemia was produced by administration of carbon monoxide or illuminating gas, and Shettles (1947) found that exposure to low oxygen tensions at normal atmospheric pressure caused the production of abnormal spermatozoa and marked degeneration of the spermatogenic epithelium in guinea-pigs.

Nutrition

In terms of protein, fat, carbohydrate or calories, the production of spermatozoa cannot be regarded as contributing greatly to the nutritional requirements of the body as a whole, even during periods of intense sexual activity. Certainly spermatogenesis in the adult is remarkably unaffected by low levels of nutrition, although the development of the testis may be disturbed by under-feeding before puberty. Walton (1949) concludes that the needs of the testis will be adequately met provided the animal receives nutrition sufficient to maintain its body health. Mason (1933, 1939) reports that the formation of spermatozoa in starved adult rats does not cease until 25 to 35 per cent of the body weight has been lost. Under these conditions, spermatids and spermatocytes become necrotic and are exfoliated but spermatogonia retain their proliferative ability and the germinal epithelium comes to resemble that of immature animals. The Sertoli cells and interstitial tissue show no characteristic changes. Complete recovery follows a return to an adequate diet. Mann and Walton (1953) observed no changes in the production of spermatozoa in an adult bull maintained on sub-maintenance rations for 23 weeks, during which body weight fell by one-sixth. On the other hand, there is evidence that spermatogenesis may be seriously affected by deficiency of specific substances, such as vitamin A (Mason, 1930, 1933, 1939 ; Evans, 1932 ; Sampson and Korenchevsky, 1932a, b ; Gunn, Sanders and Granger, 1942 ; Sapsford, 1951), vitamin E (Mattill, Carman and Clayton, 1924 ; Mason, 1926, 1929 ; Evans and Burr, 1927; Ringstead, 1934), zinc (Millar, Fischer, Elcoate and Mawson, 1958) and essential fatty acids (Holman and Aaes-Jørgensen, 1956). In rats deficient in vitamin A, spermatogenesis is gradually reduced and spermateliosis is early affected. In advanced cases of deficiency the germinal epithelium may be reduced to Sertoli cells with a few spermatogonia, but complete loss of spermatogenic cells does not occur. The depleted epithelium responds readily to vitamin-A therapy, even when the food intake is at a sub-maintenance level (Mason, 1933, 1939). Severe vitamin-E deficiency, on the other hand, leads to complete and irreversible loss of spermatogenic cells in the rat (Mason, 1933, 1939; Evans and Burr, 1927), but does not affect spermatogenesis in the mouse (Bryan and Mason, 1940; Pappenheimer, 1942). There is no definite evidence that deficiencies of vitamins B, C and D specifically affect the spermatogenic epithelium in mammals, and spermatogenesis has been observed in advanced cases of beri beri (Mattil, 1927; Evans, 1928; Marburg, 1936), and scurvy (Goettsch, 1930). In birds, however, there is evidence that spermatogenesis is affected by deficiency of vitamin B (Marrian and Parkes, 1928; Mason, 1939).

Stress

It is often stated that emotional stress and psychological disorders have an adverse effect on spermatogenesis. Sand (1933) has described damage to spermatogenesis in men sentenced to death. Meschaks (1953) states that the transportation of bulls over short distances may cause temporary damage to spermatogenesis associated with elevated excretion of neutral steroids in the urine. Harrison (1956) reports that degenerative changes in the spermatogenic epithelium of rats can be induced by the stress of daily subcutaneous injections of normal saline.   Spermatogenesis is also impaired by injections of rather large doses of adrenaline (Eguchi, 1929 ; Perry, 1941 ; VanDemark and Boyd, 1956) although Lamar (1943) failed to observe such an effect.

Sexual Activity

The number of spermatozoa that can be harvested from the ram and bull by means of the artificial vagina is greatly increased by increasing the frequency of collection (Chang, 1945 ; Almquist and Hale, 1956 ; Vandemark, 1956).   Consideration of the yields of spermatozoa obtained in this way suggests that the rate of spermatogenesis is stimulated by sexual activity, but cytological confirmation of this has not been attempted.   On the other hand, some workers believe that excessive sexual activity has a detrimental effect on spermatogenesis.

Boyd and Vandemark (1957) state that each gram of testis in the bull is capable of producing at least $2 \cdot 8 \times 10^6$ spermatozoa per day.   In the sexually active rabbit, Edwards (1940) found that each gram of testis produced about 14×10^6 spermatozoa per day.

Toxic Substances

Highly chlorinated naphthalene

Highly chlorinated naphthalene, a component of certain lubricants and an occasional contaminant of processed feeding-stuffs, causes rapid degeneration of the germinal epithelium and aspermia in the bull, when taken orally.   This condition is associated with hyperkeratosis, low vitamin-A levels in the blood plasma, squamous metaplasia of the epithelia of the epididymis and seminal vesicles and lesions in most organs of the body.   Cows are similarly affected.   Recovery occurs when administration of the chlorinated naphthalene, or contaminated food, is stopped (see Olafson, 1947 ; Olafson and McEntee, 1951 ; Olson and Cook, 1951 ; Hansel, McEntee and Olafson, 1951; Bell, 1952; McEntee and Olafson, 1953; Olson and Skidmore, 1954; Vlahos, McEntee, Olafson and Hansel, 1955).

Arsenic

Gunn, Sanders and Granger (1942) observed that the dipping of rams in arsenical sheep-dips (containing less than $0 \cdot 2$ per cent As_2O_3) to prevent blowfly strike has a profoundly adverse effect on spermatogenesis.   This is evidently caused by the absorption of arsenic through the skin.   Rams with long fine fleece are more susceptible than those with short or coarse fleece and the effects are more pronounced when the weather is warm and humid than when it is cool and dry. The dipping of rams in water, or in phenol-type sheep-dips, had no adverse effects on spermatogenesis.

Cadmium

Subcutaneous administration of cadmium salts causes dramatic destruction of the testicular tissue in rats and mice, although damage in other organs is slight

(Pařízek, 1956, 1957a, b ; Pařízek and Záhoř, 1956). Gradually the testis recovers its endocrine function but the destruction of the spermatogenic epithelium appears to be complete and irreversible. There is no similar effect with mercury and the action of cadmium can be prevented by the simultaneous administration of an excess of zinc. This suggests that cadmium acts by competitive displacement of zinc in enzymes or other important components of the testis. In this connection it may be noted that both the content of zinc and its metabolic turnover are very high in the testis (Mawson, Fischer and Riedel, 1955), and that prolonged nutritional deficiency of zinc leads to testicular damage (Millar, Fischer, Elcoate and Mawson, 1958).

Colchicine

Subcutaneous administration of colchicine causes the arrest of spermatogonial division in metaphase (Roosen-Runge, 1951a; Leblond and Clermont, 1952a). This provides a useful technique for establishing the times of spermatogonial division. Subsequently the germinal epithelium may show extensive degeneration (Barsoum, 1955).

Sensitisation to Spermatozoa and Testis Tissue

Permanent aspermatogenesis can be produced in the guinea-pig by a single intra-cutaneous injection of homologous or autologous spermatozoa or testis tissue incorporated into a water-in-paraffin oil emulsion containing killed mycobacteria (Freund, Lipton and Thompson, 1953 ; Freund, Thompson and Lipton, 1955). Under these conditions, injury to the testis is confined to the germinal epithelium and is not associated with inflammation. It first manifests itself as an inhibition of spermateliosis and progresses through the degeneration and exfoliation of the spermatids, spermatocytes and finally spermatogonia. The Sertoli cells remain relatively unaffected and often exhibit hyperplasia. In extreme cases of testis injury, however, Sertoli cells appear to degenerate and this is followed by destruction and fibrosis of the seminiferous tubules. The hyaluronidase content of the testis bcomes greatly reduced. The interstitial cells, seminal vesicles, prostate, epididymis, central nervous system, spleen, liver, kidney and lungs remain unaffected.

The anti-testis reaction shows a high degree of organ and species specificity. Similar injections with guinea-pig liver or kidney tissue, with bull spermatozoa, or with testis material from the rabbit, hamster or sheep, did not produce aspermatogenesis. Varying degrees of damage to the testis, associated with meningo-encephalomyelitis, were obtained, however, with injections of guinea-pig spinal cord and brain and in this connection it may be noted that antigenic cross-reactions between the brain and the testis have been recorded by Lewis (1933, 1934). The anti-testis reaction is dependent upon the simultaneous injection of killed mycobacteria into the same site, and injections without the adjuvant were ineffective. Killed mycobacteria in paraffin oil, without spermatozoa or testis material, also induced aspermatogenesis when injected into the testis or into nearby sites, but when injected into the site usually employed (the dorsal skin) did not injure the testis.

Although the anti-testis reaction appears to be of an immunological nature, aspermatogenesis could not be induced by the passive transfer of immune sera from sensitised guinea-pigs to untreated guinea-pigs. These sera were shown to contain antibodies that immobilise spermatozoa, fix complement in the presence of spermatozoa and inhibit hyaluronidase. In immunised animals, there appeared to be a correlation between the titre of complement-fixing antibody and the degree of testicular damage, but no such correlation was apparent for the other two antibodies.

The component of testis material responsible for producing aspermatogenesis was shown to be water-soluble, alcohol-insoluble, heat-stable and associated with the " mitochondrial " fraction. Injections of concentrated aqueous preparations of testis material, with or without mycobacteria, also elicited local and systemic anaphylactic reactions, but these reactions appear to be quite different from the anti-testis reaction, which always requires the presence of mycobacteria, and may involve different antigens.

Aspermatogenesis can also be induced in rats by intra-cutaneous injections of homologous testis material with mycobacteria, but the rat is much less sensitive to this treatment than the guinea-pig, and repeated injections are required (Freund, Lipton and Thompson, 1954). The anti-testis reaction in the rat again exhibits a high degree of organ specificity.

Ionising Radiation

Since the first observations of Albers-Schönberg (1903), many investigators have studied the destructive action of X-rays on the testis (Heller, 1948 ; Casarett, 1956). At present, it seems generally agreed that B-type spermatogonia are the most sensitive of the spermatogenic cells to radiation damage, and that spermato-cytes, spermatids and spermatozoa are of increasing resistance in the order given. (The relative sensitivity of different kinds of spermatogenic cells to the induction of transmissible genetic damage is rather different and is considered separately at the end of this Section.) The Sertoli and interstitial cells are still more resistant and may appear histologically and functionally normal after complete destruction of the spermatogenic tissue. The effects of irradiation on the seminiferous tubules are direct and are not produced when the body is irradiated with the testis shielded (Kohn, 1955). The effects of gamma-rays and neutrons are qualitatively similar to those of X-rays, but quantitatively the effects of neutrons are much greater (Lawrence and Tennant, 1937 ; Snell and Aebersold, 1937 ; Lampe and Hodges, 1943).

In the mouse, a dose of 100 r of X-rays is sufficient to destroy the B-type spermatogonia and 600 r destroys most spermatogonia of all classes, but doses as high as 1,000 r have no retarding effect on meiosis or on the development of cells irradiated as spermatids (Oakberg, 1955a, b, 1956b). As a result, spermatocytes, early spermatids and late spermatids disappear successively from the germinal epithelium as development progresses and a short period of fertility precedes a varying period of sterility. The pattern of injury is therefore quite unlike that produced by most other noxious factors. A few A-type spermatogonia usually survive quite heavy doses of irradiation and these eventually repopulate the ger-minal epithelium. In man, this period of recovery may occupy many months

(Robinson and Engle, 1949 ; Hempelmann, Lisco and Hoffman, 1952 ; Oakes and Lashbaugh, 1952) ; in small laboratory animals, recovery is much quicker (Heller, 1948 ; Eschenbrenner and Miller, 1950) and regeneration often begins before the total damage has been expressed. With still greater injury, sterility is immediate and the spermatogenic epithelium may be irrevocably destroyed. Two or three doses of irradiation applied at short intervals often appear to be more injurious than single doses of the same total amount (Schinz and Slotopolsky, 1926 ; Sartory, Sartory and Meyer, 1931 ; Ferroux, Regaud and Samssonow, 1938), but the effect of fractionation of dosage depends upon the size of each fraction, the interval between administration of each fraction and the total dose applied. With protracted administration of small doses, the injury induced is often less, presumably because the spermatogenic cells are continually being renewed and relatively few cells are subjected to total doses large enough to be seriously injurious (Kohn and Kallman, 1955). Within limits, the rate of administration of a given dose (" minute intensity ") has no influence on the degree of injury incurred (Kirchoff and Kelbling, 1937).

Qualitatively the damaging effects of X-rays are similar in all mammalian species examined, but quantitatively they vary in accordance with differences of sensitivity between species. The rabbit is relatively resistant and the dose required for permanent sterilisation appears to be in the region of 2,000 to 3,000 r (Casarett, 1956). Chronic whole-body irradiation at a rate of 1·0 r of X-rays per day for one year produced no obvious injury to the testis, but there was serious damage when the dose was increased to 10 r daily (Metcalf, Inda, Barnett and Casarett, 1954). The dog and man appear to be much more sensitive. In the dog, whole-body X-irradiation with doses of 0·5 r daily severely affects spermatogenesis and doses of 1·0 r daily result in complete atrophy of the spermatogenic epithelium (Metcalf et al., 1954 ; Casarett and Hursh, 1956). Precise information is not available for man, but Glücksmann (1947) believes that a single dose of 250 r of X-rays will produce sterility for a year, and one of 500 to 600 r will produce permanent sterility. The effects of X-rays on the testes of rats, mice, guinea-pigs, and hamsters have been investigated by many workers (rat : Wigoder, 1929 ; Ferroux, Regaud and Samssonow, 1938 ; Wattenwyl and Joël, 1942 ; Momigliano and Essenberg, 1944 ; Sacher, 1952 ; Shaver, 1953 ; Metcalf et al., 1954 ; —mouse : Snell, 1933 ; Hertwig, 1938a, b ; Henshaw, 1944a, b ; Eschenbrenner and Miller, 1950 ; Rugh, 1952 ; Fogg and Cowing, 1952, 1953 ; Oakberg, 1955a, b —guinea-pig : Wigoder, 1929 ; Warren, 1943 ; —hamster : Kivy, 1951). The rat and mouse appear to be intermediate in sensitivity between the rabbit and man. Marked temporary depletion of the spermatogenic epithelium is produced in rabbits by single doses of 800 r, in rats by 600 r and in mice by 400 r (Heller, 1948 ; Eschenbrenner and Miller, 1950 ; Casarett, 1956). Regeneration occurs in three to five months. After exposure to a dose of 600 to 800 r of X-rays the male mouse is fertile, though matings usually result in small litters, for about two weeks, and then sterile for three months (Snell, 1935). There are, however, differences between strains in the sensitivity of mice to damage from X-rays (Henshaw, 1944) and, in the rat, there is evidence that the testes of immature animals are more radiosensitive than those of adults (Casarett, 1953 ; Shaver, 1953b).

The destructive effects of gamma-rays have been studied by Russ and Scott (1939), Eschenbrenner, Miller and Lorenz (1948), Eschenbrenner and Miller

(1954), Deringer, Heston and Lorenz (1954), Carter, Lyon and Phillips (1954) and Oakberg (1957a), and of neutrons by Snell and Aebersold (1937), Lawrence and Tennant (1937), Lampe and Hodges (1943), Robinson and Engle (1949), Neary, Munson and Mole (1953) and Ely *et al.* (1954).

Other investigators have studied the induction of damage to the genetic material of spermatogenic cells and spermatozoa that have been subjected to insufficient radiation to cause their destruction (*see* Russell, 1954 ; Muller, 1955 ; Auerbach, 1957). Fertile matings following irradiation of the testis often result in a high incidence of death among fertilised eggs, early embryos and foetuses (Snell, 1935, 1941 ; Snell and Picken, 1935 ; Murphree, Whitacker, Wilding and Rust, 1952 ; Bruce and Austin, 1956 ; Bateman, 1956 ; Edwards, 1957). This is evidently caused by changes in the nature or arrangement of the genetic material of spermatozoa that do not prevent the entry of spermatozoa into eggs but do prevent the development of successful zygotes. Some of the semi-sterility induced in male mice by irradiation is transmitted to about half their progency and is believed to be caused by translocations that give rise to unbalanced chromosome complements after ferilisation (Snell, 1933, 1935 ; Snell, Bodemann and Hollander, 1934 ; Snell and Picken, 1935 ; Hertwig, 1938b, 1940 ; Koller, 1944 ; Russell, 1950 ; Auerbach and Slizynski, 1956). Similar forms of semi-sterility can be induced in male mice by intraperitoneal administration of chemical mutagens, such as nitrogen mustard and triethylene-melamine (Falconer, Slizynsky and Auerbach, 1952; Jackson and Bock, 1955; Bock and Jackson, 1957; Craig, Fox and Jackson, 1958; Cattanach, 1957; Catanach and Edwards, 1958).

Attention has also been given to the possibility that irradiation of sires may affect the sex ratio of their progeny by the induction of lethal changes in the sex chromosomes (*see* Neel and Schull, 1956). Since the X-chromosome carries more genetic material than the Y-chromosome, it should be more susceptible to radiation damage. This should lead to a reduction in the frequency of female births when sires are irradiated and a reduction in the frequency of male births when dams are irradiated. There is, however, no clear-cut evidence that such an effect occurs. Parkes (1925) observed an increase, moderate but not significant, in the proportion of male young sired by mice that mated within four days of irradiation. This was followed by a significant decrease in the proportion of males conceived at matings that occurred from 5 to 18 days after irradiation of the sires. The sex ratio in litters from subsequent matings did not depart from normal. Kalmus, Metrakos and Silverberg (1952) observed a significant increase in the proportion of male progeny of irradiated male mice, but this was not confirmed by Trasler and Metrakos (1953). Hertwig (1938b) and Russell (1954) found no significant deviation from normal in the sex ratio of the progeny of irradiated male mice, although some of Hertwig's animals, those subjected to the highest doses of irradiation, did produce a highly suggestive excess of males.

From the genetic point of view the most important effect of irradiation is the induction of mutations. These are almost invariably harmful and if recessive may not reveal themselves until several generations have elapsed. The spermatids appear to be the most sensitive of the spermatogenic cells to the mutagenic effect of X-rays. Spermatozoa are somewhat less sensitive and spermatogonia are the least sensitive. There is little available information on the relative sensitivity of different species, but the mouse is known to be considerably more sensitive than

the fruit-fly, *Drosophila*. The frequency of point-mutation is directly proportional to the total dose of irradiation and is independent of the manner in which
the exposure is spread in time. There appears to be no threshold of mutagenic
activity. Similar laws govern the frequency of induced breaks in chromosomes.
The frequency of induction of chromosome rearrangements (translocations and
deletions) is, however, dependent upon the intensity at which a dose is administered and, with the exception of neutron irradiation, does not increase linearly
with increasing dose. With X-rays and gamma-rays, it increases approximately
as the square of the dose (Auerbach, 1957). In man, it is estimated that the
present mutation rate would be doubled by a dose of between 30 and 80. r administered to the gonads during the first 30 years of life (Medical Research Council,
1956; National Academy of Sciences, 1956). For further information on the
mutagenic effects of ionizing radiation reference should be made to Muller (1954b)
and Russell (1954).

X. The Physiology of Spermatozoa within the Male Reproductive Tract

Spermatozoa are stored within the excurrent ducts of the male reproductive
tract until required for insemination and it is here that they complete their development to functional maturity. Prolonged residence within the tract leads to senility
and functional impairment of the spermatozoa. Before discussing these events
more fully, it is convenient to describe briefly the principal features of the male
reproductive tract other than the accessory glands and the copulatory organ.

The Male Reproductive Tract

The mammalian testis is enclosed within a fibrous capsule, the tunica albuginea, which carries the arterial and venous systems over the surface of the testis
and is also rich in lymphatics. Along the posterior border of the testis, the tunica
albuginea is greatly thickened and extends for a short distance into the testis to
form a mass of fibrous tissue, the mediastinum. Trabeculae of the tunica albuginea pass inwards from the surface of the capsule towards the mediastinum and
divide the testis into a number of pear-shaped lobules. Each lobule is composed
of many looped seminiferous tubules. These anastomose with straight tubules in
which spermatogenesis is usually absent. The straight tubules pass into the
mediastinum to form an anastomosing network of non-seminiferous tubules, the
rete testis. From the rete testis, a number of ducts (12 to 20 in man), the ductuli
efferentes or vasa efferentia, pass through the tunica albuginea and, after a short
but much convoluted course, combine to form a single long convoluted duct, the
ductus epididymis. This is differentiated into six histologically distinct regions
or zones of increasing diameter (Mietkiewski, 1935 ; Reid and Cleland, 1957).
The convoluted part of the vasa efferentia and the whole of the ductus epididymis
are bound together to form a discrete organ, the epididymis. This is situated
along the posterior margin of the testis and connected to it at the mediastinum.
The epididymis is usually differentiated into three anatomical regions : the head
or caput epididymis, the body, isthmus or corpus epididymis, and the tail or cauda

epididymis. The ductus epididymis leaves the cauda epididymis to form the vas deferens or vas deferens rectus. This is a relatively straight duct which passes through the inguinal canal and finally opens into the urethra. In some mammals, the terminal portion of the vas deferens widens out to form the ampulla of Henle. In man, the excretory duct of the seminal vesicle opens into the terminal portion of the vas deferens and the common duct so formed is known as the ejaculatory duct. In other mammals, the seminal vesicle may have a separate opening into the urethra.

The total length of the reproductive tract from the vasa efferentia to the urethra is estimated to be about 3 metres in the guinea-pig (Simeone and Young, 1931), about 6 metres in man (Testut, 1934), over 40 metres in the bull and over 70 metres in the stallion (Ghetie, 1939).

The epithelium of the excurrent tract is columnar. Active cilia are restricted to the vasa efferentia, but inactive stereocilia are found throughout the remaining regions. There is a progressive decrease in the height of the epithelium and a progressive increase in the diameter of the lumen of the tract from the proximal to the distal end of the epididymal duct. A layer of circular smooth muscle surrounds the ductus epididymis. In the vas deferens, the muscle is well developed and differentiated into an inner layer of longitudinal fibres, a medial layer of circular fibres and an outer longitudinal layer. On the outside of the muscles is a layer of connective tissue.

For further information on the anatomy and histology of the excurrent ducts, reference should be made to the works of Aigner (1900), Benoit (1925, 1936), Nemiloff (1926), Stieve (1930), Mietkiewski (1935), Maneely (1955) and Reid and Cleland (1957). The morphology of the seminiferous tubules has been studied by Curtis (1918), Bascom and Osternd (1925), Johnson (1934) and Hirota (1952a, b; 1955a, b). The comparative anatomy of the male reproductive tract is discussed in Chapters 2 and 8.

Maturation of Spermatozoa

Although the term spermateliosis is usually applied only to the development of the spermatid within the testis, there is evidence that spermateliosis is actually completed in the ductus epididymis for it is here that spermatozoa undergo a process of maturation during which they acquire their full functional competence. Thus it has been found that spermatozoa removed from successive levels of the tract show an increasing capacity for motility, for survival *in vitro*, and for fertility (Redenz, 1925, 1926; Young, 1929a, b; 1931; Yochem, 1930). Young (1931) found that, in the guinea-pig, spermatozoa from the distal end of the epididymis were twice as fertile as those from the proximal end. Spermatozoa taken from the testis are usually sterile (Young, 1929a; 1931). Similar observations have been made on the domestic fowl (Munro, 1935, 1938a, b). These physiological changes are accompanied by the migration of the cytoplasmic droplet from the neck of the spermatozoon to the distal end of the mid-piece (Braus and Redenz, 1924; Lasley and Bogart, 1944; Gresson and Zlotnik, 1945; Rao and Berry, 1949; Branton and Salisbury, 1947; Hancock, 1955, 1957a). In the bull, migration of the droplet appears to occur almost exclusively in the caput epididymis (Hancock, 1955) but in the boar, it commonly takes place in the corpus and cauda epididymis also

(Hancock, 1957a). At ejaculation, the droplet is usually lost from the spermatozoon. Selivanova (1937) believes that this loss is brought about not so much by the maturity of the spermatozoa as by the influence of the secretions from the accessory glands. Hancock (1957b) also considers that removal of the droplet is a function of the accessory secretions. Branton and Salisbury (1947), however, observed that the droplet is often missing from spermatozoa in the ampulla of the vas deferens. Apart from the migration of the droplet, there appears to be no appreciable change in the size or shape of spermatozoa as they pass through the epididymis, but Ånberg (1957) states that, in man, the organisation of the mitochondria into the structure of the mid-piece is completed in the epididymis.

Braus and Redenz (1924) advanced the theory that, in passing through the epididymis, the spermatozoa receive a coating of secretion that protects them from harmful substances that may be found in the female tract or in artificial media *in vitro*. Ortavant (1953) reports that permeability of epididymal ram and bull spermatozoa to eosin is greatest in the corpus epididymis, lowest in the caput and cauda epididymis and intermediate in the vas deferens. Brochart and Debatène (1953), however, state that the affinity of spermatozoa for eosin decreases progressively along the epididymal duct.

Redenz was of the opinion that the maturation changes were induced by specific secretions from the walls of the epididymis. Young, however, regards them as being essentially a continuation of processes inherent in the cell. Probably both these factors are involved. Gunn (1936) expressed doubts on the validity of Young's hypothesis, since he found that, when the rate of elimination of spermatozoa from the ram's genital tract was greatly hastened by repeated ejaculation, the spermatozoa did not lose fertilising capacity although their normal sojourn in the epididymis was greatly curtailed. On the other hand, there is evidence that excessive use of the male may diminish not only the motility of spermatozoa but also fertility (*see* Anderson, 1945a). Here, however, the effect upon the number of spermatozoa and their degree of dilution must be considered.

Concentration of Spermatozoa

According to Reid and Cleland (1957), the concentration of spermatozoa in the reproductive tract of the rat is low in the rete testis and the proximal part of the vasa efferentia, but rises rapidly in the terminal part of the vasa efferentia and more slowly in the first two zones of the ductus epididymis. In the third zone of the ductus epididymis, spermatozoon concentration falls steeply and thereafter gradually rises to about the same level as that attained in the second zone. These observations suggest that fluid is freely secreted in the testis and in the third zone of the ductus epididymis and is absorbed in other regions of the tract. Benoit's (1926) observations were slightly different from those of Reid and Cleland. He found that in many species spermatozoon concentration was low in the vasa efferentia and in the initial zone of the ductus epididymis but rose rapidly in the next zone. Similar findings were reported by Young (1933) who studied the absorptive function of the epididymis of the mouse. Reid and Cleland found that, in regions of low concentration, the spermatozoa were rather randomly distributed but, in regions of high concentration, the spermatozoa showed a high degree of orientation.

Motility and Metabolism of Spermatozoa

It is generally agreed that spermatozoa are immotile, or nearly so, while within the male reproductive tract, although they readily display motility when removed from the tract and examined on a microscope slide.   Simeone (1933) made observations through the intact wall of the excised epididymis by means of powerful illumination and was unable to detect any movement in the spermatozoa until they were liberated into the surrounding Ringer's solution.   Similar observations were made by Hartman (1939) in the bat, *Myotis*.   Gunn (1936) inserted a capillary pipette filled with medicinal paraffin, recently autoclaved to remove dissolved gases, into the vas deferens of the guinea-pig and then obtained a sample of its contents by electrical stimulation of the ejaculatory nerve centre.   The spermatozoa so obtained were immotile until exposed to air.   In the ram, slight motility was observed in the freshly ejaculated semen by a similar technique, but motility increased greatly on aeration or dilution—an observation since confirmed by Lardy, Hansen and Phillips (1945) and Walton (1956).   In the rabbit, D. W. Bishop and Mathews (1952) also observed that spermatozoa removed from the vas deferens were immotile until they made contact with air.   Walton (unpublished observation) observed that epididymal spermatozoa of the rat display active motility when exposed to air, provided that care is taken to prevent evaporation.

Nothing is known of the metabolism of spermatozoa while within the epididymis, but the rate of metabolism is presumably low.   D. W. Bishop and Mathews (1952) attribute the quiescence of spermatozoa in the epididymis to a low partial pressure of oxygen combined with a deficiency of glycolysable sugar.   Huggins and Johnson (1933) found only traces of glucose in human spermatocoele fluid and Mann (1946) and Mann and Glover (1954) found only traces of fructose in epididymal fluids of the bull, ram, rat, rabbit, cat and boar, although greater amounts may be present in the ampullae (Mann, 1948).   Walton (1956), using epididymal spermatozoa of the ram and bull, found that reversible and almost complete inhibition of motility could be produced for several hours *in vitro* by withholding both oxygen and glycolysable sugar.   Active motility was resumed when either oxygen or fructose was admitted to the spermatozoa, but maximum motility occurred only when oxygen and fructose were admitted together.   There are, however, differences between species.   According to Dott (1959), epididymal spermatozoa of the boar are active only in the presence of oxygen and epididymal spermatozoa of the stallion are active only in the presence of glycolysable sugar. In both species, maximum activity again occurred when oxygen and glycolysable substrate were present together.   Lardy and his associates found that spermatozoa removed from the epididymis of the bull have a higher metabolic efficiency, as measured by the Meyerhof oxidation-quotient, than spermatozoa from ejaculated semen.   This difference is attributed to the presence of a metabolic stimulator, believed to be a sulphite or sulphydryl compound, in the secretions of the accessory glands (Lardy, Ghosh and Plaut, 1949 ; Lardy, 1953).   Bishop (1955) and Bishop and Salisbury (1955), on the other hand, believe that the quiescence of spermatozoa in the epididymis is partly controlled by a metabolic inhibitor, and subsequent observations of Salisbury and his co-workers suggest that potassium and carbon dioxide may be implicated in this role (Salisbury and Cragle, 1956 ;   VanDemark and Sharma, 1957 ; Salisbury and VanDemark, 1957).   Sørensen and Anderson

(1956) also obtained evidence that the potassium : sodium ratio is high in the epididymis and they draw attention to the observation of Schlenk and Kahmann (1938), showing that potassium appears to be an inhibitor in trout semen.   The possible role of carbon dioxide as a metabolic inhibitor in the male tract is denied by D. W. Bishop and Mathews (1952) who concluded from measurements of pH that there are no narcotic accumulations of either carbon dioxide or lactic acid in the vas deferens of the rabbit.   Hartman (1939) cites similar hydrogen-ion concentrations (pH 6·5 to 6·7) for the tail of the epididymis of the rat, guinea-pig and bull, from the work of Lanz and Malyoth (1928a, b), Lanz (1929) and Becher (1930).   Rao and Berry (1949) believe that viscosity and high spermatozoon concentration are important factors in the inhibition of motility in the tail of the epididymis in the bull and the boar.

In general when spermatozoa are removed from the male reproductive tract, the principal activating agent appears to be the increased availability of oxygen. Greater activity is obtained by diluting the spermatozoa with seminal plasma or with physiological saline.   These observations suggest that an inhibitory substance is present, but that inhibition is incomplete in the presence of high partial pressures of oxygen.   Maximum motility, however, evidently requires a suitable exogenous source of energy.

As spermatozoa pass along the male reproductive tract, their capacity for motility increases.   This capacity is low in the testis and highest in the tail of the epididymis (White, 1932 ; Rao and Berry, 1949, 1950).   Earlier reports that spermatozoa are immotile when removed from the tract are probably attributable to post-mortem changes occurring in the tract that rapidly render spermatozoa irreversibly inactive (Redenz, 1926).

Survival of Spermatozoa

Conditions within the epididymis are exceptionally favourable for the survival of spermatozoa.   Here they retain their fertility and their capacity for motility much longer than in the female reproductive tract or *in vitro* at similar temperature. The capacity for motility is maintained for 55 to 70 days in the guinea-pig (Benoit, 1925 ; Moore, 1928, 1932, 1939 ; Young, 1929) for 60 days in the rabbit (Hammond and Asdell, 1926) and the bull (Kirillov and Morozov, 1936), for 30 to 45 days in the rat (Moore, 1932, 1939 ; White, 1932), and for several months in some bats (Guthrie, 1933).   The capacity for motility is lost first in the head of the epididymis and tends to persist for longer in the tail of the epididymis than in the vas deferens (White, 1932).   When the supply of new spermatozoa from the testis was cut off by ligature, Hammond and Asdell (1926) found that the fertility of rabbits remained at 100 per cent for 20 days, fell to 36 per cent between 20 and 30 days, to 20 per cent between 30 and 38 days and to zero after 40 days.   Similar experiments show that spermatozoa remain fertile in the epididymis for 20 to 35 days in the guinea-pig (Young, 1929a) and for 20 days in the rat (White, 1933). In some bats, spermatozoa are stored in the tail of the epididymis from the completion of spermatogenesis in the autumn until copulation in the spring (Guthrie, 1933 ; Hartman, 1939).   Senility and death of spermatozoa follow a prolonged stay in the epididymis and, when this occurs, the ability to form viable embryos is lost before the ability to fertilise eggs, and fertilising capacity is lost before motility.   Young (1931) found that the incidence of non-viable embryos in the guinea-pig could be increased from 3·6 per cent to 20 per cent by retaining spermatozoa in the epididymis for 20 to 25 days before mating.   He also noted that fertility in the distal end of the tract is lost earlier than in higher levels of the tract. The first ejaculate after prolonged abstinence often contains a high proportion of dead, inactive, and decapitate spermatozoa (Simeone and Young, 1931).

The survival of spermatozoa in the epididymis is evidently dependent upon the endocrine activity of the testis, for survival is greatly decreased if the testes or pituitary are removed (see Chapters 25 and 29).

Transport of Spermatozoa

After their formation in the germinal epithelium, the early spermatozoa are rapidly passed from the seminiferous tubules through the rete testis and the vasa efferentia to the ductus epididymis.   They show no tendency to accumulate in the testis, but the manner of their transport from this organ is obscure.   Probably it is brought about by the continuous secretion and flow of fluid from the testis to the proximal region of the epididymal duct (Young, 1933 ; Reid and Cleland, 1957) aided by the cilia of the vasa efferentia and movements of the seminiferous tubules of the kind observed by Roosen-Runge (1951b).   Transport through the ductus epididymis is almost certainly achieved by peristalic movements aided by the increasing diameter of the duct.   Cross (1955) and Risley and Turbyfill (1957) have observed peristaltic, pendular and segmentation movements in the ductus epididymis and Simeone (1933) showed that transport could be impaired by sympathetic denervation.   At ejaculation, spermatozoa are expelled into the urethra by reflex contractions of the walls of the vas deferens and the distal part of the ductus epididymis.

The time taken for the passage of spermatozoa through the epididymis has been variously estimated.   Lanz (1924) suggests that about six days are required, since it took this time for the epididymis to empty after spermatogenesis had been stopped by heat treatment of the testis.   From studies on the rate of production of spermatozoa, Edwards (1940) concluded that the passage of spermatozoa through the epididymis took 4 to 7 days in the sexually active rabbit.   Toothill and Young (1931) found that India ink introduced into the ducts of the caput epididymis of the guinea-pig appeared in the semen in 14 to 16 days.   When the supply of spermatozoa and secretion from the testis was cut off by ligature, the India ink particles appeared only after 25 to 38 days.   It was suggested, therefore, that the constant supply of material from the testis is an important factor in the passage of spermatozoa through the epididymis.   Gunn (1936) repeated these experiments on the ram.   In the sexually inactive animal, the passage took 11 days. When the rams were allowed to copulate, the passage took 9 days and, when the rams were frequently subjected to electrically induced ejaculation, the India ink appeared in about 5 days.   MacMillan and Harrison (1955) observed that radiopaque material introduced into the rete testis of the rat entered the vas deferens on the 13th post-operative day and was not detectable after the 14th day.   Contrary to the observations of Toothill and Young, MacMillan and Harrison found that the rate of passage through the epididymis was not influenced by ligation of the vasa efferentia and they conclude that the testis has no mechanical influence on the passage of spermatozoa through the ductus epididymis.   From studies on spermatozoa labelled during spermatogenesis with radioactive tracers, Edwards and Sirlin estimated that the passage of spermatozoa from the testis to the ejaculate in the mouse took about $7 \cdot 5$ days (Sirlin and Edwards, 1957b; Edwards and Sirlin, 1958). Similar estimates are given by Hertwig (1938) for mice with acute radiation damage of the testis. Ortavant (1954c), from studies of isotope incorporation, estimated that 20 days were required for spermatozoa to pass through the epididymis of the sexually inactive ram.

Storage of Spermatozoa

The tail of the epididymis and to a lesser extent the vas deferens also serve as the storage receptable wherein spermatozoa accumulate during the intervals between the periodic emission of semen (Lanz, 1924, 1926 ; Polovtzeva, 1938 ; Chang, 1945b; Ortavant, 1952; Almquist and Hale, 1956; Chang and Sheaffer, 1957). The genital tract of the ram contains up to 220×10^9 spermatozoa, of which over 70 per cent are in the cauda epididymis and less than 2 per cent are in the vas deferens. Spermatozoa are not stored, as was once supposed, in the seminal vesicles (Beams and King, 1933).

The storage capacity of the male tract can be demonstrated by repeated copulations within a short period of time. Thus, Lloyd-Jones and Hays (1918) found with rabbits that after the twentieth copulation in 4 hours the percentage fertility only fell to 36 per cent, and Hammond (1921) still obtained fertile matings with a rabbit after 39 matings within 8 hours. Almquist and Hale (1956) obtained up to 36 ejaculates in 1 hour from the bull. Other observations on domestic animals have been reviewed by McKenzie and Berliner (1937) and Anderson (1945a). Large numbers of successive matings can be made without exhausting the supply of spermatozoa and Almquist and Hale estimate that, in the bull, only about half the spermatozoa (up to 80×10^9 spermatozoa) can be evacuated in this way. The number and concentration of spermatozoa decrease in successive ejaculates (Lloyd-Jones and Hays, 1918 ; Walton, 1927 ; Macirone and Walton, 1938 ; Almquist and Hale, 1956), but there is no clear evidence that the proportion of spermatozoa with persistent cytoplasmic droplets increases (Gunn, 1936 ; Chang, 1945a). There are, of course, considerable variations between animals in their response to repeated matings, in the numbers of spermatozoa found in the genital tract, and in the period required to recover from intensive sexual activity (McKenzie and Berliner, 1937 ; Chang, 1945a ; Almquist and Hale, 1956). These differences may reflect not only variations in the storage capacity of the tract but also in the rate of passage of spermatozoa through it and in the rate of spermatogenesis. Chang, in his analysis of spermatozoon production in the ram, concludes that the content of the epididymis does not alter greatly with different rates of ejaculation, and that the number of spermatozoa is kept relatively constant either by decreased spermatogenesis or increased absorption during periods of sexual repose, or alternatively by increased spermatogenesis during periods of sexual activity.

Absorption of Spermatozoa

An additional function attributed to the vas deferens is that of dissolution and absorption of senescent spermatozoa. According to Simeone and Young (1931), dissolution of spermatozoa at the distal end of the vas (ampulla of Henle) is the normal mechanism by which superflous and effete spermatozoa are eliminated in the guinea-pig. They found no appreciable elimination of spermatozoa in the urine as described by Oslund (1928), no evidence of phagocytosis as described by Wegelin (1921), Morgenstern (1924) and Nemiloff (1926), and no evidence of disintegration of spermatozoa in the seminal vesicles. Reid and Cleland (1957), however, found no mass degeneration of spermatozoa in the vas deferens of the guinea-pig. Kirillov (1938) observed that live spermatozoa are found for only two days in the ampulla of the bull after ligation of the vas above the ampulla. Wilhelm (1935) concluded, from X-ray observation of opaque oil in the vas deferens, that there might be a continuous evacuation into the urethra independently of ejaculation. MacMillan and Harrison (1955) also observed the rapid loss of radiopaque material from the vas : they suggest, however, that this loss may be caused by absorption. Collery (1944) found evidence of spermatozoa and of nonseptic spermiophagia in the urethra of the male guinea-pig, but in view of the drastic methods used (electrical ejaculation and death by stunning) these observations are not convincing evidence that spermatozoa ordinarily pass into the urethra except by ejaculation. In marsupials, however, the elimination of spermatozoa with the urine appears to be a common occurrence (Bolliger and Carrodus, 1938). On the other hand, most males have seminal emissions without coitus, either by masturbation or otherwise, and this may be the chief means whereby excess spermatozoa are removed from the reproductive tract. Certainly, the first ejaculate after periods of sexual abstinence often contains a high proportion of dead and disintegrating spermatozoa (*see* Anderson, 1945a) but this cannot be regarded as evidence for a specific mechanism for the dissolution of spermatozoa in the ampulla. Further, it is known that the spermatozoon is extremely resistant to disintegration *in vitro*, and unless some very powerful enzymes are present in the lower part of the vas, it is difficult to envisage how rapid dissolution and absorption can occur. The frequently observed accumulation of spermatozoa in spermatocoeles in the caput and cauda epididymis, which arise after occlusion of the epididymal duct, also testifies to the absence of any powerful means for dissolving spermatozoa in these regions. Slow dissolution of spermatozoa in the isolated cauda epididymis of the rat has been observed by MacMillan (1954), but even after 127 days dissolution was not complete.

Invasion of the Epididymal Walls by Spermatozoa

The penetration of spermatozoa through the walls of the epididymal duct into the peri-tubular tissue has been described by King (1955) and others. The condition appears to be associated with infections of the epididymis, but its aetiology is not clear.

Bibliography

ADAMS, C. E. (1957). An attempt to cross the domestic rabbit (*Oryctolagus cuniculus*) and hare (*Lepus europaeus*). *Nature, Lond.*, **180**, 853.

AIGNER, A. (1900). Über das Epithel im Nebenhoden einiger Säugethiere und seine secretorische Thätigkeit. *G. B. Akad. Wien*, **109**, 1.

ALBERS-SCHÖNBERG, H. E. (1903). Uber eine bisher unbekannte Wirkung der Röntgenstrahlen auf den Organismus der Tiere. *Münch. med. Wschr.*, **50**, 1859.

ALLANSON, M., & DEANESLEY, R. (1934). The reaction of anoestrous hedgehogs to experimental conditions. *Proc. roy. Soc.* B, **116**, 170.

Allanson, M., Rowlands, I. W., & Parkes, A. S. (1934). Induction of fertility and pregnancy in the anoestrous ferret. *Proc. roy. Soc.* B, **115**, 410.

Almquist, J. O., & Hale, E. B. (1956). An approach to the measurement of sexual behaviour and semen production of dairy bulls. *Proc. Third Internat. Congr. Anim. Reprod., Cambridge*, **3**, 50.

Altland, P. D. (1949). Effect of discontinuous exposure to 25,000 feet simulated altitude on growth and reproduction of the albino rat. *J. exp. Zool.*, **110**, 1.

—— & Allen, E. (1952). Studies on degenerating sex cells in immature mammals. III: The influence of hypoxia on the degeneration of primordial and differentiating definitive germ cells in the male albino rat. *J. Morph.*, **91**, 541.

Amoroso, E. C., & Parkes, A. S. (1947). Effects on embryonic development of X-irradiation of rabbit spermatozoa *in vitro*. *Proc. roy. Soc.* B, **134**, 57.

Ånberg, Å. (1957). The ultrastructure of the human spermatozoon. *Acta obstet. gynec. scand.*, **36**, Suppl. 2.

Anderson, J. (1945a). *The semen of animals and its use for artificial insemination.* Edinburgh.

—— (1945b). Seasonal variation in the reproductive capacity of the bull. *J. agric. Sci.*, **35**, 184.

Armstrong, J. A. (1956). Histochemical differentiation of nucleic acids by means of induced fluorescence. *Exp. Cell Res.*, **11**, 640.

Asdell, S. A. (1946). *Patterns of mammalian reproduction.* New York.

—— & Salisbury, G. W. (1941a). The rate at which spermatogenesis occurs in the rabbit. *Anat. Rec.*, **80**, 145.

—— —— (1941b). The viability of spermatozoa in the abdominal epididymis and the failure of motile sperms to fertilize ova. *Amer. J. Physiol.*, **132**, 791.

Auerbach, C. (1957). Genetical effects of radiation and chemicals. *Experientia*, **13**, 217.

—— & Slizynski, B. M. (1956). Sensitivity of the mouse testis to the mutagenic action of X-rays. *Nature, Lond.*, **177**, 376.

Austin, C. R. (1951). The formation, growth and conjugation of the pronuclei in the rat egg. *J. R. micr. Soc.*, **71**, 295.

—— (1957). Fertilization, early cleavage and associated phenomena in the field vole (*Microtus agrestis*). *J. Anat., Lond.*, **91**, 1.

—— & Bishop, M. W. H. (1957). Preliminaries to fertilization in mammals. In *The Beginnings of Embryonic Development*, p. 71. Amer. Ass. Advanc. Sci., Wash.

—— —— (1958a). Capacitation of mammalian spermatozoa. *Nature, Lond.*, **181**, 851.

—— —— (1958b). Some features of the acrosome and perforatorium in mammalian spermatozoa. *Proc. roy. Soc.* B, **149**, 234.

—— —— (1958c). Role of rodent acrosome and perforatorium in fertilization. *Proc. roy. Soc.* B, **149**, 241.

—— & Sapsford, C. S. (1952). The development of the rat spermatid. *J. R. micr. Soc.*, **71**, 397.

Baker, J. R. (1931). The spermicidal powers of chemical contraceptives. II: Pure substances. *J. Hyg., Camb.*, **31**, 189.

—— (1946). The histochemical recognition of lipine. *Quart. J. micr. Sci.*, **87**, 441.

—— (1955). What is the " Golgi " controversy? *J. R. micr. Soc.*, **74**, 217.

Ballowitz, E. (1888). Untersuchungen über die Struktur der Spermatozoen, zugleich ein Beitrag zur Lehre vom feineren Bau der contraktilen Elemente. *Arch. mikr. Anat.*, **32**, 401.

—— (1891a). Weitere Beobachtungen über den feineren Bau der Saügethierspermatozoen. *Z. wiss. Zool.*, **52**, 217.

—— (1891b). Die Bedentung der Valentin' schen Querbänder am Spermatozoenkopfe der Saügethiere. *Arch. Anat. Physiol., Lpz.*, 193.

Bangham, A. D., & Hancock, J. L. (1955). A new method for counting live and dead bull spermatozoa. *Nature, Lond.*, **176**, 656.

Barer, R., Ross, K. F. A., & Thaczyk, S. (1953). Refractometry of living cells. *Nature, Lond.*, **171**, 720.

Barnett, S. A. (1956). Endothermy and ectothermy in mice at −3° C. *J. exp. Biol.*, **33**, 124.

BARNETT, S. A., & MANLY, B. M. (1954). Breeding of mice at $-3°$ C. *Nature, Lond.*, **173,** 355.

—— —— (1956). Reproduction and growth of mice of three strains after transfer to $-3°$ C. *J. exp. Biol.*, **33,** 325.

BARR, M. L. (1955). The sex chromatin and its application to errors in sex development. In *Modern trends in Obstetrics and Gynaecology.* London.

—— (1956). Cytological tests of sex. *Lancet*, **i,** 47.

—— & BERTRAM, E. G. (1949). A morphological distinction between neurones of the male and female, and the behaviour of the nucleolar satellites during accelerated nucleo-protein synthesis. *Nature, Lond.*, **163,** 676.

BARRON, D. H. (1933). The trophic influence of the spermatic nerve of the testicle. *Anat. Rec.*, **55,** 6.

BARRY, M. (1843). Spermatozoa observed within the mammiferous ovum. *Phil. Trans.*, **133,** 33.

BARSOUM, H. (1955). The effect of colchicine on the spermatogenesis of rabbits. *J. Pharmacol.*, **115,** 319.

BASCOM, K. F., & OSTERND, H. L. (1925). Quantitative studies of the testicle. II: Pattern and total tubule length in the testicles of certain common mammals. *Anat. Rec.* **31,** 159.

BATEMAN, A. J. (1956). Sensitivity of immature mouse sperm to the mutagenic effects of X-rays. *Nature, Lond.*, **178,** 1278.

BEAMS, H. W., & KING, R. L. (1933). Sperm storage function of the seminal vesicles. *J. Urol.*, **29,** 95.

BEATTY, R. A. (1956). Melanizing activity of semen from rabbit males of different geno-type. *Proc. roy. phys. Soc., Edinb.*, **25,** 39.

—— (1957). Nigrosin-eosin staining of rabbit spermatozoa and the fertility of semen. *Proc. roy. Soc., Edinb.*, **67,** 1.

BECHER, H. (1930). Die Wirkung der inkretorischen Stoffe auf die Bewegung von Säuge-tierspermien. *Anat. Anz.*, **71,** 191.

BELL, A. W. (1929). The origin of neutral fats from the Golgi apparatus of the spermatid of the dog. *J. Morph.*, **48,** 611.

BELL, L. G. E. (1953). Some observations on mouse spermatids. *Quart. J. micr. Sci.*, **94,** 37.

BELL, W. B. (1952). The production of hyperkeratosis by the administration of a lubricant. *Virginia J. Sci.*, **3,** 71.

BENDA, C. (1887). Untersuchungen über den Bau des functionierenden Samenkanälchens einiger Säugethiere und Folgerungen für die Spermatogenese dieser Werbelthierk-lasse. *Arch. mikr. Anat.*, **30,** 49.

—— (1891). Cited by Wilson, 1925, p. 838.

—— (1903). Die Mitochondria. *Ergebn. Anat. EntwGesch.*, **12,** 743.

BENOIT, J. (1924). Sur l'involution des voies excrétrices du sperme et sur la disparition de la vitalité des spermatozoides contenus dans les voies excrétrices provoquées par la castration. *C. R. Soc. Biol., Paris,* **90,** 806.

—— (1925). Recherches anatomiques, cytologiques et physiologiques sur les voies excré-trices du testicle chez les mammifères. *Bull. Histol. Tech. micr.*, **ii,** 78.

—— (1926). Recherches anatomiques, cytologiques et histophysiologiques sur les voies excrétrices du testicule chez les mammifères. *Arch. Anat., Strasbourg,* **5,** 173.

BERLINER, V., & WARBRITTON, V. (1937). The pituitary and thyroid in relation to sperm production in rams. *Proc. Amer. Soc. anim. Prod.*, **30,** 137.

VON BERTALANFFY, L., & BICKIS, I. (1956). Identification of cytoplasmic basophilia (ribonucleic acid) by fluorescence microscopy. *J. Histochem. Cytochem.*, **4,** 481.

BHARGAVA, P. M. (1957). Incorporation of radioactive amino-acids in the proteins of bull spermatozoa. *Nature, Lond.*, **179,** 1120.

—— BISHOP, M. W. H., & WORK, T. S. (1959). The chemical composition of bull semen with special reference to nucleic acids, free nucleotides and free amino acids. *Biochem. J.* **73,** 242.

BINDER, S. (1927). Spermatogenese von *Macropus giganteus* mit Berücksichtigung einiger allgemeiner Fragen der Säugerspermatogenese. *Z. Zellforsch.*, **5,** 293.

Bischoff, T. L. W. (1854). *Bestätigung des von Dr. Newport bei den Batrachiern und Dr. Barry bei den Kaninchen behaupteten Eindringens der Spermatozoïden in das Ei.* Giessen.

Bishop, D. W., & Mathews, H. P. (1952). The significance of intravas pH in relation to sperm motility. *Science*, **115**, 209.

Bishop, M. W. H. (1955a). The physiology of bull spermatozoa. Ph.D. Thesis, Cambridge.

—— (1955b). Inter-relationships of semen characteristics. *Studies on Fertility*, **6**, 81.

—— (1960). Spermatogenesis and the individuality of the spermatozoon. In *Sex differentiation and development*. Mem. Soc. Endocrinol., No. 7.

—— & Austin, C. R. (1957). Mammalian spermatozoa. *Endeavour*, **16**, 137.

—— Campbell, R. C., Hancock, J. L., & Walton, A. (1954). Semen characteristics and fertility in the bull. *J. agric. Sci.*, **44**, 227.

—— & Hancock, J. L. (1955). The evaluation of bull semen. *Vet. Rec.*, **67**, 363.

—— & Salisbury, G. W. (1955). Effect of sperm concentration on the oxygen uptake of bull semen. *Amer. J. Physiol.*, **180**, 107.

—— & Smiles, J. (1957a). Induced fluorescence in mammalian gametes with acridine orange. *Nature, Lond.*, **179**, 307.

—— —— (1957b). Differentiation between living and dead spermatozoa by fluorescence microscopy. *Nature, Lond.*, **179**, 308.

—— —— (1958). Unpublished observations.

Bissonnette, T. H. (1935). Modification of mammalian sexual cycles. III: Reversal of the cycle in male ferrets (*Putorius vulgaris*) by increasing periods of exposure to light between October second and March thirteenth. *J. exp. Zool.*, **71**, 341.

—— (1936). Sexual photoperiodicity. *Quart. Rev. Biol.*, **11**, 371.

Blandau, R. J. (1951). Observations on the morphology of rat spermatozoa mounted in media of different refractive indices and examined with the phase microscope. *Anat. Rec.*, **109**, 271.

—— & Odor, D. L. (1952). Observations on sperm penetration into the oöplasm and changes in the cytoplasmic components of the fertilizing spermatozoon in rat ova. *Fertil. Steril.*, **3**, 13.

Blom, E. (1945). Spontaneous detachment of the galea capitis in spermia of bull and stallion. *Skand. VetTidskr.*, **35**, 779.

—— (1950a). *Om Bedommelsen af Tyresperma.* Copenhagen.

—— (1950b). Interpretation of spermatic cytology in bulls. *Fertil. Steril.*, **1**, 223.

—— (1950c). A one-minute live-dead sperm stain by means of eosin-nigrosin. *Fertil. Steril.*, **1**, 176.

—— & Christensen, N. O. (1944). En modificeret Tybromol-Kataseprøve som Led: den rutinemaessige Undersøgelse af Tyresperma. *Medlemsbl. danske Dyrlaegeforen.*, **27**, 537.

—— —— (1947). Studies on pathological conditions in the testis, epididymis and accessory sex glands in the bull. I. Normal anatomy, technique of the clinical examination and a survey of the findings in 2000 Danish slaughter bulls. *Skand. VetTidskr.*, **37**, 1.

Bock, M., & Jackson, H. (1957). The action of triethylenemelamine on the fertility of male rats. *Brit. J. Pharmacol.*, **12**, 1.

Bogart, R., & Mayer, D. T. (1946). Environmental temperature and thyroid gland involvement in lowered fertility of rams. *Res. Bull. Mo. agric. Exp. Sta.*, No. 402.

Boguth, W. (1952). Über den Plasmalogengehalt in Sperma. *Naturwissenschaften*, **39**, 432.

Bolliger, H., & Carrodus, A. L. (1938). Spermatorrhoea in *Trichosurus vulpecula* and other marsupials. *Med. J. Aust.*, **ii**, 1118.

Bonnadonna, T. (1953). Esame critico di taluni metodi di colorazione per stabilire la vitalità e la morfologia dei nemaspermi. *Il Progresso Vet.*

—— & Olgiati, L. (1953). Dell' identificazione del namaspermi di "Bos taurus" vivi e morti con la colorazione bleu bromo-fenolo e nigrosina. *Zootec. e Vet.*, **8**, 195.

Bonsma, J. C. (1940). The influence of climatological factors on cattle. *Rep. Dep. Agric. S. Afr.*, No. 223.

BOVERI, T. (1891). Befruchtung. *Ergebn. Anat. EntwGesch.*, **1**, 386.

BOWEN, R. H. (1922). On the idiosome, Golgi apparatus, and acrosome in the male germ cells. *Anat. Rec.*, **24**, 159.

—— (1924). On the acrosome of the animal sperm. *Anat. Rec.*, **28**, 1.

BOYD, L. J., & VANDEMARK, N. L. (1957). Spermatogenic capacity of the male bovine. I: A measurement technique. *J. Dairy Sci.*, **40**, 689.

BRADBURY, J. T., BUNGE, R. G., & BOCCABELLA, R. A. (1956). Chromatin test in Klinefelter's syndrome. *J. clin. Endocrin.*, **16**, 689.

BRADEN, A. W. H. (1956). Studies on mammalian ova. Ph.D. Thesis. Edinburgh.

—— (1959). Strain differences in the morphology of the gametes of the mouse. *Aust. J. biol. Sci.*, **12**, 65.

BRADFIELD, J. R. G. (1953). New features of protoplasmic structure observed in recent electron microscope studies. *Quart. J. micr. Sci.*, **94**, 351.

—— (1955). Fibre patterns in animal flagella and cilia. *Symp. Soc. exp. Biol.*, **9**, 306.

—— (1956). The structure of mammalian spermatozoa. *Proc. Third Int. Conf. Electron Micr., Lond.*, 1954, p. 599. Ed. R. Ross.

BRANTON, C., & SALISBURY, G. W. (1947). Morphology of spermatozoa from different levels of the reproductive tract of the bull. *J. Anim. Sci.*, **6**, 154.

BRAUS, H., & REDENZ, E. (1924). Nebenhoden und Samenfäden. *Z. ges. Anat.* **58**, 121.

BRETSCHNEIDER, L. H. (1949). An electron-microscopical study of bull sperm. *Proc. Acad. Sci. Amst.*, **52**, 301.

BROCHART, M. (1953). Origin of half-stained spermatozoa obtained from live-dead differentiating stains. *Proc. Soc. Stud. Fert.*, **5**, 82.

—— & DABATÈNE, D. (1953). Diminution de la perméabilité à l'éosine de la capsule lipoïdique de la tête des spermatozoïdes de ruminants domestiques après l'éjaculation. *C. R. Soc. Biol., Paris*, **147**, 20.

—— & MONTROSE, S.-M. (1951). Morphologie normal et anormale du spermatozoïde de taureau. Techniques d'examen morphologique (revue). *Rec. Méd. vét.*, **127**, 449.

BROWN, H. H. (1885). On spermatogenesis in the rat. *Quart. J. micr. Sci.*, **25**, 343.

BRUCE, H. M. (1958). Genetic infertility in ruby-eyed male hamsters. *Studies on Fertility*, **9**, 90.

—— & AUSTIN, C. R. (1956). An attempt to produce the Hertwig effect by X-irradiation of male mice. *Studies on Fertility*, **8**, 121.

VON BRUNN, M. (1876). Cited by Wilson, 1925, p. 383.

—— (1884). Beiträge zur Kenntniss der Samenkörper und ihrer Entwicklung bei Säugethieren und Vogeln. *Arch. mikr. Anat.*, **23**, 108.

BRYAN, J. H. D., & GOWEN, J. W. (1958). The effects of 2560r of X-rays on spermatogenesis in the mouse. *Biol. Bull.*, **114**, 271.

BRYAN, W. L., & MASON, K. E. (1940). Vitamin E deficiency in the mouse. *Amer. J. Physiol.*, **131**, 263.

BRYSON, V. (1944). Spermatogenesis and fertility in *Mus musculus* as affected by factors at the T locus. *J. Morph.*, **74**, 131.

BULLOUGH, W. S. (1948). Mitotic activity in the adult mouse *Mus musculus* L. The diurnal cycles and their relation to waking and sleeping. *Proc. Roy. Soc. B*, **135**, 212.

BUNGE, R. G., & BRADBURY, J. T. (1956). Newer concepts of the Klinefelter's syndrome. *J. Urol.*, **76**, 758.

BURGOS, M. H., & FAWCETT, D. W. (1955). Studies on the fine structures of the mammalian testis. I: Differentiation of the spermatids in the cat (*Felis domestica*). *J. Biophys. Biochem. Cytol.*, **1**, 287.

CALANCHA, A. DE LA (1639). *Cronica moralizada de la orden de San Agustin.* Pedro Lacabellería, Barcelona.

CAMPBELL, J. A. (1935). Growth, fertility, etc., in animals during attempted acclimatization to carbon monoxide. *Quart. J. exp. Physiol.*, **24**, 271.

CAMPELL, R. C., DOTT, H. M., & GLOVER, T. D. (1956). Nigrosin-eosin as a stain for differentiating live and dead spermatozoa. *J. agric. Sci.*, **48**, 1.

—— HANCOCK, J. L., & ROTHSCHILD, LORD (1953). Counting live and dead bull spermatozoa. *J. exp. Biol.*, **30**, 44.

E*

CARTER, T. C., LYON, M. F., & PHILLIPS, R. J. S. (1954). Induction of sterility in male mice by chronic gamma irradiation. *Brit. J. Radiol.*, **27**, 418.

CARY, W. H. (1930). Sterility diagnosis; study of sperm cell migration in female secretions and interpretation of findings. *N.Y. St. J. Med.*, **30**, 131.

CASARETT, G. W. (1953). Comparison of pathologic effects of radiation in weanling and adult rats. *Arch. Path.*, **55**, 393.

—— (1956). The effects of ionizing radiations from external sources on gametogenesis and fertility in mammals: a review. Rep. UR-441. Atomic Energy Project: University of Rochester.

—— & HURSH, Y. B. (1956). Effects of daily low doses of X-rays on spermiogenesis in dogs. *Radiation Research*, **5**, 473.

CATTANACH, B. M. (1957). Induction of translocations in mice by triethylenemelamine. *Nature, Lond.*, **180**, 1364.

—— & EDWARDS, R. G. (1958). The effects of triethylenemelamine on the fertility of male mice. *Proc. roy. Soc. Edinb.*, B, **67**, 54.

CHALLICE, C. E. (1952). Some observations on the morphology of spermatozoa by electron microscopy. *Proc. Soc. Stud. Fert.*, **4**, 21.

—— (1953). Electron microscope studies of spermiogenesis in some rodents. *J. R. micr. Soc.*, **70**, 115.

CHANG, M. C. (1941). *A study of the physiology of ram spermatozoa.* Ph.D. Thesis. Cambridge.

—— (1943). Disintegration of epididymal spermatozoa by application of ice to the scrotal testis. *J. exp. Biol.*, **20**, 16.

—— (1945a). Fertilizing capacity of spermatozoa following cold treatment of the scrotal testes of rabbits. *J. exp. Biol.*, **22**, 95.

—— (1945b). The sperm production of adult rams in relation to frequency of semen collection. *J. agric. Sci.*, **35**, 243.

—— (1947). The effects of serum on spermatozoa. *J. gen. Physiol.*, **30**, 321.

—— & MCDONOUGH, J. J. (1955). An experiment to cross the cottontail and the domestic rabbit. *J. Hered.*, **46**, 41.

—— & SHEAFFER, D. (1957). Number of spermatozoa ejaculated at copulation, transported into the female tract, and present in the male tract of the golden hamster. *J. Hered.*, **48**, 107.

CHIQUOINE, A. D. (1954). The identification, origin, and migration of the primordial germ cells in the mouse embryo. *Anat. Rec.*, **118**, 135.

CLELAND, K. W. (1951). The spermatogenic cycle of the guinea-pig. *Aust. J. Sci. Res.* B, **4**, 344.

—— (1956). Acrosome formation in bandicoot spermiogenesis. *Nature, Lond.*, **177**, 387.

CLERMONT, Y. (1954). Cycle de l'epithelium seminal et mode de renouvellement des spermatogonies chez le hamster. *Rev. canad. Biol.*, **13**, 208.

—— (1956a). The Golgi zone of the rat spermatid and its role in the formation of cytoplasmic vesicles. *J. biophys. biochem. Cytol.*, **2** (Suppl. 4, Pt. 2), 119.

—— (1956b). The submicroscopic structure responsible for the cytoplasmic basophilia of the rat spermatid. *Exp. Cell Res.*, **11**, 214.

—— EINBERG, E., LEBLOND, C. P., & WAGNER, S. (1955). The perforatorium—an extension of the nuclear membrane of the rat spermatozoon. *Anat. Rec.*, **121**, 1.

—— GLEGG, R. E., & LEBLOND, C. P. (1955). Presence of carbohydrates in the acrosome of the guinea-pig spermatozoon. *Exp. Cell. Res.*, **8**, 453.

—— & LEBLOND, C. P. (1953). Renewal of spermatogonia in the rat. *Amer. J. Anat.*, **93**, 475.

—— —— (1955). Spermiogenesis of man, monkey, ram and other mammals as shown by the " Periodic acid-Schiff " technique. *Amer. J. Anat.*, **96**, 229.

—— & PEREY, B. (1957a). Quantitative study of the cell population of the seminiferous tubules in immature rat. *Amer. J. Anat.*, **100**, 241.

—— —— (1957b). The stages of the cycle of the seminiferous epithelium of the rat: practical definitions in PA-Schiff-Hematoxylin and Hematoxylin-Eosin stained sections. *Rev. canad. Biol.*, **16**, 451.

COLE, F. J. (1930). *Early theories of sexual generation.* Oxford.

COLLERY, L. (1944). Note on the physiology of the mammalian epididymis and spermatozoon. *Proc. R. Irish Acad.* B, **49**, 213.

COULOMBRE, J. L., & RUSSELL, E. S. (1954). Analysis of the pleiotropism at the w-locus in the mouse: the effects of w and w^v substitution upon postnatal development of germ cells. *J. exp. Zool.*, **126**, 277.

CRAIG, A. W., FOX, B. W., & JACKSON, H. (1958). Sensitivity of the spermatogenic process in the rat to radiomimetic drugs and X-rays. *Nature, Lond.*, **181**, 355.

CREW, F. A. E. (1922). A suggestion as to the cause of the aspermatic condition of the imperfectly descended testis. *J. anat.*, **56**, 98.

CROOK, A. C., IRVIN, J. O., & MANDL, A. M. (1949). The relative viability of human spermatozoa. *J. Hyg., Camb.*, **47**, 297.

—— & MANDL., A. M. (1947). A rapid supra-vital staining method for assessing the viability of human spermatozoa. *Nature, Lond.*, **159**, 749.

CROSS, B. A. (1955). The posterior pituitary gland in relation to reproduction and lactation. *Brit. med. Bull.*, **11**, 151.

—— & GLOVER, T. D. (1958). The hypothalamus and seminal emission. *J. Endocrin.*, **16**, 385.

CUNNINGHAM, B., & OSBORN, G. (1929). Infra-red sterility : preliminary report. *Endocrinology*, **13**, 93.

CURTIS, G. M. (1918). The morphology of the mammalian seminiferous tubule. *Amer. J. Anat.*, **24**, 339.

DALED, H. J. (1951). Étude cytochimique sur l'évolution de l'acide ribonucléique dans la spermatogenèse du rat. *Arch. Anat. micr. Morph. exp.*, **40**, 183.

DALLAM, R. D., & THOMAS, L. E. (1952). Chemical composition of mammalian sperm. *Nature, Lond.*, **170**, 377.

—— —— (1953). Chemical studies on mammalian sperm. *Biochim. biophys. Acta*, **11**, 79.

DALTON, A. J., JONES, B. F., PETERS, V. B., & MITCHELL, E. R. (1945). Organ changes in rats exposed repeatedly to lowered oxygen tension with reduced barometric pressure. *J. nat. Cancer Inst.*, **6**, 161.

—— & FELIX, M. D. (1957). Electron microscopy of mitochondria and Golgi complex. *Symp. Soc. exp. Biol.*, **10**, 148.

DAOUST, R., & CLERMONT, Y. (1955). Distribution of nucleic acids in germ cells during the cycle of the seminiferous epithelium in the rat. *Amer. J. Anat.*, **96**, 255.

DAVIDSON, J. N., LESLIE, L., & WHITE, J. C. (1951). The nucleic acid content of the cell. *Lancet*, **260**, 1287.

DAVIES, H. G., WILKINS, M. H. F., CHAYEN, J., & LA COUR, L. F. (1954). The use of the interference microscope to determine dry mass in living cells and as a quantitative cytochemical method. *Quart. J. micr. Sci.*, **95**, 271.

DAWSON, R. M. C. (1958a). The labelling of ram semen *in vivo* with radioactive phosphate and [carboxy-^{14}C]stearic acid. *Biochem. J.*, **68**, 512.

—— (1958b). Labelling of bull semen with phosphorus-32 *in vivo*. *Nature, Lond.*, **181**, 1014.

DEROBERTIS, E. D. P., NOWINSKI, W. W., & SAEZ, F. A. (1954). *General cytology*. Second edition. Philadelphia and London.

DERINGER, M. K., HESTON, W. E., & LORENZ, E. (1954). Effects of long-continued total-body gamma irradiation on mice, guinea-pigs, and rabbits. IV: Actions on the breeding behaviour of mice. In *Biological effects of external X- and gamma-radiation*. Ed. R. E. Zirkle. New York.

DHILLON, B. K. (1955). Spermatogenesis of white rat with observations under phase-contrast microscope. *Res. Bull. Punjab Univ.*, **76**, 119.

DOCTON, F. L., FERGUSON, L. C., LAZEAR, E. J., & ELY, F. (1952). The antigenicity of bovine spermatozoa. *J. Dairy Sci.*, **35**, 706.

DOHAN, F. C. (1942). Effect of low atmospheric pressure on the adrenals, thymus and testes of rats. *Proc. Soc. exp. Biol., N.Y.*, **49**, 404.

DONALD, H. P., & HANCOCK, J. L. (1953). Evidence of gene controlled sterility in bulls. *J. agric. Sci.*, **43**, 178.

DONNÉ, A. (1845). *Cours de microscopie*. Paris.

Dordick, J. L. (1949). The effect of high temperature and humidity upon cattle. *Acta trop., Basel*, **6**, 221.

Dott, H. M. (1953). Dark-ground illumination of ram spermatozoa. *Nature, Lond.*, **172**, 626.

—— (1956). Partial staining of spermatozoa in the nigrosin-eosin stain. *Proc. Third Int. Congr. Anim. Reprod., Camb.*, **3**, 42.

—— (1959). Species differences in the metabolism of epididymal spermatozoa. *Studies on Fertility*, **10**, 73.

Duesberg, J. (1908a). Les divisions des spermatocytes chez le rat. *Arch. Zellforsch.*, **1**, 399.

—— (1908b). La spermiogénèse chez le rat. *Arch. Zellforsch.*, **2**, 137.

—— (1920). Cytoplasmic structures in the seminal epithelium of the opossum. *Publ. Carneg. Instn.* **28**, 47.

Dujardin, F. (1837). Sur les zoospermes des mammifères. *Ann. Sci. nat.*, Sér. II, Zool., **8**, 291.

Easley, G. T., Mayer, D. T., & Bogart, R. (1942). Influence of diluters, rate of cooling and storage temperatures on survival of bull sperm. *Amer. J. vet. Res.*, **3**, 358.

von Ebner, V. (1888). Zur Spermatogenese bei den Säugetieren. *Arch. mikr. Anat.*, **31**, 236.

—— (1902). Die Geschlechtsorgane. *A. Kölliker's Handbuch der Gewebelehre des Menschen*. **3**. Sixth Ed. Leipzig.

Edwards, J. (1940). The effect of unilateral castration on spermatogenesis. *Proc. roy. Soc.* B, **128**, 407.

Edwards, R. G. (1957). The experimental induction of gynogenesis in the mouse. I: Irradiation of the sperm by X-rays. *Proc. roy. Soc.* B, **146**, 469.

—— & Sirlin, J. L. (1958). Radioactive tracers and fertilization in mammals. *Endeavour*, **17**, 42.

Eguchi, K. (1927). Changes of testicles due to adrenaline poisoning. (Trans.). *Jikken Igaku Zasshi*, **11**, 1129. (In *Biol. Abstr.*, **5**, 4292.)

Ehrenberg, L., Ehrenstein, G. von, & Hedgram, A. (1957). Gonad temperature and spontaneous mutation-rate in man. *Nature, Lond.*, **180**, 1433.

Elftman, H. (1950). The Sertoli cell cycle in the mouse. *Anat. Rec.*, **106**, 381.

Ely, J. O., Ross, M. H., Metcalf, R. G., Inda, F. A., Barnett, T. B., & Casarett, G. W. (1954). Clinical, pathological and hematological effects of chronic neutron radiation. In *Biological effects of external radiation*. Ed. H. A. Blair. New York.

Emik, L. O., & Sidwell, G. M. (1947). Refinining methods for using opal blue stain in evaluating ram semen. *J. Anim. Sci.*, **6**, 67.

Emmens, C. W. (1947). The motility and viability of rabbit spermatozoa at different hydrogen-ion concentrations. *J. Physiol.*, **106**, 471.

Engelgardt, V. A., & Burnasheva, S. A. (1957). Localization of the protein spermosin in sperm tails. (Trans.). *Biokhimiya*, **22**, 554.

Eriksson, K. (1938). Vererbung pathologischer Veränderungen und Zustände in den Geschlechtsorganen des Rindes. *XIII Int. Tierärztl. Kongr., Zürich.*

—— (1943). *Hereditary forms of sterility in cattle.* Lund.

—— (1950). Heritability of reproduction disturbances in bulls of Swedish Red and White cattle. *Nord. VetMed.*, **2**, 943.

Eschenbrenner, A. B., & Miller, E. (1950). Effect of roentgen rays on the testis. Quantitative histological analysis following whole-body exposure of mice. *Arch. Path.* (*Lab. Med.*), **50**, 736.

—— —— (1954). Effects of long-continued total-body gamma irradiation on mice, guinea-pigs and rabbits. Pathological observations. In *Biological effects of external X- and gamma-radiation*. Editor R. E. Zirkle. New York.

—— —— & Lorenz, E. (1948). Quantitative histologic analysis of the effect of chronic whole-body irradiation with gamma rays on the spermatogenic elements and the interstitial tissue of the testes of mice. *J. nat. Cancer Inst.*, **9**, 133.

Evans, H. M. (1928). The effect of inadequate vitamin B upon sexual physiology in the male. *J. Nutr.*, **1**, 1.

—— (1932). Testicular degeneration due to inadequate vitamin A in cases where E is adequate. *Amer. J. Physiol.*, **99**, 477.

EVANS, H. M., & BURR, G. O. (1927). The antisterility vitamine fat-soluble E. *Univ. Calif. Mem.*, **8,** 1.

EVERETT, N. B. (1945). The present status of the germ-cell problem in vertebrates. *Biol. Rev.*, **20,** 45.

FALCONER, D. S., SLIZYNSKI, B. M., & AUERBACH, C. (1952). Genetical effects of nitrogen mustard in the house mouse. *J. Genet.*, **51,** 81.

FALK, H. C., & KAUFMAN, S. A. (1950). What constitutes normal semen ? *Fertil. Steril.*, **1,** 489.

FAUST, E. C. (1913). Size dimorphism in adult spermatozoa of *Anasa tristis*. *Biol. Bull.*, **25,** 287.

FAWCETT, D. W., & BURGOS, M. H. (1956a). The fine structure of Sertoli cells in the human testis. *Anat. Rec.*, **124,** 401.

—— —— (1956b). Observations on the cytomorphosis of the germinal and interstitial cells of the human testis. *Ciba Foundation Colloquia on Ageing: Ageing in Transient Tissues*, **2,** 86.

—— & ITO, S. (1958). Observations on the cytoplasmic membranes of testicular cells, examined by phase-contrast and electron microscopy. *J. Biophys. Biochem. Cytol.*, **4,** 135.

FEDERLEY, H. (1919). Beiträge zur Kenntnis der Säugetiergametogenese. I: Die Spermatogenese von *Mus silvaticus*, L. *Acta Soc. Sci. fenn.*, **48,** 1.

FERGUSON-SMITH, M. A. (1958). Chromatin-positive Klinefelter's syndrome (primary microorchidism) in a mental-deficiency hospital. *Lancet*, **i,** 928.

—— LENNOX, B., MACK, W. S., & STEWART, J. S. S. (1957). Klinefelter's syndrome: incidence and testicular morphology in relation to nuclear sex. *Lancet*, **ii,** 167.

—— & MUNRO, L. B. (1958). Spermatogenesis in the presence of female nuclear sex. *Scot. med. J.*, **3,** 39.

FERROUX, R., REGAUD, C., & SAMSSONOW, N. (1938). Comparison des effets produits sur les testicules du lapin, au point de vue de la stérilization de l'epithelium séminal, par une même dose de rayons X, selon qu'elle à été administrée sans fractionnement au bien fractionée et étalée dans le temps. *C. R. Soc. Biol., Paris*, **128,** 173.

FEULGEN, R., & ROSSENBECK, H. (1924). Mikroskopisch-chemischer Nachweis einer Nucleinsäure von Typus der Thymonucleinsäure und die darauf beruhende elektive Färbung von Zellkern in mikroskopischen Präparaten. *Z. physiol. Chem.*, **135,** 203.

FOGG, L. C., & COWING, R. F. (1951). The changes in cell morphology and histochemistry of the testis following irradiation and their relation to other induced testicular changes. I: Quantitative random sampling of germinal cells at intervals following direct irradiation. *Cancer Res.*, **11,** 23.

—— —— (1952). Effect of direct X-irradiation on mammalian testicles. *Exp. Cell Res.*, **3,** 19.

—— —— (1953). Cytologic changes in the spermatogonial nuclei correlated with increased radio-resistance. *Exp. Cell. Res.*, **4,** 107.

FOL, H. (1879). Recherches sur la fécondation et le commencement de l'hénogenie chez divers animaux. *Mém. Soc. Phys. Genève*, **26,** 89.

FREUND, J., LIPTON, M. M., & THOMPSON, G. E. (1953). Aspermatogenesis in the guinea-pig induced by testicular tissue and adjuvants. *J. exp. Med.*, **97,** 711.

—— —— —— (1954). Impairment of spermatogenesis in the rat after cutaneous injection of testicular suspension with complete adjuvants. *Proc. Soc. exp. Biol., N.Y.*, **87,** 408.

—— THOMPSON, G. E., & LIPTON, M. M. (1955). Aspermatogenesis, anaphylaxis and cutaneous sensitization induced in the guinea-pig by homologous testicular extract. *J. exp. Med.*, **101,** 591.

FRIEDLAENDER, M. H. G., & FRASER, M. J. (1952). Cytochemical reactions of ram spermatozoa. *Exp. Cell. Res.*, **3,** 462.

FRIEND, G. F. (1936). The sperms of the British Muridae. *Quart. J. micr. Sci.*, **78,** 419.

FUKUI, N. (1923a). On hitherto unknown action of heat ray on testicles. *Japan. Med. World*, **3,** 27.

—— (1923b). Action of body temperature on the testicle. *Japan med. World*, **3,** 160.

GATENBY, J. B., & BEAMS, H. W. (1935). The cytoplasmic inclusions in the spermatogenesis of man. *Quart. J. micr. Sci.*, **78**, 1.

—— & COLLERY, L. (1943). Middle-piece beads in the *Cavia* spermatozoon. *Nature, Lond.*, **151**, 253.

—— & WIGODER, S. B. (1929). The post-nuclear body in the spermatogenesis of *Cavia cobaya* and other animals. *Proc. roy. Soc.* B, **104**.

—— & WOODGER, J. H. (1921). The cytoplasmic inclusions of the germ-cells. IX: On the origin of the Golgi apparatus and the middle-piece of the ripe sperm of *Cavia*, and the development of the acrosome. *Quart. J. micr. Sci.*, **65**, 265.

GEGENBAUER, C. (1861). Cited by Nordenskiöld (1929).

GHETIE, E. (1939). Präparation und chänge des Ductus epididymis beim Pferd und Schwein. *Anat. Anz.*, **87**, 369.

GLOVER, T. D. (1955). Some effects of scrotal insulation on the semen of rams. *Studies on Fertility*, **7**, 66.

—— (1956). The effect of scrotal insulation and the influence of the breeding season upon fructose concentration in the semen of the ram. *J. Endocrin.*, **13**, 235.

GLÜCKSMANN, A. (1947). The effects of radiation on reproductive organs. *Brit. J. Radiol.*, Suppl. 1, 101.

—— HOWARD, A., & PELC, S. R. (1955). Incorporation of ^{35}S-DL-Methionine in mouse tissues as indicated by autoradiographs. I: Testis, epididymis and seminal vesicle. *J. Anat., Lond.*, **89**, 13.

GOETTSCH, M. (1930). Relationship between vitamin C and some phases of reproduction in the guinea-pig. *Amer. J. Physiol.*, **95**, 64.

GOLDZVEIG, S. A., & SMITH, A. U. (1956). The fertility of male rats after moderate and after severe hypothermia. *J. Endocrin.*, **14**, 40.

GORDON, A. S., TORNETTA, F. J., D'ANGELO, S. A., & CHARIPPER, H. A. (1943). Effects of low atmospheric pressures on the activity of the thyroid, reproductive system and anterior lobe of the pituitary of the rat. *Endocrinology*, **33**, 366.

GORDON, M. J. (1957). Control of sex ratio in rabbits by electrophoresis of spermatozoa. *Proc. nat. Acad. Sci., Wash.*, **43**, 913.

GRAHAM, M. A., & BARR, M. L. (1952). A sex difference in the morphology of metabolic nuclei in somatic cells of the cat. *Anat. Rec.*, **112**, 709.

GRAY, A. P. (1954). *Mammalian hybrids.* Commonwealth Agricultural Bureaux, Farnham Royal, England.

GRAY, J. (1928). *Ciliary movements.* Cambridge.

—— (1931). *Experimental cytology.* Cambridge.

—— (1955). The movement of sea-urchin spermatozoa. *J. exp. Biol.*, **32**, 775.

—— (1958). The movement of the spermatozoa of the bull. *J. exp. Biol.*, **35**, 96.

—— & HANCOCK, G. J. (1955). The propulsion of sea-urchin spermatozoa. *J. exp. Biol.*, **32**, 802.

GREEN, W. W. (1940a). Chemistry and cytology of the sperm membrane of sheep. *Anat. Rec.*, **76**, 476.

—— (1940b). Seasonal trends of sperm cell types in sheep. *Proc. Amer. Soc. anim. Prod.*, **33**, 207.

GRESSON, R. A. R. (1942). A study of the male germ cells of the rat and the mouse by phase-contrast microscopy. *Proc. roy. Soc. Edinb.* B, **61**, 197.

—— (1948). *Essentials of general cytology*, Edinburgh University Press.

—— (1950). A study of the male germ cells of the rat and the mouse by phase-contrast microscopy. *Quart. J. micr. Sci.*, **91**, 73.

—— (1951). The structure and formation of the mammalian spermatozoon. *Cellule*, **54**, 398.

—— (1957). The Golgi complex of the male germ-cells of mammals. *Cellule*, **58**, 249.

—— & ZLOTNIK, I. (1945). A comparative study of the cytoplasmic components of the male germ-cells of certain mammals. *Proc. roy. Soc. Edinb.* B, **62**, 137.

—— & ZLOTNIK, I. (1948). A study of cytoplasmic components during the gametogenesis of *Bos taurus*. *Quart. J. micr. Sci.*, **89**, 219.

GRIFFITHS, J. (1893). The structural changes in the testicle of the dog, when it is replaced within the abdomnial cavity. *J. Anat., Lond.*, **27**, 483.

GRIGG, G. W., & HODGE, A. J. (1949). Electron microscopic studies of spermatozoa. I: The morphology of the spermatozoon of the common domestic fowl (*Gallus domesticus*). *Aust. J. sci. Res.*, Ser. B, **2**, 271.

GRUMBACH, M. M., BLANC, W. A., & ENGLE, E. T. (1957). Sex chromatin pattern in seminiferous tubule dysgenesis and other testicular disorders: relationship to true hermaphrodism and to Klinefelter's syndrome. *J. clin. Endocrinol.*, **17**, 703.

GULLBRING, B. (1957). Investigation on the occurrence of blood group antigens in spermatozoa from man, and serological demonstration of the segregation of characters. *Acta med. scand.*, **159**, 169.

GUNN, R. M. C. (1936). Fertility in sheep. Artificial production of seminal ejaculation and the characters of the spermatozoa contained therein. *Bull. Coun. sci. industr. Res. Aust.*, No. 94.

—— (1951). Cyclic changes in spermatogenesis in rams. *Aust. N.Z. Ass. Advanc. Sci.*, **28**, 90.

—— SANDERS, R. N., & GRANGER, W. (1942). Studies in fertility in sheep. 2: Seminal changes affecting fertility in rams. *Bull. Coun. sci. industr. Res. Aust.*, No. 148.

GUTHRIE, M. J. (1933). The reproductive cycles of some cave bats. *J. Mammal.*, **14**, 199.

HAFEZ, E. S. E., BADRELDIN, A. L., & DARWISH, Y. H. (1955). Seasonal variations in semen characteristics of sheep in the subtropics. *J. agric. Sci.*, **45**, 283.

HAMMOND, J. (1921). Further observations on factors controlling fertility and foetal atrophy. *J. agric. Sci.*, **11**, 337.

—— & ASDELL, S. (1926). The vitality of the spermatozoa in the male and female reproductive tracts. *Brit. J. exp. Biol.*, **4**, 155.

HANCOCK, G. J. (1953). The self-propulsion of microscopic organisms through liquids. *Proc. roy. Soc.*, A, **217**, 96.

HANCOCK, J. L. (1949). Evidence of an inherited seminal character associated with infertility of Friesian bulls. *Vet. Rec.*, **61**, 308.

—— (1951). A staining technique for the study of temperature-shock in semen. *Nature, Lond.*, **167**, 323.

—— (1952). The morphology of spermatozoa. Ph.D. Thesis. Cambridge.

—— (1953). The spermatozoa of sterile bulls. *J. exp. Biol.*, **30**, 50.

—— (1955). The disintegration of bull spermatozoa. *Vet. Rec.*, **67**, 825.

—— (1957a). The morphology of boar spermatozoa. *J. R. micr. Soc.*, **76**, 84.

—— (1957b). The cytoplasmic beads of boar spermatozoa. *J. Endocrin.*, **14**, xxxviii.

—— (1957c). The structure of spermatozoa. *Vet. Rec.*, **69**, 996.

—— & ROLLINSON, D. H. L. (1949). A seminal defect associated with sterility of Guernsey bulls. *Vet. Rec.*, **61**, 742.

—— & SHAW, I. G. (1955). A new difference between live and dead spermatozoa. *Nature, Lond.*, **176**, 260.

—— & TREVAN, D. J. (1957). The acrosome and post-nuclear cap of bull spermatozoa. *J. R. micr. Soc.*, **76**, 77.

HANSEL, W., McENTEE, K., & OLAFSON, P. (1951). The effects of two causative agents of experimental hyperkeratosis on vitamin A metabolism. *Cornell Vet.*, **41**, 367.

HARRENSTEIN, R. J. (1928). Uber die Funktion des Scrotums und die Behandling der retentio Testis beim Menschen. *Zbl. Chir.*, No. 28, 1734.

HARRIS, R., & HARRISON, R. G. (1955). The effect of low temperature on the guinea-pig testis. *Studies on Fertility*, **7**, 23.

HARRISON, G. A., & HARRIS, R. (1956). Thermoregulation of the testis at high temperatures. *Studies on Fertility*, **8**, 76.

HARRISON, R. G. (1956). Factors influencing the process of spermatogenesis in the experimental animal. *Brit. J. Urol.*, **28**, 422.

—— & OETTLÉ, A. G. (1950). Pathologic changes in the rat testis following ischaemia. *Proc. Soc. Stud. Fertil.*, **2**, 6.

—— & WEINER, J. S. (1949). Vascular patterns of the mammalian testis and their functional significance. *J. exp. Biol.*, **26**, 304.

HARTMAN, C. G. (1939). Ovulation, fertilization and the transport and viability of eggs and spermatozoa. In *Sex and internal secretions*. Second Ed. Editor E. Allen. London.

Hartsoeker, N. (1694). *Essay de Dioptrique.* Paris.

Harvey, C. (1955). Cytological events in the human testis in relation to abnormalities in sperm morphology. *Studies on Fertility*, **7**, 8.

—— & Jackson, M. H. (1945). Assessment of male fertility by semen analysis. *Lancet*, **ii**, 99, 134.

Heberer, G. (1937). Gibt es einen durch das Geschlechtschromosom bedingten Grössenunterschied der Spermatozoen? *Med.-Naturw. ver. Tubigen.*, **29**, 637.

Heller, M. (1948). The testis. In *Histopathology of irradiation from external and internal sources.* Ed. W. Bloom. New York.

Heller, R. E. (1929). New evidence for the function of the scrotum. *Physiol. Zoöl.*, **2**, 9.

Hempelmann, L. H., Lisco, H., & Hoffman, J. G. (1952). The acute radiation syndrome. A study of nine cases and a review of the problem. *Ann. intern. Med.*, **36**, 2.

Henle, W. (1938). The specificity of some mammalian spermatozoa. *J. Immunol.*, **34**, 325.

—— Henle, G., & Chambers, L. A. (1938). Studies on the antigenic structure of some mammalian spermatozoa. *J. exp. Med.*, **68**, 335.

—— —— Church, C. F., & Foster, C. (1940). Spermatozoal antibodies and fertility. I: Attempt to induce temporary sterility in female white mice by passive immunization with spermatozoal antisera. *J. Immunol.*, **38**, 97.

Henshaw, P. S. (1944a). Experimental roentgen injury. II: Changes produced with intermediate doses and a comparison of the relative susceptibility of different kinds of animals. *J. nat. Cancer Inst.*, **4**, 485.

—— (1944b). Experimental roentgen injury. IV: Effects of repeated small doses of X-rays on blood picture, tissue morphology and life span in mice. *J. nat. Cancer Inst.*, **4**, 513.

Herman, H. A., & Swanson, E. W. (1941). Variations in dairy bull semen with respect to its use in artificial insemination. *Res. Bull. Mo. agric. Exp. Sta.*, No. 326.

Hertwig, G. (1913). Parthenogenesis bei Wirbeltieren, hervorgernfen durch artfremden radium-bestrahlten Samen. *Arch. mikr. Anat.*, **81**, 87.

—— (1933). Die dritte Reifeteilung in der Spermatogenese des Menschen und der Katze und ihre experimentelle Auslösung durch Prolan im jugenlichen Rattenhoden. *Z. mikr.-anat. Forsch.*, **33**, 373.

Hertwig, O. (1876). Beiträge zur Kenntniss der Bildung, Befruchtung und Theilung des tierischen Eies. *Morph. Jb.*, **1**, 347.

—— (1911). Die Radiumkrankheit tierischer Keinzellen. *Arch. mikr. Anat.*, **77**, 97.

Hertwig, P. (1938a). Die Regeneration des Samenepithels der Maus nach Röntgenbestrahlung unter besonderer Berücksichtigüng der Spermatogonien. *Arch. exp. Zellforsch.*, **22**, 68.

—— (1938b). Unterschiede in der Entwicklungsfahigkeit von F_1 Mäusen nach Röntgenbestrahlung von Spermatogonien, fertigen und unfertigen Spermatozoen. *Biol. Zbl.*, **58**, 273.

—— (1940). Vererbbare Semisterilität bei Mäusen nach Röntgenbestrahlung, verursacht durch reciproke Translokationen. *Z. indkt. Abstamm.- u. VererbLehre*, **79**, 1.

Hirota, S. (1952a). The morphology of the seminiferous tubules. I: The seminiferous tubules of the mouse. *Kyushu Mem. med. Sci.*, **3**, 121.

—— (1952b). The morphology of the seminiferous tubules. II: The seminiferous tubules of the monkey. *Kyushu Mem. med. Sci.*, **3**, 129.

—— (1955a). The morphology of the seminiferous tubules. III: The seminiferous tubules of man. *Kyushu J. med. Sci.*, **6**, 180.

—— (1955b). The morphology of the seminiferous tubules. IV: The seminiferous tubules of the rabbit. *Kyushu J. med. Sci.*, **6**, 188.

Hodge, A. J. (1949). Electron microscopic studies of spermatozoa. II: The morphology of the human spermatozoon. *Aust. J. Sci. Res.*, Ser. B, **2**, 368.

Holman, R. T., & Aaes-Jørgensen, E. (1956). Effects of *trans* fatty acid isomers upon essential fatty acid deficiency in rats. *Proc. Soc. exp. Biol., N.Y.*, **93**, 175.

Holst, S. L. (1949). Sterility in boars. *Nord. VetMed. dansk Udg.*, **1**, 87.

van Hoof, L. (1912). La spermatogénèse dans les mammifères. L'évolution de l'élément chromatique dans la spermatogénèse du rat. *Cellule*, **27**, 288.

HOTCHKISS, R. D. (1948). A microchemical reaction resulting in the staining of polysaccharide structures in fixed tissue preparations. *Arch. Biochem.*, **16**, 136.

HOTCHKISS, R. G. (1945). *Fertility in men.* Philadelphia.

HOTCHKISS, R. S., BRUNNER, S. K., & GRENLEY, P. (1938). Semen analyses of two hundred fertile men. *Amer. J. med. Sci.*, **196**, 362.

HOWARD, A., & PELC, S. R. (1950). P³² autoradiographs of mouse testis. Preliminary observations on the timing of spermatogenic stages. *Brit. J. Radiol.*, **23**, 634.

HUGHES, A. F. (1955). Studies in the history of microscopy. I: The influence of achromatism. *J. R. micr. Soc.*, **75**, 1.

—— (1957). Studies in the history of microscopy. II: The later history of the achromatic microscope. *J. R. micr. Soc.*, **76**, 47.

HUGGINS, C. B., & JOHNSON, A. A. (1933). Chemical observations on fluids of the seminal tract. I: Inorganic phosphorus, calcium, non-protein nitrogen and glucose content of semen and of seminal vesicles, prostate and spermatocele fluids in man. *Amer. J. Physiol.*, **103**, 574.

JACKSON, H., & BOCK, M. (1955). Effect of triethylene melamine on the fertility of rats. *Nature, Lond.*, **175**, 1037.

JACQUET, J., PLESSIS, Y., & CASSOU, R. (1951). Hyaluronidase du sperm et fécondité des taureaux. *C. R. Acad. Sci., Paris*, **232**, 1252.

JAKWAY, J. S., & YOUNG, W. C. (1958). An inherited spermatogenic hypoplasia in the guinea-pig. *Fertility & Sterility*, **9**, 533.

JEFFRIES, M. E. (1931). Hormone production by experimental cryptorchid rat testes as indicated by the seminal vesicle and prostate cytology tests. *Anat. Rec.*, **48**, 131.

JENSEN, O. S. (1887). Untersuchungen über die Samenkörper der Säugethiere, Vögel und Amphibien. I: Säugethiere. *Arch. mikr. Anat.*, **30**, 379.

JOËL, C. A., & EICHENBERGER, E. E. (1945). Die Hyaluronidase, ein musinspaltendes Ferment, und deren Bedentung für das menschliche Sperma. *Schweiz. med. Wschr.*, **75**, 601.

JOHNSON, L. P. (1934). Dissections of human seminiferous tubules. *Anat. Rec.*, **59**, 187.

KALMUS, H., METRAKOS, J. D., & SILVERBERG, M. (1952). Sex ratio of offspring from irradiated male mice. *Science*, **116**, 274.

KATO, K. (1936). Experimental studies on the agglutination of mammalian spermatozoa with special reference to its bearing upon fertilization. *Mem. Fac. Sci. Agric. Taihoku*, **19**, 1.

KENNEDY, W. P. (1924). The production of spermatoxins. *Quart. J. exp. Physiol.*, **14**, 279.

KING, E. S. J. (1955). Spermatozoal invasion of the epididymis. *J. Path. Bact.*, **70**, 459.

KIRCHHOFF, H., KELBLING, W. (1937). Experimentelles Beitrag zum Zeitfactor-problem. (Histologische Studien am Kaninchenhoden zur Klärung des Einflusses der Protrahierung bei Coutard-Bestrahlung). *Strahlentherapie*, **60**, 444.

KIRILLOV, V. S. (1938). The role of the ampullae of the vasa deferentia in the formation of the ejaculate in the bull. (Trans.) *Probl. Zivotn.*, **2**, 189. (In *Anim. Breed. Abstr.*, **6**, 205).

—— & MOROZOV, V. A. (1936). Duration of survival of bull spermatozoa in an epididymis isolated from the testis. (Trans.). *Adv. zootech. Sci., Moscow*, **2**, 19. (In *Anim. Breed. Abstr.*, **5**, 22.)

KIVY, E. (1951). The immediate and prolonged effect of single dose X-radiation on the testes and germinal epithelium of the golden hamster (*Cricetus auratus*). *J. morph.*, **88**, 573.

KLINEFELTER, H. F. jun., RIFENSTEIN, E. C. jun., & ALBRIGHT, F. (1942). Syndrome characterized by gynecomastia, aspermatogenesis without a-Leydigism, and increased excretion of follicle stimulating hormone. *J. clin. Endocrin.*, **2**, 615.

KNOBLOCH, A., & VENDRELY, R. (1956). An estimation of the nature of nucleoproteins by an analytical method. *Nature, Lond.*, **178**, 261.

KNUDSEN, O. (1953). A karyological study of spermiogenesis in bulls. *Proc. XVth Int. Vet. Congr., Stockholm.*

—— (1954a). Cytomorphological investigations into the spermiocytogenesis of bulls with normal fertility and bulls with acquired disturbances in spermiogenesis. *Acta path. microbiol. scand.*, Suppl., 101.

KNUDSEN, O. (1954b).   Intrachromosomal aberrations causing reduced fertility in cattle. *Proc. VII Nordiske Veterinärmöte, Oslo.*

KOHN, H. I. (1955).   On the direct and indirect effects of X-rays on the testis of the rat. *Radiation Res.,* **3**, 153.

—— & KALLMAN, R. F. (1955).   The effect of fractionated X-ray dosage upon the mouse testis.   I: Maximum weight loss following 80 to 240r given in 2 to 5 fractions during 1 to 4 days. *J. nat. Cancer Inst.,* **15**, 891.

KOLLER, P. C. (1944).   Segmental interchange in mice. *Genetics,* **29**, 247.

KÖLLIKER, R. A. VON (1841).   *Beiträge zur Kenntniss der Geschlechtsverhältsnisse und der Samen-flüssigkeit wirbelloser Thiere und die Bedentung de sogenannten Samenthiere.* Berlin.

—— (1856).   Physiologische Studien uber die Samenflüssikgeit. *Z. wiss. Zool.,* **7**, 201.

—— (1899).   *Handbuch der Gewebelehre des Menschen.* Leipzig.

KOLTZOFF, N. K., & SCHRÖDER, V. N. (1933).   Artificial control of sex in the progeny of mammals. *Nature, Lond.,* **131**, 329.

KORDTS, E. (1952).   Untersuchungen über die Eignung der Elektrophorese zur Trennung der männchen-und weibchenbestimmenden Spermien beim Kaninchen (Zugleich eine Nachprüfung der Befunde von Vera Schröder). *Z. Tierz. ZüchtBiol.,* **60**, 221.

KURZROK, R., LEONARD, S. L., & CONRAD, H. (1946).   Role of hyaluronidase in human infertility. *Amer. J. Med.,* **1**, 491.

LAGERLÖF, N. (1934).   Morphologische Untersuchungen über Veränderungen im Spermabild und in den Hoden bei Bullen mit verminderter oder aufgehobener Fertilität. *Acta path. microbiol. scand.,* Suppl., 19.

—— (1938).   Infertility in male domestic animals. *XIII Int. Tierärztl. Kongr., Zürich.*

—— (1950).   Investigations on sterility in Swedish bulls during the period 1928–1949. *Vlaam. diergeneesk. Tijdschr.,* **19**, 288.

—— (1951).   Hereditary forms of sterility in Swedish cattle breeds. *Fertil. Steril.,* **2**, 230.

—— (1957).   Biological aspects of infertility in male domestic animals. *Proc. 2nd World Congr. Fertil. Steril., Naples,* **2**, 99.

LAMAR, J. K. (1943).   Epinephrine effects on young male rats. *Anat. Rec.,* **87**, 453.

LAMPE, I., & HODGES, F. J. (1943).   Differential tissue response to neutron and roentgen radiations. *Radiology,* **41**, 344.

LANDSTEINER, K. (1899).   Zur Kenntnis der spezifisch auf Blutkörperchen wirkenden Sera. *Zbl. Bakt.,* **25**, 546.

—— (1901).   Ueber Agglutinationserscheinungen normalen menschlichen Blutes. *Wien. klin. Wschr.,* **14**, 1132.

—— & LEVINE, P. (1926).   On group specific substances in human spermatozoa. *J. Immunol.,* **12**, 415.

—— & VAN DER SCHEER, J. (1927).   On the production of immune sera for tissues. *Proc. Soc. exp. Biol., N.Y.,* **25**, 140.

LANE-ROBERTS, C., SHARMAN, A., WALKER, K., & WIESNER, B. P. (1939).   *Sterility and impaired fertility.*   London and New York.

LANZ, T. VON (1924).   Die Nebenhoden einiger Säugetiere als Samenspeiches. *Verh. anat. Ges. Vers.,* **33**, 106.

—— (1926).   Ueber Bau und Funktion des Nebenhodens und seine Abhängigkeit von der Keimdrüse. *Z. Anat.,* **80**, 177.

—— (1929).   Die reelle Acidität in den einzelen Abschnitten des männlichen genitalapparates der Ratte und ihre hormonale Bedingtheit. *Pflüg. Arch. ges. Physiol.,* **23**, 181.

—— & MALYOTH, G. (1928a).   Neue Untersuchungen zur Biologie der Samenfäden.   I: Die Entwicklung underer Methode zur Bestimmung der Wasserstoffzahl im lebenden Organ.   II: Zur Steurung der Samenfäden im männlichen Genitalapparates. *S.B. Ges. Morph. Physiol. Münch.,* **38**, 52.

—— —— (1928b).   Die relle Aziditat im überlebenden Hoden und Nevenhoden des Stieres. *Pflüg. Arch. ges. Physiol.,* **218**, 535.

LARDY, H. A. (1953). Factors controlling rates of metabolism in mammalian spermatozoa. *Ciba Foundation Symposium on Mammalian Germ Cells*, p. 59.

—— GHOSH, D., & PLAUT, G. W. E. (1949). A metabolic regulator in mammalian spermatozoa. *Science*, **109**, 365.

—— HANSEN, R. G., & PHILLIPS, P. H. (1945). The metabolism of bovine epididymal spermatozoa. *Arch. Biochem.*, **6**, 41.

LASLEY, J. F. (1951). Spermatozoon motility as a measure of semen quality. *J. Anim. Sci.*, **10**, 212.

—— & BOGART, R. (1943). Some factors influencing reproductive efficiency of range cattle under artificial and natural breeding conditions. *Res. Bull. Mo. agric. Exp. Sta.*, No. 376.

—— —— (1944). A comparative study of the epididymal and ejaculated spermatozoa of the boar. *J. Anim. Sci.*, **3**, 360.

—— EASLEY, G. T., & BOGART, R. (1942). Some factors influencing the resistance of bull spermatozoa to unfavourable environmental conditions. *J. Anim. Sci.*, **1**, 79.

—— —— & McKENZIE, F. F. (1942). A staining method for the differentiation of live and dead spermatozoa. I: Applicability to the staining of ram spermatozoa. *Anat. Rec.*, **82**, 167.

—— & MAYER, D. T. (1944). A variable physiological factor necessary for the survival of bull spermatozoa. *J. Anim. Sci.*, **3**, 129.

LAURIE, E. M. O. (1946). The reproduction of the house mouse living in different environments. *Proc. roy. Soc. B*, **133**, 248.

LAWRENCE, J. H., & TENNANT, R. (1937). The comparative effects of neutrons and X-rays on the whole body. *J. exp. Med.*, **66**, 667.

LEBLOND, C. P., & CLERMONT, Y. (1952a). Spermiogenesis of rat, mouse, hamster and guinea-pig as revealed by the "periodic acid-fuchsin sulfurous acid" technique. *Amer. J. Anat.*, **90**, 167.

—— —— (1952b). Definition of the stages of the cycle of the seminiferous epithelium in the rat. *Ann. N.Y. Acad. Sci.*, **55**, 548.

LEEUWENHOEK, A. VAN (1679). Observationes de natis e semine genitali animalculis. *Phil. Trans.*, **12**, 1040.

LENHOSSEK, M. VON (1898). Untersuchungen über Spermatogenese. *Arch. mikr. Anat.*, **51**, 215.

LENNOX, B. (1956). Nuclear sexing: a review incorporating some personal observations. *Scot. med. J.*, **1**, 97.

LEUCHTENBERGER, C., LEUCHTENBERGER, R., SCHRADER, F., & WEIR, D. R. (1956). Reduced amounts of desoxyribose nucleic acid in testicular germ cells of infertile men with active spermatogenesis. *Lab. Invest.*, **5**, 422.

—— —— VENDRELY, C., & VENDRELY, R. (1952). The quantitative estimation of desoxyribose nucleic acid (DNA) in isolated individual animal nuclei by the Caspersson ultraviolet method. *Exp. cell Res.*, **3**, 240.

—— MURMANIS, I., MURMANIS, L., ITO, S., & WEIR, D. R. (1956). Interferometric dry mass and microspectrophotometric arginine determinations on bull sperm nuclei with normal and abnormal DNA content. *Chromosoma*, **8**, 73.

—— & SCHRADER, F. (1950). The chemical nature of the acrosome in the male germ cells. *Proc. nat. Acad. Sci., Wash.*, **36**, 677.

—— —— WEIR, D. R., & GENTILE, D. P. (1953). The desoxyribosenucleic acid (DNA) content in spermatozoa of fertile and infertile human males. *Chromosoma*, **6**, 61.

—— VENDRELY, R., & VENDRELY, C. (1951). A comparison of the content of desoxyribosenucleic acid (DNA) in isolated animal nuclei by cytochemical and chemical methods. *Proc. nat. Acad. Sci., Wash.*, **37**, 33.

—— WEIR, D. R., SCHRADER, F., & LEUCHTENBERGER, R. (1956). Decreased amounts of desoxyribosenucleic acid (DNA) in male germ cells as a possible cause of human male infertility. *Acta genet.*, **6**, 272.

—— —— —— & MURMANIS, L. (1955). The desoxyribosenucleic acid (DNA) content in spermatozoa of repeated seminal fluids from fertile and infertile men. *J. Lab. clin. Med.*, **45**, 851.

Lewin, S. (1956). Artificial sex regulation of mammalian offspring. *Brit. vet. J.*, **112,** 549.

Lewis, J. H. (1933). The immunologic specificity of brain tissue. *J. Immunol.*, **24,** 193.

—— (1934). The antigenic relationship of the alcohol-soluble fractions of brain and testicle. *J. Immunol.*, **27,** 473.

Leydig, F. (1883). *Untersuchungen zur Anatomie und Histologie der Thiere.* Bonn.

Lillie, F. R. (1919). *Problems of Fertilization.* Chicago.

Lindahl, P. E. (1956). Counter-streaming centrifugation of bull spermatozoa. *Nature, Lond.*, **178,** 491.

—— (1958). Separation of bull spermatozoa carrying X- and Y-chromosomes by counter-streaming centrifugation. *Nature, Lond.*, **181,** 784.

—— & Kihlström, J. E. (1952). Alterations in specific gravity during the ripening of bull spermatozoa. *J. Dairy Sci.*, **35,** 393.

Lindley, C. E. (1951). Observations on midgets in beef cattle. *J. Hered.*, **42,** 273.

Lison, L. (1955). Variation de la basophile pendant la maturation du spermatozoïde chez le rat et sa signification histochimique. *Acta histochem.*, **2,** 47.

Lloyd-Jones, A., & Hays, F. A. (1918). The influence of excessive sexual activity of male rabbits. I : On the properties of the seminal discharge. *J. exp. Zool.*, **25,** 463.

Lovelock, J. E. (1959). In *Sex differentiation and development. Mem. Soc. Endocrinol.* No. 7. Cambridge.

Lovern, J. A., Olley, J., Hartree, E. F., & Mann, T. (1957). The lipids of ram spermatozoa. *Biochem. J.*, **67,** 630.

Lush, J. L. (1925). The possibility of sex control by artificial insemination with centrifuged spermatozoa. *J. agric. Res.*, **30,** 893.

MacDonald, J., & Harrison, R. G. (1954a). Effect of low temperature on rat spermatogenesis. *Fertil. & Steril.*, **5,** 205.

—— —— (1954b). Histological appearances in the rat testis following exposure to low temperatures. *Studies on Fertility*, **6,** 14.

Macirone, C., & Walton, A. (1938). Fecundity of male rabbits as determined by " dummy matings ". *J. agric. Sci.*, **28,** 122.

MacLeod, J. (1951). Effect of chickenpox and pneumonia on semen quality. *Fertil. Steril.*, **2,** 523.

—— & Gold, R. Z. (1951). The male factor in fertility and infertility. IV : Sperm morphology in fertile and infertile marriage. *Fertil. Steril.*, **2,** 394.

—— & Heim, L. (1945). Characteristics and variations in semen specimens in 100 normal young men. *J. Urol.*, **54,** 474.

—— & Hotchkiss, R. S. (1941). The effect of hyperpyrexia upon spermatozoa counts in man. *Endocrinology*, **28,** 780.

MacMillan, E. W. (1952). The blood supply of the rat epididymis : the experimental effects of certain arterial ligations and their relation to the problems of infertility. *Proc. Soc. Stud. Fertil.*, **4,** 43.

—— (1953a). Higher epididymal obstructions in male infertility. Etiology and treatment. *Fertil. Steril.*, **4,** 101.

—— (1953b). The effects of interruption of the vasal and inferior epididymal arteries on the cauda epididymis and testis. *Proc. Soc. Stud. Fertil.*, **5,** 12.

—— (1954). Observations on the isolated vaso-epididymal loop and on the effects of experimental subcapital epididymal obstructions. *Studies on Fertility*, **6,** 57.

—— & Harrison, R. G. (1955). The rate of passage of radiopaque medium along the ductus epididymis of the rat. *Studies on Fertility*, **7,** 35.

Madden, F. W., Herman, H. A., & Berousek, E. R. (1947). The relationship between percentage of live spermatozoa and motility, longevity and fertility of semen of dairy bulls. *Res. Bull. Mo. agric. Exp. Sta.*, No. 407.

Mahovka, V. V. (1936). Control of sex-determination in the light of recent researches. (Trans.) *Probl. Zivotn.*, **1,** 86. (In *Anim. Breed. Abstr.*, **4,** 334).

—— & Schegaloff, S. B. (1935). Die Reaktion der Spermatozoen auf Konstanten Ström (Galvanotaxis). *Arch. EntwMech. Org.*, **133,** 694.

Makino, S. (1955). Notes on the cytological feature of male sterility in the mule. *Experientia*, **11,** 224.

MANEELY, R. B. (1955). The distribution of polysaccharide complexes and of alkaline glycerophosphatase in the epididymis of the rat. *Acta Anat.*, **24**, 314.

MANN, T. (1946). Studies on the metabolism of semen. III: Fructose as a normal constituent of seminal plasma. Site of formation and function of fructose in semen. *Biochem. J.*, **40**, 481.

—— (1948). Fructose content and fructolysis in semen. Practical applications in the evaluation of semen quality. *J. agric. Sci.*, **38**, 323.

—— (1954). *The Biochemistry of Semen.* London.

—— & GLOVER, T. (1954). Contribution of the seminal vesicles towards the composition of whole semen. *J. Endocrinol.*, **10**, iv.

—— LUTWAK-MANN, C. (1955). Biochemical changes underlying the phenomenon of cold-shock in spermatozoa. *Arch. Sci., biol.*, **39**, 578.

—— & WALTON, A. (1953). The effect of under-feeding on the genital functions of a bull. *J. agric. Sci.*, **43**, 344.

MARBURG, O. (1936). Über Veränderungen der Hypophyse bei Beriberi (Ein Beitrag zur Kenntnis der basophilen Hypophysen-Zellen.) *Wien. Arch. inn. Med.*, **29**, 1.

MARRIAN, G. F., & PARKES, A. S. (1928). The effects of inanition and vitamin B deficiency on the testis of the pigeon. *J. R. micr. Soc.*, **48**, 257.

MARSHALL, F. H. A. (1942). Exteroceptive factors in sexual periodicity. *Biol. Rev.*, **17**, 68.

MASON, K. E. (1926). Testicular degeneration in albino rats fed a purified food ration. *J. exp. Zool.*, **45**, 159.

—— (1929). The effect of purified diets, and their modifications, on growth and testicular degeneration in male rats. *J. Nutrit.*, **1**, 311.

—— (1930). The specificity of vitamin E for the testis. I: Relation between vitamins A and E. *J. exp. Zool.*, **55**, 101.

—— (1933). Differences in testis injury and repair after vitamin A deficiency, vitamin E deficiency, and inanition. *Amer. J. Anat.*, **52**, 153.

—— (1939). Relation of the vitamins to the sex glands. In *Sex and internal secretions*. Ed. E. Allen, H. C. Danforth and E. A. Doisy. Baltimore.

MATHEWS, A. (1897). Zur Chemi der Spermatozoen. *Z. physiol. Chem.*, **23**, 397.

MATTHEY, R. (1957). Les bases cytologiques de l'hérédité " rélativement " liée au sexe chez les mammiferes. *Experientia*, **13**, 341.

—— & VAN BRINK, J. M. (1957). Sex chromosomes in amniota. *Evolution*, **11**, 163.

MATTIL, H. A. (1927). The relation of vitamins B and E to fertility in the male rat. *Amer. J. Physiol.*, **79**, 305.

—— CARMAN, J. S., & CLAYTON, M. M. (1924). The nutritive properties of milk. III: The effectiveness of the X- substance in preventing sterility in rats on milk rations high in fat. *J. biol. Chem.*, **61**, 729.

MAURITZEN, C. M., ROY, A. B., & STEDMAN, E. (1952). The ribosenucleic acid content of isolated cell nuclei. *Proc. roy. Soc. B*, **140**, 18.

MAWSON, C. A., FISCHER, M. I., & RIEDEL, B. E. (1955). Turnover rates of zinc in certain tissues of the rat. *Communications III Congr. int. Biochim., Bruxelles*, p. 42.

MAYER, D. T. (1955). The chemistry and certain aspects of the metabolic activities of mammalian spermatozoa. In *Reproduction and Infertility*. Michigan State University, East Lansing.

—— MADERA-ORSINI, F., & BERRY, R. E. (1957). Lipoprotein complex, nucleic acids and other constituents of bovine spermatozoa. *Fed. Proc.*, **16**.

—— SQUIERS, C. D., BOGART, R., & OLOUFA, M. M. (1951). The technique for characterizing mammalian spermatozoa as dead or living by differential staining. *J. Anim. Sci.*, **10**, 226.

McELROY, W. D., & GLASS, B. (1957). *The Chemical Basis of Heredity*. Baltimore.

McENTEE, K., & OLAFSON, P. (1953). Reproductive tract pathology in hyperkeratosis of cattle and sheep. *Fertil. Steril.*, **4**, 128.

McKAY, G. D., HERTIG, A. T., ADAMS, E. C., & DANZIGER, S. (1953). Histochemical observations on the germ cells of human embryos. *Anat. Rec.*, **117**, 201.

McKENZIE, F. F., & BERLINER, V. (1937). The reproductive capacity of rams. *Res. Bull. Mo. agric. Exp. Sta.*, No. 265.

McManus, J. F. A. (1946). Histological demonstration of mucin after periodic acid. *Nature, Lond.*, **158**, 202.

McWhirter, K. G. (1956). Control of sex ratio in mammals. *Nature, Lond.*, **178**, 870.

Medical Research Council (1956). *The Hazards to Man of Nuclear and Applied Radiations.* H.M. Stationery Office, London.

Meissner, G. (1855). Beobachtungen über das Eindringen der Samenelemente in den Dotter. *Z. wiss. Zool.*, **6**, 208.

Melampy, R. M., Cavazos, L. F., & Duncan, G. W. (1955). Composition and histochemistry of bull, ram, boar and rooster testes. In *Reproduction and Infertility*, Michigan State University, East Lansing.

—— —— & Porter, J. C. (1952). Cytochemical reactions of bovine spermatozoa and seminal plasma. *J. Dairy Sci.*, **35**, 140.

Melander, Y., & Knudsen, O. (1953). The spermiogenesis of the bull from a karyological point of view. *Hereditas, Lund.*, **39**, 505.

Menzies, J. I. (1957). Gene-controlled sterility in the African mouse (*Mastomys*). *Nature, Lond.*, **179**, 1142.

Mercier, E., & Salisbury, G. W. (1947a). Seasonal variations in hours of daylight associated with fertility level of cattle under natural breeding conditions. *J. Dairy Sci.*, **30**, 749.

—— —— (1947b). Fertility levels in artificial breeding associated with season, hours of daylight and age of cow. *J. Dairy Sci.*, **30**, 817.

Merton, H. (1939). Studies on reproduction in the albino mouse. III: The duration of life of spermatozoa in the female reproductive tract. *Proc. roy. Soc. Edinb.*, **59**, 207.

Meschaks, P. (1953). The effect of transport on spermatogenesis and excretion of neutral steroids in the urine of bulls. *Ciba Foundation Symposium* on *Mammalian Germ Cells*, p. 37.

Metalnikoff, S. (1900). Études sur la spermotoxine. *Ann. Inst. Pasteur*, **14**, 577.

Metcalf, R. G., Inda, F. A., Barnett, T. B., & Casarett, G. W. (1954). Pathology in animals subjected to repeated daily exposure to X-rays. In *Biological Effects of External Radiation*. Ed. H. A. Blair. New York.

Metchnikoff, M. E. (1900a). Recherches sur l'influence de l'organisme sur les toxines. Sur la spermotoxine et l'antispermotoxine; quatrième mémoire. *Ann. Inst. Pasteur*, **14**, 1.

—— (1900b). Sur les cytotoxines. *Ann. Inst. Pasteur.*, **14**, 369.

—— (1905). *Immunity in Infective Diseases.* Cambridge.

Mèves, F. (1899). Über Struktur und Histogenesis der Samenfäden des Meerschweinschens. *Arch. mikr. Anat.*, **54**, 329.

Meyer, A. W. (1939). *The Rise of Embryology.* Stanford.

Miescher, F. (1878). Die Spermatozoen einiger Wirbelthiere Verhändlungen der Naturforschenden Gesellschaft in Basel. *Verh. naturf. Ges. Basel*, **6**, 138.

—— (1897). *Die Histochemischen und physiologischen Arbeiten.* Leipzig.

Mietkiewski, C. (1935). Recherches morphologiques, cytologiques et histophysiologiques sur l'épididyme du cobaye. *C. R. Soc. Biol., Paris*, **120**, 474.

Millar, M. J., Fischer, M. I., Elcoate, P. V., & Mawson, C. A. (1958). The effects of dietary zinc deficiency on the reproductive system of male rats. *Canad. J. Biochem. Physiol.*, **36**, 557.

Mills, R. G. (1919). The pathological changes in the testis in epidemic pneumonia. *J. exp. Med.*, **30**, 505.

Milovanov, V. K. (1934). *Principles of Artificial Insemination.* (Trans.) State Publishing House, Moscow. Leningrad.

Mirsky, A. E., & Ris, H. (1949). Variable and constant components of chromosomes. *Nature, Lond.*, **163**, 666.

—— —— (1951). The desoxyribonucleic acid content of animal cells and its evolutionary significance. *J. gen. Physiol.*, **34**, 451.

Moench, G. L. (1936). Considerations of some aspects of sterility: evaluation after 10 years. *Amer. J. Obstet. Gynec.*, **32**, 406.

—— & Holt, H. (1929). Some observations on sperm-dimorphism. *Biol. Bull.*, **57**, 267.

MOENCH, G. L., & HOLT, H (1931). Sperm morphology in relation to fertility. *Amer. J. Obstet. Gynec.*, **22**, 199.

—— —— (1932). Biometrical studies of head lengths of human spermatozoa. *J. Lab. clin. Med.*, **17**, 297.

—— —— (1933). Do sperm morphology and biometrics really offer a reliable index of fertility? *Amer. J. Obstet. Gynec.*, **25**, 410.

MOLLÉ, J. VON (1906). La spermiogénèse dans l'écureuil. *Cellule*, **23**, 5.

—— (1910). La manchette dans le spermatozoïde des mammifères. *Cellule*, **26**, 423.

MOMIGLIANO, E., & ESSENBERG, J. M. (1944). Regenerative processes induced by gonadotropic hormones in irradiated testes of the albino rat. *Radiology*, **42**, 273.

MONGE, C. (1943). Chronic mountain sickness. *Physiol. Rev.*, **23**, 166.

—— (1947). *Biologia andina y de altitud.* Facultad de Medicina, Lima.

—— (1948). *Acclimatization in the Andes.* Johns Hopkins Press.

—— & MORI CHAREZ, P. (1942). Fisiologia de la reproduccion en la altura. Le espermatogenesis en la altura. *An. Fac. Med. Lima*, **25**, 34.

MOORE, C. R. (1922). Cryptorchidism experimentally produced. *Anat. Rec.*, **24**, 383.

—— (1924a). Testicular reactions in experimental cryptorchidism. *Amer. J. Anat.*, **34**, 269.

—— (1924b). Heat application and testicular degeneration; the function of the scrotum. *Amer. J. Anat.*, **34**, 337.

—— (1926a). Scrotal replacement of experimental cryptorchid testes and the recovery of spermatogenic function (guinea-pig). *Biol. Bull.*, **51**, 112.

—— (1926b). Testis-graft reactions in different environments (rat). *Amer. J. Anat.*, **37**, 351.

—— (1928a). Spermatozoon activity and the testis hormone. *J. exp. Zool.*, **50**, 455.

—— (1928b). Hormone production in the normal testis, cryptorchid testis and non-living testis grafts as indicated by the spermatozoon motility test. *Biol. Bull.*, **55**, 339.

—— (1932). The biology of the testis. In *Sex and Internal Secretions.* Ed. E. Allen. London.

—— (1939). The biology of the testis. In *Sex and Internal Secretions.* 2nd Ed. Ed. E. Allen, C. H. Danforth, E. A. Doisy. Baltimore and London.

—— (1951). Experimental studies on the male reproductive system. *J. Urol.*, **65**, 497.

—— & OSLUND, R. (1924). Experiments on the sheep testis—cryptorchidism, vasectomy and scrotal insulation. *Amer. J. Physiol.*, **67**, 595.

—— & PRICE, D. (1948). A study at high altitude of reproduction, growth, sexual maturity and organ weights. *J. exp. Zool.*, **108**, 171.

—— & QUICK, W. J. (1924a). The scrotum as a temperature regulator for the testis. *Amer. J. Physiol.*, **68**, 70.

—— —— (1924b). Vasectomy in the rabbit. *Amer. J. Anat.*, **34**, 317.

MOORE, K. L., & BARR, M. L. (1954). Nuclear morphology according to sex in human tissues. *Acta Anat.*, **21**, 197.

—— GRAHAM, M. A., & BARR, M. L. (1953). The detection of chromosomal sex in hermaphrodites from a skin biopsy. *Surg. Gynec. Obstet.*, **96**, 641.

MOREE, R. (1947). The normal spermatogenic wave-cycle in Peromyscus. *Anat. Rec.*, **99**, 163.

MORGENSTERN, C. (1924). Zur Frage der Spermiophagie. *Virchows Arch.*, **250**, 648.

MOULE, G. R., & KNAPP, B. (1950). Observations on intra-testicular temperatures of merino rams. *Aust. J. agric. Res.*, **1**, 456.

MOXTER, M. (1900). Ueber ein specifisches Immunserum gegen Spermatozoën. *Dtsch. med. Wschr.*, **26**, 61.

MUDD, S., & MUDD, E. B. H. (1929). The specificity of mammalian spermatozoa with especial reference to electrophoresis as a means of serological differentiation. *J. Immunol.*, **17**, 39.

MULLER, H. T. (1954a). The nature of the genetic effects produced by radiation. In *Radiation Biology*, Vol. I, Part I, p. 351. Ed. A. Hollaender. New York.

—— (1954b). The manner of production of mutations by radiation. In *Radiation Biology*, Vol. I, Part 1, p. 475. Ed. A. Hollaender. New York.

MULLER, H. T. (1955). How radiation changes the genetic constitution. *Bull. atom. Sci.*, **11**, 329.

MUNRO, S. S. (1935). Motility and fertilizing capacities of fowl sperm in the execretory ducts. *Proc. Soc. exp. Biol., N.Y.*, **33**, 255.

—— (1938a). The effect of testis hormone on the preservation of sperm life in the vas deferens of the fowl. *J. exp. Biol.*, **51**, 186.

—— (1938b). Fuctional changes in fowl sperm during their passage through the excurrent ducts of the male. *J. exp. Zool.*, **79**, 71.

MURPHREE, R. L., WHITACKER, W. M., WILDING, J. L., & RUST, J. H. (1952). Effects of whole body exposure to irradiation upon subsequent fertility of male rabbits. *Science*, **115**, 709.

NATH, V. (1956). Cytology of spermatogenesis. *Int. Rev. Cytol.*, **5**, 395.

—— (1957). Animal gametes. Part III: Origin, morphology and functions of Golgi bodies and mitochondria in spermatogenesis. *Res. Bull. Punjab. Univ.*, **97**, 127.

NATIONAL ACADEMY OF SCIENCES (1956). *The Biological Effects of Atomic Radiation.* Washington.

NEARY, G. J., MUNSON, R. J., & MOLE, R. H. (1953). Effects of daily irradiation by fast neutrons on male fertility. *Nature, Lond.*, **171**, 256.

NEEL, T. V., & SCHULL, W. J. (1956). The effect of exposure to the atomic bombs on pregnancy termination in Hiroshima and Nagasaki. *Nat. Acad. Sci., Wash.*, Publ. No. 461.

NEEDHAM, J. (1931). *Chemical Embryology.* Cambridge.

NELSON, H. (1851). On the reproduction of *Ascaris mystax*. *Proc. roy. Soc.* B, **6**, 86.

NELSON, L. (1954). Enzyme distribution in fragmented bull spermatozoa. I: Adenyl-pyrophosphatase. *Biochim. Biophys. Acta*, **14**, 312.

—— (1955). Enzyme distribution in fragmented bull spermatozoa. II: Succinic dehydrogenase and cytochrome oxidase. *Biochim. Biophys. Acta*, **16**, 494.

—— (1958). Cytochemical studies with the electron microscope. I: Adenosinetriphosphatase in rat spermatozoa. *Biochim. Biophys. Acta*, **27**, 634.

NELSON, W. O. (1952). Spermatogenesis in testes of men with blocked or absent efferent ducts. In *Studies on Testis and Ovary, Eggs and Sperm.* Illinois.

—— (1956). Sex differences in human nuclei with particular reference to the " Klinefelter syndrome ", gonadal agenesis and other types of hermaphroditism. *Acta endocr., Copenhagen*, **23**, 227.

NEMILOFF, A. (1926). Histophysiologische Untersuchungen über den Nebenhoden. *Z. Anat. EntwGesch.*, **79**, 1.

NEWPORT, G. (1851). On the impregnation of the ovum in the amphibia. *Phil. Trans.*, **141**, 169.

—— (1853). On the impregnation of the ovum in the amphibia (2nd ser. revised) and on the direct agency of the spermatozoon. *Phil. Trans.*, **143**, 233.

NIESSING, G. (1897). Die Beteiligung von Centralkörper und Sphäre am Aufbau des Samensfadens bei Säugetieren. *Arch. micr. Anat.*, **49**, 111.

NIEWKOOP, P. D. (1949). The present status of the problem of the " Keimbahn " in the vertebrates. *Experientia*, **5**, 308.

NORDENSKIÖLD, E. (1929). *History of Biology: a survey.* English Edition. New York.

OAKBERG, E. F. (1955a). Degeneration of spermatogonia of the mouse following exposure to X rays, and stages in the mitotic cycle at which cell death occurs. *J. Morph.*, **97**, 39.

—— (1955b). Sensitivity and time of degeneration of spermatogenic cells irradiated in various stages of maturation in the mouse. *Radiation Res.*, **2**, 369.

—— (1956a). A description of spermiogenesis in the mouse and its use in analysis of the cycle of the seminiferous epithelium and germ cell renewal. *Amer. J. Anat.*, **99**, 391.

—— (1956b). Duration of spermatogenesis in the mouse and timing of stages of the cycle of the seminiferous epithelium. *Amer. J. Anat.*, **99**, 507.

—— (1957a). Gamma-ray sensitivity of spermatogonia of the mouse. *J. exp. Zool.*, **134**, 343.

—— (1957b). Duration of spermatogenesis in the mouse. *Nature, Lond.*, **180**, 1137.

OAKES, W. R., & LUSHBAUGH, C. C. (1952). Course of testicular injury following accidental exposure to nuclear radiations: report of a case. *Radiology*, **59**, 737.

ODOR, D. L., & BLANDAU, R. J. (1951). Observations on fertilization and the first segmentation division in rat ova. *Amer. J. Anat.*, **89**, 29.

OETTLÉ, A. G. (1948). Golgi apparatus of living human testicular cells seen with phase-contrast microscopy. *Nature, Lond.*, **162**, 76.

—— & HARRISON, R. G. (1952). The histological changes produced in the rat testis by temporary and permanent occlusion of the testicular artery. *J. Path. Bact.*, **64**, 273.

OLAFSON, P. (1947). Hyperkeratosis (X disease) of cattle. *Cornell Vet.*, **37**, 270.

—— & MCENTEE, K. (1951). The experimental production of hyperkeratosis (X disease) by feeding a processed concentrate. *Cornell Vet.*, **41**, 107.

OLIVER, J. R. (1913). The spermiogenesis of the Pribilof fur seal. *Amer. J. Anat.*, **14**, 473.

OLSON, C., & COOK, R. H. (1951). Attempts to produce bovine hyperkeratosis. *Amer. J. vet. Res.*, **12**, 261.

—— & SKIDMORE, L. V., (1954). Further observations on reproductive ability after recovery from bovine hyperkeratosis. *Vet. Med.*, **49**, 371.

ORTAVANT, R. (1952). Recherches sur la spermatogénèse des animaux domestiques. Étude des réserves chez le bélier. *C. R. Soc. Biol., Paris*, **146**, 1086.

—— (1953). Existence d'une phase critique dans la maturation épididymaire des spermatozoïdes de bélier et de taureau. *C. R. Soc. Biol., Paris*, **147**, 1552.

—— (1954a). Étude des générations spermatogoniales chez le bélier. *C. R. Soc. Biol., Paris*, **148**, 1958.

—— (1954b). Contribution à l'étude de la durée du processus spermatogénétique du bélier à l'aide du ^{32}P. *C. R. Soc. Biol., Paris*, **148**, 804.

—— (1954c). Détermination de la vitesse de transfert des spermatozoïdes dans l'épididyme de bélier à l'aide de ^{32}P. *C. R. Soc. Biol., Paris*, **148**, 866.

—— (1956a). Autoradiographie des cellules germinales du testicule de bélier; durée des phénomènes spermatogénétiques. *Arch. Anat. micr. Morph. exp.*, **45**, 1.

—— (1956b). Action de la durée d'éclairement sur les processus spermatogénétiques chez le bélier. *C. R. Soc. Biol., Paris*, **150**, 471.

—— DUPONT, S., PAUTHE, H., & ROUSSEL, G. (1952). Contribution à l'étude de la différenciation des spermatozoïdes morts et des spermatozoïdes vivants dans le sperme de taureau. *Ann. Zootech.*, 1952/1, 5.

—— & THIBAULT, C. (1956). Influence de la durée d'éclairement sur les productions spermatiques du bélier. *C. R. Soc., Biol., Paris*, **150**, 358.

OSLUND, R. M. (1928). The physiology of the male reproductive system. *J. Amer. med. Ass.*, **90**, 829.

PAGE, E. W., & HOULDING, F. (1951). Clinical interpretation of 1000 semen analyses among applicants for sterility studies. *Fertil. Steril.*, **2**, 140.

PAPANICOLAOU, G. N., & STOCKARD, C. R. (1918). The development of the idiosome in the germ cells of the male guinea-pig. *Amer. J. Anat.*, **24**, 37.

PAPPENHEIMER, A. M. (1942). Muscular dystrophy in mice on vitamin E-deficient diet. *Amer. J. Path.*, **17**, 169.

PAŘÍZEK, J. (1956). Effect of cadmium salts on testicular tissue. *Nature, Lond.*, **177**, 1036.

—— (1957a). The destructive effect of cadmium ion on testicular tissue and its prevention by zinc. *J. Endocrinol.*, **15**, 56.

—— (1957b). *Kastrice Kadmien.* (The castrating effect of cadmium. (Trans.)) Státní Zdravotnické Nakladatelství, Prague.

—— & ZÁHOŘ, Z. (1956). Effect of cadmium salts on testicular tissue. *Nature, Lond.*, **177**, 1036.

PARKES, A. S. (1923). Head length dimorphism of mammalian spermatozoa. *Quart. J. micr. Sci.*, **67**, 617.

—— (1925). The effects on fertility and sex ratio of sub-sterility exposures to X-rays. *Proc. roy. Soc. B*, **98**, 415.

PARSONS, E. F., & HYDE, R. R. (1940). An evaluation of spermatoxic sera in the prevention of pregnancy. *Amer. J. Hyg.*, **31**, Section B, 89.

Patterson, C. A., Smith, E., & Pickett, A. D. (1938). Testes and hypohyses in gassed male rats. *Proc. Soc. exp. Biol., N.Y.*, **38**, 455.

Payne, J. M. (1955). An experimental study of injury and bacterial infections of the scrotal and cryptorchid testis. *J. Path. Bact.*, **70**, 213.

—— (1956). The degenerative changes in the adult mouse testis returned to the abdominal cavity. *J. Path. Bact.*, **71**, 117.

Pelc, S. R. (1957). On the connection between the synthesis of RNA and DNA in the testis of the mouse. *Exp. Cell. Res.*, **12**, 320.

—— & Howard, A. (1956). A difference between spermatogonia and somatic tissues of mice in the incorporation of (8-^{14}C)-adenine into deoxyribonucleic acid. *Exp. Cell. Res.*, **11**, 128.

Peltier, J. C. A. (1835). Observations microscopiques sur les animalcules. *Bull. Soc. Sci. nat., Paris*, p. 92.

—— (1838). Sur l'origine et le développement des zoospermes de la grenouille. *Soc. Philom. Proc. Verb. Paris l'Institut*, **6**.

Pernot, E. (1956). Recherches sur les constituants antigéniques des spermatozoïdes de cobayes. *Bull. Soc. Chim. biol., Paris*, **38**, 1041.

Perry, J. C. (1941). Gonad response of male rats to experimental hyperadrenalism. *Endocrinology*, **29**, 592.

Phillips, R. W., Fraps, R. M., & Frank, A. H. (1945). Hormonal stimulation of estrus and ovulation in sheep and goats. *Amer. J. vet. Res.*, **6**, 165.

—— & McKenzie, F. F. (1934). The thermo-regulatory function and mechanism of the scrotum. *Res. Bull. Mo. agric. Exp. Sta.*, No. 217.

Pilz, A. (1952). Das Verhalten der Säugetierspermien in elektrischen Feld. *Z. Tierz. ZüchtBiol.*, **60**, 315.

Plunkett, E. R., & Barr, M. L. (1956). Cytologic tests of sex in congenital testicular hypoplasia. *J. clin. Endocrin.*, **16**, 829.

Pollak, O. J., & Joel, C. A. (1939). Sperm examination according to the present state of research. *J. Amer. med. Ass.*, **113**, 395.

Pollister, A. W., & Mirsky, A. E. (1946). The nucleoprotamine of trout sperm. *J. gen. Physiol.*, **30**, 101.

Polovtzeva, V. V. (1938). The rate of movement and the time of maturation of spermatozoa in the epididymis of the ram. (Trans.) *Dokl. Akad. seljskoloz. Nauk*, No. 15/16, 43. (In *Anim. Breed. Abstr.*, **8**, 52.)

Popa, G. T., & Marza, V. D. (1931). Biologie des spermatozoides. *Arch. roum. Path. exp. Microbiol.*, **4**, 301.

Porter, J. C., Shankman, S., & Melampy, R. M. (1951). Chemical composition of bovine spermatozoa. *Proc. Soc. exp. Biol., N.Y.*, **77**, 53.

Poucher, H. (1943). Relation of number of injections to the titer of sperm iso-agglutinins in mice. *Proc. Soc. exp. Biol., N.Y.*, **54**, 261.

Prasad, M. R. N. (1956). Reproductive cycle of the male Indian gerbille, *Tatera indica cuvierii* (Waterhouse). *Acta zool. Stockh.*, **38**, 87.

Prévost, J. L., & Dumas, J. B. A. (1824a). Nouvelle théorie de la génération. *Ann. Sci. nat., Paris*, **1**.

—— —— (1824b). De la génération dans les mammifères, et les premiers indices du développement de l'embryon. *Ann. Sci. nat., Paris*, **3**, 113.

Punnett, R. C. (1928). Ovists and animalculists. *Amer. Nat.*, **62**, 481.

Pursley, G. R., & Herman, H. A. (1950). Some effects of hypertonic and hypotonic solutions on the livability and morphology of bovine spermatozoa. *J. Dairy Sci.*, **33**, 220.

Rajasekarasetty, M. R. (1954). Studies on a new type of genetically determined quasi-sterility in the house mouse. *Fertil. Steril.*, **5**, 68.

Randall, J. T., & Friedlaender, M. H. G. (1950). The microstructure of ram spermatozoa. *Exp. Cell. Res.*, **1**, 1.

Rao, C. K. (1956). Studies on the differential staining of live and dead sperm. *Indian vet. J.*, **33**, 180.

—— (1957). Studies on certain factors affecting live and dead differential sperm staining. *Vet. Rec.*, **69**, 544.

RAO, C. K., & BERRY, R. O. (1949). The cytoplasmic drop and the cytoplasmic cap in the development of boar spermatozoa. *Amer. J. vet. Res.*, **10**, 357.

———— —— (1950). Observations on the cytoplasmic drop and cytoplasmic cap in sperm development in domestic sheep, domestic goats and wild barbary sheep (*Ammotragus lervia*). *Indian J. vet. Sci.*, **20**, 47.

RAU, A. S., & BRAMBELL, F. W. R. (1925). Staining methods for the demonstration of the Golgi apparatus in fresh vertebrate and invertebrate material. *J. R. micr. Soc.*, **45**, 438.

REDENZ, E. (1925). Versuch einer biologischen Morphologie des Nebenhoden. II: Die Bedeutung elekrolytarmer Losungen für die Bewegung der Spermien. *Arch. EntwMech. Org.*, **106**, 290.

—— (1926). Nebenhoden und Spermienbewegung. *Würzburg. Abh. prakt. Med.*, **4**, 5.

REGAUD, C. (1900). Direction hélicoidale du movement spermatogénètique dans les tubes séminifères du rat. *C. R. Soc. Biol., Paris*, **52**, 1042.

—— (1901). Études sur la structure des séminifères et sur la spermatogénèse chez mammifères. *Arch. Anat. micr.*, **4**, 101.

REID, B. L., & CLELAND, K. W. (1957). The structure and function of the epididymis. I: The histology of the rat epididymis. *Aust. J. Zool.*, **5**, 223.

RETZIUS, G. (1902). Weitere Beitrage zur Kenntniss der Spermia des Menschen und einiger Säugethiere. *Biol. Untersuch., N. F. Jena*, **10**, 45.

—— (1906). Die Spermien der Amphibien. Die Spermien der Reptilien. Die Spermien der Monotremen. Die Spermien der Marsupialier. Die Spermien der Edentaten. Die Spermien der Vespertilionen. *Biol. Untersuch., N. F., Jena*, **13**, 49, 71, 75, 77, 87, 91.

—— (1909). Die Spermien der Vögel. Die Spermien von Didelphys. Die Spermien von Bradypus. Die Spermien der Insektivoren. Die Spermien der Nagetiere. Die Spermien der Huftiere. Die Spermien der Waltiere. Die Spermien der Carnivoren. Die Spermien der Halbaffen. Die Spermien der Affen. Die Spermien des Menschen. *Biol. Untersuch., N. F., Jena*, **14**, 89, 123, 127, 129, 133, 163, 179, 185, 199, 201, 205.

RICHTER, J. (1936). Sterilität männlicher Tiere. *Berl. tierärzltl. Wschr.*, **52**, 757.

RINGSTED, A. (1934). Histological investigations on the causes of sterility in albino rats kept on a normal butter diet. *Acta path. microbiol. scand.*, **11**, 197.

RISLEY, P. L., & TURBYFILL, C. (1957). Studies *in vivo* of the contractile behaviour of the epididymis. *Anat. Rec.*, **128**, 607.

ROBINSON, J. N., & ENGLE, E. T. (1949). Effect of neutron radiation on the human testis: case report. *J. Urol.*, **61**, 781.

ROLLINSON, D. H. L. (1951). Studies on the abnormal spermatozoa of bull semen. *Brit. vet. J.*, **107**, (5), 203; (6) 258; (11) 251.

ROLSHOVEN, E. (1941). Zur Frage des "Alterns" der generativen Elemente in den Hodenkanälchen. *Anat. Anz.*, **91**, 1.

—— (1951). Ueber die Reifungsteilungen bei der Spermatogenese mit einer Kritik des bisherigen Begriffes der Zellteilung. *Verh. anat. Ges.*, **49**, 189.

ROOSEN-RUNGE, E. C. (1951a). Quantitative studies on spermatogenesis in the albino rat. II: The duration of spermatogenesis and some effects of colchicine. *Amer. J. Anat.*, **88**, 163.

—— (1951b). Motions of the seminiferous tubules of rat and dog. *Anat. Rec.*, **190**, 413.

—— (1952). Kinetics of spermatogenesis in mammals. *Ann. N.Y. Acad. Sci.*, **55**, 574.

—— (1955). Untersuchungen über die Degeneration samenbildender Zellen in der normalen Spermatogenese der Ratte *Z. Zellforsch.*, **41**, 221.

—— & GIESEL, L. O. (1950). Quantitative studies on spermatogenesis in the albino rat. *Amer. J. Anat.*, **87**, 1.

ROTHSCHILD, LORD (1953). The movements of spermatozoa. *Ciba Foundation Symposium on Mammalian germ cells*, p. 122.

—— (1958). The human spermatozoon. *Brit. med. J.*, Feb. 8, p. 301.

RUGH, R. (1939). Developmental effects resulting from exposure to X-rays. I: Effect on the embryo of irradiation of frog sperm. *Proc. Amer. phil. Soc.*, **81**, 447.

—— (1952). Fetal X-irradiation and fertility. *Proc. Soc. exp. Biol., N.Y.*, **80**, 388.

RUGH, R., & EXNER, F. (1940). Developmental effects resulting from exposure to X-rays. II: Development of leopard-frog eggs activated by bull-frog sperm. *Proc. Amer. phil. Soc.*, **83**, 607.

RUSS, S., & SCOTT, G. M. (1939). Biological effects of gamma radiation. *Brit. J. Radiol.*, **12**, 440.

RUSSELL, W. L. (1950). The incidence of sterility and partial sterility in the descendents of X-irradiated mice. *Genetics*, **35**, 689.

—— (1954). Genetic effects of radiation in mammals. In *Radiation Biology*, Vol. I, Part I, p. 825. Ed. A. Hollaender. New York.

RYLE, M. (1957). Studies on possible serological blocks to species hybridization in poultry. *J. exp. Biol.*, **34**, 365.

SACHER, G. A. (1952). Effects of total body X-irradiation on rats. II: Effects of single and periodic doses on weight. A. The growth of rats exposed to small daily doses of X-rays. *Rep. CH-3902*. Metallurgical Laboratory, University of Chicago.

SALISBURY, G. W., & CRAGLE, R. G. (1956). Freezing point depressions and mineral levels of fluids of the ruminant male reproductive tract. *Proc. 3rd Int. Congr. Anim. Reprod., Cambridge*, **1**, 25.

—— & VANDEMARK, N. L. (1957). Carbon dioxide as a reversible inhibitor of spermatozoan metabolism. *Nature, Lond.*, **180**, 989.

—— WILLETT, E. L., & SELIGMAN, J. (1942). The effect of the method of making semen smears upon the number of morphologically abnormal spermatozoa. *J. Anim. Sci.*, **1**, 199.

SAMPSON, M. M., & KORENCHEVSKY, V. Changes in the testes of rats kept on a diet deficient in vitamin A. *J. Path. Bact.*, **35**, 875.

—— —— (1932b). The influence of vitamin A deficiency on male rats in paired feeding experiments. *Biochem. J.*, **26**, 1322.

SAND, K. (1921). Études expérimentales sur les glandes sexuelles chez les mammifères. Cryptorchidie expérimentale. *J. Physiol. Path. gén.*, **19**, 515.

—— (1933). *Die Physiologie des Hodens*. Leipzig.

SAPSFORD, C. S. (1951). Seasonal changes in spermatogenesis in rams: their relation to plane of nutrition and to vitamin A status. *Aust. J. agric. Res.*, **2**, 331.

—— (1957). The development of the Sertoli cell. *J. Endocrin.*, **15**, lv.

—— (1958). Personal communication.

SARKAR, B. C. R., LUECKE, R. W., & DUNCAN, C. W. (1947). The amino acid composition of bovine semen. *J. biol. Chem.*, **171**, 463.

SARTORY, A., SARTORY, R., & MEYER, J. (1931). Phénomènes apportes par l'irradiation sur les tissu cutane et sur la glands génital mâle du lapin en fonction du mode d'application du rayonnement. *C. R. Acad. Sci., Paris*, **192**, 447.

SAVAGE, A., WILLIAMS, W. W., & FOWLER, N. M. (1927). A statistical study of the head-length variability of bovine spermatozoa and its application to the determination of fertility. *Trans. roy. Soc. Can.*, **31**, 425.

SCHAEFER, H. (1939). Die Fertilität von Mäusemännchen nach Bestralung mit 200r. *Z. mikr.-anat. Forsch.*, **46**, 121.

SCHINZ, H. R., & SLOTOPOSKY, B. (1926). Experimentelle Beitrage zur Frage der Röntgenallergie. *Acta radiol.*, **7**, 365.

SCHLENK, W., JR., & KAHMANN, H. (1938). Die chemische Zusammensetzung des Spermaliquors und ihre physiologische Bedeutung, Untersuchung an Forellensperma. *Biochem. Z.*, **295**, 383.

SCHMIDT, G., & THANNHAUSER, S. J. (1945). A method for the determination of desoxyribonucleic acid, ribonucleic acid, and phosphoproteins in animal tissues. *J. biol. Chem.*, **161**, 83.

SCHMIDT, W. J. (1937). *Die Doppelbrechung von Karyoplasma, Zytoplasma und Metaplasma*. Berlin.

SCHNEIDER, W. C. (1945). Phosphorus compounds in animal tissues. I: Extraction and estimation of desoxypentose nucleic acid and of pentose nucleic acid. *J. biol. Chem.*, **161**, 293.

SCHOENFELD, H. (1900). La spermatogénèse chez le taureau. *Bibliogr. anat.*, **8**, 74.

—— (1902). La spermatogénèse chez le taureau et chez les mammifères en général. *Arch. Biol., Liége*, **18**, 1.

SCHRADER, F., & LEUCHTENBERGER, C. (1951). The cytology and chemical nature of some constituents of the developing sperm. *Chromosoma*, **4**, 404.

SCHRÖDER, V. N. (1934). Physico-chemical analysis of the physiology of spermatozoa. V: Artificial control of sex in mammals. (Trans.). *Biol. Zh. (Mosk.)*, **3**, 465. (In *Anim. Breed. Abstr.*, **3**, 166.)

—— (1936a). The nature of the electric charge on living cells. (Trans.). *Biol. Zh. (Mosk.)*, **5**, 657. (In *Chem. Zbl.*, **2**, 3180.)

——(1936b). Die physikalishc-chemische Analyse der Spermienphysiologie. VI: Uber die Natur der Elektrischen Ladung der Kannichenspermien. *Biol. Zh. (Mosk.)*, **5**, 690.

—— (1937). Physico-chemical analysis of the physiology of mammalian spermatozoa. VII: On the physico-chemical nature of the bio-colloids of the anode and cathode spermatozoa of the rabbit. (Trans.). *Biol. Zh. (Mosk.)*, **6**, 1235. (In *Anim. Breed. Abstr.*, **7**, 375.)

—— (1940a). Über die künstliche Geschlechtsregulation bei den Säugetieren mittels der Elektrophorese und deren biologische Kontrolle. *C. R. Acad. Sci., U.R.S.S.*, **26**, 687.

—— (1940b). Die physikalisch-chemische Analyse der Spermienphysiologie (Säugetierspermien). Über die Natur der Lipoide der anodisch und kathodisch wandernden. Kaninchenspermien. *C. R. Acad. Sci., U.R.S.S.*, **26**, 692.

—— (1941a). Künstliche Geschlechtsregulation der Nachkommenschaft der Säugetiere und ihre biologische Kontrolle. *Z. Tierz. ZüchtBiol.*, **50**, 1.

—— (1941b). Über die biochemischen und physiologischen Eigentümlichkeiten der X- und Y-Spermien. *Z. Tierz. ZüchtBiol.*, **50**, 16.

——(1956). The role of metabolism of the parent on the sex ratio of the progeny. (Trans.). *Usp. sovr. Biol.*, Moscow, **42**, 33. (In *Anim. Breed. Abstr.*, **25**, 191.)

SCHULTZ-LARSEN, J., & HAMMEN, R. (1956). The submicroscopic morphology of human spermatozoa. *Dan. med. Bull.*, **3**, 141.

SCHWEIGGER-SEIDEL, O. (1865). Ueber die Samenkörperchen und ihre Entwickelung. *Arch. mikr. Anat.*, **1**, 309.

SELIVANOVA, O. (1937). Movement of the kinoplasmic drop in spermatozoa of farm animals. (Trans.). *Adv. zootech. Sci.*, Moscow, **4**, 67.

SERTOLI, E. (1865). Dell' esistezia di particolari cellule ramificate nei canalicoli seminiferi del testicolo umano. *Morgagni*, **7**, 31.

SHAFFER, H. E., & ALMQUIST, J. O. (1948). Vital staining of bovine spermatozoa with an eosin-aniline blue staining mixture. *J. Dairy Sci.*, **31**, 668.

—— —— (1949). Relation of the eosin–aniline blue staining method to the quality of bull semen. *J. Dairy Sci.*, **32**, 723.

SHARMA, G. P., CHANDHURI, G. C., & SATTEE, V. S. (1953). The guinea-pig sperm. *Res. Bull. East Punjab Univ.*, **38**, 157.

SHAVER, S. L. (1953a). X-irradiation injury and repair in the germinal epithelium of male rats. I: Injury and repair in adult rats. *Amer. J. Anat.*, **92**, 391.

—— (1953b). X-irradiation injury and repair in the germinal epithelium of male rats. II: Injury and repair in immature rats. *Amer. J. Anat.*, **92**, 433.

—— & MASON, K. E. (1950). Selective testicular damage in rats due to X-rays. *Anat. Rec.*, **106**, 246.

SHETTLES, L. B. (1947). Effects of low oxygen tension on fertility in adult male guinea-pigs. *Fed. Proc.*, **6**, 200.

SILJANDER, A. A. (1936). Sex control in farm animals by means of sperm electrophoresis. (Trans.). *Sbornik Trudov Zootek. s.l. Skol. Kirov.*, **148**, 166. (In *Anim. Breed. Abstr.*, **7**, 376.).

SIMEONE, F. A. (1933). A neuromuscular mechanism in the ductus epididymis and its impairment by sympathetic denervation. *Amer. J. Physiol.*, **103**, 582.

—— & YOUNG, W. C. (1931). A study of the function of the epididymis. IV: The fate of non-ejaculated spermatozoa in the genital tract of the male guinea-pig. *J. exp. Biol.*, **8**, 163.

Sirlin, J. L., & Edwards, R. G. (1955). The labelling of mouse sperm by adenine-8-C-14. *Exp. Cell. Res.*, **9**, 396.

—— —— (1957a). Sensitivity of immature mouse sperm to the mutagenic effects of X-rays. *Nature, Lond.*, **179**, 725.

—— —— (1957b). Duration of spermatogenesis in the mouse. *Nature, Lond.*, **180**, 1138.

Slizynski, B. M. (1954). The sex bivalent of *Mus musculus* L. *J. Genet.*, **53**, 591.

Smelser, G. K. (1935). Spontaneous sterility in the male rat. *Anat. Rec.*, **64**, Suppl. 1, 53.

Smith, A. U. (1949a). Some antigenic properties of mammalian spermatozoa. *Proc. roy. Soc.* B, **136**, 46.

—— (1949b). The antigenic relationship of some mammalian spermatozoa. *Proc. roy. Soc.* B, **136**, 472.

Smith, P. E. (1930). Hypophysectomy and a replacement therapy in the rat. *Amer. J. Anat.*, **45**, 205.

Snell, G. D. (1933). X-ray sterility in the male house mouse. *J. exp. Zool.*, **65**, 421.

—— (1935). The induction by X-rays of hereditary changes in mice. *Genetics*, **20**, 545.

—— (1941). The induction by roentgen rays of hereditary changes in mice. *Radiology*, **36**, 189.

—— (1944). Antigenic differences between the sperm of different inbred strains of mice. *Science*, **100**, 272.

—— & Aebersold, P. C. (1937). The production of sterility in male mice by irradiation with neutrons. *Proc. nat. Acad. Sci., Wash.*, **23**, 374.

—— Bodemann, E., & Holländer, W. (1934). A translocation in the house mouse and its effect on development. *J. exp. Zool.*, **67**, 93.

—— & Picken, D. I. (1935). Abnormal development in the mouse caused by chromosome unbalance. *J. Genet.*, **31**, 213.

Sørensen, E., & Anderson, S. (1956). The influence of sodium and potassium ions upon the motility of sperm cells. *Proc. 3rd Int. Congr. Anim. Reprod., Cambridge*, **1**, 45.

Spallanzani, L. (1780). *Dissertazioni di isica Animale e Vegetabile.* Modena. English Edition: *Dissertations relative to the natural history of animals and vegetables.* London, 1784.

Starke, N. C. (1949). The sperm picture of rams of different breeds as an indication of their fertility. II: The rate of sperm travel in the genital tract of the ewe. *Onderstepoort J. vet. Sci.*, **22**, 415.

Steudal, H. (1926). Physikalische und chemische Eigenschaften des Spermes und der Eisubstanzen, nebst Umban von Körperorganen in Generations organe. *Handb. norm. path. Physiol.*, **14**, 156.

Stickney, J. C., & Liere, E. J. van (1953). Acclimatization to low oxygen tension. *Physiol. Rev.*, **33**, 13.

Stieve, H. (1930). *Möllendorff's Handbuch der mikroskopischen Anatomie des Menschen.* Berlin.

Stone, E. J., Johnstone, J. E., & Mixner, J. P. (1950). Live spermatozoa relationships and fertility of dairy bull semen. *J. Dairy Sci.*, **33**, 442.

Swanson, E. W., & Bearden, H. J. (1951). An eosin-nigrosin stain for differentiating live and dead bovine spermatozoa. *J. Anim. Sci.*, **10**, 981.

Swift, H. H. (1950). The desoxy-ribose nucleic acid content of animal nuclei. *Physiol. Zoöl.*, **23**, 169.

Swyer, G. I. M. (1947a). The hyaluronidase content of semen. *Biochem. J.*, **41**, 409.

—— (1947b). The release of hyaluronidase from spermatozoa. *Biochem. J.*, **41**, 413.

Taylor, Sir Geoffrey (1951). Analysis of the swimming of microscopic organisms *Proc. roy. Soc.* A, **209**, 447.

—— (1952). The action of waving cylindrical tails in propelling microscopic organisms. *Proc. roy. Soc.* A, **211**, 225.

Testut, L. (1934). *Traité d'anatomie humaine.* 8me Edit. Paris.

Teunissen, G. H. B. (1946). Een Afwijkning van het Acrosom (Kopkap) bij de Spermatozoiden van een Stier. *Tijdschr. Diergeneesk.*, **71**, 292.

Tibbs, J. (1957). The nature of algal and related flagella. *Biochim. Biophys. Acta*, **23**, 275.

TOBIAS, P. V. (1956). *Chromosomes, Sex-cells and Evolution in a Mammal.* Lund, Humphries & Co., London.

TOOTHILL, M. C., & YOUNG, W. C. (1931). The time consumed by spermatozoa in passing through the ductus epididymis of the guinea-pig as determined by India-ink injections. *Anat. Rec.*, **50**, 95.

TOSIC, J., & WALTON, A. (1950). Metabolism of spermatozoa. The formation and elimination of hydrogen peroxide by spermatozoa and effects on motility and survival. *Biochem. J.*, **47**, 199.

TRASLER, D. G., & METRAKOS, J. (1953). Sex ratio of offspring from irradiated male mice. *Genetics*, **38**, 697.

TURNER, C. D. (1938). Intra-ocular homotransplantation of prepuberal testes in the rat. *Amer. J. Anat.*, **63**, 101.

LA VALETTE ST. GEORGE (1865). Ueber die Genese der Samenkörper. *Arch. mikr. Anat.*, **1**.

VAN BENEDEN, E. (1875). La maturation de l'oeuf, la fécondation et les premières phases du développement embryonnaire des mammifères d'après des recherches faites chez le lapin. *Bull. Acad. roy. Soc., Belg.*, Ser. II, **40**, 687.

—— (1883). Recherches sur la maturation de l'oeuf, la fécondation et la division cellulaire. *Arch. Biol.*, **4**.

VANDEMARK, N. L. (1956). Quantitative aspects of semen production in bulls. *Proc. III Int. Congr. Anim. Reprod., Cambridge*, p. 80.

—— & BOYD, M. S. (1956). The effect of epinephrine upon testicular function in rabbits. *Internat. J. Fertil.*, **1**, 245.

—— & SHARMA, U. D. (1957). Preliminary fertility results from the preservation of bovine semen at room temperatures. *J. Dairy Sci.*, **40**, 438.

VENDRELY, C., KNOBLOCH, A., & VENDRELY, R. (1956). Contribution à l'étude biochimique comparée de diverses désoxyribonucléoprotéines d'origine animale. *Biochim. Biophys. Acta.* **19**, 472.

VENDRELY, R., KNOBLOCH, A., & VENDRELY, C. (1957). An attempt of using biochemical methods for cytochemical problems. The desoxyribonucleoprotein of spermatogenic cells of bull testis. *Exp. Cell Res.*, Suppl. 4, p. 279.

—— & VENDRELY, C. (1948). La teneur du noyau cellulaire en acid désoxyribonucleique à travers les organes, les individus et les espèces animales. Techniques et premiers résultats. *Experientia*, **4**, 434.

—— —— (1953). Arginine and deoxyribonucleic acid content of erythrocyte nuclei and sperm of some fishes. *Nature, Lond.*, **172**, 30.

VLAHOS, K., MCENTEE, K., OLAFSON, P., & HANSEL, W. (1955). Destruction and restoration of spermatogenesis in a bull experimentally poisoned with highly chlorinated naphthaline. *Cornell Vet.*, **45**, 198.

WALDEYER, W. (1906). Die Geschlectszellen. In *Handbuch der vergleichenden und experimentellen Entwicklungslehre der Wirbeltiere.* Jena.

WALKER, P. M. B., & YATES, H. B. (1952). Nuclear components of dividing cells. *Proc. roy. Soc. B*, **140**, 274.

WALSH, L. S. N. (1925). Natural auto and homoio spermotoxins in guinea-pig serum. *J. Immunol.*, **10**, 803.

WALTON, A. (1927). The relation between " density " of sperm suspension and fertility as determined by artificial insemination of rabbits. *Proc. roy. Soc. B*, **101**, 303.

—— (1947). Unpublished observations.

—— (1949). Spermatogenesis and nutrition. *Brit. J. Nutrit.*, **3**, 83.

—— (1956). The initiation of motility in mammalian spermatozoa. *Studies on Fertility*, **8**, 53.

—— & URUSKI, W. (1946). The effects of low atmospheric pressure on the fertility of male rabbits. *J. exp. Biol.*, **23**, 71.

WARREN, S. (1943). Effects of radiation on normal tissues. VIII : Effects on the gonads. *Arch. Path.*, **35**, 124.

WATSON, M. L. (1952). Spermatogenesis in the albino rat as revealed by tissue sections in the electron microscope. *Biochim. Biophys. Acta*, **8**, 369.

WATTENWYL, H. VON, & JOËL, C. A. (1942). Die Wirkung der Röntgenstrahlen auf den Rattenhoden. IV: Verlauf der Degeneration bzw. Regeneration des Samenepithels nach Bestrahlung mit 150 bis 2400r von 75 bis zu 300 Tagen nach der Bestrahlung. *Strahlentherapie*, **72**, 62.

WEGELIN, C. (1921). Über Spermiophagie in menslichen Nebenhoden. *Beitr. path. Anat.*, **69**, 281.

WEICHARDT, W. (1901). Recherches sur l'antispermotoxine. *Ann. Inst. Pasteur*, **15**, 832.

WEIR, J. A. (1955). Male influence on sex ratio of offspring in high and low blood-pH lines of mice. *J. Hered.*, **46**, 277.

WEISMAN, A. I. (1941). *Spermatozoa and Sterility*. New York.

WELLS, L. J., & ZALESKY, M. (1940). Effects of low environmental temperature on the reproductive organs of male mammals with annual aspermia. *Amer. J. Anat.*, **66**, 429.

WERTHESSEN, N. T., BERMAN, S., GREENBURG, B. E., & GARGILL, S. L. (1945). Technique for the assay of hyaluronidase in human semen and its correlation with sperm concentration. *J. Urol.*, **54**, 565.

WHITE, J. C., LESLIE, I., & DAVIDSON, J. N. (1953). Nucleic acids of bone marrow cells, with special reference to pernicious anaemia. *J. Path. Bact.*, **66**, 291.

WHITE, M. J. D. (1942). *The Chromosomes*. London.

—— (1954). *Animal Cytology and Evolution*. Second Ed. Cambridge.

WHITE, W. E. (1932). The effect of hypophysectomy on the survival of spermatozoa in the male rat. *Anat. Rec.*, **54**, 253.

—— (1933). The duration of fertility and the histological changes in the reproductive organs after ligation of the vasa efferentia in the rat. *Proc. roy. Soc.* B, **113**, 544.

WIGODER, S. B. (1929). The effect of X-rays on the testes. *Brit. J. Radiol.*, **2**, 213.

WILHELM, S. (1935). Observations on emptying of vasa deferentia and seminal vesicles. *J. Urol.*, **34**, 284.

WILLIAMS, J. R., & SMITH, E. (1935). Blood picture, reproduction, and general condition during daily exposure to illuminating gas. *Amer. J. Physiol.*, **110**, 611.

WILLIAMS, W. L., & CUNNINGHAM, B. (1940). Histological changes in the rat testis following heat treatment. *Yale J. Biol. Med.*, **12**, 309.

WILLIAMS, W. W. (1947). Routine semen examinations and their interpretation. *West. J. Surg.*, **55**, 451.

—— & POLLAK, O. J. (1950). A study of sperm vitality with the aid of eosin-nigrosin stain. *Fertil. Steril.*, **1**, 178.

—— & SAVAGE, A. (1925). Observations on the seminal micropathology of bulls. *Cornell Vet.*, **15**, 353.

WILSON, E. B. (1925). *The Cell in Development and Heredity*. Third Ed. New York.

WILSON, L. (1954). Sperm agglutinins in human semen and blood. *Proc. Soc. exp. Biol., N.Y.*, **85**, 652.

WISLOCKI, G. B. (1949). Seasonal changes in the testis, epididymides and seminal vesicles of the deer investigated by histochemical methods. *Endocrinology*, **44**, 167.

—— (1950). Cytochemical reactions of human spermatozoa and seminal plasma. *Anat. Rec.*, **108**, 645.

WITSCHI, E. (1948). Migration of the germ cells of human embryos from the yolk sac to the primitive gonadal folds. *Contr. Embryol. Carneg. Instn*, **32**, 67.

—— NELSON, W. O., & SEGAL, S. J. (1957). Genetic, developmental and hormonal aspects of gonadal dysgenesis and sex inversion in man. *J. clin. Endocrin.*, **17**, 737.

WODSEDALEK, J. E. (1913). Spermatogenesis of the pig with special reference to the accessory chromosomes. *Biol. Bull.*, **25**, 58.

—— (1914). Spermatogenesis of the horse with special reference to the accessory chromosome and the chromatoid body. *Biol. Bull.*, **27**.

—— (1916). Causes of sterility in the mule. *Biol. Bull.*, **30**, 1.

—— (1920). Studies on the cells of cattle with special reference to spermatogenesis, oögonia and sex-determination. *Biol. Bull.*, **38**, 290.

WYATT, G. R. (1951). The purine and pyrimidine composition of deoxypentose nucleic acids. *Biochem. J.*, **48**, 584.

YAMAKAMI, K. (1926). The individuality of semen, with reference to its property of inhibiting specifically isohemoagglutinin. *J. Immunol.*, **12**, 185.

YASUZUMI, G. (1956). Spermatogenesis in animals as revealed by electron microscopy. I: Formation and submicroscopic structure of the middle-piece of the albino rat. *J. Biophys. Biochem. Cytol.*, **2**, 445.

YEATES, N. T. M. (1949). The breeding season of the sheep with particular reference to its modification by artificial means using light. *J. agric. Sci.*, **39**, 1.

YOCHEM, D. E. (1930). A study of the motility and resistance of rat spermatozoa at different levels in the reproductive tract. *Physiol. Zoöl.*, **3**, 309.

YOUNG, W. C. (1927). The influence of high temperature on the guinea-pig testis. Histological changes and effects on reproduction. *J. exp. Zool.*, **49**, 459.

—— (1929a). A study of the function of the epididymis. I: Is the attainment of full spermatozoan maturity attributable to some specific action of epididymal secretion? *J. Morph.*, **47**, 479.

—— (1929b). A study of the function of the epididymis. II: The importance of an ageing process in sperm for the length of the period during which fertilizing capacity is retained by sperm isolated in the epididymis of the guinea-pig. *J. Morph.*, **48**, 475.

——(1931). A study of the function of the epididymis. III: Functional changes undergone by spermatozoa during their passage through the epididymis and vas deferens of the guinea-pig. *J. exp. Biol.*, **8**, 151.

—— (1933). Die Resorption in den Ductuli efferentes der Maus und ihre Bedentung für das Problem der Unterbindung in Hoden-Nebenhoden system. *Z. Zellforsch.*, **17**, 729.

ZAWADOWSKY, M. M. (1931). Zebu-yak hybrids. Sterility of bulls, fertility of cows and material on the genetics of zebu-yak hybrids. *J. Hered.*, **22**, 296.

ZELENY, C., & FAUST, E. C. (1914). Size difference in spermatozoa from single testes. *Science*, **39**, 440.

—— —— (1915a). Size dimorphism in the spermatozoa from single testes. *J. exp. Zool.*, **18**, 187.

—— (1915b). Dimorphism in size of spermatozoa and its relation to the chromosomes. *Proc. nat. Acad. Sci.*, **1**, 91.

—— & SENAY, C. T. (1915). Variation in head length of spermatozoa in seven additional species of insects. *J. exp. Zool.*, **19**, 505.

ZITTLE, C. A., & O'DELL, R. A. (1941a). The determination of cystine: the use of cuprous oxide for simultaneous reduction and precipitation of cystine as the cuprous mercaptide. *J. biol. Chem.*, **139**, 753.

—— —— (1941b). Chemical studies of bull spermatozoa. Lipid, sulfur, cystine, nitrogen, phosporus and nucleic acid content of whole spermatozoa and of parts obtained by physical means. *J. biol. Chem.*, **140**, 899.

—— —— (1941c). Chemical studies of bull spermatozoa. The methionine content of whole spermatozoa and of the parts obtained by physical means. *J. biol. Chem.*, **141**, 239.

ZLOTNIK, I. (1943). A nuclear ring in the developing male germ-cells of dog and cat. *Nature, Lond.*, **151**, 670.

CHAPTER 8

COPULATION AND NATURAL INSEMINATION

By Arthur Walton

A description of the mammalian testis, of the spermatozoon, and of the spermatic tract as far as the vas deferens has been given in the preceding chapter. It
remains to describe the functional relations of the rest of the male tract ; the
urethra, with the accessory glands, and the penis ; and to relate these to the mechanism of copulation and the preliminaries to internal fertilisation in the female.

I. Evolution of Copulation

The evolution of copulation as a preliminary to internal fertilisation can be
regarded from several standpoints (Walton, 1938b). First of all it ensures the production of offspring with the greatest economy of gametes ; especially the ova.
In most marine organisms, many of which are sedentary, the gametes are simply
liberated into the surrounding sea water. In this medium the gametes can survive,
but their period of life is determinate and dependent upon the exhaustion of
endogenous sources of energy. The probability of fertilisation will depend upon
the number of pairs of gametes which happen to come in contact during the period
of their active life. This probability will be affected by the number of gametes
liberated by each sex and the distance the gametes are apart in space and time
at the moment of liberation. Distance apart in time is of prime importance owing
to the limited length of life of the gametes outside the body. Distance apart in
space is of importance in relation to dispersal affecting the chances of encounter
between male and female gametes. The wastefulness of free fertilisation is
represented by the enormous number of gametes liberated. This wastage would
be greater were it not for the existence of temporal and spacial co-ordination in
the liberation of the sexual products. Temporal co-ordination may occur through
seasonal influences, as when spawning of both sexes is restricted to certain times
of the year or is initiated by some specific environmental stimulus. A classical
example of the latter is the swarming of the Palolo worms which at full moon
rise to the surface of the ocean to spawn. Temporal co-ordination is also illustrated in the case of chemical stimulation of spawning. It has been shown that in
Neiris limbata (Townsend, 1938a, b) and in *Ostrea virginica* (Galtsoff, 1938, 1940),
liberation of the gametes is stimulated by the presence of eggs or spermatozoa in the
surrounding water. Co-ordination in space may result from a restricted colonial
habitat, or in the case of non-sedentary animals from the habit of living together
in shoals or congregating in special areas for breeding, as in the case of many fish.
From colonial aggregation or gregarious habit there is a series of evolutionary

stages leading to the close individual association of the sexes in pairs, to amplection with external fertilisation as in many fish and amphibia, and finally to the development of true copulation with intromittent organs and internal fertilisation as is characteristic of birds and mammals.

From a second standpoint the evolution of copulation may be regarded as a mechanism to ensure protection of the gametes from an unfavourable external environment. As soon as the gametes are liberated, survival will depend not only upon the limitations imposed by the cell structure and endogenous sources of energy but on the severity of the conditions which the gametes meet in the external medium. The conquest of fresh water, which is anisosmotic, illustrates this principle. Free fertilisation in an isosmotic environment is most characteristic of marine organisms. Fresh-water animals show highly developed mechanisms which ensure close approximation of the gametes at the time of fertilisation ensuring the minimum exposure to the environment. In some fresh-water fish, e.g. *Gasterosteus* and *Salmo*, " nests " are formed where the eggs are laid and then immediately fertilised. In the newt a spermatophore is laid on the pond bottom and picked up by the cloaca of the female. Many fresh-water fish and amphibia copulate and in some fertilisation is internal.

Although the spermatozoa of fresh-water animals and amphibia may survive in pure water for a longer time than do those of sea organisms and mammals, the adaptation to this hostile medium is not complete, as is shown by the fact that the addition of neutral salts which raise the osmotic pressure of the water prolongs survival of the spermatozoa (Scheuring, 1925, 1928 ; Gaschott, 1925). It is also of interest to note that mammalian spermatozoa retain to some extent, perhaps as a vestige of their previous ancestry, a considerable tolerance to hypotonic solutions.

With the development of internal fertilisation, protection against a hostile outside environment is complete, but new problems arise. Sea and fresh water provide an aerated medium in which spermatozoa can swim freely and fertilise the liberated ova. With internal fertilisation the place of sea or fresh water as a medium for fertilisation is taken by the secretions of the male and female tract. Unlike fresh water these are approximately isosmotic to the body tissues, but differ from both sea and fresh water by containing complex organic secretions including possible substrates for exogenous metabolism. How far these secretions simply fulfil the function of providing an " internal private pond " for the meeting of spermatozoon and ovum and how far they provide nourishment for the spermatozoa will be discussed later.

From a third standpoint the evolution of copulation can be regarded as an essential step towards providing a safe environment for the development of the fertilised ovum and embryo. In birds, the egg must be fertilised internally before it receives the protective coating of the albumen and shell. In mammals internal fertilisation necessarily precedes uterine development of the embryo.

Copulation is rendered possible by the development of highly specialised copulatory organs and complex patterns of sexual behaviour which involve the higher senses and even the mental faculties. In most birds, copulation is performed by the approximation of the cloacae and by transfer by ejaculation of semen from the male tract to the female. In a few birds, e.g. the duck, a rudimentary penis is developed. The physical contact of the sexes in birds is a relatively simple process, but is in most species conditioned by elaborate behaviour patterns

—courtship, display, feeding, nest building, and other sexual activities. As Darling (1938) has shown, these psychological functions not only serve the needs of reproduction, but may become an integral part of the social life of the bird community. Conversely, the social life may be important for successful reproduction.

In mammals, copulatory organs, especially male organs, are highly specialised and present very great diversity of structure, and there is equally great diversity in patterns of sexual behaviour, the functional significance of which is not always clear in our present stage of knowledge. However, many behaviour patterns and anatomical features can be interpreted in terms of the primary requirement for successful mating, namely the coincidence in time and space of the gametes at the site of fertilisation. Spacially the site of internal fertilisation is limited and bounded by the confines of the female tract ; nevertheless, when compared with the size of the spermatozoon, the " dispersal area " is large and by no means negligible.

In the development of mechanisms which ensure temporal coincidence of the gametes the mammals are most highly specialised. The oestrous cycle is a typical example of this. A relatively small number of ova is liberated at specific intervals. Each ovulation is preceded by a short oestrous period during which the female exhibits sexual desire and will readily copulate : the male attempts coitus when opportunity offers. This ensures a high probability that spermatozoa will be present at the site of fertilisation, at, or shortly before, the time when the ova are liberated (see p. 229). In those mammals (e.g. rabbit, ferret, mink, cat) in which ovulation occurs, not spontaneously, but as a consequence of copulation, there is a most exact mechanism for bringing about the temporal coincidence of ovulation with the presence of spermatozoa in the Fallopian tube, and in this respect these animals may be regarded as having a highly specialised and efficient pattern of sexual behaviour. It is not inconsistent with this view of the evolution of copulation, that other highly evolved animals, including man, should lack an accurate timing mechanism relating copulation to ovulation. In man coitus occurs at any time in the menstrual cycle, and ovulation is spontaneous and not conditioned by sexual stimulation. Consequently, the number of pregnancies which follow a given number of copulations is relatively small, and in this respect human reproduction is very inefficient. But in man and to a less extent in primates and in some other social mammals, copulation has a significance which is not exclusively related to reproductive ends. Zuckerman (1932) has shown that in monkeys and apes, sexual behaviour plays an integral part in the development of individual relationships and social structure (cf. also Darling, above, for birds). In man, the social implications of sexual relationships are still more highly developed. Love, courtship, mating, and hence marriage, family life and our social structure are largely founded on intimate sexual intercourse between man and woman. If, for example, coitus in man was confined, as it is in many of the lower animals, to a single short oestrous period, preceding an annual pregnancy, with no sexual desire on the part of the female outside oestrous, our way of life would assuredly be very different. We would be without that which gives not only intense sexual gratification but is also the foundation of much of our social and cultural life. It is in these respects that man can claim a higher evolutionary status, as regards sexual relationships, than the lower animals.

II. The Male Genital Tract

Although the comparative morphology of the male reproductive tract has been described by Eckstein and Zuckerman in Chapter 2, some short account of the anatomy of the tract must precede the description of physiological functions if only to provide a logical sequence for the account of the various accessory glands and

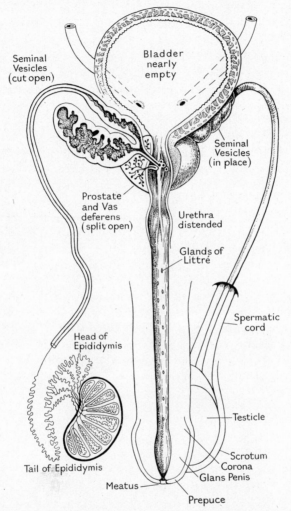

Fig. *8.1*—The male genital tract in man.　(From Dickinson, 1933.)

parts of the tract.　In order to simplify this account as much as possible it will deal most fully with the one species, namely man, about which probably most is known of the anatomy and functional physiology of the accessory glands.　Already an account of the testis and its main function, spermatogenesis, has been given in Chapter 7, and only the following parts of the male tract need be described here.

A diagrammatic representation of this part of the human male tract is shown in Fig. *8.1*.

The Vas deferens and Ampulla

The vas deferens rectus near its junction with the urethra becomes enlarged and sacculated by the formation of thin septa from the interior epithelium. The enlargement is called the ampulla, although the implied function of containing fluid, and specifically the seminal fluid, is indeed doubtful. The cavities between the walls of the septa contain a jelly-like substance. Spermatozoa may be found in the central lumen of the duct, but in many dissections of the ampulla in sexually mature domesticated and laboratory animals, the sectioned ampulla has been found practically devoid of spermatozoa. This casts doubt on the validity of the contention that the ampullae act as seminal reservoirs (Disselhorst, 1904), but may give support rather to the theory of Young and Simeone (1930) that the main function of the lower section of the vas deferens is the absorption of liquefied products of sperm dissolution (see p. 100). In man the ampulla on either side receives the duct or terminal portion of the corresponding seminal vesicle and the common passage is continued as the ejaculatory duct, which traverses the prostate and opens into the floor of the urethra on the surface of a slight eminence, the verumontanum or colliculus seminalis. Some anatomists consider the ejaculatory duct to be a continuation of the duct of the seminal vesicle and the ampulla of the vas deferens to be a tributary. This is based upon the more acute angle which the vas makes with the ejaculatory duct (Gutierrez, 1942). The embryological evidence, however, makes it clear that the seminal vesicle develops as a diverticulum of the mesonephric (Wolffian) duct and is therefore to be regarded as a tributary of the vas deferens. The similarity in anatomical and histological structure of the epithelium supports this view.

In many species there is no ejaculatory duct and the seminal vesicles open separately into the urethra close to the openings of the vas deferens. In the rabbit, the seminal vesicles fuse to form a bi-lobed gland with a common lumen which opens by a single orifice into the urethra. This organ has previously been described as the uterus masculinus but the embryological study of Davies and Mann (1947) clearly established its origin from the mesonephric ducts.

The Urethra

The urethra serves as the common channel for both urine and seminal fluid. It is lined by a columnar epithelium, supported by a vascular corium which is further surrounded by two layers of muscular fibres : the inner longitudinal and the outer circular. The upper or pelvic portion of the urethra is continuous with the bladder and it receives in the course of its passage to the exterior a number of tributaries. The first are openings of Home's glands on the subtrigonal portion of the urethra. The second are the openings of a group of small glands lying on the floor of the urethra between the subtrigonal portion and the verumontanum. These are known as the subcervical (Albarran's) tubules. No specific function of these two groups of glands is known, but they probably contribute a secretion to moisten the surface of the urethra and increase the volume of the ejaculate. Lower down, the elevation on the floor of the urethra, known as the verumontanum, receives medially the opening of the uterus masculinus or utriculus prostaticus. This vestigial structure is derived from the Müllerian

ducts and is the homologue of the uterus and vagina of the female.   In the goat
and deer it is more developed than in most mammals (Disselhorst, 1904).   Lateral
to the opening of the uterus masculinus on the verumontanum are the two openings of the ejaculatory ducts.   Surrounding the urethra at this level is the prostate
gland with several apertures.   According to Lowsley *et al.* (1942) the human
prostate is derived from five outgrowths from the embryonic prostatic urethra
forming the median lobe, two lateral lobes, one anterior and one posterior.   Hirsch
(1931a), however, from a comparative study of the organ in a number of different
species, casts doubt on the existence of unpaired glands.   The lobes of the human
prostate according to Lowsley *et al.* (1942) together contribute about 64 prostatic
ducts opening on the floor of the urethra.   The homologue of the prostate is
represented in the female by the para-urethral glands of Skene.   Below the prostate, the continuation of the urethra is known as the phallic portion, since it forms
the canal of the intromittent organ or penis.   This will be described as a separate
organ below.   In the phallic portion of the urethra are the paired bulbo-urethral
glands (Cowper's glands) and there are also small glands in the wall of the urethra
known as the glands of Littré.

The Glandulae vesiculares (Seminal Vesicles)

As already described the glandulae vesiculares or seminal vesicles are outgrowths
from the lower portions of the Wolffian ducts.   According to Guterriez (1942),
in man each gland consists of a coiled tube with six or more diverticula.   The
gland is about 5 cm. long and when uncoiled about double this length.   The
cubic capacity is estimated to be from 1·5 to 11 ml.   The wall of the gland consists
of three layers : (1) an external fibrous layer, (2) a relatively thick muscular coat
comprising two layers, the outer longitudinal and the inner circular, and (3) a
mucous layer.   The surface of the mucosa is greatly increased by the formation
of linear projections forming a network with alveoli between.

There has been some dispute as to the function of the seminal vesicles.
According to earlier observers they were regarded as receptacles for the spermatozoa before ejaculation.   Most recent authorities, however, are now agreed that
their main function is secretory, first to add bulk to the seminal fluid and aid the
mechanical transference of the spermatozoa through the urethra in the course
of ejaculation, and secondly to provide substrates which can be utilised by the
active ejaculated spermatozoa.   Most of the evidence for the storage function is
based upon the discovery of spermatozoa in the contents of the gland on autopsy,
but the evidence at best is very contradictory.   Beams and King (1933) reviewed
the early literature and concluded that the evidence was against storage.   In
most cases in man where spermatozoa have been found in the seminal vesicles
(*see* Thomas and Harrison, 1917 ; Gutierriez, 1942) no attempt has been made
to give quantitative estimates and the descriptions of spermatozoa being " present,"
" few," " many," " plentiful," etc., may only indicate a relatively small number
of cells which have entered the glands *post mortem* or through operative interference (Hotchkiss, 1945).   In other animals than man, the evidence is almost
entirely negative.   Marshall (1911), who examined the contents of the vesicles of
the hedgehog at all seasons of the year, including the breeding period, failed to
find spermatozoa after most careful search.   Beams and King (1933) did not find
spermatozoa in the seminal vesicles of the rat *post mortem*.   In the writer's experience

spermatozoa are not found in any significant numbers in the seminal vesicles of the rabbit, bull, or ram, and the few which are found occasionally are non-motile and degenerate.

The seminal vesicles contribute an important fraction of the constituents of the seminal fluid. Lode (1895) first proved their secretory function by showing that when one testis was removed from a young animal, the corresponding gland continued to grow and became filled with its characteristic fluid, which evidently was not derived from the testis or epididymis.

The seminal vehicles, although certainly of functional significance, are not essential to reproduction. As Ivanov (1900, 1907) and others have shown, normal fertility can be obtained with spermatozoa taken from the vas deferens, which proves that the secretions of the seminal vesicles and other accessory glands are not essential. McKenzie, Miller and Bauguess (1938) found that removal of the seminal vesicles of the boar did not impair fertilising capacity and even slightly increased the survival of the spermatozoa *in vitro*. The latter effect may have been due to increased concentration of the spermatozoa in the ejaculates. In some rodents fertility may be impaired by removal of the seminal vesicles (Steinach, 1894 ; Schüller, 1931). This may be due to absence of formation of the vaginal plug (*see* below, p. 152). Both in quantity and character, the secretion of the seminal vesicles varies considerably in different species, the quantity depending upon the relative development of the organs. The seminal vesicles are absent or rudimentary in the dog, cat, ferret and other carnivora, and also in cetacea and some ruminants (*see* Hirsch, 1931a ; Broek, 1933 ; and Asdell, 1946).

The Prostate

The prostate in man and other animals surrounds the urethra at the base of the bladder and opens into it by a number of small ducts, which have their orifices close to the aperture of the vasa defferentia and seminal vesicles. A comprehensive study of the human prostate is given by Lowsley *et al.* (1942). The prostate is covered by the prostatic facia, which is rich in blood vessels. The gland itself is enclosed in a fibrous muscular capsule and from it prolongations extend into the gland separating the outer portion of the lobes. Within the gland there is con-siderable muscle and elastic fibre. Smooth muscle fibres surround each tubule and its duct, and by their contraction expel the contents of the gland into the urethra. Although the sphincter muscles of the urethra are intimately con-nected with the sheath and muscular stroma of the prostate, the innervation is independent. The prostate does not contract during the act of urination, and expression of the contents normally only occurs during emission of semen. Like the seminal vesicles, the only certain function of the prostate is its secretory activity and the contribution of this secretion to the ejaculate.

The milky appearance of the prostatic secretion of man is due to granules and concretions of various types. Similar bodies are found in the prostatic secretion of the rabbit but are not characteristic of the semen of other domesticated animals.

The prostate of rodents was found by Camus and Gley (1896–1922) to contain an enzyme, " vesiculase," which coagulates the secretion of the seminal vesicles to form the vaginal plug. In the rat a separate anterior lobe of the prostate, the so-called " coagulating " gland, is the source of this enzyme (Walker, 1910 ; Moore, 1939 ; Mann, 1954).

The Urethral Glands

The bulbo-urethral or Cowper's glands are small tubulo-racemose glands which communicate with the urethra by two ducts opening, in man, about two inches below the orifices of the vasa defferentia.   The lobules of the glands are surrounded by a firm investing membrane containing muscle fibres.   They are lined by secretory epithelium.   The exact significance of the viscous secretion which these glands produce is still unknown.   It has been suggested that the secretion, which, in man, is commonly exuded from the penis prior to intromission, serves to cleanse the urethral tract or lubricate the glans and vagina and assist penetration.   In the boar the bulbo-urethral glands are proportionately very large.   Removal of the glands does not affect breeding capacity (Barrington, 1914 ; McKenzie, Miller and Bauguess, 1938).

The glands of Littré or Morgagni are small dispersed secretory glands opening on the surface of the urethra.   According to Hirsch (1927) true submucous glands of Littré are confined to man.   Urethral glands of superficial structure are well developed in lower classes of mammals.   In some higher forms they are either absent or poorly developed.   In the boar the urethral glands contribute a considerable portion of the seminal fluid (McKenzie, Miller and Bauguess, 1938).   The homologues of the glands of Littré in the female are the lesser vestibular glands.

In the above descriptions of the accessory glands little reference has been made to the chemical constituents.   This important aspect will be discussed in relation to the metabolism of the spermatozoon in Chapter 9A.

The Penis

The structure of the penis differs considerably in different species of animal, but two extreme types are recognisable, the vascular and the fibro-elastic.   Between the two extremes are many intermediates (cf. Slijper, quoted by Asdell, 1946).   The penis of man (Fig. 8.2) will be described as an example of the vascular type, and the penis of the bull (Fig. 8.3) as an example of the fibro-elastic.   In many species with vascular penes, the glans may have various outgrowths of papillae, horny styles, bristles, etc., which may serve to retain the penis in the vagina or possibly to stimulate the female.   Whether such structures are essential for the induction of the orgasm in male or female, or through nervous pathways stimulate ovulation, and whether they affect fertility is conjectural.   In certain species of ruminants (fibro-elastic type) there is a prolongation of the urethral passage beyond the glans known as the filiform process (Fig. 8.4).   In the dog, ferret, and some other carnivora and rodentia there is a cartilaginous or bony structure, the os penis, the under surface of which is grooved and surrounds the urethra.   The function of these penile structures will be discussed below.

The vascular type of penis (man)

The function of the vascular penis as an intromittent organ depends upon the power of erection as a result of sexual excitement.

The erectile tissue of the penis is contained in three tracts ; the two corpora cavernosa which are situated one on each side, and are united in the middle line

F*

by a septum penis, and the small corpus spongiosum (cavernosum urethrae) which is placed inferiorly and surrounds the urethral passage. The corpora cavernosa are covered with an integument (tunica albuginea) containing numerous elastic fibres as well as white fibres. From the integument, branching trabeculae

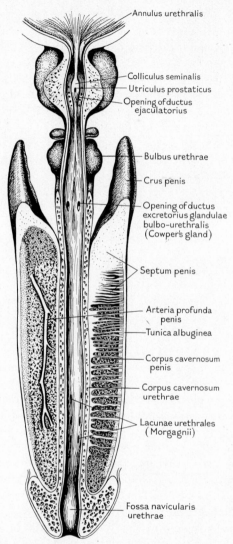

Fig. 8.2—Section of human urethra and penis.
(After Toldt. From Dickinson, 1933.)

pass inwards and divide the substance of the cavernous bodies into a large number of irregularly shaped cavities. The trabeculae contain plain muscle fibres. The cavities are continuous with the arterial and venous system and are lined with endothelium. According to Testut (1931) they represent enlarged capillaries. During erection the cavities become distended with blood. There is complete continuity between the cavities throughout each corpus cavernosum and inter-communication between the two corpora by means of passages through the septum.

Fluid injected at any place in the corpora cavernosa spreads with great ease throughout the whole system and passes from one corpus to another. The distal ends of the corpora cavernosa form separate cones which are covered by the glans penis. The posterior continuations of the corpora diverge at the level of the pubic symphysis and each root on its superior surface forms a close attachment to the descending branch of the pubis. The roots are surrounded below by the ischio-cavernosi muscles.

The corpus spongiosum (corpus cavernosus urethrae) is an unpaired organ lying in the inferior groove formed by the junction of the two corpora cavernosa. It completely surrounds the urethra. At its distal end the corpus becomes enlarged forming the glans penis, the internal structure of which is the same as the rest of the corpus. At its proximal end the corpus spongiosum is enlarged to form the urethral bulb, which is surrounded by the bulbo-cavernosus muscle (or ejaculator urinae).

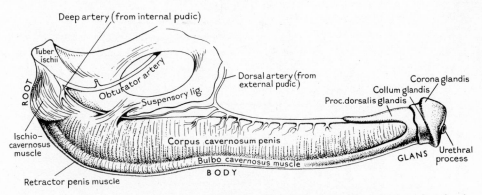

Fig. 8.3—Penis of horse. (From Sisson-Grossman: *The Anatomy of Domestic Animals,* 4th ed., 1953, Philadelphia, W. B. Saunders Company.)

The integument of the penis is thin and pliable and consists of four layers. The skin is continuous with that of the pubic region and the scrotum. It is provided with hairs and sebaceous glands, but these become less frequent towards the distal end. The dermis consists almost entirely of connective tissue and elastic fibres. In the mid-line of the inferior surface a slight thickening of the skin (the raphe) marks the position of fusion of the lips of the embryonic uro-genital trough. Below the skin is a muscular layer which is continuous with the dartos of the scrotum. Contraction of this layer is held by some authors to compress the superficial veins of the penis and by raising the internal pressure to contribute to the mechanism of erection (*see* p. 141). Below the dartos is a loose layer of connective tissue (tela subcutanea penis) containing many elastic fibres. It is this layer which gives the skin of the penis its great mobility, enabling the skin of the penis itself and of the prepuce to be pushed back so that the glans is exposed. Below the connective tissue layer is a tough elastic fascia penis which encloses the erectile organs. The fascia penis, by restricting the expansion of the erectile organs and raising the internal pressure, is also said to contribute to the mechanism of erection.

The integument of the penis with its various layers is prolonged and inverted at its distal end to form a loose fold. This is the prepuce, or foreskin, which generally covers the glans. Accumulation between the prepuce and the glans of cast epithelial cells together with some sebaceous secretion, may give rise to the formation of smegma.

The penis is very sensitive to external stimulation, its surface being beset with simple and compound end-bulbs and Pacinian corpuscles, especially in the region of the glans. The various kinds of end-organs in the external genital organs of both sexes have been described at some length by Luciani (1917). There are

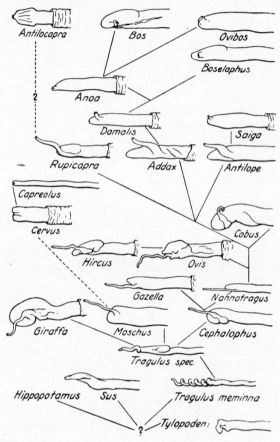

Fig. 8.4—Penes of various types of ruminants. (After Gerhardt, 1933.)

genital corpuscles, the nerve fibres to which divide into five branches, which end in knobs (Krause's end-bulbs), as well as typical Meissner's corpuscles which are capsulated and usually oval or elongated in shape, with a complex and variable structure, and a series of transitional forms passing imperceptibly from Pacinian corpuscles to more elaborate structures.

The vascular system of the penis is of particular interest since it is largely through an alteration in the blood flow and the distention of the intertrabecular spaces with blood that erection is brought about. The anatomy of the vascular system has been fully described by Kiss (1921) and the histology by Stieve (1930). A comprehensive review with many illustrations is given by Dickinson (1933).

Some of the arterial branches enter the intertrabecular spaces of the erectile tissue and form coiled vessels known as the helicine arteries. In these arteries the intima is folded and capable of great distention. The blood is carried away from the erectile tissue by veins which are provided with special valves or funnels which obstruct the rapid flow of blood and hence raise the pressure in the inter-trabecular spaces, but permit a steady slow flow which maintains circulation during erection and enables the penis to relax when erection ceases. The blood is carried away from the penis by two sets of veins, the one set uniting to form the dorsal vein, and the other communicating with the prostatic plexus and the pudendal veins.

The fibro-elastic type of penis (bull)

The penis of the bull is relatively long and of small diameter. Even in the non-erect state it is markedly firm and almost rigid. The tunica albuginea is very thick and composed of dense white fibrous tissue. Although corpora caver-nosa and corpus spongiosum bear the same relationship as in the vascular type, the amount of erectile tissue is very small, except at the root. The walls of the cavernous spaces of the erectile tissue into which the blood flows during erection are fibro-elastic and not muscular. The result is that during erection the penis becomes rather more rigid, but does not increase greatly in diameter or length. Protrusion of the penis on erection and an apparent increase in length of about 15 inches, is brought about by relaxation of the retractor penis, a pair of muscles which are attached to the second curve of the sigmoid flexure of the penis, lying just behind the scrotum. The prepuce of the bull is long, and completely incloses the retracted penis. Round the orifice of the prepuce are relatively long preputial hairs. The glans penis is about three inches in length and the extremity slightly twisted so that the urethral meatus opens laterally in a slight prolongation.

The mechanism of erection and ejaculation

The erection of the penis in both types is brought about mainly by the dilata-tion of the arteries and the filling of the intertrabecular spaces with blood. During the state of relaxation of the organ the tonus of the muscles in the arterial walls restricts the flow of blood into the intertrabecular spaces. Erection is initiated by a relaxation of this muscular control. As the organ dilates, the fascia penis and the dartos exert a certain restriction to complete dilatation and aid in raising the tumescence of the organ. Although at one time it was held that the muscles round the base of the penis played the chief part in inducing venous stasis, this view is no longer tenable (Kiss, 1921). Actually during erection the total blood flow to the organ is not restricted but greatly increased, as was shown experi-mentally by Eckhard (1863). Muscular control by contraction can, however, play some part in erection as is shown by the voluntary elevation of the penis when in the semi-erect stage brought about by constriction of the bulbo-caver-nosus muscle. Muscular control is very noticeable in the stallion, especially during masturbation. Moreover, although the penis can be made to erect in animals in which the muscular mechanism has been paralysed by the injection of curare, the erection in such cases is incomplete (Marshall, 1922).

Tumescence is strongest in the corpora cavernosa, which in full erection become almost incompressible. The corpus spongiosum with the glans, however, becomes much less tumid. This prevents complete closure of the urethral passage and by rendering the glans soft and compressible aids penetration of the organ into the vagina and prevents injury to the female (Dickinson, 1933). This difference between the extent of tumescence of the corpora cavernosa and the corpus spongiosum is very noticeable in the stallion. The glans is hardly erected at all until after the penis has entered the vagina and ejaculation is about to take place ; it then becomes markedly turgid and about doubles in diameter. On retraction of the penis the glans may remain distended, although the corpora cavernosa are flaccid and the penis pendulous. In animals with the fibro-elastic type of penis, enlargement of the organ is not marked on erection, and hence differential tumescence of the corpora cavernosa and the corpus spongiosum is not so noticeable.

Ejaculation involves a series of co-ordinated contractions. Those which propel the spermatozoa probably begin in the walls of the epididymis and pass thence along the vas deferens. The spermatozoa enter the urethra where they mix with the prostatic fluid similarly expelled from the prostate by muscular contraction of its walls. The secretions of the urethral glands are also added to the seminal fluid. Entrance of the seminal fluid to the bladder is prevented by the erection of the crista urethrae, and by the contraction of the sphincter of the bladder. The final discharge is brought about by the rhythmical contractions of the bulbo-cavernosus and ischio-cavernosus muscles, which have the effect of emptying the canal from behind forward and so ejecting the semen mixed with the various glandular secretions into the vaginal passage of the female. In those animals in which ejaculation is extremely rapid, as in the sheep and bull, exact demarcation of the sequence is not possible, since the various constituents of the ejaculate appear at the urethral meatus simultaneously, but in those animals in which the course of ejaculation is prolonged, the semen as it emerges from the penis can be collected in separate fractions and each fraction identified. Ivanov (1917) studied the ejaculation of semen from the dog by this method. The first part of the ejaculate was clear and watery and probably came from the urethral glands. The middle portion was milky white and contained numerous spermatozoa in suspension. The third portion was again clear and watery. Similar observations have been made for man (MacLeod and Hotchkiss, 1942 ; Lundquist, 1949; Harvey, 1956), horse (Walton, 1938a ; Day, 1940 ; Mann et al., 1957), and boar (McKenzie et al., 1938 ; Mann and Glover, 1954). The identification of the separate contributions of each accessory gland to each fraction has been greatly aided by the chemical identification of the substances specific for each portion of the male tract (Mann, 1954). The fact that each fraction retains its identity without much admixture during ejaculation adds to the hypothesis that the main function of the accessory secretions is mechanical, viz. to wash the spermatozoa through the track, and is not directly related to the metabolic needs of the spermatozoa.

III. Nervous Control of the Male Sexual Organs

It has been shown experimentally that stimuli applied directly to the brain or to the upper part of the cord can induce both erection and ejaculation. Thus Budge (1858) and Eckhard (1863) were able to cause the penis to erect by electrical stimulation of the cervical cord, the pons and the crura cerebri.   The same result was obtained by Pussep (1902) by exciting a region of the cerebral cortex.   It is stated also that hanging and decapitation in man are sometimes followed by erection (Götze, 1898).   According to Spina (1897), who experimented with the guinea-pig, section of the spinal cord near the last costo-vertebral articulation is invariably succeeded by erection and ejaculation.   Dusser de Barenne and Koskoff (1932, 1934) have shown that spinal transection after decerebration produces a strong flexor rigidity in the hind limbs and erection of the penis of the

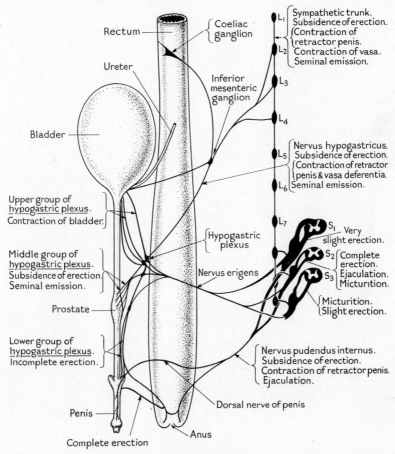

Fig. *8*.5—Innervation of the male cat genital system.   (From Semans and Lang-worthy, 1937.)

cat which may last for 24 hours.   This reflex is elicited by exteroceptive stimuli applied to the abdomen and inner surfaces of the thighs.   Dorso-flexion of the tail (which normally occurs at copulation in the cat) or tapping on the animal's dorsal lumbar region produces augmentation of erection and the ejaculation of semen. A more complete analysis of the functional innervation of the genital organs of the male cat has been provided by Semans and Langworthy (1938), whose diagrammatic summary is reproduced here as Fig. *8*.5.

    The points of great interest to note are the extreme complexity of the various nervous pathways both from the autonomic and central nervous system, and the diversity of response. For example, according to the nervous pathway stimulated, erection may be incomplete or complete, seminal emission is to be distinguished from ejaculation, and contraction of the vasa and contraction of the retractor penis are separately innervated. It must be clear that no isolated " centres " of erection or of ejaculation control the process of sexual activity in the male.

Much study has been devoted to the induction of ejaculation by electrical stimulus applied to the intact animal, since this method of obtaining semen may be of value to the experimental physiologist and to commercial centres for artificial insemination. Batelli (1922) found that if one of a pair of electrodes were placed under the skin on the nape of the neck and the other placed in the mouth of the guinea-pig, ejaculation of semen took place when an alternating current of about 30 volts was passed. Two shocks of a few seconds' duration and with a short interval between the shocks were necessary. Moore and Gallagher (1930) used this method to make regular collections of seminal fluid in assaying male hormone. The ejaculation takes place without erection of the penis. Gunn (1936) found that this method was inapplicable to the ram, but that in this animal erection and ejaculation could be obtained by direct stimulation of the lumbar and sacral nerves by means of an alternating current of about 30 volts passed between a needle inserted into the longissimus dorsi muscle parallel to and close to the spines of the lumbar vertebrae, and a blunt electrode, insulated except for the tip, inserted about four inches into the rectum. By varying the situation of the needle and the rectal pole, and the strength of the current, he obtained various effects according to which nerve tracts were stimulated. In the methods described above, the direct stimulation across the spinal column involved strong stimulation of sensory and motor nerves and the animals experienced symptoms of distress. So severe were the muscle contractions of the hind limbs that large animals such as the horse or bull could not be used for fear of permanent injury. Laplaud and Cassou (1945) improved the method of stimulation by use of a bipolar electrode inserted into the rectum. The nerves which mediate emission and ejaculation are then stimulated by the spread of current round the poles. Motor reactions are much less severe, but the animals may posture with the hind limbs extended as they would for copulation or masturbation. The method can be used for bulls and horses. For bulls or calves, a simpler type of electrode consisting of two copper rings placed on the fingers of a rubber-gloved hand inserted into the rectum has been used by Rowson and Murdoch (1954) and Davies, Mann and Rowson (1957). When held near the junction of the ampullae with the urethra, ejaculation with emission of semen can be most easily induced. Marden (1954), using a bipolar electrode similar to that designed by Laplaud, Ortavant and Thibault (1948) and Thibault, Laplaud and Ortavant (1948), finds that erection and ejaculation can be produced regularly with the minimum of motor reaction, by using an electrical a.c. pulse of sine wave form and reducing the a.c. frequency from the usual 50 c/s. to about 25 c/s. With this modification, quite low current strengths, 5 volts and 0·9 amp, can be used.

Reflexes of Emission and Ejaculation

The penis of the male is sensitive to both temperature change and pressure. In most cases the copulatory thrust is given as soon as the erect penis comes in contact with the warm, moist surface of the vagina.   To elicit this reflex in the bull the interior surface of the artificial vagina must have a temperature equal to or slightly higher than that of the body, but not be more than about three degrees below.   Pressure and possibly friction between the surface of the vagina and the penis may also be components of the effective stimulus to ejaculation but are less important.   In the case of the stallion, pressure on the penis, and particularly on the glans, is most critical, while temperature can be varied considerably.   In the pig and dog, in which copulation is unusually prolonged, temperature also is not so important, but continual pressure or traction applied to the glans or rhythmical pulsation simulating the peristalsis of the vagina during natural coitus is necessary. In man, the moist, warm pressure of the vagina and the friction set up by copulatory movements elicit ejaculation, but friction alone, as in manual masturbation, is also sufficient.   In the domesticated animals masturbation is not uncommonly seen in the horse and bull, but less often in the pig and ram.   In primates, including man, masturbation is a usual feature of normal sexuality.

In addition to the physical stimuli which mediate direct reflexes, the latter can become highly conditioned by environmental stimuli.   Sexual excitement may be aroused by tactile sensations in the so-called erogenous zones ; the penis and perineum generally, the breast and abdomen, the lips and other sensitive surfaces of the face and hands.   Erotic stimulation can also be obtained through visual, olfactory and auditory paths.   This excitation when not accompanying coitus may lead to masturbation or " spontaneous " ejaculation.

IV. Sex Drive

Early concepts of the hormone control of sexual activity were relatively simple : it was held that in the male the testis secreted male hormone which was responsible for sexual differentiation, growth until puberty of the sexual organs, the onset of spermatogenesis, the development and secretory activity of the accessory glands, the development of the secondary sexual characteristics, and, finally, typical male behaviour.   Analogous changes took place in the female under the hormonal influence of the ovary.   Particularly with regard to behaviour, these concepts require modification.   For example, under certain conditions intact males may exhibit female behaviour, and vice versa.   Castration generally results in loss or impairment of specific sexual behaviour but not always, and administration of male or female hormones may initiate or reinforce appropriate specific sexual behaviour, but not invariably.   The issues are complicated by the parts played by the anterior pituitary and the adrenal cortex in the sexual syndrome, and also by the extent to which behaviour may become conditioned or learned.   Notwithstanding these difficulties of interpretation, it is certain that to a considerable extent endocrine activity determines sexuality and that a higher output of testosterone from the testis or a higher concentration of this hormone at the target organs will raise the excitability of the male, or lower the threshold of response of the male to a sexually excitatory object (such as an oestrous female), thus bringing into action the innate sexual drive.   How the hormone acts on the nervous system to produce these effects is entirely unknown.

The copulatory behaviour pattern, in sub-primates at least, is almost entirely dependent upon innate and genetic endowment (Beach, 1942, 1948).   Chicks and male rats raised to sexual maturity in isolation display copulatory behaviour indistinguishable from sexually experienced males.   In some species, and more particularly the primates, however, the complete pattern does not appear so spontaneously and sexual experience seems to play a part in its development.   There are, however, in all animals marked individual differences in sexual excitability which are innate and not entirely due to differences in sexual experience.

In eliciting male behaviour there are marked differences in the excitatory value of various stimulus objects.   In experiments with the use of the " dummy " rabbit in the collection of semen, Macirone and Walton (1938) conclude that performance of the sexual pattern depends not only upon the sexual drive or excitability of the male but also upon the suitability or excitatory value of the object which elicits sexual activity.   Thus a male with strong sexual drive would sometimes complete the sexual pattern and ejaculate when the hand only of the operator was introduced into the animal's cage to serve as a mount.   Other males would respond only if the hand was covered with fur and an artificial vagina with the correct temperature and pressure presented to the penis.   Others again would respond only to the receptive real female.   Copulation usually follows a definite pattern of behaviour, and the rate at which it is performed or completed may reflect the intensity of the sex drive.   Thus Macirone and Walton (1938) list the following sequence in the behaviour pattern of the male rabbit : (1) exploration, (2) smelling, (3) jumping, (4) chin rubbing, (5) mounting, (6) gripping with teeth, (7) pelvic oscillations, (8) exploratory movements with erect penis, (9) intromission, (10) ejaculation with orgasm.   The highly excitable male will ejaculate even with an object of low excitatory value, and he will pass very rapidly through the complete sequence.   In fact some of the early stages may apparently be missed out altogether.   With a less ardent male the full sequence will appear.   A male with very low excitability may show either no response at all, or the first reactions of the copulatory sequence, and then only if the excitatory value of the stimulus object is high (e.g. a receptive female).   Furthermore, the time occupied in passing from stage to stage may be prolonged (Fig. 8.6).

Some of the reactions of the male can best be described as unconditioned or innate reflexes, especially those of later sequence order, e.g. pelvic oscillation, erection and exploratory movements with the erect penis, intromission, and ejaculation.   The last two may be elicited only if the stimulus is suitable within fairly narrow limits.   For example males will not ejaculate within the artificial vagina unless the pressure is suitable and the temperature just a little above that of the body (bull, ram).   These reflexes may become highly " conditioned " in the sense of the term used by Pavlov.   This is not so easily demonstrated in the case of the rabbit as it is with the larger domesticated animals.   Use of the artificial vagina for the collection of semen in commercial artificial insemination centres provides valuable information on the physiology of reflex sexual behaviour.   This has been specifically investigated by Milovanov and Smirnov-Ugrumov (1940), whose attention was drawn to the subject by the frequency with which bulls at insemination centres become impotent or partially impotent by the development of inhibitions, often highly conditioned to outside stimuli.   These inhibitions decreased sexual excitability, with the result that the reflexes of intromission and ejaculation were weakened and semen of poor quality obtained.   Further development of inhibition might lead to delay in the fulfilment of the reaction sequence (the bull becomes slow) or to the sequence being incompleted (refusing to mount or to ejaculate when mounted). Raising the excitatory value of the stimulus object such as the use of a different oestrous female might restore potency. Removal of conditioned stimuli to inhibition was also often effective, as when the stimulus object was presented in a different environment, when the stimulus object was changed (a different cow used), or even when the herdsman who used the artificial vagina changed the colour of his coat. An interesting case of the release of inhibition by removal of conditioned stimuli came to the present writer's notice. A bull

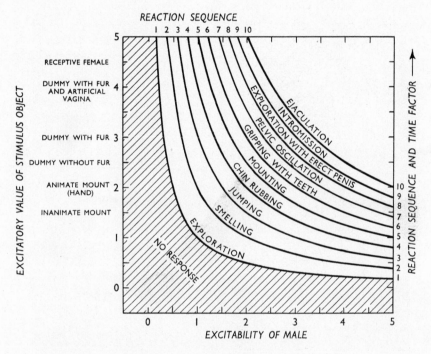

Fig. *8*.6—Diagram to illustrate sexual arousal as a product of excitability of the male and excitatory value of stimulus object with contours to show the graded sequence of sexual consummation.

which had become completely inhibited to the use of the artificial vagina was accidentally blinded in the left eye. Although he continued to refuse even to mount the cow if the operator stood on the right side, he mounted and ejaculated quite normally if collection was made from the blind side (*see also* Walton, 1952, 1955). An example of how sexual reflexes may become conditioned to inhibitory stimuli is provided by an experiment at a commercial A.I. station by which it was shown that inhibitions to the collection of semen or to the production of semen of good quality might be built up inadvertently but could be removed by increasing sexual excitation by introducing more foreplay (Kerruish, 1955).

In the species of animal most studied the stimulus required to elicit sexual behaviour in the male is quite simple. The stallion, bull, ram and boar will mount and attempt to copulate with a " dummy " consisting of a metal framework covered with a sack or hide (Fig. 8.7). Sometimes the male will do this at the first presentation, sometimes a " learning " period intervenes. If, when the male has mounted, an artificial vagina of appropriate design is presented to the penis, intromission is immediate and a normal ejaculation follows. Apparently any object of about the right size to mount will provide an adequate stimulus, and if the mounted object remains stationary the sequence of copulatory behaviour described on p. 147 is set in action. Males will attempt to mount females which are not in oestrus and also other males provided these remain stationary long enough. Homosexual behaviour is not of itself evidence of endocrine disfunction or of psychopathic disorder; it appears regularly when males are kept in isolation together.

Fig. 8.7—Boar mounted and serving a " dummy " sow.

A " peck order " of male dominance may be established. Homosexual behaviour may denote a high level of sexual excitability in the dominant male, who consequently responds to an object of less than the normal excitatory value. The behaviour pattern so established may be reinforced by conditioned reflexes and become permanent.

The functions of the male tract in conveying semen to the female have been described, but successful deposition of the semen in the genital tract of the female and a satisfactory culmination of the sex act, requires the co-operation of the female and the normal functioning of her sexual organs. In the female, as in the male, the pattern of sexual behaviour is conditioned both by hormonal influences and factors acting through the senses. In the section which follows, the process of copulation will be described for certain typical species, in which the mutual response of male and female is well illustrated.

V. Copulation

Copulation in man has been very fully described in various works on general sexology and for pornographic purposes. For accuracy and scientific objectivity, Dickinson's *Topographical Hand Atlas of Human Sex Anatomy* (1933) deserves first consideration.

During normal coitus in man the semen is ejaculated at the upper end of the vagina round the entrance of the cervix. There has been considerable speculation as to the function of the orgasm and the part which it may play in forwarding the entrance of the spermatozoa into the uterus. Kristeller (1871) thought that expressions of mucus from the cervix might provide a means for the ascent of the spermatozoa, and Beck (1872) postulated sucking movements of the cervix. These mechanisms, either alone or in combination, have at various times been put forward to explain the function of the orgasm in forwarding sperm transport. Dickinson (1933) discusses the subject exhaustively and is definitely of the opinion that in the human no such mechanism is possible, and that spermatozoa enter the cervix by their own activity.

Recently, interest in the subject has reopened in the light of experiments on various animal species. In a review, Hartman (1957) concludes that the evidence favours the view that spermatozoa are transported through the cervix and up the uterine tract by muscular movements of the uterus and that sperm motility plays little part except perhaps in the passage of the utero-tubal junction and in the immediate approach to the ovum and in fertilisation. There are, however, very large differences between species and it would be unwise to generalise from one species to another without very careful investigation of each individual case.

Among the few species which have been closely studied in this respect differences arise from the differing anatomical structures of the sexual organs, from differences in behaviour pattern at copulation and from differences in the properties of the semen and accessory secretions. Certain types of insemination may be distinguished and can be classified according to the place of main deposition of the semen, and the mode of its conveyance through the uterine tract. This classification is an arbitrary one and if more species were examined might well require revision.

(a) Uterine insemination with voluminous semen and distension of cervix (horse).

(b) Uterine insemination with voluminous semen and retention of the penis during copulation (dog, pig).

(c) Uterine insemination with vaginal plug and spasmodic contraction of vagina (guinea-pig, rat, mouse).

(d) Vaginal insemination with incipient plug or slight coagulation of the semen (rabbit, human).

(e) Vaginal insemination with little accessory fluid and semen of high sperm concentration (bull, ram).

Uterine Insemination with Voluminous Semen and Distension of Cervix (horse)

In the horse, the penis is of the typical vascular type. When mating takes place freely in the open, a period of courtship and sex play precedes a gradual erection of the penis which is almost entirely confined to enlargement and increased rigidity of the corpora cavernosa.   Intromission is aided by the relaxed condition of the glans and by the mare " showing " (i.e. erecting the clitoris and partly everting the labiae).   The penis is not so sensitive to temperature as in the bull and ejaculation is initiated by the pressure and friction exerted on the penis by the vagina and fornix.   Several pelvic oscillations are usually performed before ejaculation commences.   The penis is then kept quite still in the vagina.   The glans distends very markedly and this distends the orifice of the cervix, which during the period of maximum oestrus is quite relaxed.   In this position the urethral orifice of the penis is brought into close opposition to the os and the semen ejaculated straight into the uterus.   A large volume (20–100 ml.) of semen is ejaculated of low sperm density (200–600 $\times$ 10^6 sperm/ml.), owing to considerable dilution with accessory fluids.   Uterine insemination, however, may not always succeed, especially in mares which are not in full oestrus and the cervix is not completely relaxed.   In this case much of the semen may be deposited in the vagina and is extruded with the withdrawal of the penis or shortly after by contractions of the vagina.   This extrusion of the semen may reduce the chances of pregnancy.   The extruded semen may be used for artificial insemination, as shown by Marshall and Crosland (1918).

The presence of seminal plasma along with spermatozoa within the uterus of the mare has been detected chemically by Mann, Polge and Rowson (1956), who found citric acid from the seminal vesicles and ergothionine from the ampullae in reduced concentration in a small quantity of fluid (3 ml.) which was present in the uterus of a mare killed 50 minutes after coitus.   Copulation in the horse and the composition of seminal fractions have also been described by Mann, Short, Walton, Archer and Miller (1957).

Uterine Insemination with Retention of Penis (dog, boar)

In the dog the penis is of the vascular type ; there is considerable sex play before intromission, and coitus is prolonged by retention of the penis within the vagina.   The glans penis is elongated anteriorly and pointed.   At the base it is enlarged to form the bulbus glandis.   After intromission this organ erects (cf. horse) and serves to retain the penis in the vagina, which in coitus is constricted by a muscular spasm equivalent to vaginismus in women.   This muscular constriction would tend to obliterate the urethral lumen, were the latter not protected by the os penis which covers the dorsal aspect of the urethra and is grooved ventrally. When intromission is completed and the penis locked in the vagina, the dog dismounts by throwing one leg over the back of the female.   A certain amount of traction is thus exerted on the penis during ejaculation.   Ejaculation of semen is a relatively slow process.   Seminal vesicles and bulbo-urethral glands are absent but the prostrate is well developed.   The seminal fluid is rapidly transported by vaginal and uterine contractions to the distal ends of the uterine horns (Evans, 1933).   The anatomical structures and pattern of copulation of the dog, ferret and mink are similar.

Although the penis of the boar is fibro-elastic and of small diameter, erection takes longer than in the bull or ram and there is usually a period of sexual play and courtship before the boar mounts and begins erection and intromission.   Use

of the artificial vagina demonstrates that the penis is not very sensitive to temperature, but that ejaculation is elicited by waves of pressure exerted especially on
the distal end.   It is possible that in natural mating intermittent pressure is effected
by peristaltic contractions of the vagina and possibly also of the cervix of the sow.
The lumen of the cervix may be penetrated by the " corkscrew "-like penis of the
male and semen in bulk can readily pass through into the body and horns of the
uterus.   Coitus lasts several minutes (5–20).   The volume of semen is large
(100–500 ml.).   Two or three separate ejaculations may take place before the

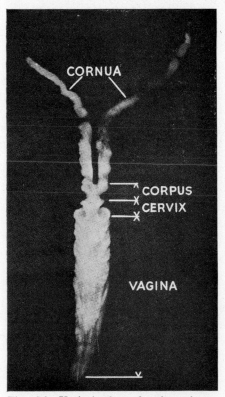

Fig. 8.8—Vaginal plug of guinea-pig as
dissected from the female tract 5
minutes after copulation.

boar dismounts.   It is probable that the semen which enters the uterine horns is
conveyed to their distal ends by peristaltic movements.   A thick " tapioca "-like
secretion is ejaculated with the semen.   This may be analogous to the vaginal
plug of some rodents and serve to prevent back-flow of semen from the uterus,
but the functional significance of the jelly has not been accurately assessed.   As
mentioned above, McKenzie, Miller and Bauguess (1938) found that removal of the
accessory glands which produce the secretion did not prevent fertility.   As in the
case of the mare, the presence of seminal plasma in the uterus of the sow can be
detected chemically.   Mann, Polge and Rowson (1956) found fructose, ergothionine and citric acid in fluid distributed throughout the uterus of a sow killed
10 minutes after copulation.   In a sow killed 6 hours after mating, these substances
could still be detected although very little fluid remained in the uterus.

Uterine Insemination with Vaginal Plug (chiefly rodents)

In many rodents, but also in the opossum, and the chimpanzee, the most characteristic feature of the copulatory pattern is the formation of the vaginal plug. Camus and Gley (1896–1922) in a series of short papers on the subject found that the plug was formed from the secretion of the seminal vesicles and coagulated by an enzyme present in the proximal lobe of the prostate sometimes referred to as the coagulatory gland. The enzyme was termed vesiculase. Van Wagenen (1936) showed that the enzyme was not species specific and that prostatic coagulating fluid from the monkey would coagulate fluid from the seminal vesicles of the rat and vice versa. The plug has probably a functional significance in those animals in which it is well developed, and prevents the back-flow of semen from the vagina, but in other animals such as the boar, rabbit and man, where only partial coagulation of the semen occurs, the functional significance of the process is not so clear. In the rat and mouse, the formation of the plug apparently plays a part in the nervous stimulation of the anterior pituitary of the female and determines a short prolongation of the sexual cycle prior to nidation or, if the ovum is not fertilised, to pseudopregnancy. In these animals, the plug is seldom found beyond the cervix. In the guinea-pig the plug may be formed even within the uterus, which is convincing proof of the almost instantaneous transport of semen from the vagina to the uterus by a spasmodic contraction of the vagina (see Fig. 8.8). In the photograph, breaks in the continuity of the cast of the upper end of the uterine horns represent the presence of the sperm-rich portion of the ejaculate which did not coagulate.

Vaginal Insemination with Incomplete Plug Formation (rabbit)

In the rabbit ejaculated semen frequently contains a gel-like substance which originates from the glandulae vesiculares (Mann, 1954). The gel is not always present, and, as it contains no spermatozoa except possibly by contamination with the sperm-rich fraction, it is often disregarded when semen volume or sperm-density is recorded. Other secretions from the accessory glands are, however, present, and in consequence the sperm-density is relatively low (100–200 × 10^6 spermatozoa/ml.). In the rabbit, copulation initiates afferent impulses from the vagina and cervix to release ovulating hormone from the anterior pituitary. Ovulation occurs $9\frac{1}{2}$–10 hours later. Absence of a fully formed plug in the vagina does not appear to influence this neuro-hormonal mechanism. Copulation is performed rapidly, and to judge from the relative size of penis and vagina the semen is deposited in the upper part of the vagina beyond the brim of the pelvis.

It has been the subject of much controversy whether the spermatozoa of the rabbit gain access to the uterus by their own motility or are transported by peristaltic contractions of the vagina. Heape (1898) thought the latter might take place since he observed " sucking " movements in the exposed uterus and cervix on faradic stimulation of the vulva. Walton (1930) concluded from the evidence derived from coloured fluids deposited in the vagina prior to copulation that the fluid part of the semen remained in the vagina (Fig. 8.9). Florey and Walton (1931) could not detect instantaneous fluid transport in the rabbit by the uterine fistula technique, although it was demonstrable by this method in the rat and guinea-pig. Parker (1930, 1931, 1932) reached a different conclusion with regard to the rabbit.   He killed does almost immediately after coitus and found spermatozoa at the uterine end of the cervix in 4 minutes, but not before this time.   In most cases spermatozoa appeared later than this.   There was no evidence of instantaneous fluid transport of semen as in the dog, rat or guinea-pig, but Parker

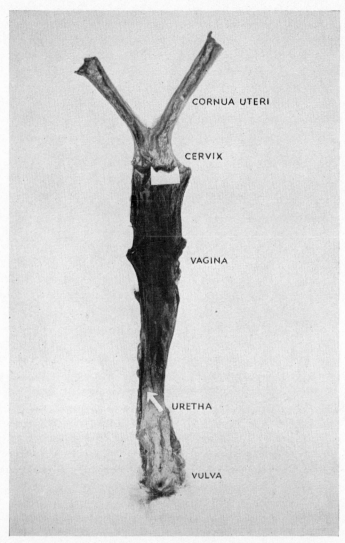

Fig. 8.9—Vagina of rabbit showing failure of liquid (dye) to penetrate
beyond the external os of the cervix during and after coitus with
the male.   (From Walton, 1930.)

nevertheless concluded that the rate of transport through the cervix was faster than could be attained by motility of the spermatozoa themselves.   This conclusion, however, is faulty since he calculated the rate of sperm travel from observations made *in vitro* at room temperature.   If similar observations are made at body temperature the rate of sperm travel is adequate for spermatozoa to traverse the cervix in the minimum time found by Parker.   If any valid conclusions are to be drawn from Parker's data, they are that semen is not instantaneously drawn into the uterus at the moment of coitus, and that the spermatozoa pass the cervix in the time they would do if moved by their own energy and not more rapidly.

Krehbiel and Carstens (1939) claimed to have obtained evidence from fluoroscopic studies on the rabbit that gives support to the original observations of Heape. Their technique has, however, been criticised by Noyes, Adams and Walton (1958) on the grounds that the posture of the rabbit was unphysiological and distorted pictures obtained. Noyes, Adams and Walton found no evidence that semen was sucked into the uterus, and concluded that only actively motile spermatozoa gain access to the uterus through the cervical barrier under normal conditions. They accept the view that, having passed the cervical barrier by their own motility, muscular movements might affect a rapid dispersal of the spermatozoa within the uterus, but the exact point in the cervix at which self-progression gives place to muscularly assisted passage was not determinable.

Vaginal Insemination with Small Volume of Semen of High Sperm Density (bull, ram)

In the bull the penis is of the fibro-elastic type, erection is rapid and extrusion mainly due to relaxation of the retractor penis. There is very little preliminary courtship or sex play. The relatively small diameter and pointed glans make for easy intromission. Sensitivity of the glans to temperature rather than to pressure aids a rapid release of the reflex of thrust and ejaculation. Service is completed in a few seconds. The relatively small development of the accessory glands results in a small volume of semen of high density (about 5 ml. of semen containing 1×10^9/ml. sperm being deposited at the mouth of the cervix). The cervix of the cow is long and rigid and the lumen tortuous ; fluid transport in bulk is impossible. The spermatozoa undoubtedly obtain access to the uterus by their own motility, and possibly by the mechanism described below. Copulation in the ram is similar to that in the bull, and is also of short duration. A peculiar feature of the penis is the prolongation of the urethra to form the vermiform appendix. This was found by Marshall (1901) to be provided with erectile tissue, and was thought by him to be inserted into the cervix. In view of the rigidity of the cervix and tortuous lumen, this is unlikely. Close observation of the penis during collection of semen with the artificial vagina suggests however a slighly different function. The penis is introduced into the artificial vagina, with corpora cavernosa rigid, but with little distention of the glans and with the filiform appendage relaxed and reflected back alongside of the penis. Immediately after the copulatory thrust is completed, the glans, which may be visible in the glass collecting cup, distends slightly and the vermiform appendage tends to erect just at the moment of withdrawal and as the semen appears at the orifice. If this same sequence is followed in natural mating the result will be that the urethral orifice, with the semen spurting from it, is kept longer in contact with the cervix than would be the case if the vermiform appendage were absent. Although this mechanism may slightly increase the chances of spermatozoa gaining access to the cervix, the advantage gained is probably small. Robert Wallace informed Marshall (1901) that it used to be a regular practice to cut off the vermiform appendage of rams in order to prevent conceptions. E. I. Ivanov (1929) found, however, that removal of the appendage did not prevent conception.

Although the actual passage of seminal plasma into the uterus of the cow or sheep following coitus has not been detected it has been inferred from the discovery of spermatozoa within the tract in cows killed a few minutes after copulation or insemination (VanDemark and Moeller, 1951). When considering the significance of this it is necessary to take into account certain quantitative aspects. From the description of the methods used to find spermatozoa in the tract, both by these authors and by others who have either confirmed their results or failed to do so (Dauzier and Wintenberger, 1952), it must be assumed that even in the successful trials the number of spermatozoa which enter the tract within the time specified must be quite small. For sake of illustration we may assume the number to be of the order of a few million spermatozoa. Since the concentration of spermatozoa in the semen of the bull is about 1×10^9/ml., and in the semen of the ram about 3×10^9/ml., the volume of semen required to provide the number of spermatozoa found to have entered the uterine tract from the vagina is of the order of a few μl. or less. This volume of seminal plasma diluted with the uterine contents would not be easily identifiable by known chemical analysis. On the other hand, the size of the minute volume of fluid, identifiable only by its contents of spermatozoa, which can be inferred to have entered the cervix, rules out the likelihood that in the cow or sheep semen passes the cervical barrier either by direct uterine insemination as in the horse, dog, or boar, or that it is forced into the uterine tract by a spasmodic contraction of the vagina at the instant of coitus, as in the rat, mouse and guinea-pig.

A more likely explanation is that bovine spermatozoa in very small numbers are carried up the tract by muscular movements of the uterus, but again quantitative aspects of this hypothesis have to be considered before it can be accepted as a complete explanation. The female tract can be considered as an elastic-walled tube of varying internal diameter, being wide in the vagina, very narrow and tortuous through the cervix, wide and relatively straight through the corpus and cornus, very narrow at the utero-tubal junction and first half of the Fallopian tube, but finally widening out towards the fimbriated end. The walls of the tract are virtually in contact except for a film of mucous secretion and the cavity of the organ is potential rather than actual.

Now, if the undistended elastic-walled tube constituting the female tract constricts in one section of its length, the fluid contents of the tube will move from this constriction in the direction of least resistance, along or into a wide potential cavity, but not into or along a narrow cavity. Most probably this distribution of flow will be inversely proportional to the relative diameters of the cavities on each side of the constriction. The volume of fluid moved will be proportional to the diameter of the lumen, but the distance which a given volume is moved will be inversely proportional to the diameter of the lumen.

When the walls of the tube are near together laminar flow will determine that while the velocity of flow will be a minimum at the wall surface it will be at a maximum midway between the surfaces. Since spermatozoa are flow-orientated (Walton, 1952), laminar flow will orientate spermatozoa in the central axis of the lumen and aid dispersal along its length. Yamane and Ito (1932) found that in stallion spermatozoa the velocity of movement increased with the increase in rate of flow of the suspending fluid. Without knowing more about the hydrodynamics of the uterine tract and particularly about laminar flow and its effect on the orientation of the spermatozoa, it would be unwise to dogmatise about the passage or non-passage of spermatozoa or inert particles through the cervix. Spermatozoa may pass the barrier partly as a result of their own motility and partly as a result of movements of the uterus. There is, however, no substantial evidence of " sucking action" taking place following normal coitus, and no evidence that seminal plasma in measurable quantity can be found in the uterus of the cow or sheep *post coitum*. Rowson (1955) used a radio opaque fluid to demonstrate the transport of fluid within the uterus and tubes of the cow, but none was found to pass the cervix when the fluid was deposited in the vagina (Rowson, 1955; Fig. *8.10*).

There is little reason to doubt the efficacy of muscular contractions of the uterus in causing a rapid mixing of the uterine contents, which if they should include spermatozoa or inert particles which have entered from the cervix will, of course, be transported more or less rapidly to the utero-tubal end. When dis-

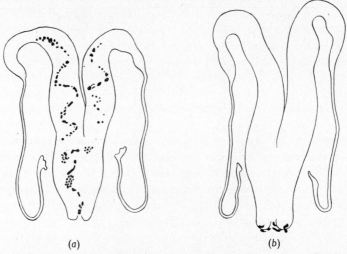

(a)   (b)

Fig. *8.10*—Diagram showing the dispersal of radio-opaque substance injected into the genital tract of the cow. (a) Rapid dispersal 5 minutes after injection into the uterus. (b) Failure to enter the uterus $2\frac{1}{4}$ minutes after deposition at the cervix. (From Rowson, 1955.)

persed over the uterine surface the spermatozoa will be in contact with sufficient oxygen and metabolisable substrates to enable them to be fully motile and independent of the substrates in the seminal plasma (Bishop, 1956; Walton and Dott, 1956).

Sperm motility and uterine muscular motility would provide an adequate means of dispersal throughout the uterus. Cilliary currents (Parker, 1931) and peristalsis in the direction of the ovary have also been postulated, but Lim and Chao (1927) found that reversing segments of the uterus of the rabbit, which would presumably reverse both cilliary action and the direction of peristalsis, did not affect fertility.

It is still doubtful if the rate of transport of spermatozoa from the vagina to the site of fertilisation will significantly affect fertility. An increase in the rate might indeed bring spermatozoa more quickly in contact with the egg or increase the number which accumulate there, but if several hours must elapse before the spermatozoa become capacitated the advantages of rapid transport are not very obvious. On the other hand, if capacitation takes place primarily in contact with the uterine mucosa and is reversed or inhibited by seminal plasma (Chang, 1957), a rapid dispersal of spermatozoa over the mucosa might mean more rapid capacitation. This introduces the subject of the physiological functions of the spermatozoa in the female tract which is dealt with in Chapter 9, and the changes in the spermatozoon which precede fertilisation which are discussed in Chapter 10.

The observations on the differences of copulatory function in different species which are made in this chapter are sufficient to demonstrate the existence of complicated organs, physiological mechanisms and behaviour patterns which ensure transport of spermatozoa from the male tract to within the female. By very different paths, these mechanisms fulfil the primary function of copulation, which is to ensure the approximation in time and space of the gametes with a relative economy in gamete production. The diversity of pattern in different species must be due to considerable diversity of genotype, and these different genotypes can only have arisen by mutations continually subject to natural selection. That the balance between fertility and infertility is a critical one for most species appears evident from the importance which is attached to fertility problems in man, in the domesticated animals, in laboratory stocks, and in wild animals kept in captivity or studied in the field. Any mutation which might swing the balance from one side to the other would have a very direct effect in determining the number of possible progeny and hence the chances of survival of the mutant genes. It is perhaps to this critical balance that we owe the diversity of the sexual organs and patterns. It is true that some characteristics of the mating pattern may be vestigial or emergent, such as the incomplete or inconstant formation of a vaginal plug in the pig and rabbit, or the filiform appendage of the penis in the ram, but our measurements of their functional significance may be too crude to detect slight differences in fertility which would however " in the long run " tend to swing the balance one way or another.

Bibliography

ASDELL, S. A. (1946). *Patterns of mammalian reproduction.* Ithaca.

BARRINGTON, F. J. F. (1941). The variations in the mucin content of the bulbo-urethral glands. *Int. Mschr. Anat. Physiol.,* 30.

BATTELLI, F. (1922). Une méthode pour obtenir l'emission complète du liquide des vesicules seminales chez le cobaye. *C. R. Soc. Phys. Hist. nat. Genève,* **39,** 73.

BEACH, F. A. (1942). Analysis of factors involved in the arousal, maintenance and manifestation of sexual excitement in male animals. *Psychosom. Med.,* **4,** 173.

—— (1948). *Hormones and behaviour.* New York.

BEAMS, H. W., & KING, R. L. (1933). Sperm storage of seminal vesicles. *J. Urol.,* **29,** 95.

BECK, J. R. (1872). How do spermatozoa enter the uterus ? *Amer. J. Obstet. Gynec.,* **7,** 353.

BISHOP, D. W. (1956). Oxygen concentrations in the rabbit genital tract. *III int. Congr.-Anim. Reprod., Cambridge.* Section 1, p. 53.

BROEK, A. J. P. VAN DEN (1933). Gonaden und Ausführungsgänge. *Bolk et Al. Hand-b. vergl. Anat. Wirbeltiere,* **7.** Berlin.

BUDGE, J. (1858). Ueber das Centrum genitospinale des Nervus sympathicus. *Virchows Arch.,* **15,** 115.

CAMUS, L., & GLEY, E. (1896–1922). Action coagulante du liquide prostatique sur le contenu des vésicules séminales. *C. R. Soc. Biol., Paris,* **48,** 787—87, 320.

CHANG, M. C. (1957). A detrimental effect of seminal plasma on the fertilising capacity of sperm. *Nature, Lond.,* **179,** 258.

DARLING, F. FRASER (1938). *Bird flocks and the breeding cycle.* Cambridge.

Dauzier, L., & Wintenberger, S. (1952). Analyse des conditions de la fécondation chez la brebis. *II int. Congr. Anim. Reprod. Copenhagen*, I, 113.

Davies, D. V., & Mann, T. (1947). Functional development of accessory glands and spermatogenesis. *Nature, Lond.*, **160**, 295.

—— & Rowson, L. E. A. (1957). Effect of nutrition on the onset of male sex hormone activity and sperm formation in monozygous bull-calves. *Proc. Roy. Soc.*, B, **147**, 332.

Day, F. T. (1940). The stallion and fertility. The technique of sperm collection and insemination. *Vet. Rec.*, **52**, 597.

Dickinson, R. L. (1933). *Human sex anatomy.* Baltimore.

Disselhorst, R. (1904). Ausführapparat und Anhangsdrüsen der männlichen Geschlechtsorgane. *Oppels Lehrbuch der Micros. Anat. d. Wirbeltiere.* Vol. 4. Jena.

Dusser de Barenne, J. G., & Koskoff, Y. D. (1932). Flexor rigidity of the hind legs and priapism in the " secondary " spinal preparation of the male cat. *Amer. J. Physiol.*, **102**, 75.

—— (1934). Further observations on flexor rigidity in the hind legs of the spinal cat. *Amer. J. Physiol.*, **107**, 441.

Eckhard, C. (1863). Untersuchungen über der Erektion der Penis beim Hunde. *Beitr. Anat. Physiol., Giessen*, **3**, 123.

Evans, E. I. (1933). The transport of spermatozoa in the dog. *Amer. J. Physiol.*, **105**, 287.

Florey, H., & Walton, A. (1931). Uterine fistula used to determine the mechanism of ascent of the spermatozoa in the female genital tract. *J. Physiol.*, **74**, 5P.

Gaschott, O. (1925). Beiträge zur Reizphysiologie des Forellenspermas. I. Die optimalen Konzentrationen einiger Salzlösungen. *Arch. Hydrobiol. (Plankt.)*, Suppl. **4**, 441.

Gerhardt, U. (1933). V. Kloake und Begattungsorgane. Bolk *et al.* Handb. vergl. Anat. Wirbeltiere, Berlin.

Galtsoff, P. S. (1938). Physiology of reproduction of *Ostrea virginica.* II : Stimulation of spawning in the female osyter. *Biol. Bull., Wood's Hole*, **75**, 286.

—— (1940). Physiology of reproduction of *Ostrea virginica.* III : Stimulation of spawning in the male oyster. *Biol. Bull., Wood's Hole*, **78**, 117.

Götz (1898). Über Erektion und Ejaculation bei Erhängten. Cited from Marshall (1922), p. 265.

Gunn, R. M. C. (1936). Fertility in sheep. Artificial production of seminal ejaculation and the characters of the spermatozoa contained therein. *Bull. Coun. sci. industr. Res. Aust.*, No. 94.

Gutierrez, A. B. (1942). Surgery of the seminal vesicles, ampullae, vasa deferentia and spermatic cord. Cited from Lowsley *et al.*, 1942.

Hartman, C. G. (1957). How do sperms get into the uterus ? *Fertility & Sterility*, **8**, 403.

Harvey, C. (1956). The use of partitioned ejaculates in investigating the role of accessory secretions in human semen. *Studies on Fertility*, **8**, 3.

Heape, W. (1898). The artificial insemination of mares. *Veterinarian, Lond.*, **71**, 202.

Hirsch, E. W. (1927). Comparative histology of the urethral mucosa and its relation to gonococcal infections. *J. Urol.*, **17**, 575.

—— (1931a). A note on the comparative anatomy of the prostate gland. *J. Urol.*, **25**, 669.

—— (1931b). The so-called arterial valves in the penile arteries. *J. Urol.*, **25**, 61.

Hotchkiss, R. S. (1945). *Fertility in men.* London.

Ivanow, E. (1900). Sur la fonction des vésicules séminales et de la glande prostatique. *J. Physiol. Path. gén.*, **2**, 95.

—— (1907). De la fécondation artificielle chez les mammifères. *Arch. Sci. biol., St Pétersb.* **12**, 377.

—— (1917). Observations sur le processus d'éjaculation du sperme chez le chien. Durée et volume des différentes portions de la sécretion spermatique. *C. R. Soc. Biol., Paris*, **80**, 514.

IVANOW E. (1929). The experimental verification of the question as to the purpose of the filiform process on the ram's penis; and the possibility of producing sterility by amputation. *Vet. J.*, Sept. 29, 351.

KERRUISH, B. M. (1955). The effect of sexual stimulation prior to service on the behaviour and conception rate of bulls. *Brit. J. Anim. Behaviour*, **3**, 125.

KISS, F. (1921). Anatomische-histologische Untersuchungen über die Erektion. *Z. ges. Anat.*, **61**, 455.

KREHBIEL, R. H., & CARSTENS, H. P. (1939). Roentgen studies of the mechanism involved in sperm transportation in the female rabbit. *Amer. J. Physiol.*, **125**, 571.

KRISTELLER, S. (1871). Beiträge zu den Bedingungen der Conception. *Berl. klin. Wschr.*, **27**, 215 and 325.

LAPLAUD, M., & CASSOU, R. (1945). Nouveau procédé de recolte du sperme par electrode bipolaire rectale unique. *C. R. Acad. Agric. Ann.*, 37.

LIM, R. K-S., & CHAO, C. (1927). On the mechanism of the transportation of ova. I : Rabbit uterus. *Chin. J. Physiol.*, **1**, 175.

LODE, A. (1895). Experimentelle Beiträge zur Physiologie der Samenblasen. *S. B. Akad. Wiss. Wien.*, Pt. 3, **104**, 33.

LOWSLEY, O. S., HINMAN, F., SMITH, D. R., & GUTIERREZ, R. (1942). *The sexual glands of the male.* New York.

LUCIANI, L. (1917). *Human physiology*, **4**, 81. (English Trans.) London.

LUNDQUIST, F. (1949). Aspects of the biochemistry of human semen. *Acta physiol. scand.*, **19**, Suppl. 66.

MACIRONE, C., & WALTON, A. (1938). Fecundity of male rabbits as determined by " dummy matings." *J. agric. Sci.*, **28**, 122.

MCKENZIE, F., MILLER, J. C., & BAUGUESS, L. C. (1938). The reproductive organs and semen of the boar. *Res. Bull. Univ. Missouri*, 279.

MACLEOD, J., & HOTCHKISS, R. S. (1942). Distribution of spermatozoa and of certain chemical constituents in human ejaculate. *J. Urol.*, **48**, 225.

MANN, T. (1954). *The Biochemistry of Semen.* London.

—— & GLOVER, T. (1954). Contribution of the seminal vesicles towards the composition of whole semen. *J. Endocrin.*, **10**, iv.

—— POLGE, C., & ROWSON, L. E. A. (1956). Participation of seminal plasma during the passage of spermatozoa in the female reproductive tract of the pig and horse. *J. Endocrin.*, **13**, 133.

—— SHORT, R. V., WALTON, A., ARCHER, R. K., & MILLER, W. C. (1957). The " tail-end sample " of stallion semen. *J. agric. Sci.*, **49**, 301.

MARDEN, W. G. R. (1954). New advances in the electroejaculation of the bull. *J. Dairy Sci.*, **37**, 556.

MARSHALL, F. H. A. (1901). The copulatory organ in the sheep. *Anat. Anz.*, **20**, 261.

—— (1911). The male generative cycle in the hedgehog. *J. Physiol.*, **43**, 247.

—— (1922). *The physiology of reproduction.* 2nd Ed. London.

—— & CROSLAND, W. P. (1918). Sterility in mares with recommendations to breeders of heavy horses. *J. Bd. Agric.*, **24**, 1357.

MILOVANOV, V. K., & SMIRNOV-UGRUMOV, D. V. (1940). The problem of rational utilisation of pedigree sires in the light of Pavlov's teaching. *Zhivotnovodstoo*, **5**, 138.

MOORE, C. R. (1939). Biology of the testes. Chap. 7 in *Sex and Internal Secretions.* Ed. E. Allen. London.

—— & GALLAGHER, T. F. (1930). Seminal vesicle and prostate function as a testis-hormone indicator ; the electric ejaculation test. *Amer. J. Anat.*, **45**, 39.

NOYES, R., ADAMS, C. A., & WALTON, A. (1958). Transport of spermatozoa into the uterus of the rabbit. *Fertility & Sterility*, **9**, 288.

PARKER, G. H. (1930). The passage of the spermatozoa and the ova through the oviducts of the rabbit. *Proc. Soc. exp. Biol., N.Y.*, **27**, 826.

—— (1931). The passage of sperms and eggs through the oviducts in terrestrial vertebrates. *Philos. Trans.*, B., **219**, 381.

—— (1932). The passage of sperms and eggs through the oviducts of the rabbit and of the human being with a consideration of Sampson's theory of hemorrhagic or chocolate cysts. *Amer. J. Obstet. Gynec.*, **23**, 619.

PUSSEP (1902).   Cited from Marshall (1922), p. 265.

ROWSON, L. E. A. (1955).   The movement of radio-opaque material in the bovine uterine tract.   *Brit. Vet. J.*, **111**, 334.

—— & MURDOCH, M. I. (1954).   Electrical ejaculation in the bull.   *Vet. Rec.*, **66**, 326.

SCHEURING, L. (1925).   Biologische und physiologische Untersuchungen an Forellen-sperma.   *Arch. Hydrobiol. (Plankt.)*, Suppl. **4**, 181.

—— (1928).   Weitere biologische und physiologische Untersuchungen an Salmoniden-sperma.   *Zool. Jb.*, **45**, 651.

SCHÜLLER, H. (1931).   Studien zur Regeneration und zur vergleichenden Physiologie der Prostata.   *Proc. II int. Congr. Sex. Res., Edinburgh*, p. 130.

SEMANS, J. H., & LANGWORTHY, O. R. (1938).   Observations on the neurophysiology of sexual function in the male cat.   *J. Urol.*, **40**, 836.

SISSON, S. (1945).   *The anatomy of the domestic animals.*   4th Edn.   Revised by J. D. Gross-man.   Philadelphia.

SLIJPER.   Cited from Asdell, 1946.

SPINA (1897).   Experimentelle Beiträge zu der Lehre von der Erektion und Ejaculation.   Cited from Marshall, 1922, p. 265.

STEINACH, E. (1894).   Untersuchungen zur vergleichenden Physiologie der männlichen Geschlechtsorgane, insbesondere der accessorischen Geschlechtsdrüsen.   *Pflüg. Arch. ges. Physiol.*, **56**, 304.

STIEVE, H. (1930).   *Möllendorff's Handbuch. mikros. Anat. Mensch.*   Berlin.

TESTUT, L. (1931).   *Traité d'Anatomie Humaine.*   8th Ed.   Paris.

THIBAULT, C., LAPLAUD, M., & ORTAVANT, R. L. (1948).   Electroejaculation chez le taureau.   *C. R. Acad. Sci., Paris*, **226**, 2006.

THOMAS, B. A., & HARRISON, F. G. (1917).   Bacteriology and microscopy of the seminal vesicles post mortem.   *J. Urol.*, **1**, 59.

TOWNSEND, G. (1938a).   The spawning reaction of *Nereis limbata* with emphasis upon chemical stimulation.   *Biol. Bull., Wood's Hole*, **75**, 363.

—— (1938b).   Physiological assays concerning the nature of fertilizin.   *Biol. Bull., Wood's Hole*, **75**, 364.

VANDEMARK, N. L., & MOELLER, A. N. (1951).   Speed of spermatozoan transport in reproductive tract of estrous cow.   *Amer. J. Physiol.*, **165**, 674.

VAN WAGENEN, G. (1936).   The coagulating function of the cranial lobe of the prostate gland in the monkey.   *Anat. Rec.*, **66**, 411.

WALKER, G. (1910).   The nature of the secretion of the vesiculae seminales.   *Johns Hopk. Hosp. Bull.*, **21**, 185.

WALTON, A. (1930).   On the function of the rabbit cervix during coitus.   *J. Obstet. Gynaec.*, Brit. Emp., **37**, 1.

—— (1938a).   Preservation of fertilising capacity of horse semen.   *XXXI Annu. Mtg. Amer. Soc. Anim. Prod.*, 238.

—— (1938b).   The quantitative basis of fertility.   *Folia morph., Warsz.*, **8**, 270.

—— (1952).   Flow orientation as a possible explanation of " wave-motion " and " rheo-taxis " of spermatozoa.   *J. exp. Biol.*, **29**, 520.

—— (1955).   Sexual behaviour.   Chap. 13.   Hammond's *Progress in the Physiology of Farm Animals*, Vol. 2.   London.

—— & DOTT, H. M. (1956).   The aerobic metabolism of spermatozoa.   *III int. Congr. Anim. Reprod., Cambridge*, **2**, 33.

YAMANE, J., & ITO, T. (1932).   Über die Geschwindigkeit der Pferdespermatozoen in strömenden und nicht strömenden Flüssigheiten.   *Cytologia*, **3**, 188.

YOUNG, W. C., & SIMEONE, F. A. (1930).   Development and fate of spermatozoa in the epididymis and vas deferens in the guniea-pig.   *Proc. Soc. exp. Biol., N.Y.*, **27**, 838.

ZUCKERMAN, S. (1932).   *The Social Life of Monkeys and Apes.*   London.

CHAPTER 9

THE BIOLOGY OF SPERMATOZOA AND ARTIFICIAL INSEMINATION

By A. S. Parkes

I. Semen Collection and Artificial Insemination

Introduction

Investigation of the properties of spermatozoa *in vitro* involves either the preparation of spermatozoal suspensions from the epididymis or vas deferens of the male, or the collection of ejaculated semen from the male or from the reproductive tract of the female after mating. Collection from the female tract is now attempted only for special purposes ; the applicability of the other methods of obtaining spermatozoa depends entirely on the species concerned. The practicability of collecting semen or spermatozoa makes possible the complementary techniques of artificial semination (A.S.) of the egg mass in forms in which fertilisation is external, or artificial insemination (A.I.) of the female in forms with internal fertilisation. Some of the numerous uses of these techniques are listed below.

The idea of extra-coital insemination features largely in mythology and legend. There is, for instance, the well-known fourteenth-century story of the Arab who successfully inseminated his own mare with semen stolen from a stallion belonging to another tribe. Moreover, the subject has attracted several of those, including Eustachius and Malpighi, whose names are familiar from eponymous terminology. The first authenticated experiments, as might be expected, were carried out on animals in which fertilisation is external, and Jacobi's (1765) experiments with fish appear to have been outstandingly successful. It remained, however, for the great Italian biologist Spallanzani to demonstrate conclusively the possibilities of the technique. Spallanzani passed on from successful work with lower animals to his famous experiment on the dog, in which he demonstrated for the first time under laboratory conditions the practicability of A.I. in mammals and the essential function of the spermatozoon. The following account of the original experiment, taken from a contemporary translation of the " Dissertations " (Spallanzani, 1784), was cited by Marshall (1922):

" I chose a bitch spaniel of moderate size which had before had whelps. Suspecting from certain appearances, that she would soon be in heat, I confined her in an apartment, where she continued a long time, as will be seen below. For greater security, that she might never be let loose, I fed her myself, and kept the key the whole time. On the thirteenth day she began to show evident signs of being in heat ; the external parts of generation were tumid, and a thin stream of blood flowed from them.   On the twenty-third day she seemed fit for the admission of the male, and I attempted to fecundate her artificially in the following manner.   A young dog of the same breed furnished me, by a spontaneous emission, with nineteen grains of seed, which were immediately injected into the matrix, by means of a small syringe introduced into the vagina.   As the natural heat of the seed of animals of warm blood may be a condition necessary to render fecunda-tion efficacious, I had taken care to give the syringe the degree of heat which man and dogs are found to possess, which is about 30° (or between 99° and 100°F.).   Two days after the injection, the bitch went off her heat, and in twenty days her belly appeared swollen, which induced me to set her at liberty on the twenty-sixth.   Meanwhile the swelling of the belly increased ; and sixty-two days after the injection of the seed, the bitch brought forth three lively whelps, two male and one female, resembling in colour and shape not the bitch only, but the dog also from which the seed had been taken.   Thus did I succeed in fecundating this quadruped ; and I can truly say, that I never received greater pleasure upon any occasion, since I first cultivated experimental philosophy."

Having worked his way up from silkworms to dogs it is likely that Spallanzani would have progressed to man had his position in the priesthood been compatible with such an extension of his experiments.   As it was, A.I. in man is reported to have been carried out first by John Hunter (Home, 1799) at about the same time as Spallanzani was working, but the documentation of the case is inadequate ; it is not certain that John Hunter made the insemination himself, and the exact date is unknown.

Unlike most biological discoveries, the importance of Spallanzani's work was recognised by his contemporaries.   According to Schellen (1957), who does not state the source of the translation, Charles Bonnet, the French biologist, wrote to Spallan-zani, " I am not so sure but what you have discovered may not some day have consequences for mankind of no mean significance."   Following Spallanzani, reports of successful A.I. in animals, including lower mammals and man, became progressively more numerous, and by the end of the century the possibilities and potentialities of the technique were becoming recognised among biologists. Historical matters are discussed in detail by Iwanow (1907), Rohleder (1934) and Schellen (1957).   In modern times, the development of efficient methods of col-lecting spermatozoa and of A.I. in many animals has played a big part in the study of sexual physiology and in controlled animal breeding and much of the credit for the application of the technique to agriculture and biological problems must go to Russian workers (see Iwanow, 1930).

The following may be considered as some of the more important uses of A.I.

1. It enables insemination to be made from a selected male in circumstances where such control would otherwise be impossible.   The empyrean nuptials of the queen bee, for instance, are beyond human control, but, so far as the bee-breeder is concerned, can be replaced adequately by A.I. (see p. 164).

2. A.I. enables individuals of different breeds to be cross-bred in spite of what would otherwise be prohibitive differences in size.   The case of the Shire horse and Shetland pony cross is mentioned by Hammond in Volume II, p. 690, and among dogs it is difficult to imagine, say, a Great Dane and a Pekinese being crossed by any other means than A.I.

3. A.I. permits attempts at hybridisation between species which would not mate normally, or would do so only rarely.   Recent success in obtaining cross-

fertilisation between birds of different species and even genera has been facilitated by the use of A.I., e.g. fowl and pheasant (Marchlewski, 1952).

4. A.I. permits the insemination of a known number of spermatozoa, so that the minimum number compatible with fertilisation can be determined. This, in turn, enables the vast excess of spermatozoa normally produced at one ejaculation to be distributed between many females so that the reproductive potential of an outstanding male can be more fully utilised, and the total male population reduced and centralised. These advantages are to be seen in the modern application of A.I. to cattle breeding.

5. In medical and veterinary practice A.I. may be of assistance in dealing with sterility arising from mechanical causes.

6. A.I. permits examination of the effect on fertilising power and genetic properties of spermatozoa of *in vitro* treatments such as storage, fractionation, irradiation, freezing, and thawing, subjection to spermicides, antisera, and so on.

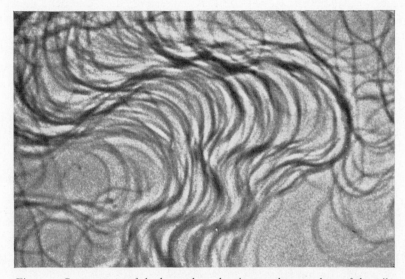

Fig. 9.1—Spermatozoa of the honey-bee, showing synchronous beat of the tails. (From the material of Rothschild, 1955.)

7. A.I. permits insemination for experimental purposes at a time (e.g. pseudopregnancy) when the female mammal does not normally accept the male.

Insects

The honey-bee, because of its intrinsic interest and commercial value, has received more attention than any other species of insect. Spermatozoa can be obtained from the seminal vesicles of the male or more easily by everting the penis to cause ejaculation. On slight dilution, the semen shows wave motion which has the appearance of numerous spiral eddies, due presumably to the synchronous beat of the tails (Fig. 9.1), which was noted by Bishop (1920) and studied in some detail by Rothschild (1955). The earliest attempts at A.I. in bees consisted merely of squeezing semen from the penis into the vagina of the queen (McLain, 1885), but injection from a syringe was used soon afterwards. The instrumental insemination of queens was developed into a routine procedure by Watson (1927), who used a microsyringe. Results, however, were still not good, and Laidlaw (1944) after a detailed study of the anatomy of the reproductive tract introduced the technique of holding down the valvefold, which normally blocks direct entrance to the median oviduct from the vagina, so that the semen can be put into the oviducts at insemination. The vagina is then closed with a mucous plug. Further improvements were introduced by Mackensen (1954), and the observation that CO_2 is a good anaesthetic for bees has greatly increased the ease with which the queen can be immobilised. These refinements of technique have much improved results, and A.I. is now becoming widely used in apiculture.

Fish

It has already been mentioned that fish were the first subjects of successful A.S., and reference has been made to the work of Jacobi (1765). This pioneer fish-breeder obtained spawn and milt by massaging the abdomens of the fish, and mixed the gametes in an incubator. His most successful experiments were with trout. This work attracted little attention at the time, but a century later artificial pisciculture was introduced into France and an institute of fish breeding established by Napoleon III (*see* Schellen, 1957). Since then, the technique has been used extensively, and for a long time without any great elaboration, in experimental work on the breeding of both fresh-water and marine fish.

Many general accounts have been given of the practical aspects of stripping trout and other fish, and the A.S. of the egg mass (e.g. Davis, 1903). More recently, there have been several investigations designed to refine the technique and to assess the variables involved. Nursall and Hasler (1952) worked on the minimum number of spermatozoa required, and Shuman (1950) on the effective range of salmon spermatozoa. Wharton (1957) evolved improved methods of obtaining ova and spermatozoa, and studied optimal conditions for fertilisation.

Spawn and milt can, of course, also be obtained by dissection of the ripe gonad, but in many cases the life of the gamete in the dead fish is very short (*see* Blaxter, 1955). Attempts to induce deposition of gametes by injection or other administration of gonadotrophins have given varied results (*see* Dodd, Chapter 11).

Successful A.I. of fish with internal fertilisation, so far as the writer knows, has not been reported.

Amphibians

The spermatozoa of the chief laboratory anurans can be obtained by various devices at normal amplexus, or by dissecting the testis or vasa, and such methods were used by the earlier workers with reasonable success. In 1929, however, Houssay and Gonzales discovered that spermiation could be induced in male frogs and toads within about two hours by the injection of gonadotrophins, and that spermatozoa could then conveniently be collected from the cloaca. This reaction is dealt with further in Chapter 11 in considering the effects of gonadotrophic hormones on amphibia. The application of the reaction to pregnancy diagnosis by Galli Mainini (1947) led to a great deal of quantitative work. The reaction occurs in almost all the Anura which have been investigated, including *Bufo* spp. and *Rana* spp. A check list of some forty species which have been used is given by Frazer (1954). Sensitivity varies greatly between different species. A 50 per cent response in a group of animals was obtained with 8 i.u. of chorionic gonadotrophin in a group of Rana esculenta (Thorborg and Hansen, 1951) (Fig. 9.2) and with 38 i.u. in Bufo arenarum (Schweitzer and Bas, 1948). Bufo viridis was found by Sulman and Sulman (1950) to be less sensitive. A detailed treatment of the dose/response relationship in Bufo bufo and the tree frog Hyla arborea was given by Frazer (1956), who found an ED 50 of 1·13 i.u. of chorionic gonadotrophin. Frazer also considered seasonal and thermal variations in response.

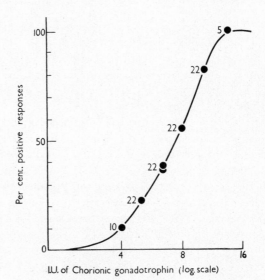

Fig. 9.2—Dose-response curve for spermiation in Rana esculenta injected with chorionic gonadotrophin. (From Thorborg and Hansen, 1951.)

There is thus no difficulty in obtaining anuran spermatozoa, many of which have interesting characteristics (see Fig. 9.3), but so far their properties in vitro have been little studied. The shape of the head differs greatly between genera and even species. It may be twisted like a corkscrew, spindle-shaped, cylindrical, or some other shape. In Bufo vulgaris and Discoglossus the tail has an undulating membrane. Overall, the spermatozoa of Discoglossus are enormous, reaching the astonishing length of 3 mm. Anuran spermatozoa are normally deposited into fresh water and therefore tolerate hypotonicity far better than the spermatozoa of birds and mammals. It appears, in fact, that hypotonicity has a stimulating effect, though sur-

Fig. 9.3—Spermatozoon of Rana showing undulating membrane on tail. (From the material of Frazer.)

vival in fresh water may be short (Rugh, 1934). The in vitro behaviour of the spermatozoa of Bufo bufo is described by Frazer and Glenister (1956) as follows:

" Whereas in 0·6 per cent saline (which is isotonic with amphibian tissue fluid) the sperms have a gentle swaying activity, usually without forward progression, tap water, distilled water and other distinctly hypotonic solutions (e.g. 0·3 per cent saline) all increase the activity of the spermatozoa, which vibrate and wriggle violently. Hypertonic solutions have a depressing effect on motility, as has pH higher than 6·5 or 7."

A.S. is effected merely by bringing together the spermatozoa and the ova, and the technique has been used, as in Hertwig's classic experiments, to study the effects of *in vitro* treatment of the spermatozoa and in experiments on hybridisation between different species in which male and female would not normally mate.

In contrast to the Anura, which copulate but have external fertilisation, many of the urodeles have internal fertilisation but do not mate (e.g. *Salamandra atra* and *Nectophrynoides torneri*). In this case the spermatozoa are enclosed in a gelatinous spermatophore, which is deposited in the water. The female then picks it up between her cloacal lips and squeezes out the spermatozoa into the oviduct. From this brief account of well-known facts it would appear that there should be no difficulty in obtaining urodele spermatozoa, or in performing artificial insemination. The writer, however, is not aware that the properties of spermatozoa in the spermatophores have been investigated or that attempts have been made to perform artificially this strange form of natural insemination.

Birds

Birds are well adapted to the collection of spermatozoa and to artificial insemination, but very little was done before 1936, and so far the techniques have been applied only to domestic fowl and a few other birds. According to Munro (1938c) spermatozoa removed from the testis or epididymis of the cock are not capable of effecting fertilisation even after several days in the oviduct. This observation implies that some special maturation of the spermatozoon takes place in the male tract, and it means that for A.I. spermatozoa must be obtained by ejaculation.

Early methods of collecting semen followed the usual lines : aspiration from the cloaca of the hen after mating (Payne, 1914 ; Craft, McElroy and Penquite, 1926 ; Jull and Quinn, 1931), the interception of the ejaculate during mating attempts (Dunn, 1927 ; Warren and Kilpatrick, 1929 ; Hutt, 1929), the use of an artificial cloaca attached to the hen (Ischikawa, 1930 ; Adamstone and Card, 1934) or a semen collector attached to the male (Parker, 1939) and, lastly, electrical stimulation to ejaculation (Letard and Tinet, 1937). All these methods, however, were superseded by the technique of manual stimulation introduced by Burrows and Quinn (1935) and afterwards used by them in extensive investigations (Burrows and Quinn, 1938, 1939) in which they clarified many of the variables associated with semen collection and A.I. in fowl. The technique of collection and its anatomical basis has been described by Polge (1950) as follows:

" In the cock the lower regions of the vasa deferentia, passing through the walls of the cloaca, are considerably changed. The semen is stored in these ampullae prior to ejaculation. The ducts terminate in two small papillae on the ventral wall of the cloaca. By the method of Burrows and Quinn the cock is so held that a rapid massage can be applied to the abdominal region. This causes a protrusion of the copulatory organ which is then gripped between the thumb and forefinger of the operator. A steady squeezing pressure on the sides of the cloaca will force the semen from the ampullae through the papillae. The semen can then be collected in any suitable glass vessel. Further stimulation leads to a complete ejaculatory response which acts to refill the ampullae. The squeezing operation can then be repeated until no more semen is obtained."

Some birds are very susceptible to manipulation of this kind, others less so. In any case, male birds used should be isolated both from hens and other cocks and collections should not be more frequent than twice weekly. The Burrows–Quinn technique has been widely used by later workers, including Munro (1938a), Black and Scorgie (1942) and Polge (1950, 1955). Lake (1957) examined the fluid components of the ejaculate obtained by the massage method.

In Polge's experience, the average volume of semen collected by the manual method was 0·76 ml. The largest amount ever obtained was 2·83 ml. Polge,

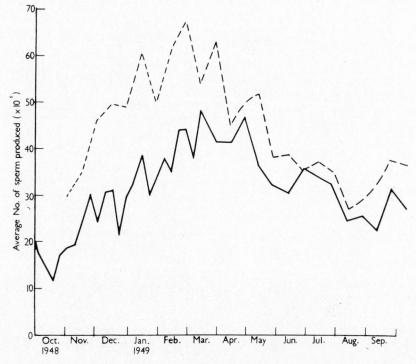

Fig. 9.4—Seasonal production of spermatozoa in two groups of white Leghorn cocks. (From Polge, 1955.)

like others, observed great individual and time to time variation in the amounts of semen produced and in sperm density. Fowl semen is free from accessory secretions and is therefore highly concentrated without being sticky or stringy. Polge (1950) found an average density of 3,400 million spermatozoa per ml., but the semen varied from a watery fluid containing few spermatozoa to a dense white cream containing 12,400 million per ml. The average number of spermatozoa per ejaculate was 2,600 million. The largest number in one ejaculate was 13,000 million, which, as Polge says, would be considered noteworthy even for a bull. There was considerable seasonal variation in production of spermatozoa (Fig. 9.4) but at no time did the average for a group fall below 1,000 million per ejaculate, even when the birds were moulting. According to Burrows and Titus (1939) the rate of semen production is related to testis size, not to comb size or sexual activity. Variation in semen production occurs not only between different breeds (Williams and McGibbon, 1956), but also between high- and low-fertility strains of the same breed (Jones and Lamoreux, 1942). The spermatozoa are remarkable for their elongated heads (Fig. 9.5).

Methods for inseminating the hen were described by Quinn and Burrows (1936) and by Munro (1935). Both involve introduction of the semen straight into the oviduct. Polge (1950) described Munro's method as follows : " The hen is held upside-down so that the abdomen can be compressed. This everts the lower portion of the oviduct which will then protrude into the cloaca, and the semen is inserted through a glass syringe. The pressure on the abdomen is released at the same time and the oviduct returns to its normal position." Munro

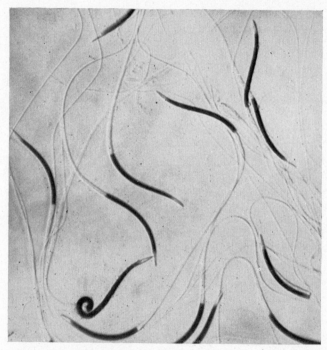

Fig. 9.5—Ultra-violet photograph of fowl semen diluted with Ringer's solution. The sperm head is needle-shaped, about 10 μ long and 1 μ in diameter, bearing at the tip a small acrosome. The mid-piece is about 5 μ long, and the tail about 100 μ. (From Polge, 1950.)

(1938a) records that it is necessary to inseminate more than one million spermatozoa to obtain fertile eggs. Burrows and Quinn (1938) found that the insemination of 0·05 ml. once weekly was necessary to give good fertility ; with 0·02 ml., fertility was only 54 per cent. Rowell and Cooper (1957), however, observed that dilutions greater than 1 : 1 decreased fertility because of inadequate numbers of spermatozoa. Intraperitoneal insemination of hens by injection was introduced by Van Drimmelen (1945), who reported that the fertility rate was at least as good as that found after insemination into the cloacol end of the oviduct.

Burrows and Marsden (1938) found that similar techniques could be applied to turkeys with similar results. The semen is less abundant and is thicker and more sticky ; the amounts required for insemination are similar to those in fowl. Many additional details about A.I. in turkeys were given by Burrows and Quinn (1939), and the use of diluents with turkey semen has been investigated by Van Tienhoven and Steel (1957). The technique has also been extended to geese (Johnson, 1954) and ducks (Watanabe and Sugimori, 1957).

A.I. in poultry has many possibilities. As in farm mammals, it can obviously be used, in view of the enormous excess of spermatozoa in one ejaculate, to increase the reproductivity of an outstanding male. Polge used the technique to study problems of fertility in battery hens for which normal mating would be impossible. There is evidence that this use will increase (e.g. Burton, 1957 ; Gabriel, 1957). Polge also used the technique, as others before him, to study the effects of *in vitro* treatment of the spermatozoa. Skaller (1951) reported the large-scale use of A.I. in comparing different breeding systems in fowl. Possibly the most interesting use, however, as already mentioned, is in effecting hybridisation between species which will not cross-mate. Warren and Scott (1935) cross-inseminated fowl and turkeys and obtained fertile eggs from both the turkey and fowl hens. However, most of the embryos died at an early stage and no living chicks were produced. The pheasant–fowl cross is of particular interest. The pheasant cock and the domestic hen occasionally mate spontaneously ; the reverse cross does not happen naturally. Presumably the domestic cock is less versatile than the pheasant cock. By A.I., however, Sandnes and Landauer (1938) repeatedly obtained offspring from pheasant eggs fertilised by fowl spermatozoa. Marchlewski (1937) by similar means obtained fertile eggs from domestic fowl × guinea fowl but viable chicks were not produced. Vojtíšková (1958) succeeded in rearing similar hybrids when immunological tolerance to the other species had been induced in the hen, and it is possible that the combination of A.I. and immunological techniques will greatly extend the range of avian and mammalian hybrids that can be obtained.

Domestic Mammals

In all the common farm animals, cattle, horses, pigs, sheep, goats, semen is now almost always collected by the use of an artificial vagina or by electrical stimulation. So far as horses, cattle, and sheep are concerned, the techniques of collection and A.I. are described fully by Hammond (1952). Later developments in the production of ejaculation by electrical stimulation have been discussed by Walton in the preceding chapter. Reviews by other authors are numerous ; especial attention may be directed to Anderson (1952), who deals with semen quality, and Frank (1952) and Emmens and Blackshaw (1956), who review the whole field of A.I. in cattle and sheep. Only brief references need therefore be made here to horses, cattle and sheep. More attention will be given to pigs, goats, and dogs, for which most of the information is comparatively new.

Collection of sperm from the epididymis is not, of course, a practicable routine in domestic animals, but there seems to be scope for more experimental work on the comparative properties of epididymal and ejaculated sperm in these species. According to Lasley and Mayer (1944), epididymal spermatozoa of the bull are more resistant to thermal shock than are ejaculated spermatozoa. With boar spermatozoa, Lasley and Bogart (1944) found that resistance to thermal shock and viability on storage depended on the distance from the testis at which

G*

they were obtained ; those from the head of the epididymis were most and ejaculated spermatozoa least resistant.

Cattle

A vast literature has grown up on the collection and properties of bull semen. Much of this has been considered by Hammond (1952) and by Walton in the preceding chapter. The quality and quantity of an ejaculate vary enormously according to circumstances—individual variation and frequency of collections being two important factors. Bratton and Foote (1954), for instance, found that over the period of a year, 60 per cent more motile spermatozoa were obtained by collection

TABLE I

NUMBER OF COWS INSEMINATED IN GREAT BRITAIN 1944-1958

Year (April to March)	Total (thousands)
1943/44	2
1944/45	10
1945/46	25
1946/47	65
1947/48	172
1948/49	387
1949/50	599
1950/51	773
1951/52	1,046
1952/53	1,122
1953/54	1,343
1954/55	1,472
1955/56	1,694
1956/57	1,791
1957/58	1,865

at 4-day intervals than by collection at 8–day intervals. The figures given by Hammond (1952) show that an average ejaculate from a bull amounts to 4 to 5 ml. with a sperm density of 300 to 2,000 million per ml., and that a single ejaculate can be diluted to inseminate 40 to 50 cows.

The use of A.I. in cattle breeding in Great Britain continues to increase (Table I); by December 1958, ten million cows had been inseminated from Milk Marketing Board centres alone. In the United States, the annual total now approaches that figure, and the number of cows bred per sire has doubled in ten years. Over the world some scores of millions of calves have now been produced by the use of the technique. The extent to which cattle have been upgraded by this increased use of the reproductive potential of selected bulls is perhaps debatable, but it is at least certain that no harmful effects can be attributed directly to the use of A.I. In this vast industry, small improvements in efficiency are obviously important, and large-scale field trials are commonly carried out (e.g. Willett, Ohms and Torrie, 1955). An experiment on many thousands of cows is required to show that an apparent change of 1 per cent in the conception rate is statistically signi-ficant. Recent developmental work has concentrated on the *in vitro* assessment of the potential fertilising capacity of different samples of semen (e.g. Bishop, 1955), on the most efficient degree of dilution of the semen, on its conservation, and on various other factors affecting conception rate. The sexual psychology of A.I. bulls in relation to semen production has also received much attention (e.g. Almquist and Hale, 1956). The low-temperature preservation of bull semen is dealt with in detail below. For comparison with other animals it may be noted that the conception (non-return) rate for first inseminations is between 65 per cent and 70 per cent. The application to the buffalo of methods of semen col-lection and examination and A.I. has been studied by a number of workers (Prabhu and Sharma, 1955 ; Shalash, 1956).

Insemination of heifers by intraperitoneal injection of semen, tried by McDonald and Sampson (1957), may result in pregnancy.

Horse

The work of Walton (1938, 1945) and Day (1940) showed that semen collec-tion, by means of an artificial vagina, and A.I. could satisfactorily be applied to horses. This method was used by Walton and Hammond (1938) to obtain Shire–Shetland crosses. Progress was reviewed in 1941 by Berliner. Bielanski (1956) found that the ejaculates from 1,710 stallions had a mean volume of $61 \cdot 60 \pm 1 \cdot 04$ ml., the amount being greater for the stallions of heavier breeds. The sperm density was 410 million to 430 million per ml., giving total numbers per ejaculate varying between 26,367 million and 45,521 million according to the breed. Day (1942) found that good fertility resulted from the insemination of two billion spermatozoa, and in a personal communication states that the total ejaculate in a horse varies from 50 to 150 ml., and sperm density varies between about 70 million and 200 million per ml. The decreasing use of the horse in Great Britain (apart from thoroughbreds in which A.I. is not permitted) has prevented any wide application of the technique to this animal.

Sheep

Semen is collected from rams either by means of an artificial vagina or by electrical stimulation. The volume of an ejaculate is small, about 1 ml., and the sperm density very high, 800–4,000 million per ml. (Hammond, 1952). After dilution, a single ejaculate may be used for 30–40 ewes. Insemination into the uterus is not possible because of the numerous cervical folds. There is some doubt as to whether intracervical insemination is desirable, as thought by Keast and Morley (1949), or whether deposition of the semen in the vagina is adequate (Albornoz-Bustamante, 1952). There is difference of opinion as to the optimal time of insemination during oestrus, but most observers consider that 14–32 hours after the onset of oestrus is the most likely time to effect conception (*see* Emmens and Blackshaw, 1956). One of the more interesting recent developments is the facilitation of A.I. in sheep by synchronising oestrus in a group of ewes by the use of PMS and progesterone (Robinson, 1956).

A.I. in sheep was originally developed by Russian workers, but its use is now spreading rapidly in many parts of the world, including Australia (Emmens and Blackshaw, 1956) and South America (Mies and Ramos, 1956). The use of A.I. in sheep may well come to exceed that in cattle, as the following figures, taken from Kuznetsov (1956), suggest :

TABLE II

A.I. in Sheep in the U.S.S.R.

Year	No. inseminated (millions)
1928	0·005
1932	1·015
1936	8·9
1940	23·0
1950	21·0
1955	28·0

Pig

The boar is of especial interest because of the large volume of semen and the huge numbers of spermatozoa produced, and because the prolonged ejaculation enables the semen to be fractionated. A method of collection was described by McKenzie (1931) using a sow and a simple form of artificial vagina. Workers elsewhere found that a dummy sow was adequate and elaborated the artificial vagina (Milovanov, 1932 ; Rodolfo, 1934 ; Rodin and Lipatov, 1935). Observations on the nature of the semen were also made by these and other workers. The most striking characteristic is, of course, the volume, which varies between 100 and 500 ml. and is usually of the order of 200 ml. The sperm density ranges from 10 to 1,000 million per ml., with an average of 1,000 million per ml. There is no regular relation between volume of semen and density or total number of spermatozoa. The total number, however, is usually much greater than in other species because of the large volume, but no wave motion is seen microscopically in the semen because of the comparatively low density.

The concentration of spermatozoa in the epididymis is very high (Novoseljcev, 1951), so that the bulk of the semen is evidently derived from the accessory glands, and it can be calculated that the contribution of the epididymis is only 1 to 5 per cent of the total ejaculate. Systematic removal of different glands enabled McKenzie, Miller and Bauguess (1938) to show that the ejaculate was derived to the extent of 20 per cent from the seminal vesicles, 15 per cent from Cowper's glands, 62 per cent from the prostate and urethral glands, and 3 per cent from the epididymis. The vesicular secretion can be identified by the fact that it is the only source of fructose, citric acid, and certain other substances in the semen (Mann, 1948, 1951) ; by comparison of the vesicular and seminal fructose concentrations, Glover and Mann (1954) confirmed the estimate of McKenzie *et al.* that

20 per cent of the semen was of vesicular origin. The effects of various experimental treatments on the amount and nature of the semen were also investigated by Wallace (1949), whose work is referred to in Volume III Chapter 29.

The boar is remarkable for the complicated pattern of its prolonged ejaculation, already referred to by Walton in the preceding chapter, and graphically described by Polge (1956b), who continues :

" If the collecting vessels for the semen are changed at intervals during the course of ejaculation, it is possible to distinguish three quite distinct fractions which correspond to the phases described above (Rodolfo, 1934 ; McKenzie et al., 1938). The first fraction contains no sperm and is generally termed the ' pre-sperm ' fraction ; the second contains a very high concentration of sperm and is termed the ' sperm-rich ' fraction ; the final fraction, as the fluid becomes clear again, contains a much lower concentration of sperm and is termed the ' post-sperm ' fraction."

Boar semen offers unusual opportunities for chemical investigation, and in addition to the references given above, Mann and Leone (1953) and Humphrey and Mann (1949) may be consulted. Boar semen differs chemically from that of other mammals by having a low concentration of fructose and a high one of ergothionine and mesoinositol.

The physiological significance of the qualitative and quantitative peculiarities of boar semen is not known, though it may be noted that du Mesnil du Buisson and Dauzier (1955) and Mann, Polge and Rowson (1956) found that in pigs killed soon after mating the uterine horns were full of semen. With all this emphasis on the accessory secretions it is salutary to record that McKenzie et al. (1938) found boars to be normally fertile after removal of all their accessory glands.

A.I. in pigs was first carried out experimentally by the Russian workers already cited, and was afterwards developed in Japan (Ito et al., 1948a, b). Later, serious consideration to the problems involved was given by Wiggins, Grummer and Casida (1951) in the United States, by Polge (1956a, b) in Great Britain, and by du Mesnil du Buisson and Dauzier (1956) in France. The greatest practical difficulty lies in the proper timing of insemination in relation to oestrus. As ovulation occurs about the middle of oestrus insemination may be made too late. Reports differ as to the amount of semen required. According to Polge (1956b), 100 ml. is adequate for a gilt, but not for a sow, though the earlier workers had reported good results with 50 ml. Du Mesnil du Buisson and Dauzier (1956) found that the number of eggs fertilised was not affected by the amount of semen inseminated between 50 ml. and 250 ml., but that the pregnancy rate was much higher with the larger dose. This observation, if confirmed, may help to answer the question as to whether the copious male secretions perform any function.

Goat

Methods of semen collection and A.I. in the goat have developed along lines similar to those for other farm animals. Semen is collected from the billy-goat in an artificial vagina and, according to Cowie (personal communication), the essential feature of the technique is to get someone else to do the job. Sharma, Suri and Vali (1957) give the following data for the semen: volume of ejaculate averaged 1·3 ml. in summer and 0·8 ml. in winter; sperm density averaged 5424·7 million per ml., being lowest in spring and highest in winter. Motility was greatest in autumn. Baudet, Dauzier, Pécard and Wintenberger (1954) state that fertilising capacity is quickly lost *in vitro*, although motility persists much longer. Blokhuis (1957) diluted with a medium containing 3 per cent sodium citrate and 5 per cent egg-yolk, together with a bacteriostat, and performed A.I. with the aid of a vaginal speculum and a head-lamp. During 1955/6 he obtained 48 per cent of pregnancies after one insemination per nanny, and 72 per cent after a maximum of three. In the next year, using the above diluent, 58·1 per cent of 364 goats became pregnant. Very similar results were obtained by Dauzier (1956) using milk or egg-yolk sodium citrate buffer for dilution of the semen.

Dog

Although the dog was the first mammal to be artificially inseminated successfully (*see* p. 161), no systematic work was carried out on this species until recent years. Casual experiments were, however, made by several biologists, including Heape (1897) and Marshall (1922), especially for the crossing of breeds of very different size. Earlier workers appear to have relied for semen collection on digital manipulations, but this method was abandoned by Harrop (1956a) " on aesthetic grounds and also because it was inadequate in respect of the quantity and quality of semen obtained." Harrop, having found existing types of artificial vagina not to be entirely satisfactory for the dog, developed a new type which provided stimulation by a pulsating lining and did away with the need for a teaser bitch (Harrop, 1954a). An apparatus for obtaining ejaculation in the dog by electrical stimulation has also been described (Christensen and Dougherty, 1955).

The following account of the characteristics of canine semen is taken mainly from Harrop (1956a). The average ejaculate is about 10 ml., dogs of smaller breeds giving lesser amounts than those of larger breeds. The pH is about 6·75. The ejaculate consists of three fractions. The first is a clear watery fluid, devoid of spermatozoa, probably derived from the urethral mucosa and amounting to 0·25 ml. to 2·0 ml. The second fraction contains the spermatozoa and is whitish in colour and viscous in consistency and amounts to 0·5 ml. to 3·5 ml. The third fraction consists of watery prostatic secretion, 3 to 20 ml. in volume and with a pH of 7·2, higher than that of the other two fractions.

As with other animals, sperm density in the semen of the dog varies with breed, individual and time. A mass of information about the use of the artificial vagina for dogs in comparison with other methods and about the collection and characteristics of dog semen is given by Garcia (1957). His frequency curves show that small, medium and large dogs produced modal volumes of semen of 3·5 ml., 15 ml. and 40 ml. respectively. Average sperm concentration was 60 million per ml. The evaluation of semen quality in the dog and the effects on it of frequency of collection have been considered by Boucher, Foote and Kirk (1958). In Harrop's experience, the number of spermatozoa in more than 100 ejaculates varied from 4 to 540 million per ml., the average being about 125 million per ml. For insemination, Harrop deposited about 5 ml. of a 1 to 8 dilution of fraction 2 in the anterior part of the vagina. Insemination through the cervix was found to be difficult or impossible. The optimal time of insemination was about two days after the first acceptance of the male.

Letard, Szumowski and Théret (1957) give detailed figures for volume of the ejaculate and motility and density of the spermatozoa. They found, using fresh semen, that 60 per cent of the bitches became pregnant and produced litters of from one to nine pups. If the semen was concentrated to 150,000 spermatozoa per mm³, the insemination of 1 ml. was adequate. According to these authors, insemination might be effective, in extreme cases, when carried out a week or more after the beginning of heat.

Cat

Amoroso and Goffin (1957) have illustrated a procedure for A.I. in the cat.

Laboratory Mammals

Rabbit

Among laboratory animals, the rabbit is the most satisfactory animal for A.I. Semen collection can be made by means of the artificial vagina developed by Macirone and Walton (1938), and A.I. is simple. The technique has been used in many hundreds of experiments on the effects of dilution, on factors affecting survival of the spermatozoa and on the effects of *in vitro* treatment, which are described later. Unfortunately, rabbit semen is not abundant and even so is comparatively dilute. An ejaculate of 1 ml. containing 100 million spermatozoa is considered to be a good specimen. Experimental work is further complicated by the presence of large amounts of adventitious material, including, sometimes, blobs of jelly. On the other hand, the conception rate following A.I. is very high, and 40–50 eggs may be fertilised in a superovulated rabbit by this means. The fact that the doe rabbit ovulates 10–11 hours after mating, or gonadotrophin injection, means that insemination can be timed accurately in relation to ovulation and has made the rabbit a favourite subject for experiments on the survival of eggs and spermatozoa, and similar problems. Further information is given by Hammond (1952), by Walton in the preceding chapter of this volume, and in Sections V and VI of the present chapter.

Rowlands (1944), in confirmation of Walton's earlier results (Walton, 1927), found that it was necessary to inseminate of the order of one million spermatozoa to obtain full fertility. Fertility was much reduced when one-fifth of this number was used, and disappeared when only 100,000 spermatozoa were inseminated. Cheng and Casida (1948), on the other hand, obtained maximal fertility with 90,000, and partial fertility even when the number was decreased to 16,000. Chang's work (1946), however, implies that both total number of spermatozoa and density must be taken into account in such experiments. Moreover, the efficiency of a minimal number of rabbit spermatozoa in the female tract may be affected by the medium in which they are suspended before insemination. Chang (1949) found that human or rabbit seminal plasma increased the effectiveness of minimal numbers, as did suspensions in fructose-Ringer of dead spermatozoa of man, rabbit, or bull.

Guinea-pig

Other laboratory animals at present available are much less satisfactory than the rabbit. In the guinea-pig, ejaculation can be caused with moderate regularity by passing 33 volts through the head (Battelli, 1922), and the technique was extensively used by Moore and Gallagher (1930) in their work on the stimulation of the accessory glands by androgenic preparations. The reaction is apparently specific, and causes neither urination nor defaecation. The ejaculate consists of the contents of the seminal vesicles, prostate, vasa and Cowper's glands. According to Moore and Gallagher, first ejaculates were usually between 3 and 4 g. On regular weekly stimulation the average was about 2 g. Ejaculation in the guinea-pig can also be caused by the subcutaneous injection of 30–50 mg. of " Gravitol " (the di-ethyl-amino-ethyl-ether of 2-methoxy-6-allyl-phenol in the form of its hydrochloride) (Barkan, 1942). The ejaculate, however produced, instantly coagulates into a tough rubbery mass (see Chapter 8, p. 152), which was handy for weighing in Moore's work, but from which it is almost impossible to separate

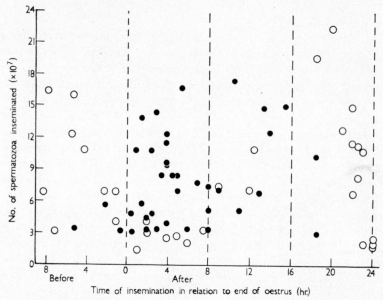

Fig. 9.6—Result of intraperitoneal insemination in the guinea-pig, according to stage of cycle and number of spermatozoa inseminated. (From Rowlands, 1957.)
  ● pregnancy
  ○ no pregnancy

spermatozoa for *in vitro* use or insemination unless drastically treated in some such way as described by Freund (1958). Fortunately, the vasa deferentia of the male guinea-pig contain masses of closely packed spermatozoa, which can easily be extruded. A coarse sperm suspension can also be made by macerating the epididymides in a suitable medium. Insemination must be made in relation to sexual receptivity which begins about 10 hours before ovulation (Myers, Young and Dempsey, 1936). There is no consistent relation between the nature of the vaginal smear and the occurrence of sexual receptivity (Young, 1937). Frequent observations must therefore be made after the opening of the vaginal membrane ; Blandau and Young (1939), for instance, tested the females for the copulatory response day and night at half-hourly intervals. Young (1931) inseminated 0·5 ml. of suspension through the cervix into the uterus and obtained 68 per cent of conceptions. Blandau and Young (1939) inseminated into the vagina and obtained an 83 per cent conception rate. Soderwall and Young (1940) were less successful with a rate of only 50 per cent, but their animals were thought to have intercurrent infection.

Other methods of insemination in guinea-pigs have been described. Kelly. *et al.* (1929) inseminated spermatozoa from the vasa deferentia direct into the ovarian bursa during the first stage of oestrus as defined by Stockard and Papanicolaou (1917) and obtained about two-thirds of pregnancies. Results of great interest were obtained by Rowlands (1957, 1958) in seeking a method of insemination which could be used at all stages of the reproductive cycle. Rowlands prepared, under aseptic conditions, a suspension of the contents of both vasa of an adult male in 0·6 ml. of Baker solution (Baker, 1931a) and injected 0·5 ml. intraperitoneally at various times in relation to the beginning of heat, which was determined by frequent testing of the females with males between 7 a.m. and midnight after opening of the vaginal orifice. His results are shown in Fig. 9.6, which indicates a high proportion of conceptions from insemination made 0 to 16 hours after the beginning of heat, but a very small proportion before or after that period. This intriguing experiment opens up many interesting questions as does its possible application to other mammals.

Rat and mouse

In the rat and mouse, collection of semen presents greater difficulties even than in the guinea-pig. Loewe (1937) reported that in mice the injection of a mixture of pernostone and yohimbin would cause ejaculation, and later that the response was facilitated by the use of parasympathomimetic drugs such as pilocarpine (Loewe, 1938). Electrically-induced ejaculation has also been described in the rat (Durfee, Lerner and Kaplan, 1940). Such methods are not very suitable for sperm collection, partly because they are not very reliable and partly because the ejaculate soon coagulates. For practical purposes, therefore, good suspensions of rat and mouse spermatozoa can be obtained only from the epididymis and vasa deferentia. Because the suspension has to be introduced into the female through a fine needle, the spermatozoa must be obtained by stripping from the lumen, not by maceration of the tissue. Methods used by various authors differ in detail, as do the media (saline, Locke's solution, etc.) in which the cells are collected. Dense suspensions are, however, readily obtained for *in vitro* treatment and A.I.

Coitus in the mouse and rat leads not only to the formation of a vaginal plug, but also to the stimulation of the cervix necessary to activate the adenohypophysis and so prolong the life of the corpora lutea of ovulation to allow the implantation of the embryos, which would otherwise be prevented by the recurrence of the five-day cycle. Artificial insemination in the rat may be effective without plug formation, provided that the cervix is stimulated by other means. In the mouse, electrical stimulation of the cervix is not effective (Shelesnyak and Davies, 1953). Long and Mark (1911) carried out A.I. on post-partum mice and obtained a number of animals with fertilised eggs. It is not very likely, however, that the fertilised eggs would have become implanted without stimulation of the cervix, the need for which was not recognised at the time.

A.I. in mice was attempted again by Merton (1939), who recorded a series of not very convincing experiments, but it remained for Snell and his co-workers to establish the practicability of the technique in mice. Insemination should be made during the period of sexual receptivity, which normally occurs in mice during the night. This cycle is light conditioned, and to permit observation to be made during the daytime Snell, Hummel and Abelmann (1944) used light-reversed animals, i.e. mice kept in the dark but illuminated artificially from 10.30 p.m. to 10.30 a.m. They carried out insemination direct into the uterus with the aid of a speculum, a head mirror and a blunt-pointed No. 19 needle. By turning the point to one side or the other in the cervix the needle could be introduced into either horn of the uterus as required (Fig. 9.7). The inseminated mice were then immediately placed with a vasectomised buck. Under these circumstances, a.m. matings produced 44·0 per cent and p.m. matings 69·0 per cent of pregnancies. The corresponding figures for normal matings were 46·2 per cent and 91·2 per cent. The time of onset of oestrus showed a clear mode 4–6 hours after the beginning of darkness. A technique similar to that of Snell and his co-workers was used by Edwards (1957a) in his work on experimental gynogenesis. Kile (1951), on the other hand, made intra-uterine injections of sperm suspensions at laparotomy within 1½ to 4½ hours of mating with a vasectomised buck. The pregnancy rate (71·8 per cent), however, was not obviously superior to that of Snell *et al.*

Fig. 9.7—A.I. in the mouse, showing method of introducing sperm-suspension through the cervix into one or other uterine horn. (By permission of the publisher from Fig. 2, Snell, G. D., Hummel, K. D., & Abelmann, W. H., *Anat. Rec.*, 1944, **90**, 248.)

Apart from the use of an artificial vaginal plug, and of electrical stimulation of the cervix, and the avoidance of any form of mating, the technique of Blandau and Jordan (1941) for the rat was the same as that described for the mouse, and according to the authors was as successful as normal mating. Ogawa and Suzuki (1955) described a method involving electrical stimulation of the cervix without the use of a vaginal plug, and state that the conception rate was almost normal.

Man

The collection of semen from normal men presents no difficulties. It may be obtained as a by-product of coitus, but the most obvious method is the best, and masturbation specimens are routinely used for seminological examinations in fertility clinics. Similar specimens are normally used for A.I. whether from the husband or a donor. Precautions to be taken in collection are outlined by Brown (1944a). The partitioning of ejaculates during collection, and the nature of the fractions, has also been described (e.g. MacLeod and Hotchkiss, 1942; Lundquist, 1949; Harvey, 1957). With abnormal men the collection of semen or spermatozoa may present difficulties, and in cases of impotence, anatomical defect and the like, many different devices have been used, including electrical stimulation, collection of nocturnal emissions, and testicular puncture. Hanley (1957) has recently described the successful use by A.I. of spermatozoa collected from an epididymal cyst artificially formed in a man with congenital absence of the vasa.

In man, as in other male animals, the volume of the ejaculate and the number, density and morphology of the spermatozoa vary greatly, even in individuals of known fertility, according to the individual and his general state of health, and particularly to the interval between ejaculations (e.g. Brown, 1943). Counts below a total of 20 million normal motile spermatozoa are usually held to be incompatible with fertility, but there are well authenticated exceptions to this rule. The total count in fertile men is usually between 100 million and 500 million. At the upper extreme counts approaching 1,000 million total, or 500 million per ml., have been recorded. The characteristics of 24 specimens of semen successfully used for A.I. are shown in Table III, taken from Farris (1950). The number of spermatozoa produced by man is paltry compared with that found in farm animals

TABLE III

SEMEN ANALYSES OF SPECIMENS USED IN SUCCESSFUL ARTIFICIAL INSEMINATION
(All samples taken after five days of abstinence)

	Median	Range
1. No. of men .	24	—
2. No. of analyses	24	—
3. Volume of ejaculate (ml.)	3·13	1·2–5·8
4. Active and inactive spermatozoa per ml. (millions) .	130	71–240
5. Active spermatozoa per ml. (millions)	57·5	31–123
6. Active and inactive spermatozoa in total ejaculate (millions)	412·5	82–899
7. Active spermatozoa in total ejaculate (millions) .	190	38–370
8. Percentage of active spermatozoa	46	30–66
9. Speed of spermatozoa (seconds to traverse 0·05 mm.)	0·9	0·6–1·6
10. Percentage of oval forms	86·3	78–93

(From Farris, 1950)

(see Hammond, 1952), among which the density record is held by the ram (up to 4,000 million per ml.) and the total number record by the boar (up to 250,000 million). The low density of spermatozoa in human semen and the abundance of adventitious matter makes the material inferior for metabolic and other in vitro studies. A mass of specialised information on human semen is, however, available in standard works on andrology, especially as to prognosis of fertility, nature and significance of abnormal forms of spermatozoa, and so on.

The use of A.I. in man at the present time is very restricted. It may be effective in overcoming certain forms of sterility in the male, e.g. hypospadias, congenital absence of the excurrent ducts and impotence, so long as spermato-genesis is not impaired. Its value in the much more numerous cases of oligo-spermia is less certain though it permits the selective use of partitioned ejaculates (Jackson, 1957a), and in general both the extent and the efficacy of A.I. from the husband, where the woman does not conceive as the result of normal coitus, is difficult to assess.   There is, of course, a field for A.I.H. in cases of unavoidable absence of the husband.   Where the husband is irrevocably sterile and the parental urge is strong, A.I. from a donor may be prefered to adopting a child.   The indications required to justify the use of A.I.D. have been debated at great length, and its moral and legal implications, being man-made, are of more interest to the ethnologist and the psychologist than to the biologist.   In Great Britain A.I.D. is a development of the last 20 years, and even now its use is very limited ; it may be doubted if more than a few score of children are born here each year as a result of the procedure.

Whether A.I.H. or A.I.D. is involved, the prospects of success depend on the insemination of an adequate number of viable spermatozoa at an appropriate time in the menstrual cycle, and the biological interest of A.I. in man turns on the assessment of these two requirements.   Insemination is usually made intra-cervically, and amounts of the order of 0·5 ml. can readily be introduced in this way.   With normal undiluted semen this amount will contain a great excess of spermatozoa over the 20 million usually regarded as the minimum number likely to be effective when introduced by coitus.   Unfortunately, the scarcity of cases has prevented any systematic determination of the minimum effective number, but by intra-cervical insemination it is likely to be less than by deposition into the vagina.

The time of ovulation during the menstrual cycle of women and methods of determining it have been considered in Volume I, Part 1 (Eckstein and Zuckerman, 1956).   The only safe conclusion is that ovulation usually occurs about the middle of a normal 28-day cycle, but that the time is subject to unpredictable variations and methods of determining it in any particular cycle are unreliable.   In all the circumstances, and allowing for administrative difficulties and the comparatively short survival of the spermatozoa in the female tract (*see* p. 233), it is not surprising that A.I.H. is a procedure of limited value when normal coitus has failed to result in pregnancy (Schellen, 1957—p. 193).   By contrast, the use of A.I.D. in uncom-plicated cases in man may be regarded as comparatively successful.   Schellen (1957), summarising individual reports, almost all post-1940 and from Great Britain, Europe and the United States, found that 778 patients out of a total of 1,311 had conceived by A.I.D.   The average number of inseminations per conception was not given.   Three reports may be considered individually, two of them relating to Great Britain.

Murphy and Farris (1953) used the excretion of gonadotrophin as determined by the rat hyperaemia test (*see* Chapter 25) to determine the time of ovulation. They obtained 66 conceptions in 52 women from 170 inseminations, a conception rate of 39 per cent.   Some of the inseminations were deliberately performed at an unfavourable time of the cycle.   Barton (1955), reviewing 10 years' experience with A.I.D., gives figures for 1951–2, during which pregnancy was obtained in 57·6 per cent of 66 cases, and for a more recent series of 24 patients of whom 54 per cent became pregnant.   The mean number of cycles for which treatment was required was 4·3.   The success rate was increased to 67·7 per cent if women showing stigmata of infertility were excluded.   In Barton's experience there was no dramatic fall in the conception rate in women over 35 years of age.

Finally, Jackson (1957b, c) reported that 57 women conceived out of 136 receiving A.I.D.   Of the failures, however, a substantial number gave up treatment, disappeared, or were probably infertile. Jackson determined the optimal time of cycle by combining all the information available from basal temperature charts, vaginal smears, cervical mucus and average length of cycle. Eighty-five per cent of the successful inseminations were done between 10 and 14 days after the beginning of menstruation. In one patient, Jackson brought about four successive pregnancies by A.I.D. Allowing for the general difficulties in carrying out A.I.D. under present conditions, for the difficulty of determining the time of ovulation, and for other adverse factors, these various conception rates, even though they are based on the number of patients rather than on the number of inseminations, are not unimpressive when compared with the non-return rate of 65–70 per cent obtained in cows after a single insemination made under the most favourable conditions. Barton reports that the miscarriage rate was no higher in A.I.D. pregnancies than in normal ones, and Jackson considers the health and intelligence of the children to be above average. Biologically, therefore, A.I.D. in man is a practicable and successful procedure, capable when methods of " banking " semen are more advanced (*see* p. 201) of almost unlimited development.

II. SURVIVAL OF SPERMATOZOA *IN VITRO* ABOVE 0° C.

Among vertebrates, studies on the survival of spermatozoa *in vitro* under various conditions are almost limited to fish, domestic fowl, laboratory and farm animals and man. The largest body of substantial and detailed information is available for the economically important cattle and sheep. Survival *in vitro* can obviously be assessed in various ways, especially by the retention of motility, of metabolic activity or of fertilising power. With bulls, the motility of the spermatozoa gives a fair indication of the fertilising capacity of the sample of semen (Bishop, Campbell, Hancock and Walton, 1954) but in other animals there may be great differences in the results given by the three indices. Generally speaking, only the capacity to effect normal fertilisation and give rise to a normal embryo is unequivocal evidence of functional survival. Even here the proportion of effectively surviving spermatozoa can be assessed only by a careful check on the number of spermatozoa inseminated in comparison with the number normally necessary.

Survival *in vitro* at temperatures above freezing point depends on many factors, of which temperature and the speed of changes therein, the nature of the medium and the degree of dilution, are the most important (*see* White, 1956). With these factors many variables are possible, but they have been little investigated except in the case of fowl, farm animals and the rabbit.

Fish

The retention of fertilising capacity in fish spermatozoa stored at temperatures above 0° C. has been discussed by Blaxter (1955). Dilution of the semen activates the spermatozoa, which then soon become exhausted ; this effect has been reported for several species, including salmonids (Huxley, 1930 ; Ellis and Jones, 1939) and the Volga herring (Stroganov, 1938). Storage experiments have therefore usually been carried out with undiluted " dry " material.

Early reports indicated that milt might retain partial fertility for some days, and Nakano and Nozawa (1925) and Kawajiri (1927) found that lower temperatures tended to be advantageous in the case of salmonid milt.   Trout spermatozoa stored under liquid paraffin at 2·2° to 3·3°C. by Butcher (1944) were fertile after 5 days, and those of the chum salmon stored " dry " by Barrett (1951) lost less than 10 per cent of their fertilising capacity in 36 hours.   Rucker (1949) preserved the fertilising capacity of salmon milt for 14 days at refrigerator temperature.

A more detailed investigation was carried out by Yanagimachi (1953), who found that herring spermatozoa retained fertilising capacity to a small extent for 12 hours in sea-water at 8° to 10°C., and for more than double this time in diluted Ringer and sea-water.   Blaxter (1955) compared the survival of fertilising capacity in herring spermatozoa stored " dry ", in sea-water, and in buffered sea-water with

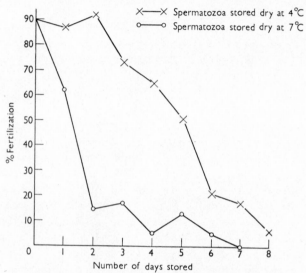

Fig. 9.8—Decline in fertilising capacity of herring spermatozoa stored at different temperatures. (From Blaxter, 1955.) (From Scottish Home Department, Marine Research No. 3, by permission of the Controller of H.M. Stationery Office.)

and without egg-yolk.   The addition of egg-yolk appeared to be beneficial, but the diluted preparations did not retain fertilising capacity as well as those stored " dry ".   Temperature also was found to be important (Fig. 9.8).

Detlaf and Ginsburg (1954) discuss in some detail the physiology of sturgeon spermatozoa *in vitro* and describe the results of earlier workers, of whom two may be mentioned here.   Shmidtov (1936) preserved the spermatozoa of the sturgeon and the " small sturgeon " at + 1°C. to + 4°C. and tested their viability by artificial semination.   The spermatozoa of the first species retained fertilising capacity for 5 to 8 days, and of the second for 12 days.   Persov (1941) found that sturgeon spermatozoa stored at + 1° to + 3°C. retained full fertilising capacity for 6 days, but then deteriorated.

Birds

Motility

Fowl spermatozoa will remain active for about 24 hours in neat semen kept at room temperature (Polge, 1950), and at 20°C. the spermatozoa are much more active than those of most mammals. Only when cooled to temperatures approaching 0°C. do they become completely immotile (Munro, 1938b ; Polge, 1955). In undiluted semen stored at 0°C. many of the spermatozoa show motility after 10–12 days when the specimen is re-warmed (Wheeler and Andrews, 1943 ; Polge, 1955 ; Ferrand and Bohren, 1948). Unlike the spermatozoa of many mammals, fowl spermatozoa in undiluted semen are comparatively resistant to thermal shock caused by sudden changes of temperature. Polge (1955) collected semen from birds direct into containers at 40°C., 10°C. and 0°C. Only at the lowest of these temperatures was there any irreversible change in the spermatozoa, and even then the majority regained motility on re-warming.

The effect of various diluents on the retention of motility in fowl spermatozoa was studied by Koch and Robillard (1945), who obtained their best results with

TABLE IV

DURATION OF MOTILITY OF FOWL SPERMATOZOA IN DILUTED SEMEN AT 2°C.

Diluent	Half-life of sperm (days)	Maximum life of sperm (days)
Ringer . . .	2	3
Ringer-Locke . .	2	4
Yolk-Ringer . .	3	6
Albumen-Ringer . .	4	7
Milk-Ringer . .	4	6
C.G.S. . . .	6	11
A.C.G.S. . . .	9	24
Oviduct-extract . .	8	15
Albumen . . .	6	14
Milk	1	3

(From Polge, 1955)

Ringer containing 2 per cent glucose, and by Grodzinski and Marchlewski (1935), who found a medium composed of serum, embryo extract and egg albumen to be superior to Tyrode's solutions for the maintenance of motility. More detailed observations on the effects of composition and pH of the medium were made by Jasper (1950), Hofkens (1950) and Bogdonoff and Shaffner (1954). Lorenz and Tyler (1951) recorded the interesting observations that motility at 22°C. was extended by the addition of glycine to the medium. Smith (1949a) devised a medium (C.G.S.) consisting of saline, glucose and egg-white, buffered with citrate, in which some spermatozoa retained potential motility for 19 days at $+ 2$°C. Polge's (1955) results were as shown in Table IV. In general, the use of diluents did not extend dramatically the survival of motility either at 20° or 0°C.

Fertilising capacity

In contrast to the long retention of motility, fowl spermatozoa retain fertilising capacity for only a very short time on storage above freezing point by present methods. Garren and Shaffner (1952) found that the optimal temperature was 10°C., though even here the practical storage time was only 6 hours. Fertilising capacity decreased more rapidly on storage at + 15°C. and was negligible after 90 minutes at 20°, 30° or 40°C. At 0° or 5°C. fertilising capacity dropped sharply after a few minutes. Polge (1950, 1955) found that:—

(a) the best results with neat semen were obtained on storage at + 10°C., but even so fertilising capacity had almost disappeared at 24 hours.

(b) rapid cooling damaged fertilising capacity much more than it had been found to damage motility.

(c) the best of the diluents (ACGS; glucose, NaCl, citrate-phosphate buffer, and thin egg-white) improved the fertilising capacity of spermatozoa stored for

TABLE V

Fertilising Capacity of Semen Diluted 1/10 with A.C.G.S. and Stored at 20°C. and 2°C.

(1·0 ml. diluted semen inseminated per bird)

Time stored (hours)	Percentage fertility of eggs laid following a single insemination			
	Stored at 20°C.		Stored at 2°C.	
	1st week (days 2–7)	2nd week (days 8–14)	1st week (days 2–7)	2nd week (days 8–14)
0	76	30	—	—
1	66	24	68	31
2	46	10	53	15
4	38	3	77	24
8	30	0	41	3
24	0	0	0	0
48	3	0	0	0

(From Polge, 1955)

periods up to 8 hours at 20° or 2°C., the effect being most evident in the improved fertility of eggs laid during the second week after a single insemination, i.e. in the longer survival of the spermatozoa in the oviduct (Table V). Polge obtained essentially similar results with a diluent made by mixing equal quantities of cow's milk and buffered citrate-glucose-saline.

Undiluted semen was found by Hunsaker, Aitken and Lindblad (1956) to retain fertilising capacity better at 10°C. to 20°C. than at 0° and 30°C. for periods up to 9 hours.

This failure of fowl semen to maintain fertilising capacity for more than a few hours, although maintaining motility for several days, contrasts sharply not only with results obtained with mammalian spermatozoa, but also with the long survival of fowl spermatozoa in the oviduct. It accords, however, with results obtained on turkey semen, in which fertilising capacity declines rapidly after one hour *in vitro* (Harper, 1955).

Domestic Mammals

The survival of motility and fertilising capacity in the spermatozoa of farm animals maintained *in vitro* at temperatures above 0°C. has been reviewed by Hammond (1952) and is further considered in Chapter 9A of the present volume. Only salient features and recent work will be considered here in order to give base-lines for the results of long-term storage described in Section III.

Bull spermatozoa retain motility for only a few hours at body temperature, and for about 12 hours at room temperature. The optimal temperature for storage above freezing point is about + 4°C., provided that the temperature is lowered gradually to avoid thermal shock. Efforts to devise media which would improve the performance of bull spermatozoa led to the introduction of egg-yolk buffer medium by Lardy and Phillips (1939). This medium was found to decrease liability to thermal shock and to extend the useful life of semen stored at + 4°C. from 3 days to 5 days. Fertilising capacity, and to a lesser extent motility, have, however, already decreased at 3 days and both fall rapidly after this period (Hagelberg, 1952).

Many attempts have been made to improve survival still further both by the elaboration of synthetic media and by the introduction of new preparations. Frank, Smith and Eichhorn

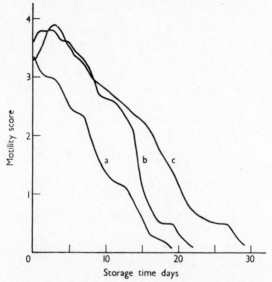

Fig. 9.9—Motility of bull spermatozoa stored at 4°C. in (*a*) 3·2 per cent sodium citrate egg-yolk, (*b*) 3·0 per cent glycine egg-yolk, and (*c*) 4·5 per cent glycine egg-yolk. (From Bishop, 1954.)

(1941) secured prolonged motiltiy of bull spermatozoa at + 2°C. by the use of embryo extract, but fertilising capacity was not recorded. Interesting observations were initiated by Tyler and Tanabe (1952), who found that the addition of glycine to the medium extended the motility of bull spermatozoa at 38·5°C., but not at 4°C. This work was extended by Roy and Bishop (1954), and Fig. 9.9, taken from Bishop (1954), shows that the addition of 4·5 per cent glycine to the yolk-citrate buffer nearly doubles the time for which a moderate motility (score 2) is maintained. Unfortunately, fertilising capacity was found not to be correspondingly prolonged. Another diluent which has been extensively investigated, since its introduction by Mihailov (*see* Emmens and Blackshaw, 1956) as a horse semen diluent, is whole or skimmed milk. Reports, summarised by Emmens and Blackshaw (1956), as to its value with bull semen differ, but several workers, including Kerruish (1956), have come to the conclusion that it is superior to yolk-citrate medium. Willett and Ohms (1958a) call attention to the reversible immobilisation caused by lactate and point out the inadequacy of motility as a criterion of viability. The value of the luminal fluids of the cow's genital tract as diluents for bull semen was investigated by Olds and VanDemark (1957), who found that under anaerobic conditions at 37°C. spermatozoa remain motile for 7 hours in uterine fluid, 9 hours in cervical mucus, 12 hours in oviducal fluid, and 19 hours in follicular fluid.

Much information on dilution and diluents is summarised by Salisbury (1957) and by Emmens and Blackshaw (1956), whose conclusion about storage of bull semen above 0°C. is as follows :

" As long as temperature shock is avoided semen for A.I. is best stored, unless deeply frozen, at a little above freezing point. A temperature of 4–5°C. is commonly employed. Although the time for which semen may be stored successfully at such temperatures depends on the nature of the diluent, none has proved capable of extending the storage time beyond a matter of days without a fall in motility and fertility. Recent data from a variety of sources are in good general agreement that, even with the best of modern diluents, a fall of 5 or 6 per cent per day of storage occurs in the fertility of bull semen."

Chang and Walton (1940) found that ram spermatozoa, judged by respiratory rate and survival, were susceptible to temperature shock. The maintenance of motility and fertilising capacity of ram spermatozoa has since received considerable attention (Dauzier, Thibault and Wintenberger, 1954). Quinlan and Steyn (1941) concluded that dilutors with a pH of 6·9 to 6·99 gave the best result, and that ram semen could safely be stored for 12 hours but that fertilising power afterwards decreased up to 72 hours and was then lost. According to Kuznetsov (1956) a technique of maintaining ram spermatozoa for several days at 0°C. was evolved by scientists in the U.S.S.R., but the fertilising capacity decreased. Roy, Gupta, Srivastava and Pandey (1956) reported that glycine-containing media were beneficial to ram spermatozoa stored at + 4°C. For the pig, Niwa (1958) gives figures which show that if the semen is used within 24 hours the conception rate per insemination may be as high as 76·8 per cent, but that by the third day of storage the rate has fallen to 28·6 per cent. In the goat, Blokhuis (1957) found that a diluent composed of 3 per cent citrate buffer and 5 per cent egg-yolk was by far the most efficient in respect of both conception rate and survival of motility.

The use of antibiotic and sulpha drugs to check bacterial growth in stored semen has been much investigated, and experiments on a vast scale have been carried out. There is general agreement that conception rates are improved by the use of the bacteriostatic substances. Willett and Ohms (1954) record results based on 104,000 inseminations, for which the basic medium was egg-yolk citrate. Results were : no antibiotics, 63·2 per cent ; streptomycin, 500 µg./ml., 67·0 per cent. ; streptomycin 500 µg./ml. plus penicillin 500 U./ml., 67·2 per cent. ; streptomycin, 500 µg./ml. plus sulphanilamide 300 mg./100 ml., 70·2 per cent. The subject is fully reviewed by Emmens and Blackshaw (1956) and is further discussed in Chapter 9A.

The constant effort to increase the efficiency with which semen is used in insemination centres has prompted much work on dilution effects. The degree of dilution is important in two ways. Firstly, it may be so great as to reduce the number of spermatozoa inseminated below the minimum number required to give a high probability of the egg or eggs being fertilised. Two investigations among the many in cattle may be mentioned. Salisbury and his colleagues (1945, 1946a, b, 1948) found a drop of 0·8 per cent in the non-return rate for each decrease of one million in the number of spermatozoa inseminated, between two million and 15 million. Willett (1953) found in a large-scale field experiment that the non-return rate of cows dropped significantly from 68·2 per cent to 62·4 per cent when dilution was increased from 1/100 to 1/300. Secondly, dilution affects the retention of motility. There is some difference of opinion, summarised by Willett (1953), as to the extent to which this effect operates in bull semen stored above 0°C. at dilutions not greater than 1/100. There is agreement that very high dilution results in rapid loss of motility and fertilising capacity. The effect is much influenced by the nature of the medium.

According to Emmens (1947), the capacity to resist the dilution effect was the basis of Milovanov's test for assessing the value of a semen specimen for A.I. Blackshaw (1953), in 5-hour tests, compared the retention of motility in bull and ram spermatozoa at densities of 20 million and 0·4 million per ml. In glucose–sodium citrate medium full motility was retained in the 5-hour test with the higher density, but almost lost at the lower one. A clue to the nature of this effect is to be found in the observation that it can be avoided by making the dilution with fresh bull seminal plasma or certain other substances, and that repeated washing of ram and bull spermatozoa causes irreversible immobilisation. Blackshaw (1953) concludes that the latter effect is due to the leaching out of potassium salts from the cell. It may also be recalled that the replacement of the seminal plasma in a stored specimen with the supernatant fluid of a fresh specimen revives the failing motility of the spermatozoa. According to Szumowski (1952) this effect is due to the renewal of fructose, buffering substances and protective substances which prevent the fatal increase in permeability of the cell wall.

Dog

Recent interest in A.I. in the dog has led to several studies on the preservation of the semen. Bederke (1933) recorded that normal dog semen remained alive for 21 hours, and Freiberg (1935) that the spermatozoa survived better if the fraction containing them, the second part of the ejaculate, was separated from the other two. Gutiérrez Nales (1957) also recommended that for storage the sperm-containing fraction should be separated from the rest of the ejaculate, and he found that when the semen was diluted with yolk-citrate medium the spermatozoa retained motility for 240 hours at +5°C. Brochart and Coulomb (1952) noted that dog spermatozoa showed a 50 per cent motility after 4 days' storage in a hypotonic medium composed of sodium citrate, egg-yolk, and fructose, the hypotonicity being a favourable factor. These authors did not, however, study the fertilising capacity of the preserved specimens. Harrop (1954b) diluted the sperm-containing fraction of a greyhound ejaculate 1:8 with pasteurised milk and stored the preparation at 4°C. Four days later the diluted semen was used for inseminating a bitch in the 12th day of heat. Two male pups were subsequently produced. Similar preparations were later flown to the United States, where one conception was achieved with 6-day-old semen (Harrop, 1956b). Analogous observations are recorded by Bendorf and Chung (1958), who sent semen from California to the Hawaiian Islands.

As Harrop points out, the international exchange of canine semen is of special interest because of the quarantine difficulties surrounding the import and export of entire dogs.   Antibiotics were found by Bendorf and Chung (1958) not to increase survival time.   A careful comparison of various media including milk and yolk-citrate has been made by Davoine (1958).

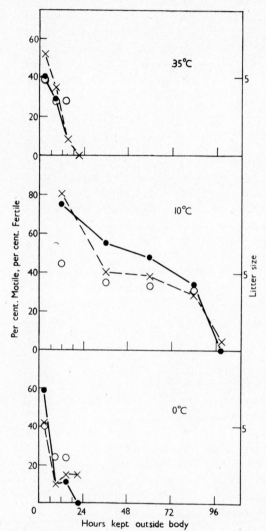

Fig. 9.10—Effect of temperature of storage on motility and fertilising capacity of rabbit spermatozoa, and on number in resulting litters. (From Hammond, 1930.)

   × ---- = motility
   ● ——— = fertilising capacity
   ○   = number in litter

Laboratory Mammals

Rabbit

In early experiments, Hammond (1930) found that rabbit spermatozoa obtained from the vagina of a matéd female retained fertilising power for 84 hours at 10°C. Temperatures higher or lower were less favourable.   Spermatozoa from the vas deferens, stored under liquid paraffin, behaved similarly except that the maximum survival time was longer, about 7 days.   Hammond's results (Fig. 9.10) were of interest in showing that loss of motility and fertilising capacity was about as rapid at 0°C. as at 35°C.

Cole, Waletzky and Shackelford (1940) record that no motility was seen in rabbit spermatozoa outside the range of pH 5·0–8·8, and Casida and Murphree (1942) found that the addition of 5 per cent sodium bicarbonate to rabbit semen often immobilised the spermatozoa.   More extensive observations were made by Emmens (1947), who worked at room temperature and who observed that acid pHs were more damaging than alkaline ones, and some of whose results are shown in Figs. 9.11 and 9.12.   It will be seen that at the optimal pH survival was good for more than 24 hours.   It was also found that brief immobilisation due to acidity could be reversed by the addition of alkali.   Emmens later (1948) investigated the interaction of pH and tonicity and found that at pH 7·0–8·7 hypo- and hypertonicity were about equally harmful, whereas hypotonicity was more so at low pHs and hypertonicity at high pHs.   In neither experiment was the fertilising

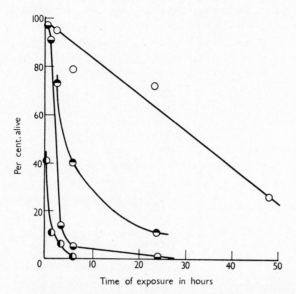

Fig. 9.11—Survival of rabbit spermatozoa after exposure
to different hydrogen-ion concentrations (acid pHs).
(Initial percentage living = 100.) (From Emmens,
1947.)
O—O pH 7·5
●—● pH 6·5
●—● pH 5·5
◖—◖ pH 4·5

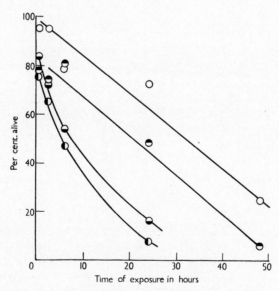

Fig. 9.12—Survival of rabbit spermatozoa after exposure to different hydrogen-ion concentrations
(alkaline pHs). (Initial percentage living = 100.)
(From Emmens, 1947.)
O—O pH 7·5
●—● pH 8·7
●—● pH 9·7
◖—◖ pH 10·2 approximately

capacity of the spermatozoa investigated. The dilution effect in rabbit semen was investigated by Emmens and Swyer (1947), who found that motility was normal and well maintained for 24 hours at a dilution of 20 million cells per ml., but almost abolished when dilution was increased to give only 400,000 cells per ml. They also found that the addition of starch, glycogen and serum protein had a temporary protective effect.

Guinea-pig

Baker (1930) used guinea-pig epididymal spermatozoa in work designed to find a diluent which would keep mammalian spermatozoa in maximum activity for the maximum time. Baker's semen diluent has become so well known that a typical experiment carried out by him at 37°C. with spermatozoa from one guinea-pig is cited in Table VI :

TABLE VI

Hours after start of experiment	Buffered glucose-saline	Ringer
$1\frac{1}{2}$	The majority very active	Less than 50 per cent moderately active
3	The majority moderately active	Less than 50 per cent moderately active
$5\frac{1}{2}$	The majority very active	Slight movement detected in a few sperms
$7\frac{1}{4}$	The majority moderately active	All dead
$9\frac{1}{2}$	Rather less than 50 per cent moderately active	All dead

His diluent, as slightly improved later by increasing its alkalinity (Baker, 1931a) contained:

Glucose	3·0 g.
$Na_2HPO_4.12H_2O$	0·6 g.
Sodium chloride	0·2 g.
KH_2PO_4	0·01 g.
Distilled water	100 c.c.

With the advent of A.I. in the guinea-pig, Locke's fluid appears to have been adequate for the rapid dilution and insemination of epididymal spermatozoa (Blandau and Young, 1939).

Mouse and rat

Few systematic attempts have yet been made to preserve the spermatozoa of the smaller laboratory rodents at temperatures above 0°C., or to study the effect of different media. The various workers mentioned in Section I all used the ordinary physiological media, Locke's, Tyrode's, saline or slight modifications of them. According to Edwards (1957a), mouse spermatozoa tolerate 0·75 per cent NaCl better than rat spermatozoa.   Ogawa and Suzuki (1956) investigated the survival time of rat spermatozoa in various artificial media and tissue homogenates.   In liver extract with glucose the spermatozoa maintained activity for 24 days.

Man

Human semen is not good experimental material and much less is known about the survival of spermatozoa *in vitro* under different conditions than might be expected.

Joël and Pollak (1939) record that 80 per cent of spermatozoa showed normal motility in isotonic glucose, but motion ceased after 16 hours.   Isotonic glucose–Mg salt mixtures were most potent in restoring or increasing motility. Jackson (1957b) records that semen for A.I. can satisfactorily be diluted with buffered-glucose medium and kept at + 4°C. Under these conditions fertilising capacity may be maintained for up to 15 hours.   She also reports, however, that an exceptional specimen, kept without special precautions for 28 hours, retained normal fertilising capacity in the sense that its use for A.I. led to a normal live birth.

Harvey (personal communication) summarises her observations as follows :

" In undiluted plasma spermatozoa may survive at room temperature (15–20°C.) for 5 days, but at this time the seminal fluid is usually heavily contaminated with bacteria.   The survival time in buffered glucose + antibiotics is about 24 hours longer for any

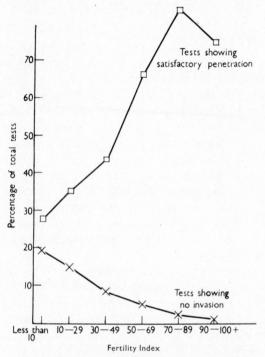

Fig. 9.13—Penetration of human cervical mucus *in vitro* according to fertility index of semen. (From Harvey, 1953.)

given specimen, i.e. spermatozoa surviving 3 days in plasma will survive 4 days in diluted plasma.   The actual percentage motility after 24 hours is very low, usually less than 10 per cent in plasma and not more than 25 per cent in diluent.   At temperatures near 37°C. only 1 to 5 per cent of the spermatozoa will remain progressively active for 24 hours in diluted semen.   In a few cases progressing spermatozoa have been found after 48 hours at 35°C.   At domestic refrigerator temperatures the behaviour of human spermatozoa is erratic, but we have had 10 per cent motility after 7 days in one instance (diluted with an equal volume of buffered glucose).   After 24 to 48 hours one may get 25 per cent progressing, but the speed of movement is greatly reduced.   All these figures are for really good semen, and even some first-class samples succumb very quickly."

Harvey (1953) has described a method for calculating a fertility index from the observed motility, density and morphology of the spermatozoa, top score being 140, and correlated the results with the capacity of the spermatozoa to penetrate cervical mucus *in vitro* (Fig. 9.13). In the human subject great difficulty naturally arises in comparing any *in vitro* index with conception rate. With natural insemination time-to-time variation in semen quality presents an unknown variable and systematic investigation by A.I. is not possible. In an investigation on sub-fertile couples Harvey concluded that if the man had a fertility index over 70, the infertility was mainly due to the woman ; if below 30, the man was likely to be infertile in his own right.

III. EFFECTS OF FREEZING AND THAWING : LONG-TERM PRESERVATION OF SPERMATOZOA

Experiments on the biological effects of sub-zero temperatures have been carried out sporadically for centuries. Much of this work had as its background the idea that the biochemical processes of life would be arrested at low temperatures so that if a living cell could be frozen without damage it could be held in a state of suspended animation. Unfortunately, almost all the normal cells of vertebrates were found to be extremely sensitive to freezing and thawing. Spermatozoa conformed to this generalisation, with one exception. As long ago as 1866, Mantegazza had shown that a proportion of human spermatozoa would withstand freezing to $- 17°$C. and subsequent thawing. Work during the present century confirmed this observation, though the exact conditions of the manipulation were obviously critical. Little attention was paid to the exceptional resistance of the human spermatozoon, and the prospects of being able to preserve animal spermatozoa at sub-zero temperatures were generally considered to be poor.

In general, two different approaches have been made to the problem of avoiding the damage caused by freezing. The first arose from Luyet's work on vitrification. According to this author, if minute amounts of material are cooled ultra-rapidly in one of the liquid gases, at say $100°$ C. per sec., the formation of ice crystals is prevented and the water solidifies amorphously in a way which is not damaging to the cell. Hoagland and Pincus (1942) failed signally to revive rabbit or bull spermatozoa treated in this way, but, according to Kuznetsov (1956), Smirnov in 1947–9 obtained living young with rabbit semen, and later with ram and bull semen, vitrified by rapid cooling. Smirnov gave a vague account of his methods in 1951.

Much greater progress has been made along the second approach—the use of protective substances. Indifferent results were obtained with sugars, but two suggestive indications were obtained with other materials. The first was Luyet and Hartung's (1941) observation that ethylene glycol, used by them as a dehydrating agent, greatly assisted the eel-worm to resist the damaging effects of freezing and thawing. The second pointer was Rostand's (1946) observation that a larger proportion of frog spermatozoa regained motility after exposure to $- 4°$ or $- 6°$C. if 10 per cent of glycerol was added to the fluid in which they were suspended. The significance of these clues to the use of protective substances was not appreciated at the time and the extensive use of glycerol and other neutral solutes to protect living cells against the effects of freezing and thawing derives from the chance observation, made by Polge, Smith and Parkes in 1949, that the

addition of 10 per cent glycerol to the medium had a remarkable effect in protect-
ing fowl spermatozoa against the otherwise fatal effects of freezing and thawing.

Fish

Blaxter (1953) successfully applied the glycerol-freezing technique to herring
spermatozoa.   Testis tissue was removed from the newly dead fish and placed in
sea-water diluted with four volumes of distilled water, and fortified with 12·5 per
cent glycerol w/w.   Diluted sea-water was used to minimise hypertonicity effects
to which herring spermatozoa had been found to be sensitive.   The material was
bottled in plastic-topped tubes left at about 8°C. for 30 minutes and then frozen
and stored at − 79°C.   Preparations thawed after 14 days or after about 6 months
retained fertilising power not significantly different from that of fresh preparations.   Slow addition or removal of the glycerol was not necessary.   By contrast,
preparations stored at − 28·9°C. were not fertile after 6 months.   By means of
this technique Blaxter was able, for the first time, to cross spring- and autumn-
spawning races of herring.

Sneed and Clemens (1956) applied the technique to the preservation of carp
milt, and revived about 20 per cent of the spermatozoa after 60 hours' storage at
− 73°C.   Fertilising capacity was not investigated.   The authors emphasised
that no spermatozoa survived freezing in the absence of protective substances and
that further work was required to improve the basic medium.

Amphibians

In 1938, Luyet and Hodapp reported that they had been able to revive a proportion of frog spermatozoa which had been partially dehydrated in 2M sucrose,
frozen in a thin film in liquid air and thawed rapidly at + 20°C.   Rostand's subsequent experiment on frog spermatozoa treated with glycerol has been noted
above.   No attempt was made by these workers to test the fertilising capacity of
the resuscitated spermatozoa.

Birds

Laevulose had been used by Luyet and Gehenio (1940) to effect partial
dehydration of cells before freezing, and this technique, though not apparently
ultra-rapid freezing, was applied by Shaffner, Henderson and Card (1941) to fowl
spermatozoa.   These authors added laevulose to semen samples in amounts calculated to give 0·7 M, and froze them to − 76°C. between cakes of solid CO_2.
On thawing, up to 35 per cent of the spermatozoa resumed motility.   Long-term
freezing, up to 14 months, did not much affect the revivability of the spermatozoa.
Experiments on fertilising capacity of the frozen and thawed spermatozoa were,
however, disappointing ; some fertile eggs were obtained following insemination
of spermatozoa which had been frozen for 1 hour in CO_2, but in no case did
embryonic development proceed more than 15 hours (Shaffner, 1942).

Attempts by Polge, Smith and Parkes (1949) to repeat these experiments were
unsuccessful, but in the course of the work they made the observation, referred
to above, of the protective action of glycerol.   The optimal concentration of
glycerol was 10 to 15 per cent and the prolongation of freezing for some days
did not detectably affect the result.   Insemination of the frozen and thawed

semen, however, failed to result in fertilisation (Smith and Polge, 1950b). It was then found that the addition of 15 per cent glycerol destroyed the fertilising capacity of fowl semen, frozen or unfrozen, although motility was if anything enhanced. Two per cent was the maximum that could safely be added without affecting the fertilising capacity of the semen. This low concentration of glycerol gave scant protection against freezing, but three chicks were obtained, which served to show that there was nothing inherently incompatible between exposure to low temperatures and the retention of fertilising capacity. Further progress was not made until parallel experiments with red blood cells (Smith, 1950; Sloviter, 1951) had suggested that the infertility of treated fowl semen might be due to osmotic stresses set up when the glycerolised spermatozoa

TABLE VII

FERTILISING CAPACITY OF SEMEN AFTER LONG-TERM STORAGE AT — 79°C. AND — 192°C.

(Semen frozen in 15 per cent glycerol, dialysed after thawing. 1·0 ml. inseminated per bird)

| Time semen stored | Percentage fertility of eggs laid following a single insemination | | | |
| | Semen stored at —79°C. | | Semen stored at —192°C. | |
	1st week (days 2–7)	2nd week (days 8–14)	1st week (days 2–7)	2nd week (days 8–14)
1 week	18	6	21	4
2 weeks	10	2	26	2
5 ,,	7	0	12	0
10 ,,	4	0	12	2
20 ,,	0	0	12	0
30 ,,	0	0	14	0
1 year	0	0	0	0

(From Polge, 1955).

made contact with the normal fluids of the oviduct. The glycerol was therefore removed by slow dialysis from unfrozen specimens, which were then found to have retained normal fertility. Dialysis of the frozen and thawed specimens caused the death of about 50 per cent of the spermatozoa ; insemination of the surviving ones in *pro rata* numbers led to more than half of the eggs laid in the first week after insemination being fertile ; hatchability was 71 per cent and the chicks (35 in all) were normal (Polge, 1951). Semen frozen for more than one hour had decreased fertilising power, but some live chicks were obtained from semen held at — 79°C. for 33 days. This evidence of an unexpected loss of viability at — 79°C. suggested that physical as well as biochemical activity would have to be considered in the low-temperature preservation of living cells. Polge (1955) fully confirmed the loss of viability, but showed that preservation of fowl spermatozoa was better at — 192° C. in liquid air. His results for the first year are shown in Table VII.

So far little other work has been done on the freezing of fowl spermatozoa, though Allen and Bobr (1955) confirmed Polge's observations on the failure of glycerolised spermatozoa to effect fertilisation, and found that the disability could be avoided to some extent by insemination higher into the tract.

Cattle

The practical value of being able to preserve spermatozoa for indefinite periods in the frozen state was, of course, most obvious in cattle, in which it seemed likely that such a technique would greatly increase the efficiency of A.I. centres, permit the nomination of sires, facilitate progeny testing to a remarkable extent, and promote international exchange of genetic material. For this reason, Smith and Polge (1950a), having made progress with fowl spermatozoa, turned their attention to bull spermatozoa, and a vast amount of work has now been carried out on this material. Various general accounts and reviews may be consulted for further details, e.g. Polge and Parkes (1952), Parkes (1954, 1956), Smith (1954), Emmens and Blackshaw (1955), Bruce (1956), Polge (1957), Rowson (1956).

The work of Smith, Polge and Rowson

Smith and Polge found that bull spermatozoa tolerated diluents containing 10 per cent glycerol and could be returned abruptly to a normal medium without damage. However, the comparatively quick freezing obtained by plunging a small tube into alcohol cooled with CO_2, which had proved satisfactory for fowl spermatozoa, was fatal to bull spermatozoa.

At this stage, Smith and Polge, recognising the necessity for slow cooling above zero, introduced the idea of slow cooling below zero, and found that more than half of the spermatozoa resumed motility on warming if the glycerolised semen was cooled slowly at the rate of about 2°C. per min. to − 15°C. and then more rapidly. This slow cooling was achieved by step-wise transference to successively cooler alcohol baths. The general nature of the cooling curve is shown in Fig. 9.14. Later, an insulated container, which gave about the same rate of cooling when surrounded by alcohol at − 79°C., was designed by Polge and Lovelock (1952). In the first experiment on the fertilising capacity of the frozen and thawed semen, at Shinfield, one cow out of five inseminated produced a calf (Stewart, 1951), but a larger-scale experiment at Cambridge gave no results except to show that glycerol alone did not affect fertilising capacity. In the following year, a second trial was carried out in Cambridge during which Polge introduced two modifications in the handling of the semen : (a) the addition of glycerol-containing citrate buffer to the semen in egg-yolk diluent already cooled to + 5°C., and (b) the overnight equilibration of the spermatozoa with the glycerol-containing medium. The results were dramatic. Thirty-eight cows were inseminated with semen which had been frozen at − 79°C. for periods varying from 2 hours to 8 days, and 6 weeks later thirty of them were diagnosed clinically as being pregnant (Polge and Rowson, 1952a). In the light of these results a " bank " of bull semen was laid down and by the end of the year Polge and Rowson (1952b) were able to report that semen stored for up to 8 months at −79° C. had shown an overall conception rate on 128 cows of 69 per cent. Results for up to one year with this same batch of semen were given by Rowson and Polge (1953) and are shown in Table VIII, which is reproduced because it constitutes a landmark in both cattle breeding and experimental biology. Various references to later results with this original material have been made from time to time in the writings of Rowson and Polge. The history of the work on the freezing and long-term preservation of semen in Great Britain, 1949–52, has been given by Parkes (1957a).

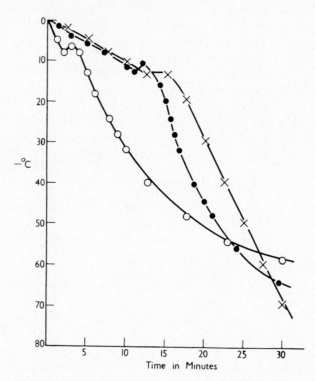

Fig. 9.14—Cooling of 1·0 ml. of a 15 per cent glycerol solution contained in a 1 cm. diameter ampoule. (From Polge and Lovelock, 1952.)

    ×—× By successive transfer through increasingly colder baths.

    O—O By immersion of the ampoule insulated with polythene in a bath at −79°C.

    ●—● By immersion of the ampoule, contained in a cooling vessel, in a bath at −79°C.

Investigation of variables

Early confirmation of the results of Polge and Rowson was forthcoming from both Great Britain and elsewhere. Since 1952 almost every technical detail of the methods of freezing bull semen has been worked over, and many variations of technique have been introduced as to the nature of the medium, time of equilibration, rate of freezing, rate of thawing, and so on. General consideration of variables has been made by Jones, Perkins and Seath (1956) and VanDemark, Miller, Kinney, Rodriguez and Friedman (1957).

Nature of the diluent. The addition of glycerol to the medium was repeatedly found to be innocuous (Bruce, 1953 ; Holt, 1953 ; Dunn, Larson and Willet, 1953) ; but its presence interfered with the live-dead staining reaction (Saroff and Mixner, 1954, and others). Conception rates of 70 to 75 per cent were obtained by several of the comparatively early workers (Holt, 1953 ; Stower, 1953 ; Swanney, 1953). Replacement of the sodium citrate by potassium buffers increased the damage to the semen (Moss, 1953). Lower concentrations of glycerol were reported to be effective by some workers (Miller and VanDemark, 1953). Emmens and Blackshaw (1950) and Blackshaw (1955) found the addition of certain sugars, such as arabinose, to be beneficial. The egg-yolk diluent can be replaced

TABLE VIII

LONG-TERM STORAGE OF BULL SEMEN AT − 79°C.

(Dilution, 1 : 4. Final concentration of glycerol, 10 per cent)

Time of storage (weeks)	Number of cows	Conception rate (per cent)
1–4	16	50
5–8	16	69
9–12	16	63
13–16	16	63
17–20	16	50
21–24	16	69
25–28	16	38
29–32	16	56
33–36	16	69
37–40	16	69
41–44	16	56
45–48	16	75
49–52	16	75

(From Rowson and Polge, 1953)

by milk (Graham and Marion, 1953 ; Amann and Almquist, 1957). Other aspects of the method of dilution and nature of the diluent were examined by Dyrendahl (1954), Rowson (1956), Hafs and Elliott (1955), de Groot (1955), Kinney and VanDemark (1954), Saroff and Mixner (1955), Cragle *et al.* (1955), Polge (1957), O'Dell and Almquist (1954), Erickson, Graham and Frederick (1954).

Time of equilibration. The optimal time of equilibration has been a subject of some controversy. Emmens and Blackshaw (1955), Emmens and Martin (1957) and others, found no great advantage in prolonged equilibration, and O'Dell and Hurst (1955) considered that it might even be harmful. On the other hand, Blackshaw *et al.* (1957), Bruce (1956), Miller and VanDemark (1954) and others, obtained better results when equilibration was allowed to proceed for 6–18 hours. Evidently, the nature of the diluent, the previous treatment of the semen, the rate of freezing and various other factors affect experiments of this kind (*see* Polge, 1957).

Rate of freezing. A radical alteration in the original technique of Smith and Polge may be foreshadowed by the work of Luyet and Keane (1955). These workers used semen which had been diluted with sodium citrate, egg-yolk and 7 per cent glycerol in the usual way, equilibrated for 24 hours and distributed into tubes 9 mm. in diameter, in 0·2 ml. quantities. The tubes were immersed abruptly in freezing mixtures at temperatures ranging from — 20°C. to —50°C. Five minutes later the tubes were transferred to liquid nitrogen at —196°C. When the intermediate-stage temperature was —20C°. no spermatozoa could be revived. Maximal viability, amounting to 75 per cent, was found when the semen was rested at —27°C. The results of Luyet and Keane were confirmed and extended by Polge (1957). The fertilising capacity of bull spermatozoa frozen by the two-stage method has not yet been investigated. Various attempts to maintain the semen at temperatures between 0°C. and — 79°C. gave unpromising results (Dunn, Hafs and Young, 1953). Other information about freezing rate is given by O'Dell, Almquist and Marsh (1958).

Rate of thawing. An interesting observation related to the temperature at which the material was thawed. It is important to raise the temperature rapidly through the critical range (Polge, 1953b), but samples thawed in water at + 20°C. or at + 5°C. showed higher motility than those thawed at + 38°C. to +40°C. (Stower, 1953 ; Miller and VanDemark, 1953, 1954). This apparent discordance seems to have been resolved by Polge (1957), who found maximal revival in specimens thawed in water at +38°C. provided the ampoule was removed immediately the last of the ice had disappeared. Leaving the thawed semen at + 38°C. was rapidly deleterious, It seems, therefore, that under strictly controlled conditions the best results are obtained by thawing at + 40°C. (Hafs and Elliott, 1954 ; Foote and Dunn, 1955 ; Foote and Bratton, 1956). In other circumstances it is safer to thaw at +5°C. or 20°C. (Bruce, 1956 ; Mixner, 1955).

Aging of the semen up to 60 hours after thawing, was found to be slightly more harmful than similar aging of unfrozen material (Bratton, Foote and Cruthers, 1955).

Other variables. Many authors have commented on the individual and time-to-time variation in the freezability of semen. Successive ejaculates on the same day from the same bull also vary in their resistance to freezing. Kinney and VanDemark (1954) found that when 20 ejaculates were collected over a period of 4 hours the maximum revival after freezing was obtained with the fourth sample, subsequent ones being progressively more sensitive. Epididymal spermatozoa may be less resistant than ejaculated spermatozoa, but nevertheless retain a considerable degree of fertilising capacity after prolonged storage at — 79°C. (Baker, 1954). According to Willett and Ohms (1958b) spermatozoa from the small ducts are more resistant to freezing than epididymal spermatozoa, an observation which they relate to their other finding that the second ejaculate freezes better than the first.

Use of anti-bacterial agents. It is generally agreed that the addition of sulphanilamide to the medium is harmful to bull spermatozoa during freezing and thawing (e.g. Dunn, Larson and Willett, 1953). Antibiotics are less damaging.

The effect of sulphanilamide may have accounted for some of the early comparative failures with the freezing technique.

The use of frozen bull semen

By 1955 the technique was in operation in all the major cattle-breeding countries of the world and some centres had come to rely entirely on frozen semen (Henderson, Macpherson and Snyder, 1956; Snyder, 1955). Frozen semen, packed in CO_2 at $- 79°C.$, had been sent from Great Britain to South Africa and New Zealand, from Canada to Great Britain, and from Italy to Abyssinia and Eritrea with good results (van Rensburg and Rowson, 1954; James and Fyvie, 1955; Macpherson, 1954; Bonnadonna, 1955).

A curious and unexpected side use of the freezing technique as originally employed by Polge and Rowson is that it may free the semen of *Trichomonas foetus* (Barthel, 1954; Joyner and Bennett, 1956). The elimination of *Vibrio foetus* is more difficult (Dunn, 1955).

Some samples of semen have maintained good motility for several years at $- 70°C.$ to $-79°C.$ Mixner and Wiggin (1957a) obtained a 60–90-day non-return rate of 65·7 per cent with material frozen one year, and later (1957b) an identical rate after 2 years. MacPherson (1955) also obtained good results with 2-year-old semen. Van Drimmelen (1956) obtained a good conception rate with material which had been frozen for $2\frac{2}{3}$ years in a glycerol-containing medium. The record is held by the 1952 material in the Cambridge semen bank, which still retained fertilising capacity in 1958. Other samples of semen may show a decrease in motility and fertilising capacity in the comparatively short time of 2 to 3 years (Rowson, 1956). It is likely that under the best conditions known at present there is a gradual deterioration in semen held at $- 79°C.$ Experience with fowl spermatozoa and other cells and tissues suggests that further modification of the diluent might be helpful, but that the most effective way of improving long-term preservation would be to lower the temperature of storage. The use of the liquid gases for storing bull semen presents certain practical difficulties, but is apparently being found to be feasible on a large scale in the U.S.A. An alternative, of course, is to use mechanical refrigeration, which is now being developed to give temperatures around $- 100°C.$ and which will undoubtedly play a large part in the future of cryobiology. For instance, Etgen, Ludwick and Hess (1955) found that spermatozoa maintained at $- 90°C.$ by mechanical refrigeration maintained motility better for short periods than those in semen kept at $- 73°C.$ in solid CO_2.

The possibilities arising from the prolonged storage of bull semen have been discussed by many writers (e.g. Foote and Bratton, 1956). It is indeed difficult to exaggerate " the magnitude of the revolution in animal breeding initiated by the possibility of long-term preservation of spermatozoa " (Parkes, 1956).

Other Domestic Mammals

A large proportion of ram spermatozoa can be revived after freezing to $- 79°C.$ by the technique devised for bull spermatozoa (Smith and Polge, 1950b; Emmens and Blackshaw, 1950). Respiration and glycolysis are greatly depressed, however, even when the thawed specimens are highly motile (White, Blackshaw and Emmens,

1954). In keeping with this *in vitro* indication of damage, fertilising capacity is seriously impaired ; Emmens and Blackshaw (1955) obtained pregnancy in only 5 per cent of the ewes inseminated with frozen and thawed semen, and Dauzier (1956) was no more successful. Emmens (1956) later reported a conception rate of 15–20 per cent among 2,000 ewes receiving frozen semen. According to Kuznetsov (1956) Russian workers have obtained conception rates of 15 to 33 per cent with ram semen frozen for up to 50 days. Graça Araujo (1955) obtained a conception rate of 31·2 per cent with ram semen frozen at − 79°C. for 45 days. Evidently further work is required to find out what diluents, freezing rates, etc., are required to deal with the special properties of ram spermatozoa.

Early work with spermatozoa of the goat (Smith and Polge, 1950b) showed that good motility could be obtained after freezing and thawing by the glycerol/slow-cooling technique used for bull spermatozoa. Up to date, however, there seem to be no reports of the fertilising capacity of goat semen so treated.

With other domestic animals, horse, pig and dog, preliminary work was much less promising, and it is likely that special methods of dilution and freezing will be required for the long-term preservation of the spermatozoa of these animals. Whole semen of the stallion treated by the method effective for bull semen showed very poor recovery when thawed (Smith and Polge, 1950b), but about 25 per cent resumed motility when the seminal plasma was removed from the spermatozoa before addition of the glycerol-containing diluent. Results were no better with media containing egg-yolk, but the further addition of glucose or glycine, together with 10 per cent glycerol, permitted the revival of 80 per cent or more of the spermatozoa (Szumowski, 1954 ; Roy, 1955). Baker and Gandier (1957) report that one mare became pregnant following the insemination of epididymal spermatozoa which had been suspended in whole milk and stored at − 79°C. for 30 days.

Spermatozoa of the boar are very sensitive to glycerol, motility *in vitro* being reduced rapidly by a concentration of 10 per cent and fertilising capacity by any concentration exceeding 5 per cent (Polge, 1956a, 1957). Roy (1955) showed that the addition of glycine was beneficial and that about 50 per cent of boar spermatozoa survived after freezing to − 79°C. in a glycine egg-yolk medium containing 10 per cent glycerol. Such thawed semen, however, was found by Polge (1957) not to have retained fertilising capacity.

Working on dog spermatozoa, Davoine (1958) failed to obtain significant revivals after freezing in milk-glucose media containing 7 or 10 per cent glycerol. He obtained better results, however, with hypotonic media. With a diluent composed of 2–3 per cent glucose, 0·5 per cent " leciphos " and 2·6 per cent egg-yolk in distilled water he obtained up to 30 per cent revival of the spermatozoa. Gutiérrez-Nales (1957), by contrast, reported that he had been able to preserve dog spermatozoa in the separated sperm-containing fraction of the ejaculate in a citrate diluent containing 5·5 per cent glycerol and 37·5 per cent egg-yolk for 8 months in solid CO_2.

Laboratory Mammals

The spermatozoa of the rabbit are very sensitive to hypertonic salt solutions at temperatures above zero (*see* p. 188) ; the same appears to be true with the hypertonic residual fluid produced when water is frozen out of the medium at temperatures below 0°C. (Lovelock, and Polge 1954). The spermatozoa are also damaged readily by a rise in the concentration of glycerol in the suspending medium (Smith and Polge, 1950b). This poor prognosis for reviving frozen rabbit spermatozoa is borne out in practice. Only about 30 per cent of the spermatozoa regained motility after cooling in media containing 10 per cent glycerol or 7·5 ethylene glycol (Smith and Polge, 1950b ; Emmens and Blackshaw, 1950). Gradual addition of the glycerol by dialysis allowed concentrations up to 30 per cent to be used. This resulted in good motility being regained after thawing, but on insemination the semen had lost fertilising capacity.

Little progress has been made with the low-temperature preservation of the spermatozoa of laboratory rodents, which because of their larger acrosomes appear to be particularly susceptible to the stresses of freezing.

Man

Mantegazza (1866) appears to have been the first to record that a proportion of human spermatozoa would survive cooling to temperatures well below zero (— 17°C.). He foresaw that this observation might facilitate A.I. and gave his paper the sub-title " Honi soit qui mal y pense ". Mantegazza's observation was recalled in 1897 by Davenport, but nothing more happened until 1938, when Jahnel, working on *Treponema pallidum*, noted that although the spirochaetes were killed by freezing to and storage at — 79°C. in CO_2, — 196°C. in liquid nitrogen, and — 269°C. in liquid helium, a proportion of the associated spermatozoa survived. Shettles (1940) froze undiluted semen in 0·2-mm. capillary tubes and found that up to 10 per cent of the spermatozoa survived after 5-minute periods at — 79°C., — 196°C., or at — 269°C. The revival rate varied with different donors, but not according to the temperature. Revival was less good with stale specimens, and with those kept for long periods at — 79°C.

Attempts to apply Luyet's vitrification technique to human spermatozoa by Hoagland and Pincus (1942) were unsuccessful, but this result was reconciled with those of the previous workers by Parkes (1945), who showed that freezing minute amounts of semen to — 79°C. or — 192°C. in capillary tubes or thin films was fatal to the spermatozoa, but that a substantial number revived when comparatively large amounts were frozen in ampoules. Considered retrospectively, the enhanced survival of the ampouled material was obviously an effect of slower cooling, but the significance of the result was missed at the time. Whether the sensitivity to ultra-rapid cooling is to be regarded as a form of thermal shock is uncertain. At slower rates of cooling, human spermatozoa do not show this reaction (Sherman, 1955). With the discovery of the protective properties of glycerol some attention was again given to human spermatozoa. Polge, Smith and Parkes (1949) reported that the addition of glycerolised Baker solution to human spermatozoa to give a final concentration of 5 per cent glycerol improved the revival after freezing, but the extent of the improvement was trifling compared to that seen with fowl spermatozoa.

Many variations of technique have been tried without success, and the difficulty of testing the fertilising capacity of thawed human semen has retarded work. Mainly, however, the slow progress seems to be due to a marked lack of enthusiasm

H*

for the idea of telegenesis in man (Parkes, 1956). An exception is to be seen in the work of Sherman and Bunge (1953a), who showed that the avoidance of dilution increased the revivability of frozen glycerolised human spermatozoa. They added 10 per cent of absolute glycerol to liquified semen and after slow freezing obtained a revival rate of 67 per cent. The surviving spermatozoa showed normal staining reactions (Sherman and Bunge, 1953b). Bunge and Sherman (1953), and Bunge Keettel and Sherman (1954) later reported the birth of four normal children following the insemination of frozen and thawed semen. Evidently, much work remains to be done on the optimal conditions for the long-term storage of human spermatozoa, but there can be no doubt that telegenesis in man has arrived. " We have therefore to contemplate the possibility of a man (or an animal) begetting progeny long after his death. This idea does not violate the biological concept that the soma is merely a temporary and often inadequate vehicle for the essential germplasm, but it is one which will disturb deeply many who regard themselves as more than mere germplasm containers " (Parkes, 1951).

The Nature and Prevention of the Damage Caused by Freezing

There has been much discussion about the nature of the damage caused by freezing and thawing a living cell. Comprehensive reviews of the subject are to be found in Luyet and Gehenio (1940), Smith (1954, 1958), Meryman (1956), Parkes (1957b) and Parkes and Smith (1959). The oldest and simplest idea was that the formation of extracellular ice, necessarily larger in volume than the water it replaced, damaged the cell mechanically by distortion or rupture. At the same time, the formation of intracellular ice destroyed the internal organisation of the cell. This idea that the damage caused by freezing was essentially mechanical in nature implied that it would not occur if the formation of ice crystals could be avoided by vitrification of the water or partial dehydration of the cell. Vitrification, if in a strict sense it occurs at all, involves cooling the cell at about 100°C. per sec. to pass it so quickly through the range of temperature at which crystallisation occurs that the water becomes solidified without crystallisation. There is, of course, little hope of using this method with cells which show cold shock, or with large amounts of material, but Luyet found it to be effective with minute amounts of red blood cells.

A second possible method of discouraging the formation of crystals of ice is to use strong sugar solutions or similar hypertonic media to dehydrate the cell as far as is compatible with its survival. Work based on this idea has been referred to on p. 192, but for the most part both the vitrification and the dehydration approaches to the problem of freezing damage have been unfruitful. A quite different approach was made by Moran (1929) and by Breedis (1942). These authors emphasise the fact that as intra- or extra-cellular water crystallises, the salts become concentrated until saturation point is reached for any particular electrolyte and temperature. This means that as water freezes out the residual fluid becomes progressively more hypertonic and the cells are subject to severe osmotic stresses. Lovelock and Polge (1954) provided valuable confirmation of the importance of this factor by correlating the sensitivity of cells to hypertonic salt solutions at 0°C. with the amount of damage that they sustained on being frozen to various temperatures. Exposure of the cell to the hypertonic residual fluids is shortened by rapid freezing, and the efficacy of ultra-rapid freezing may depend on this factor as much as on " vitrification " of the water.

The dilemma which arises in freezing living cells thus becomes obvious. " If freezing is sufficiently rapid to avoid the effects of the hypertonic residual fluid thermal shock occurs with many types of cell ; if freezing is slow enough to avoid thermal shock the cells are destroyed by being pickled in their own brine " (Parkes, 1956). Bull spermatozoa illustrate well this dual vulnerability.

It seems probable that the first effect of thermal shock above zero is to cause the loss of lipoproteins from the cell membrane and that this loss is minimised when these constituents are in equilibrium with or have poor solubility in the medium, as when egg-yolk is added thereto (Tosic and Walton, 1947). It is likely that below freezing point the effect is augmented by the hypertonicity of the residual fluid and that where gradual loss of viability occurs on prolonged storage at low temperature the same process is continuing at a slower rate. The results of Bialy, Ludwick, Hess and Ely (1957), who found that " freezability " was improved by the addition of 5 per cent lipoprotein to the medium, is in keeping with the view that loss of lipoprotein by the cell to the medium is one of the major factors in freezing damage.

The addition of glycerol or a similar neutral solute to the medium alters conditions radically. In the first place the volume of the residual fluid present at any particular temperature is increased, and with it, of course, the spaces between the ice crystals. Photomicrography of the process of freezing in biological media with and without glycerol shows this effect clearly (Smith, Polge and Smiles, 1951), but it also shows that the formation of ice crystals, while it may be modified, is certainly not prevented (Smith and Smiles, 1953). It is very doubtful, however, if the presence of cavities in which the cells can escape from the ice crystals has any significant part in the protective action of glycerol because it is known that to be effective the substance must penetrate the cell. It is now generally thought that the fatal increase in the concentration of electrolytes caused by freezing is prevented by the presence of glycerol, which not only increases the volume of the residual fluid but has a strong affinity for salts. This protective effect allows freezing to be carried out slowly enough to avoid thermal shock without causing osmotic damage to the cell.

Freeze-drying of Spermatozoa

Many micro-organisms can now be preserved by freeze-drying—that is by vacuum sublimation of the water from the frozen preparation. This technique has the great advantage that the preparation can then be kept on the shelf at room temperature rather than in the deep-freeze. A great deal is now known about the optimal conditions of freeze-drying and the factors influencing the shelf-life of dried preparations (Parkes and Smith, 1959).

The refinement of freeze-drying methods on the one hand, and the development of methods of retaining viability in frozen spermatozoa on the other, stimulated interest in the possibility of freeze-drying spermatozoa and a great deal of time and thought has already been expended on the problem. It is not likely that any quick and easy solution will be found, but it is also unlikely that the problem is insoluble. Negative results have been reported by Sherman (1954) with human spermatozoa, by Schmid and Neumann (cited by Leidl 1956), Bialy and Smith (1957) and Albright, Erb and Ehlers (1958) with bull spermatozoa, and somewhat equivocal results by others. Some success has already been claimed by Russian workers.

At — 79°C. all free water is converted to ice. In theory, therefore, the cells are dry as well as frozen, and it should be immaterial to them whether or not the ice crystals are left in position or removed. This simple concept, however, meets a host of difficulties, especially that of sublimating the water at a temperature at which the spermatozoa will remain viable for a sufficient length of time. At — 79°C. the removal of water is usually regarded as being impossibly slow. At the temperatures commonly used for freeze-drying, — 20°C. to — 40°C., the spermatozoa are in a dangerous temperature range, though the studies of Luyet and Keane (1955) and the development of more efficient apparatus, as by Rey (1957), should assist here.

In the case of cells which survive freezing and thawing only in the presence of a protective substance, further difficulties arise. The best of these substances, glycerol, being non-volatile, remains with the dried material at a concentration which is certainly toxic at room temperature. Polge, Smith and Parkes (1949) were able to remove about 90 per cent of the water from glycerolised fowl semen at a temperature of — 25°C. The preparations were reconstituted by the addition of distilled water at + 1°C. and on warming active spermatozoa were seen regularly. If the preparation was allowed to remain at room temperature before reconstitution no motile spermatozoa were found. Somewhat similar experiments were carried out with bull spermatozoa by Leidl (1956), who removed up to 95 per cent of the water from frozen glycerolised preparations and revived a proportion of the spermatozoa on reconstitution and re-warming. Albright, Erb and Ehlers (1958) report having obtained progressive movement in 5–10 per cent of bull spermatozoa reconstituted after freeze-drying from diluted whole milk. Leidl calls attention to the complications caused by the use of glycerol, and a volatile protective agent would obviously be an advantage. For this reason trimethyleneglycol was investigated by Smith and Polge (1950b), but the substance proved of low effectiveness. It is probable that progress could be made by the use of other volatile substances, e.g. methanol (Lovelock, 1954 ; Parkes, 1959), dimethyl sulphoxide (Lovelock and Bishop, 1959) or of substances innocuous in high concentration at room temperature, which would not require removal, e.g. xylose (Polge and Soltys, 1959).

Work along different lines has been reported from the U.S.S.R. on bull, ram, and rabbit spermatozoa (Juščenko, 1957). The semen was diluted with a synthetic medium and cooled for 3–4 hours at 0°C. More diluent containing 7·5–20 per cent glycerol was added. After equilibration the preparation was poured into a test-tube containing a mixture of freon and heptane. The spermatozoa were freed from the seminal plasma by centrifugation and frozen at — 20°C. to — 78°C. and then subjected to vacuum sublimation to remove the residual water of the spermatozoa and the organic fluids. The author claims that dried bull spermatozoa retained potential motility for 18–20 months at room temperature, and that fertilised eggs were obtained from does inseminated with reconstituted, dried rabbit spermatozoa. Later, Meryman and Kafig (1959) reported that bull spermatozoa, freeze-dried from nylon gauze, showed motility when reconstituted and that a cow inseminated with a comparatively small number of such spermatozoa became pregnant.   Confirmation of these reports will be awaited with interest.

IV. Effect of Physical, Chemical and Immunological Agents on Spermatozoa

The development of methods of collecting spermatozoa and of artificial insemination has made possible a great variety of experiments on functional changes in spermatozoa treated *in vitro* in different ways.   In general, the results have been far more clear-cut than those obtained in attempts to influence the mature spermatozoa in the male before ejaculation or in the female tract after coitus.   The experiments have fallen mainly into one or other of four categories: (*a*) attempts to produce genetic effects by subjecting the spermatozoa *in vitro* to radiation or radiomimetic or polyploidogenic substances, (*b*) the study of spermicidal or fertilisation-inhibiting substances in the interests of fertility control, (*c*) investigation of the immunological properties of spermatozoa, and (*d*) attempts to alter the ratio of X- and Y-spermatozoa so as to modify the sex-ratio of the young conceived.

Ionising Radiations

Lower vertebrates

One of the outstanding observations of experimental biology was made in 1911 by O. Hertwig, who exposed frog spermatozoa to radium emanations, and found that up to a certain level there was increasing embryonic mortality and abnormality as dosage increased, but that the higher doses were compatible with the production of apparently normal young.   The explanation of this paradoxical result offered by Hertwig was that slightly damaged spermatozoa both penetrated the eggs and effected syngamy, so that dominant lethals appeared, but that the badly damaged spermatozoa only penetrated the eggs without syngamy, and stimulated them to gynogenetic development (*see* Chapter 10, p. 382).   Dalcq and Simon (1931), in carrying out similar experiments, came to the conclusion that the Hertwig paradox was much more variable and complex than the original discoverers believed, and that paternal chromatin often took part in several mitoses before being extruded.   They reported negative results with spermatozoa of *Rana fusca* subjected to high doses of X-rays.   Hertwig's work was further extended by Rugh (1939), who used X-irradiation and modern calibration of dosage in the treatment of the spermatozoa of *Rana pipiens*.   With exposure of the spermatozoa to doses between 15 r and 10,000 r there was a progressive increase in embryonic mortality and death, so that at the higher level only 1·6 per cent of the embryos were viable.   With larger doses, the trend was reversed, and 90·5 per cent of the embryos hatched when the dose to the spermatozoa was raised to 50,000 r.   These embryos were evidently produced by gynogenesis because they resembled haploids obtained by other means.

These observations, and their general implication, were confirmed in decisive experiments on inter-generic crosses in amphibians.   G. Hertwig (1913) seminated the eggs of *Bufo vulgaris* with normal spermatozoa of *Rana temporaria*.   Hybridisation was effected, but the embryos failed to develop to gastrulation.   When the experiment was repeated with heavily irradiated spermatozoa, larvae were produced which proved to be gynogenetic *Bufo*. A similar demonstration of the effect of massive irradiation was made by Rugh and Exner (1940), who seminated the eggs of the Leopard frog with spermatozoa from the bull frog. When normal spermatozoa were used, the embryos did not develop beyond the gastrula stage.

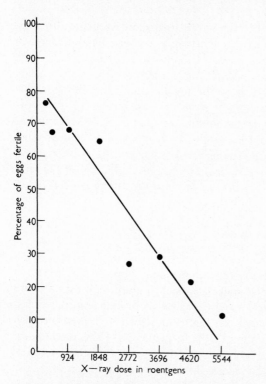

When the spermatozoa were exposed to 66,000 r X-irradiation, 80 per cent of the embryos hatched and developed into typical Leopard frog tadpoles.

Essentially similar observations were also made at about the same time on trout by Oppermann (1913), and on *Gobius* and *Triton* by P. Hertwig (1916), and later, on *Triturus alpestris* × *T. palmatus* (Fischberg, 1947).

The experiments on frogs and toads gave the first clear demonstration that the spermatozoon performs two distinct functions : activation of the egg and contribution of male genetic material. The wider significance of the work is discussed in Chapter 10, p. 380.

Fig. 9.15—Effect of X-irradiation on fertilising capacity of fowl spermatozoa, according to dosage and percentage of fertile eggs laid in the 10 days after a single insemination. With one exception, control figures for untreated spermatozoa in the different experiments were all above 80 per cent. (After Kosin, 1944.)

Birds

The first part of the Hertwig effect was produced in domestic fowl by Kosin (1944). Semen was obtained as described on p. 166 and was irradiated with graded doses of soft X-rays. Fertilising capacity was lost when the dose was raised to 5,544 r or 6,488 r (Fig. 9.15). Increase of the dosage even to 152,000 r gave no indication of activation of the eggs to gynogenetic development. Within the lower dose range the spermatozoa showed no change in motility or morphology, but there was increasing embryonic mortality with increasing dosage (Fig. 9.16), which appeared to result in the chicks hatched being preponderantly male. The survival time of the spermatozoa in the female tract was reduced but was normal up to 10 days.

Mammals

Spermatozoa in the epididymis. The well-known effects of ionising radiation on spermatogenesis (Chapter 7, p. 91) have prompted many experiments on the breeding performance of males after irradiation but before the onset of sterility. Moreover, the formed spermatozoa in the epididymis are inevitably irradiated along with the testis, and as an alternative to irradiation of spermatozoa *in vitro* irradiation of the genital region of the male has been used to determine the effect of irradiation on the fertilising capacity and genetic properties of spermatozoa. In this technique, however, there is usually some confusion, because spermatozoa, probably defective, produced by the testis immediately following irradiation soon appear in the epididymis along with the spermatozoa irradiated when fully formed. During the latter part of the post-irradiation fertile period the ejaculate will contain both kinds of spermatozoa.   Such admixture can, of course, be prevented

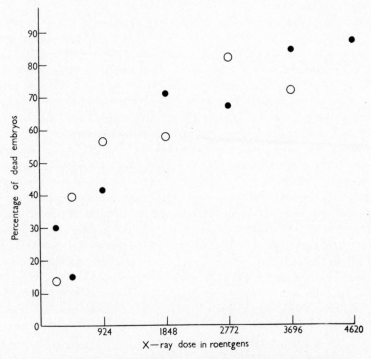

Fig. 9.16—Effect of X-irradiation of fowl spermatozoa on embryonic mortality, according to dosage and percentage of dead embryos in eggs laid in the 10 days after a single insemination. (After Kosin, 1944.) ○ =eggs laid 1–5 days after insemination of irradiated sperm ● =eggs laid 6–10 days after insemination. Control figures in experiments with untreated spermatozoa were all below 40 per cent and mostly below 20 per cent.

by ligation of the efferent ducts immediately before irradiation, but this precaution has not usually been taken.

There is abundant evidence of the production of the first part of the Hertwig effect by irradiation of spermatozoa in the epididymis.   Very early in the study of irradiation damage, Régaud and Dubreuil (1908) reported that the failure of irradiated male rabbits to produce offspring was due in part to non-viability of the embryos following fertilisation of the eggs by spermatozoa existing at the time of irradiation or produced soon afterwards.   Strandskov (1932), too, found that litters sired by irradiated male guinea-pigs were smaller than usual and contained more dead young.   Detailed studies were carried out by Snell (1933), who exposed male mice to 800 r and found that the passage of spermatozoa from the testis to the epididymis stopped within a week or two of irradiation. Motile spermatozoa, however, were found in the epididymis for 6 to 7 weeks after ligation of the efferent ducts and irradiation, about the same time as after ligation alone, so that the survival time of the spermatozoa was little affected by the irradiation. Such males remained fertile for 10 to 14 days after irradiation, but litter size decreased with increasing dosage up to 800 r, because of increasing prenatal mortality. With 800 r, litter size was reduced to 2·4. Failure of fertilisation was not involved. The sex-ratio of the offspring was normal. Genetic findings in this work are discussed in Chapter 7, p. 93.

Brenneke (1937) exposed male rats and mice to doses of X-rays between 220 r and 800 r. In confirmation of Snell, she found that the fertilising capacity of the spermatozoa was not decreased in the 2 weeks following irradiation, but that there was heavy embryonic mortality. Henson (1942) irradiated male rats with graded doses of X-rays, 100 r, 500 r, 1,000 r, 3,000 r. With the two low doses, litters sired within one week of irradiation were of normal size but low survival value. Subsequent litters were normal. With 1,000 r, litters sired over the first 3 weeks were of small size because of heavy embryonic mortality and of increasingly low survival value. Subsequent matings were sterile. With a dose of 3,000 r the spermatozoa lost their activating and fertilising capacity within 2 days and no litters were sired thereafter. In all these experiments, doses far below that required to produce gynogenesis in frogs were used, and to improve the chances of securing the second phase of the Hertwig effect Bruce and Austin (1956) gave doses of 10,000 r, 30,000 r and 100,000 r locally to the genital region of male mice which were then each paired immediately with females of a genetically marked strain. With the highest dose, about one-third of the males mated within 24 hours, and none later; with 30,000 r, about four out of five mated within 4 days; with the lowest dose, matings were frequent at the start but declined after the first week. No young were born following the matings and there was evidence of implantation only in three of the 82 females which mated. Spermatozoa receiving 100,000 r failed almost entirely to penetrate the egg. Those receiving the two smaller doses effected penetration and mostly formed pronuclei, but syngamy was delayed temporarily or permanently. No evidence of continued gynogenetic development was obtained.

Spermatozoa in vitro. The first observation of the effects of irradiation on mammalian spermatozoa *in vitro* appears to have been made by Bergonié and Tribondeau (1904), who found that, superficially, human spermatozoa were remarkably resistant. The first *in vitro* irradiations followed by A.I. were carried out by Asdell and Warren (1931), who came to the conclusion that the exposure of rabbit spermatozoa to " huge " doses of X-rays was compatible with the production of normal young. Amoroso and Parkes (1947) made a detailed investigation with rabbit spermatozoa exposed to doses of X-rays ranging from 50 r to 100,000 r before insemination into females in which ovulation was brought about by injection of gonadotrophin. Doses up to and including 100 r had no effect on fertilisation or segmentation and apparently normal young were produced. With doses of 250 r, 500 r, and 1,000 r, an increasing proportion of ova obtained at 40 hours after ovulation showed arrested segmentation. With 500 r the number of pregnancies and the size of litter were much reduced, but some young, not

obviously abnormal, were produced. With doses of 1,000 r or more no established
pregnancies were observed. With doses of 2500 r or more all tubal ova were
delayed or arrested, at a stage roughly proportional to the dose (Fig. 9.17) (Parkes
1947). Spermatozoa penetrated the eggs at all dose levels, but with the higher
doses the male pronucleus was abnormal, syngamy delayed and irregular, and
many activated ova failed to divide. A few eggs showed signs of activation
without syngamy, but none of continued gynogenetic development. Chang,
Hunt and Romanoff (1957) have described similar experiments, with similar
results, on the exposure of rabbit spermatozoa to a radiocobalt source.

The development of methods of A.I. in mice (*see* p. 177) has made possible
experiments on the effects of *in vitro* irradiation of mouse spermatozoa, thus avoiding the complications which beset work on the effects of irradiating spermatozoa

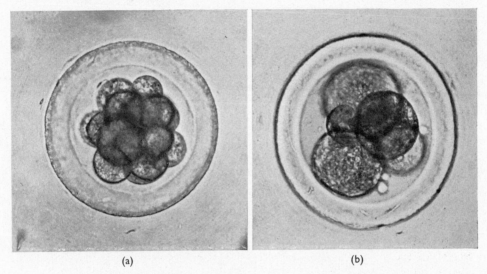

(a)   (b)

Fig. 9.17—Effect of X-irradiation of rabbit spermatozoa *in vitro* on segmentation of the fertilised
egg. (From Parkes, 1947.)
(a) Egg obtained about 50 hr. after insemination of normal spermatozoa, showing normal
segmentation.
(b) Egg obtained about 50 hr. after insemination of spermatozoa exposed to 25,000 r,
showing irregular and arrested segmentation.

in the epididymis. Edwards (1957a) subjected mouse spermatozoa to doses ranging
from 100 r to 50,000 r. There was no obvious decline in activity of the spermatozoa except with the higher doses. Irradiation did not usually prevent syngamy,
but paternal chromosomes were lost during development, so that with increasing
dosage, the embryos, examined at $3\frac{1}{2}$ days gestation, tended increasingly towards
haploidy (Fig. 9.18). Gynogenetic development was very brief. With 30,000 r
and 50,000 r, development was restricted to the first cleavage.

Ultra-violet Irradiation

Comparatively little work has been carried out on the exposure of spermatozoa
to ultra-violet irradiation, though the effects are no less dramatic than those produced by ionising radiations. According to Dalcq and Simon (1931, 1932),

exposure of the spermatozoa to ultra-violet rays produced the Hertwig effect in *Rana fusca* more clearly and definitely than radium irradiation, in that the paternal chromatin was eliminated at the first division. Drebinger (1951) claims to have produced some gynogenetic *R. fusca* by U.V. irradiation, and Fischberg and Selman (1952) found that gynogenesis occurred regularly in newt larvae following similar exposure of the spermatozoa. For many years, information for the mammal was apparently confined to the report of Pincus and Enzmann (1936), who irradiated rabbit spermatozoa *in vitro* from an ultra-violet lamp and examined the tubal

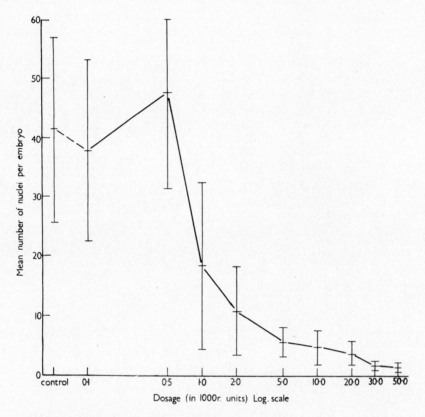

Fig. 9.18—Effect of X-irradiation of mouse spermatozoa *in vitro* on development of 3½-day embryo, according to dosage and number of nuclei in the embryo. The vertical lines at each point represent one standard error above and below the mean. (From Edwards, 1957a.) (*Proc. Roy. Soc.*, B, 1957, **146**, 469.)

eggs of inseminated females. They reported that the spermatozoa penetrated the eggs but that the male pronucleus was abnormal and the first division delayed and irregular.

Recently, Edwards (1957b) has reported on extensive experiments in the mouse. He obtained suspensions of spermatozoa by stripping the excised vasa deferentia into 0·75 per cent NaCl, and irradiated them for between 15 seconds and 30 minutes. The longest exposure gave 156·6 × 10^5 ergs per sq. cm. on the surface of the suspension, the wavelength being between 2,100 and 3,200 Å, with the peak output close to the absorption maximum for nucleic acids. Immediate effects on the cells were seen in that activity and regularity of movement decreased with increasing exposure, so that motility was greatly reduced in most of the spermatozoa receiving the longer exposure. Developmental effects were determined at all stages especially by examination of the embryos at $3\frac{1}{2}$ days. Both the proportion of mice with embryos and the number of eggs fertilised per female were less in the mice receiving irradiated spermatozoa, especially those exposed for longer periods, than in the control series receiving normal spermatozoa. Embryos derived from

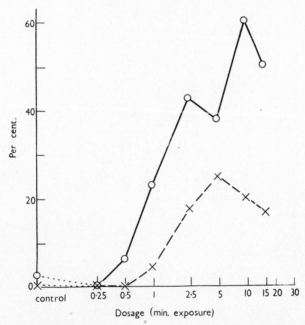

Fig. 9.19—Effect of U.V. irradiation of mouse spermatozoa *in vitro* on development of $3\frac{1}{2}$-day embryos, according to time of exposure and classification of embryos. (From Edwards, 1957b.) (*Proc. Roy. Soc.*, B, 1957. **146**, 488.)

○ =not diploid
× =haploid or near haploid

lightly irradiated spermatozoa, presumably diploids, had a high mortality rate about the time of implantation. One of the few offspring was deformed. Many of the embryos were grossly retarded when examined at $3\frac{1}{2}$ days, as shown by the number of nuclei in them; the proportion of retarded embryos increased with prolonged exposure and some were haploid or near haploid (Fig. 9.19). A $3\frac{1}{2}$-day embryo with only two nuclei, both haploid, in comparison with a control, is shown in Fig. 9.20. It was evident that in many instances the irradiated spermatozoa had penetrated and activated the eggs without effecting syngamy and had initiated gynogenetic development. It is also evident, however, that the haploid embryos were not viable beyond a few divisions. The genetic implications of Edwards's work are considered in Chapter 10.

Trypaflavine, Toluidine Blue, Nitrogen Mustard and Colchicine

G. Hertwig (1924) produced the Hertwig effect in *R. fusca* by subjecting the spermatozoa to trypaflavine, and also in the *Bufo communis* × *R. fusca* cross.

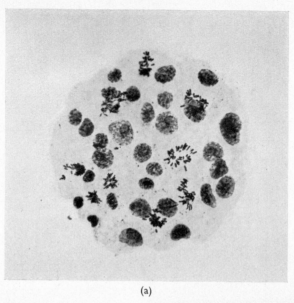

(a)

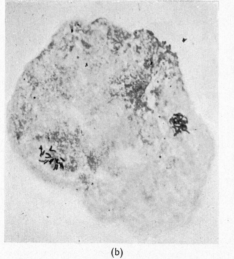

(b)

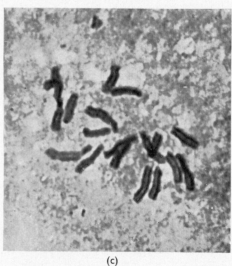

(c)

Fig. 9.20—Effect of U.V. irradiation of mouse spermatozoa *in vitro* on development at $3\frac{1}{2}$ days, as seen in whole-embryo squashes. (From Edwards, 1957b.) (*Proc. Roy. Soc.*, B, 1957, **146**, 488.)
(a) Normal $3\frac{1}{2}$-day diploid blastocyst, after insemination of normal spermatozoa.
(b) $3\frac{1}{2}$-day haploid embryo, obtained after insemination with spermatozoa exposed to U.V. irradiation for 5 min. Two nuclei only, both being in division.
(c) Enlargement of left-hand nucleus seen in (b), showing 19 chromosomes instead of the usual 40.

Dalcq (1929) obtained the same result in *R. fusca*, and later (1931) showed that although the male pronucleus derived from the trypaflavinised spermatozoon became apposed to the female one, it did not resolve into chromosomes and was eliminated.   Dalcq and Simon (1932) considered that the effect of trypaflavine was even more definite than that of radium or U.V.   The effectiveness of trypa-flavine was further confirmed by Drebinger (1951) on *R. fusca*, and by Briggs, Green and King (1951) on *R. pipiens*.   An identical effect can be obtained with toluidine blue (Briggs, Green and King, 1951 ; Briggs, 1952).   Drebinger (1951) came to the conclusion that the action of these fluorescent dyes was essentially photodynamic.   The effect depends on exposure of the treated spermatozoa to light and is then irreversible.   Attempts to produce gynogenesis in mammals with trypaflavine and toluidine blue have given equivocal results (Thibault, 1949 ; Edwards, 1958a).

Nitrogen mustard applied to the spermatozoa *in vitro* is a highly effective gynogenesis-inducing agent in amphibia (Drebinger, 1951) but is dubiously so in mammals in which heteroploidy is a more usual result of thus treating the sper-matozoa (Edwards, 1958a).

Several experiments have been made on subjecting spermatozoa *in vitro* to colchicine, the classical polyploidogenic agent in plants (Blakeslee, 1937). Chang (1944) treated rabbit semen with colchicine *in vitro* and inseminated the mixture.   He records having obtained some abnormal young.   In an experiment of this kind the spermatozoa will be superficially contaminated with colchicine, which may then be carried into the egg and produce an effect quite independent of the male chromatin.   Häggqvist and Bane (1950, 1951) used a similar technique on rabbits and pigs and claimed to have produced heteroploids which, according to Melander (1950, 1951), were triploids.   Attempts to confirm the results in the rabbit and to reproduce them in the cow (Beatty and Rowson, 1954 ; Venge, 1954a, b) were not successful, and the work has been severely criticised (Beatty, 1957a).   Edwards's work (1958b), based on a different technique of exposing the gametes to colchicine, is discussed in Chapter 10, p. 382.

Ultrasonic Vibration ; Hydrostatic Pressure

Spermatozoa have been subjected to ultrasonic vibration to fracture the mid-piece and so separate the head from the tail, as in Henle's work on the respective antigenic properties of heads and tails.   For chemical work, similar treatment has been pushed further to disintegrate the spermatozoa completely.   A more surprising effect of ultrasonic vibration has been described by Maupoumé and Verain (1957), who reported that mild subjection of fresh bull spermatozoa to ultra-sonic waves increased survival time *in vitro* by about 3 days, whether neat or diluted semen was used.   Stale semen was not affected in the same way.

Hydrostatic pressure of 544 atms. applied to frog spermatozoa had no effect on motility or fertilising capacity, or on the resulting larvae (Marsland and Rugh, 1940).

Antibodies against Spermatozoa

The antigenic properties of spermatozoa have been discussed in Chapter 7, p. 30, where it was recorded that spermatozoa administered parenterally evoked the formation of antibodies which agglutinate spermatozoa *in vitro*.   It remains to consider here the biological potentialities of these properties.   Heterologous spermatozoa are far more effective as antigens than are homologous spermatozoa ;

however, weak isoimmunisation has been described by Henle (1938) in rabbits and rats, though Parsons and Hyde (1940) failed to detect it in guinea-pigs.

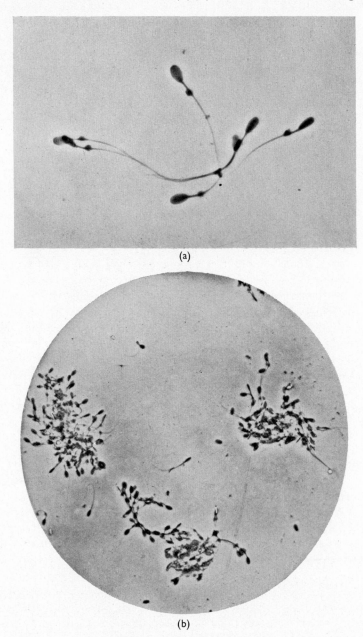

(a)

(b)

Fig. 9.21—Tail agglutination of rabbit epididymal spermatozoa by serum of sheep immunised against rat spermatozoa. (From Smith, 1949b.) (*Proc. Roy. Soc.*, B, 1949, **136**, 46.)
  (*a*) Early stage after 2 min. in 1/20 dilution.
  (*b*) Later stage after 4 min.

Spermatozoal antigens show a considerable degree of tissue specificity in that antisera react with the spermatozoa but not with the serum of the homologous species, while antiserum against the serum of a species does not react with the spermatozoa of that species.   Antispermatozoal sera, however, show some degree of species specificity in that they react most strongly with homologous spermatozoa. Nevertheless, considerable cross-reaction is found, especially in related species such as the rabbit, guinea-pig, rat and mouse (Smith, 1949c) and the bull, sheep and deer (Henle, 1938).   Some cross-reaction may also occur between unrelated species, being shown by the spermatozoa of bull and man (Henle, 1938) and of laboratory rodents and carnivores (Smith, 1949c).

The reaction between spermatozoa and antisera can be shown by the microscopical examination of hanging drops in which spermatozoa agglutinate in the absence of, and are killed in the presence of complement.   Specific head and tail

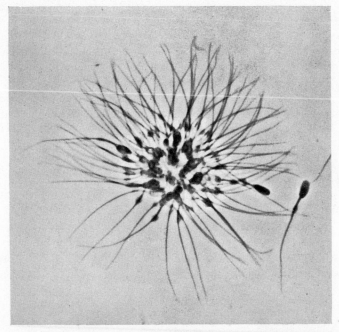

Fig. 9.22—Spontaneous head agglutination of rabbit epididymal spermatozoa after 4 hr. at room temperature in Baker's solution. (From Smith, 1949b.)   (*Proc. Roy. Soc.*, B, 1949, **136**, 46.)

agglutinins have been described but clear-cut tail agglutination is the usual reaction to antisera prepared against whole spermatozoa.   Starting with foci consisting of a few spermatozoa entangled by their tails, the agglutinating spermatozoa, still highly active, rapidly build up into dense masses leaving the rest of the medium clear (Fig. 9.21).   The reaction occurs at a speed proportional to the concentration of antibody, and typically is so rapid as to be clearly distinguishable from any non-specific tail-to-tail agglutination.   Antispermatozoal sera tend to be weak by immunological standards, though they can be improved by administering the antigen in Freund's adjuvant (Edwards, personal communication).   The nominal titre can be increased by improving the sensitivity of the *in vitro* test (Kibrick, *et al.*, 1952) which depends on many factors, including density of sperm and presence of seminal plasma (Smith, 1949b) which contains antigens similar to those of spermatozoa (Weil *et al.*, 1956; Weil and Finkler, 1958).   Head agglutination (Fig. 9.22) is to be regarded with suspicion because it is often seen in stale preparations, as well as under various experimental conditions not involving an immunological situation. Alternatively to slide tests, complement fixation or precipitin tests may be used.

The effectiveness of antispermatozoal sera *in vitro* posed the question of their action *in vivo* and gave rise to the attractive idea of immunising against pregnancy. The problem of immunisation by homologous spermatozoa is relevant in connection with the fate of the spermatozoa in the female tract (p. 240); spermatozoa penetrating or resorbed by the wall of the female tract might be as effective antigenically as when administered parenterally. There is no evidence that isoimmunisation occurs naturally as the result of insemination (though it has been evoked to explain the alleged sterility of prostitutes), or that the reaction, as it can be demonstrated experimentally, is sufficiently strong to offer a basis for immunological contraception. It may be recalled, however, that Parsons and Hyde (1940) produced a potent haemolysin for sheep cells by insemination of guinea-pig spermatozoa into the rabbit. The chance of immunisation by way of the vagina does therefore exist. There are two other possibilities. The female could be immunised actively against heterologous spermatozoa showing antigenic overlap with the homologous spermatozoa, or she could be immunised passively by the transfer of antiserum made in another species against homologous spermatozoa. In spite of early optimistic reports about the *in vivo* effect of " spermatoxins ", as the antibodies were originally known, it seems that no unequivocal positive results have been obtained.

Dittler (1920), using rabbits, and McCartney (1923), using rats, claimed to have induced temporary sterility in females by the subcutaneous injection of spermatozoa or testicular mashes. Dittler, who used as his antigen the vaginal contents of the newly-mated female, specifically noted that ovulation was not inhibited in the immunised rabbits which failed to become pregnant. Similar reports of isoimmunisation in female guinea-pigs were made by Kennedy (1924) and in female rabbits by Pommerenke (1928). Other positive results were reported by Baskin (1932) and Ardelt (1931). Later work, however, gave no support to these authors. Conclusively negative results were obtained by Wang (1936), who actively immunised female rats against rat, dog or ram spermatozoa ; by Oslund (1926) working with rats, rabbits and guinea-pigs ; by Parsons and Hyde (1940) who failed to prevent pregnancy in rabbits by active immunisation against sheep, guinea-pig or rabbit spermatozoa, and in rats by active immunisation against bull, sheep, rat or guinea-pig spermatozoa, or passive immunisation with anti-rat spermatozoal rabbit serum ; by Henle and Henle (1940), who obtained a positive antibody response in 60 to 77 per cent of guinea-pigs isoimmunised with homologous spermatozoa but no decrease in fertility, and a 100 per cent antibody response against bull spermatozoa, with a weak cross-reaction against guinea-pig spermatozoa, but again with no effects on fertility ; and by Henle, Henle, Church and Foster (1940), who passively immunised female mice with antisera against rat and mouse spermatozoa. Female fowl may also react against homologous spermatozoa, as shown by the appearance of antibodies in the blood ; but, again, no effect on fertility was observed by Lamoreux (1940).

It should be noted that at least three different sources of antigen have been used in these experiments, sperm suspensions from testis or epididymis, ejaculated semen, and fluid obtained from the vagina of the mated rabbit. All three will differ in the nature of the adventitious substances and therefore in their total antigenic properties. It is possible, though perhaps not likely, that such differences affected the reported results.

A curious result was reported by Brunner (1941), who failed to sterilise rabbits by injection of bull phospholipid in sheep serum, but noticed an unusual number of hermaphrodites among the young.

Success in immunising the female against spermatozoa would imply that it should be possible to immunise the male in such a way as to destroy his spermatozoa *in vivo*, but here again, in spite of early reports (e.g. Guyer, 1922), unequivocal positive results seem to be lacking. Oslund (1926), for instance, found that spermatoxins developed in the blood of the male animal have no effect on spermatogenesis or epididymal spermatozoa. Freund and his co-workers (Chapter 7, p. 90), however, by the use of adjuvant to potentiate antigenic activity of homologous testis tissue, was able to damage severely the testis of the guinea-pig, and to a much lesser extent that of the rat. The serum of the treated animals immobilised spermatozoa *in vitro*, but did not damage the testis of another animal by passive transference. The relevance of these results to those of the earlier work described above is not yet clear.

The lack of *in vivo* effect of antispermatozoal bodies is curious but is probably due to one or more of the following factors :

(*a*) Active immunisation with heterologous spermatozoa may fail because of the weakness of the cross-reaction between the hetero- and the homologous spermatozoa.

(*b*) Passive immunisation may be vitiated by the fact that antibodies originating in a different species are not always acceptable to animal tissues.

(*c*) Isoimmunisation probably produces titres too low to affect fertility.

In general it seems certain that the antibodies do not reach the necessary site of *in vivo* action in sufficient concentration, allowing for the capacity of inert matter to interfere with their action. Smith (1949b), for instance, found that the vaginal fluids of an immunised rabbit had no *in vitro* effect on homologous spermatozoa, but that the vaginal fluids of a normal rabbit had an inhibitory effect on antiserum *in vitro* and would reverse existing agglutination. In keeping with this, spermatozoa agglutinated *in vitro* by the addition of antiserum are more effective in fertilising eggs after insemination than would be expected from their *in vitro* appearance. It may be that these various observations are related to the sperm antagglutins described in the female rabbit by Lindahl and Nilsson (1954) and referred to on p. 239.

At present, therefore, effective immunisation of the female against spermatozoa in the reproductive tract is not in sight, but further work may alter the prospect, especially as Wilson (1954) has reported the occurrence of auto-immunisation against endogenous spermatozoa in two sterile men.

Hyaluronidase Inhibitors

The role of hyaluronidase in fertilisation is discussed in Chapter 10. The early suggestion that hyaluronidase in bulk, supplied by a mass of spermatozoa at the site of fertilisation, is necessary to disintegrate the cumulus and so permit fertilisation to take place is not now tenable. For one thing, comparatively few spermatozoa are to be found in the Fallopian tube (*see* p. 319), and, for another, disintegration of the cumulus is not always a prerequisite for fertilisation (*see* p. 326). It is possible, however, that an individual spermatozoon's own supply of the enzyme plays a part in enabling the spermatozoon to penetrate between the corona cells which usually still surround the ovum at the time of fertilisation, and which are cemented together by a complex of hyaluronic acid. The idea that hyaluronidase is essential in some way for fertilisation has prompted two lines of experiment : (*a*) addition of the enzyme to the material inseminated with the aim of improving marginal fertility, and (*b*) use of hyaluronidase inhibitors to prevent fertilisation.

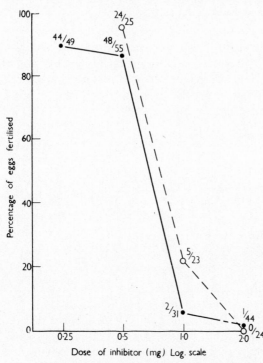

Fig. 9.23—Effect of hyaluronidase inhibitors added to rabbit semen *in vitro* on percentage of eggs fertilised. The proportion of the observed eggs which were fertilised is indicated at each point. (From Parkes, Rogers and Spensley, 1954.)

○ ——— = rehibin
● ——— = compound 53

Rowlands (1944) obtained some indication that the fertilising effect of marginal numbers of spermatozoa in the rabbit could be increased by the addition of preparations of hyaluronidase. However, clinical work in cases of oligospermia gave no support to the idea (Swyer, personal communication), and in view of the negative results later obtained by Chang (1950) on rabbits, the potentiation of marginal numbers of spermatozoa must at best be slight.

The use of hyaluronidase inhibitors has given much more decisive and instructive results. The earliest experiment was carried out by Pincus, Pirie and Chang (1948), who added excess of hyaluronic acid complex to rabbit semen and obtained some evidence of interference with fertilisation. Chang and Pincus (1953) used phosphorylated hesperidin, one of the earlier inhibitors of hyaluronidase, and decreased the fertilisation rate, but did not obtain complete inhibition of fertilisation even when 1·0 per cent of the compound was added. With the introduction of highly active inhibitors of hyaluronidase more detailed work was possible. Parkes (1953) used " rehibin "—trigentisic acid—and showed that fertilisation could be prevented routinely by the addition of 5 mg. per 1·0 ml. of original semen. The substance had no visible spermicidal activity and its effect was presumably due to the inhibition of hyaluronidase or some other essential enzyme. Rehibin had a low solubility in water, and Parkes, Rogers and Spensley (1954) used a formaldehyde polymer of hydroquinone sulphonic acid (Compound 53), which inhibited hyaluronidase strongly *in vitro* and was readily soluble in water. This compound, on addition to diluted semen, proved to be rather more effective than rehibin in preventing fertilisation. Dose-response curves for the two are shown in Fig. 9.23. Removal of the seminal plasma from semen treated with inhibitor, and subsequent washing of the spermatozoa, did not restore fertilising power, so that an effective amount of inhibitor adheres to the spermatozoa presumably as a surface layer, that part remaining in the seminal plasma being without effect. In keeping with this conclusion, (*a*) attempts to remove the negatively-charged inhibitor with positively-charged protamine resulted in rapid head agglutination of the spermatozoa, and (*b*) spermatozoa freed from seminal plasma and washed before treatment could be rendered non-functional with much smaller amounts of inhibitor. Compound 53 had no spermicidal action, but it inhibited other enzymes than hyaluronidase and possibly had non-specific effects, so that the anti-fertilisation effect was not necessarily due directly to inhibition of hyaluronidase. In view of the results with protamine it is possible that the treated spermatozoa failed to traverse the tract.

Spermicidal Substances

Almost from the day of their discovery spermatozoa were seen to be killed or immobilised by inimical substances or conditions. Inhibition of motility under various conditions was recorded by Leeuwenhoek (1678) and Spallanzani (1776). Leeuwenhoek noted that dilution with rain-water rendered dog spermatozoa motionless, and the nature of this effect was shown by Kölliker (1856), who found that motility could be restored in such circumstances by the immediate addition of salt. De Quatrefages (1850, 1853) described the toxic effect of salts of copper, mercury and lead, Newport (1853) noted the " narcotising " effect of chloroform vapour, and Kölliker (1856) showed that organic as well as inorganic substances might be toxic.

In more recent times, growing knowledge of cell biochemistry in general, and of spermatozoal metabolism in particular, has provided much information about substances which interfere with the functional activity of spermatozoa. This fundamental approach has been accompanied by more or less empirical work designed to find substances with high spermicidal activity and suitable for human use.

In the latter context, the work of Baker (1931b, 1932a, b, 1935) was outstanding, both for the application of scientific experiment to chemical contraception, and for his success in determining the relative *in vitro* activity of a large number of compounds. His researches led to widespread use of phenyl mercuric acetate, benzoate or nitrate, as the active principles of contraceptive preparations (Baker, Ranson and Tynen, 1939a, b). Much work has since been done on these lines, and many reviews have appeared, e.g. Millman (1952), Pirie (1952) and Gamble (1953).

The combination of fundamental and empirical researches has given rise to certain general considerations.

(*a*) Although the spermatozoal nucleus is in a resting state and the cell neither grows nor divides, it has an active metabolism designed to maintain fertilising capacity and the motility required therefor. Associated with the active metabolism is a high permeability to a great variety of substances.

(*b*) Spermicidal substances act in different ways; some inhibit essential enzymes, others damage the cell membrane, and so on. Moreover, immobilisation may be permanent or reversible, and Mann (1958) has drawn attention to the important distinction between spermicidal and spermistatic substances. The effect of the latter may well be reversed in the female tract, where their concentration will decrease continuously, so that spermatozoa apparently dead *in vitro* may effect fertilisation *in vivo*. Moreover, inimical substances may act rapidly or slowly so that in any comparison of effectiveness the time of making the observation becomes important.

Biochemical basis of spermicidal activity

A full account of this subject has been given by Mann (1958) based on a similar but earlier and shorter paper (Mann, 1954). According to Mann the great majority of spermicides fall into one or other of three categories, with some overlap. The first comprises the enzyme inhibitors; these may affect mainly respiration, e.g. cyanide or carbon monoxide, or they may affect mainly fructolysis, e.g. glyceraldehyde or fluoride. A suitable concentration of fluoride, for instance, will inhibit fructolysis and therefore motility, but affect respiration only partly (Mann and Lutwak-Mann, 1948).

The second category comprises the sulphydryl-binding substances. These inhibit the sulphydryl groups essential for motility and metabolism of the spermatozoon, and include copper ions, hydrogen peroxide, iodobenzoic acid and mercury salts. The effect of these substances may be counteracted by the presence of sulphydryl-containing substances, such as the ergothioneine normally present in semen, or by cysteine and glutathione added *in vitro*.

The third group comprises certain long-chain compounds, detergents and soaps e.g. cetrimide, which cause irreversible immobilisation by detaching the lipoprotein outer layer from the cell membrane so that there is fatal leakage of the cell contents.

Chemical contraception

Lists of contraceptive gels, pastes and creams, and of the spermicidal substances included in them, have been given among others by Gamble (1953) and by Mann (1958). Almost all contain sulphydryl-binding substances, mainly phenyl mercuric acetate, nitrate or benzoate, or one or other of the surface-active substances. It is difficult to obtain accurate estimates even *in vitro* of the relative effectiveness of the various preparations. The assay of spermicidal power, like all biological assays, should properly be carried out by comparison with the effect of a simultaneously tested reference substance. But, in the case of contraceptive preparations, it would be necessary to know the nature of the contained spermicide and to choose a reference substance with the same type of action. Moreover, it would be necessary to dispense the reference substance in a base similar to that used for the preparation under test. The importance of this precaution is shown by the fact that Gamble, (1957), in carrying out *in vitro* tests, found that a gel based on rice flour and containing 30 per cent NaCl in its aqueous component, immobilised human spermatozoa more rapidly than any one of a large number of commercial contraceptive gels and pastes. The difficulties in the way of carrying out a convincing biological assay of chemical contraceptives *in vitro* are thus formidable, but they are not scientifically greater than those that have been met and overcome in the biological assay of other active substances. The same applies to the correlation of *in vitro* spermicidal activity with *in vivo* contraceptive activity, though in the special circumstances surrounding it, this is likely to be a major task of organisation and perseverance.

The possibility of finding spermicidal substances effective by mouth has been a subject of some debate. Mann (1958) has pointed out that certain substances, e.g. ethanol and sulphonamide, appear in the seminal plasma after oral ingestion, so that there is no insuperable barrier between orally administered substances and the reproductive organs. However, no substance is yet known which, taken by mouth in doses non-toxic to the organism, has spermicidal activity in male or female. Substances such as cadmium, which destroy the seminiferous tubules of the testis, belong, of course, to a different category.

Attempts to Alter the Ratio of X- and Y-Spermatozoa

Recognition that mammalian spermatozoa are of two kinds, Y (male-producing) and X (female-producing), opened up an unlimited field for attempts to separate the two types *in vitro*, or to alter the ratio between them sufficiently to cause a demonstrable effect on the sex-ratio at birth. Such attempts were encouraged by the fact that in many mammals it appears that more males are conceived than females (Parkes, 1926), so that somewhere along the line between the start of meiosis and fertilisation the ratio of X- to Y-spermatozoa is presumably altered by naturally-occurring factors. Various supposed properties of spermatozoa have been invoked as a basis for the experimental alteration of the ratio, including differences in size or density of the two types arising from the extra chromatin present in the X-spermatozoon, differences in electrical charge and differences in tolerance of pH effects. All these matters have been discussed by Crew (1952) and their theoretical basis considered by Bishop and Walton in Chapter 7 of the present volume. It remains to discuss here only the more practical aspects of recent work.

Electrophoresis

Schröder (*see* Chapter 7, p. 125) subjected rabbit spermatozoa to electrophoresis and claimed that spermatozoa migrating to the anode were predominantly female-determining (X) and those migrating to the cathode predominantly male-determining (Y). The success of the separation was said to depend on the nature of the diluting fluid (optimum pH 7·1), on temperature (optimum 10°C.), on the difference in potential and on current strength (optimum about 80–90 volts and 17–20 milliamps). At higher temperatures the direction of migration was reversed ; at higher voltages and current strengths all spermatozoa migrated to the cathode. Many biological variables such as the age and sexual history of the animal, as well as the season of the year, were also indicated. Under optimal conditions separation, as indicated by the sex of the offspring arising from insemination of the semen fractions, was said to be 80 per cent successful. Schröder's optimal conditions appear to have been somewhat esoteric and various workers failed to reproduce her results (*see* p. 30). Gordon (1957), however, claimed to be more successful. He found that orientation of rabbit spermatozoa in the electric

field was immediate, passive, and tail first ; the separation was 71 per cent successful for Y-spermatozoa. In some samples the separation was excellent, but in
others it was very poor. The fertility of treated spermatozoa was low and only
31 litters resulted from 201 inseminations. The anodic samples yielded 62 females
and 25 males ; the cathodic 29 females and 51 males. The differences from the
expected sex-ratio were highly significant ($P < 0.001$).

It is remarkable that, 25 years after the publication of Schröder's first papers,
no decision as to the validity of her important claims has been reached.

Centrifugation

The question of whether size or density differences between X- and Y-spermatozoa could be sufficient to allow of differential centrifugation has recently been
revived by Lindahl and his co-workers, using a counter-streaming centrifuge in
which the cells are simultaneously subjected to centrifugal force and to a fluid
stream running counter to it. Lindahl and Kihlström (1952a) came to the conclusion that the density of the spermatozoon increased as it matured, and that
this increase was sufficiently great to mask completely any likely difference between
X- and Y-spermatozoa. Nevertheless, Lindahl (1956) reports two experiments
carried out on bull spermatozoa under slightly different conditions in the counter-
streaming centrifuge. In the first, about one-half of the material was retained
in the centrifuge and 187 out of 376 cows inseminated with it became pregnant.
There was no alteration in the sex-ratio. In the second experiment, the speed of
the counter-stream was increased so that only one-fifteenth to one-twentieth of
the material was retained. The spermatozoa in this fraction showed low motility,
but insemination of 24 cows resulted in the birth of 11 calves which were all male.
Attempts to repeat this second experiment led to equivocal results (Lindahl,
1958).

pH changes

One of the hoariest legends about the sex-ratio is that alkalinity in some way
assists the male-producing spermatozoa and acidity the female-producing ones.
A strange assortment of " evidence " has been adduced in support of this idea,
ranging from the supposed daughter-producing propensity of sour-tempered
women to the alleged effect of alkaline vaginal douches in promoting the conception
of males. In more modern times, the idea has been resuscitated by Weir (1955),
who claimed that two strains of mice differing in blood pH, i.e. 7.42 and 7.46, produced 40 ♂ : 60 ♀ and 60 ♂ : 40 ♀ respectively. Reciprocal crossing between
the strains showed that the source of the abnormal sex-ratio lay in the male not
the female. The pH idea has been further elaborated by McWhirter (1956) to
explain the sex-ratios in the offspring of human athletes and of rats kept at high
altitudes. However, treatment of spermatozoa in vitro with lactic acid or sodium
bicarbonate (Casida and Murphree, 1942) seems to have lent little support to
these suppositions.

V. Survival of Spermatozoa in the Genital Tract of the Female

The survival time of spermatozoa in the genital tract of the female can be estimated in various ways. Viable spermatozoa may be recovered from the tract

at various times after coitus, the time between coitus and fertilisation of the egg can be determined, and finally, further information may be obtained by the experimental alteration of the normal time relation between insemination and ovulation. Work along these lines has given remarkable results. Survival differs enormously between different animals ; in the mouse it is no more than a few hours, in the queen bee and many reptiles it is a few years. Even among mammals, survival time, as in some species of bats, may extend to several months. In the account that follows, a number of outstanding examples of storage of spermatozoa in insects and lower vertebrates are mentioned for purposes of comparison, but no attempt is made to deal generally with invertebrates, and only birds and mammals are considered in detail.

Insects

Many female insects mate only once, the single insemination being adequate for the fertilisation of eggs produced over a long period. The necessary storage of spermatozoa is usually carried out in special diverticulae of the female tract, the spermathecae, which may be some distance from the female genital opening. In *Oncopeltus*, the semen is deposited direct into the spermatheca through the medium of a long flagellum-like penis (Bonhag and Wick, 1953). In most insects, however, the semen is contained in a spermatophore, which is deposited in the bursa copulatrix of the female at the time of mating, and from which the spermatozoa migrate to the oviduct and thence to the spermatheca, where they are stored until required. There has been some difference of opinion about the mechanism of this migration, but Davey (1958) has shown that in *Rhodnius polixus* the process is a passive one. He found that the spermatozoa began to arrive in the spermathecae 5–10 minutes after mating, and by a number of ingenious experiments he established that this rapid migration was brought about by rhythmic contraction of the oviduct initiated through a peripheral nervous system by the accessary secretions of the male. Davey, whose paper should be consulted for references to earlier work, considers that a similar process may operate in other insects in which the semen is contained in spermatophores.

The survival time of spermatozoa in the spermathecae of insects differs enormously from species to species, and a good deal of information is now available. By far the best known case of long survival is provided by the queen Honey-bee. In this insect, semen is found in the oviducts immediately on return from the nuptial flight, which lasts 15–20 minutes (Laidlaw, 1944). Migration to the spermatheca takes longer, about 6 hours according to Bishop (1920). The spermatheca is a small round sac, about 1 mm. in diameter, connected to the common oviduct by a short duct, through which the spermatozoa first enter the spermatheca and are later extruded by a muscular "sperm pump" (Bresslau, 1906) as required for fertilisation of eggs destined to become queens or workers. The spermatozoa are held back when the eggs are required to produce the parthenogenetic drones.

Queen bees may mate more than once, but always within the space of a day or two, and sexual receptivity is lost for ever at the age of about 4 weeks. Plural mating, however, is unnecessary, as shown by the results of a single mating or a single A.I. The queen starts to lay within a few days of mating. She continues to lay for 24 hours a day and at her peak fertility is producing an average of about 1,500 eggs per day, with a maximum of some 2,000. She thus lays upwards of

100,000 eggs in a season, the great majority of them fertilised. After two full seasons, her stock of spermatozoa is much reduced and she lays fewer fertile eggs. As she gets older, the proportion of unfertilised eggs increases, the stock becomes weak and she is superseded. The arithmetic of this process is interesting. Estimates of the number of spermatozoa originally stored in the spermatheca vary from 4 million to 200 million (Snelgrove, 1946).

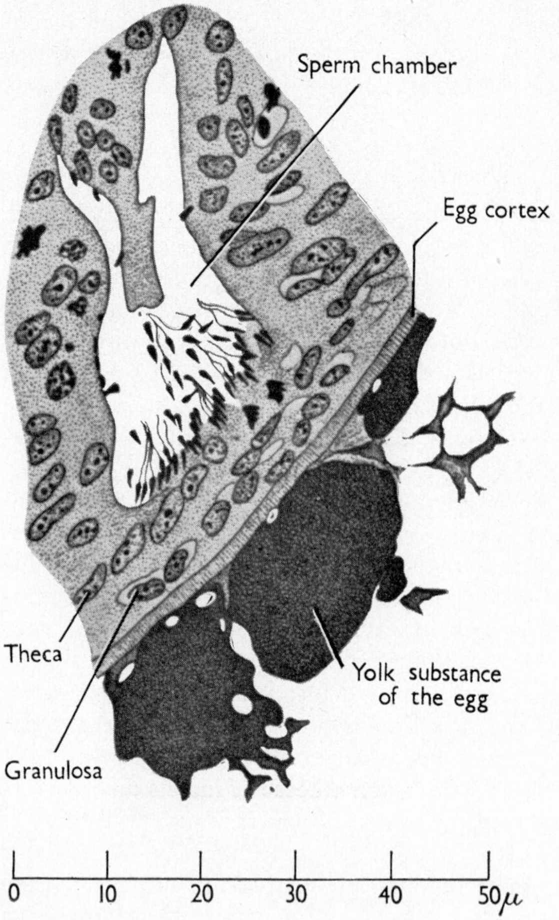

Fig. 9.24—Sperm chamber in ovary of *Lebistes* (From Stolk, 1950.)

Roberts (1944) counted about 7 million. From this store the queen fertilises perhaps 250,000 eggs. In other words, on Robert's figures, one spermatozoon in thirty introduced into the female tract succeeds in fertilising an egg, many of them being a year or even two years old at the time. This is efficiency of an order which, perhaps fortunately, is unknown among mammals.

Fish

Many instances are recorded of the long survival of spermatozoa in female viviparous fish, many of which produce a succession of broods after a single insemination. According to Philippi (1908), in the viviparous teleost, *Glaridichthys januarius*, the spermatozoa are stored partly in folds in the oviduct and partly in crypts in the ovary adjacent to the immature eggs. A similar state of affairs was found by Schmidt (1920) in *Lebistes reticulatus* and by van Oordt (1928) in *Xiphophorus helleri*. Several later publications refer to *Lebistes*. Winge (1922) has a photomicrograph of a clump of spermatozoa in an ovarian crypt lying with their heads orientated towards an immature egg and their tails twined together. Purser (1937) obtained eight broods of young over a period of about 4 months from a female *Lebistes* isolated from males, and Winge (1937) has the following to say about the survival of spermatozoa and selective fertilisation :

" Plainly enough there is competition between the spermatozoa, and it is remarkable that when a female has been fertilized by a male of one race of *Lebistes* and has produced some few broods within a few months, and then a new male of another race of *Lebistes* put into the tank immediately after a birth, the next brood will be from fertilization by the new male. The old spermatozoa cannot compete with the fresh ones. Ordinarily a mixed brood is only obtained when both males are together with the female at the same time."

Further reference to *Lebistes* is made by Stolk (1950), whose illustration of a nest of spermatozoa in the ovary is reproduced in Fig. 9.24.

Reptiles

Some of the most remarkable examples of storage of spermatozoa in the female are found among the reptiles. Marshall (1922), for instance, cites Rollinat (1898), who recorded that in the snake *Tropidonotus viperinus* insemination took place in the autumn though the eggs were not laid until the following summer. Again, the observations of Barney (1922) made it very likely that in terrapins spermatozoa might retain functional activity for years. Numerous observations followed on snakes (e.g. Woodward, 1933) and more recently on lizards (Atsatt, 1953). Some of the evidence is equivocal, but most of the conclusions are soundly based on the finding of active spermatozoa in the tract of females isolated from males for known periods, or on the laying of fertile eggs under similar control conditions.

The following are some typical records. Woodward (1933) isolated a female African Night Adder. During the next 5 months she produced four clutches of eggs, of which the first two clutches were 100 per cent, the third 64·7 per cent, and the fourth 55·5 per cent fertile. Later clutches were infertile. Ewing (1943) isolated four female Box Turtles in September 1933 ; one laid fertile eggs up to 1935 and two up to 1936. The fourth laid fertile eggs in 1934, 1936 and 1937. Eggs laid in the next 3 years were infertile. Carson (1945) kept a female Indigo Snake at home and away from all other snakes. After $4\frac{1}{3}$ years of "solitary confinement" she laid five eggs, at least one of which was fertile. Haines (1940) acquired a snake which had come from South America in a bunch of bananas, and isolated it in a cage in August 1934. In 1936 it laid seven eggs, of which one had been fertilised, in 1938 six eggs, of which two were fertile, and in 1939, eleven eggs, of which six were fertile.

Available information based on the finding of motile spermatozoa in, or the laying of fertile eggs by isolated females was summarised by Fox (1956), whose list leaves little doubt, reproduced in Table IX, that " delayed fertilisation " can occur in many reptiles. To what extent the more extreme possibilities occur under natural conditions is perhaps less certain.

Histological examination has not produced evidence of the existence of specialised spermathecae in reptiles, and it has generally been thought that the spermatozoa are stored in the oviduct (e.g. Ludwig and Rahn, 1943). Fox (1956) came to the conclusion that in the autumn-mating Garter Snake the spermatozoa spent most of the winter in the lower part of the oviduct and during February or March moved up into modified glands at the base of the infundibulum, which acted as spermathecae until ovulation took place (Fig. 9.25). Fox considered that spermatozoa did not normally survive in these receptacles after the birth of the young but might sometimes carry over from one breeding season to the next.

TABLE IX

SURVIVAL OF SPERMATOZOA IN REPRODUCTIVE TRACT OF ISOLATED FEMALE REPTILES

Species	Maximum period of demonstrated viability	Reference
Turtles		
Malaclemmys centrata (*Malaclemmys terrapin centrata*) Diamondback terrapin	4 years	Barney (1922) Hildebrand (1929)
Terrapene carolina Common box turtle	4 years	Ewing (1943)
Lizards		
Microsaura pumila pumila Dwarf chameleon	6 months	Atsatt (1953)
Solenoglyphic snakes		
Vipera aspis European asp	over winter	Rollinat (1946)
Causus rhombeatus African night adder	5 months	Woodward (1933)
Ancistrodon contortrix Copperhead	11 days	Gloyd (1933)
Crotalus viridis viridis Prairie rattlesnake	over winter	Rahn (1942)
Aglyphic colubrid snakes		
Tropidoclonion lineatum Lined snake	over winter	Gloyd (1928) Force (1931)
Coronella austriaca European smooth snake	over winter	Rollinat (1946)
Thamnophis sirtalis Common garter snake	over winter 3 months	Blanchard (1942) Rahn (1940)
Natrix natrix Common grass snake	over winter	Rollinat (1946) Petter-Rousseaux (1953)
Natrix vittata	$1\frac{1}{2}$ years	Kopstein (1938)
Natrix subminiata	5 months	Kopstein (1938)
Storeria dekayi Brown snake, DeKay's snake	4 months	Trapido (1940)
Drymarchon corais couperi Indigo snake	$4\frac{1}{2}$ years	Carson (1945)
Opisthoglyphic colubrid snakes		
Xenodon merremi	1 year	Graber (1940)
Leimadophis viridis	delayed fertilisation ; duration not stated	Mertens (1940)
Leptodeira annulata polysticta	6 years	Haines (1940)
Leptodeira albofusca	1 year	Kluth (1936)
Boiga multimaculata	1 year	Kopstein (1938)

Birds

Almost all the animals in which prolonged storage of spermatozoa in the female tract has been described are either normally poikilothermic (e.g. reptiles) or are poikilothermic during the period of storage (e.g. the hibernating bat). Against this background, the domestic fowl and certain other birds, with their high body temperature and comparatively long sperm-survival in the oviduct, are remarkable. Hammond (1952), however, has called attention to the possibly related fact that spermatogenesis proceeds at full body temperature in the abdominal testis of birds, and that survival in the male tract is prolonged (Munro, 1938c).

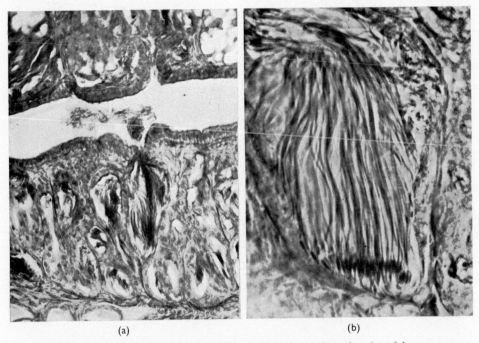

(a)   (b)

Fig. 9.25—Seminal receptacles of Garter Snake killed on April 25, after migration of the spermatozoa to the glands of the upper oviduct. (From the material of Fox, 1956.)
(a) Crypt full of spermatozoa, connecting with the lumen.
(b) Higher magnification of similar crypt, showing orderly arrangement of spermatozoa.

The fact that hens continue to lay fertile eggs after removal of the cock must have been known for centuries. Barfurth (1896) came to the conclusion that fertile eggs could be laid for as long as 4 weeks after a single mating, but found that in the later stages embryonic development might be faulty. Other workers, such as Gilbert (*cited by* Nalbandov and Card, 1943), Philips (1918) and Crew (1926), observed periods of fertility ranging from 8 to 20 days after a single mating, but all noted decreased viability of the embryos as the spermatozoa became stale. Nalbandov and Card (1943) examined the specific point of the effect of stale spermatozoa. They found that at 16–20 days after removal of the male, fertility was down from more than 90 per cent to about 10 per cent, and hatchability from about 65 per cent to 0 per cent. Dunn (1927) and Warren and Kilpatrick (1929), however, failed to find decreased hatchability in the later stages of the period of

fertility following a single mating.   Polge (1955) investigated the retention of fertility following a single A.I. in Leghorn hens, and obtained the results shown in
Fig. 9.26.   He found no decrease in hatchability in the second week after a single
insemination, which according to his curve is the period of rapidly falling fertility.
Analogous results following A.I. in turkeys were recorded by Burrows and
Marsden (1938).   In ring-doves, also, fertile eggs may be laid up to 8 days after
removal of the male, according to Riddle and Behre (1921).

The striking and easily observed retention of fertility in de-mated hens aroused
the curiosity of the celebrated observer Buffon (1771), who believed that it was due
to the fertilisation of immature oöcytes.   This theory was afterwards accepted

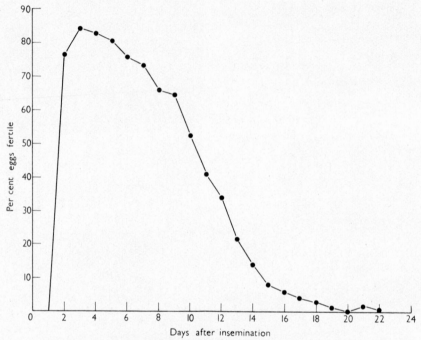

Fig. 9.26—Survival of spermatozoa in oviduct of hen, as shown by time for which
fertile eggs were laid after a single insemination. (From Polge, 1955.)

by Iwanow (1924) on the grounds that hens continued to lay fertile eggs after
irrigation of the oviduct with spermicidal fluid.   This curious experiment was
repeated by Walton and Whetham (1933), who confirmed Iwanow's finding but
offered the explanation that many spermatozoa lying deep in folds and crevices
of the oviduct would be protected from the spermicide.   This suggestion was
given substance by Van Drimmelen (1946), who observed " sperm nests " in
shallow crypts of the cranial part of the oviduct.   The structure of the sperm
nests in the hen and the nature of the release mechanism has been investigated
by Grigg (1957), and the mechanism of sperm transport by Allen and Grigg (1957).
The story was taken a stage further by the ingenious experiment of Olsen and Neher
(1948), who transferred newly ovulated eggs from unmated pullets into the oviducts
of mated hens, and, reciprocally, transferred eggs obtained by *in vitro* ovulation
from the ovaries of mated hens into the oviducts of unmated birds.   Only in the

mated birds were the eggs fertile, showing that fertilisation was oviducal rather than ovarian. Nevertheless, Olsen (1952) proceeded to the further experiment of applying spermatozoa to the surface of the ovary of birds 4 to 17 weeks old with the result that four apparently fertile eggs were obtained from the birds as long as 5 to 6 months later. The full implications of this remarkable result await further work, but if substantiated it seems that in some instances the spermatozoa are able to penetrate the follicular wall and enter the immature ovum in the ovary, an event reminiscent of the ovarian fertilisation characteristic of many groups of lower vertebrates. So far as normal mating or insemination is concerned, however, the balance of the evidence favours the view that the continued fertility of the de-mated hen is due to the survival of the spermatozoa in the oviduct for a period of 2 to 3 weeks.

Mammals

In most female mammals sexual receptivity is closely related to ovulation and the spermatozoa ascend the female genital tract rapidly. There is thus no teleological reason why the mammalian spermatozoa should have a prolonged survival time in the female tract and, with the notable exception of the bats, their survival does, in fact, appear to be brief.

Domestic animals

Information about the survival of spermatozoa in the female genital tract of domestic animals is summarised in Volume II by Hammond (1952). In the cow the spermatozoa retain fertilising power or motility for about 28 hours, in the mare for 5 to 6 days, in the ewe for about 30 to 36 hours, in the sow for less than 24 hours, and in the bitch for about 2 days. According to du Mesnil du Buisson and Dauzier (1955, 1956) natural insemination in the sow is followed by rapid resorption of spermatozoa in the uterine horns so that most of the spermatozoa disappear from this part of the tract within 5 hours of service. Viable spermatozoa were found in the Fallopian tubes at 22 to 30 hours, but not at 50 hours after service. No surviving spermatozoa were recovered from the vagina later than 5 hours after service. Mann, Polge and Rowson (1956) found that not only the spermatozoa but also the seminal plasma, present in abundance in the uterus of the newly mated sow, had largely disappeared within 6 hours. Burkhardt's (1949) figures for the horse are concordant with earlier ones in that he obtained pregnancy in a mare in which there was an interval of 126–138 hours between mating and gonadotrophin-induced ovulation. There is little doubt, therefore, that among domestic animals the spermatozoa of the stallion survive longest in the female tract. The implications of these findings, especially as to the time of insemination during oestrus, are discussed by Hammond (1952), and recent work is reviewed by VanDemark (1958).

Laboratory animals

The rabbit has been a favourite subject for experiments on the longevity of spermatozoa in the female tract because of the ease with which mating or A.I. can be carried out at known times before ovulation. Hammond and Asdell (1926), in their classical work, concluded that rabbit spermatozoa might retain fertilising power in the female tract for up to 30 hours, but that only small litters were produced from conceptions occurring towards the end of this period.   Satisfactory information is also available for other laboratory animals.   In the mouse, Merton (1939) found that, following A.I., spermatozoa reached the Fallopian tube in $1\frac{1}{4}$ hours, and there retained fertilising power for 6 hours and motility for $13\frac{1}{2}$ hours.   Soderwall and Young (1940) carried out a massive experiment on guinea-pigs, in which they inseminated 185 female guinea-pigs before the beginning of oestrus and found that 22 hours was the maximum time for which the spermatozoa retained fertilising capacity.   Up to 17 hours, the percentage of successful inseminations and litter size were not affected.   After that time, the number of successful inseminations decreased, but the young developed normally.   Analogous results were obtained by Soderwall and Blandau (1941) in an experiment involving artificial insemination of 184 female rats.   Conceptions were obtained from inseminations made as long as 14 hours before ovulation, but when the interval was more than 10 hours the proportion of successes and litter size decreased. Again, however, no evidence was found that fertilisation by stale spermatozoa affected embryonic development.   As would be expected, motility lasts longer than fertilising power ; Yochem (1929) observed feeble motility among guinea-pig spermatozoa after 41 hours and among rat spermatozoa after 17 hours in the female genital tract.   In every case the short survival time in the female tract is in marked contrast with the long survival in the epididymis of the male (*see* Chapter 7) and it may be doubted whether the slight difference in temperature between the two environments is more than a minor factor.

The bat

Many bats in the northern temperate zone mate in the autumn, though ovulation and fertilisation of the egg are delayed to the spring.   As a result, the vagina (in Rhinolophidae) or the uterus (in Vespertilionidae), as first noted by Pagenstecher (1859), is gorged with spermatozoa during the winter hibernation, but pregnancies do not occur until the spring (*see* Eckstein and Zuckerman, 1956) (Fig. 9.27).   This sequence of events was generally supposed to indicate that the spermatozoa survived in the female tract throughout the winter ; the alternative explanation of arrested development of the embryo, put forward by Van Beneden, received little credence.   Hartman (1933) reviewed all the existing evidence and came to the conclusion that spermatozoa undoubtedly remained alive in the tract during the whole winter.   He emphasised, however, the uncertainty as to whether such spermatozoa retained fertilising capacity, because the females of certain species often mated again in the spring or even during temporary awakenings during hibernation.   This problem has been attacked in several ways.   Harrison Matthews (1937) found that in the British horseshoe bats the vagina was sealed as a result of the autumn mating with a vaginal plug which was retained in position until the early stages of pregnancy in spring, and which would discourage if not actually prevent supplementary matings.   It seemed likely, therefore, that fertilisation was effected by spermatozoa stored for many months in the female tract.   An experimental approach to the problem was made by Caffier (1934) and Caffier and Kolbow (1934), who induced ovulation in the hibernating female by injection of gonadotrophin and in several cases obtained fertilised eggs, even from torpid animals.   Caffier concluded that the stored spermatozoa retained fertilising power. Guthrie and Jeffers (1938), however, recovered fertilised eggs from hibernating bats injected on February 20th, but not from those injected on December 4th or January 7th ; they concluded that the stale spermatozoa present at the earlier dates failed to fertilise the newly ovulated eggs, and that the February eggs were fertilised as the result of more recent matings.

Fortunately, the decisive experiment called for by Hartman (1933) of isolating hibernating females until the spring breeding season was later carried out by Folk (1940) and Wimsatt (1942, 1944). Folk found two embryos on April 28th in a bat which had been isolated from males since January 8th. Wimsatt worked on a bigger scale and his conclusions may be cited.

" Females of two species of bats, *Myotis l. lucifugus* and *Eptesicus f. fuscus*, were collected in the fall and early winter, isolated from males, and placed in hibernation under

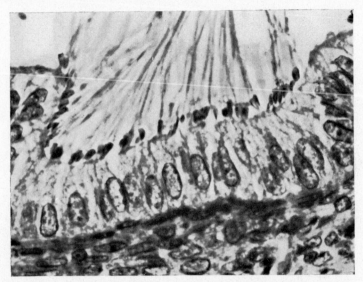

Fig. 9.27—Spermatozoa in the uterus of pipistrelle bat in April, showing orderly arrangement in shallow crypt, coinciding with a fertilised egg in the Fallopian tubes. (From the material of Deanesly and Warwick, 1939.)

laboratory conditions. The genital tracts of those autopsied during hibernation were examined, and the presence of highly motile sperm was noted as many as 159 days following isolation. The genital tracts of those animals which were kept at room temperature for a time before being killed were examined histologically. The presence of normal embryos was observed in all thirty specimens surviving hibernation of a total of fifty-five females of *E. f. fuscus*, and in five of seven female *M. l. lucifugus* that had ovulated following prolonged artificial hibernation. The two females which had been separated longest from males and which contained normal embryos were isolated 138 (*Myotis*) and 156 (*Eptesicus*) days respectively. It is evident, therefore, that the stored spermatozoa retain their ability to fertilise the ova released spontaneously from the ovaries in the spring." (Fig. 9.28.)

It should be added that in many bats, including the familiar Pipistrelle, spermatogenesis begins in May and ends in September (Courrier, 1927), the spermatozoa being stored in the enlarged tail of the epididymis during the autumn and

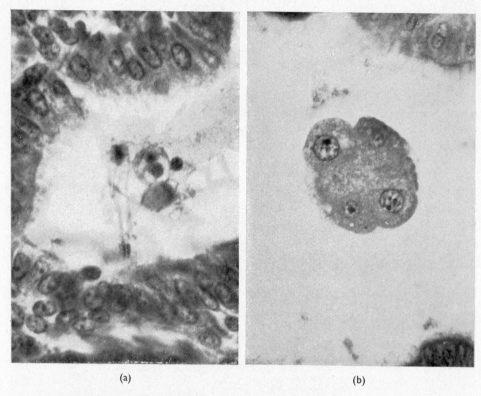

(a)   (b)

Fig. 9.28—Little brown bat (*Myotis lucifugus lucifugus*) isolated in artificial hibernation on December 12th. Removed to room temperature (70°F.) on April 21st and killed on May 1st. Period of isolation 139 days. (From the material of Wimsatt, 1942.)

(a) Spermatozoa in uterine gland crypt, together with phagocyte.

(b) 10-celled ovum in uterine lumen, about 8 days after fertilisation.

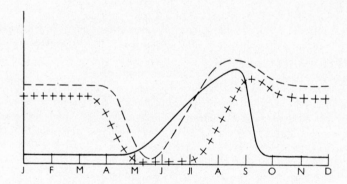

Fig. 9.29—Male pipistrelle bat; relative times of development of
+ + + + secondary sexual characters
– – – – interstitial tissue
——————— spermatogenesis
(From Courrier, 1927.)

winter (Fig. 9.29). Fertilisation of the eggs in spring, therefore, implies prolonged survival of the spermatozoa in the male if not in the female.

Man

It is known that under ordinary conditions the survival time of spermatozoa in the human vagina is limited to a few hours. Huhner (1913) considered that almost all were dead within an hour, while Belonoschkin (1939) recovered motile spermatozoa only for up to $2\frac{1}{2}$ hours after insemination. MacLeod et al. (1958) observed that spermatozoa might be decapitated in the vagina. Stemmer (1940) related the short survival time to the fact that the optimal pH for spermatozoa is 8·0, while the pH of the vagina is 4·5. By contrast, according to the first of these authors, spermatozoa may survive in the cervical mucus for up to 48 hours. Others have noted a similar or even greater survival period (Moench, 1934 ; Cary, 1936 ; Stein and Cohen, 1950). These observations can again be related to pH effects, the pH of the cervical mucus being about 8·0 (Stemmer, 1940). Breckenridge, Pederson and Pommerenke (1950) found that the intracervical pH measured through ten menstrual cycles fluctuated narrowly on the slightly alkaline side. It is not obvious, however, how the supposed pH effect correlates with the results of Goldfarb (1952), who found motile spermatozoa in the vagina up to 48 hours and in the cervical mucus up to 96 hours after the artificial insemination of an ejaculate to which had been added 100,000 units of penicillin.

Notwithstanding the favourable climate usually provided by the cervical mucus it is recognised that in some individuals and at certain times of the cycle it may present a formidable barrier to the progress of the spermatozoa. As a result there have been many attempts to study in vitro the properties of the cervical mucus by capillary tube (Lamar, Shettles and Delfs, 1940) or coverslip (Barton and Wiesner, 1946) techniques. Harvey and Jackson (1948), using a specially designed calibrated microscope slide in which there were grooves to hold strips of mucus, distinguished four grades of penetration of cervical mucus by spermatozoa ; these ranged from almost total failure of the spermatozoa to enter the mucus, to penetration so complete and rapid that the mucus was swarming with spermatozoa to a depth of 3 cm. within 30 minutes.

The comparatively prolonged survival of spermatozoa in the cervical mucus is the basis of the so-called post-coital test commonly used in fertility clinics. This test involves the examination of the cervical mucus for the presence of motile spermatozoa a few hours after coitus and gives an indication of the vigour and numbers of the spermatozoa, of the penetrability of the cervical mucus, and as to whether there is any unusual hostility towards the particular spermatozoa in question. In the experience of Donald (1953) a satisfactory post-coital test, in the sense that large numbers of active spermatozoa were found embedded in the mucus, was obtained in about two-thirds of the cases where the husband had a sperm count of 20 million/ml. to 90 million/ml. With lower counts satisfactory tests amounted to only 25 per cent of the total : with higher counts satisfactory tests were surprisingly infrequent. Further clinical data were given by Bishop (1953). According to Harvey (1953) the in vitro fertility index (referred to on p. 191) correlates well with the capacity of the spermatozoa to penetrate the mucus (Fig. 9.13).

There is now a considerable body of evidence indicating that cyclic variations

1*

occur in the nature of human cervical mucus. According to Clift (1945) and Clift, Glover and Scott Blair (1950) at mid-cycle it is homogeneously translucent, more "runny" and has increased flow elasticity and "Spinnbarkeit". This mid-cycle change is associated with indications of ovulation obtained by basal temperature charts (Viergiver and Pommerenke, 1946; Pommerenke and Viergiver, 1947) and may be assumed to result from the action of oestrogens (Abarbanel, 1946) produced at the climax of the follicular phase of the cycle. *In vitro* studies show that mucus obtained at this stage is more easily, and at other times less easily penetrated by spermatozoa (Lamar, Shettles and Delfs, 1940; Harvey, 1954; Pommerenke, 1946). The present significance of these observations is that if the spermatozoa have difficulty in penetrating the cervical mucus their survival time in the female tract will necessarily be brief. According to Schwartz and Zinsser (1955), however, high activity of the spermatozoa in the cervical mucus is not necessarily correlated either with the stage of the cycle or the fertility of the couple.

Accurate determination of the survival time of spermatozoa in the upper part of the genital tract of the human female is extraordinarily difficult. Early estimates, references to which are given by Marshall (1922) and Knaus (1934), based on the finding of motile spermatozoa *post mortem*, or in parts of the tract removed by surgery, ranged up to several weeks, but no importance is now attached to these observations. Belonoschkin (1939) did not find spermatozoa in the female tract 2½ days after coitus. Knaus (1934), reviewing all the evidence then available about the time for which spermatozoa retained fertilising capacity in the female tract, concluded that 3 days (Hoehne and Behne, 1914) was probably an overestimate, and that the time was probably less than 48 hours. Information of this kind was essential to Knaus's theories about the "safe" and "fertile" periods of the human menstrual cycle, which depended on knowing approximately the time of ovulation and the duration of functional survival of egg and spermatozoon. For obvious reasons it is extremely difficult to assess the results of organised "trials" of the restriction of coitus to the "safe period", and reports such as that of Latz and Reiner (1942), who recorded 11,249 cycles with 49,356 intercourses in the calculated safe period without a single conception, must be regarded with some caution. Nevertheless, allowing for the difficulty of determining the time of ovulation some days in advance, even a modest degree of success in fertility control attending the limitation of intercourse to the "safe period" (Knaus, 1950) indicates clearly the limited time for which spermatozoa retain fertilising power in the genital tract of the human female. A similar conclusion may be drawn from the results of A.I. at different times of the menstrual cycle mentioned in Section I of this chapter.

VI. TRANSPORT, SELECTION AND FATE OF SPERMATOZOA IN THE FEMALE MAMMAL

Transport of Spermatozoa in the Female Genital Tract

Species differences in survival time of the spermatozoa do not appear to be correlated with the site of deposition of the semen at coitus or with its mode of transport in the female tract. Some aspects of this subject have been considered

by Hammond in Chapter 22 and by Walton in Chapter 8.   It remains to consider
in more detail the question of active motility of the spermatozoa *versus* passive
transportation in the tract and in particular the role of the neurohypophysis.

Many authors have called attention to the rapidity with which the spermatozoa
appear at the ovarian end of the tract after coitus and have emphasised that the
automotility of the spermatozoa (*see* Chapter 9A) could not alone be responsible
(*see* review by VanDemark, 1958).   The work of Florey and Walton (*see* p. 152)
showing that semen spread through the uterus of the rat within a few seconds
of coitus was confirmed by several observers.   Blandau (1945) pointed out that
this was a remarkable fact, because at oestrus the rat uterus is distended with
fluid under pressure.   He considered that the necessary temporary relaxation of
the cervical musculature was brought about by the formation of the vaginal plug,
because spermatozoa from a male deprived of its seminal vesicles did not pass
through the cervix.   Other observations on speed of transport include the following : Evans (1933), by means of a uterine fistula, showed that in the bitch
spermatozoa arrived in the Fallopian tube within 25 seconds of ejaculation by the
male.   He concluded that they were transported by peristaltic movement of the
uterus and that their own motility played little part.   Adams (1956) ligated the
utero-tubal junction in rabbits at various times after mating, and found that,
although a few spermatozoa reached the Fallopian tube very quickly, effective
numbers appeared only after 25 minutes.   VanDemark and Moeller (1951) found
spermatozoa in the Fallopian tube of the cow $2\frac{1}{2}$ minutes after A.I. and at the
ampulla in 5 minutes.   Brown (1944b) observed that spermatozoa traversed an
excised human uterus and tubes in an average time of 69 minutes, which, as Hartman
(1957) points out, would be possible by active motility only if the spermatozoa
kept up top speed in the right direction.   Dauzier and Wintenberger (1952a, b),
in contrast to other authors (Schott and Phillips, 1941 ; Phillips and Andrews,
1937 ; Starke, 1949), found that in the sheep the spermatozoa do not reach the
upper part of the Fallopian tube until 8 hours after mating.   Rommer (1947)
and Rubenstein (1943) consider that, in man, vaginal contractions are important
in forcing the semen into the cervix, and Rubenstein *et al.* (1951) report having
recovered live spermatozoa from the Fallopian tube of a woman 30 minutes after
coitus.   The function of the orgasm in promoting transport of spermatozoa in
women has been much debated, but it is certain that an orgasm is not essential for
fertility (*see* Marshall, 1922).

Another line of approach has been to study the movement of inert matter (*see*
p. 156), but the results have been somewhat inconclusive.   Dauzier (1955a, b)
investigated the movement of killed spermatozoa in the genital tract of the ewe
and concluded that when alive they moved by passive transport in the uterus,
but by their own motility in the Fallopian tube.   Conditions, however, vary in
different animals.   In the mated rabbit spermatozoa decrease gradually in numbers
between the cervix and Fallopian tube ; in the rat spermatozoa are more evenly
distributed in the uterus, but are held up by the utero-tubal " valve " through
which only a few hundred spermatozoa ascend into the Fallopian tube (Blandau
and Money, 1944).   Heterologous spermatozoa introduced into the uterus of the
rat are blocked completely by this valve (Leonard and Perlman, 1949).

The relative importance of uterine contraction and intrinsic motility in trans-
porting spermatozoa has been considered by Hübner (1955) and reviewed in some

detail by Hartman (1957). Hartman emphasises the evidence that the manipulation of the female's genitalia before and during copulation reflexly stimulates the posterior pituitary lobe and thereby causes increased contractions of the uterus. Millar (1952) measured the intra-uterine pressure in the mare and found that a negative pressure was set up during coitus. In two mares tested, 79 ml. and 80 ml. of fluid were sucked up into the uterus in 5 seconds, amounts which slightly exceed the volume of the stallion's ejaculate. A pressure difference of 0·7 lb. per sq. in. was indicated. VanDemark and Hays (1952), using an intra-uterine balloon, recorded movements in the cow uterus before and during coitus. Each successive phase of the process led to increased activity, and ejaculation resulted in tetanic

(a)

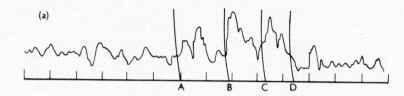

(b)

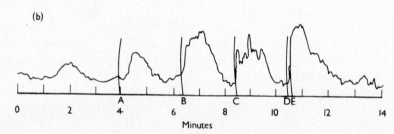

Fig. 9.30—Response of the uterus of a cow to sexual stimulation, measured by an intra-uterine balloon. (After VanDemark and Hays, 1952.)

    (a) A.I.   A–B, massage of anal region
                    B–C, massage of cervix
                    C–D, insertion of insemination tube
    (b) Natural mating.
             A.   Bull brought into sight of cow.
             B.   Bull allowed to muzzle vulva and hindquarters of cow.
             C.   Bull allowed to mount but not copulate.
             D.   Bull allowed to mount.
             E.   Bull copulated.

contractions (Fig. 9.30). A.I. had a similar effect (VanDemark and Hays, 1951) and a corresponding uterine motility pattern was produced in the absence of other stimulation by 15 units of oxytocin (VanDemark and Hays, 1955). VanDemark and Moeller (1951) obtained movement of spermatozoa in the isolated uteri of cows slaughtered in oestrus or during the follicular phase, but the movement was enhanced by the addition of oxytocin to the perfusate ; during the luteal phase, movement was not obtained with the addition of oxytocin.

Harris (1955) has reviewed the evidence that the posterior pituitary body is involved in the transport of spermatozoa in the female tract, and pointed out that while direct evidence is lacking, mammary effects known to be caused by sudden release of oxytocin may also be brought about by stimulation of the genitalia and

by mating ; thus, manipulation of the vulva and cervix of the cow causes a rise
in intra-mammary pressure (Hays and VanDemark, 1953) and coitus in a lactating
woman may cause a sudden flow of milk (Campbell and Petersen, 1953).   Hartman (1957) also called attention to the work of Eränkö, Friberg and Karvonen
(1953), who found water retention in the newly mated rat similar to that produced
by the antidiuretic principle of the neurohypophysis (Fig. 9.31).

It is thus almost certain that the increased tone and contraction of the uterus
caused by sexual stimulation and mating is due to reflex stimulation of the posterior
pituitary gland and the consequent outpouring of oxytocin (VanDemark and Hays,
1954).   In this connection we may recall the observation made by Knaus (*see*

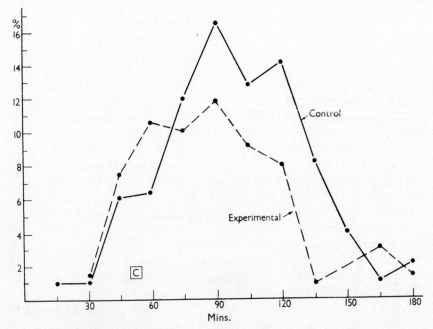

Fig. 9.31—Urine excretion of female rats as percentage of hydrating doses of water.
(From Eränkö *et al.*, 1953.)
● ————— ● In control animals
● – – – – ● In females after copulation at C

Marshall and Moir, 1952) that oestrogen increases and progesterone decreases the
sensitivity of the myometrium to oxytocin so that the uterus is most sensitive at
oestrus when mating occurs, and least during pregnancy or pseudopregnancy
when mating is less likely.   Evidently it is probable that the passive transport of
spermatozoa will be much affected by the stage of the cycle at which they are
introduced into the female tract, and Dauzier and Wintenberger (1952a) found that
both movement and motility of spermatozoa were much less in the anoestrous or
dioestrous than in the oestrous sheep.   It seems that here is a further reason why,
in an animal such as the rabbit, A.I. rarely brings about the fertilisation of eggs
resulting from ovulation induced during pseudopregnancy (Wislocki and Snyder,
1931; Austin, 1949).   Conversely, Austin and Bruce (1956) observed that
administration of oestrogen seemed to increase the number of spermatozoa
reaching the site of fertilisation in the mouse.

Selective Fertilisation

Why does one particular spermatozoon fertilise the egg when a million fail ? Why in some animals, including man, is the ovum more often fertilised by a Y-spermatozoon than by an X-spermatozoon ? Why may one male regularly be prepotent over another when their semen is mixed in equal quantities before insemination ? No definite answers can yet be given to these questions, though many relevant observations have been made.

The older literature contains various odd accounts of the results of double mating. Robertson (1917) recorded that the mule breeders of Kansas had the custom of mating the mare with a horse stallion a few minutes before putting her to the donkey stallion. This practice was brought to light by the anomalous appearance of a horse and a mule as twins, but normally only mules resulted. It seems, therefore, that, at least in Kansas, donkey spermatozoa had some advantage in the mare compared with horse spermatozoa. Cole and Davis (1914) mated doe rabbits with a pair of bucks in rapid succession and found that the offspring always took after the same buck. When this prepotent male was treated with ethyl alcohol the young took after the other buck, although the treated one was still fertile when used alone. King (1929) records a comparatively large number of litters showing selective fertilisation after double mating in rats. In natural matings of this kind it is impossible, of course, to standardise either the volume of semen or the number of spermatozoa, so it may be that the prepotent spermatozoa triumphed by sheer weight of numbers rather than by superior speed, longevity or fertilising power. King's experiments, however, included reciprocal double matings and seemed to show that the unlike male was prepotent. In mice, Gowen and Schott (1933) obtained a small number of mixed litters from females which had mated at one oestrus with two males of different strains and Michie (1955) records a mixed litter in mice equally divided between C_{57} and C_3H sires.

The advent of A.I. made possible more accurate observations of this kind, and Marshall (1922) described an experiment in which a Dandie Dinmont bitch was inseminated with a mixture of approximately equal amounts of Dandie Dinmont and mongrel semen, and produced an all-mongrel litter. In more recent times the subject of heterospermic [1] inseminations came into prominence again with Russian work, reviewed by Kushner (1954). This purported to show the existence of " heterospermic vigor " by increase in conception rate, birth rate, birth weight and growth and viability of young, presumably as the result of somatic fertilisation, heteropolyspermic penetration of the eggs, or interaction between embryos of different genetic makeup. Beatty (1957b) was unable to confirm the existence of " heterospermic vigor " by any of the criteria mentioned, but obtained some interesting data on selective fertilisation. Working with rabbits, he used the mixed semen of two genetically marked bucks (S and L) on 35 does. The semen of one buck was much more effective than that of the other ; a 50–50 mixture gave rise to litters which were mainly S hybrids. To produce a 50–50 mixture of young required about 70 per cent of L semen in the mixture

---

[1] This term would be expected to mean the insemination of mixed semen from sires of different species. It implies here, however, the mixed semen of two sires of the same species.

(Fig. 9.32). Beatty standardised the semen by volume but not by number of spermatozoa, so that his results could be explained by greater sperm density in the S semen.

In a series of experiments on mice, Edwards (1955) made sperm mixtures from three inbred strains in which the hybrids were genetically distinguishable (C_3H, REB, G).   In the C_3H + REB mixture C_3H spermatozoa were found to be significantly more effective in producing offspring.

An example of a possible mechanism of male prepotency is to be seen in the report of Kelly (1937), who found that Dorset rams were equally fertile with either Dorset or Merino ewes, but that Merino rams were less fertile with Dorsets than with Merinos.   He explained these results on the grounds that the Merino

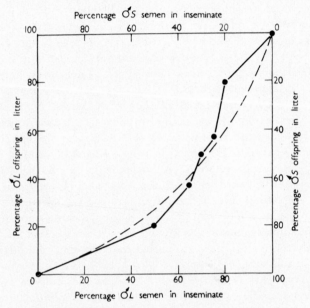

Fig. 9.32—Proportion of young derived from each of two male rabbits (L and S), according to proportion of semen from each in mixed inseminate. (From Beatty, 1957b.)

spermatozoa were shorter-lived than the Dorset spermatozoa, and although effective in association with the short oestrus and rapid ovulation of the Merino ewe, were less effective with the more prolonged oestrus and less certain ovulation time of the Dorsets.

It may be that the sperm antagglutins described by Lindahl and Kihlström (1952b) have some bearing on the problem of selective fertilisation.   The authors claim to have obtained not only from seminal plasma (Lindahl and Kihlström, 1954) (*see* p. 296) but also in the tubal secretions of the rabbit and in the ovarian follicles of cattle and pigs, a substance capable of inhibiting the spontaneous head-to-head agglutination of stale spermatozoa.   Lindahl and Nilsson (1957) report the " isolation " of an active substance from liquor folliculi of the cow and indicate some of its chemical properties.   According to Lindahl, Ingelman-Sundberg, Furuhjelm and Nilsson (1956) the female antagglutinic factor is found in women in the ovarian follicles, the Fallopian tube and the cervical mucus. The evaluation of these results and of their relation to the antagglutination effect of rabbit vaginal washings described by Smith (1954) and to the fertilisin of mammalian eggs described by Bishop and Tyler (1956), will be awaited with interest.

Fate of Redundant Spermatozoa

In most animals which have been investigated, large numbers of spermatozoa are found in the uterus after coitus, as a result either of intra-uterine ejaculation or of ascent through the cervix from the vagina (*see* Chapter 8). Comparatively few spermatozoa reach the site of fertilisation in the upper Fallopian tube, and very few penetrate the eggs. The enormous majority of those entering the uterus must therefore be disposed of in some way. Blandau and Odor (1949), working on the rat, described a relaxation of the cervix in metoestrus, so that the uterine contents were evacuated and spermatozoa reappeared in the vaginal washing. The distension of the uterus of the oestrous rat and mouse with fluid might facilitate such a mechanism, but it may be assumed that in most animals redundant spermatozoa are disposed of *in situ*. The idea that many penetrate the wall of the female tract or survive to penetrate the embryo, and thereby effect some kind of " somatic fertilisation " is considered in Chapter 10, and while some spermatozoa undoubtedly penetrate the tubal mucosa in certain species (Austin and Bishop, 1959; Austin, 1959), there is little doubt that, dead or alive, most redundant spermatozoa are removed by phagocytosis in the uterine lumen. This suggestion was put forward by Hoehne (1914) and Hoehne and Behne (1914), who studied the fate of human, rabbit and guinea-pig spermatozoa in the peritoneal cavity, and to whom their removal by phagocytosis represented the usual reaction of the animal to foreign bodies. Several later workers, including Yochem (1929) and Merton (1939), have supported the view that redundant spermatozoa are removed in this way.

Austin (1957) made a detailed study of the rat and mouse. He found that in mice killed 2–6 hours after coitus the uterine fluid, amounting to about 0·1 ml., contained some 20 million spermatozoa and very few leucocytes. Twelve hours later leucocytes had increased to 25 million and the spermatozoa had decreased to 11 million, most of which were being phagocytosed (Fig. 9.33). About 20 hours after coitus the uterine contents were evacuated in spite of the continued presence of a plug. Phagocytosis was also observed, but on a lesser scale, in the rat, in which the uterine contents are evacuated earlier. The phagocytes observed by Austin were polymorphonuclear leucocytes for which one spermatozoon was a heavy meal, and he called attention to this difference from the results of Hoehne and Behne, who described and figured phagocytes large enough to accommodate a dozen spermatozoa, and whose results may therefore not be applicable to the intra-uterine disposal of spermatozoa.

According to Austin, the phagocytes may engulf a live spermatozoon, making one more hazard between the spermatozoon and the egg, but the leucocytes do not wander back into the uterine tissues; they are evacuated from the uterus when the cervix relaxes. The state of affairs may be different in women, in whom immunisation against spermatozoa has been adduced as a possible cause of sterility. The idea, however, receives no support from animal work, and the serum of ten women

sterile for no obvious reason, examined by Swyer (personal communication), showed
no obvious agglutinins against human spermatozoa.   However, both the absorption

(a)   (b)

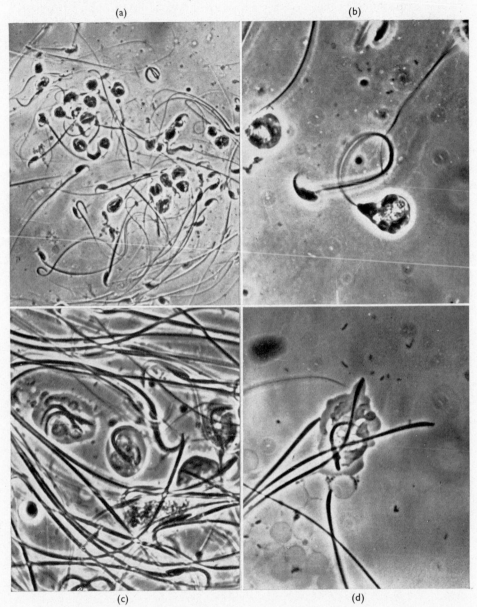

(c)   (d)

Fig. 9.33—Fate of mouse and rat spermatozoa in female tract. (From Austin, 1957.)
   (a) Uterine contents of a mouse killed 14–18 hr. after coitus, showing many leucocytes,
a few intact free spermatozoa and several headless forms. Some of the leucocytes can be seen
to be engaged in phagocytosis. × 200.
   (b) Early stage of phagocytosis of mouse spermatozoa.
   (c) and (d) Phagocytosis of rat spermatozoa. Preparations flattened to show cell details.

of antigens from the vagina and the antigenicity of homologous spermatozoa (see
p. 213) would be involved in such a reaction.   It remains to be seen whether
heterologous spermatozoa are antigenic by vaginal administration.

Austin (1959) points out that " somatic fertilisation " together with the phago-
cytic ingestion of spermatozoa, if they occur, provide a conceivable but barely
credible explanation of telegony, the supposed influence of a sire on the offspring
of the same female by a later sire. Belief in telegony received a great fillip during
the nineteenth century from the case of Lord Morton's quagga—a mare bred with
a quagga stallion was said later to have had a striped foal by a horse stallion (*see*
Darwin, 1905). Many attempts, all unsuccessful, have been made under controlled conditions to obtain positive evidence of the occurrence of telegony.
Cossar Ewart (1899) obtained only negative results from extensive experiments
with a zebra and various mares, as well as with other animals. Minot (1904) and
Pearson (1900) found no evidence for the alleged phenomenon in guinea-pigs and
man respectively. The idea is now generally supposed to be discredited, but it
died hard, if it is dead. It will be interesting to see whether it is resuscitated by the
verification of somatic fertilisation.

Bibliography

ABARBANEL, A. R. (1946). Artificial reproduction of the cyclic changes in cervical mucus in
human castrates. *Endocrinology*, **39**, 65.

ADAMS, C. E. (1956). A study of fertilization in the rabbit: the effect of post-coital ligation
of the Fallopian tube or uterine horn. *J. Endocrin.*, **13**, 296.

ADAMSTONE, F. B., & CARD, L. E. (1934). A study of the spermatozoon of the fowl, with
particular reference to osmiophilic bodies in the sperm head. *J. Morph.*, **56**, 325.

ALBORNOZ-BUSTAMANTE, A. (1952). Analyse de trois années de fécondation artificielle faite
avec du bétail à laine karakul. *Zootec. e Vet.*, **7**, 373.

ALBRIGHT, J. L., ERB, R. E., & EHLERS, M. H. (1958). Freeze-drying bovine spermatozoa.
J. Dairy Sci., **41**, 206.

ALLEN, T. E., & BOBR, L. W. (1955). The fertility of fowl spermatozoa in glycerol diluents
after intra-uterine insemination. *Poult. Sci.*, **34**, 1167.

—— & GRIGG, G. W. (1957). Sperm transport in the fowl. *Aust. J. agric. Res.*, **8**, 788.

ALMQUIST, J. O., & HALE, E. B. (1956). An approach to the measurement of sexual
behaviour and semen production of dairy bulls. *III int. Congr. Anim. Reprod.*,
Cambridge, Plenary Pap., p. 50.

AMANN, R. P., & ALMQUIST, J. O. (1957). Freezing of bovine semen. II: Effect of milk
solids level, glycerol level, and fructose on freezability of bull spermatozoa in
reconstituted and fresh skim milk diluents. *J. Dairy Sci.*, **40**, 1542.

AMOROSO, E. C., & GOFFIN, A. (1957). The artificial insemination of the domestic cat.
J. Physiol., **135**, 38P.

—— & PARKES, A. S. (1947). Effects on embryonic development of X-irradiation of rabbit
spermatozoa *in vitro*. *Proc. Roy. Soc.*, B, **134**, 57.

ANDERSON, J. (1952). The examination of semen and its relationship to fertility. *Report
of the Second International Congress of Physiology and Pathology of Animal Reproduction and of Artificial Insemination*, **3**, 7.

ARDELT, F. (1931). Erzeugung von temporarer Sterilitat beim weiblichen Kaninchen durch
Spermtoxine. *Arch. Gynæk.*, **145**, 474.

ASDELL, S. A., & WARREN, S. L. (1931). The effect of high voltage roentgen radiation (200
kv.) upon the fertility and motility of the sperm of the rabbit. *Amer. J. Roentgenol.*,
25, 81.

ATSATT, S. R. (1953). Storage of sperm in the female chameleon, *Microsaura pumila pumila*.
Copeia, Feb. 26, No. 1, 59.

AUSTIN, C. R. (1949). Fertilisation and the transport of gametes in the pseudopregnant
rabbit. *J. Endocrin.*, **6**, 63.

—— (1957). Fate of spermatozoa in the uterus of the mouse and rat. *J. Endocrin.*, **14**,
335.

AUSTIN, C. R. (1959). Entry of spermatozoa into the Fallopian tube mucosa. *Nature, Lond.*, **183,** 908.

—— & BISHOP, M. W. H. (1959). Presence of spermatozoa in the uterine-tube mucosa of bats. *J. Endocrin.*, **18,** viii.

—— & BRUCE, H. M. (1956). Effect of continuous oestrogen administration on oestrus, ovulation and fertilization in rats and mice. *J. Endocrin.*, **13,** 376.

BAKER, C. A. V. (1954). Low temperature preservation of bovine epididymal spermatozoa. *Canad. J. comp. Med.*, **18,** 390.

—— & GANDIER, J. C. C. (1957). Pregnancy in a mare resulting from frozen epididymal spermatozoa. *Canad. J. comp. Med.*, **21,** 47.

BAKER, J. R. (1930). A fluid for mammalian sperm-suspensions. *Quart. J. exp. Physiol.*, **20,** 67.

—— (1931a). An improved fluid for mammalian sperm-suspensions. *Quart. J. exp. Physiol.*, **21,** 139.

—— (1931b). The spermicidal powers of chemical contraceptives. II. Pure substances. *J. Hyg., Camb.*, **31,** 189.

—— (1932a). The spermicidal powers of chemical contraceptives. IV: More pure substances. *J. Hyg., Camb.*, **32,** 171.

—— (1932b). The spermicidal powers of chemical contraceptives. V: A comparison of human sperms with those of the guinea-pig. *J. Hyg., Camb.*, **32,** 550.

—— (1935). *The chemical control of conception.* London.

—— RANSON, R. M., & TYNEN, J. (1939a). The chemical composition of the Volpar contraceptive products. 1. Phenyl mercuric acetate as a spermicide. *Eug. Rev.*, January 1939.

—— —— —— (1939b). The chemical composition of the Volpar contraceptive products. 2. Vehicles for phenyl mercuric acetate. *Eug. Rev.*, April 1939.

BARFURTH, D. (1896). Versuche über die parthenogenetische Furchung des Hühnereies. *Arch. EntwMech. Org.*, **2,** 303.

BARKAN, G. (1942). Ejaculation induced by a uterine drug. (Gravitol.) *Proc. Soc. exp. Biol., N.Y.*, **51,** 52.

BARNEY, R. L. (1922). Further notes on the natural history and artificial propagation of the diamond-back terrapin. *Bull. U.S. Bur. Fish.*, **38,** 91.

BARRETT, I. (1951). Fertility of salmonid eggs and sperm after storage. *J. Fish. Res. Bd Can.*, **8,** 125.

BARTHEL, H. (1954). A short report on experiences with the use of deep frozen semen in artificial insemination. *Tierarztl. Umsch.*, **9,** 403.

BARTON, M. (1955). Fertility in women. *Studies on Fertility*, **7,** 99.

—— & WIESNER, B. P. (1946). Receptivity of cervical mucus to spermatozoa. *Brit. med. J.*, ii, 606.

BASKIN, M. J. (1932). Temporary sterilization by the injection of human spermatozoa. *Amer. J. Obstet. Gynec.*, **24,** 892.

BATTELLI, F. (1922). Une méthode pour obtenir l'émission complète du liquide des vésicules séminales chez le cobaye. *C. R. Soc. Phys. Hist. nat. Genève*, **39,** 73.

BAUDET, —., DAUZIER, L., PÉCARD, —., & WINTENBERGER, S. (1954). Remarques sur l'insémination artificielle appliquée aux brebis et aux chèvres. *Elevage et Insem.*, No. 24, 13.

BEATTY, R. A. (1957a). *Parthenogenesis and polyploidy in mammalian development.* Cambridge.

—— (1957b). A pilot experiment with heterospermic insemination in the rabbit. *J. Genet.*, **55,** 325.

—— & ROWSON, L. E. A. (1954). Note on motility and fertility of colchicine-treated bull and rabbit sperm. *J. agric. Sci.*, **45,** 254.

BEDERKE, G. (1933). Untersuchungen über den Einfluss verschiedener Konservierungsmethoden auf die Vitalität von Hunde-spermien. *Arch. Tierernähr. Tierz.*, **9,** 585.

BELONOSCHKIN, B. (1939). Life expectation of human spermatozoa. *Münch. med. Wschr.*, **86,** 847.

BENDORF, R. P., & CHUNG, N. Y. (1958). Preservation of canine semen: preliminary observations. *Amer. J. Vet. Sci.*, **39,** 54.

BERGONIÉ, J., & TRIBONDEAU, L. (1904). Action des rayons X sur les spermatozoïdes de l'homme. *C. R. Soc. Biol., Paris*, **57**, 595.

BERLINER, V. R. (1941). Problems of artificial insemination in horse and mule production. *J. Amer. vet. med. Ass.*, **98**, 384.

BIALY, G., LUDWICK, T. M., HESS, E. A., & ELY, F. (1957). Influence of lipoprotein on the freezing of bovine spermatozoa. *J. Dairy Sci.*, **40**, 1189.

——— & SMITH, V. R. (1957). Freeze-drying of bovine spermatozoa. *J. Dairy Sci.*, **40**, 739.

BIELAŃSKI, W. (1956). Results of extensive researches of the semen of stallions. *III. int. Congr. Anim. Reprod. Cambridge*, Section III, p. 85.

BISHOP, D. W., & TYLER, A. (1956). Fertilisin in mammalian eggs. *J. exp. Zool.*, **132**, 575.

BISHOP, G. H. (1920). Fertilization in the honey-bee. I: The male sexual organs; their histological structure and physiological functioning. *J. exp. Zool.*, **31**, 225.

BISHOP, M. W. H. (1954). Some aspects of the dilution effect in bovine spermatozoa. *Studies on Fertility*, **6**, 81.

——— (1955). Inter-relationships of semen characteristics. *Studies on Fertility*, **7**, 48.

——— CAMPBELL, R. C., HANCOCK, J. L., & WALTON, A. (1954). Semen characteristics and fertility in the bull. *J. agric. Sci.*, **44**, 227.

BISHOP, P. M. F. (1953). Post-coital tests. Ciba Foundation Symposium: *Mammalian Germ Cells*, p. 275.

BLACK, D. J., & SCORGIE, N. J. (1942). The collection of semen and artificial insemination in the domestic fowl. *Vet. J.*, **98**, 108.

BLACKSHAW, A. W. (1953). The effects of potassium and calcium salts on the motility of ram, rabbit and bull spermatozoa. *J. Physiol.*, **120**, 465.

——— (1955). The effect of equilibration and the addition of various sugars on the revival of spermatozoa from −79°C. *Aust. vet. J.*, **31**, 124.

——— EMMENS, C. W., MARTIN, I., & HEYTING, J. (1957). The preparation of deep frozen semen. *A. I. Digest*, **5**, 6.

BLAKESLEE, A. F. (1937). Cytologie vegetale. Dedoublement du nombre de chromosomes chez les plantes par traitement chimique. *C. R. Acad. Sci., Paris*, **205**, 476.

BLANCHARD, F. C. (1942). A test of fecundity of the Garter Snake *Thamnophis sirtalis sirtalis* (Linnaeus) in the year following the year of insemination. *Pap. Mich. Acad. Sci.*, **28**, 313.

BLANDAU, R. J. (1945). On the factors involved in sperm transport through the cervix uteri of the albino rat. *Amer. J. Anat.*, **77**, 253.

——— & JORDAN, E. S. (1941). A technique for the artificial insemination of the white rat. *J. Lab. clin. Med.*, **26**, 1361.

——— & MONEY, W. L. (1944). Observations on the transport of spermatozoa in the female genital tract of the rat. *Anat. Rec.*, **90**, 255.

——— & ODOR, D. L. (1949). The total number of spermatozoa reaching various segments of the reproductive tract in the female albino rat at intervals after insemination. *Anat. Rec.*, **103**, 93.

——— & YOUNG, W. C. (1939). The effects of delayed fertilization on the development of the guinea-pig ovum. *Amer. J. Anat.*, **64**, 303.

BLAXTER, J. H. S. (1953). Sperm storage and cross-fertilization of spring and autumn spawning herring. *Nature, Lond.*, **172**, 1189.

——— (1955). Herring rearing—I. The storage of herring gametes. Scottish Home Department. Marine Research No. 3.

BLOKHUIS, J. (1957). Praktische toepassing van de K.I. bij geiten. *Tijdschr. Diergeneesk.*, **82**, 570.

BOGDONOFF, P. D., & SHAFFNER, C. S. (1954). The effect of pH on *in vitro* survival, metabolic activity, and fertilizing capacity of chick semen. *Poult. Sci.*, **33**, 665.

BONHAG, P. F., & WICK, J. R. (1953). The functional anatomy of the male and female reproductive systems of the milkweed bug. *J. Morph.*, **93**, 171.

BONNADONNA, T. (1955). The possibilities of using deep frozen bull semen in tropical countries. *Dtsch. tierärztl. Wschr.*, **62**, 444.

BOUCHER, J. H., FOOTE, R. H., & KIRK, R. W. (1958). The evaluation of semen quality in the dog and the effects of frequency of ejaculation upon semen quality, libido, and depletion of sperm reserves. *Cornell Vet.*, **48**, 67.

BRATTON, R. W., & FOOTE, R. H. (1954). Semen production and fertility of dairy bulls ejaculated either once or twice at intervals of either four or eight days. *J. Dairy Sci.*, **37**, 1439.

—— —— & CRUTHERS, J. C. (1955). Preliminary fertility results with frozen bovine spermatozoa. *J. Dairy Sci.*, **38**, 40.

BRECKENRIDGE, M. A. B., PEDERSON, D. P., & POMMERENKE, W. T. (1950). A pH study of human cervical secretions. *Fertility & Sterility*, **1**, 427.

BREEDIS, C. (1942). The action of extreme cold on leukaemic cells of mice. *J. exp. Med.*, **76**, 221.

BRENNEKE, H. (1937). Strahlenschadigung von Mause- und Rattensperma, beobachtet an der Frühentwicklung der Eier. *Strahlentherapie*, **60**, 214.

BRESSLAU, E. VON (1906). Der Samenblasengang der Bienenkönigin. *Zool. Anz.*, **29**, 299.

BRIGGS, R. (1952). An analysis of the inactivation of the frog sperm nucleus by toluidine blue. *J. gen. Physiol.*, **35**, 761.

—— GREEN, E. U., & KING, T. J. (1951). An investigation of the capacity for cleavage and differentiation in *Rana pipiens* eggs lacking "functional" chromosomes. *J. exp. Zool.*, **116**, 455.

BROCHART, M., & COULOMB, J. (1952). Research on the dilution and conservation of dog semen. *Bull. Acad. vet. France*, February, p. 59.

BROWN, R. L. (1943). Effect of repeated ejaculation on semen and spermatozoa in man. *Urol. cutan. Rev.*, **47**, 372.

—— (1944a). On the care of human sperm. *J. Lab. clin. Med.*, **29**, 211.

—— (1944b). Rate of transport of spermia in human uterus and tubes. *Amer. J. Obstet. Gynec.*, **47**, 407.

BRUCE, H. M., & AUSTIN, C. R. (1956). An attempt to produce the Hertwig effect by X-irradiation of male mice. *Studies on Fertility*, **8**, 121.

BRUCE, W. (1953). In Symposium on *"The storage of bull semen at low temperatures."* *Vet. Rec.*, **65**, 557.

—— (1956). The application of the low temperature storage of bull semen for artificial insemination. *Proc. III int. Congr. Anim. Reprod., Cambridge*. Section III, p. 27.

BRUNNER, E. K. (1941). An experiment in temporary immunization against pregnancy. *Human Fertility*, **6**, 10.

BUFFON, G. L. (1771). *Histoire Naturelle des Oiseaux*. Paris.

BUNGE, R. G., KEETTEL, W. C., & SHERMAN, J. K. (1954). Clinical use of frozen semen. *Fertility & Sterility*, **5**, 520.

—— & SHERMAN, J. K. (1953). Fertilizing capacity of frozen human spermatozoa. *Nature, Lond.*, **172**, 767.

BURKHARDT, J. (1949). Sperm survival in the genital tract of the mare. *J. agric. Sci.*, **39**, 201.

BURROWS, W. H., & MARSDEN, S. J. (1938). Artificial breeding of turkeys. *Poult. Sci.*, **17**, 408.

—— & QUINN, J. P. (1935). A method of obtaining spermatozoa from the domestic fowl. *Poult. Sci.*, **14**, 251.

—— —— (1938). Effective dosages of undiluted semen in artificial insemination of chickens. *Poult. Sci.*, **17**, 131.

—— —— (1939). Artificial insemination of chickens and turkeys. *Tech. Bull. U.S. Dep. Agric.*, Circular No. 525.

—— & TITUS, H. W. (1939). Semen production in the male fowl. *Poult. Sci.*, **18**, 8.

BURTON, H. W. (1957). The use of artificial insemination in poultry breeding. *Qd agric. J.*, **83**, 413.

BUTCHER, A. D. (1944). Preliminary observation on the storage of the milt of trout. *Aust. J. Sci.*, **7**, 23.

CAFFIER, P. (1934). Hormonale Schwangerschaftserzeugung bei der winterschlafenden Fledermaus. *Zbl. Gynäk.*, **58**, 2354.

—— & KOLBOW, H. (1934). Anatomisch-physiologische Genitalstudien an Fledermäusen zur Klärung der therapeutischen Sexualhormonwirkung. *Z. Geburtsch. Gynäk.*, **108**, 185.

Campbell, B., & Petersen, W. E. (1953). Milk "let-down" and the orgasm in the human female. *Human Biol.*, **25**, 165.

Carson, H. L. (1945). Delayed fertilization in a captive indigo snake with notes on feeding and shedding. *Copeia*, Dec. 31, No. 4, 222.

Cary, W. H. (1936). Duration of sperm cell migration in uterine secretions. *J. Amer. med. Ass.*, **106**, 2221.

Casida, L. E., & Murphree, R. L. (1942). Fertility and sex-ratios in the rabbit from semen treated *in vitro* with lactic acid and sodium bicarbonate. *J. Hered.*, **33**, 434.

Chang, M. C. (1944). Artificial production of monstrosities in the rabbit. *Nature, Lond.*, **154**, 150.

—— (1946). Effect of dilution on fertilizing capacity of rabbit spermatozoa. *Science*, **104**, 361.

—— (1949). Effects of heterologous seminal plasma and sperm cells on fertilizing capacity of rabbit spermatozoa. *Proc. Soc. exp. Biol., N.Y.*, **70**, 32.

—— (1950). Further study of the role of hyaluronidase in the fertilization of rabbit ova *in vivo*. *Science*, **112**, 118.

—— Hunt, D. M., & Romanoff, E. B. (1957). Effects of radiocobalt irradiation of rabbit spermatozoa *in vitro* on fertilization and early development. *Anat. Rec.*, **129**, 211.

—— & Pincus, G. (1953). Does phosphorylated hesperidin affect fertility? *Science*, **117**, 274.

—— & Walton, A. (1940). The effects of low temperature and acclimatization on the respiratory activity and survival of ram spermatozoa. *Proc. Roy. Soc.*, B, **129**, 517.

Cheng, P., & Casida, L. E. (1948). Fertility in rabbit as affected by the dilution of semen and the number of spermatozoa. *Proc. Soc. exp. Biol., N.Y.*, **69**, 36.

Christensen, G. C., & Dougherty, R. W. (1955). A simplified apparatus for obtaining semen from dogs by electrical stimulation. *J. Amer. vet. med. Ass.*, July, 50.

Clift, A. F. (1945). Observations on certain rheological properties of human cervical secretion. *Proc. R. Soc. Med.*, **39**, 1.

—— Glover, F. A., & Scott Blair, G. W. (1950). Rheology of human cervical secretions: effects of menstrual cycle and pregnancy. *Lancet*, **i**, 1154.

Cole, L. J., & Davis, C. L. (1914). The effect of alcohol on the male germ cells, studied by means of double matings. *Science*, **39**, 476.

—— Waletzky, E., & Shackelford, M. (1940). A test of sex control by modification of the acid-alkaline balance. *J. Hered.*, **31**, 501.

Courrier, R. (1927). Étude sur le déterminisme des caractères sexuels secondaires chez quelques mammifères à activité testiculaire périodique. *Arch. Biol., Paris*, **37**, 173.

Craft, W. A., McElroy, C. H., & Penquite, R. (1926). The influence of certain feeds upon the production of spermatozoa by the domestic chicken. *Poult. Sci.*, **5**, 187.

Cragle, R. G., Myers, R. M., Waugh, R. K., Hunter, J. S., & Anderson, R. L. (1955). The effects of various levels of sodium citrate, glycerol and equilibration time on survival of bovine spermatozoa after storage at $-79°$C. *J. Dairy Sci.*, **38**, 508.

Crew, F. A. E. (1926). On fertility in the domestic fowl. *Proc. Roy. Soc., Edinb.*, **46**, 230.

—— (1952). The factors which determine sex. Chapter 22 in *Marshall's Physiology of Reproduction*. Ed. A. S. Parkes. Volume II, p. 741.

Dalcq, A. (1929). A propos des effets de l'irradiation des gemètes chez les amphibiens. *Arch. Anat. micr.*, **25**, 336.

—— (1931). Étude cytologique des oeufs fecondes par du sperme trypaflavine. *Arch. Biol., Paris*, **41**, 143.

—— & Simon, S. (1931). Contribution à l'analyse des fonctions nucléaires dans l'ontogénèse de la grenouille. III. Étude statistique et cytologique des effets de l'irradiation d'un des gametes sur la gastrulation chez *Rana fusca*. *Arch. Biol., Paris*, **42**, 107.

—— —— (1932). Contribution à l'analyse des fonctions nucléaires dans l'ontogénèse de la grenouille. II: Le rôle dynamique des chromosomes mis en évidence par lésion mécanique ou irradiation des gamètes. *Protoplasma*, **14**, 497.

Darwin, C. (1905). *The variation of animals and plants under domestication*. London. Popular Edn.

Dauzier, L. (1955a). Recherches sur les facteurs de la remontée des spermatozoïdes dans les voies génitales femelles (cornes utérines). Étude chez la brebis. *C. R. Soc. Biol., Paris*, **149**, 1872.

DAUZIER, L. (1955b). Recherches sur les facteurs de la remontée des spermatozoïdes dans les voies génitales femelles (trompe de Fallope). Étude chez la brebis. *C. R. Soc. Biol., Paris*, **149**, 1941.

—— (1956). Quelques résultats sur l'insémination artificielle des brebis et des chèvres en France. *Proc. III int. Congr. Anim. Reprod., Cambridge.* Section III, p. 12.

—— THIBAULT, C., & WINTENBERGER, S. (1954). Conservation du sperme de bélier après dilution et maintien de son pouvoir fécondant. *Ann. Endocr., Paris*, **15**, 341.

—— & WINTENBERGER, S. (1952a). Recherches sur la fécondation chez les mammifères : la remontée des spermatozoides dans le tractus génital de la brebis. *C. R. Soc. Biol., Paris*, **146**, 67.

—— —— (1952b). Recherches sur la fécondation chez les mammifères. Durée du pouvoir fécondant des spermatozoïdes de bélier dans le tractus génital de la brebis et durée de la période de fécondité de l'oeuf après l'ovulation. *C. R. Soc. Biol., Paris*, **146**, 660.

DAVENPORT, C. B. (1897). *Experimental morphology:* I. *Effect of chemical and physical agents upon protoplasm.* New York.

DAVEY, K. G. (1958). The physiology of reproduction in an insect, *Rhodnius prolixus* Stål. Thesis (University of Cambridge).

DAVIS, H. S. (1903). *Culture and diseases of game fishes.* Berkeley and Los Angeles.

DAVOINE, J. (1958). Le lait comme base de dilution du sperme de chien. Thèse Doctorat Vétérinaire, Alfort.

DAY, F. T. (1940). The stallion and fertility. The technique of sperm collection and insemination. *Vet. Rec.*, **52**, 597.

—— (1942). Survival of spermatozoa in the genital tract of the mare. *J. agric. Sci.*, **32**, 108.

DEANESLY, R., & WARWICK, T. (1939). Observations on pregnancy in the common bat (*Pipistrellus pipistrellus*). *Proc. Zool. Soc.*, A, **109**, 57.

DETLAF, T. A., & GINSBURG, A. S. (1954). *Embryonic development of sturgeons (Sevruga, Ossétr, Beluga) in relation to the problem of their breeding.* Moscow.

DITTLER, —. (1920). Die Sterilisierung des weiblichen Tierkörpers durch parenterale Spermazufuhr. *Munch. med. Wschr.*, **67**, 1495.

DONALD, I. (1953). Results of post-coital tests where pregnancy ensued. Ciba Foundation Symposium: *Mammalian Germ Cells*, p. 287.

DREBINGER, K. (1951). Kerngifte und Lichstrahlung. Eine Studie an Froschspermien zur Wirkingsanalyse der Kergifte. *Roux Arch. EntwMech. Org.*, **145**, 174.

Du MESNIL DU BUISSON, F., & DAUZIER, L. (1955). Distribution et résorption du sperme dans le tractus génital de la truie : survie des spermatozoïdes. *Ann. Endocr., Paris*, **16**, 413.

—— —— (1956). Donnes experimentales sur l'insemination naturelle et artificielle de la truie. *Proc. III int. Congr. Anim. Reprod., Cambridge.* Section III, 62.

DUNN, H. O. (1955). The problem of disease organisms in frozen semen. *Proc. VIIIth Ann. Conv. Nat. Ass. Artif. Breeders, U.S.A.*, p. 196.

—— HAFS, H. D., & YOUNG, G. F. (1953). Laboratory and field studies with frozen semen. *J. Anim. Sci.*, **12**, 893.

—— LARSON, G. L., & WILLETT, E. L. (1953). The effects of freezing bovine spermatozoa in extenders containing antibacterial agents. *J. Dairy Sci.*, **36**, 728.

DUNN, L. C. (1927). Selective fertilization in fowls. *Poult. Sci.*, **6**, 201.

DURFEE, T., LERNER, M. W., & KAPLAN, N. (1940). Artificial production of seminal ejaculation. *Anat. Rec.*, **76**, 65.

DYRENDAHL, I. (1954). Some studies of the methods of freezing bull semen. I: The influence of different brands of glycerol on the survival of spermatozoa. *Nord. VetMed.*, **6**, 780.

ECKSTEIN, P., & ZUCKERMAN, S. (1956). The oestrous cycle in the mammalia. Chapter 4 in *Marshall's Physiology of Reproduction*, Ed. A. S. Parkes. Volume I, Part 1, p. 226.

EDWARDS, R. G. (1955). Selective fertilization following the use of sperm mixtures in the mouse. *Nature, Lond.*, **175**, 215.

EDWARDS, R. G. (1957a). The experimental induction of gynogenesis in the mouse. I: Irradiation of the sperm by X-rays. *Proc. Roy. Soc.*, B, **146,** 469.

—— (1957b). The experimental induction of gynogenesis in the mouse. II: Ultra-violet irradiation of the sperm. *Proc. Roy. Soc.* B, **146,** 488.

—— (1958a). The experimental induction of gynogenesis in the mouse. III: Treatment of sperm with trypaflavine, toluidine blue, or nitrogen mustard. *Proc. Roy. Soc.* B, **149,** 117.

—— (1958b). Colchicine-induced heteroploidy in the mouse. I: The induction of triploidy by treatment of the gametes. *J. exp. Zool.*, **137,** 317.

ELLIS, W. G., & JONES, J. W. (1939). The activity of the spermatozoa of *Salmo salar* in relation to osmotic pressure. *J. exp. Biol.*, **15,** 530.

EMMENS, C. W. (1947). The motility and viability of rabbit spermatozoa at different hydrogen-ion concentrations. *J. Physiol.*, **106,** 471.

—— (1948). The effect of variations in osmotic pressure and electrolyte concentration on the motility of rabbit spermatozoa at different hydrogen-ion concentrations. *J. Physiol.*, **107,** 129.

—— (1956). Discussion following papers by Professor Almquist and Russian speakers. *III int. Congr. Anim. Reprod., Cambridge*, Plenary Papers, p. 68.

—— & BLACKSHAW, A. W. (1950). The low temperature storage of ram, bull and rabbit spermatozoa. *Aust. vet. J.*, **26,** 226.

—— —— (1955). The fertility of frozen ram and bull semen. *Aust. vet. J.*, **31,** 76.

—— —— (1956). Artificial insemination. *Physiol. Rev.*, **36,** 277.

—— & MARTIN, I. (1957). Fertility of bull semen deep-frozen by two different techniques. *Aust. vet. J.*, **33,** 63.

—— & SWYER, G. I. M. (1947). Maintenance of spermatozoal motility in dilute suspension. *Nature, Lond.*, **160,** 718.

ERÄNKÖ, O., FRIBERG, O., & KARVONEN, M. J. (1953). Effect of the act of copulation on water diuresis in the rat. *Acta endocr., Paris*, **12,** 197.

ERICKSON, W. E., GRAHAM, E. F., & FREDERICK, E. C. (1954). The effect of antibiotics, levels of glycerol and rates of freezing on revival rate of bovine spermatozoa in yolk citrate and milk extenders. *J. Dairy Sci.*, **37,** 651.

ETGEN, W. M., LUDWICK, T. M., & HESS, E. A. (1955). The use of mechanical refrigeration for storage of frozen semen. *J. Dairy Sci.*, **38,** 604.

EVANS, E. I. (1933). The transport of spermatozoa in the dog. *Amer. J. Physiol.*, **105,** 287.

EWART, Cossar (1899). *The Penicuik Experiments*, London.

EWING, H. E. (1943). Continued fertility in female box turtles following mating. *Copeia*, June 30, No. 2, 112.

FARRIS, E. J. (1950). *Human fertility and problems of the male*. New York.

FERRAND, R. H. Jr., & BOHREN, N. B. (1948). The effect of carotenols on fertilizing capacity of fowl sperm. *Poult. Sci.*, **27,** 759.

FISCHBERG, M. (1947). Experimentelle Auslösung von haploider und diploider Partheno-genese bei den Urodelen *Triton palmatus* und *Triton alpestris*. *Arch. Klaus-Stift. VererbForsch.*, **22,** 331.

—— & SELMAN, G. G. (1952). Heteroploidy in Amphibia. *Quinquennial Report*, 1947–1951, Institute of Animal Genetics, Edinb., p. 13.

FOLK, G. E. Jr. (1940). The longevity of sperm in the female bat. *Anat. Rec.*, **76,** 103.

FOOTE, R. H., & BRATTON, R. W. (1956). Frozen semen: past, present, future. *Farm Res.*, **21,** No. 249.

—— & DUNN, H. O. (1955). Buffers, extenders and methods of freezing semen. *Mimeo Routine Lab. Procedure* No. 11. Cornell Univ. & N.Y. A.B.C. Sept.

FORCE, E. (1931). Habits and birth of young of the lined snake, *Tropidoclonion lineatum* (Hallowell). *Copeia*, p. 51.

FOX, W. (1956). Seminal receptacles of snakes. *Anat. Rec.*, **124,** 519.

FRANK, A. H. (1952). Artificial insemination in livestock breeding. *Tech. Bull. U.S. Dep. Agric.*, Circ. No. 507.

—— SMITH, C. A., & EICHHORN, A. (1941). Preliminary report on prolonging the viability of spermatozoa *in vitro*. *J. Amer. Vet. Med. Ass.*, **99,** 287.

FRAZER, J. F. D. (1954). Some applications of the use of amphibia for human pregnancy tests. Thesis (University of Oxford).

—— (1956). The sperm-shedding response of male toads and treefrogs after the injection of two types of gonadotrophin. *Brit. J. Pharmacol.*, **11**, 248.

—— & GLENISTER, T. W. (1956). Factors affecting the motility of toad spermatozoa and their application in a rapid test for pregnancy. *J. Physiol.*, **135**, 49P.

FREIBERG, E. A. (1935). Artificial insemination of the dog. *Anim. Breed. Abs.*, **3**, 411.

FREUND, M. (1958). Collection and liquefaction of guinea-pig semen. *Proc. Soc. exp. Biol., N.Y.*, **98**, 538.

GABRIEL, I. (1957). A complete one-man technique for the collection of cock semen and the insemination of caged hens. *Poult. Sci.*, **36**, 1035.

GALLI MAININI, C. (1947). Pregnancy test using the male toad. *J. clin. Endocrin.*, **7**, 653.

GAMBLE, C. J. (1953). An improved test of spermicidal activity without dilution of mixing. *J. Amer. med. Ass.*, **152**, 1037.

—— (1957). Spermicidal times as aids to the clinician's choice of contraceptive materials. *Fertility & Sterility*, **8**, 174.

GARCIA, T. P. (1957). Aportaciones a los metodo de recogida y centrastacion del esperma de perro. *Revista del Patronato de Biologia Animal*, **3**, 97.

GARREN, H. W., & SHAFFNER, C. S. (1952). The effect of temperature and time of storage on the fertilizing capacity of undiluted fowl semen. *Poult. Sci.*, **31**, 137.

GLOVER, T., & MANN, T. (1954). On the composition of boar semen. *J. agric. Sci.*, **44**, 355.

GLOYD, H. K. (1928). The amphibians and reptiles of Franklin Co., Kansas. *Trans. Kansas Acad. Sci.*, **31**, 115.

—— (1933). Studies on the breeding habits and young of the copperhead, *Agkistrodon mokasen* Beauvois. *Pap. Mich. Acad. Sci.*, **19**, 587.

GOLDFARB, W. (1952). Viability of human spermatozoa mixed with Penicillin G and inseminated in the female. *Amer. J. Obstet. Gynec.*, **63**, 1322.

GORDON, M. J. (1957). Control of sex ratio in rabbits by electrophoresis of spermatozoa. *Proc. nat. Acad. Sci., Wash.*, **43**, 913.

GOWEN, J. W., & SCHOTT, R. C. (1933). A genetic technique for differentiating between acquired and genetic immunity. *Amer. J. Hyg.*, **18**, 668.

GRABER, R. (1940). Beobachtungen an *Ophis* (syn. *Xenodon*) *kerreimi* und *O. severus*. *Wschr. Aquar.- u. Terrarienk.*, **37**, 291.

GRAÇA ARAUJO, P. (1955). Verificação da fertilidade do sêmen congelado de carneiro, conservado a −79°C. *Bol. Insem. art.*, **7**, 5.

GRAHAM, E. F., & MARION, G. B. (1953). A technique of freezing and factors affecting the revival of bovine spermatozoa. *J. Dairy Sci.*, **36**, 597.

GRIGG, G. W. (1957). The structure of stored sperm in the hen and the nature of the release-mechanism. *Poult. Sci.*, **36**, 450.

GRODZINSKI, Z., & MARCHLEWSKI, J. (1935). Studies on the motility of spermatozoa of the domestic cock outside the organism. *Bull. int. Acad., Cracovie*, B.II, 347.

DE GROOT, B. (1955). Een apparaat voor het automatisch toevoegen van de glycerine verdunner aan diepvries sperma. *Tijdschr. Diergeneesk.*, **80**, 662.

GUTHRIE, M. J., & JEFFERS, K. R. (1938). The ovaries of the bat *Myotis lucifugus* after injection of hypophyseal extract. *Anat. Rec.*, **72**, 11.

GUTIÉRREZ-NALES, N. (1957). Contribución al estudio de la diluyo-conservación del esperma de perro. *Rev. Patron. Biol. anim. (Madr.)*, **3**, 189.

GUYER, M. F. (1922). Studies on cytolysins. III: Experiments with spermatotoxins. *J. exp. Biol.*, **35**, 207.

HAFS, H. D., & ELLIOTT, F. I. (1954). Effect of thawing temperatures and extender composition on the fertility of frozen bull semen. *J. Anim. Sci.*, **13**, 958.

—— —— (1955). Effect of methods of adding egg yolk and monosaccharides on survival of frozen bull spermatozoa. *J. Dairy Sci.*, **38**, 811.

HAGELBERG, R. (1952). The effect of storage time on the fertilizing capacity of semen. *Rep. II int. Congr. Anim. Reprod.*, **3**, 83.

HÄGGQVIST, G., & BANE, A. (1950). Polyploidy in rabbits induced by colchicine. *Nature, Lond.*, **165,** 841.

—— —— (1951). Kolchizin-induzierte Heteroploidie beim Schwein. *K. svenska Veten-skAkad. Handl.*, **3,** 1.

HAINES, T. P. (1940). Delayed fertilization in *Leptodeira annulata polysticta*. *Copeia*, July 28, No. 2, 116.

HAMMOND, J. (1930). The effect of temperature on the survival *in vitro* of rabbit sperm-atozoa obtained from the vagina. *J. exp. Biol.*, **7,** 175.

—— (1952). Fertility. Chapter 21 in *Marshall's Physiology of Reproduction*. Ed. A. S. Parkes. Volume II, p. 648.

—— & ASDELL, S. A. (1926). The vitality of the spermatozoa in the male and female reproductive tracts. *Brit. J. exp. Biol.*, **4,** 155.

HANLEY, H. G. (1957). Pregnancy following artificial insemination from epididymal cyst. *Studies on Fertility*, **8,** 20.

HARPER, J. A. (1955). The effect of holding time of turkey semen on fertilizing capacity. *Poult. Sci.*, **34,** 1289.

HARRIS, G. W. (1955). *Neural control of the pituitary gland*. London.

HARROP, A. E. (1954a). A new type of canine artificial vagina. *Brit. Vet. J.*, **110,** 194.

—— (1954b). Artificial insemination of a bitch with preserved semen. *Brit. Vet. J.*, **110,** 424.

—— (1956a). Canine artificial insemination. *Proc. III int. Congr. Anim. Reprod., Cam-bridge*. Section III, p. 95.

—— (1956b). Artificial insemination in dogs. The first transatlantic conception. *Brit. Vet. J.*, **112,** 338.

HARTMAN, C. G. (1933). On the survival of spermatozoa in the female genital tract of the bat. *Quart. Rev. Biol.*, **8,** 185.

—— (1957). How do sperms get into the uterus ? *Fertility & Sterility*, **8,** 403.

HARVEY, C. (1953). A fertility index derived from semen analysis. *J. clin. Path.*, **6,** 232.

—— (1954). An experimental study of the penetration of human cervical mucus by spermatozoa *in vitro*. *J. Obstet. Gynaec., Brit. Emp.*, **61,** 480.

—— (1957). The use of partitioned ejaculates in investigating the role of accessory secre-tions in human semen. *Studies on Fertility*, **8,** 3.

—— & JACKSON, M. C. N. H. (1948). Penetration of cervical mucus by spermatozoa. *Lancet*, ii, 723.

HAYS, R. L., & VANDEMARK, N. L. (1953). Effect of stimulation of the reproductive organs of the cow on the release of an oxytocin-like substance. *Endocrinology*, **52,** 634.

HEAPE, W. (1897). The artificial insemination of mammals and subsequent possible fertilisation or impregnation of their ova. *Proc. Roy. Soc.*, **61,** 52.

HENDERSON, J. A., MACPHERSON, J. W., & SNYDER, R. G. (1956). The use of frozen semen in routine insemination of cattle. *Proc. III int. Congr. Anim. Reprod., Cambridge*. Section III, p. 15.

HENLE, W. (1938). The specificity of some mammalian spermatozoa. *J. Immunol.*, **34,** 325.

—— & HENLE, G. (1940). Spermatozoal antibodies and fertility. II: Attempt to induce temporary sterility in female guinea-pigs by active immunization against sperm-atozoa. *J. Immunol.*, **38,** 105.

—— —— CHURCH, C. F., & FOSTER, C. (1940). Spermatozoal antibodies and fertility. I: Attempt to induce temporary sterility in female white mice by passive immun-ization with spermatozoa antisera. *J. Immunol.*, **38,** 97.

HENSON, M. (1942). The effect of roentgen irradiation of sperm upon the em-bryonic development of the Albino Rat (*Mus Norvegicus albinus*). *J. exp. Biol.*, **91,** 405.

HERTWIG, G. (1913). Parthenogenesis bei Wirbeltieren, hervorgerufen durch artfremden radium-bestrahlten Samen. *Arch. mikr. Anat.*, **81,** 87.

—— (1924). Trypaflavin als Radiumersatz zur Gewinnung haploidkerniger Froschlarven. *Verh. anat. Ges. Jena*, **58,** 223.

HERTWIG, O. (1911). Die Radiumkrankheit tierischer Keimzellen. Ein Beitrag zur experimentellen Zeugungs- und Vererbungslehre. *Arch. mikr. Anat.*, **77,** 97.

HERTWIG, P. (1916). Durch Radiumbestrahlung verursachte Entwicklung von halbkernigen Triton-und Fischembryonen. *Arch. mikr. Anat.*, **87,** 63.

HILDEBRAND, S. F. (1929). Review of experiments on artificial culture of diamond-back terrapin. *Bull. U.S. Bur. Fish.*, **45,** 25.

HOAGLAND, H., & PINCUS, G. (1942). Revival of mammalian sperm after immersion in liquid nitrogen. *J. gen. Physiol.*, **25,** 337.

HOEHNE, O. (1914). Experimentelle Unterschungen über das Schicksal arteigener und artfremder Spermatozoen im Weiblichen Genitalapparat und in der Bauchhöhle. *Verh. dtsch. Ges. Gynäk.*, **15,** 514.

—— & BEHNE, K. (1914). Uber die Lebensdauer homologer und heterologer Spermatozoen im weiblichen Genitalapparat und in der Bauchhöhle. *Zbl. Gynäk.*, 1914, 5.

HOFKENS, C. (1950). Sperma-onderzoek bij hanen. *Vlaam. diergeneesk. Tijdschr.*, **19,** 130.

HOLT, A. F. (1953). The effect of glycerolisation of bull semen on fertility. *Vet. Rec.*, **65,** 624.

HOME, E. (1799). An account of the dissection of an hermaphrodite dog. To which are prefixed some observations on hermaphrodites in general. *Phil. Trans.*, **1,** 158.

HOUSSAY, B. A., & GONZALES, L. (1929). L'hypophyse et le testicule chez le crapaud *Bufo marinus* (L.) Schneid. *C. R. Soc. Biol., Paris*, **101,** 938.

HÜBNER, K. A. (1955). Tierexperimentelle Untersuchungen über den Transport des Sperma im weiblichen Genitaltrakt. *Zbl. Gynäk.*, **77,** 1220.

HUHNER, M. (1913). *Sterility in the male and female.* New York.

HUMPHREY, G. F., & MANN, T. (1949). Studies on the metabolism of semen. 5: Citric acid in semen. *Biochem. J.*, **44,** 97.

HUNSAKER, W. G., AITKEN, J. R., & LINDBLAD, G. S. (1956). The fertilising capacity of fowl semen as affected by time and temperature of storage. *Poult. Sci.*, **35,** 649.

HUTT, F. B. (1929). On the relation of fertility in fowls to the amount of testicular material and density of sperm suspension. *Proc. Roy. Soc., Edinb.*, **49,** 102.

HUXLEY, J. S. (1930). The maladaptation of trout spermatozoa to fresh water. *Nature, Lond.*, **125,** 494.

ISCHIKAWA, H. (1930). The life duration of cock spermatozoa outside the body. *Proc. IV World Poultry Congr.*, p. 90.

ITO, S., NIWA, T., & KUDO, A. (1948a). Studies on the artificial insemination in swine. I: On the method of collection of semen and the condition of ejaculation. *Res. Bull.*, 55, *Zootec. Exp. Sta., Chiba*, Japan, p. 1.

—— —— —— (1948b). Studies on the artificial insemination in swine. III: On the method of injection of semen and the results in fecundation. *Bull. zootech. Exp. Sta. Chiba-Shi*, No. 55, p. 57.

—— —— —— & MIZUHO, A. (1948). Studies on the artificial insemination in swine. II: Observations on the semen and its storage. *Bull. zootech. Exp. Sta. Chiba-Shi*, No. 55, p. 17.

IWANOW, E. J. (1907). De la fécondation artificielle chez les mammifères. *Arch. Sci. biol., St. Pétersb.*, **12,** 377.

—— (1924). Recherches expérimentales à propos du processus de la fécondation chez les poules. *C. R. Soc. Biol., Paris*, **91,** 54.

—— (1930). Artificial insemination of mammals. Scientific and zootechnical method. (Trans. by Henry Fox.) *Vet. Rec.*, January 11th.

JACKSON, M. C. N. H. (1957a). Brief evaluation of some therapeutic measures used in an infertility clinic during the past twenty years. *Studies on Fertility*, **8,** 100.

—— (1957b). Artificial insemination (donor). *Eugen. Rev.*, **48,** 203.

—— (1957c). Discussion on artificial insemination. *Proc. R. Soc. Med.*, **50,** 683.

JACOBI, L. (1765). *Künstliche Fischzucht.* Hannover, Magazin.

JAHNEL, F. (1938). Über die Widerstandsfähigkeit von menschlichen Spermatozoen gegenüber starker Kälte. Wiederauftreter der Beweglichkeit nach Abkühlung auf −196°C. (flüssiger Stickstoff) und −269·5°C. etwa 3·7° vom absoluten Nullpunkt entfernt (flüssiges Helium). *Klin. Wschr.*, **17,** 1273.

JAMES, J. P., & FYVIE, A. A. (1955). Technique and results of low temperature bull semen storage. *Proc. N.Z. Soc. Anim. Prod.*, **15,** 126.

JASPER, A. W. (1950). Storage studies of diluted cock semen for use in artificial insemination of chickens. *Poult. Sci.*, **29**, 812.

JOËL, K., & POLLAK, O. J. (1939). Human spermatozoa. *Mschr. Geburtsh. Gynäk.*, **109**, 91.

JOHNSON, A. S. (1954). Artificial insemination and the duration of fertility of geese. *Poult. Sci.*, **33**, 638.

JONES, D. G., & LAMOREUX, W. F. (1942). Semen production of White Leghorn males from strains selected for high and low fecundity. *Poult. Sci.*, **21**, 173.

JONES, W. M., PERKINS, J. R., & SEATH, D. M. (1956). The effect of glycerol level and rate of freezing, for various extenders, on the survival of bovine spermatozoa frozen and stored at −79°C. *J. Dairy Sci.*, **39**, 1574.

JOYNER, L. P., & BENNETT, G. H. (1956). Observations on the viability of *Trichomonas foetus* during the process of freezing to −79°C. and thawing in the presence of glycerol. *J. Hyg. Camb.*, **54**, 335.

JULL, M. A., & QUINN, J. P. (1931). Inheritance of body weight in domestic fowl. *J. Hered.*, **22**, 283.

JUŠČENKO, N. P. (1957). Proof of the possibility of preserving mammalian spermatozoa dry (Trans.). *Dokl. Akad. seljskohoz. Nauk. Lenin.*, **22**, 37.

KAWAJIRI, M. (1927). On the preservation of the eggs and sperm of *Oncorhynchus masou* (Walbaum). *J. Fish. Inst., Tokyo*, **23**, 11.

KEAST, J. C., & MORLEY F. H. W. (1949). Some observations on artificial insemination of sheep. *Aust. Vet. J.*, **25**, 281.

KELLY, G. L., FULGHUM, C. B., GOODWIN, T. W., & TODD, W. A. (1929). Artificial insemination by way of the ovarian bursa in the guinea-pig. *Surg. Gynec. Obstet.*, **48**, 200.

KELLY, R. B. (1937). Studies in fertility of sheep. *J. Coun. sci. industr. Res. Aust.*, No. 12.

KENNEDY, W. P. (1924). The production of spermatoxins. *Quart. J. exp. Physiol.*, **14**, 279.

KERRUISH, B. M. (1956). A field-trial comparison of milk and egg-yolk citrate as semen dilutors. *Proc. III int. Congr. Anim. Reprod., Cambridge.* Section III, p. 65.

KILE, J. C. (1951). An improved method for the artificial insemination of mice. *Anat. Rec.*, **109**, 109.

KIBRICK, S., BELDING, D. L., & MERRILL, B. (1952). Methods of detecting antibodies against mammalian spermatozoa. *Fertility & Sterility*, **3**, 430.

KING, H. D. (1929). Selective fertilisation in rats. *Arch. EntwMech. Org.*, **116**, 202.

KINNEY, W. C., & VANDEMARK, N. L. (1954). The effect of yolk and citrate levels and stage of maturity on the survival of bull spermatozoa at sub-zero storage temperatures. *J. Dairy Sci.*, **37**, 650.

KLUTH, F. (1936). Ungewöhnlich späte Eiablage bei Schlangen. *Bl. Aquar.- u. Terrarienk.*, **47**, 20.

KNAUS, H. (1934). *Periodic fertility and sterility in woman. A natural method of birth control.* Vienna.

—— (1950). *Die Physiologie der Zeugung des Menschen.* Wien.

KOCH, P., & ROBILLARD, E. (1945). Survie des spermatozoides de coq dans divers milieux et a différentes températures. *Rev. Canad. Biol.*, **4**, 163.

KÖLLIKER, A. (1856). Physiologische Studien über die Samenflüssigkeit. *Z. wiss. Zool.*, **7**, 201.

KOPSTEIN, F. (1938). Ein Beitrag zur Eierkunde und zur Fortpflanzung der malaiischen Reptilien. *Bull. Raffles Mus.*, **14**, 81.

KOSIN, I. L. (1944). Some aspects of the biological action of X-rays on cock spermatozoa. *Physiol. Zoöl.*, **17**, 289.

KUSHNER, K. F. (1954). The effect of heterospermic insemination in animals and its biological nature. (Trans.). *Izvestia Akad. Nauk. USSR*, Ser. Biol., No. 1, 32.

KUZNETSOV, M. (1956). Artificial insemination of sheep in the U.S.S.R. *III int. Congr. Anim. Reprod., Cambridge.* Plenary Papers, p. 64.

LAIDLAW, H. H., Jr. (1944). Artificial insemination of the queen bee (*Apis mellifera* L.): Morphological basis and results. *J. Morph.*, **74**, 429.

LAKE, P. E. (1957). Fowl semen as collected by the massage method. *J. agric. Sci.*, **49**, 120.

LAMAR, J. K., SHETTLES, L. B., & DELFS, E. (1940). Cyclic penetrability of human cervical mucus to spermatozoa *in vitro*. *Amer. J. Physiol.*, **129**, 234.

LAMOREUX, W. F. (1940). Spermatozoa antibodies and infertility in fowl. *J. exp. Zool.*, **85**, 419.

LARDY, H. A., & PHILLIPS, P. H. (1939). Preservation of spermatozoa. *Proc. Amer. Soc. Anim. Prod.*, p. 219.

LASLEY, J. F., & BOGART, R. (1944). A comparative study of epididymal and ejaculated spermatozoa of the boar. *J. Anim. Sci.*, **3**, 360.

—— & MAYER, D. T. (1944). A variable physiological factor necessary for the survival of bull spermatozoa. *J. Anim. Sci.*, **3**, 129.

LATZ, L. J., & REINER, E. (1942). Further studies on the sterile and fertile periods in women. *Amer. J. Obstet. Gynec.*, **43**, 74.

LEEUWENHOEK, A. VAN (1678). Letter addressed to the Secretary of the Royal Society (N. Grew) and published in the *Phil. Trans.* **12**, 1044.

LEIDL, W. (1956). Experiments in freeze-drying of bull semen. *Proc. III int. Congr. Anim. Reprod., Cambridge.* Section III, p. 39.

LEONARD, S. L., & PERLMAN, P. L. (1949). Conditions affecting the passage of spermatozoa through the utero-tubal junction of the rat. *Anat. Rec.*, **104**, 89.

LETARD, E., SZUMOWSKI, P., & THÉRET, M. (1957). Insémination artificielle chez le chien. *Rec. Méd. vét.*, **133**, 261.

—— & TINET, E. (1937). L'insémination artificielle chez les oiseaux et les procédes électriques d'obtention du sperme. *Rev. Zootech., Rio de J.*, **12**, 425.

LINDAHL, P. E. (1956). Counter-streaming centrifugation of bull spermatozoa. *Nature, Lond.*, **178**, 491.

—— (1958). Separation of bull spermatozoa carrying *x*- and *y*-chromosomes by counter-streaming centrifugation. *Nature, Lond.*, **181**, 784.

—— INGELMAN-SUNDBERG, A., FURUHJELM, M., & NILSSON, A. (1956). The sperm ant-agglutinic factor in women. *J. Obstet. Gynaec., Brit. Emp.*, **63**, 363.

—— & KIHLSTRÖM, J. E. (1952a). Alterations in specific gravity during the ripening of bull spermatozoa. *J. Dairy Sci.*, **35**, 393.

—— —— (1952b). On ripening and agglutination in bull spermatozoa. *Proc. II int. Congr. Anim. Reprod., Copenhagen.* Vol. I, p. 70.

—— —— (1954). An antagglutinic factor in mammalian sperm plasm. *Fertility & Sterility*, **5**, 241.

—— & NILSSON, A. (1954). On the occurrence of sperm antagglutin in the female rabbit. *Ark. Zool.*, **7**, 223.

—— —— (1957). The isolation of sperm antagglutin from the follicle fluid, and some of its properties. *Biochim. biophys. Acta*, **25**, 22.

LOEWE, S. (1937). A pharmacological ejaculation test for bio-assay of male sex hormone. *Proc. Soc. exp. Biol., N.Y.*, **37**, 483.

—— (1938). Influence of autonomic drugs on ejaculation. *J. Pharmacol.*, **63**, 70.

LONG, J. A., & MARK, E. L. (1911). The maturation of the egg of the mouse. *Publ. Carneg. Instn*, No. 142, 1.

LORENZ, F. W., & TYLER, A. (1951). Extension of motile life span of spermatozoa of the domestic fowl by amino acids and proteins. *Proc. Soc. exp. Biol., N.Y.*, **78**, 57.

LOVELOCK, J. E. (1954). The protective action of neutral solutes against haemolysis by freezing and thawing. *Biochem. J.*, **56**, 265.

—— & BISHOP, M. W. H. (1959). Prevention of freezing damage to living cells by dimethyl sulphoxide. *Nature, Lond.*, **183**, 1394.

—— & POLGE, C. (1954). The immobilisation of spermatozoa by freezing and thawing and the protective action of glycerol. *Biochem. J.*, **58**, 618.

LUDWIG, M., & RAHN, H. (1943). Sperm storage and copulatory adjustment in the prairie rattlesnake. *Copeia*, p. 15.

LUNDQUIST, F. (1949). Aspects of the biochemistry of human semen. *Acta physiol. scand.*, **19**, Suppl. 66.

LUYET, B. J., & GEHENIO, P. M. (1940). *Life and death at low temperatures.* Biodynamica, Normandy, Missouri.

LUYET, B. J., & HARTUNG, M. C. (1941). Factors in revival of *Anguillula aceti* after its solidification in liquid air. *Amer. J. Physiol.*, **133**, 368.

—— & HODAPP, E. L. (1938). Revival of frog's spermatozoa vitrified in liquid air. *Proc. Soc. exp. Biol., N.Y.*, **39**, 433.

—— & KEANE, J. (1955). A critical temperature range apparently characterized by sensitivity of bull semen to high freezing velocity. *Biodynamica*, **7**, 281.

McCARTNEY, J. L. (1923). Studies on the mechanism of sterilization of the female by spermatoxin. *Amer. J. Physiol.*, **63**, 207.

McDONALD, L. E., & SAMPSON, J. (1957). Intraperitoneal insemination of the heifer. *Proc. Soc. exp. Biol., N.Y.*, **95**, 815.

MACIRONE, C., & WALTON, A. (1938). Fecundity of male rabbits as determined by "dummy matings". *J. agric. Sci.*, **28**, 122.

MACKENSEN, O. (1954). Some improvements in method and syringe design in artificial insemination. *J. econ. Ent.*, **47**, 765.

McKENZIE, F. F. (1931). A method for the collection of boar semen. *J. Amer. Vet. Med. Ass.*, **78**, 244.

—— MILLER, J. C., & BAUGUESS, L. C. (1938). The reproductive organs and semen of the boar. *Res. Bull. Mo. Agric. Exp. Sta.*, No. 279.

McLAIN, N. W. (1885). Artificial fertilization. Report on experiments in apiculture. Quoted by Laidlaw, 1944.

MacLEOD, J., & HOTCHKISS, R. S. (1942). Distribution of spermatozoa and of certain chemical constituents in human ejaculate. *J. Urol.*, **48**, 225.

—— MARTENS, F., SILBERMAN, C., & SOBRERO, A. J. (1958). The post-coital and post-insemination cervical mucus and semen quality. *Studies on Fertility*, **10**, 41.

MACPHERSON, J. W. (1954). Use of frozen semen in Canada. *Proc. VIIth Ann. Conv. Nat. Ass. Artif. Breeders*, p. 201.

—— (1955). Long-term dry ice storage of bovine semen. *Canad. J. comp. Med.*, **19**, 287.

McWHIRTER, K. G. (1956). Control of sex-ratio in mammals. *Nature, Lond.*, **178**, 870.

MANN, T. (1948). Fructose contents and fructolysis in semen: practical application in the evaluating of semen quality. *J. agric. Sci.*, **38**, 323.

—— (1951). Inositol, a major constituent of the seminal vesicle secretion of the boar. *Nature, Lond.*, **168**, 1043.

—— (1954). The mode of action of spermicidal agents. *Studies on Fertility*, **6**, 41.

—— (1958). Biochemical basis of spermicidal activity. *Studies on Fertility* **9**, 3.

—— & LEONE, E. (1953). Studies on the metabolism of semen. *Biochem. J.*, **53**, 140.

—— & LUTWAK-MANN, C. (1948). Studies on the metabolism of semen. 4: Aerobic and anaerobic utilization of fructose by spermatozoa and seminal vesicles. *Biochem. J.*, **43**, 266.

—— POLGE, C., & ROWSON, L. A. E. (1956). Participation of seminal plasma during the passage of spermatozoa in the female reproductive tract of the pig and horse. *J. Endocrin.*, **13**, 133.

MANTEGAZZA, P. (1866). Sulla sperma umano. *R. C. Ist. lombardo*, **3**, 183.

MARCHLEWSKI, J. H. (1937). Guinea fowl and common fowl hybrids obtained by means of artificial insemination. *Bull. Acad. Polonaise Sci.*, (B), **2**, 127.

—— (1952). The Golden Pheasant hen *Chrysolophus pictus* L. and the Domestic Cock *Gallus domesticus* L. hybrids obtained by means of artificial insemination. *Bull. int. Acad. Cracovie*, 1951, B VI, 443.

MARSHALL, F. H. A. (1922). *The physiology of reproduction*. 2nd Ed. London.

—— & MOIR, J. C. (1952). Parturition. Chapter 19 in *Marshall's Physiology of Reproduction*. Ed. A. S. Parkes. Vol. II, p. 496.

MARSLAND, D. A., & RUGH, R. (1940). Resistance of sperm of *Rana pipiens* to hydrostatic compression; effect upon embryonic development. *Proc. Soc. exp. Biol., N.Y.*, **43**, 141.

MATTHEWS, L. HARRISON (1937). The female sexual cycle in the British horseshoe bats. *Trans. zool. Soc. Lond.*, **23**, 224.

MAUPOUMÉ, R., & VERAIN, A. (1957). Éffets des ultrasons sur les spermatozoïdes de taureau. *C. R. Soc. Biol., Paris*, **151**, 1502.

MELANDER, Y. (1950). Chromosome behaviour of a triploid adult rabbit as produced by Häggqvist and Bane after colchicine treatment. *Hereditas*, **36,** 335.

—— (1951). Polyploidy after colchicine treatment of pigs. *Hereditas*, **37,** 288.

MERTENS, R. (1940). Neuere Beobachtungen über die Fortpflanzung der Schlangen. *Wschr. Aquar.- u. Terrarienk.*, **37,** 489.

MERTON, H. (1939). Studies on reproduction in the albino mouse. III: The duration of life of spermatozoa in the female reproductive tract. *Proc. Roy. Soc., Edinb.*, **59,** 207.

MERYMAN, H. T. (1956). Mechanics of freezing in living cells. *Science*, **124,** 515.

—— & KAFIG, E. (1959). Survival of spermatozoa following drying. *Nature, Lond.*, **184,** 470.

MICHIE, D. (1955). Towards uniformity in experimental animals. *Collected Papers*, Laboratory Animals Bureau, **3,** 37.

MIES, A., & RAMOS, A. A. (1956). Semen production of rams in Brazil. *III int. Congr. Anim. Reprod., Cambridge*, Section III, p. 101.

MILLAR, R. (1952). Forces observed during coitus in thoroughbreds. *Aust. Vet. J.*, **28,** 127.

MILLER, W. J., & VANDEMARK, N. L. (1953). Factors affecting survival of bull spermatozoa at sub-zero temperatures. *J. Dairy Sci.*, **36,** 577.

—— —— (1954). The influence of glycerol level, various temperature aspects, and certain other factors on the survival of bull spermatozoa at sub-zero temperatures. *J. Dairy Sci.*, **37,** 45.

MILLMAN, N. (1952). A critical study of methods of measuring spermicidal action. *Ann. N.Y. Acad. Sci.*, **54,** 806.

MILOVANOV, V. K. (1932). The present position of artificial insemination in the pig. (In Russian.) *Probl. Zivotn.*, **4,** 31. *Anim. Breed. Abstr.* (1933), **1,** 112.

MINOT, C. S. (1904). An experiment with telegony. *Brit. Ass. Rep. (Cambridge Meeting)*.

MIXNER, J. P. (1955). Processing, storing and shipping frozen bull semen. *N.J. Agric. Exp. Sta. Circ.*, 573.

MIXNER, J. P., & WIGGIN, S. H. (1957a). Fertility results with frozen semen stored up to one year. *J. Dairy Sci.*, **40,** 537.

—— —— (1957b). Fertility results with frozen semen stored for two years. *J. Dairy Sci.*, **40,** 1650.

MOENCH, G. L. (1934). Viability of sperm in female genital tract. *J. Amer. med. Ass.*, **102,** 866.

MOORE, C. R., & GALLAGHER, T. F. (1930). Seminal-vesicle and prostate function as a testis hormone indicator: the electric ejaculation test. *Amer. J. Anat.*, **45,** 39.

MORAN, T. (1929). Critical temperature of freezing living muscle. *Proc. Roy. Soc.*, B, **105,** 177.

MOSS, J. A. (1953). The storage of bull semen at low temperatures. *Vet. Rec.*, **65,** 564.

MUNRO, S. S. (1935). Motility and fertilizing capacities of fowl sperm in the excretory ducts. *Proc. Soc. exp. Biol., N.Y.*, **33,** 255.

—— (1938a). Effect of dilution and density on the fertilising capacity of fowl sperm suspensions. *Canad. J. Res.*, **16,** 281.

—— (1938b). Effect of temperature and medium on fowl sperm motility. *Quart. J. exp. Physiol.*, **27,** 281.

—— (1938c). Functional changes in fowl sperm during their passage through the excurrent ducts of the male. *J. exp. Zool.*, **79,** 71.

MURPHY, D. P., & FARRIS, E. J. (1953). The day of ovulation as indicated by 66 conceptions following A.I. *Proc. I World Congr. Fertil. Steril., N.Y.*, p. 372.

MYERS, H. I., YOUNG, W. C., & DEMPSEY, E. W. (1936). Graafian follicle development throughout the reproductive cycle in the guinea-pig, with especial reference to changes during oestrus (sexual receptivity). *Anat. Rec.*, **65,** 381.

NAKANO, S., & NOZAWA, A. (1925). On the vitality of the eggs and sperm of *Oncorhynchus masou* (landlocked). *J. Fish. Inst. Tokyo*, **21,** 17.

NALBANDOV, A., & CARD, L. E. (1943). Effect of stale sperm on fertility and hatchability of chicken eggs. *Poult. Sci.*, **22,** 218.

Newport, G. (1853). On the impregnation of the ovum in the Amphibia. And on the direct agency of the spermatozoon. *Phil. Trans.*, **143**, 233.

Niwa, T. (1958). Artificial insemination with swine in Japan. *Nat. Inst. agric. Sci.*, August.

Novoseljcev, D. V. (1951). The quantity of spermatozoa in the boar's epididymides and principles governing it. (Trans.) *Sovetsk. Zooteh.*, **6**, 76. *Anim. Breed. Abstr.*, **20**, 272.

Nursall, J. R., & Hasler, A. D. (1952). A note on experiments designed to test the viability of gametes and the fertilisation of eggs by minute quantities of sperm. *Progr. Fish Cult.*, **14**, 165.

O'Dell, W. T., & Almquist, J. O. (1954). Techniques for freezing bull spermatozoa in heated milk and preliminary breeding results. *J. Dairy Sci.*, **37**, 652.

——— & Marsh, L. A. (1958). Freezing bovine semen. III: Effect of freezing rate on bovine spermatozoa frozen and stored at −79°C. *J. Dairy Sci.*, **41**, 79.

O'Dell, G. D., & Hurst, V. (1955). The effect of glycerol equilibration time in egg yolk citrate and skim-milk semen diluters. *J. Dairy Sci.*, **38**, 623.

Ogawa, S., & Suzuki, Y. (1955). Studies on artificial insemination in the rat. I: Induction of pseudopregnancy, collection of semen and technique of insemination. *Jap. J. Anim. Reprod.*, **1**, 67.

——— (1956). Studies on artificial insemination in the rat. II: Storage of semen with "Organ homogenate diluent". *Jap. J. Anim. Reprod.*, **2**, 55.

Olds, D., & VanDemark, N. L. (1957). The behaviour of spermatozoa in luminal fluids of bovine female genitalia. *Amer. J. Vet. Res.*, **18**, 603.

Olsen, M. W. (1952). Intra-ovarian insemination in the domestic fowl. *J. exp. Zool.*, **119**, 461.

——— & Neher, B. H. (1948). The site of fertilization in the domestic fowl. *J. exp. Zool.*, **109**, 355.

Oppermann, K. (1913). Die Entwicklung von Forelleneiern nach Befruchtung mit radium-bestrahlten Samenfäden. II: Das Verhalten des Radiumchromatins während der ersten Teilungsstadien. *Arch. mikr. Anat.*, **83**, 307.

Oslund, R. M. (1926). Physiologic effects of spermatoxin in rats, rabbits and guinea-pigs. *J. Amer. Med. Ass.*, **86**, 1755.

Pagenstecher, H. A. (1859). Über die Begattung des *Vesperugo pipistrellus*. *Verh. naturh.-med. Ver. Heidelb.*, **1**, 194.

Parker, J. E. (1939). An avian semen collector. *Poult. Sci.*, **18**, 455.

Parkes, A. S. (1926). The mammalian sex-ratio. *Biol. Rev.*, **2**, 1.

——— (1945). Preservation of human spermatozoa at low temperatures. *Brit. med. J.*, **ii**, 212.

——— (1947). Effects on early embryonic development of irradiation of spermatozoa. *Brit. J. Radiol.*, Suppl. 1, p. 117.

——— (1951). Storage of mammalian spermatozoa at low temperatures. *Proc. Soc. Study Fertility*, No. 2, p. 12.

——— (1953). Prevention of fertilisation by a hyaluronidase inhibitor. *Lancet*, **ii**, 1285.

——— (1954). Transplantation of testis tissue after storage at very low temperatures. *J. Endocrin.*, **10**, vii.

——— (1956). Preservation of living cells and tissues at low temperatures. *Proc. III int. Congr. Anim. Reprod.*, *Cambridge*, Plenary Papers, p. 69.

——— (1957a). The development in Gt. Britain, 1949–52, of the technique of preserving bull semen in the frozen state. *Vet. Rec.*, **69**, 463.

——— (1957b). Ed. A discussion on viability of mammalian cells and tissues after freezing. *Proc. Roy. Soc.*, B, **147**, 424.

——— (1960). Freeze-drying of viable grafts: problem and possibilities. *Recent Research in Freezing and Drying*. Oxford.

——— Rogers, H. J., & Spensley, P. C. (1954). Biological and biochemical aspects of the prevention of fertilization by enzyme inhibitors. *Studies on Fertility*, **6**, 65.

——— & Smith, A. U. (1960). Editors: *Recent Research in Freezing and Drying*. Oxford.

Parsons, E. I., & Hyde, R. R. (1940). An evaluation of spermatoxic sera in the prevention of pregnancy. *Amer. J. Hyg.*, B, **31**, 89.

PAYNE, L. F. (1914). Vitality and activity of sperm cells and artificial insemination of the chicken. *Okla. agric. exp. Sta. Circ.*, 30.

PEARSON, K. (1900). *The grammar of science.* London.

PERSOV, G. M. (1941). Some facts about the survival of sturgeon sperm (*Acipenser stellatus*). *C. R. Acad. Sci. U.R.S.S.*, **33**, 327.

PETTER-ROUSSEAUX, A. (1953). Recherches sur la croissance et le cycle d'activité testiculaire de *Natrix natrix helvetica* (Lacepede). *Terre et la Vie*, **4**, 175.

PHILIPPI, E. (1908). Fortpflanzungsgeschichte der viviparen Teleosteer *Glaridichthys januarius. Zool. Jb.*, **27**, Pt. 1.

PHILIPS, A. G. (1918). Brief study of the mating of fowls with a test for the value of a single mating. *J. Amer. Ass. Poult. Husb.*, **4**, 30.

PHILLIPS, R. W., & ANDREWS, F. N. (1937). The speed of travel of ram spermatozoa. *Anat. Rec.*, **68**, 127.

PINCUS, G., & ENZMANN, E. V. (1936). The comparative behaviour of mammalian eggs *in vivo* and *in vitro*. II: The activation of tubal eggs of the rabbit. *J. exp. Zool.*, **73**, 195.

—— PIRIE, N. W., & CHANG, M. C. (1948). Effects of hyaluronidase inhibitors on fertilization in the rabbit. *Arch. Biochem.*, **19**, 388.

PIRIE, N. W. (1952). The biochemistry of conception control. *Eugen. Rev.*, **44**, 129.

POLGE, C. (1950). Artificial insemination in fowl. *Proc. Soc. Study of Fertility*, No. II, 16.

—— (1951). Functional survival of fowl spermatozoa after freezing at −79°C. *Nature, Lond.*, **167**, 949.

—— (1953a). Storage of bull semen at low temperatures. *Vet. Rec.*, **65**, 557.

—— (1953b). The preservation of spermatozoa at low temperatures. *Ciba Foundation Symposium: Mammalian Germ Cells*, p. 108.

—— (1955). Artificial insemination in fowl. Thesis (University of London).

—— (1956a). Techniques for artificial insemination in pigs. *Proc. III int. Congr. Anim. Reprod., Cambridge.* Section III, p. 59.

—— (1956b). Artificial insemination in pigs. *Vet. Rec.*, **68**, 62.

—— (1957). Low temperature storage of mammalian spermatozoa. *Proc. Roy. Soc.*, B, **147**, 498.

—— & LOVELOCK, J. E. (1952). Preservation of bull semen at −79°C. *Vet. Rec.*, **64**, 396.

—— & PARKES, A. S. (1952). Possibilities of long-term storage of spermatozoa at low temperatures. *Anim. Breed. Abstr.*, **20**, 1.

—— & ROWSON, L. E. A. (1952a). Fertilizing capacity of bull spermatozoa after freezing at −79°C. *Nature, Lond.*, **169**, 626.

—— —— (1952b). Results with bull semen stored at −79°C. *Vet. Rec.*, **64**, 851.

—— SMITH, A. U., & PARKES, A. S. (1949). Revival of spermatozoa after vitrification and dehydration at low temperatures. *Nature, Lond.*, **164**, 666.

—— & SOLTYS, M. A. (1960). The preservation of trypanosomes by freezing. *Recent Research in Freezing and Drying.* Oxford.

POMMERENKE, W. T. (1928). Effects of sperm injections into female rabbits. *Physiol. Zoöl.*, **1**, 97.

—— (1946). Cyclic changes in the physical and chemical properties of cervical mucus. *Amer. J. Obstet. Gynec.*, **52**, 1023.

—— & VIERGIVER, E. (1947). Relationship between cervical mucus and basal temperature cycles. *Amer. J. Obstet. Gynec.*, **54**, 676.

PRABHU, S. S., & SHARMA, U. D. (1955). Sex-drive and semen production in water buffalo. *Indian J. vet. Sci.*, **25**, 89.

PURSER, G. L. (1937). Succession of broods of *Lebistes. Nature, Lond.*, **140**, 155.

QUATREFAGES, A. DE (1850). Recherches experimentales sur les spermatozoides des hermelles et des tarets. *Ann. Sci. nat. (Ser. 3 Zool.)*, **13**, 111.

—— (1853). Recherches sur la vitalité des spermatozoides de quelques poissons d'eau douce. *Ann. Sci. Nat. (Ser. 3 Zool.)*, **19**, 341.

QUINLAN, J., & STEYN, H. P. (1941). Observations on artificial insemination of sheep with fresh and stored semen. *Onderstepoort J. vet. Sci.*, **16**, 263.

QUINN, J. P., & BURROWS, W. H. (1936). Artificial insemination of fowls. *J. Hered.*, **27**, 31.

RAHN, H. (1940). Sperm viability in the uterus of the Garter Snake, *Thamnophis*. *Copeia*, July 28, p. 109.

—— (1942). The reproductive cycle of the prairie rattler. *Copeia*, p. 233.

RÉGAUD, C., & DUBREUIL, G. (1908). Perturbations dans le développement des oeufs fécondés par des spermatozoïdes roentgénisés chez le lapin. *C. R. Soc. Biol., Paris*, **64**, 1014.

REY, L. R. (1957). Studies on the action of liquid nitrogen on cultures *in vitro* of fibroblasts. *Proc. Roy. Soc.*, B, **147**, 460.

RIDDLE, O., & BEHRE, E. J. (1921). Studies on the physiology of reproduction in birds. IX: On the relation of stale sperm to fertility and sex in ring-doves. *Amer. J. Physiol.*, **57**, 228.

ROBERTS, W. C. (1944). Multiple mating of queen bees proved by progeny and flight tests. *Glean. Bee Cult.*, **72**, 6, 255.

ROBERTSON, W. R. B. (1917). A mule and a horse as twins, and the inheritance of twinning. *Kansas Univ. Sci. Bull.*, **10**, 293.

ROBINSON, T. J. (1956). The artificial insemination of the Merino sheep following the synchronization of oestrus and ovulation by progesterone injected alone and with pregnant mare serum gonadotrophin (PMS). *Aust. J. agric. Res.*, **7**, 194.

RODIN, I. M., & LIPATOV, V. I. (1935). Artificial insemination of pigs. (In Russian.) *Probl. Zivotn.*, No. 9, 108. *Anim. Breed. Abstr.*, (1936), **4**, 205.

RODOLFO, A. (1934). The physiology of reproduction in swine. *Philipp. J. Sci.*, **53**, 183; **55**, 13 and 165.

ROHLEDER, H. (1934). *Test tube babies. A history of the artificial impregnation of human beings.* New York.

ROLLINAT, R. (1898). Sur l'accouplement des ophidiens à la fin de l'été et au commencement de l'automme. *Bull. Zool. Soc. France*, **23**.

—— (1946). *La vie des reptiles de la France Centrale.* 3rd Ed., Paris.

ROMMER, J. J. (1947). Psychoneurogenic causes of sterility and their treatment with preliminary remarks on allergenic sterility. *West. J. Surg.*, **55**, 278.

ROSTAND, J. (1946). Glycérine et résistance du sperme aux basses températures. *C. R. Acad. Sci., Paris*, **222**, 1524.

ROTHSCHILD, Lord (1955). The spermatozoa of the honey bee. *Trans. Roy. ent. Soc., Lond.*, **107**, 289.

ROWELL, J. G., & COOPER, D. M. (1957). The relation between fertility in the fowl and the dilution rate of the semen using a glycine diluent. *Poult. Sci.*, **36**, 706.

ROWLANDS, I. W. (1944). Capacity of hyaluronidase to increase the fertilizing power of sperm. *Nature, Lond.*, **154**, 332.

—— (1957). Insemination of the guinea-pig by intraperitoneal injection. *J. Endocrin.*, **16**, 98.

—— (1958). Insemination by intra-peritoneal injection. *Studies on Fertility*, **10**, 150.

ROWSON, L. E. A. (1956). The low temperature preservation of germinal cells. *Proc. III int. Congr. Anim. Reprod., Cambridge*, Plenary Papers, p. 75.

—— & POLGE, C. (1953). Storage of bull semen at −79°C. and fertility results for up to 12 months. *Vet. Rec.*, **65**, 677.

ROY, A. (1955). Storage of boar and stallion spermatozoa in glycine–egg-yolk medium. *Vet. Rec.*, **67**, 330.

—— & BISHOP, M. W. H. (1954). Effect of glycine on the survival of bull spermatozoa *in vitro*. *Nature, Lond.*, **174**, 746.

—— GUPTA, H. C., SRIVASTAVA, R. K., & PANDEY, M. D. (1956). Storage of ram spermatozoa *in vitro*. I: Preservation in glycine–egg-yolk medium. *Indian vet. J.*, **33**, 18.

RUBENSTEIN, B. B. (1943). The transportation and survival of sperm in the vaginal and cervical canals. In *Problems of Human Fertility*. Ed. E. T. Engle. Menasha, Wisconsin.

—— STRAUSS, H., LAZARUS, M. L., & HANKIN, H. (1951). Sperm survival in women: motile sperm in the fundus and tubes of surgical cases. *Fertility & Sterility*, **2**, 15.

RUCKER, R. R. (1949). Fact and fiction in spawntaking: addenda. *Prog. Fish. Cult.*, **11**, 75.

RUGH, R. (1934). Induced ovulation and artificial fertilisation in the frog. *Biol. Bull.*, **66**, 22.

—— (1939). Developmental effects resulting from exposure to X-rays. I: Effect on the embryo of irradiation of frog sperm. *Proc. Amer. phil. Soc.*, **81**, 447.

—— & EXNER, F. (1940). Developmental effects resulting from exposure to X-rays. II: Development of leopard frog eggs activated by bullfrog sperm. *Proc. Amer. phil. Soc.*, **83**, 607.

SALISBURY, G. W. (1946a). The glycolysis, livability and fertility of bovine spermatozoa as influenced by their concentration. In *The Problem of Fertility*. Ed. E. T. Engle. Princeton.

—— (1946b). Fertility of bull semen diluted at 1:100. *J. Dairy Sci.*, **29**, 695.

—— (1957). Recent developments with bull semen diluents. *Anim. Breed. Abstr.*, **25**, No. 2, 111.

—— & BRATTON, R. W. (1948). Fertility level of bull semen diluted at 1:400 with and without sulfanilamide. *J. Dairy Sci.*, **31**, 817.

—— ELLIOTT, F. I., & VANDEMARK, N. L. (1945). Further studies of the effect of dilution rate on the fertility of bull semen used for artificial insemination. *J. Dairy Sci.*, **28**, 233.

SANDNES, G. C., & LANDAUER, W. (1938). The sex ratio in the cross of *Phasianus torquatus* ♀ × *Gallus domesticus* ffl. *Amer. Nat.*, **72**, 180.

SAROFF, J., & MIXNER, J. P. (1954). The relationship of diluter composition and glycerol equilibration time to survival of bull spermatozoa after freezing. *J. Dairy Sci.*, **37**, 651.

—— (1955). The relationship of egg-yolk and glycerol content of diluters and glycerol equilibration time to survival of bull spermatozoa after low temperature freezing. *J. Dairy Sci.*, **38**, 292.

SCHELLEN, A. (1957). *Artificial insemination in the human*. Texas.

SCHMIDT, J. (1920). The genetic behaviour of a secondary sexual character. *C. R. Lab. Carlsberg*, **14**, No. 8.

SCHOTT, R. G., & PHILLIPS, R. W. (1941). Rate of sperm travel and time of ovulation in sheep. *Anat. Rec.*, **79**, 531.

SCHWARTZ, R., & ZINSSER, H. H. (1955). Some factors modifying sperm progress. *Fertility & Sterility*, **6**, 450.

SCHWEITZER, F. L., & BAS, J. A. (1948). Valoración y diferenciación de las distintas hormonas gonadotrofinas por su acción sobre el sapo macho. *Sem. méd., B. Aires*, **55**, 703 & 980.

SHAFFNER, C. S. (1942). Longevity of fowl spermatozoa in frozen condition. *Science*, **96**, 337.

—— HENDERSON, E. W., & CARD, C. G. (1941). Viability of spermatozoa of the chicken under various environmental conditions. *Poult. Sci.*, **20**, 259.

SHALASH, M. R. (1956). Some applied aspects in A.I. of buffaloes. A rapid method of standardisation of the density of buffalo semen. *Vet. Rec.*, **68**, 8.

SHARMA, G. P., SURI, K. R., & VALI, K. N. (1957). A study of the "reaction time" and some of the semen characteristics of the Betal breed of goat. *Res. Bull. E. Panjab Univ., Zool.*, No. 101, 217.

SHELESNYAK, M. C., & DAVIES, A. M. (1953). Relative ineffectiveness of electrical stimulation of the cervix for inducing pseudopregnancies in the mouse. *Endocrinology*, **52**, 362.

SHERMAN, J. K. (1954). Freezing and freeze-drying of human spermatozoa. *Fertility & Sterility*, **5**, 357.

—— (1955). Temperature shock in human spermatozoa. *Proc. Soc. exp. Biol., N.Y.*, **88**, 6.

—— & BUNGE, R. G. (1953a). Observations on preservation of human spermatozoa at low temperatures. *Proc. Soc. exp. Biol., N.Y.*, **82**, 686.

—— & BUNGE, R. G. (1953b). Effect of glycerol and freezing on some staining reactions of human spermatozoa. *Proc. Soc. exp. Biol., N.Y.*, **84**, 179.

SHETTLES, L. B. (1940). The respiration of human spermatozoa and their responses to various gases and low temperature. *Amer. J. Physiol.*, **128**, 408.

SHMIDTOV, A. E. (1936). Concerning the survival of sturgeon sperm under different conditions. *C. R. Acad. Sci., U.R.S.S.*, **3**, 89.

SHUMAN, R. F. (1950). On the effectiveness of spermatozoa of the Pink Salmon (*Oncorhynchus gorbuscha*) at varying distances from the point of dispersal. *Fish. Bull., U.S.*, **51**, 359.

SKALLER, F. (1951). Artificial insemination applied on a large scale to poultry breeding research. *Rep. IX World's Poult. Congr. Paris*, **3**, 124.

SLOVITER, H. A. (1951). Recovery of human red blood cells after freezing. *Lancet*, **i**, 823.

SMIRNOV, I. V. (1951). The storage of livestock semen at a temperature of −78°—183°. (Trans.). *Socialist Zivotn.*, **1**, 94.

SMITH, A. U. (1949a). The control of bacterial growth in fowl semen. *J. agric. Sci.*, **39**, 194.

—— (1949b). Some antigenic properties of mammalian spermatozoa. *Proc. Roy. Soc.*, B, **136**, 46.

—— (1949c). The antigenic relationship of some mammalian spermatozoa. *Proc. Roy. Soc.*, B, **136**, 472.

—— (1950). Prevention of haemolysis during freezing and thawing of red blood cells. *Lancet*, **ii**, 910.

—— (1954). Effects of low temperature on living cells and tissues. In *Biological Applications of Freezing and Drying*, Ed. R. J. C. Harris. New York.

—— (1958). The resistance of animals to cooling and freezing. *Biol. Rev.*, **33**, 197.

—— & POLGE, C. (1950a). Storage of bull spermatozoa at low temperatures. *Vet. Rec.*, **62**, 115.

—— —— (1950b). Survival of spermatozoa at low temperatures. *Nature, Lond.*, **166**, 668.

—— —— & SMILES, J. (1951). Microscopic observation of living cells during freezing and thawing. *J. R. micr. Soc.*, **71**, 186.

—— & SMILES, J. (1953). Microscopic studies of mammalian tissues during cooling to −79°C. *J. R. micr. Soc.*, **73**, 134.

SNEED, K. E., & CLEMENS, H. P. (1956). Survival of fish sperm after freezing and storage at low temperatures. *Prog. Fish. Cult.*, **18**, 99.

SNELGROVE, L. E. (1946). *Queen rearing*. Somerset.

SNELL, G. D. (1933). X-ray sterility in the male house mouse. *J. exp. Zool.*, **65**, 421.

—— HUMMEL, K. P., & ABELMANN, W. H. (1944). A technique for the artificial insemination of mice. *Anat. Rec.*, **90**, 243.

SNYDER, R. (1955). Problems encountered in converting to an all-frozen semen programme. *Proc. VIII Convention Nat. Ass. Artif. Breeders, U.S.A.*, p. 199.

SODERWALL, A. L., & BLANDAU, R. J. (1941). The duration of the fertilizing capacity of spermatozoa in the female genital tract of the rat. *J. exp. Zool.*, **88**, 55.

—— & YOUNG, W. C. (1940). The effect of ageing in the female genital tract on the fertilising capacity of guinea-pig spermatozoa. *Anat. Rec.*, **78**, 19.

SPALLANZANI, L. (1776). *Opuscoli di Fisica Animale, e Vegetabile*. Modena.

—— (1784). *Dissertations relative to the natural history of animals and vegetables, translated from the Italian of the Abbé Spallanzani*, Vol. II. London.

STARKE, N. C. (1949). The sperm picture of rams of different breeds as an indication of their fertility. II: The rate of sperm travel in the genital tract of the ewe. *Onderst. J. vet. Sci.*, **22**, 415.

STEIN, I. F., & COHEN, M. R. (1950). Sperm survival at estimated ovulation time: prognostic significance. *Fertility & Sterility*, **1**, 169.

STEMMER, W. (1940). Examination of semen and female sterility. *Med. Welt.*, **14**, 351.

STEWART, D. L. (1951). Storage of bull spermatozoa at low temperatures. *Vet. Rec.*, **63**, 65.

STOCKARD, C. R., & PAPANICOLAOU, G. N. (1917). The existence of a typical oestrous cycle in the guinea-pig—with a study of its histological and physiological changes. *Amer. J. Anat.*, **22**, 225.

STOLK, A. (1950). Histo-endocrinological analysis of the gestation phenomena in the cyprinodont, *Lebistes reticulatus*. (Trans.). Thesis, University of Utrecht.

STOWER, J. (1953). The storage of bull semen at low temperatures. *Vet. Rec.*, **65**, 560.

STRANDSKOV, H. H. (1932). Effects of X-rays in an inbred strain of guinea-pigs. *J. exp. Zool.*, **63**, 175.

STROGANOV, N. S. (1938). The survival capacity of sperm in the Volga herring (*Caspiolosa volgensis*) under external conditions. *Zool. Zh.*, **17**, 316.

SULMAN, F. G., & SULMAN, E. (1950). Pregnancy test with the male frog (*R. ridibunda*). *J. clin. Endocrin.*, **10**, 933.

SWANNEY, J. M. (1953). The storage of bull semen at low temperatures. *Vet. Rec.*, **65**, 563.

SZUMOWSKI, P. (1952). De quelques effets du plasma séminal frais sur les spermatozoïdes de sperme de taureau conservé. *Proc. II int. Congr. Anim. Reprod., Copenhagen*, **1**, 80.

—— (1954). Essais de congélation du sperme de cheval. *C. R. Acad. Agric. Fr.*, **40**, 156.

THIBAULT, C. (1949). L'œuf des mammifères. Son développement parthénogénétique. *Ann. Sci. nat. (Zool.)*, **11**, 136.

THORBORG, J. V., & HANSEN, K. (1951). The use of *Xenopus laevis*, *Bufo bufo*, and *Rana esculenat* as test animals for gonadotrophic hormones. III: Quantitative investigations on the sensitivity of the animals to chorionic gonadotrophin. *Acta endocr., Copenhagen* **6**, 51.

TOSIC, J., & WALTON, A. (1947). Effect of egg yolk and its constituents on the respiration and fertilizing capacity of spermatozoa. *J. agric. Sci.*, **37**, 69.

TRAPIDO, H. (1940). Mating time and sperm viability in *Storeria*. *Copeia*, July 28, No. 2, p. 107.

TYLER, A., & TANABE, T. Y. (1952). Motile life of bovine spermatozoa in glycine and yolk-citrate diluents at high and low temperatures. *Proc. Soc. exp. Biol., N.Y.*, **81**, 367.

VANDEMARK, N. L. (1958). Spermatozoa in the female genital tract. *Int. J. Fertil.*, **3**, 220.

—— & HAYS, R. L. (1951). The effect of oxytocin, adrenalin, breeding techniques and milking on uterine motility in the cow. *J. Anim. Sci.*, **10**, 1083.

—— —— (1952). Uterine motility response to mating. *Amer. J. Physiol.*, **170**, 518.

—— —— (1954). Rapid sperm transport in the cow. *Fertility & Sterility*, **5**, 131.

—— —— (1955). Sperm transport in the perfused genital tract of the cow. *Amer. J. Physiol.*, **183**, 510.

—— MILLER, W. J., KINNEY, W. C., RODRIGUEZ, C., & FRIEDMAN, M. E. (1957). Preservation of bull semen at sub-zero temperatures. *Bull. Ill. agric. Exp. Sta.*, No. 621.

—— & MOELLER, A. N. (1951). Speed of spermatozoan transport in the reproductive tract of the oestrous cow. *Amer. J. Physiol.*, **165**, 674.

VAN DRIMMELEN, G. C. (1945). Intraperitoneal insemination of birds. *J. S. Afr. vet. med. Ass.*, **16**, 1.

—— (1946). "Spermnests" in the oviduct of the domestic hen. *J. S. Afr. vet. med. Ass.*, **17**, 42.

—— (1956). Low temperature storage of living organisms. *S. Afr. J. Sci.*, **52**, 267.

VAN OORDT, G. J. (1928). The duration of life of spermatozoa in the fertilized female of *Xiphophorus Nelleri*, Regan. *Tijdschr. ned. dierk. Ver.*, Ser. 3, Pt. I, No. 2.

VAN RENSBURG, S. W. J., & ROWSON, L. E. A. (1954). The fertilising capacity of frozen bull semen after long distance aerial transport. *Vet. Rec.*, **66**, 385.

VAN TIENHOVEN, A., & STEEL, R. G. D. (1957). The effect of different diluents and dilution rates on fertilizing capacity of turkey semen. *Poult. Sci.*, **36**, 473.

VENGE, O. (1954a). A simplified method for spreading the chromosomes in the rabbit blastocyst. *Nature, Lond.*, **174**, 608.

—— (1954b). Experiments on polyploidy in the rabbit. *Kungl. Lautbruk. Annal.*, **21**, 417.

VIERGIVER, E., & POMMERENKE, W. T. (1946). Cyclic variations in the viscosity of cervical mucus and its correlation with amount of secretion and basal temperature. *Amer. J. Obstet. Gynec.*, **51**, 192.

VOJTÍŠKOVÁ, M. (1958). Distant hybrids from parents with reduced immunological reactivity. *Nature, Lond.*, **181**, 927.

WALLACE, C. (1949). The effects of castration and stilboestrol treatment on the semen production of the boar. *J. Endocrin.*, **6**, 205.

WALTON, A. (1927). The relation between "density" of sperm-suspension and fertility as determined by artificial insemination of rabbits. *Proc. Roy. Soc.*, B, **101**, 303.

—— (1938). *Notes on artificial insemination of sheep, cattle and horses*, 2nd Ed. Holborn Surgical Instrument Co., London.

—— (1945). *The technique of artificial insemination*, 3rd Ed. Holborn Surgical Instrument Co., London.

—— & HAMMOND, J. (1938). The maternal effects of growth and conformation in Shire horse–Shetland pony crosses. *Proc. Roy. Soc.*, B, **125**, 311.

—— & WHETHAM, E. O. (1933). The survival of spermatozoa in the domestic fowl. *J. exp. Biol.*, **10**, 204.

WANG, Y. (1936). Effect of spermatozoon injections on the fertility of female albino rats. *Chin. J. Physiol.*, **10**, 53.

WARREN, D. C., & KILPATRICK, L. (1929). Fertilization in the domestic fowl. *Poult. Sci.*, **8**, 237.

—— & SCOTT, H. M. (1935). An attempt to produce turkey-chicken hybrids. *J. Hered.*, **26**, 105.

WATANABE, M., & SUGIMORI, Y. (1957). Studies on artificial insemination in ducks. *Zootec. e Vet.*, **12**, 119.

WATSON, L. R. (1927). Controlled mating of queen bees. Quoted by Laidlaw, 1944.

WEIL, A. J., & FINKLER, A. E. (1958). Antigens in rabbit semen. *Proc. Soc. exp. Biol.*, *N.Y.*, **98**, 794.

—— KOTSERVATOR, O., & WILSON, L. (1956). Antigens of human seminal plasma. *Proc. Soc. exp. Biol.*, *N.Y.*, **92**, 606.

WEIR, J. A. (1955). Male influence on sex ratio of offspring in high and low blood-pH lines of mice. *J. Hered.*, **46**, 277.

WHARTON, J. C. F. (1957). A preliminary report on new techniques for the artificial fertilisation of trout ova. *Fisheries Contribution* No. 6. From Snob's Creek Fisheries Research Station, Victoria, Australia.

WHEELER, N. C., & ANDREWS, F. N. (1943). The influence of season on semen production in the domestic fowl. *Poult. Sci.*, **22**, 361.

WHITE, I. G. (1956). Studies relating to the storage of mammalian spermatozoa. *Studies on Fertility*, **8**, 36.

—— BLACKSHAW, A. W., & EMMENS, C. W. (1954). Metabolic and motility studies relating to the low temperature storage of ram and bull spermatozoa. *Aust. Vet. J.*, **30**, 85.

WIGGINS, E. L., GRUMMER, R. H., & CASIDA, L. E. (1951). Minimal volumes of semen and number of sperm for fertility in artificial insemination of swine. *J. Anim. Sci.*, **10**, 138.

WILLETT, E. L. (1953). Decline in fertility of bull semen with increase in storage time as influenced by dilution rate. *J. Dairy Sci.*, **36**, 1182.

WILLETT, E. L., & OHMS, J. I. (1954). Field trials with semen containing various combinations of anti-bacterial agents. *J. Dairy Sci.*, **37**, 649.

—— —— (1958a). Inactivation of spermatozoa by lactate and reactivation with alkali. *J. Dairy Sci.*, **41**, 275.

—— —— (1958b). Influence of seminal plasma and maturity of bovine spermatozoa upon their freezability. *J. Dairy Sci.*, **41**, 90.

—— —— & TORRIE, J. H. (1955). Factors influencing experimental error in field trials in artificial insemination. *J. Dairy Sci.*, **38**, 1375.

WILLIAMS, C., & McGIBBON, W. H. (1956). The yields of semen among inbred lines and crosses of S.C. White Leghorns. *Poult. Sci.*, **35**, 617.

WILSON, L. (1954). Sperm agglutinins in human semen and blood. *Proc. Soc. exp. Biol.*, *N.Y.*, **85**, 652.

WIMSATT, W. A. (1942). Survival of spermatozoa in the female reproductive tract of the bat. *Anat. Rec.*, **83**, 299.

—— (1944). Further studies on the survival of spermatozoa in the female reproductive tract of the bat. *Anat. Rec.*, **88**, 193.

WINGE, Ö. (1922). A peculiar mode of inheritance and its cytological explanation. *J. Genet.*, **12**, 137.

—— (1937). Succession of broods in *Lebistes*. *Nature, Lond.*, **140**, 467.

Wislocki, G. B., & Snyder, F. F. (1931). On the experimental production of super-foetation. *Bull. Johns Hopk. Hosp.*, **35**, 246.

Woodward, S. F. (1933). A few notes on the persistence of active spermatozoa in the African Night Adder, *Causus rhombeatus*. *Proc. Zool. Soc.* (1933), p. 189.

Yanagimachi, R. (1953). Effect of environmental salt concentration on fertilisability of herring gametes. *J. Fac. Sci. Hokkaido Univ.*, **11**, 481.

Yochem, D. E. (1929). Spermatozoon life in the female reproductive tract of the guinea-pig and rat. *Biol. Bull., Wood's Hole*, **56**, 274.

Young, W. C. (1931). A study of the function of the epididymis. III: Functional changes undergone by spermatozoa during their passage through the epididymis and vas deferens in the guinea-pig. *J. exp. Biol.*, **8**, 151.

—— (1937). The vaginal smear picture, sexual receptivity and the time of ovulation in the guinea-pig. *Anat. Rec.*, **67**, 305.

CHAPTER 9A

METABOLISM AND MOTILITY OF MAMMALIAN SPERMATOZOA

By Marcus W. H. Bishop and Arthur Walton

I. Metabolism

Early observations on the metabolism of spermatozoa were confined to marine invertebrates, such as the sea-urchin, in which fertilisation is external. It was soon discovered that these spermatozoa swim and respire very actively in sea-water. Since sea-water contains no metabolic substrates, it may be concluded that the energy for movement is obtained solely from the catabolism of intracellular substrates, and it follows that exhaustion of this source of energy will limit the independent life of the cell. In 1919, Lillie summarised the then prevailing views as follows : " Spermatozoa are probably incapable of receiving nourishment outside of the gonad after they are fully differentiated : certainly in the case of all forms with external insemination there is no opportunity for the restitution of substance. We must therefore regard these cells as charged with their full available store of energy in the testes and their capacity for locomotion as thus determined and limited. They therefore have a strictly limited period of life, the duration of which will be determined by their activity. The store of energy is saved when they are motionless and expended when in motion. Thus we find that sperm suspensions will retain their fertilising power for a relatively long time if activity is reduced, and will lose it rapidly if activity is great."

Subsequently, work on mammalian spermatozoa showed that they too swim and respire actively in saline solutions without added metabolic substrate, even when prior admixture with secretions of the accessory glands is prevented. It soon became evident, however, that the metabolism of these cells, unlike those of the sea-urchin, is not restricted to aerobic oxidation, for Amantea and Krzyszkowsky (1921), Walton, Hammond and Asdell (1928) and Walton (1930) found that mammalian spermatozoa can survive for long periods under anaerobic conditions, and McCarthy, Stepita, Johnston and Killian (1927) demonstrated glycolysis in human semen. Other workers found that various organic substances of possible nutritive value prolonged the survival of spermatozoa suspended in saline solutions, but it remained for Redenz (1930, 1933) to be the first to show conclusively that mammalian spermatozoa can utilise extracellular substrates. Working in Meyerhof's laboratory and using the latest manometric techniques of Warburg, Redenz showed that epididymal spermatozoa of the bull could derive energy for motility, under both aerobic and anaerobic conditions, from the glycolytic breakdown of exogenous glucose, fructose or mannose to lactic acid. Under aerobic conditions, the lactic acid produced by glycolysis was further degraded to carbon dioxide and water. Redenz's discovery was independently confirmed by Ivanov (1931), who showed that dog spermatozoa retained their motility under anaerobic conditions, or in the presence of cyanide, provided that the suspending medium contained glucose. Subsequent observations by many workers have firmly established that mammalian spermatozoa can obtain energy for their physiological activities by the following three processes : (1) aerobic and anaerobic glycolysis of certain exogenous hexose sugars to pyruvic acid or lactic acid, (2) aerobic oxidation of the terminal products of glycolysis, and of a variety of other exogenous substrates, to carbon dioxide and water, and (3) aerobic oxidation of intracellular substrates, probably lipid in nature, that are laid down during spermatogenesis. There is, however, still disagreement about the relative importance of these three processes in the normal physiology of the cell. Under anaerobic conditions, only glycolysis can occur, but in the presence of oxygen it is probable that respiratory metabolism of exogenous substrate is the chief source of energy. It is also likely that oxidation of endogenous substrate, though probably the primitive form of catabolism in spermatozoa, only takes place when extracellular substrate is not readily available.

The principal earlier reviews on spermatozoon metabolism are those of Anderson (1945) and Mann (1949, 1951, 1954a). For general information on the metabolic pathways used by spermatozoa, reference should be made to standard texts on biochemistry, such as those of Baldwin (1952), Fruton and Simmonds (1953), White, Handler, Smith and Stetten (1954) and Neilands and Stumf (1955).

Glycolysis

Redenz (1933) observed that glucose, fructose, mannose and maltose would support glycolysis by bull spermatozoa, but that sucrose, lactose and glycogen would not. Macleod (1941a) found that glucose, mannose, fructose, maltose and glycogen could be utilised by human spermatozoa, but not lactose, sucrose or galactose. Lardy and Phillips (1941a, 1945a) state that ejaculated bull spermatozoa metabolise glucose, fructose and maltose equally, that galactose and sucrose are not utilised, and that maltose is utilised only weakly by epididymal spermatozoa. The ability of spermatozoa to catabolise glucose, fructose and mannose is a property of all mammalian species so far examined, but the extent to which disaccharides and polysaccharides can be utilised is still uncertain. Mayer (1955) states that ram spermatozoa do not possess enzymes that hydrolyse α- and β-glucosidic linkages and consequently cannot use di- and polysaccharides. Such enzymes may, however, be present in the seminal plasma of some species. It was originally believed that the reducing sugar in semen was glucose, and that this was the naturally-occurring substrate for spermatozoon metabolism. Mann (1946), however, has shown that the seminal hexose is almost entirely $D(-)$fructose : its metabolic degradation is therefore more appropriately termed fructolysis. When fructose and glucose are present together, however, glucose is utilised preferentially (Mann, 1951 ; Van Tienhoven, Salisbury, VanDemark and Hansen, 1952).

The metabolic degradation of hexoses by mammalian spermatozoa is carried out through the Embden–Meyerhof glycolytic system in the same manner as that known to occur in other animal tissues and in yeast. The principal stages of this degradation, together with the enzymes and co-enzymes involved, are illustrated in Fig. 94,1. Many of these stages and enzymes have been demonstrated in intact

K*

living spermatozoa by Mann (1945a). It can be seen from Fig. 9A,1 that during the early stages of glycolysis the substrate is phosphorylated in two steps by the

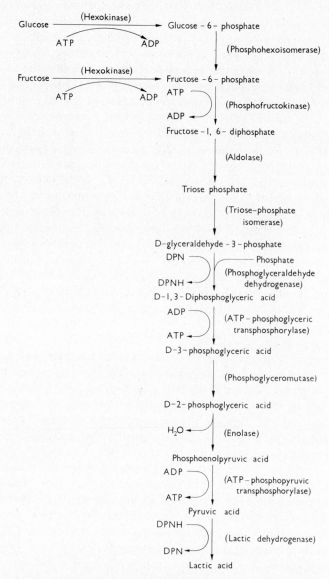

Fig. 9A.1—Diagrammatic representation of the probable glycolytic pathway occurring in mammalian spermatozoa. Enzymes are indicated in parenthesis. Coupled reactions are indicated by arrows that do not enter the main chain of events. Theoretically, all reactions are reversible. (ATP=adenosine triphosphate; ADP=adenosine diphosphate; DPN = oxidized diphosphopyridine nucleotide; DPNH = reduced diphosphopyridine nucleotide; triosephosphate is a mixture of dihydroxyacetone phosphate and D-glyceraldehyde-3-phosphate.)

co-enzyme adenosine triphosphate (ATP) in the presence of appropriate enzymes. During this phosphorylation, ATP acts as a phosphate donor and is broken down to adenosine diphosphate (ADP). The phosphorylated molecule is then split into two and oxidised by a special mechanism that is coupled with the conversion of ADP to ATP. Subsequently, it is hydrated and dephosphorylated to give pyruvic acid, which in the absence of oxygen is converted to lactic acid. As a result of the various transformations, two high-energy phosphate bonds are utilised, but four are synthesised. The net increase of two high-energy bonds represents that part of the free energy of the hexose substrate that is trapped by the cell and can be made available for its physiological activities. Two high-energy bonds contain about 21,000 calories, which is about 36 per cent of the 58,000 calories of free energy that are theoretically available when glucose is degraded to lactic acid. In the presence of oxygen, the final transformation of pyruvic acid to lactic acid is inhibited and reversed, and pyruvic acid is oxidised through the tricarboxylic-acid cycle (*see* below). Other methods of hexose catabolism, such as the hexose-monophosphate shunt, are known in some biological systems but have not so far been demonstrated in spermatozoa.

Spermatozoon fructolysis is inhibited by fluoride (which inhibits enolase), by iodoacetate (which inhibits triosephosphate dehydrogenase), by chloromercuribenzoate, iodosobenzoate and hydrogen peroxide (which probably act by virtue of their sulphydryl-binding properties), and by DL-glyceraldehyde (*see* MacLeod, 1941b ; Lardy and Phillips, 1943b ; Mann, 1954b, 1958). The rate of fructolysis is considerably slower under aerobic conditions than under anaerobic conditions (Redenz, 1933 ; Melrose and Terner, 1951) : this is the well-known Pasteur effect (Pasteur, 1876).

Other investigators of the glycolytic activity of mammalian spermatozoa include Bernstein (1933a,b), Killian (1933), Goldblatt (1935a), Shergin (1937), Comstock (1939), MacLeod (1939, 1943, 1951), Lardy and Phillips (1941a, 1943b), Moore and Mayer (1941), Henle and Zittle (1942), Comstock, Green, Winters and Nordskog (1943), Salisbury and VanDemark (1945), Salisbury (1946), Mann (1945b, 1948), Mann and Lutwak-Mann (1948), Roy, Luktuke, Bhattacharya and Bhattacharya (1950), Plaut and Lardy (1950), Eichenberger and Goossens (1950), Anderson (1946, 1951, 1952), Rollinson (1951), Melrose and Terner (1951), Brochart (1951), Melrose (1952), Gassner and Hill (1952), Flipse (1954), Bishop, Campbell, Hancock and Walton (1954), Bishop and Hancock (1955), Bishop (1955a, b), Flipse and Almquist (1955), Erb, Flerchinger, Ehlers and Gassner (1956), Ehlers and Erb (1956), Hopwood, Rutherford and Gassner (1956), Mixner, Mather and Freund (1957) and MacLeod and Freund (1958a, b).

Respiration

In the presence of oxygen, mammalian spermatozoa exhibit considerable respiratory activity. Metabolic substrates that support this activity include glycolysable sugars, lactate, pyruvate, acetate, propionate, butyrate and oxaloacetate (Lardy and Phillips, 1944, 1945 ; Mann and Lutwak-Mann, 1948 ; Humphrey and Mann, 1949 ; Melrose and Terner, 1952, 1953). Succinic acid and citric acid have little effect on the oxygen uptake of intact mammalian spermatozoa although the former will support respiration in spermatozoa damaged by treatment with detergents (Koefoed-Johnsen and Mann, 1954). Even without exogenous oxidisable substrate, mammalian spermatozoa can respire actively for an appreciable length of time (Lardy and Phillips, 1941c, 1945 ; Bishop, 1954 ; Bishop and Salisbury, 1955b ; Fig. 9A.2).

The respiratory metabolism of spermatozoa proceeds through the cytochrome–cytochrome oxidase system and Krebs' tricarboxylic-acid cycle in the same manner as that known to occur in a large variety of animal and plant cells. This is a remarkable cyclic series of transformations wherein pyruvic acid acetylates co-enzyme-A (3-phospho-ADP-pantoyl-β-alanyl-cysteamine) and is itself decarboxy-lated. The acetyl-coenzyme-A so produced reacts with oxaloacetic acid to produce citric acid. This is then degraded through a series of tri-carboxylic and dicarboxylic acids, until oxaloacetic acid is regenerated and becomes available for further reaction with acetyl-coenzyme-A. The mechanism by which this is achieved is not yet completely understood, but the principal features of the cycle are illustrated in Fig. 9A.3. During the cycle, carbon dioxide, hydrogen and electrons are removed from the substrate (actually one acetic-acid equivalent is oxidised to carbon dioxide and water in each circuit of the cycle), and a large part of the free energy released, probably over 60 per cent, is trapped in the form of newly syn-thesised high-energy phosphate bonds. The role of molecular oxygen, without which the cycle cannot proceed, is that of ultimate acceptor of electrons. These are transferred from the substrate through a complex system of elec-tron carriers, involving pyridine nucleotides, flavoproteins and cyto-chromes, to cytochrome oxidase. The reduced cytochrome oxidase is oxidised by oxygen and the reduced oxygen so formed combines with hydrogen to form water. It is, indeed, during these transfer reactions that the high-energy phosphate bonds are synthesised.

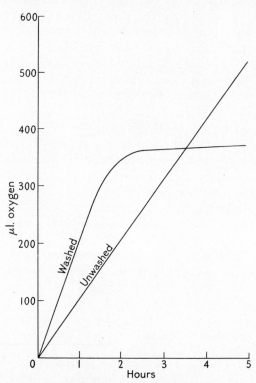

Fig. 9A.2—The oxygen uptake of washed bull sper-matozoa suspended in 0·9 per cent NaCl solu-tion and of unwashed spermatozoa, from the same ejaculate at the same concentration of cells, in seminal plasma. The washed cells respired actively for two hours by the oxidation of intra-cellular substrate; respiration then ceased. Respiration in the unwashed cells, though slower, was sustained by extracellular substrate in the seminal plasma. Each sample contained $1\cdot3 \times 10^9$ spermatozoa. (From Bishop, 1954.)

Since some 630,000 calories of free energy are theoretically liberated when lactic acid is degraded to carbon dioxide and water, and since the efficiency of conversion of this energy into high-energy phosphate bonds is high, it can be seen that respiration is an extremely productive source of energy for the cell. In many biological systems glycerol, fatty acids and amino acids can also be metabolised by means of the tricarboxylic-acid cycle and there is evidence that mammalian spermatozoa degrade glycerol and fatty acids in this way (*see* pages 270 and 271). Glycerol is thought to enter the cycle through glycerol phosphate and pyruvate, fatty acids through fatty-acid oxidative systems and acetyl-coenzyme-A, and amino acids through amino-acid degradative systems and pyruvate (*see* Fig. 9A.6).

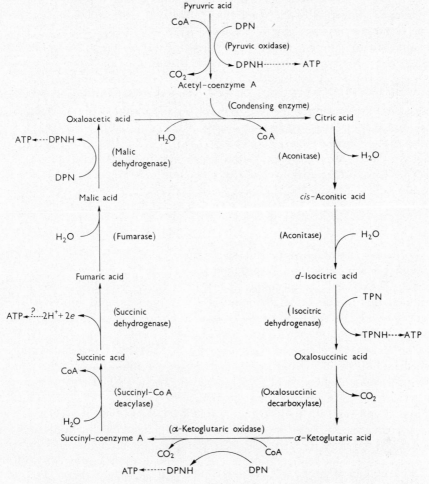

Fig. 9A.3—Diagrammatic representation of the Krebs' tricarboxylic-acid cycle. Dotted arrows indicate the sites at which coupled reactions lead to the synthesis of high-energy phosphate bonds. Enzymes are indicated in parenthesis. Coupled reactions are indicated by arrows that do not enter the main chain of events. (CoA=coenzyme A; DPN=oxidised diphosphopyridine nucleotide; DPNH=reduced diphosphopyridine nucleotide; TPN = oxidised triphosphopyridine nucleotide; TPNH = reduced triphosphopyridine nucleotide; ATP=adenosinetriphosphate.)

The tricarboxylic-acid cycle is, indeed, the common terminal pathway of oxidation for all foodstuffs.

Spermatozoon respiration is inhibited by carbon monoxide, cyanide, azide, hydroxylamine and hydrazine (all of which inhibit the cytochrome system), by malonate (which inhibits succinic dehydrogenase), and by maleate, benzoate, hydroquinone, indole, selenite, arsenite and quinone (*see* Lardy and Phillips, 1943a; Mann, 1954b, 1958). It is depressed by glucose (Lardy and Phillips, 1941a), by fluoride (Mann and Lutwak-Mann, 1948) and by phosphate (Bishop, 1954, 1955a ; Bishop and Salisbury, 1955b ; Mann and White, 1956). It is stimulated by dilution with 0·9 per cent NaCl solution or with Ringer's solution (Bishop, 1954, 1955 ; Bishop and Salisbury, 1955b) (*see* Fig. 9A.11), by sulphite (Schultze and Mahler, 1952) and by dinitrophenol (Melrose and Terner, 1951).

Other investigators of the respiratory activity of mammalian spermatozoa include Ivanov (1930, 1931, 1936), Redenz (1933), Windstosser (1935), Walton and Edwards (1938), Shergin (1939), Comstock and Green (1939), MacLeod (1939, 1941a, 1943), Shettles (1940a), Chang and Walton (1940), Winchester and Mc-Kenzie (1941b), Henle and Zittle (1941, 1942), Ross, Miller and Kurzrok (1941), D. W. Bishop (1942), Comstock, Green, Winters and Nordskog (1943), Lardy, Hansen and Phillips (1945), Lardy, Winchester and Phillips (1945), Mann (1945a), Tosic and Walton (1945, 1946, 1947, 1950), Salisbury (1946), Tosic (1947), Romijn (1947, 1950), Ghosh, Casida and Lardy (1949), Lardy, Ghosh and Plaut (1949), Maqsood (1950), Brochart (1951), Lardy and Ghosh (1952), Lardy (1953), Terner (1953), White (1953a), Bishop *et al.* (1954), Bishop and Hancock (1955), Bishop and Salisbury (1955a, b, c), Mayer (1955), Glew (1956) and Salisbury and Nakabayashi (1957).

Lipid Metabolism

As already noted, mammalian spermatozoa can, under aerobic conditions, maintain their motility and respiratory activity for an appreciable time in the absence of extracellular metabolic substrate. Lardy and his co-workers have attributed this to the oxidation of intracellular phospholipid and have ascribed great importance to this form of metabolism as a source of energy for spermatozoa while within the epididymis (Lardy and Phillips, 1941a, b, 1945 ; Lardy, Hansen and Phillips, 1945). These workers observed that the lipid-phosphorus content of washed bull spermatozoa decreased, and the acid-soluble phosphorus increased, during aerobic storage without glycolysable substrate. When glucose was added, however, the level of lipid phosphorus remained constant. They also found that respiration and motility could be supported by the addition of certain phospholipid preparations. These observations were explained by the supposition that spermatozoa can liberate fatty acid from phospholipid by hydrolysis, and obtain energy by the aerobic oxidation of fatty acid through the tricarboxylic-acid cycle. Bomstein and Steberl (1957) concluded that bull spermatozoa do not have the ability to oxidise phospholipids to any great extent, but substantial support for Lardy and Phillips' observations is provided by recent findings of Hartree and Mann (1958). Lovern, Olley, Hartree and Mann (1957) found that the predominant intracellular phospholipid of ram spermatozoa is choline-based plasmalogen (*see* Chapter 7). Hartree and Mann (1958) found that there was no degradation of this plasmalogen when spermatozoa were incubated in the presence of fructose, but without fructose there was a progressive decrease in the acyl-ester content of the spermatozoon lipid. This change, however, was not associated with any appreciable decrease in the intracellular content of either lipid phosphorous or fatty aldehyde. The mean respiratory quotient of washed ram spermatozoa was found to be 0·71. The results suggest that intracellular plasmalogen loses one molecule of fatty acid, which is then oxidised to carbon dioxide and water. There is evidence that sea-urchin spermatozoa obtain energy for motility by a similar method (Rothschild and Cleland, 1952). Since lipid is a characteristic component of mitochondria, it is probable that the intracellular food reserves of spermatozoa are situated within the mitochondria in the mid-piece.

Preliminary observations of Lovelock and Bishop (1958) suggest that spermatozoa may also be able to synthesise lipid. These workers found that bull spermatozoa *in vitro* can incorporate methyl-^{14}C-acetate into their lipid fatty acids.

Glycerol Metabolism

Humphrey and Mann (1949) and Mann (1954a) concluded that glycerol was not oxidised by bull and ram spermatozoa. White, Blackshaw and Emmens (1954), however, found that glycerol increased both the oxygen consumption and the lactic-acid production of washed bull and ram spermatozoa, although no such effect occured in the presence of fructose. Subsequently, O'Dell, Flipse and Almquist (1956) showed that glycerol-1-^{14}C entered bull spermatozoa and, under anaerobic (*sic*) conditions, was oxidised by washed cells to ^{14}C-carbon dioxide. No radioactive carbon dioxide was produced in the presence of seminal plasma. These observations were extended by Mann and White (1956, 1957) and White (1957), who found that glycerol was actively metabolised by washed bull and ram spermatozoa under aerobic conditions, but not under anaerobic conditions. Glycerol had no appreciable effect on the anaerobic utilisation of fructose, but did have a sparing effect on the aerobic breakdown of fructose. Dihydroxyacetone had similar effects on metabolism to those produced by glycerol, and α- and β-phosphoglycerols also supported spermatozoon respiration. These observations suggest that glycerol is metabolised by conversion to dihydroxyacetone-phosphate via phosphoglycerol and that dihydroxyacetone-phosphate enters the glycolytic system by conversion to D-glyceraldehyde-3-phosphate (*see* Fig. 9A.6). This is then degraded to pyruvate and lactic acid, which can be further oxidised through the tricarboxylic-acid cycle. More work is required, however, before the pathway of glycerol metabolism can be described with certainty.

Mann and White also observed that sorbitol was oxidised by washed spermatozoa and that this was accompanied by increased oxygen uptake and the formation of lactic acid and fructose. They could find no indication that inositol, mannitol, dulcitol, erythritol or glycerylphosphorylcholine could be metabolised by spermatozoa. Recently, the metabolism of sorbitol has been further investigated by King and Mann (1958).

Amino-acid Metabolism

Tosic and Walton observed that bull spermatozoa in the presence of oxygen can oxidatively deaminate certain L-amino acids (L-tryptophane, L-phenylalanine and L-tyrosine) with the formation of ammonia and hydrogen peroxide, but, so far as is known, this mechanism plays no important role in the physiology of the spermatozoon (Tosic and Walton, 1945, 1946, 1947, 1950; Tosic, 1947, 1951). Hydrogen peroxide is very toxic to spermatozoa *in vitro* on account of their lack of catalase (*see* Chapter 7): its formation by spermatozoa was first postulated by MacLeod (1943) and further evidence of its evolution and toxic effects has been obtained by VanDemark, Salisbury and Bratton (1949) and by Bishop and Salisbury (1955c).

Roy and Bishop observed that relatively large amounts of glycine had a beneficial effect on the survival of bull, boar and stallion spermatozoa, but they were unable to show that glycine was metabolised (Roy and Bishop, 1954; Bishop, 1954; Roy, 1955). Ahmed (1955) made similar observations with ram spermatozoa. Subsequently, Flipse (1956) and Flipse and Benson (1957) showed that ^{14}C-glycine was catabolised by washed bull spermatozoa to formate and carbon dioxide. The significance of these observations is not clear. As yet, there is no indication that spermatozoa can obtain energy by the degradation of amino acids although it is well known that many other organisms can oxidise amino acids through the tricarboxylic-acid cycle.

Bhargava (1957) and Bhargava, Bishop and Work (1959) found that bull spermatozoa *in vitro* can incorporate small amounts of mixed ^{14}C-amino acids into their proteins. The significance of this finding is unknown, but it is of especial interest in view of the vital role that ribonucleic acid is believed to play in protein synthesis (*see* Brachet, 1955; Gale, 1956; Speigelman, 1956) and the virtual absence of ribonucleic acid from spermatozoa (*see* Chapter 7). Spermatozoa do, of course, contain deoxyribonucleic acid, but this is believed to be metabolically inert on account of its highly condensed state.

Creatine-phosphate Synthesis

In many cells, ATP reacts with creatine to form creatine phosphate which acts as a store of readily available high-energy phosphate bonds. Torres (1935) claims that bull spermatozoa are capable of this synthesis, but this was refuted by Ivanov (1937) and the question remains open.

Reduction of Methylene Blue

Methylene blue, by acting as a hydrogen acceptor in oxidations catalysed by dehydrogenases, becomes reduced to its colourless leucoform and thereby serves as a simple colour indicator of dehydrogenase activity (Michaelis, 1930; Thunberg, 1936; Umbreit, Burris and Stauffer, 1949). This technique has been applied to studies on mammalian semen by Lardy and Phillips (1941a), Klein and Saroka (1941), Sørensen (1942), Beck and Salisbury (1943), VanDemark, Mercier and Salisbury (1945), Bönner (1947), Milovanov and Sokolovskaya (1947), Brochart (1948), Rottensten (1950), Roy *et al.* (1950), Branton, James, Patrick and Newsom (1951), Buckner, Willett and Bayley

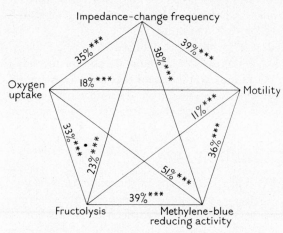

Fig. 9A.4—Interrelationships of measures of impedance-change frequency, spermatozoon motility, methylene-blue reducing activity, fructolysis and oxygen uptake, in bull semen. All relationships are positive and highly significant (*** indicates p < 0·001). The percentage figures indicate the amount of variation in a characteristic that can be explained by variation in the related characteristic; they are calculated as 100r^2, where r is the correlation coefficient. (From Bishop, 1955a, b.)

(1954), Bishop *et al.* (1954) and Bishop (1955a, b). Other workers have used the dye resazurin for the same purpose (Erb and Ehlers, 1950; Erb, Ehlers, Mikota and Schwartz, 1950; Erb, Ehlers and Flerchinger, 1952; Erb, Flerchinger, Ehlers and Mikota, 1955).

Sørensen (1942) demonstrated that the methylene-blue reducing activity of semen was associated with the spermatozoa and not with the seminal plasma. It is directly related to respiratory activity and to glycolytic activity (Fig. 9A.4). It is depressed by glucose and lactate and stimulated by succinate (Lardy and Phillips, 1941c).

Heat Production

The anaerobic heat production of bull spermatozoa has been studied by Bertaud and Probine (1956) and by Clarke and Rothschild (1957). The latter authors state that the anaerobic heat production of 10^9 living spermatozoa in undiluted semen during one hour at $37°C$. is about 220 microcalories—an observation consistent with the supposition that anaerobic heat production is associated with the breakdown of fructose to lactic acid. During the second hour of incubation, however, the heat production (about half that of the first hour) was sometimes greater than that expected from fructolysis. There was also suggestive evidence that heat production continued after spermatozoon motility had ceased.

Enzymes and Co-enzymes

The presence of ATP in spermatozoa was suggested by Lardy and Phillips (1945b) and Lardy, Hansen and Phillips (1945), and confirmed by Mann (1945a, c) and Ivanov, Kassavina and Fomenko (1946). Diphosphopyridinenucleotide (DPN) was demonstrated by Winberg (1941), the cytochromes by MacLeod (1943) and Mann (1945a, c, 1951), and various enzymes of the glycolytic system by Mann (1945b). The distribution of adenosinetriphosphatase, succinic dehydrogenase and cytochrome oxidase has been studied by Nelson (1954, 1955, 1958).

The metabolic enzymes appear to be all contained within the spermatozoon tail. From knowledge of the distribution of enzyme systems generally, it may be concluded that the respiratory enzymes are probably confined to the mitochondria (i.e. to the mid-piece region of the tail : *see* Chapter 7), but the glycolytic enzymes may be more widely distributed throughout the tail. The large surface area of the tail will greatly facilitate the transfer of metabolites between the cell and its environment, but there is no evidence to support the often-stated belief that the intact membrane is actually more permeable than that of other kinds of cell.

Metabolism and Cell Function

It has been shown above that mammalian spermatozoa can metabolise a variety of exogenous substrates, and some endogenous ones, and convert a large part of the free energy liberated into high-energy phosphate bonds. The synthesis of these bonds is the only effective means known whereby the cell can couple the production of energy with its utilisation. Without this synthesis, the liberation of energy from metabolic substrates is of little biological significance.

Metabolism for motility

Much of the energy trapped by the spermatozoon in the form of high-energy bonds is undoubtedly used for motility. The precise nature of the contractile material of the spermatozoon tail and the manner in which it uses energy are unknown, but, superficially at least, the parallel between this system and that of muscle contraction is striking. Accordingly, it is supposed that energy obtained by the hydrolysis of ATP is transferred to an actomysin-like substance in the contractile filaments of the spermatozoon tail and that this energy transfer brings about changes in the molecular arrangement of the actomysin-like substance that result in contraction. Certainly, the pivotal role that ATP plays in spermatozoon motility can hardly be doubted. Mann (1945a, b, c) found that a fall in the ATP content of spermatozoa was invariably accompanied by a fall in their motility. D. W. Bishop (1958) observed that ATP induced vigorous rhythmic lashing movements in the tails of glycerol-extracted spermatozoa, although there was no propagation of organised waves of contraction along the tail and no significant forward progression. Nelson (1958) obtained histochemical evidence that an enzyme capable of specifically dephosphorylating ATP is present on those filaments of the tail that are believed to have a contractile function (*see* Chapter 7). There is evidence that the rate of metabolism in mammalian spermatozoa is usually related to their degree of motility (Bishop *et al.*, 1954 ; Bishop and Hancock, 1955 ; Bishop, 1955a, b; Fig. 9A.4) but it is also known that this relationship is not an invariable one. Spermatozoa treated with certain detergents will, for example, respire actively in the presence of succinate but remain quite immotile (Koefoed-Johnsen and Mann, 1954). Similarly, spermatozoa treated with 0·02 N sodium fluoride exhibit a considerable, though reduced, rate of oxygen uptake even though motility is abolished (Mann and Lutwak-Mann, 1948). (It should be noted that this experiment does not indicate that energy for motility is obtainable only from glycolysis, since fluoride, under the conditions used, is not a specific inhibitor of enolase.) Evidently, under these conditions, either the degradation of metabolic substrate is dissociated from the normal production of high-energy bonds, or else the mechanism by which energy is transferred from these bonds to the motor apparatus, is disrupted. Lardy and Phillips (1941c) believe that spermatozoa can retain their motility for a short time when both glycolysis and respiration are simultaneously blocked by inhibitors, but this requires critical re-evaluation.

Metabolism for maintenance

Some of the energy trapped by the spermatozoon must be used to maintain the integrity of the cell against losses caused by diffusion and other physical processes, and this part may well be much greater than is generally appreciated. Rothschild (1953a) believes that the energy available from fructolysis is greatly in excess of that required for motility. Unfortunately, no technique for measuring the " basal or resting metabolism " of spermatozoa has yet been devised. Suggestive evidence that spermatozoa may be capable of repairing the damage of wear and tear to a greater extent than is usually supposed is provided by recent studies on protein and lipid synthesis in bull spermatozoa (Bhargava, 1957 ; Bhargava *et al.*, 1959 ; Lovelock and Bishop, 1958). The synthetic abilities of the spermatozoon are, however, likely to be severely limited by its lack of ribonucleic acid and by the apparent metabolic inactivity of its deoxyribonucleic acid (*see* Chapter 7). It is unlikely, for example, that spermatozoa can synthesise highly specific materials, such as enzymes, since it is generally believed that the specifications for such syntheses are contained within nucleic acids and that synthesis cannot proceed without the active participation of nucleic acids. The synthetic requirements of spermatozoa are, of course, much less than those of most other cells since spermatozoa neither grow, divide nor secrete.

Relative importance of glycolysis and respiration

The observations of Redenz (1930, 1933), Ivanov (1931) and others, that mammalian spermatozoa can remain active when deprived of oxygen, together with the demonstration of glycolysable substrate in seminal plasma, has led to the widespread opinion that the catabolic metabolism of these cells is primarily glycolytic. MacLeod (1943, 1946) believes that the metabolism of human spermatozoa is almost entirely glycolytic, even though they possess a cytochrome system.

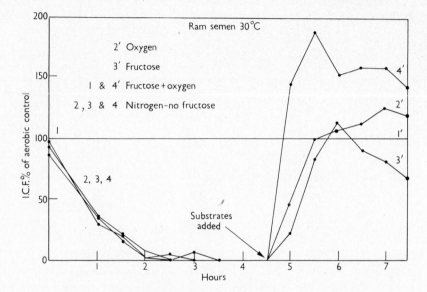

Fig. 9A.5—The effect of oxygen and fructose on the motility of ram spermatozoa. Motility was measured as impedance-change frequency (I.C.F.) and is plotted relative to motility in the control sample, in which oxygen and fructose were both continuously present. (From Walton and Dott, 1956.)

Tyler (1955) states " it is now well established that mammalian sperm have a predominantly glycolytic metabolism even under aerobic conditions, and that the substrate is a reducing sugar present in the seminal fluid." Mann (1954a) states that it is " an established fact that the metabolism of spermatozoa in several mammalian species, including man, ram and bull, is predominantly of a glycolytic character," although he concedes that " lactic acid can be efficiently oxidised by spermatozoa even when the partial pressure of oxygen has been reduced to a level as low as that which normally prevails in animal tissues." Rothschild (1953a) suggests that " the aerobic metabolism of mammalian spermatozoa is unimportant for provision of energy for movement " and that respiration functions mainly as " a mopping-up process which, by continuously removing lactate, keeps the environment from becoming too acid." It is inherently unlikely, however, that the large amounts of energy derived from respiration, at least ten to fifteen times more than that available from glycolysis, will be simply dissipated from the cell.

This view is supported by the observed depressive effect that oxygen has on gly-colysis (i.e. the Pasteur effect), for, if useful energy is obtained from respiration, the energy requirement from glycolysis will be reduced. Further, Bishop and his associates obtained evidence that the rate of oxygen consumption by bull sperm-atozoa is more closely related to their motility than is the rate of fructolysis

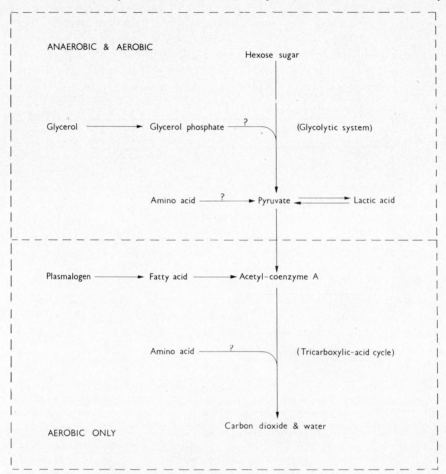

Fig. 9*A*.6—Diagrammatic summary of the probable metabolic pathways available to mammalian spermatozoa for the provision of energy. The main chain of events is indicated by the vertical line joining hexose sugar with carbon dioxide and water. Glycolysis can take place under both anaerobic and aerobic conditions. The tricar-boxylic-acid cycle can only operate under aerobic conditions and when it is functioning it depresses glycolysis. The oxidation of fatty acid probably only occurs in the absence of pyruvate. The precise manner of glycerol oxidation is not definitely known. The indicated role of amino acids is speculative and based on knowledge obtained from other biological systems.

(Bishop *et al.*, 1954; Bishop and Hancock, 1955; Bishop, 1955a, b). These workers also found that measures of the rates of fructolysis, methylene-blue reducing activity and oxygen uptake were highly significantly interrelated, even though these three kinds of measurement were each made under different experi-mental conditions (Fig. 9*A*.4). The problem was tackled more directly by Walton and Dott (1956), who were able to show that motility was greater with oxygen and no glycolysable substrate than it was with glycolysable substrate without oxygen. Maximum motility, however, was achieved when both oxygen and glycolysable substrate were present together. In the absence of both factors, the spermatozoa were quickly immobilised, but regained their motility when either fructose or oxygen was admitted (*see* Fig. 9A,5).

The available evidence on spermatozoon metabolism, together with that on cell metabolism in general, suggests that the various catabolic pathways available to the spermatozoon are best regarded as part of a common metabolic system (*see* Fig. 9A,6). These pathways combine in a complex manner and have as a common function the synthesis of high-energy phosphate bonds. The factors that control metabolism and decide which pathways shall have priority are poorly understood (*see* Krebs, Kornberg and Burton, 1957; Krebs, 1957), but two of the main considerations are likely to be the availability of substrate and the requirement for energy. This control is, of course, also influenced by environmental conditions (*see* Section III). There is evidence that the precise nature of metabolism varies somewhat between species (Dott, 1958). In some, glycolysis may perhaps predominate, but, in most, there seems no reason to doubt that respiration is the principal source of energy for the spermatozoon whenever oxygen is available.

In animals with external fertilisation in the sea or in fresh water, it is probable that energy for spermatozoon motility can only be obtained by the aerobic oxidation of intracellular lipids (*see* p. 270). In these circumstances, only endogenous substrates are available for metabolism, and whereas spermatozoa appear to possess no reserves of metabolisable carbohydrate they do contain large amounts of lipid (*see* Chapter 7). Lipids, furthermore, are known to provide highly concentrated sources of energy. It appears, therefore, that the aerobic degradation of intracellular lipid is the primitive form of catabolism in spermatozoa and that the extensive utilisation of extracellular substrate by mammalian spermatozoa represents a later adaptation to internal fertilisation.

Metabolism within the female reproductive tract

The nature of spermatozoon metabolism within the female genital tract can at present only be deduced from observations made *in vitro* considered in conjunction with the limited information that is available about the conditions within the tract.

Immediately following ejaculation, the spermatozoa, already suspended in the seminal plasma, are further diluted by admixture with the secretions of the female tract. The proportionate contribution made by the seminal plasma varies widely between different species. Its contribution to the total environment will depend upon its volume, its distribution throughout the tract, the rate of its absorption from the tract and the abundance of the female secretions. In animals such as the pig, a large volume of semen with a low concentration of spermatozoa is injected directly into the uterus at mating (*see* Chapter 8). There is no evidence, however, that seminal plasma enters the Fallopian tubes, and even within the uterus it appears to be rather rapidly removed (Mann, Polge and Rowson, 1956). In other animals, such as cattle, sheep and man, a small volume of much more concentrated semen is deposited in the vagina and most of it appears to remain there. In the oestrous rabbit, there is a considerable flow of fluid down the Fallopian tube into the uterus (D. W. Bishop, 1956c). In the oestrous rat, the uterus is often distended with accumulated fluid which will greatly dilute constituents of the semen that enter the uterus (Warren, 1938 ; Leonard, 1950). In the cow, vaginal discharge during oestrous is said to amount to over 100 ml. (Masuda, Quishi and Kudo, 1951). The evidence suggests, therefore, that the influence of the seminal plasma upon spermatozoon metabolism in the female tract is likely to be limited to the site of deposition of the semen for a rather short period following ejaculation. It is at this time, of course, that the spermatozoa exist together at their greatest concentration and will be most demanding of metabolic substrates. The spermatozoa destined to be available for fertilisation appear to be rather rapidly dispersed throughout the upper regions of the tract, where the influence of the seminal plasma is likely to be negligible.

Much of the available information on conditions in the female genital tract has been summarised by Olds and VanDemark (1957a) and the general physiology of spermatozoa within this environment has been recently discussed by Austin and Bishop (1957). Glucose is a known constituent of cervical mucus in women at the time of ovulation (*see* Breckenridge and Pommerenke, 1951 ; Doyle, 1958), and glycolysis may therefore play an important role in enabling spermatozoa to penetrate this mucus. Olds and VanDemark (1957b) also found considerable amounts of reducing sugar in fluids from the uterus and oviduct of the cow. On the other hand, Campbell (1932) found that the partial pressure of oxygen within the rabbit uterus is comparable to that in many other tissues of the body (20–45 mm. Hg.) and similar observations have been made by D. W. Bishop (1956a). Oxygen tensions of this order should be adequate to support spermatozoon respiration. D. W. Bishop (1956b) also observed that lactate was present in the oviduct fluids of the rabbit, but glucose appeared to be absent. Bovine follicular fluid, which may contribute to the environment of the Fallopian tubes at the time of fertilisation, contains glucose and lactate (Lutwak-Mann, 1954). It is also known to contain oestrogen. Olds and VanDemark (1957c) observed that both glycolysis and respiration proceed actively *in vitro* in bull spermatozoa suspended in diluted fluids from the reproductive tract of the cow. From these considerations and those given earlier, it may be concluded that spermatozoa within the female tract probably obtain energy by both glycolysis and respiration. It is unlikely that the aerobic production of hydrogen peroxide by spermatozoa will inhibit their metabolism within the female tract on account of the presence of catalase in the endometrial mucosa.

Metabolism within the male reproductive tract

The nature of spermatozoon metabolism within the male reproductive tract is much more difficult to account for (*see* Chapter 7). Here, metabolism appears to remain at a steady basic level in a deficiency of both glycolysable substrate and oxygen. Perhaps the limited supply of these metabolites is itself the main restraining influence on the metabolic processes. At ejaculation, the controlling influences, whatever they may be, are removed and spermatozoa respond to the changed environment by an immediate outburst of metabolic activity (*see* Chapter 7). In most instances, this activation irrevocably directs the physiology of the spermatozoon into a path of rather rapid exhaustion. In some bats, however, there is evidence that activation can be reversed within the female genital tract and, in bull spermatozoa, reversal can be readily achieved *in vitro* by the storage of spermatozoa at low temperatures (*see* Chapter 9).

Relationships between metabolism and fertility

Many attempts have been made to relate the metabolic activity of spermatozoa to their fertility in the hope of establishing criteria that would be of value in assessing the fertility of males. Bishop *et al.* (1954), Bishop and Hancock (1955) and Bishop (1955a, b) obtained significant relationships between certain measures of the metabolic activity of bull semen and the fertility of the samples examined, but these relationships were not very close (i.e. the correlation coefficients were low ; *see* Fig. 9A.7). Similar results have been obtained by other workers (*see* Emmens and Blackshaw, 1956). The reasons for this lack of correspondence between metabolism and fertility become apparent when the complex nature of fertilisation is considered. Measures of metabolism provide information on the

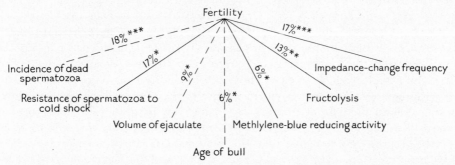

Fig. 9A.7—Relationships of various characteristics of bull semen, and of age of bull, to fertility. Broken lines indicate negative correlations ; unbroken lines indicate positive correlations * indicates p < 0·05 ; ** indicates p < 0·01 ; *** indicates p < 0·001 ; the percentage figures indicate the closeness of the relationships and are calculated as $100r^2$ where r is the correlation coefficient. (From Bishop and Hancock, 1955.)

ability of spermatozoa to degrade certain metabolic substrates. Within limits, they also supply information on the motility of spermatozoa. They probably provide little information on the ability of spermatozoa to enter eggs, or on the ability of spermatozoa to activate eggs, or on the quality of the genetic material carried by the spermatozoa. Simple examples will serve to illustrate these points. In the bull, decapitate spermatozoa and spermatozoa with deformed acrosomes (*see* Chapter 7) metabolise actively, but are completely sterile. Spermatozoa in which the genetic material has been so badly damaged by X-irradiation that the successful development of penetrated eggs is prevented are actively motile and presumably, therefore, able to metabolise actively (*see* Chapter 9). Certain hyaluronidase inhibitors can prevent successful fertilisation but have little effect on spermatozoon motility (*see* Chapter 9). A further serious limitation to the value of metabolic measurements for the prediction of fertility arises from the fact that such measurements provide only average values for large numbers of spermatozoa. They furnish no information on the metabolic performances of individual spermatozoa or on the frequency distribution of such performances throughout the population.

II. MOTILITY

The structure of the spermatozoon tail and the probable mechanism by which it beats have already been discussed in Chapter 7, and the methods whereby spermatozoa obtain energy for motility are described in the preceding Section. The present Section deals with the characteristics of spermatozoon movement, with the methods that can be used to obtain measures of this movement, and with the significance of movement.

The Method of Swimming

Spermatozoa swim by the rhythmic propagation of transverse waves of bending in the tail. These waves originate at or near the anterior end of the tail and pass distally to its tip. In so doing they exert pressure on the surrounding medium and the cell is propelled forwards. The mechanics of this kind of movement have been discussed at length by Taylor (1951, 1952a, b), Rothschild (1953a), Hancock (1953), Gray and Hancock (1955), Gray (1955, 1958) and Rikmenspoel (1957).

Characteristics of the bending movements of the tail have been carefully studied in bull spermatozoa by Gray (1958). These movements occur in a plane coincident with the transverse plane of the head (*see also* Walton, 1952). The maximum extent to which an element of the tail bends during its contractile cycle, the amplitude of transverse movement relative to the head, and the angle at which the tail crosses the axis of propulsion, all increase progressively along the tail towards the distal end. The length and speed of propagation of the bending wave decrease progressively along the tail. In Gray's experiments, the average frequency of the bending cycles at $37°$C. was $9 \cdot 1$ per second, and the average forward movement with each contractile cycle was $8 \cdot 3\mu$.

During swimming, the front end of the cell acts as a fulcrum, against which the tail exerts its propulsive effort. As the waves of bending are propagated, the head is displaced laterally, and, during the bending cycle, oscillates from side to side. It also tends to rotate somewhat about the long axis of the cell and this gives rise to a characteristic " flashing effect " when seen under dark-ground illumination. These movements of the head have suggested to some investigators that the path of progression of the spermatozoon is in the form of a narrow helix, but it seems likely that this interpretation is erroneous.

Spermatozoon tails that have become detached from the head often display active motility (*see* Chapter 7), but their speed of progression does not appear to be greater than that of intact spermatozoa (Gray, 1958). Kihlström (1952) believes that the heads of bull spermatozoa are capable of slight independent movement, but this seems very unlikely and the observation has not been confirmed.

In view of the localisation of mitochondria in the anterior region of the tail (*see* Chapter 7) the problem of whether or not active bending is restricted to this region is one of considerable interest. Gray (1955), discussing the question of where energy is applied to the tail of the sea-urchin spermatozoon, concludes that " all the evidence strongly suggests that the tail of a spermatozoon cannot be regarded as a passive rod oscillated by a localised source of power. The concept of sources of energy distributed along the whole tail—or at any rate the greater part of it—seems inescapable. At the same time, it is probably going too far to maintain that the passive elastic properties of the tail play no part in the mechanism of movement." It seems likely that these conclusions are valid for the spermatozoa of mammals also.

Wave-motion

A characteristic feature of dense suspensions of highly active spermatozoa is " wave-motion." This is the term commonly used to describe the swirling bands or waves of increased opacity that may be seen in semen when examined with a microscope (Fig. 9A.8) and which are apparent to the naked eye as a moving mottled pattern. Wave-motion is seen most frequently in the dense semen of the ram and bull, but it can also be observed in semen of the boar, stallion and other animals after concentration by centrifugation. Its discovery appears to be of some antiquity, for Blumenbach, commenting in 1792 on Hooke's demonstration

Fig. 9A.8—Wave-motion in bull semen. (From Blom, 1946.)

to King Charles II, states that the King commanded the spermatozoa to be presented to him swimming and frisking in their native fluid, when, " in the semen of the ram they beheld them moving in a troop with great gravity like a flock of sheep " (Cole, 1930).

The nature of wave-motion has been investigated by Walton (1952), who points out that suspensions of small rod-shaped bodies are readily orientated by flow currents, and, even when at rest, do not exist in a state of random disorder, since the orientation of any one body will tend to influence the orientation of those adjacent to it. The resting pattern of arrangement is called a " short-range order " (Fig. 9A.9). Such an order can be detected in dense suspensions of immotile spermatozoa and flow orientation can be readily produced by stirring such suspensions or by propelling them through narrow passages. When strongly orientated by flow, suspensions of spermatozoa exhibit marked optical and electrical anisotropy—the former being readily apparent as birefringence in ordinary light, and the latter as differences of electrical conductivity dependent upon the direction of orientation of the cells. In dense suspensions of actively motile spermatozoa, flow currents set up by moving spermatozoa will strengthen the resting order of arrangement, and Walton suggests that this results in the formation of moving streams of spermatozoa with a common orientation. These streams will themselves induce flow orientation and thereby increase in size. They will move through the suspension until they meet opposing streams, and the interplay of the various streams, with their associated optical effects, would constitute wave-motion. A further point of relevance is the observation that in some species the tails of closely adjacent spermatozoa have a tendency to wave in unison. Taylor (1951) gives evidence showing that this is caused by a reaction, due to viscous stress in the fluid between the tails, that tends to force the two waves into phase. This will further assist the arrangement of spermatozoa into orderly groups moving in a common direction. Rothschild (1949a) believes that wave-motion represents " a periodic aggregation of spermatozoa, the tails of which

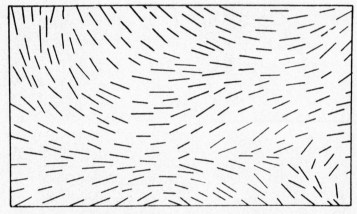

Fig. 94.9—Diagram illustrating short-range order of rod-shaped particles. (From Kratky, 1934.)

probably beat synchronously in the aggregations." This implies that wave-motion is associated with changes in the concentration of spermatozoa. Walton (1952) suggests that the optical effects of wave-motion are caused by anisotropy rather than by differences in concentration, but he also points out that highly orientated spermatozoa may possibly become more closely packed than those moving in a more random manner. Blom (1946) observed that dead spermatozoa in semen samples displaying wave-motion tend to accumulate in strands, and suggested that obstruction to free movement caused by these strands was the primary mechanism for orientating spermatozoa during the generation of wave-motion. Walton, however, believes that the segregation of dead cells is a consequence of wave-motion and not a cause of it.

Impedance-change Frequency

Samples of semen showing active wave-motion also exhibit well defined cyclic changes in electrical impedance, the frequency of which is directly related to the degree of spermatozoon motility as judged by examination of the undiluted semen with a microscope (Rothschild, 1948, 1949b, 1950). The amplitude of impedance change is directly related to the concentration of spermatozoa in the semen and such changes cannot easily be detected in concentrations of less than 400 million cells per ml. No spontaneous changes are shown in inactive semen. Walton (1952) has demonstrated experimentally a relationship between spermatozoon orientation and impedance change, and there is little doubt that impedance-change frequency in semen is directly associated with the changes in arrangement (and perhaps also of concentration) of spermatozoa that constitute wave-motion. Walton observed that impedance-change can be induced in concentrated suspensions of tobacco mosaic virus by flow orientation, and occurs spontaneously in concentrated suspensions of *Glaucoma pyriformis*, an elongate ciliate.

Bishop and associates found that impedance-change frequency in bull semen was directly related to visual estimates of motility, to the proportion and concentration of living spermatozoa present, to rates of fructolysis, oxygen uptake and methylene-blue reduction (Fig. 9A.4), and to the resistance of spermatozoa to cold shock (Bishop *et al.*, 1954; Bishop and Hancock, 1955; Bishop, 1955a, b; Bishop and Campbell, 1959). These results show that measures of impedance-change frequency provide measures of the physical and metabolic activity in unit volumes of semen, and that this activity depends upon the number of living spermatozoa present and their degree of activity. Cummings (1954) has also examined impedance-change frequency in bull semen, and Walton and Dott (1956) have shown that impedance-change frequency in ram semen is supported by both glycolytic and respiratory metabolism (Fig. 9A.5).

Rheotaxis and Chemotaxis

It has been shown above that spermatozoa readily become orientated in flow currents. Since the spermatozoon consists of a long narrow tail with a relatively wide head attached at one end, the resistance of the head to displacement by flow will be greater than that of the tail. Spermatozoa situated in a flow stream will therefore tend to rotate about the head until they become aligned along the direction of flow with the head pointing upstream. These considerations apply both to immotile spermatozoa and to motile ones. In consequence, motile spermatozoa show a distinct tendency to swim against the current—a form of behaviour referred to as positive rheotaxis. Rheotaxis in spermatozoa has been observed by many workers, but the simple mechanical basis of this phenomenon has not been generally appreciated.

In his studies on rheotaxis, Adolphi (1905) concluded that the rate of progression of spermatozoa, relative to the current, was independent of the velocity of the current. Yamane and Ito (1932), however, claim that the velocity of movement of stallion spermatozoa, relative to the current, increases with the velocity of flow up to a maximum of about 200μ per second. This maximum was about twice the velocity of movement in a still medium. It seems possible that these findings arose from errors of observation, for, if a current is caused to flow through a suspension of spermatozoa under observation with a microscope, only those cells that are sufficiently active to stem the current will remain within the field of view. This selection will increase with increasing velocity of current until only the most active spermatozoa remain. On the other hand, when spermatozoa are orientated and moving in the same direction, interference between cells may be greatly reduced and an increase in absolute velocity of movement for the same expenditure of energy may result. Taylor (1951) has indeed postulated that when the tails of neighbouring spermatozoa are in phase, very much less energy is dissipated in the fluid between them than when the waves are in opposite phase.

It has often been suggested that the direction in which spermatozoa swim may be influenced by chemical gradients—a form of behaviour known as chemotaxis. Striking examples of chemotaxis are shown by the spermatozoids of some lower plants (Cook, 1945 ; Hawker, 1951 ; Rothschild, 1951a, 1952 ; Brokaw, 1958a, b) but as yet there is no conclusive evidence that chemotaxis is ever exhibited by the spermatozoa of animals (Buller, 1903 ; Tyler, 1955 ; Rothschild, 1956).

Measurement of Motility

In studies on the physiology of spermatozoa, motility is an easily detected and meaningful characteristic, but its precise measurement presents great difficulties. It is, of course, easy to examine a drop of a suspension of spermatozoa with a microscope and express an opinion on its degree of activity. Impressions thus obtained can be recorded by allocating to them numerical values from some arbitrarily chosen scale of grades of activity, but it is impossible to obtain strictly quantitative and objective measures of motility in this way. The problem is made more difficult by the heterogeneity that exists in any sample. Inactive cells are usually present even in freshly collected samples, and among the active cells there may be many different degrees of activity. With time, both the number of active cells and their degree of activity decrease exponentially. Despite these difficulties, however, careful and experienced investigators can obtain useful and reproduceable results by methods of this kind (for example, see Emmens, 1947, 1948 ; Blackshaw and Emmens, 1951).

Methods of assessing the activity of spermatozoa by visual inspection can be broadly classified into two groups : those in which attention is directed to the general mass effect of motility in concentrated suspensions of cells, and those in which attention is directed to the movements of individual spermatozoa in dilute suspensions. Methods belonging to the first group employ a minimum of experimental manipulation, and artefacts can be more easily avoided, but they lack sensitivity and are of limited value. They are extensively used in the United Kingdom for evaluating the quality of bull semen before use for artificial insemination—active wave-motion usually being considered an essential characteristic of suitable samples. Methods belonging to the second group can be adapted to give more detailed information on the manner in which individual spermatozoa contribute to the total activity. Bishop and Salisbury (1955a), for example, describe a method in which the proportion of motile cells and their degree of activity are estimated separately—the former as a percentage of total cells, and the latter as a rating on an arbitrarily chosen 0–4 scale of activity. Crude frequency distributions of activity within a sample can be obtained in this way. Bishop and Salisbury expressed total activity within a sample as the product of the estimate of proportion and the estimate of activity (or as the sum of such products when more than one category of activity within the sample is assessed separately), the maximum rating of total activity being 400 (i.e. 100 per cent of cells with an activity rating of 4). Estimates of this kind can be supplemented by the use of simple, but more strictly quantitative techniques. The proportion of motile cells can be determined more accurately by counting the number that are immotile and comparing it with counts of the total number of cells after fixation in osmic acid vapour (Brady and Gildow, 1939 ; Harvey, 1945 ; Lasley, 1951 ; Bane, 1952). The proportion of cells that are actually dead can be determined fairly accurately by the use of differential staining techniques (*see* Chapter 7). The velocity of movement of individual spermatozoa can be measured directly as the time required for cells to move across a given distance. The simplest method of doing this is by use of a microscope with an eyepiece micrometer. This method has the disadvantage that measurements can only be made on relatively few spermatozoa within a reasonable time, and those selected for measurement may not be representative of the population as a whole. Moeller and VanDemark (1955) studied the speed of movement of bull spermatozoa in this way : they obtained a mean speed of 114 μ per second with a range of 10 to 352 μ per second. Some results by earlier workers, taken from Bonnadonna (1946) without critical examination of the conditions under which measurements were made, are given in Table I.

TABLE I

RATE OF MOVEMENT OF SPERMATOZOA
(From Bonadonna, 1946)

Species	Rate of movement (μ/sec.)	Authority
Fowl	17	Adolphi
Cavy	60	,,
Pigeon	20	Milovanov
Rabbit	18–33	,,
Rat	71	,,
Ram	50	,,
Bull	67	,,
Dog	43	,,
Stallion	87	Yamane and Ito
Man	33–50	Tigersted

Other workers have measured the rate of movement of spermatozoa along capillary tubes (Grave and Downing, 1928 ; Yamane and Ito, 1932 ; Phillips and Andrews, 1937), and similar methods have been used to measure the rate of penetration of human spermatozoa into cervical mucus (Lamar, Shettles and Delfs, 1940 ; Harvey and Jackson, 1948).

Methods devised to give more objective measures of motility can also be divided into those that give measures of total activity within a sample and those that give information on the motility characteristics of individual spermatozoa. Two methods fall into the first category. The first of these is measurement of impedance-change frequency (*see* p. 282). This provides, with much greater sensitivity and objectivity, the same kind of information as that obtainable by the first of the visual inspection methods described above (Bishop *et al.*, 1954). It is usually recorded in terms of visual counts of movements of a trace on an oscilloscope screen, but photographic recorders or pen recorders can be used if required.

Measurement of impedance-change frequency can only be made on dense suspensions of spermatozoa : objective measures of total activity in much more dilute suspensions (though not in very dilute ones) can be made by means of the second method in this category. This will be termed " optical measurement of relaxation time." It involves optical measurement of the time required for flow-orientated suspensions of spermatozoa to return to the degree of disorientation that was present before the orientating force was applied. This measurement is directly related to the degree of total activity in the suspension (Walton, 1952).

Very accurate measurements of the rate and direction of movement in individual spermatozoa in dilute suspensions can be obtained by the use of photomicrography. In the " dark-ground-track " method, a suspension of spermatozoa is illuminated with a dark-ground condenser and a photographic plate is exposed for a known time above the suspension. Since the spermatozoon head scatters more light than the tail, a light track corresponding to the progress of the head is recorded on the photographic plate. The length of this track divided by the exposure time gives the speed of movement (Rothschild and Swann, 1949 ; Rothschild, 1951b, 1953a). Other workers have followed the movements of spermatozoa by high-speed cinematography (Schlenk and Kahmann, 1938 ; Rothschild, 1950, 1953b, c ; Rikmenspoel, 1957 ; Gray, 1958). This method can provide detailed information on the frequency distribution of speeds of movement throughout the population. It is, however, extremely laborious, since, in addition to the photographic work involved, it entails plotting the movements of large numbers of individual spermatozoa through successive frames of film, and measuring the distances travelled by each over known time intervals. The mean speed of movement can, however, be determined from cinematograph records by merely counting the number of spermatozoa in an area of known size in consecutive photographs (Rothschild, 1953b, c). This method depends upon a phenomenon known in mathematics as the " probability-after-effect " (*see* Chandrasehkar, 1943). Rothschild (1953c) made a cinematograph record of movement in a suspension of bull spermatozoa and determined the mean speed of movement both by plotting individual movements and by the probability-after-effect method. By the first method, the mean speed of movement of motile spermatozoa was 123 μ per second with a standard deviation of 39. When immotile spermatozoa were included, the mean speed became 117 μ per second. By the second method, the mean speed of movement, including immotile spermatozoa, was 111 μ per second with a standard error of 24·5. A method developed by Baker, Cragle, Salisbury and VanDemark (1957) appears to give very similar information without resort to photography and elaborate apparatus, but has not yet been checked against other methods of measurement. It is based upon the principle that the number of free-swimming spermatozoa passing through a segment of a plane in a given time is dependent upon the dimensions of the segment, the concentration of spermatozoa in suspension, and the velocity of movement. It involves determining the frequency at which spermatozoa in a suspension of known concentration cross a line segment in a cytometer chamber. By this method, Baker *et al.* estimated the mean speed of movement in bull spermatozoa, excluding immotile cells, at 70·5 μ per second with a standard deviation of 2. An electronic apparatus designed to provide measures of spermatozoon motility with a maximum of objectivity has been described by Bosselaar and Spronk (1952) and Bosselaar, Spronk and Van

Dam (1955). In this, dark-ground images of spermatozoa are projected on to a screen, in the centre of which is a small aperture. Light signals produced by images passing across this aperture are recorded by a photomultiplier and an electronic counter. The frequency of these signals is determined by the concentration of cells and their speed of movement. Frequency distributions of spermatozoon speed of movement obtained by this method appear to be in good agreement with those determined from cinematograph records (Rikmanspoel, Van Herpen and Van Dam, 1956; Rikmenspoel, 1957) but more information is required before the utility of the method can be properly assessed. Preliminary observations with two other types of electronic equipment are described by Van-Demark, Salisbury, Moeller and Berkley (1958).

It may be concluded that there is as yet no fully satisfactory method of measuring the motility of spermatozoa, although promising techniques are under development. The main requirements of a satisfactory method are that it should be rapid and objective and provide measurements of both the rate of movement and the frequency distribution of these rates within the population. Ideally it should discriminate between normal and abnormal movement, and should be applicable to suspensions over a wide range of population densities. Finally, it should be mentioned that in any valid method of measurement, the strictest attention must be paid to the conditions to which the spermatozoa are subjected. Some of the factors that are known to affect the motility of spermatozoa are discussed in Section III.

Significance of Motility

Spermatozoa are immotile within the ductus epididymis, and motility appears to play no part in the passage of spermatozoa through the male reproductive tract (*see* Chapter 7). Within the female tract, on the other hand, spermatozoa exhibit active motility for several hours after ejaculation, and it has often been suggested that the function of motility is to enable spermatozoa to reach the ampulla of the Fallopian tube (or in some species the peri-ovarian sac or even the ovary) where the first stages of fertilisation take place. Anderson (1945), for example, states that " spermatozoa must be motile to reach the Fallopian tubes." In many species, however, spermatozoa are known to reach the upper levels of the Fallopian tubes very much more quickly than they could by their own motility and, in the cow, dead spermatozoa reach this site as rapidly as do living ones (*see* VanDemark and Hays, 1953, 1954; Austin and Bishop, 1957; Hartman, 1957). Evidently, the transport of spermatozoa from the site of deposition at coitus to the site of fertilisation is very largely brought about by muscular activity of the female reproductive tract, and the classic concept of successful spermatozoa requiring an athletic constitution to travel through the female tract becomes no longer tenable. It is very unlikely, however, that spermatozoon motility plays no important role in the events preceding fertilisation, for all the available evidence indicates that motility is essential for fertility. Probably motility assists the passage of spermatozoa through such barriers as the cervix and the utero-tubal junction, and it almost certainly plays a vital role in enabling spermatozoa to penetrate the cumulus oophorus and the zona pellucida of the egg.

To the experimentalist, motility is a characteristic of great importance because it signifies a high degree of physiological integrity in the cell, but its utility in this respect is at present severely limited by the difficulties of measurement discussed earlier in this Section. It must also be remembered that motility is by no means an indicator of complete functional competence : abnormal spermatozoa may be very motile and yet completely sterile, and normal spermatozoa are known to lose their fertility before they lose their motility (*see* Van Drimmelen and Oettlé, 1949 ; Bishop and Hancock, 1951 ; Austin and Bishop, 1957).

Bishop *et al.* (1954) found that measures of impedance-change frequency in bull semen were more closely related to fertility than were measures of spermatozoon metabolism, but the relationship obtained between impedance-change frequency and fertility was none the less not very close (*see* Fig. 9A.7). It may be concluded from this that impedance-change frequency provides a better index of functional competence than does metabolism, but that fertility is largely determined by factors that are not reflected either in differences of impedance-change frequency or in differences of metabolic activity. More precise measures of motility may well provide better indices of fertility, but the correlation between these two characteristics can never be complete for the reasons already indicated.

III. Factors that Affect Metabolism and Motility

There have been many studies on environmental factors that affect spermatozoon metabolism and motility, more especially the latter (*see* Anderson, 1945 ; Mann, 1954a), but much of this work is rather uncritical and the results of different workers frequently appear to be at variance. These studies do clearly show, however, that spermatozoa are very responsive to environmental change, although it is also true that they are remarkably tolerant of such change. This tolerance is doubtless associated with the requirements of the free-living existence that spermatozoa lead after their expulsion from the male tract. In general, conditions that stimulate metabolism appear also to increase motility, but to decrease survival time. Conditions that affect the survival and fertility of spermatozoa are discussed in Chapter 9.

For a more general treatment of the factors discussed in this Section, reference should be made to standard works on general physiology such as those of Heilbrunn (1952) and Giese (1957).

Hydrogen-ion Concentration

The optimum pH for spermatozoon motility and metabolism appears to be about $7 \cdot 5$, but the range of tolerance is remarkably wide and extends from about pH 5 to about pH 10 (Redenz, 1926 ; Gellhorn, 1931 ; Shergin, 1939 ; Cole, Waletzky and Shackleford, 1940 ; Moore and Mayer, 1941 ; Winchester and McKenzie, 1941a, b; Lardy and Phillips, 1943c; Emmens, 1947, 1948; Blackshaw and Emmens, 1951 ; Kok, 1953 ; Wales and White, 1958a). The effects of changes of pH appear to vary slightly between species, and also be to dependent upon other prevailing conditions, but, in general, spermatozoa are not nearly as sensitive to pH changes as is popularly supposed. Bishop and Salisbury (1955b) observed very active oxygen uptake and motility in bull spermatozoa at pH levels as low as $5 \cdot 62$.

A major difficulty in studying the effects of hydrogen-ion concentration is that of finding a buffer that does not itself affect cell physiology by virtue of properties other than the regulation of hydrogen-ion concentration. Phosphate buffers have been widely used on studies with mammalian spermatozoa, but these have been shown to depress respiration and motility and to encourage the accumulation of lactic acid (Bishop, 1955a, b ; Bishop and Salisbury, 1955b ; Salisbury and Nakabayashi, 1957 ; Mann and White, 1956). They also precipitate important cations, such as calcium, manganese, magnesium and ferrous ion. Citrate buffers have also been commonly employed, but these are open to objection on account of their chelating properties. Carbonate-bicarbonate buffers appear to depress motility in dog spermatozoa (Wales and White, 1958a).

Osmotic Pressure

The optimum osmotic requirements of mammalian spermatozoa approximate to isosmosity with blood plasma (freezing point about −0·55°C.). It is not generally appreciated, however, that osmotic pressures calculated from measures of freezing point or vapour pressure are theoretical pressures such as would develop against a perfect semipermeable membrane. The osmotic pressure that a solution exerts against a living cell is determined by the permeability characteristics of the living cell membrane to the substances in solution. This pressure will be inversely related to the ease with which the substances concerned pass through the cell membrane. Solutes that pass freely through the membrane can exert only transient osmotic pressures, for the cell rapidly comes into osmotic equilibrium with its environment. There is, therefore, a difference between solutions that are theoretically isosmotic among themselves and those that are actually isosmotic for a given cell. The latter are called isotonic solutions, a term that is much abused in the literature relating to the reactions of spermatozoa to osmotic conditions and often used in the incorrect sense of isosmotic with seminal plasma. Tonicity can only be measured against living cells, and

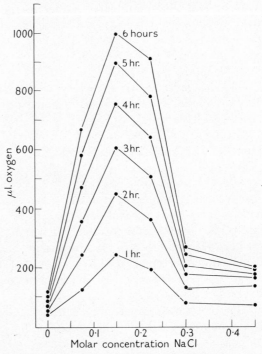

Fig. 9A.10—The effects of a 1:4 dilution with distilled water and with sodium chloride solutions of various concentration on the oxygen uptake of bull semen. (From Bishop, 1954, 1955a.)

in mammalian spermatozoa this cannot be done directly since these cells do not shrink, swell or lyse under anisosmotic conditions. The response of motility or metabolic activity can, however, be easily observed, and, in most instances, estimates of tonicity made in this way are probably satisfactory.

Fig. 9A.10 illustrates the effect of various concentrations of sodium chloride on the oxygen uptake of bull spermatozoa. In this experiment, maximum oxygen consumption occurred when the concentration of NaCl was 0·15 molar (freezing point −0·54°C.). In 0·225 molar NaCl solution, oxygen uptake was reduced to 90 per cent of its maximum value ; in 0·075 molar NaCl, it was reduced to 66 per cent ; and, in 0·3 molar NaCl, it was reduced to only 26 per cent. Motility was good in 0·15 molar NaCl, slightly less in 0·225 molar NaCl, and very poor or completely lacking in the other diluents. Evidently, 0·15 molar NaCl solution is approximately isotonic for bull spermatozoa, and both hypotonic and hypertonic solutions are associated with serious disruption of normal physiology. Mann (1958) has since shown that fructolysis by ram spermatozoa is similarly affected by hypertonic solutions of NaCl. As pointed out in the preceding paragraph, however, the effect of variation in osmotic pressure depends upon the nature of the dissolved substances that contribute to the osmotic activity. In general, electrolytes penetrate cell membranes much more slowly than do non-electrolytes and are consequently much more damaging on an equi-osmotic basis. (Electrolytes are also known to be injurious to cell membranes by virtue of properties other than their osmotic activity—see below.) The tolerance that bull spermatozoa show to high concentrations of glycine has been described by Bishop (1954), and their tolerance to high concentrations of glycerol is amply demonstrated by the numerous studies in which diluents containing considerable amounts of this solute have been used for preserving spermatozoa at sub-zero temperatures (see Chapter 9).

Other investigators of the effects of osmotic conditions on mammalian spermatozoa include Gellhorn (1920), Dubincik (1934), Milovanov (1934), Emmens (1948), Salisbury, Knodt and Bratton (1948), Swanson (1949), Pursley and Herman (1950), Blackshaw and Emmens (1951), Smith, Mayer and Herman (1953) and Wales and White (1958a).

Electrolytes

Electrolytes are simultaneously both stimulating and injurious to spermatozoa, and for this reason survival time tends to be greatest in diluents with a fairly low electrolyte : non-electrolyte ratio. A certain amount of electrolyte is necessary for normal irritability and the stimulating effect of sodium chloride can be readily demonstrated on senescent bull spermatozoa (Weber, 1938 ; Bishop and Salisbury, 1955b). In diluents containing electrolytes only, spermatozoa swim very actively at first but die rather quickly.

The precise action of any electrolyte, though not well understood, depends both upon the anion and the cation. It varies somewhat between species and is influenced by other prevailing conditions. The injuriousness of anions increases approximately in the following order : sulphate, tartrate, phosphate, citrate, acetate, chloride, chlorate, nitrate, bromide, iodide, thiocyanate (see Redenz, 1926 ; Milovanov, 1934 ; Dubincik, 1934 ; Anderson, 1945). This order resembles the Hofmeister lyotropic series. Redenz interprets this as evidence that electrolyte damage is mainly caused by the removal of lipid from the cell surface—an idea that is supported by Milovanov and by Lovelock's more recent observations on red blood cells (Lovelock, 1954, 1955). Lovelock found that lipid and lipoprotein diffuse rapidly from red blood cells suspended in 0·16 molar sodium chloride solution, and that this loss from the cell is much smaller in solutions of sodium citrate or sodium acetate. With spermatozoa, the injuriousness of chloride appears to be greater under alkaline conditions than under acid conditions (Blackshaw and Emmens, 1951 ; Wales and White, 1958a). A further effect of electrolytes on the surface properties of spermatozoa manifests itself as an increased tendency of spermatozoa to agglutinate. This is brought about by neutralisation of charge on the cell surface by oppositely charged ions in solution. Certain anions, as noted in Section I, are powerful inhibitors of metabolism and motility.

The action of different cations on spermatozoa is less distinctive than that of anions. There is little evidence of antagonism between cations such as is usually found with other cells and tissues, and simple salt solutions, such as $0 \cdot 15$ molar NaCl, appear to be tolerated as readily as are balanced salt solutions, such as Ringer's solution. Bishop (unpublished observations), for example, found that unwashed bull spermatozoa can respire and swim actively for at least four hours in pure isosmotic solutions of NaCl, $CaCl_2$, $MgCl_2$ and KCl. This suggests that the cell membrane is highly impermeable to Na^+, Ca^{++}, Mg^{++} and K^+. There is evidence, however, that calcium depresses motility in bull and ram spermatozoa (but apparently not in dog spermatozoa), that magnesium stimulates motility and glycolysis, that potassium and rubidium stimulate motility, and that lithium is toxic (Lardy and Phillips, 1943c ; White, 1953b, c, d ; 1956a; Blackshaw, 1953a, b; Wales and White, 1958b). Gellhorn (1922a), working with guinea-pig spermatozoa, arranged cations in the following order of increasing injuriousness : potassium, rubidium, sodium, ammonium, caesium, lithium. Dubincik (1934) gives the order ; potassium, sodium, ammonium, calcium, zinc, iron. The effects of heavy metals have been recently investigated by White (1955a, b ; 1956a, b). These tend to be toxic on account of their sulphydryl-binding properties. The degree of toxicity varies considerably between species, and is often not nearly as great as might be expected. The use of the salts of heavy metals as spermicides is discussed in Chapter 9.

Beneficial results obtained from the partial replacement of electrolytes by non-electrolytes are described by Bogart and Mayer (1950), Kampschmidt, Mayer, Herman and Dickerson (1951), Kampschmidt, Mayer and Herman (1953), Kok (1953) and Bishop (1954).

Extent of Dilution

It has been generally assumed that the metabolic activity of unit numbers of spermatozoa is independent of the concentration of cells in the suspensions studied. Bishop and Salisbury, however, have shown that the oxygen uptake of bull spermatozoa is substantially increased by the addition of seminal plasma, Ringer solution or $0 \cdot 15$ molar NaCl solution (*see* Fig. 9A.11), and there is evidence that fructolysis is affected in the same way (Bishop, 1955a, b ; Bishop and Salisbury, 1955a, b, c). A similar phenomenon occurs when sea-urchin spermatozoa are diluted with sea-water : this was first described by Gray (1928) and later extensively studied by other workers (*see* Rothschild, 1951a). In both the bull and the sea-urchin, this response to dilution is almost certainly related to the phenomenon of activation that normally accompanies the release of spermatozoa from the male reproductive tract. Its nature is complex and poorly understood. Bishop and Salisbury believe that the increased metabolism observed in their experiments was probably caused by the dilution of some inhibiting substance together with the stimulating effect of electrolytes. As yet, there is no direct evidence of a naturally-occurring inhibitor in the semen of mammals, but there is evidence that potassium inhibits the movements of spermatozoa in the semen of the salmon and trout (Schlenk and Kahmann, 1938).

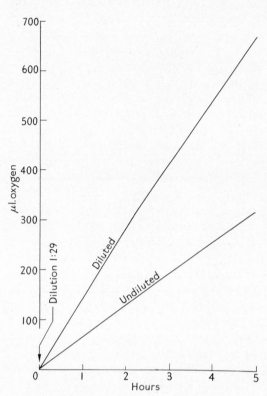

Fig. 9A.11—The effect of a 1:29 dilution with 0·9 per cent NaCl solution on the oxygen uptake of bull semen. Each sample contained 1 × 10⁹ spermatozoa. (From Bishop, 1954.)

As might be expected, the dilution response varies with the nature of the diluent used. Bishop and Salisbury found, for example, that the oxygen uptake and motility of bull spermatozoa were depressed by diluents containing phosphate—the depression often following a brief period of stimulation.

The dilution of semen with a favourable diluent prolongs the survival of spermatozoa *in vitro* beyond that of those in undiluted controls (*see* Chapter 9). In any given diluent, however, the survival time and fertility of spermatozoa decrease when the extent of dilution exceeds a certain optimum level (*see* Salisbury, Beck, Cupps and Elliott, 1943 ; Chang, 1946a, b ; Emmens and Swyer, 1948 ; Cheng, Casida and Barrett, 1949 ; Willett, 1953) This effect, which is seen even in seminal plasma, is most marked in diluents with a high content of electrolytes. It probably arises from irreparable decay of enzymes in the actively metabolising cells, and from breakdown of the selective permeability of the cell membrane on account of loss of lipid from the surface. Extensive dilution with " isotonic " (1 per cent) sodium chloride solution is extremely injurious and results in almost instantaneous immobilisation of spermatozoa (Milovanov, 1934).

Washing

The effects of washing spermatozoa are similar to those of dilution. Bishop and Salisbury (1955b) observed that the oxygen uptake of bull spermatozoa was stimulated by washing and resuspension in 0·15 molar NaCl solution, even though the washed cells were suspended at the same concentration as in the original sample. The results of such an experiment, in which the initial rate of oxygen uptake was doubled by the washing treatment, are shown in Fig. 9A.2. The early decline of respiration in this experiment was caused by exhaustion of metabolic substrate and could have been prevented by the inclusion of glucose or fructose in the suspending fluid. Washing and resuspension in fluids containing phosphate, on the other hand, depresses the oxygen uptake of bull spermatozoa. Washing, like dilution, is ultimately harmful to spermatozoa, and extensive washing is accompanied by extensive injury. Repeated washings in small volumes of fluid are, however, less injurious than the equivalent replacement of seminal plasma by dilution (Emmens and Swyer, 1948; Walton, 1950). This suggests that injury from dilution is probably caused by the loss of vital material from the cell. Some of the consequences of washing for motility and metabolism have been studied by White (1953a, b, c), Smith, Mayer and Merilan (1957) and Wales and White (1958b). Bhargava, Bishop and Work (1959) observed that the incorporation of amino acids into the proteins of bull spermatozoa was greatly affected by washing.

Temperature

The upper limit of temperature at which spermatozoa can survive is about 45°C., and death, preceded by a brief period of reversible heat rigor, occurs at about 48°C. (Stigler, 1913; Amantea and Krzyszkowsky, 1921; Walton, 1930). As temperature is lowered below that of body temperature (about 38°C.), metabolic activity and motility become reduced and movement ceases at 5° to 10°C. This reduction of activity is almost completely reversible, an observation first made by Spallanzani (1776), provided that the rate of cooling is sufficiently slow. If, however, the rate of cooling is rapid, large numbers of spermatozoa are killed—a phenomenon known as " temperature shock " or " cold shock " (Milovanov, 1934; Birillo and Puhaljskii, 1936; Gladcinova, 1937; Skatkin, 1940; Chang and Walton, 1940; Easley, Mayer and Bogart, 1942; Hancock, 1951; Bishop et al., 1954). Cold shock appears to be virtually an " all or nothing " phenomenon so far as individual cells are concerned and is accompanied by a sudden increase in the permeability of the cell membrane. In populations of cells, it is associated with a decrease in oxygen uptake, fructolysis, ATP synthesis and motility, and with an increase in ammonia formation and the rate of leakage of cytochrome c into the suspending medium (Chang and Walton, 1940; Hancock, 1951; Bishop and Hancock, 1951; Mayer, 1955; Mann and Lutwak-Mann, 1955). Provided that the lethal high temperature is not reached, there are no similar effects from suddenly raising the temperature. The resistance of spermatozoa to cold shock varies between species and between individuals within a species, is greater in epididymal spermatozoa than in ejaculated spermatozoa, and can be greatly increased by protective substances, such as hen egg-yolk (Lasley and Bogart, 1944; Lasley and Mayer, 1944; Hancock, 1952; Bishop et al., 1954). It appears to be inversely related to the age of the cell (Bishop, 1955b).

When the harmful effects of cooling are avoided, the longevity of spermatozoa in vitro can be greatly extended by lowering the environmental temperature, and extensive use has been made of this in the storage of bull spermatozoa for artificial insemination (see Chapter 9). The usual temperature for storage is +4°C., a temperature at which metabolism appears to be just about sufficient to maintain the integrity of the cell against the destructive effects of physical agencies, such as diffusion. At slightly lower temperatures, metabolism ceases and death of the cell quickly occurs, but at temperatures of −79°C. and below, where physical forces are reduced to a very low level of activity, bull spermatozoa can be preserved in fully functional condition for several years (see Chapter 9).

The dependence of the metabolic activity of spermatozoa upon temperature has been studied by Bernstein (1933a, b), Shergin (1939), Gladcinova (1940), Moore and Mayer (1941), Beck and Salisbury (1943), Mann (1946), and Blackshaw, Salisbury and VanDemark (1957). The last-named group of workers report the following temperature coefficients for bull spermatozoa : fructolysis, 4·0 between 37° and 21°C. and 1·6 between 37° and 5°C. ; lactic acid accumulation, 4·1 between 37° and 21°C. and 2·2 between 37° and 5°C. ; oxygen uptake, 2·8 between 37° and 21°C. and 4·2 between 37° and 5°C. The temperature coefficient for impedance-change frequency, between 16° and 36°C., is about 2 (Rothschild, 1948).

Oxygen and Carbon-dioxide Tensions

Measurement of the respiratory activity of spermatozoa is usually made with a gas phase of carbon-dioxide-free air, and little is known of the effects that variations in partial pressure of oxygen and carbon dioxide may exert on metabolism.

On *a priori* grounds, one would expect spermatozoa to be able to utilise oxygen effectively at partial pressures equivalent to those found in tissues. The only direct observation relevant to this appears to be Mann's (1954a) finding that suspensions of ram spermatozoa respire as actively in a gas phase containing 1 per cent oxygen as they do in air. Recently, VanDemark and Sharma (1957) and Salisbury and VanDemark (1957) have claimed that high concentrations of carbon dioxide reversibly inhibit motility and metabolism in bull spermatozoa and prolong their survival *in vitro*.

Hormones

Various workers have examined the effects of thyroxine on the physiology of spermatozoa but the results obtained are rather inconclusive (Carter, 1931, 1932; Lardy and Phillips, 1943d ; Schultze and Davis, 1948, 1949 ; Maqsood, 1952). Adrenaline and noradrenaline are said to inhibit aerobic fructolysis in bull semen, but not anaerobic fructolysis (Brochart, 1951). Nothing appears to be known of the influence that other hormones may have on spermatozoon physiology.

Antibiotics

Ivanov (1917, 1923) found that ethyl alcohol tended to reduce bacterial growth in semen without appearing to harm the spermatozoa, and that salvarsan, in concentrations sublethal to spermatozoa, would kill the trypanosomes of equine dourine. In recent years, various antibiotics have been extensively used in diluents for bull semen, and some have been shown to improve both the survival and fertility of the spermatozoa (*see* Emmens and Blackshaw, 1956). The extent to which these results are brought about merely by the control of contaminating bacteria is, however, not known.

In general, spermatozoa are very resistant to the action of antibiotics at usual bacteriostatic concentrations, but at higher concentrations most antibiotics are toxic to a varying degree. Henle and Zittle (1942) found that gramicidin at first stimulated oxygen uptake by bull spermatozoa and subsequently inhibited it. Knodt and Salisbury (1946) found that sulphanilamide depressed glucose utilisation and oxygen uptake of bull semen and improved their survival. White (1954b) observed that chloromycetin in high concentration depressed both respiration and glycolysis, and that aureomycin stimulated the respiration of ram spermatozoa at the expense of glycolysis, but had the reverse effect on bull spermatozoa. Other investigators of the effects of antibiotics on spermatozoa include Shettles (1940b) (sulphanilamide and sulphapyridine), Phillips and Spitzer (1946) (sulphonamides and streptomycin), Almquist, Thorp and Knodt (1946) (penicillin), Myers and Almquist (1951) (streptomycin), Foote and Bratton (1950) (polymyxin), Stallcup and McCartney (1953) (terramycin).

Seminal Plasma

At ejaculation, spermatozoa are mingled with secretions from the accessory glands and this fluid forms the bulk of the seminal plasma. A very much smaller contribution accompanies the spermatozoa from the epididymis. Since seminal plasma can be regarded as the naturally occurring diluent for spermatozoa, it is appropriate to conclude this chapter with a brief discussion of its properties and significance.

The complex composition of seminal plasma has been discussed in detail by Anderson (1945) and Mann (1954a) and will not be treated at length here. A notable feature of this composition, relative to that of other body fluids, is its great variability. This variability, is, of course, greatest between species, but is none the less considerable both within species and within individual males. It is determined both by variations in the proportionate contributions of the various accessory glands and by variations in the composition of the secretions of the glands themselves. Differences between species are in some instances very striking. Thus, gel-forming substances are a prominent feature of semen of the boar, stallion, rabbit and many rodents—they are present to a much smaller extent in the semen of man and are absent from the semen of the bull and ram. Ergothioneine and inositol occur in very much greater amount in the semen of the boar than in the semen of other species studied, and the same is true for spermine in human semen. Fructose, a characteristic component of the semen of most mammals, appears to be absent from the semen of the dog and cat. This variability is difficult to explain in terms of differing physiological requirements between species. Seminal gels, by forming vaginal or uterine plugs, are generally supposed to assist insemination by preventing loss of semen from the female tract. They may also have the function of mechanically stimulating muscular movements of the tract that assist the transportation of spermatozoa to the site of fertilisation. It is difficult however, to visualise why such a mechanism should be necessary or advantageous in some species and not in others. Variability in other components of semen is even more puzzling. The variability in composition that is encountered within any species suggests that the precise composition of seminal plasma is, within fairly wide limits, of little physiological importance. It has indeed been observed that fairly wide variations in the content of substances such as fructose are not related to fertility.

The extent to which spermatozoa are diluted by the accessory secretions is also very variable. In the semen of the ram, the spermatozoa constitute about 25 per cent of the total volume, whereas, in the semen of the boar, this proportion is only about 1 per cent. This difference is also reflected in the volume of the ejaculate—about 1 ml. in the ram and up to half a litre in the boar. The consequences of dilution with the accessory fluids resemble those described earlier for dilution with artificial diluents. The spermatozoa are stimulated to vigorous activity and their life-span is greatly shortened. The injurious effects of dilution again increase with the extent of dilution. The viability of boar spermatozoa *in vitro* is much lower than that of bull spermatozoa, but can be greatly improved by concentrating the suspension of spermatozoa and discarding most of the seminal plasma. The fertility of stallion semen can be prolonged by concentrating the spermatozoa (Walton, 1938).

The pH of seminal plasma is buffered at about neutrality by bicarbonate, citric acid, proteins, amino acids and other substances. The content of inorganic phosphate is small. The buffer capacity, though considerable, is insufficient to prevent changes in pH brought about by the metabolic activity of spermatozoa. With loss of carbon dioxide, the pH may rise a little, but with accumulation of lactic acid, it falls rather rapidly (Smith and Asdell, 1940 ; Laing, 1944).

Seminal plasma is approximately isosmotic with blood plasma (Salisbury, Knodt and Bratton, 1948 ; Rothschild and Barnes, 1954). Much of the osmotic activity of seminal plasma is created by organic constituents such as fructose, citric acid, lactic acid, amino acids, urea, glycerylphosphocholine and inositol. The electrolyte content is small and is characterised by a remarkably high potassium : sodium ratio and a low concentration of calcium and magnesium. It seems likely that the major significance of the organic constituents of fairly small molecular size lies in their ability to provide an adequate osmotic environment with a low proportion of electrolytes in relation to non-electrolytes, and this may explain the variety of rather unusual organic compounds that occurs in seminal plasma. As mentioned earlier in this Section, a low electrolyte : nonelectrolyte ratio appears to be of considerable importance in ameliorating the harmful effects of dilution and in maintaining the integrity of the spermatozoon. Substances of larger molecular size, such as various lipids, proteins, polypeptides and other protein-like substances, may also help to protect the spermatozoon membrane from the harmful effects of dilution. Lindahl and Kihlström (1954a, b) believe that a mucoprotein present in seminal plasma acts as a highly potent " antagglutin." It is suggested that this antagglutin is produced in the prostate, is reversibly oxidisable, and becomes attached, while in the reduced form, to the surface of the spermatozoon and thereby prevents agglutination. On oxidation, the antagglutin becomes detached from the spermatozoon and agglutination takes place. The active agent is apparently stabilised in semen by the presence of reducing substances, such as ascorbic acid and ergothioneine.

A further possible function of ergothioneine and of other sulphydryl compounds such as cysteine and reduced glutathione, stems from their ability to absorb sulphydryl-binding agents and thereby protect essential sulphydryl groups in spermatozoa from inactivation. Protection of this kind can be readily demonstrated *in vitro* (Mann and Leone, 1953), but has not been shown to be of importance *in vivo*. Haag and Werthessen (1956), on the other hand, claim that high non-protein sulphydryl levels in stallion semen are associated with infertility.

Many workers have attached great importance to the presence in seminal plasma of substrates that can be catabolised by spermatozoa, but their significance under conditions of natural mating is doubtful (*see* p. 277). The principal metabolic substrates of seminal plasma are fructose and lactic acid. Glucose is present only in very small amounts, presumably because it is freely metabolised by the accessory glands, and for this reason cannot be concentrated in extracellular fluids. Seminal phospholipids and fatty acids may perhaps be catabolised to a limited extent.

Other constituents of seminal plasma that may be of physiological importance include its enzymes, its hormones, its vitamins and its antigenic substances. The enzymes include various proteolytic enzymes, various phosphatases, various glyco-sidases, choline esterase, diamine oxidase and lactic dehydrogenase. The hormones include choline, adrenaline, noradrenaline and small amounts of oestrogen and androgen. The vitamins include ascorbic acid, inositol and riboflavin. Goldblatt (1935b) found that human seminal plasma induced strong stimulation in smooth muscle and contained a powerful vaso-dilator.

In conclusion, it may be stated that the only known important function of seminal plasma under conditions of natural mating is to provide the fluid medium that carries the spermatozoa from the male tract to the female tract. The ejaculated semen is rapidly diluted with secretions of the female tract, and these secretions appear to provide the spermatozoon with all its physiological requirements. The fertility of the spermatozoon is certainly not dependent upon admixture with the accessory secretions (Ivanov, 1926 ; Hammond, 1930 ; Walton, 1930), and Lardy and Ghosh (1952) found that, when epididymal bull spermatozoa were used for artificial insemination of cows, the resulting incidence of conception was approximately the same as that which had previously been obtained with ejaculated spermatozoa from the same bulls. Further, seminal plasma by no means provides the ideal medium for the survival of spermatozoa. Survival *in vitro* is much better after dilution in certain artificial diluents that are quite unlike seminal plasma than it is in the natural diluent alone. Seminal plasma does, however, have an important influence on the physiology of spermatozoa *in vitro* and this must be carefully considered in interpreting the results of experimental work.

Bibliography

ADOLPHI, H. (1905). Die Spermatozoen der Säugetiere schwimmen gegen den Strom. *Anat. Anz.*, **26**, 549.

AHMED, S. I. (1955). Effect of glycine on storage of ram semen. *J. agric. Sci.*, **46**, 165.

ALMQUIST, J. O., THORP, W. T. S., & KNODT, C. B. (1946). The effect of penicillin upon the livability, fertility and bacterial content of bull semen. *J. Anim. Sci.*, **5**, 400.

AMANTEA, G., & KRZYSZKOWSKY, K. N. (1921). Richerche fisiologiche sugli spermatozoi. *Riv. Biol.*, **3**, 569.

ANDERSON, J. (1945). *The Semen of Animals and its use for Artificial Insemination.* Edinburgh.

—— (1946). The sugar content of bull semen and its reduction during storage. *J. agric. Sci.*, **36**, 260.

—— (1951). Notes on the semen of sterile and sub-fertile bulls. *Vet. Rec.*, **63**, 733.

—— (1952). Fructolysis in bull semen in relation to fertility and infertility. *Proc. 2nd Int. Congr. vet. Zootech., Madrid*, paper 25.

AUSTIN, C. R., & BISHOP, M. W. H. (1957). Preliminaries to fertilization in mammals. In *The Beginnings of Embryonic Development*, American Association for the Advancement of Science, Washington.

BAKER, F. N., CRAGLE, R. G., SALISBURY, G. W., & VANDEMARK, N. L. (1957). Spermatozoan velocities in vitro. A simple method of measurement. *Fertility & Sterility*, **8**, 149.

BALDWIN, E. (1952). *Dynamic Aspects of Biochemistry*, 2nd ed. Cambridge.

L*

BANE, A. (1952). A study on the technique of hemocytometric determination of sperm motility and sperm concentration in bull semen. *Cornell Vet.*, **42**, 518.

BECK, G. H., & SALISBURY, G. W. (1943). Rapid methods for estimating the quality of bull semen. *J. Dairy Sci.*, **26**, 483.

BERNSTEIN, A. D. (1933a). Problems of artificial insemination. (Translated title.) *Probl. Anim. Husb., Moscow*, No. 1, 77. (In *Anim. Breed. Abstr.*, **1**, 82.)

—— (1933b). Studies on the physiology of spermatozoa. Glucose metabolism of spermatozoa. (Translated title.) *Trans. vet. Path., Orenburg vet. Inst.*, No. 1, 9. (In *Anim. Breed. Abstr.*, **3**, 478.)

—— (1933c). Studies on the physiology of spermatozoa. Artificial nutrient media and mineral solutions as sperm diluents. (Translated title.) *Trans. vet. Path., Orenburg vet. Inst.*, No. 1, 116. (In *Anim. Breed. Abstr.*, **3**, 479.)

—— & SLOVOKOTOV, I. (1933). Studies on the physiology of spermatozoa. Lactic acid metabolism of spermatozoa. (Translated title.) *Trans. vet. Path., Orenburg vet. Inst.*, No. 1, 26. (In *Anim. Breed. Abstr.*, **3**, 478.)

BERTAUD, S., & PROBINE, M. C. (1956). Rate of heat production by bull spermatozoa. *Nature, Lond.*, **178**, 933.

BHARGAVA, P. M. (1957). Incorporation of radioactive aminoacids in the proteins of bull spermatozoa. *Nature, Lond.*, **179**, 1120.

—— BISHOP, M. W. H., & WORK, T. S. (1959). Incorporation of ^{14}C-amino acids into the proteins of bull spermatozoa. *Biochem. J.*, **73**, 247.

BIRILLO, I. M., & PUHALJSKII, L. H. (1936). Problems of prolonged storage of bull and ram sperm. (Translated title.) *Probl. Anim. Husb., Moscow*, No. 10, 24. (In *Anim. Breed. Abstr.*, **5**, 219.)

BISHOP, D. W. (1942). Oxygen consumption of fox sperm. *Biol. Bull., Wood's Hole*, **83**, 353.

—— (1956a). Oxygen concentrations in the rabbit genital tract. *Proc. 3rd Int. Congr. Anim. Reprod., Cambridge*, **1**, 53.

—— (1956b). Metabolic conditions within the oviduct of the rabbit. *Proc. 2nd World Congr. Fertil. Steril., Naples*.

—— (1956c). Active secretion in the rabbit oviduct. *Amer. J. Physiol.*, **187**, 347.

—— (1958). Motility of the sperm flagellum. *Nature, Lond.*, **182**, 1638.

BISHOP, M. W. H. (1954). Some aspects of the dilution effect in mammalian spermatozoa. *Studies on Fertility*, **6**, 81.

—— 1955a). *The Physiology of Bull Spermatozoa*. Ph.D. Thesis, University of Cambridge.

—— (1955b). Inter-relationships of semen characteristics. *Studies on Fertility*, **7**, 48.

—— & CAMPBELL, R. C. (1959). Spermatozoon motility and impedance change frequency in bull semen. *J. agric. Sci.* (in press).

—— —— HANCOCK, J. L., & WALTON, A. (1954). Semen characteristics and fertility in the bull. *J. agric. Sci.*, **44**, 227.

—— & HANCOCK, J. L. (1951). Unpublished observations.

—— —— (1955). The evaluation of bull semen. *Vet. Rec.*, **67**, 363.

—— & SALISBURY, G. W. (1955a). The effect of sperm concentration on the oxygen uptake of bull semen. *Amer. J. Physiol.*, **180**, 107.

—— —— (1955b). The effect of dilution with saline and phosphate solutions on the oxygen uptake of bull semen. *Amer. J. Physiol.*, **181**, 114.

—— —— (1955c). The effect of dilution with a yolk-containing extender on the oxygen uptake and motility of bull spermatozoa. *J. Dairy Sci.*, **38**, 202.

BLACKSHAW, A. W. (1953a). The effects of potassium and calcium salts on the motility of ram, rabbit and bull spermatozoa. *J. Physiol.*, **120**, 465.

—— (1953b). The motility of ram and bull spermatozoa in dilute suspension. *J. gen. Physiol.*, **36**, 449.

—— & EMMENS, C. W. (1951). The interaction of pH, osmotic pressure and electrolyte concentration on the motility of ram, bull and human spermatozoa. *J. Physiol.*, **114**, 16.

—— SALISBURY, G. W., & VANDEMARK, N. L. (1957). Factors influencing metabolic activity of bull spermatozoa. 1. 37, 21 and 5° C. *J. Dairy Sci.*, **40**, 1093.

BLOM, E. (1946). A comparing-chamber for microscopic examination of undiluted bull semen. *Vet. J.*, **102**, 252.

BOGART, R., & MAYER, D. T. (1950). The effects of egg yolk on the various physical and chemical factors detrimental to spermatozoan viability. *J. Anim. Sci.*, **9**, 143.

BOMSTEIN, R. A., & STEBERL, E. A. (1957). Utilization of phospholipids by bovine spermatozoa. *Exp. Cell Res.*, **12**, 254.

BONNADONNA, T. (1946). *Nozioni di Tecnica della Fecondazione Artificiale degli Animali*. Milan.

BÖNNER, G. (1947). Die Dehydrierungsfähigkeit der menschlichen Spermatozoen in ihrer Beziehung zur Fertilität. *Klin. Wschr.*, **24**, 756.

BOSSELAAR, C. A., & SPRONK, N. (1952). A physical method for determination of the motility and concentration of spermatozoa. *Nature, Lond.*, **169**, 18.

—————— & VAN DAM, G. C. (1955). An apparatus for measuring the motility of sperm cells. *J. agric. Sci.*, **46**, 417.

BRACHET, J. (1955). The biological role of pentose nucleic acids. In *The Nucleic Acids*, editors E. Chargaff and J. N. Davidson, New York.

BRADY, D. E., & GILDOW, E. M. (1939). Characteristics of ram semen as influenced by the method of collection. *Proc. Amer. Soc. Anim. Prod.*, 1939.

BRANTON, C., JAMES, C. B., PATRICK, T. E., & NEWSOM, M. H. (1951). The relationship between certain semen quality tests and fertility and the inter-relationship of these tests. *J. Dairy Sci.*, **34**, 310.

BRECKENRIDGE, M. A. B., & POMMERENKE, W. T. (1951). Analysis of carbohydrates in human cervical mucus. *Fertility & Sterility*, **2**, 29.

BROCHART, M. (1948). Controle du sperm de taureau par le test au bleu de methlene, suivant la technique en tube capillaire. *Rec. Méd. Vét.*, **124**, 64.

—— (1951). Influence de l'adrenaline et de la nor-adrenaline sur la glycolyse et la respiration des spermatozoides de taureau. *Bull. Soc. Chim. biol., Paris*, **33**, 1777.

BROKAW, C. J. (1958a). Chemotaxis of bracken spermatozoids: the role of bimalate ions. *J. exp. Biol.*, **35**, 192.

—— (1958b). Chemotaxis of bracken spermatozoids: implications of electrochemical orientation. *J. exp. Biol.*, **35**, 197.

BUCKNER, P. J., WILLETT, E. L., & BAYLEY, N. (1954). Laboratory tests, singly and in combination, for evaluating fertility of semen and of bulls. *J. Dairy Sci.*, **37**, 1050.

BULLER, A. H. R. (1903). Is chemotaxis a factor in the fertilization of the eggs of animals? *Quart. J. micro. Sci.*, **46**, 145.

CAMPBELL, J. A. (1932). Normal gas tensions in the mucous membrane of the rabbit's uterus. *J. Physiol.*, **76**, 13P.

CARTER, G. S. (1931). Iodine compounds and fertilization. II: The oxygen consumption of suspensions of sperm of *Echinus esculentus* and *Echinus miliaris*. *J. exp. Biol.*, **8**, 176.

—— (1932). The effects of thyroxine and desiodothyroxine on the oxygen consumption of the sperm of the rabbit. *J. exp. Biol.*, **9**, 378.

CHANDRASEHKAR, S. (1943). Stochastic problems in physics and astronomy. *Rev. mod. Phys.*, **15**, 1.

CHANG, M. C. (1946a). Effect of dilution on fertilizing capacity of rabbit spermatozoa. *Science*, **104**, 361.

—— (1946b). Fertilizing capacity of rabbit spermatozoa. In *The Problem of Fertility*. Princeton.

—— & WALTON, A. (1940). The effects of low temperature and acclimatization on the respiratory activity and survival of ram spermatozoa. *Proc. Roy. Soc. B*, **129**, 517.

CHENG, P. L., CASIDA, L. E., & BARRETT, G. R. (1949). The effects of dilution on motility of bull spermatozoa and the relation between motility in high dilution and fertility. *J. Anim. Sci.*, **8**, 81.

CLARKE, E. W., & ROTHSCHILD, Lord. (1957). Anaerobic heat production of bull spermatozoa. *Proc. Roy. Soc. B*, **147**, 316.

COLE, F. J. (1930). *Early Theories of Sexual Generation*. Oxford.

COLE, L. J., WALETZKY, E., & SHACKELFORD, M. (1940). Test of sex control by modification of acid-alkaline balance. *J. Hered.*, **31**, 501.

COMSTOCK, R. E. (1939). A study of the mammalian sperm cell. I: Variations in the glycolytic power of spermatozoa and their relation to motility and its duration. *J. exp. Zool.*, **81**, 147.

—— & GREEN, W. W. (1939). Methods for semen evaluation. I: Density, respiration, glycolysis of semen. *Proc. Amer. Soc. Anim. Prod.*, **32**, 213.

—— —— WINTERS, L. M., & NORDSKOG, A. W. (1943). Studies of semen and semen production. *Tech. Bull. Minn. agric. Exp. Sta.*, No. 162.

COOK, A. H. (1945). Algal pigments and their significance. *Biol. Rev.*, **20**, 115.

CUMMINGS, J. N. (1954). Testing fertility in bulls. *Tech. Bull. Minn. agric. Exp. Sta.*, No. 212.

DOTT, H. M. (1958). Species differences in the metabolism of epididymal spermatozoa. *Studies on Fertility*, **10**, 73.

DOYLE, J. B. (1958). Cervical tampon-synchronous test for ovulation. Simultaneous assay of glucose from cervix and follicular fluid from cul-de-sac and ovary by culdotomy. *J. Amer. med. Ass.*, **167**, 1464.

DUBINCIK, J. (1934). The influence of physico-chemical factors on vitality of spermatozoa. *Ginekologia*, No. 3, 79. (In *Anim. Breed. Abstr.*, **4**, 256.)

EASLEY, G. T., MAYER, D. T., & BOGART, R. (1942). Influence of diluters, rate of cooling, and storage temperatures on survival of bull sperm. *Amer. J. vet. Res.*, **3**, 358.

EHLERS, M. H., & ERB, R. E. (1956). Metabolism of bull semen. V: Influence of dilution rate and time. *Tech. Bull. Wash. agric. Exp. Sta.*, No. 20.

EICHENBERGER, E., & GOOSSENS, O. (1950). Fructose und Fructolyse im menschlichen Samen. *Schweiz. med. Wschr.*, **80**, 1073.

EMMENS, C. W. (1947). The motility and viability of rabbit spermatozoa at different hydrogen-ion concentrations. *J. Physiol.*, **106**, 471.

—— (1948). The effect of variations in osmotic pressure and electrolyte concentration on the motility of rabbit spermatozoa at different hydrogen-ion concentrations. *J. Physiol.*, **107**, 129.

—— & BLACKSHAW, A. W. (1956). Artificial insemination. *Physiol. Rev.*, **36**, 277.

—— & SWYER, G. I. M. (1948). Observations on the motility of rabbit spermatozoa in dilute suspension. *J. gen. Physiol.*, **32**, 121.

ERB, R. E., & EHLERS, M. H. (1950). Resazurin reducing time as an indicator of bovine semen fertilizing capacity. *J. Dairy Sci.*, **33**, 853.

—— —— & FLERCHINGER, F. H. (1952). Modified resazurin reduction test for estimating fertilizing capacity of bull semen. *J. Dairy Sci.*, **35**, 881.

—— —— MIKOTA, L. E., & SCHWARTZ, E. (1950). The relation of simple semen quality tests to fertilizing capacity of bull semen. *Tech. Bull. Wash. agric. Exp. Sta.*, No. 2.

—— FLERCHINGER, F. H., EHLERS, M. H., & GASSNER, F. X. (1956). Metabolism of bull semen. II: Fructolysis relationships with sperm concentration and fertility. *J. Dairy Sci.*, **39**. 326.

—— —— & MIKOTA, L. E. (1955). Semen metabolism studies. IV: Relationships among physical measurements, metabolic activity and fertility. *Tech. Bull. Wash. agric. Exp. Sta.*, No. 18.

FLIPSE, R. J. (1954). Metabolism of bovine semen. Uptake of glucose -C^{14} by bovine spermatozoa. *J. Dairy Sci.*, **37**, 425.

—— (1956). Metabolism of glycine by bovine spermatozoa. *Science*, **124**, 228.

—— & ALMQUIST, J. O. (1955). Metabolism of bovine semen. II: Qualitative anaerobic catabolism of glucose -C^{14} by spermatozoa. *J. Dairy Sci.*, **38**, 782.

—— & BENSON, A. A. (1957). Catabolism of glycine -C^{14} by washed bovine spermatozoa. *Exp. Cell Res.*, **13**, 611.

FOOTE, R. H., & BRATTON, R. W. (1950). Motility of spermatozoa and control of bacteria in bovine semen extenders containing sulfanilamide, polymyxin and aureomycin. *J. Dairy Sci.*, **33**, 539.

FRUTON, J. S., & SIMMONDS, S. (1953). *General Biochemistry*. New York and London.

GALE, E. F. (1956). Nucleic acids and enzyme synthesis. In *Enzymes: Units of Biological Structure and Function*, a Henry Ford Hospital Symposium, New York, p. 49.

—— (1957). *Nucleic acids and protein synthesis. The Harvey Lectures, Series LI.* New York.

GASSNER, F. X., & HILL, H. J. (1952). Correlation of fructose content of semen and rate of fructolysis to breeding efficiency of bulls. *Rep. 2nd Int. Congr. Physiol. Path. Anim. Reprod., Copenhagen*, **3**, 62.

GELLHORN, E. (1920). Beiträge zur vergleichenden Physiologie der Spermatozoen. I: Mitteilung. *Pflüg. Arch. ges. Physiol.*, **185**, 262.

—— (1922a). Beiträge zur vergleichenden Physiologie der Spermatozoen. II: Weitere Studien über Salzwirkungen. *Pflüg. Arch. ges. Physiol.*, **193**, 555.

—— (1922b). Beiträge zur vergleichenden Physiologie der Spermatozoen. III: Weitere Studien über Salzwirkungen, besonders über Elektrolytgemische. *Pflüg. Arch. ges. Physiol.*, **193**, 576.

—— (1931). *Lehrbuch der allgemeinen Physiologie.* Leipzig.

GHOSH, D., CASIDA, L. E., & LARDY, H. A. (1949). A study of the metabolic activity of bull semen and spermatozoa in relation to their fertilizing ability. *J. Anim. Sci.*, **8**, 265.

GIESE, A. C. (1957). *Cell Physiology.* Philadelphia and London.

GLADCINOVA, E. F. (1937). The influence of marked drops in temperature on the survival of spermatozoa. (Translated title.) *Adv. zootech. Sci., Moscow*, **4**, 56. (In *Anim. Breed. Abstr.*, **7**, 373.)

—— (1940). The effects of low temperatures on the processes of metabolism in the sperm. (Translated title.) *Trud. Lab. ishusst. Osemen. Zhivotn. (Mosk.)*, **1**, 214. (In *Anim. Breed. Abstr.*, **13**, 37.)

GLEW, G. (1956). An investigation into the relationship between the metabolism of pyruvate in bull spermatozoa and fertility. *J. agric. Sci.*, **48**, 155.

GOLDBLATT, M. W. (1935a). Constituents of human seminal plasma. *Biochem. J.*, **29**, 1346.

—— (1935b). Properties of human seminal plasma. *J. Physiol.*, **84**, 208.

GRAVE, B. H., & DOWNING, R. C. (1928). The longevity and swimming ability of spermatozoa. *J. exp. Zool.*, **51**, 383.

GRAY, J. (1928). The effect of dilution on the activity of spermatozoa. *J. exp. Biol.*, **5**, 337.

—— (1955). The movement of sea-urchin spermatozoa. *J. exp. Biol.*, **32**, 775.

—— (1958). The movement of the spermatozoa of the bull. *J. exp. Biol.*, **35**, 96.

—— & HANCOCK, G. J. (1955). The propulsion of sea-urchin spermatozoa. *J. exp. Biol.*, **32**, 802.

HAAG, F. M., & WERTHESSEN, N. T. (1956). Relationship between fertility and the non-protein sulfhydryl concentration of seminal fluid in the thoroughbred stallion. *Fertility & Sterility*, **7**, 516.

HAMMOND, J. (1950). The effect of temperature on the survival of rabbit spermatozoa obtained from the vagina. *J. exp. Biol.*, **7**, 175.

HANCOCK, G. J. (1953). The self-propulsion of microscopic organisms through liquids. *Proc. Roy. Soc.* A, **217**, 96.

HANCOCK, J. L. (1951). A staining technique for the study of temperature shock in semen. *Nature, Lond.*, **167**, 323.

—— (1952). *The Morphology of Spermatozoa.* Ph.D. Thesis, University of Cambridge.

HARTMAN, C. G. (1957). How do sperms get into the uterus? *Fertility & Sterility*, **8**, 403.

HARTREE, E. F., & MANN, T. (1958). Plasmalogen in ram semen and its role in sperm metabolism. *Biochem. J.*, **69**, 50 P.

HARVEY, C. (1945). A method of estimating the activity of spermatozoa. *Nature, Lond.*, **155**, 368.

—— & JACKSON, M. H. (1948). Penetration of cervical mucus by spermatozoa. *Lancet*, ii, 723.

HAWKER, L. E. (1951). Biochemistry of sexual reproduction in plants. *Symp. biochem. Soc.*, **7**, 52.

HEILBRUNN, L. V. (1952). *An Outline of General Physiology.* 3rd ed. Philadelphia and London.

HENLE, G., & ZITTLE, C. A. (1941). Effect of gramicidin on metabolism of bovine spermatozoa. *Proc. Soc. exp. Biol., N.Y.*, **47**, 193.

—— —— (1942). Studies on the metabolism of bovine epididymal spermatozoa. *Amer. J. Physiol.*, **136**, 70.

Hopwood, M. L., Rutherford, E. R., & Gassner, F. X. (1956). The concept of fructose utilization by bull sperm and its relation to fertility. *J. Dairy Sci.*, **39**, 51.

Humphrey, G. F., & Mann, T. (1949). Studies on the metabolism of semen. 5: Citric acid in semen. *Biochem. J.*, **44**, 97.

Ivanov, E. (1917). Moyen de rendre le sperme infecté des mammifères incapable de transmettre l'infection. *C.R. Soc. Biol.*, Paris, **80**, 765.

—— (1923). Experiments on the disinfection of sperm in mammals, especially in relation to dourine in horses. *Parasitology*, **15**, 122.

—— (1926). Durée de conservation de la propriété fécondatrice des spermatozoïdes des mammifères dans l'epididyme separé de l'organisme. *C. R. Acad. Sci.*, Paris, **183**, 456.

Ivanov, E. E. (1930). Action de la sécrétion prostatique sur la respiration des spermatozoïdes. *C.R. Soc. Biol.*, Paris, **103**, 57.

—— (1931). Zurfrage der Energetik der Spermatozoen-Bewegung. *Z. Zücht. B.*, **20**, 404.

—— (1936). Sur le quotient respiratoire des spermatozoïdes. *Bull. Soc. Chim. biol.*, Paris, **18**, 1613.

—— (1937). Participation of phosphocreatine in the metabolism of spermatozoa, and the possibility of esterification of phosphopyruvic acid and creatine in spermatozoa. *Biochemistry, Leningr.*, **2**, 926. (In *Chem. Abstr.*, **32**, 2584.)

Ivanov, I. I., Kassavina, B. S., & Fomenko, L. D. (1946). Adenosine triphosphate in mammalian spermatozoa. *Nature, Lond.*, **158**, 624.

Kampschmidt, R. F., Mayer, D. T., & Herman, H. A. (1953). Viability of bull spermatozoa as influenced by various sugars and electrolytes in the storage medium. *Res. Bull. Mo. agric. Exp. Sta.*, No. 519.

—— —— —— & Dickerson, G. E. (1951). Viability of bull spermatozoa as influenced by electrolyte concentration, buffer efficiency and added glucose in storage media. *J. Dairy Sci.*, **34**, 45.

Kihlström, J. E. (1952). On the movements of isolated sperm heads in bull semen. *Ark. Zool.*, **4**, 141.

Killian, J. A. (1933). Metabolism of spermatozoa in semen. *Amer. J. Surg.*, **19**, 76 and 103.

King, T. E., & Mann, T. (1958). Sorbitol dehydrogenase in spermatozoa. *Nature, Lond.*, **182**, 868.

Klein, M. D., & Saroka, M. (1941). Studies on the viability of human spermatozoa; preliminary report. *Amer. J. Obstet. Gynec.*, **42**, 497.

Knodt, C. B., & Salisbury, G. W. (1946). The effect of sulfanilamide upon the livability and metabolism of bovine spermatozoa. *J. Dairy Sci.*, **29**, 285.

Koefoed-Johnsen, H. H., & Mann, T. (1954). Studies on the metabolism of semen. 9. Effect of surface active agents with special reference to the oxidation of succinate by spermatozoa. *Biochem. J.*, **57**, 406.

Kok, J. C. N. (1953). Some factors influencing the longevity of bull sperm cells *in vitro*. In *Mammalian Germ Cells*, a Ciba Foundation Symposium, London.

Kratky, O. (1934). Zum Deformationsmechanismus der Faserstoffe. II: Die Ordnung der Mizellen von Filmen in kleinsten Bereichen. *Kolloidzschr.*, **68**, 347.

Krebs, H. A. (1957). Control of metabolic processes. *Endeavour*, **16**, 125.

—— Kornberg, H. L., & Burton, K. (1957). A survey of the energy transformations in living matter. *Ergebn. Physiol.*, **49**, 212.

Laing, J. A. (1944). Observations on the characteristics of semen in relation to fertility in bulls. *J. agric. Sci.*, **35**, 1.

Lamar, J. K., Shettles, L. B., & Delfs, E. (1940). Cyclical penetration of human cervical mucus to spermatozoa in vitro. *Amer. J. Physiol.*, **129**, 234.

Lardy, H. A. (1953). Factors controlling rates of metabolism in mammalian spermatozoa. In *Mammalian Germ Cells*, a Ciba Foundation Symposium, London, p. 59.

—— & Ghosh, D. (1952). Comparative metabolic behaviour of epididymal and ejaculated spermatozoa. *Ann. N.Y. Acad. Sci.*, **55**, 594.

—— —— & Plaut, G. W. E. (1949). A metabolic regulator in mammalian spermatozoa. *Science*, **109**, 365.

LARDY, H. A., HANSEN, R. G., & PHILLIPS, P. H. (1945). The metabolism of bovine epididymal spermatozoa. *Arch. Biochem.*, **6**, 41.

—— & PHILLIPS, P. H. (1941a). The interrelation of oxidative and glycolytic processes as sources of energy for bull spermatozoa. *Amer. J. Physiol.*, **133**, 602.

—— —— (1941b). Phospholipids as a source of energy for motility of bull spermatozoa. *Amer. J. Physiol.*, **134**, 542.

—— —— (1941c). The effect of certain inhibitors and activators on sperm metabolism. *J. biol. Chem.*, **138**, 195.

—— —— (1943a). Inhibition of sperm respiration and reversibility of the effects of metabolic inhibitors. *J. biol. Chem.*, **148**, 333.

—— —— (1943b). Inhibition of sperm glycolysis and reversibility of the effects of metabolic inhibitors. *J. biol. Chem.*, **148**, 343.

—— —— (1943c). Effect of pH and certain electrolytes on the metabolism of ejaculated spermatozoa. *Amer. J. Physiol.*, **138**, 741.

—— —— (1943d). The effect of thyroxine and dinitrophenol on sperm metabolism. *J. biol. Chem.*, **149**, 177.

—— —— (1944). Acetate utilization for maintenance of motility of bull spermatozoa. *Nature, Lond.*, **153**, 168.

—— —— (1945). Studies of fat and carbohydrate oxidation in mammalian spermatozoa. *Arch. Biochem.*, **6**, 53.

—— WINCHESTER, B., & PHILLIPS, P. H. (1945). The respiratory metabolism of ram spermatozoa. *Arch. Biochem.*, **6**, 33.

LASLEY, J. F. (1951). Spermatozoan motility as a measure of semen quality. *J. Anim. Sci.*, **10**, 211.

—— & BOGART, R. (1944). A comparative study of the epididymal and ejaculated spermatozoa of the boar. *J. Anim. Sci.*, **3**, 360.

—— & MAYER, D. T. (1944). A variable physiological factor necessary for the survival of bull spermatozoa. *J. Anim. Sci.*, **3**, 129.

LEONARD, S. L. (1950). The reduction of uterine sperm and uterine fluid on fertilization of rat ova. *Anat. Rec.*, **106**, 607. (In *Anim. Breed. Abstr.*, **19**, 92.)

LINDAHL, P. E., & KIHLSTRÖM, J. E. (1954a). An antiagglutinic factor in mammalian sperm plasm. *Fertility & Sterility*, **5**, 241.

—— —— (1954b). A constituent of male sperm antagglutin related to vitamin E. *Nature, Lond.*, **174**, 600.

LOVELOCK, J. E. (1954). Physical instability and thermal shock in red cells. *Nature, Lond.*, **173**, 659.

—— (1955). The physical instability of human red blood cells. *Biochem. J.*, **60**, 692.

—— & BISHOP, M. W. H. (1958). Unpublished observations.

LOVERN, J. A., OLLEY, J., HARTREE, E. F., & MANN, T. (1957). The lipids of ram spermatozoa. *Biochem. J.*, **67**, 630.

LUTWAK-MANN, C. (1954). Note on the chemical composition of bovine follicular fluid. *J. agric. Sci.*, **44**, 477.

McCARTHY, J. F., STEPITA, C. T., JOHNSTON, M. B., & KILLIAN, J. A. (1927). Glycolysis in semen. *Proc. Soc. exp. Biol., N.Y.*, **25**, 54.

MACLEOD, J. (1939). The metabolism of spermatozoa. *Proc. Soc. exp. Biol., N.Y.*, **42**, 153.

—— (1941a). The metabolism of human spermatozoa. *Amer. J. Physiol.*, **132**, 193.

—— (1941b). The effect of glycolysis inhibitors and of certain substrates on the metabolism and motility of human spermatozoa. *Endocrinology*, **29**, 583.

—— (1943). The role of oxygen in the metabolism and motility of human spermatozoa. *Amer. J. Physiol.*, **138**, 512.

—— (1946). Metabolism and motility of human spermatozoa. In *The Problem of Fertility* (ed. by E. T. Engle). Princeton.

—— (1951). Sulphydryl groups in relation to the metabolism and motility of human spermatozoa. *J. gen. Physiol.*, **34**, 705.

—— & FREUND, M. (1958a). The carbohydrate metabolism of human spermatozoa in seminal plasma. *Studies on Fertility*, **10**, 52.

—— —— (1958b). Influence of spermatozoal concentration and initial fructose level on fructolysis in human semen. *J. appl. Physiol.*, **13**, 501.

MANN, T. (1945a). Studies on the metabolism of semen. 1: General aspects, occurrence and distribution of cytochrome, certain enzymes and coenzymes. *Biochem. J.*, **39**, 451.

—— (1945b). Studies on the metabolism of semen. 2: Glycolysis in spermatozoa. *Biochem. J.*, **39**, 458.

—— (1945c). Anaerobic metabolism of spermatozoa. *Nature, Lond.*, **156**, 80.

—— (1946). Studies on the metabolism of semen. 3: Fructose as a normal constituent of seminal plasma, site of formation and function of fructose in semen. *Biochem. J.*, **40**, 481.

—— (1948). Fructose content and fructolysis in semen. Practical application in the evaluation of semen quality. *J. agric. Sci.*, **38**, 324.

—— (1949). Metabolism of semen. *Advanc. Enzymol.*, **9**, 329.

——— (1951). Mammalian semen: composition metabolism and survival. *Symp. biochem. Soc.*, **7**, 11.

—— (1954a). *The Biochemistry of Semen.* London.

—— (1954b). The mode of action of spermicidal agents. *Studies on Fertility*, **6**, 41.

—— (1958). Biochemical basis of spermicidal activity. *Studies on Fertility*, **9**, 3.

—— & LEONE, E. (1953). Studies on the metabolism of semen. 8: Ergothioneine as a normal constituent of boar seminal plasma. Purification and crystallization. Site of formation and function. *Biochem. J.*, **53**, 140.

—— & LUTWAK-MANN, C. (1948). Aerobic and anaerobic utilization of fructose by spermatozoa and seminal vesicles. *Biochem. J.*, **43**, 266.

—— —— (1955). Biochemical changes underlying the phenomenon of cold-shock in spermatozoa. *Arch. Sci. biol.*, **39**, 578.

—— POLGE, C., & ROWSON, L. E. A. (1956). Participation of seminal plasma during the passage of spermatozoa in the female reproductive tract of the pig and horse. *J. Endocrin.*, **13**, 133.

—— & WHITE, I. G. (1956). Metabolism of glycerol, sorbitol and related compounds by spermatozoa. *Nature, Lond.*, **178**, 142.

—— —— (1957). Glycerol metabolism by spermatozoa. *Biochem. J.*, **65**, 634.

MAQSOOD, M. (1950). *In vitro* effects of thyroxine on oxygen consumption of mammalian spermatozoa. *Comm. 18th Int. physiol. Congr., Copenhagen*, p. 353.

—— (1952). Thyroid functions in relation to reproduction of mammals and birds. *Biol. Rev.*, **27**, 281.

MASUDA, S., QUISHI, N., & KUDO, A. (1951). Studies on oestrus in the cow. *Res. Bull. zootech. Exp. Sta.*, No. 56. (In *Anim. Breed. Abstr.*, **12**, 195.)

MAYER, D. T. (1955). The chemistry and certain aspects of the metabolic activities of mammalian spermatozoa. In *Reproduction and Infertility*, Centennial Symposium, Michigan State University, p. 45.

MELROSE, D. R. (1952). Evaluation of semen quality by the fructose utilization test. *Brit. vet. J.*, **108**, 260.

—— & TERNER, C. (1951). The influence of 2:4-dinitrophenol on the Pasteur effect in bull spermatozoa. *Biochem. J.*, **49**, i.

—— —— (1952). Pyruvate metabolism and assessment of semen quality. *Proc. Soc. exp. Biol., N.Y.*, **80**, 298.

—— —— (1953). The metabolism of pyruvate in bull spermatozoa. *Biochem. J.*, **53**, 296.

MICHAELIS, L. (1930). *Oxidation—Reduction Potentials.* Philadelphia.

MILOVANOV, V. K. (1934). *Principles of Artificial Insemination.* (Translated title.) Moscow and Leningrad.

—— & SOKOLOVSKAYA, I. I. (1947). *Stockbreeding and the Artificial Insemination of Livestock.* (Translated by A. G. Morton.) London.

MIXNER, J. P., MATHER, R. E., & FREUND, M. (1957). Bovine semen metabolism. I: Methods for expressing fructolytic activity. *J. Dairy Sci.*, **40**, 142.

MOELLER, A. N., & VANDEMARK, N. L. (1955). In vitro speeds of bovine spermatozoa. *Fertility & Sterility*, **6**, 506.

MOORE, B. H., & MAYER, D. T. (1941). The concentration and metabolism of sugar in ram semen. *Res. Bull. Mo. agric. Exp. Sta.*, No. 338.

MYERS, R. M., & ALMQUIST, J. O. (1951). A comparison of the effects of aureomycin, penicillin and streptomycin upon spermatozoan livability and control of bacteria in bovine semen. *J. Anim. Sci.*, **10**, 322.

NEILANDS, J. B., & STUMF, P. K. (1955). *Outlines of Enzyme Chemistry*. New York and London.

NELSON, L. (1954). Enzyme distribution in fragmented bull spermatozoa. I: Adenyl-pyrophosphatase. *Biochim. biophys. Acta*, **14**, 312.

—— (1955). Enzyme distribution in fragmented bull spermatozoa. II: Succinic dehydrogenase and cytochrome oxidase. *Biochim. biophys. Acta*, **16**, 494.

—— (1958). Cytochemical studies with the electron microscope. I: Adenosinetriphosphatase in rat spermatozoa. *Biochim. biophys. Acta*, **27**, 634.

O'DELL, W. T., FLIPSE, R. J., & ALMQUIST, J. O. (1956). Metabolism of bovine semen. III: Uptake and metabolic utilization of glycerol-1-C^{14} by bovine spermatozoa. *J. Dairy Sci.*, **39**, 214.

OLDS, D., & VANDEMARK, N. L. (1957a). Physiological aspects of fluids in female genitalia with special reference to cattle—a review. *Amer. J. vet. Res.*, **18**, 587.

—— —— (1957b). Composition of luminal fluids in bovine female genitalia. *Fertil. & Steril.*, **8**, 345.

—— —— (1957c). The behavior of spermatozoa in luminal fluids of bovine female genitalia. *Amer. J. vet. Res.*, **18**, 603.

PASTEUR, L. (1876). *Études sur la Bière*. Paris.

PHILLIFS, P. H., & SPITZER, R. R. (1946). A synthetic pabulum for the preservation of bull semen. *J. Dairy Sci.*, **29**, 407.

PHILLIPS, R. W., & ANDREWS, F. N. (1937). Speed of travel of ram spermatozoa. *Anat. Rec.*, **68**, 127.

PLAUT, G. W. E., & LARDY, H. A. (1950). Metabolism of ejaculated bull spermatozoa with particular reference to the glycolysis of maltose. *Amer. J. Physiol.*, **162**, 598.

PURSLEY, G. R., & HERMAN, H. A. (1950). Some effects of hypertonic and hypotonic solutions on the livability and morphology of bovine spermatozoa. *J. Dairy Sci.*, **33**, 220.

REDENZ, E. (1926). Nebenhoden und Spermienbewegung. *Würzburg. Abh. ges. Med.*, **4**, 5.

—— (1930). Uber Atmung und Glykolyse der Saugetier-spermatozoen. *Proc. 2nd Int. Congr. Sex. Res.*, Lond.

—— (1933). Uber den Spaltungstoffwechsel der Spermatozoen in Zusammenhaug mit der Beweglichkeit. *Biochem. Z.*, **257**, 234.

RIKMENSPOEL, R. (1957). *Photoelectric and Cinematographic Measurements of the "Motility" of Bull Sperm Cells*. Utrecht.

—— VAN HERPEN, G., & VAN DAM, G. C. (1956). Physical investigations on the movements of bull sperm cells. *Proc. 3rd Int. Congr. Anim. Reprod., Cambridge*, **1**, 19.

ROLLINSON, D. H. L. (1951). Fructose estimation and fructolysis of abnormal semen: results obtained in the field. *Vet. Rec.*, **63**, 548.

ROMIJN, C. (1947). Physiologisch spermaonderzoek. *Tijdschr. Diergeneesk.*, **72**, 628.

—— (1950). De invoed van eidooier op het metabolisme van stierensperma. *Tijdschr. Diergeneesk.*, **75**, 95.

ROSS, V., MILLER, E. G., & KURZROK, R. (1941). Metabolism of human sperm. *Endocrinology*, **28**, 885.

ROTHSCHILD, Lord. (1948). The activity of ram spermatozoa. *J. exp. Biol.*, **25**, 219.

—— (1949a). Electrical measurement of bull sperm activity. The effect of small electric currents on fertilizing capacity. *J. agric. Sci.*, **39**, 295.

—— (1949b). Measurement of sperm activity before artificial insemination. *Nature, Lond.*, **163**, 358.

—— (1950). Electrical measurement of bull sperm activity. Comparison with visual assessment. *J. agric. Sci.*, **40**, 82.

—— (1951a). Sperm-egg interacting substances and metabolic changes associated with fertilization. *Symp. biochem. Soc.*, **7**, 40.

—— (1951b). Sea-urchin spermatozoa. *Biol. Rev.*, **26**, 1.

—— (1951c). Cytochrome-catalysis of the movements of bracken spermatozoids. *Proc. Roy. Soc. B*, **138**, 272.

ROTHSCHILD, Lord (1952). Spermatozoa. *Sci. Progr.*, **40**, No. 157, 1.

—— (1953a). The movements of spermatozoa. In *Mammalian Germ Cells*, Ciba Foundation Symposium, London, p.122.

—— (1953b). A new method of measuring sperm speeds. *Nature, Lond.*, **171**, 512.

—— (1953c). A new method of measuring the activity of spermatozoa. *J. exp. Biol.*, **30**, 178.

—— (1956). *Fertilization*. London.

—— & BARNES, H. (1954). Constituents of bull seminal plasma. *J. exp. Biol.*, **31**, 561.

—— CLELAND, K. W. (1952). The physiology of sea-urchin spermatozoa. The nature and location of the endogenous substrate. *J. exp. Biol.*, **29**, 66.

—— & SWANN, M. M. (1949). The fertilization reaction in the sea-urchin egg. A propagated response to sperm attachment. *J. exp. Biol.*, **26**, 164.

ROTTENSTEN, K. (1950). Jagttagelser og under søgelser over nedsat frugtbarked hos kvaeg. *Beretn. Forsøgslab. Kbh.*, No. 247.

ROY, A. (1955). Storage of boar and stallion spermatozoa in glycine-egg-yolk medium. *Vet. Rec.*, **67**, 330.

—— & BISHOP, M. W. H. (1954). Effects of glycine on the survival of bull spermatozoa *in vitro*. *Nature, Lond.*, **174**, 746.

—— LUKTUKE, S. N., BHATTACHARYA, S., & BHATTACHARYA, P. (1950). Studies on the reducing substances of semen. Relation of sperm concentration and semen volume to fructose content, fructolysis and methylene-blue reduction time. *Indian J. Dairy Sci.*, **3**, 161.

SALISBURY, G. W. (1946). The glycolysis, livability and fertility of bovine spermatozoa as influenced by their concentration. In *The Problem of Fertility*, Princeton, p. 134.

—— BECK, G. H., CUPPS, P. T., & ELLIOTT, I. (1943). The effect of dilution rate on the livability and fertility of bull spermatozoa used for artificial insemination. *J. Dairy Sci.*, **26**, 1057.

—— KNODT, C. B., & BRATTON, R. W. (1948). The freezing point depression of bull semen and its relation to the diluter problem. *J. Anim. Sci.*, **7**, 283.

—— & NAKABAYASHI, N. T. (1957). Effect of phosphate and chloride ions on aerobic metabolism of bovine spermatozoa. *J. exp. Biol.*, **34**, 52.

—— & VANDEMARK, N. L. (1945). Stimulation of livability and glycolysis by addition of glucose to the egg-yolk citrate diluent for ejaculated bovine semen. *Amer. J. Physiol.*, **143**, 692.

—— —— (1957). Carbon dioxide as a reversible inhibitor of spermatozoan metabolism. *Nature, Lond.*, **180**, 989.

SCHLENK, W., & KAHMANN, H. (1938). Die chemische Zusammensetzung des Sperma-liquors und ihre physiologische Bedeutung, Untersuchung an Forellensperma. *Biochem. Z.*, **295**, 383.

SCHULTZE, A. B., & DAVIS, H. P. (1947). Some effects of adding thyroxine to bovine semen. *J. Dairy Sci.*, **30**, 543.

—— —— (1948). Effect of thyroxine on oxygen consumption of bovine spermatozoa and semen. *J. Dairy Sci.*, **31**, 946.

—— —— (1949). Effect of thyroxine on fertility of bovine semen. *J. Dairy Sci.*, **32**, 322.

—— & MAHLER, D. (1952). The effect of sodium arsenite on the respiration of bovine semen and the relation of this response to the fertilizing ability of semen. *J. Dairy Sci.*, **35**, 906.

SHERGIN, N. P. (1937). Glycolysis in the sperm of farm animals. (Translated title.) *Probl. Anim. Husb.*, Moscow, No. 12, 126. (In *Anim. Breed. Abstr.*, **7**, 181.)

—— (1939). Respiration of sperm of farm animals. (Translated title.) *Proc. Lenin Acad. agric. Sci.*, Nos. 2/3, 60. (In *Anim. Breed. Abstr.*, **7**, 181.)

SHETTLES, L. B. (1940a). The respiration of human spermatozoa and their response to various gases and low temperatures. *Amer. J. Physiol.*, **128**, 408.

—— (1940b). Resistance of human spermatozoa *in vitro* to sulfanilamide and sulfapyridine. *Proc. Soc. exp. Biol. N.Y.*, **44**, 392.

SKATKIN, P. N. (1940). Temperature shock of spermatozoa of the stallion. *Proc. Lenin Acad. agric. Sci.*, No. 8, 29. (In *Anim. Breed. Abstr.*, **8**, 344.)

SMITH, J. T., MAYER, D. T., & HERMAN, H. A. (1953). Osmotic pressure of extended bovine semen during storage. *Res. Bull. Mo. agric. Exp. Sta.*, No. 538.

—— —— & MERILAN, C. P. (1957). Effect of washing upon the dehydrogenase activity of bovine spermatozoa. *J. Dairy Sci.*, **40,** 521.

SMITH, S. E., & ASDELL, S. A. (1940). The buffering capacity of bull semen. *Cornell Vet.*, **30,** 499.

SØRENSEN, E. (1942). The dehydrogenation power of sperm cells as a measure for the fertility of semen. *Skand. VetTidskr.*, **32,** 358.

SPALLANZANI, L. (1776). *Opuscoli di Fisica Animale e Vegetabile.* Modena. (English edition, Edinburgh, 1799.)

SPEIGELMAN, S. (1956). On the nature of the enzyme-forming system. In *Enzymes: Units of Biological Structure and Function,* a Henry Ford Hospital Symposium, New York, p. 67.

STALLCUP, O. T., & McCARTNEY, H. K. (1953). Toxicity to bull spermatozoa of terramycin hydrochloride and its use as an anti-bacterial agent in diluents. *J. Dairy Sci.*, **36,** 293.

STIGLER, R. (1913). Wärmelähmung und Wärmestarre der menschlichen Spermatozoen. *Pflüg. Arch. ges. Physiol.*, **155,**

SWANSON, E. W. (1949). The effect of varying proportions of egg yolk and sodium citrate buffer in bull semen diluters upon sperm motility. *J. Dairy Sci.*, **32,** 345.

TAYLOR, Sir Geoffrey. (1951). Analysis of the swimming of microscopic organisms. *Proc. Roy. Soc.* A, **209,** 447.

—— (1952a). The action of waving cylindrical tails in propelling microscopic organisms. *Proc. Roy. Soc.* A, **211,** 225.

—— (1952b). Analysis of the swimming of long and narrow animals. *Proc. Roy. Soc.* A, **214,** 158.

TERNER, C. (1953). Aerobic metabolism and semen quality. In *Mammalian Germ Cells,* a Ciba Foundation Symposium, London.

THUNBERG, T. (1936). *Die Methodik der Dehydrogenasen.*

TORRES, I. (1935). Über Kreatinphosphorsäuresynthese in Organextrakten und in lebenden Spermatozoen. *Biochem. Z.*, **283,** 128.

TOSIC, J. (1947). Mechanism of hydrogen peroxide formation by spermatozoa and the role of amino acids in sperm motility. *Nature, Lond.*, **159,** 544.

—— (1951). Hydrogen peroxide formation by spermatozoa and its relation to sperm survival. *Symp. biochem. Soc.*, **7,** 22.

—— & WALTON, A. (1945). Respiration of spermatozoa in egg-yolk medium. *Nature, Lond.*, **156,** 507.

—— —— (1946). Formation of hydrogen peroxide by spermatozoa and its inhibitory effect upon respiration. *Nature, Lond.*, **158,** 485.

—— —— (1947). Effect of egg yolk and its constituents on the respiration and fertilizing capacity of spermatozoa. *J. agric. Sci.*, **37,** 69.

—— —— (1950). Metabolism of spermatozoa. The formation and elimination of hydrogen peroxide by spermatozoa and effects on motility and survival. *Biochem. J.*, **47,** 199.

TYLER, A. (1955). Gametogenesis, fertilization and parthenogenesis. In *Analysis of Development,* Philadelphia, p. 170.

UMBREIT, W. W., BURRIS, R. H., & STAUFFER, J. F. (1949). *Manometric Techniques and Tissue Metabolism,* Minneapolis.

VANDEMARK, N. L., & HAYS, R. L. (1953). Motility patterns in the female reproductive tract. *Iowa St. Coll. J. Sci.*, **28,** 107.

—— —— (1954). Rapid sperm transport in the cow. *Fertility & Sterility*, **5,** 131.

—— MERCIER, E., & SALISBURY, G. W. (1945). The methylene-blue reduction test and its relation to other measures of quality in bull semen. *J. Dairy Sci.*, **28,** 121.

—— SALISBURY, G. W., & BRATTON, R. W. (1949). Oxygen damage to bull spermatozoa and its prevention by catalase. *J. Dairy Sci.*, **32,** 353.

—— —— MOELLER, A. N., & BERKLEY, C. (1958). Exploration of electronic methods for evaluating sperm motility. *Science*, **127,** 286.

VANDEMARK, N. L. & SHARMA, U. D. (1957). Preliminary fertility results from the preservation of bovine semen at room temperatures. *J. Dairy Sci.*, **40**, 438.

VAN DRIMMELEN, G. C., & OETTLÉ, A. G. (1949). Changes in sperm quality. *Proc. Soc. Stud. Fertil.*, **1**, 5.

VAN TIENHOVEN, A., SALISBURY, G. W., VAN DEMARK, N. L., & HANSEN, R. G. (1952). The preferential utilization by bull spermatozoa of glucose as compared to fructose. *J. Dairy Sci.*, **35**, 637.

WALES, R. G., & WHITE, I. G. (1958a). The interaction of pH, tonicity and electrolyte concentration on the motility of dog spermatozoa. *J. Physiol.*, **141**, 273.

—— —— (1958b). The effect of the ions of the alkali metals magnesium and calcium on dog spermatozoa. *J. Physiol.*, **142**, 494.

WALTON, A. (1930). The effect of temperature on the survival in vitro of rabbit spermatozoa from the vas deferens. *Brit. J. exp. Biol.*, **7**, 201.

—— (1938). Preservation of fertilising capacity of horse semen. *Proc. Amer. Soc. Anim. Prod.*

—— (1950). Activity of spermatozoa *in vitro*. *Proc. Soc. Stud. Fertil.*, **2**, 63.

—— (1952). Flow orientation as a possible explanation of "wave-motion" and "rheotaxis" of spermatozoa. *J. exp. Biol.*, **29**, 520.

—— & DOTT, H. M. (1956). The aerobic metabolism of spermatozoa. *Proc. 3rd Int. Congr. Anim. Reprod., Cambridge*, **1**, 33.

—— & EDWARDS, J. (1938). Criteria of fertility in the bull. 1: The exhaustion test. *Proc. Amer. Soc. Anim. Prod.*, **31**, 254.

—— HAMMOND, J., & ASDELL, S. A. (1928). On the vitality of the spermatozoa in the male and female genital tracts and outside the body. *Proc. 1st Int. Congr. Sex. Res., Berlin*, **2**, 217.

WARREN, M. R. (1938). Observations on the uterine fluid of the rat. *Amer. J. Physiol.*, **122**, 602.

WEBER, H. (1938). The physiology of bull sperm with reference to artificial insemination. (Translated title.) *Vet. Med. Dissertation, Leipzig.* (In *Anim. Breed. Abstr.*, **6**, 16.)

WHITE, A., HANDLER, P., SMITH, E. L., & STETTEN, DEW., Jr. (1954). *Principles of Biochemistry*, New York, Toronto and London.

WHITE, I. G. (1953a). The effect of washing on the motility and metabolism of ram, bull and rabbit spermatozoa. *J. exp. Biol.*, **30**, 200.

—— (1953b). The effect of potassium on the washing and dilution of mammalian spermatozoa. *Aust. J. exp. Biol. med. Sci.*, **31**, 193.

—— (1953c). Metabolic studies of washed and diluted ram and bull spermatozoa. *Aust. J. biol. Sci.*, **6**, 706.

—— (1953d). Studies on the alkali metal requirements of ram and bull spermatozoa. *Aust. J. biol. Sci.*, **6**, 716.

—— (1954a). The effect of some seminal constituents and related substances on diluted mammalian spermatozoa. *Aust. J. biol. Sci.*, **7**, 379.

—— (1954b). The toxicity of some antibacterials for bull, ram, rabbit and human spermatozoa. *Aust. J. exp. Biol. med. Sci.*, **32**, 41.

—— (1955a). Studies on the spermicidal activity of chelating agents. *Aust. J. biol. Sci.*, **8**, 387.

—— (1955b). The toxicity of heavy metals to mammalian spermatozoa. *Aust. J. exp. Biol. med. Sci.*, **33**, 359.

—— (1956a). The effect of some inorganic ions on mammalian spermatozoa. *Proc. 3rd Int. Congr. Anim. Reprod., Cambridge*, Section 1, 23.

—— (1956b). The interaction between metals and chelating agents in mammalian spermatozoa. *J. exp. Biol.*, **33**, 422.

—— (1957). Metabolism of glycerol and similar compounds by bull spermatozoa. *Amer. J. Physiol.*, **189**, 307.

—— BLACKSHAW, A. W., & EMMENS, C. W. (1954). Metabolic and motility studies relating to the low temperature storage of ram and bull spermatozoa. *Aust. vet. J.*, **30**, 85.

WILLETT, E. L. (1953). Decline in fertility of bull semen with increase in storage time as influenced by dilution rate. *J. Dairy Sci.*, **36**, 1182.

WINBERG, H. (1941). The cozymase content of bird sperm. *Ark. Kemi Min. Geol.*, **15 B**, 1.

WINCHESTER, C. F., & McKENZIE, F. F. (1941a). Relative metabolic rates of semen, seminal plasma, and bacteria in semen of boar. *Proc. Soc. exp. Biol.*, *N.Y.*, **46**, 455.

—— —— (1941b). Influence of cell concentration on respiration rate of sperm. *Proc. Soc. exp. Biol.*, *N.Y.*, **48**, 648.

WINDSTOSSER, K. (1935). Uber die Atmung der Säugetierspermien. *Klin. Wschr.*, **14**, 193.

YAMANE, J., & ITO, T. (1932). Ueber die Geschwindegkeit der Pferdespermatozoen in strömenden und nicht-strömenden Flüssigkeiten. *Cytologia, Tokyo*, **3**, 188.

CHAPTER 10

FERTILISATION

By C. R. Austin and Arthur Walton

I. Introduction

Much progress has been made and many new facts have been discovered since Harvey (1651) wrote his famous works on generation and on " The Efficient Cause of the Chicken." Not long after Harvey's death, Leeuwenhoek (1677) described the occurrence in semen of spermatozoa, and thus the identity of the male germ-cell was first recognised (*see* Chapter 7), but the identity of the mammalian egg evaded recognition for many years despite the painstaking search of numerous investigators. In Harvey's day, the mammalian embryo was thought to originate in the uterus, and objects in that location, presumably blastocysts, were commonly referred to as eggs. De Graaf (1672) was one of the first to ascribe the source of eggs to the ovary, but he seems to have believed that the ovarian follicles were either the eggs themselves or else contained something analogous to eggs. Like many who succeeded him, De Graaf was conscious of the difficulty that though the follicles resembled the uterine " eggs," the Fallopian tubes were much too small to permit their passage from the ovary to the uterus. Much later, Cruickshank (1797) succeeded in recovering developing eggs from the Fallopian tubes of the rabbit, and these were of such small size that they clearly could not be explanted follicles and presumably must have originated within the follicle. Following this line of thought, Prévost and Dumas (1824) examined follicles with care and reported seeing a small object about 1 mm. in diameter that emerged when the follicle was ruptured. This may well have been the oöcyte surrounded by cumulus oöphorus, but unfortunately for them Prévost and Dumas saw no reason to examine it more closely. It was left to von Baer (1827), an outstanding investigator, to define precisely the structure of the follicle and the disposition of the egg within it. (The history of the search for and discovery of the mammalian egg is most ably told by Corner, 1933.)

In 1843, Barry first observed the spermatozoon within the perivitelline space in the egg of the rabbit, and a little later reports were published on the entry of the spermatozoon into the eggs of the round-worm, *Ascaris* (Nelson, 1851), and the frog (Newport, 1853). These findings were confirmed by Bischoff (1854), who had earlier strenuously maintained that the spermatozoon had but a subordinate function, namely, that of keeping the semen well stirred. Later, Hensen (1876), who acceded precedence to Weil, reported the presence of the spermatozoon within the cytoplasmic part of the egg, the vitellus. In 1877, Fol described in great detail the penetration of the spermatozoon into the sea-urchin egg and first put forward the theory that the fertilisation membrane was an adaptation to prevent polyspermy. It was, however, Van Beneden (1875) and O. Hertwig (1876) who were responsible for the most significant advances of this era. These workers showed that a nucleus of new formation, developing as a result of spermatozoon entry, eventually united with the egg nucleus. The immense significance of these observations was quickly appreciated and it was during the succeeding twenty years of that century that the general concept of fertilisation as we know it today was established (for a brief outline, *see* Austin, 1953b).

With these basic facts elucidated, theories of fertilisation developed along two main lines : one was concerned mainly with the mechanism by which the spermatozoon and egg coming together initiate development, and the other, with the significance of fertilisation in the life cycle, and the part that it plays in heredity and evolution. Up to the end of the last century, fertilisation was regarded as being concerned primarily with the means whereby continuity and increase of living organisms were assured. Asexual reproduction and parthenogenesis were thought to be exceptional phenomena. More recently, however, this outlook changed. Asexual reproduction in plants and in some animals was shown to be quite capable of maintaining continuity and increase, and parthenogenesis was observed as a normal process in many organisms and could often be induced by relatively simple procedures. On the other hand, the discovery of Mendelian inheritance, the origin of variation by mutation, the chromosomal mechanism, and the complex processes involved in meiosis have led to the realisation that sexuality, the formation of gametes, and fertilisation are intimately concerned with hereditary transmission. This outlook changed our attitude towards the significance of fertilisation. When reproduction was regarded as the chief end of fertilisation, emphasis was laid upon the function of the spermatozoon in " activating " the egg or " initiating " the development of a new individual from the egg. If, however, we consider sexuality and fertilisation as concerned equally with amphimixis the essential equivalence of the gametes acquires greater importance. Amphimixis and its hereditary consequences belong to the special field of genetics and genetical cytology, and will not be treated fully here. We are primarily concerned with the actual mechanism involved rather than with the consequences. (Broader issues are discussed by Wilson, 1928; White, 1954; Haldane, 1955; and Austin, 1959b).

With the formation of the gametes, the sequence of somatic cellular reproduction ceases. The gametes leave their sites of origin in the gonads and if fertilisation does not ensue they decay and eventually die. Normally, only when one male gamete and one female gamete have come in contact and the haploid nuclei have united, is life continued. The proper study of the process of fertilisation therefore covers the period from the formation of the gametes up to the first zygotic cleavage. This Chapter is concerned with the final development and the retention of fertilising capacity by the gametes, the mutual reaction of the gametes to one another prior to penetration, the morphology and physiology of the fertilisation reaction, and the initiation of cleavage. It also deals with such phenomena as parthenogenesis, gynogenesis and polyspermy, the analysis of which is of interest in itself, and gives much useful information on the nature of the normal processes as they occur in sexual reproduction.

II. The Egg

Maturation

In the formation of the male gametes, the spermatocytes undergo meiosis involving reduction of chromosomes to the haploid condition before any major differentiation of the cellular structure is apparent. Not until the spermatid is

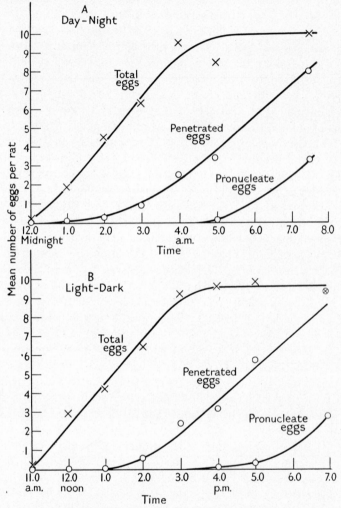

Fig. *10*. 1—Showing the time intervals between ovulation, spermatozoon penetration, and pro-nucleus formation as observed in rats maintained under normal conditions of illumination and in artificial (reversed) lighting. (From Austin and Braden, 1954a.)

formed, do the definitive structures of the spermatozoon appear (*see* Chapter 7). In the female gametes, on the other hand, differentiation appears first in the oöcyte as increased growth and yolk formation, and meiosis is delayed until after the ovum is fully formed (*see* Chapter 5). The primary oöcytes are produced by mitotic division of oögonia and are characterised by the possession of a large spherical nucleus, the germinal vesicle, containing usually a single nucleolus. Maturation entails two meiotic divisions. At the beginning of maturation, the nucleus moves towards the surface of the oöcyte and loses the nuclear membrane, the nucleolus disappears and the chromosomes complete their condensation. The first maturation spindle forms, meiosis proceeds to telophase, the spindle rotates and part of the cytoplasm is extruded to form the first polar body (*see* p. 347). The cell is now a secondary oöcyte. The second meiotic division and the extrusion of the second polar body occur in essentially the same manner as the first, giving rise to the oötid. Both meiotic divisions are reductional, the number of centromeres being reduced in the first and the number of chromatids being reduced in the second. (The behaviour of the chromosomes in meiosis is discussed by White, 1954; in connection with spermatogenesis, *see* p. 46. Knowledge of spindles, asters and centrosomes has been summarised by De Robertis, Nowinski and Saez, 1954 ; Ris, 1955 ; Brachet, 1957).

Both hormonal and physical influences apparently affect the maturation of eggs in mammals. There is good evidence that pituitary gonadotrophin plays a part in the initiation of meiosis (*see* Vol. 3, p. 75). On the other hand, Pincus and Enzmann (1935) and Pincus (1939b) reported that the culture *in vitro* of oöcytes resulted in typical maturation phenomena and that these changes were unaffected by the presence of pituitary hormones in the medium. It would seem, therefore, that isolation of the eggs from the granulosa, whether by the action of hormones or by explantation, is itself sufficient to induce maturation. This conclusion is further supported by the work of Noyes (1952) and Chang (1955c, d), who found that rat and rabbit oöcytes matured after transfer to a host animal or in culture.

There is some evidence that certain as yet undefined changes in the properties of the investments surrounding the eggs are normally completed after ovulation in rodents and are a necessary preliminary to spermatozoon penetration. Close study of the time relations involved in the fertilisation of rat (Fig. *10.1*), mouse and hamster eggs showed that penetration did not occur until after 4 hours after ovulation, although it could be assumed that the spermatozoa present were fully capable of fertilisation when ovulation took place (Austin and Braden, 1954a ; Braden and Austin, 1954b ; Strauss, 1954, 1956 ; Austin, 1956d). That these changes are independent of the maturation of the egg itself is implied by the finding that spermatozoa can enter the perivitelline space of the primary oöcytes occasionally ovulated in the mouse (Austin and Braden, 1954c).

Relationship between Maturation, Ovulation and Fertilisation

As a general rule, fertilisation begins soon after ovulation and the egg is penetrated just before, during or just after maturation. This is true for the great majority of animals but not for all. Exceptions among the invertebrates include a number of forms such as the marine annelids *Histribodella, Dinophilus* and *Saccocirrus*, and some free-living flatworms, in which the spermatozoon penetrates the early oöcyte but remains quiescent until the latter has completed its growth (Marshall, 1922 ; Wilson, 1928). A similar possibility was suggested for the fowl by Ivanov (1924) (*see also* Walton and Whetham, 1933). Hartman (1937), however, has pointed out that experiments by Warren and Kilpatrick (1929) make this interpretation unlikely. As noted later, a departure from the general rule is represented among the mammals by the tenrecs in which spermatozoa are reported to enter the eggs before ovulation. Figure *10. 2* illustrates the four classes in which most animals can be grouped.

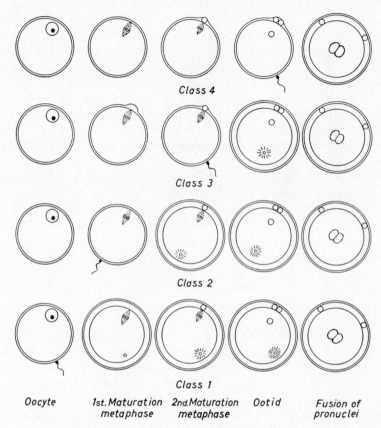

Fig. *10. 2*—The stages of maturation at which the eggs of different animals are penetrated by spermatozoa. (From Rothschild, 1956, after Dalcq, 1952b.)

Class I : Fertilisation begins before the germinal vesicle of the oöcyte has broken down.

> Examples : *Nereis, Spisula, Urechis, Ascaris, Sagitta,* and the sponges.

Class II : Fertilisation begins at the first maturation division.

> Examples : *Ciona, Chaetopterus, Cumingia, Mytilus, Habrobracon.* Precocious spermatozoon penetration into the oöcytes of *Chaetopterus* has been reported by Lillie (1923).

Class III : Fertilisation begins at the second maturation metaphase.

> Examples : *Branchiostoma* and all vertebrates, except that in the dog and fox (Van der Stricht, 1923 ; Pearson and Enders, 1943) and in the horse (Hamilton and Day, 1945) spermatozoa may enter the eggs in the stage of the intact germinal vesicle as in Class I.

Class IV : Fertilisation occurs after completion of the second maturation division. Examples : coelenterates and echinoderms. In these, the polar bodies are normally formed before the egg leaves the ovary. Sometimes, spermatozoa will penetrate sea-urchin eggs that have not extruded polar bodies ; fertilisation proceeds when maturation has taken place (Wilson, 1928).

Loss of the Capacity for Fertilisation

The eggs of all species lose the capacity for becoming fertilised rather rapidly. Spallanzani found that the eggs of the frog became unfertilisable after about half an hour in water. The fertile life of the eggs of the sea-urchin, *Arbacia punctulata*, is 36–52 hours (Harvey, 1956).

The duration of fertilising capacity of the mammalian egg has been determined by experiment in a few species. Hammond (1925) found in the rabbit that the percentage of eggs fertilised diminished rapidly if mating occurred at the time of ovulation or later. In a more extensive series of experiments, the time that the eggs remain fertilisable was estimated to be about 6 hours (Hammond, 1934). Pincus (1936a) considers that this period may be a little too short and places it at about 7 hours, at which time the eggs leave the cumulus mass and, passing down the Fallopian tube, become coated with mucinous material. Chang (1953b), assesses the fertile period at 8 hours, and San Martin and Fernandez (1949) at 8–9 hours. The acquisition by the rabbit egg of an additional layer during its passage through the Fallopian tube seems to have been observed by Cruickshank (1797) and was described by Barry (1839), Bischoff (1842), Meissner (1855), and later by many others. For long called the " albumen " layer, it was shown by Braden (1952, 1955) and Bacsich and Hamilton (1954) to be composed of an acid mucoprotein. Its production seems to be under hormonal control, for Greenwald (1957) reports that oestrogen administration reduces the amount deposited on the eggs. This coating is impervious to spermatozoa (Pincus, 1930) and so is probably responsible for the loss of fertilisability. Chang's (1952a, b ; 1953a, 1955c) results certainly show that rabbit eggs kept *in vitro* retain their fertilisability for longer than *in vivo*. The time limits were found to vary with the temperature of storage : about $\frac{1}{2}$ hour at 45° C., 24 hours at 38° C., 24 hours at 24° C., 96 hours at 10° C., and 72 hours at 0° C. Though these eggs were capable of undergoing fertilisation and early cleavage, most of the embryos degenerated before birth.

Hammond and Walton (1934) found that ferret eggs were fertilisable for about 36 hours. Hartman (1924) has shown that the eggs of the opossum are definitely degenerate when they reach the uterus in about 24 hours. As with rabbit eggs, however, the fertile life of marsupial eggs may be limited by the deposition of the layer of " albumen " that they receive in the Fallopian tube (Caldwell, 1887 ; Hill, 1910, 1918 ; Hartman, 1916, 1919 ; McCrady, 1938 ; Sharman, 1955b). The fertile life of cow and sheep eggs is probably less than 24 hours (Quinlan, Mare and Roux, 1932 ; Green and Winters, 1935 ; Trimberger and Davis, 1943). It is possible that the dog egg retains fertility for longer than those of other species, namely, 5 or 6 days and perhaps as long as 8 days (Whitney, 1927 ; Evans and Cole, 1931).

Observations on the guinea-pig indicate that the egg becomes unfertilisable about 20 hours after ovulation (Young and Blandau, 1936 ; Young, 1937 ; Blandau and Young, 1939). The hamster egg probably remains fertilisable for little more than 10 hours (Strauss, 1956). Data for the mouse (Long, 1912) and rat (Blandau and Jordan, 1941) showed that the eggs were fertilisable for at least 12 hours. More recent experiments by Runner and Palm (1953), involving recovery of eggs from immature mice after artificially induced ovulation and transfer to adult recipients, seemed to suggest a very short fertile life, between 4 and 8 hours, for mouse eggs. Braden and Austin (1954d), however, pointed out that manipulation may have accelerated the normal rate of ageing and that their own observations on delayed coitus indicated a fertile life of at least 10 hours for both mouse and rat eggs. In addition, eggs ovulated in immature rats following hormone administration were often found to deteriorate rapidly, apparently because of some inherent weakness (Austin, 1950b). Early deterioration of artificially ovulated eggs may also be attributable to conditions within the immature female tract, since the proportion of such eggs capable of undergoing normal fertilisation is quite high if they are transferred to adult animals (Adams, 1954 ; McLaren and Michie, 1956 ; Gates, 1956).

In the fowl, the egg is apparently fertilisable for only a few hours after it leaves the ovary (Crew, 1926 ; Dunn, 1927).

An estimate of the duration of fertile life in the eggs of any species is subject to considerable variance because differences inevitably exist between eggs and between individuals. In addition, the ageing process is a gradual one, in which various functions in the egg are successively overwhelmed. An early effect of ageing is that the resulting embryos are not fully viable and perish at some time before birth (Blandau and Young, 1939 ; Blandau and Jordan, 1941 ; Chang, 1952b ; Young, 1953 ; Blandau, 1954). Further ageing leads to abnormalities in fertilisation, involving particularly the pronuclei (Blandau, 1952). The rate of reaction of the egg to the entry of the spermatozoon also becomes slower, so that the defence mechanisms against polyspermy deteriorate (Austin and Braden, 1953a, b, 1956 ; Odor and Blandau, 1956). Failure to undergo fertilisation and normal development may sometimes be due to inherent abnormality of the eggs (Corner, 1923 ; Austin, 1950b ; Chang, 1952c ; Hartman, 1953).

Fate of Unfertilised Eggs

Unfertilised eggs pass down the Fallopian tube in the same way as fertilised eggs, though their release from the cumulus mass is apt to be slower owing to the absence of spermatozoon-borne hyaluronidase. The eggs apparently break up in the uterus ; Hartman (1939) remarks that in thousands of washings from the vagina of the monkey no egg was ever encountered.

During their passage through the Fallopian tube, unfertilised eggs undergo degeneration which is exhibited both by nuclear and cytoplasmic changes and which may sometimes be interpreted as an abortive attempt at development. One of the earliest changes seen in unfertilised eggs involves the second maturation spindle. Most often, this structure simply fades and the chromosomes undergo chromatolysis or become scattered through the egg cytoplasm. Sometimes, however, the second meiotic division is spontaneously resumed and the second polar body is extruded. This may be followed by the formation of a single nucleus, resembling a pronucleus, but more often several subnuclei develop, presumably from scattered chromosomes. Alternatively, the meiosis may be completed without polar-body extrusion and thus two nuclei may develop which simulate male and female pronuclei. Later, the unfertilised egg may undergo one or more divisions giving rise to apparent cleavage stages but nearly always the

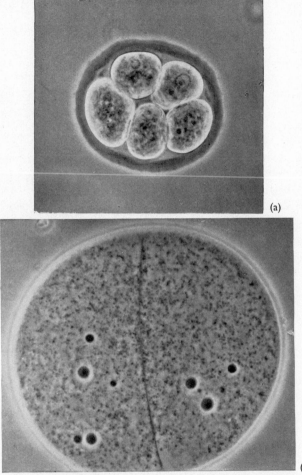

(a)

(b)

Fig. *10*.3—Unfertilised rat eggs undergoing spontaneous fragmentation. The egg in (b) has been compressed to demonstrate the abnormal nuclear state. (From Austin, 1949b.)

resulting fragments are clearly abnormal in size and form. Fragmenting rat eggs, especially in immature animals after induced ovulation, sometimes rather closely resemble cleaved fertilised eggs, but the nuclear state generally renders distinction easy ; instead of a normal nucleus there may be two or more subnuclei, or else no nuclear structure at all is visible (Austin, 1949b ; and see Fig. *10*. 3). The occurrence of enucleate fragments implies that much of the subdivision of the egg cytoplasm may take place by amitotic division—a process rarely encountered in somatic cells (Swann, 1952).

In spite of these observations, the possibility cannot be excluded that unfertilised eggs in mammals may very occasionally undergo protracted embryonic development and even give rise to living young. This phenomenon, to which the term " parthenogenesis " is applied, is discussed later (*see* p. 384).

III. Union of the Gametes
Probability of Fertilisation

In preceding Chapters it was shown that the main function of copulation was to ensure a close approximation in time and space of the male and female gametes under such conditions that fertilisation will be assured with the minimum of waste. In general, the probability of fertilisation will depend upon a number of independent variables such as the chances of a meeting between male and female, the fitness of each to perform the sexual act and the viability of the gametes. Where, however, the scope of the enquiry is confined to the contingencies in the female tract after successful coitus and immediately preceding fertilisation, the number of variables is considerably reduced. Even then a quantitative measurement of the chances of fertilisation cannot be so easily computed as it can in experiments *in vitro* with the gametes of marine invertebrates. Rothschild and Swann (1949, 1951b) and Rothschild (1956) calculated the probability of a successful collision between the spermatozoa and eggs of the sea-urchin, *Psammechinus miliaris*, when mixed *in vitro*. In mammals, however, such assessments have not been attempted. Even the site of fertilisation, the volume that it contains, the concentrations of ova and spermatozoa, and the velocity of movement of the spermatozoon in the vicinity of the ovum are as yet most imperfectly known.

In mammals, the most common site of fertilisation, where the spermatozoon penetrates the ovum, is the Fallopian tube. In some species, part of the ampulla becomes distended with fluid after ovulation and the eggs are held here for several hours ; it is evidently within this region that fertilisation generally takes place (rat, Tafani, 1889 ; mouse, Sobotta, 1895 ; guinea-pig, Lams, 1913 ; elephant shrew, Van der Horst and Gillman, 1941 ; hamster, Strauss, 1954, 1956 ; field vole, Austin, 1957c). It is possible that spermatozoon penetration may sometimes occur in the ovarian bursa whilst the eggs are passing through, for spermatozoa have been reported in this location in the bat (Van der Stricht, 1909), ferret (Hammond and Walton, 1934), and rat (Blandau and Odor, 1949). In the rabbit, fertilisation takes place in the ampulla (Hammond, 1934 ; Braden, 1953). The tenrecs of Madagascar are exceptional in that spermatozoa apparently enter the ovarian follicles and there penetrate the eggs which are then ovulated in the pronuclear stage of development (*Hemicentetes*, Bluntschli, 1938 ; *Ericulus*, Strauss, 1938 ; *Centetes*, Strauss, 1950). Pearson (1944) believed that in the short-tailed shrew, also, penetration occurred in the follicle. Although fertilisation commonly begins in the Fallopian tube, a high degree of development is not reached there. In the opossum, *Didelphis virginiana* (Hartman, 1928), and in the wallaby, *Setonix brachyurus* (Sharman, 1955a, b), eggs reach the uterus while still in the pronucleate stage. In most mammals, however, the eggs enter the uterus as morulae.

Only a tentative estimate can be given of the actual number of spermatozoa present at the site of fertilisation but some counts of the number found there have been recorded. Hammond and Walton (1934) reported finding in the ovarian bursae of ferrets numbers of spermatozoa that ranged from 0 to 1,600. The counts were made at different times after copulation. Between 0–100 spermatozoa have been recorded in the ampullae of rats, mice and hamsters at about the time of fertilisation (Austin, 1948b, 1956d ; Blandau and Odor, 1948, 1949 ; Moricard and Bossu, 1951 ; Braden and Austin, 1954a), between 28 and 360 in the field vole (Austin, 1957c), about 1,000 in the rabbit ampulla (Austin, 1948b ; Moricard and Bossu, 1949b ; Chang, 1951b ; Braden, 1953), and between 36 and 1,350 in the sheep ampulla (Braden and Austin, 1954a). In the fowl, it is estimated that from 7,000 to 70,000 spermatozoa reach the infundibulum after intravaginal insemination with 2×10^8 spermatozoa (Allen and Grigg, 1957). These data are not sufficient for a reliable estimation to be made of the probability of fertilisation along the lines adopted by Rothschild and Swann for marine organisms. Nevertheless, an approximate figure can be given for the frequency of penetration of the rabbit ovum with spermatozoa because in this species the zona pellucida does not become impermeable to spermatozoa after penetration, and spermatozoa continue to enter the egg for several hours after ovulation. It was found that with normal mating, when about 50 to 100 million spermatozoa might be liberated into the vagina, each rabbit egg received an effective sperm collision about once every two minutes (Braden and Austin, 1954a). From other considerations, notably from the proportion of eggs to become penetrated during a specified time, the successful collision frequency in the rat was found to be about once every 10 minutes. The small number of spermatozoa found at the site of fertilisation, and hence the small number of effective collisions that occur, is the basis of the thesis advanced by Chang (1951b) and developed by Austin and Braden (1952), Braden (1953) and Braden and Austin (1953b) that an important function of the female tract is to control the number of spermatozoa arriving at the site of fertilisation so that all eggs when ovulated will have a favourable chance of being fertilised, while the risk of polyspermy, against which the egg itself has inadequate protection, is reduced. The reality of this risk can be inferred from the data in Table I,

TABLE I

NUMBER OF EXTRA SPERMS IN THE EGGS OF ANY ONE FALLOPIAN TUBE AND ITS RELATION
TO THE NUMBER OF SPERMS ABOUT THE EGGS, AND THE NUMBER OF POLYSPERMIC
(DISPERMIC) EGGS (BRADEN AND AUSTIN, 1954a)

Number of extra sperms (within eggs) per tube	Number of tubes	Number of sperms about the eggs		Total number penetrated eggs	Dispermic eggs	
		Total	Mean per tube		Total	Per cent
0	50	1785	35·7	211	0	—
1	35	1379	39·4	174	3	1·7
2	17	749	44·1	80	2	1·5
3	10	563	56·3	42	1	2·4
4–5	11	720	65·5	59 ⎫		
6–8	6	399	66·5	30 ⎬ 107	3	2·8
>8	3	408	136	18 ⎭		

which show that there is a highly significant association between the numbers of extra spermatozoa entering the eggs of any one Fallopian tube and the numbers of spermatozoa observed at the site of fertilisation. The figures also suggest a positive association between the incidence of polyspermy and the numbers of spermatozoa at the site of fertilisation, but the number of polyspermic eggs encountered was too small for the results to be statistically significant.

In the discussion so far, there is the tacit assumption that all spermatozoa reaching the site of fertilisation have equal chances of fertilising eggs. That this is not necessarily so is a conclusion to be derived from work on " selective fertilisation " (see p. 238).

The features of the female genital tract that contribute to its regulatory action upon the passage of spermatozoa are considered in a recent review (Austin and Bishop, 1957a). Evidence that the function is under hormonal influence is set out in Chapter 9, p. 234.

Chemotaxis

It has been suggested that the spermatozoon is attracted towards the egg by chemical substances. The difficulty of envisaging some mechanism by which this effect could be produced has not helped the analysis of a subject that has long been a matter of controversy (see Morgan, 1927). In the plant kingdom, however, the operation of chemotaxis is now well established and has been demonstrated particularly in the ferns, mosses, horse-tails, liverworts and quillworts (see Rothschild, 1956; Brokaw, 1957, 1958a, b). There is evidence that l-malic acid is the agent in the bracken fern. If a capillary tube containing this acid is dipped into a suspension of bracken spermatozoa the movements of most of the spermatozoa soon cease to be random. The cells move quickly towards the source of l-malic acid and gather about the tip of the capillary tube where the concentration is highest. According to Rothschild, study of the behaviour of bracken spermatozoa indicates that they must possess something analogous to a sense organ that is capable of detecting l-malic acid, but the position of any sensory region, whether in the head or tail, and the precise mechanics of the response in terms of spermatozoon movements, are still quite obscure.

Buller (1902), who discussed the question of chemotaxis at some length and performed numerous experiments, stated that he was unaware of a single instance where chemotaxis had been proved to play a part in the fertilisation of the eggs of animals. Dakin and Fordham (1924), however, repeated Buller's experiments and came to a contrary conclusion. They found that the spermatozoa of sea-urchins entered capillary tubes containing acid and egg secretions to a much greater extent than control tubes containing only sea-water. Since the spermatozoa passed further up the experimental tubes than the control tubes they concluded that the effect was not due to an inhibition of motility acting as a trapping mechanism. Lillie (1923) and Lillie and Just (1924) described the reaction of spermatozoa to a drop of egg secretion introduced into a spermatozoon suspension beneath a cover slip—" a ring of active spermatozoa forms round the drop separated by a clear zone almost devoid of spermatozoa from the general suspension. If the clear zone be examined carefully under the microscope, spermatozoa may be seen swimming directly across it from the general suspension to the drop of egg water for some minutes.   The clear zone thus gives the range of some directive influence proceeding from the drop." Hartmann and Schartau (1939), using the capillary tube technique, also claimed support for a chemotactic effect of egg secretions, but their conclusions have been criticised by Cornman (1941), who considers that a trapping mechanism was not rigorously excluded.   For the same reason, both Tyler (1955) and Rothschild (1956) believe that unequivocal evidence for chemotaxis in animals is still lacking.

Although chemotaxis has not been conclusively demonstrated in animal spermatozoa, the orientation of spermatozoa in response to the flow of the suspending medium is well recognised (*see* Walton, 1952).

Capacitation

In mammals of most species, coitus is restricted to a relatively short time in the cycle when ripe follicles are present in the ovaries and the animal comes into oestrus.   Since the spermatozoa and eggs have but a brief period of survival after liberation, the relationship of this receptive phase to the time of ovulation is important.   If oestrus is very short, the chances of a successful sexual encounter with a male are relatively small.   If the period of receptivity were too prolonged, the interval between coitus and ovulation or between ovulation and subsequent coitus might be longer than the survival of the spermatozoon in the first case or of the unfertilised egg in the second.   By this hypothesis alone, it would appear that the most favourable timing would be for copulation and ovulation to be nearly coincident, the former preceding the latter by just sufficient time for spermatozoa to reach the newly ovulated eggs.   Examination of the relevant data shows, however, that on the average spermatozoa reach the site of fertilisation very soon after coitus and usually several hours before ovulation.

In those species that do not ovulate without the stimulus of coitus, the true relationship is fairly accurately ascertained.   In the rabbit, for example, ovulation does not occur until $9\frac{1}{2}$–10 hours after copulation (Barry, 1839 ; Bischoff, 1842 ; Heape, 1905 ; Walton and Hammond, 1928 ; Hammond, 1934).   It is estimated that spermatozoa reach the Fallopian tube in about an hour after mating (Adams, 1956a, b ; Greenwald, 1956a), and the ampulla in 3–4 hours (Heape, 1905 ; Parker, 1931 ; Florey and Walton, 1932 ; Hammond, 1934 ; San Martin, 1951 ; Braden, 1953).   Chang (1952a) has evidence that the time may be as short as 1 hour.   It is apparent, therefore, that some spermatozoa may be present at the site of fertilisation 6 or more hours before ovulation.   In the ferret, the interval between copulation and the ovulation that it induces is about 30 hours and spermatozoa reach the ovarian capsule 3–6 hours after coitus (Hammond and Walton, 1934).   Spermatozoa may therefore be present at the site of fertilisation in this species for a whole day before the eggs arrive.

In species that ovulate spontaneously, the interval that may elapse between coitus and ovulation is not so easily defined.   In the rat, coitus early in oestrus can precede ovulation by about 10 hours (Boling, Blandau, Soderwall and Young, 1941), and as the spermatozoa take only $\frac{1}{2}$ to 1 hour to reach the ovarian end of the Fallopian tubes (Blandau and Money, 1944), spermatozoa may be 9 hours at the site of fertilisation before the eggs.   In the cow, ovulation occurs about 14 hours after the end of the heat, but the conception rate of inseminations made at this time is very low, and the optimum time is from about 12 hours before to about

6 hours after the end of oestrus, or from 6 to 24 hours before ovulation (Trimburger and Davis, 1943 ; Laing, 1957). In the ewe and sow, ovulation occurs towards the end of the heat period, but as in the former the heat is of very short duration, and in the latter ovulation occurs over a rather long period, the evidence for a latent period between service (or insemination) and ovulation is not so obvious (Polge, 1956 ; Laing, 1957). A latent period appears to be lacking also in the mouse, in which coitus and ovulation are often contemporaneous (Braden and Austin, 1954b).

The relatively long period that may elapse between the arrival of the spermatozoa at the site of fertilisation and subsequent arrival of eggs suggests that it may be *necessary* for the spermatozoa to be present within the female tract some time before fertilisation. An indication that this is so can be seen in the evidence obtained by Hammond (1934) that in rabbits mated 1 hour after ovulation some 79 per cent of eggs failed to undergo fertilisation. About 7 hours after ovulation, rabbit eggs become impervious to spermatozoa (*see* p. 315), so that spermatozoa introduced after ovulation may not acquire fertilising capacity before the eggs become unfertilisable. More direct evidence began to accumulate when experiments were performed involving the injection of suspensions of spermatozoa directly into the Fallopian tubes of rabbits at laparotomy ; it was found that though spermatozoa were able to fertilise eggs when introduced into the Fallopian tubes 4 to 6 hours before ovulation (Austin, 1948b, 1949a), they could rarely do so when introduced at the time of or shortly after ovulation (Chang, 1951a, 1955a, b ; Austin, 1951a, 1955b). Chang also made the observation that rather more fertilised eggs could be obtained by introducing spermatozoa at this time if the spermatozoa had previously been incubated in the uterus of another doe. Austin extended the investigation to the rat, noting that spermatozoa injected into the periovarian sac after ovulation rapidly attained the site of fertilisation but did not penetrate eggs until 4 or more hours later. Noyes (1953) found that in rats the interval between introduction of spermatozoa into the uterus and the penetration of spermatozoa into the eggs was shorter with uterine than with epididymal spermatozoa. It was concluded that the spermatozoa acquired fertilising capacity by undergoing some kind of physiological preparation in the female environment. Since lack of fertilisation could be attributed to failure of the spermatozoa to pass through the zona pellucida, it was suggested that the physiological preparation involved the activation of an enzyme capable of acting upon the zona. Evidence was also obtained in intact rats : when coitus occurred after ovulation, spermatozoa began to accumulate at the site of fertilisation within an hour but did not proceed to enter the eggs until at least 2 hours after mating. As there had been no operative interference with the animals, nor dilution of the spermatozoa with artificial media, there seemed no doubt that the necessary sojourn of the spermatozoon in the female tract could not be attributed to artefact and the preparatory process that the spermatozoon evidently had to undergo was termed " capacitation " (Austin, 1952b). The time required for capacitation appears to be not less than 2 hours in the rat and 4 hours in the rabbit (Austin and Braden, 1954a). In the hamster, too, the period seems to be about 2–4 hours (Strauss, 1956). Recently, Chang (1957a) has produced evidence that capacitation is reversible and that spermatozoa brought again into contact with the seminal plasma require to be recapacitated before being able to effect fertilisation.

A morphological change in the spermatozoon, that may be the visible evidence
of capacitation, has been described by Austin and Bishop (1958a, c), who found
that living spermatozoa recovered from the Fallopian tubes showed distinct alterations of the acrosome (Fig. *10*. 4).   Spermatozoa with their heads in the thickness
of the zona pellucida, or within eggs, clearly lacked the acrosome (Figs. *10*. 4, 19
and 21a).   These authors concluded that capacitation involves a loosening of the

(a)   (b)

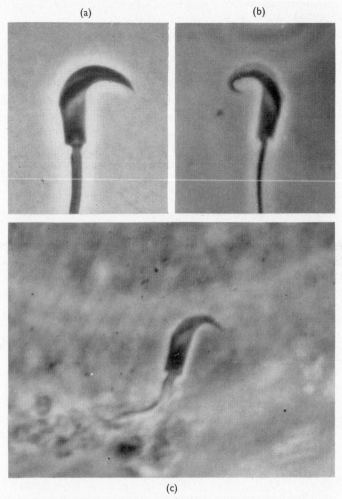

(c)

Fig. *10*. 4—Heads of hamster spermatozoa (a) from the epididymis,
(b) from the Fallopian tube, (c) embedded in the zona pellucida.
Alteration and loss of the acrosome is believed to be attributable
to capacitation. (From Austin and Bishop, 1958b, c.)

attachment of the acrosome to the spermatozoon head, as a result of which the
acrosome becomes detached when the spermatozoon makes contact with the zona
pullucida.   Removal of the acrosome evidently exposes the perforatorium (Austin
and Bishop, 1958b ; *and see* page 10) which may play an important role in the
penetration of the zona pellucida (*see* page 329).

From the experiments described above (involving the introduction of spermatozoa into the Fallopian tube) it is evident that spermatozoa need not pass through

the uterus and that capacitation can take place wholly in the Fallopian tube. This probably accounts for the fact that eggs may be fertilised following the injection of spermatozoa into the peritoneal cavity, a result that has been reported in the fowl (Van Drimmelen, 1951), rabbit (Ott, 1882 ; Dauzier and Thibault, 1956), bitch (Albrecht, 1895, 1899), guinea-pig (Rowlands, 1957a, b, 1958), and heifer (Skjerven, 1955 ; McDonald and Sampson, 1957). It seems likely the spermatozoa found their way into the Fallopian tubes and there underwent capacitation and penetrated the eggs. An alternative explanation is that capacitation occurred in the peritoneal cavity, but this is contra-indicated by some of Dauzier and Thibault's observations. They tied off the ovarian ends of the Fallopian tubes before intraperitoneal insemination, and noted that none of the eggs subsequently recovered from the peritoneal cavity were fertilised. Nevertheless, it now seems clear that the conditions responsible for producing the state of capacitation are not entirely specific to the female genital tract : Noyes, Walton and Adams (1958a, b) have demonstrated that capacitation can occur, to some extent at least, in non-genital organs, namely, bladder, colon, and the anterior chamber of the eye.

Fertilisins and Antifertilisins

When the water in which sea-urchin eggs have been standing (" egg water ") is added to a suspension of spermatozoa of the same species, the cells become aggregated into groups which gradually increase in size. Close examination shows that the spermatozoa are generally agglutinated head to head, but sometimes also tail to tail, or head to tail (see Tyler, 1955). The substance responsible for this effect evidently diffuses from the eggs into the surrounding medium and it was named " fertilisin " by Lillie (1912, 1913a, b). Lillie believed that fertilisin from the egg reacted with a specific substance, " antifertilisin," in the spermatozoon and drew an analogy with a serological reaction. Since that time, a great volume of work has been published on this subject and the progress made has been appraised in recent reviews by Tyler (1948, 1949, 1955), Bielig and Medem (1949), Runnström (1949), Rothschild (1956, 1958) and Metz (1957).

The present state of knowledge may be briefly described as follows. Fertilisin (also called Gynogamone II) is a mucopolysaccharide or glycoprotein with a molecular weight of rather more than 82,000, and it largely composes the jelly coat of the echinoderm egg. It has been identified in a number of invertebrates and also in some fish and amphibia. Serological tests indicate that its nature varies between different animals, and cross-reactions between the egg water of one species and the spermatozoa of another are seldom as strong as the homologous reactions. The agglutination is not permanent : after a time, spermatozoa become free again, but their properties have now changed. They can no longer be agglutinated, even by fresh egg-water, and they have lost their fertilising capacity but not their motility. The reactions between fertilisin and spermatozoa thus resemble in several particulars the agglutination phenomena that are familiar to immunologists. In addition to agglutination of spermatozoa, egg water causes an increase in the motility of the cells ; this effect is probably attributable to a different substance which is distinguished by the name Gynogamone I.

Antifertilisin (Androgamone II) is evidently present on the nuclear part of the spermatozoon head and is of the nature of an acidic protein. When extracted from the spermatozoon it reacts with the fertilisin about the egg to form a precipitation membrane and is also capable of agglutinating a suspension of eggs. An antifertilisin of essentially the same chemical and serological properties can be extracted from the interior of sea-urchin eggs.

The function of the fertilisins and antifertilisins is still largely hypothetical. Agglutination of the spermatozoon onto the surface of the egg would probably ensure against its escape and the relative species-specificity of the reaction would tend to reduce the chances of cross-fertilisation. Tyler (1949) suggests that once the spermatozoon is attached to the egg it is transported through the jelly coat by interaction of its antifertilisin with successively deeper layers of fertilisin until it reaches the cytoplasmic part of the egg. Hagström (1956a, b, c) believes, however, that the jelly coat of the sea-urchin egg represents a general obstacle to spermatozoon penetration, for he found that fertilisation took place normally but with much lower spermatozoon concentrations after the jelly coat had been removed. The role of the egg antifertilisin is even less clear—it may conceivably be involved in the formation of the fertilisation membrane by reacting with a layer of fertilisin on the vitelline membrane.

The existence in mammals of a spermatozoon-agglutinating substance similar to fertilisin is suggested by the observations of Popa (1927), Corrias and Novarini (1950) and Tyler (1954). Recently, Bishop and Tyler (1956) have produced further evidence of a type of fertilisin-antifertilisin reaction between mammalian gametes. When rabbit eggs were placed in a suspension of spermatozoa in physiological saline solution on a glass slide, the spermatozoa showed a strong tendency to become agglutinated head to head. Agglutination of this kind is very commonly presented by mammalian spermatozoa in artificial media and is well known to be augmented by the absence of non-electrolytes from the medium (*see* Chapter 9). In Bishop and Tyler's experience, however, the agglutination was shown more distinctly near the eggs than further away. Moreover, the agglutinating agent could be extracted by solutions at pH 3 or by hypertonic solutions. The effect was not observed among spermatozoa in the vicinity of rabbit eggs that had acquired a mucoprotein layer. Cross-tests between rabbit, mouse, bull and human spermatozoa and rabbit, mouse and cow eggs gave evidence of some species-specificity. Bishop and Tyler believe that the zona pellucida is the source of the agent, which they suggest may be referred to as a fertilisin.

P. E. Lindahl and his co-workers (*see* p. 239) have described the presence of an " antagglutin " in the semen and in the follicles and Fallopian tubes ; whether it plays any part in fertilisation is unknown.

Egg-membrane Lysins

From the spermatozoa of various animals, certain enzymes or lytic agents may be extracted that possibly play a part in the penetration of the spermatozoon into the egg. Three such lysins are now recognised.

The eggs of a number of molluscs and lower vertebrates develop a tough membrane soon after they are shed and through this the spermatozoon must pass to effect fertilisation. Solutions prepared from the spermatozoa by centrifugation of dense suspensions, by freezing and thawing, by extraction with alkaline media or by extraction of lyophilised suspensions have been shown to exert a powerful solvent action on the egg membrane of the keyhole limpet, *Megathura spp.*, and abalone, *Haliotis spp.* (Tyler, 1939, 1949 ; von Medem, 1942), of the mussel, *Mytilus edulis* (Berg, 1950 ; Wada, Collier and Dan, 1956), of the polychaete worm, *Pomatoceros triqueter* (Monroy, 1948), and the toad, *Discoglossus* (Hibbard, 1928 ; Wintrebert, 1929 ; Parat, 1933). The active agent seems to be a protein

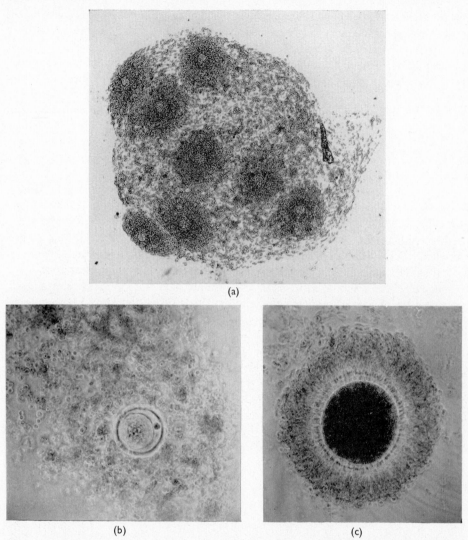

(a)

(b)   (c)

Fig. *10*. 5—Tubal eggs surrounded by cumulus oöphorus: (a) rat, (b) hamster, (c) ferret. (a., from Austin and Smiles, 1948.)

and evidence has been advanced to show that it is carried by the acrosome of the spermatozoon (Parat, 1933 ; Tyler, 1949 ; Wada, Collier and Dan, 1956 ; Colwin, Colwin and Philpott, 1957).

Another kind of lysin, called Androgamone III, has been reported in methanolic extracts of frozen-dried salmon and sea-urchin spermatozoa (Runnström, Tisselius and Lindvall, 1945 ; Runnström, 1949 ; Rothschild, 1958). This appears to

be an 18-carbon fatty acid and its specific action is on the cytoplasmic surface
or on the vitelline membrane of the egg. The action resembles that of certain
chemical detergents in rendering the egg more prone to cytolysis. Runnström
suggests that the lysin may be involved in the initiation of the block to polyspermy.

The only lytic agent so far reported in mammalian material is the enzyme
hyaluronidase, which is also discussed briefly in Chapter 7. The eggs of many
mammals, notably the rabbit, the rodents and the carnivores, retain a voluminous
investment of cumulus oöphorus for some hours after ovulation (Fig. *10*. 5) ; in

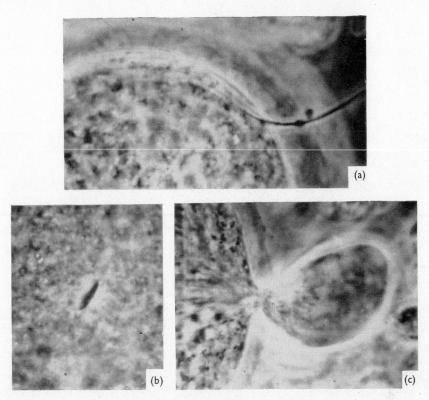

Fig. *10*. 6—(a) Profile view of rat spermatozoon with its head and part of its tail
    embedded in the vitellus and the rest of its tail projecting through the zona
    pellucida. In plan view, the tail could be seen to project through a slit such as
    that shown in (b). (c) The same egg as in (b) after it had been rolled under
    pressure so as to cause leakage of vitellus through the slit. (From Austin, 1951.)

other species, including the ungulates and man, most of the cumulus apparently
breaks down spontaneously within a short time. When whole semen, or preparations containing hyaluronidase, are applied *in vitro* to eggs in cumulus, the hyalu-
ronic-acid matrix is rapidly dissolved (McClean and Rowlands, 1942 ; Fekete and
Duran-Reynals, 1943).

Because of its position on the leading surface of the spermatozoon, the acrosome
is the logical place for the storage of hyaluronidase ; although there is as yet no
direct evidence for this, the histochemical properties of the acrosome are at least
consistent with the presence there of the enzyme (*see* p. 10). Spermatozoa can
be washed a number of times without freeing them of hyaluronidase (Hechter and

Hadidian, 1947 ; Swyer, 1947a) and so they may be considered capable of carrying the enzyme with them in their passage through the female genital tract to the site of fertilisation. Although there is some factor in the Fallopian tube that is evidently responsible in part for the denudation of eggs (Swyer, 1947b), and which

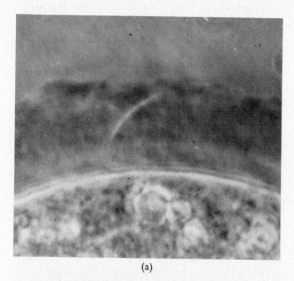

(a)

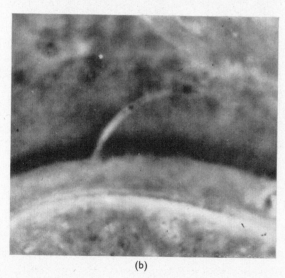

(b)

Fig. 10. 7—Profile views of slits made by penetrating spermatozoa in the eggs of (a) the guinea-pig, and (b) the Libyan jird. (From Austin and Bishop, 1958c.)

may possibly involve ascorbic acid (Rödel and Karg, 1955), eggs certainly become divested of their surrounding cumulus much earlier in animals that have mated with fertile males than in those that have not.

Actual denudation of the eggs is not a prerequisite of spermatozoon penetration, for recently penetrated rodent and rabbit eggs are commonly found with intact cumulus (Lewis and Wright, 1935 ; Leonard, Perlman and Kurzrok, 1947 ; Austin, 1948a ; Moricard and Bossu, 1949b, 1951 ; Odor and Blandau, 1951b ; Chang, 1951c ; Bowman, 1951). Complete denudation was, in fact, once thought to prevent spermatozoon penetration (Chang and Pincus, 1951), but this does not seem to be true, at least for rat and rabbit eggs (Austin, 1951a ; Chang, 1953b).

Although the corona radiata and the cumulus oöphorus are generally described as a "barrier" which the spermatozoa must pass to fertilise the egg, it is by no means certain that fertilisation is in fact impeded by these structures. Since active spermatozoa tend to accumulate on concave surfaces with heads orientated towards the concavity (see p. 281), it is possible that spermatozoa entering the interstices between the corona cells are orientated towards the egg, and thus aided in their approach to the egg. It is deduced, nevertheless, that a function of hyaluronidase may be to permit individual spermatozoa to make their way between the cumulus cells by means of their complement of enzyme. If this is true, it should be possible to prevent fertilisation by neutralising the hyaluronidase. Rabbit semen has indeed been treated with various hyaluronidase inhibitors prior to artificial insemination and has then been found to have lost its fertility (Pincus, Pirie and Chang, 1948 ; Chang and Pincus, 1953 ; Parkes, 1953 ; Parkes, Rogers and Spensley, 1954). It is uncertain, however, that the agents inhibited only the hyaluronidase and exerted no influence upon the other enzymes of the spermatozoon, including those required for its survival (*see also* p. 217).

Apart from its likely function in facilitating spermatozoon penetration, hyaluronidase may conceivably be of value to the early embryo by expediting the removal of the surrounding mass of actively metabolising follicle cells, which otherwise might impede transfer of its metabolites.

As yet, it has not been found possible to demonstrate a spermatozoon lysin capable of attacking the material of the zona pellucida. Some evidence for the existence of such an agent is provided by the fact that in rat, guinea-pig and Libyan-jird eggs a small slit made in the zona pellucida by the penetrating spermatozoon persists and is recognisable for some hours afterwards (Figs. *10.* 6 and *10.* 7).

Since observations on several rodent species indicate that the spermatozoon perforatorium is exposed when the acrosome is removed (*see* p. 10 and Fig. *10.* 4), it is suggested that an agent capable of acting on the substance of the zona pellucida, a " zona lysin," is disposed on the surface of the perforatorium. In this position, the lysin is supposed to modify the zona substance immediately in front of the spermatozoon head, enabling the spermatozoon to make its way through (Austin and Bishop, 1958a, b, c).

The Acrosome Reaction

In the course of his study of fertilisation in the starfish, *Asterias*, Fol (1877a, b, 1879) believed that he saw a slender, tapering process, the " attraction cone," grow out from the surface of the egg proper in the direction of a spermatozoon approaching through the jelly coat. According to Fol, the process extended until it met and became attached to the spermatozoon ; it then contracted, apparently drawing the spermatozoon into the egg. The same kind of thing has been described by Chambers (1923, 1930) and Hörstadius (1939a, b). Just (1929), however, believed that the filament came from the head of the spermatozoon and made contact with the egg surface. Recent work seems to have reconciled these apparently conflicting views.

In 1952, Dan described a reaction in sea-urchins that was evoked in the structure of the spermatozoon acrosome by egg water, by alkaline sea-water (pH 9·2) or by attachment of the spermatozoon to a collodion membrane. Later, she found that it was also induced by contact with glass surfaces but was inhibited in calcium-deficient media (Dan, 1954a). The reaction appeared to involve breakdown of the acrosome membrane and release of a labile mass of substance that Dan suggested might represent the lysin that mediated spermatozoon penetration of the vitelline membrane. This suggestion was consistent with Tyler's (1949) observations on the extraction of the egg-membrane lysin and has received support in the recent work of Wada, Collier and Dan (1956). When starfish spermatozoa were investigated, they were found to react to egg water by producing a fine long filament of surprising rigidity from the region of the acrosome (Dan, 1954b). It seemed likely that the filament permitted contact to be made with the reactive

M*

cytoplasm of the egg before the spermatozoon had passed through the jelly coat.
Dan thought that this contact was responsible for the formation of Fol's attraction
cone and, consistently, Colwin and Colwin (1954) have observed in the acorn worm,
Saccoglossus, that connection by means of the filament between the spermatozoon
head and the egg surface exists before the cone becomes visible.   A similar order
of events was seen in the sea-cucumber, *Holothuria* (Fig. *10*. 8) (Colwin and

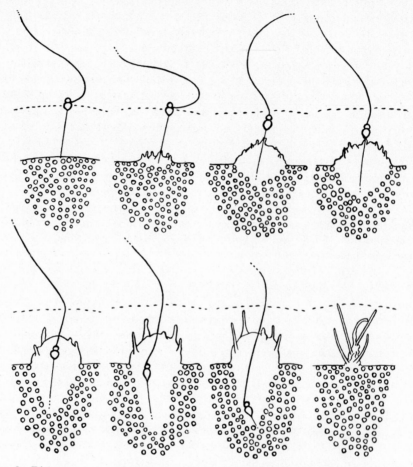

Fig. *10*. 8—Diagrams representing the successive stages of spermatozoon penetration in the sea-
cucumber, *Holothuria atra*.   The dotted line represents the surface of the jelly-coat.   (From
Colwin and Colwin, 1955.) (By permission of the publisher from *J. Morph.*, 1955, **97**, 547.)

Colwin, 1955), in which it could be discerned that part of the cone grows out
around the filament and thus comes into contact with the head of the spermatozoon.   Both kinds of reaction—breakdown of the acrosome and the extrusion of
a filament—have also been recognised in several species of molluscs (Dan and Wada,
1955).   Rothschild and Tyler (1955), too, have reported that they were able to
demonstrate filaments in many spermatozoa of species of chiton, mussel and sea-
urchin (*Strongylocentrotus*, *Echinocardium*, *Lepidochitona*, *Mopalia* and *Mytilus*),
but they were not altogether convinced that extrusion of filaments constituted a
response to egg water because their observations were made in the absence of this

agent. Colwin and Colwin (1956) obtained quantitative data on the proportions of spermatozoa with and without filaments in the sea-cucumber, *Thyone* ; they found that very few untreated spermatozoa possessed filaments, whereas of those treated with egg water the great majority displayed these structures. It is supposed that those spermatozoa that show the reaction in the absence of egg water have responded to non-specific stimuli. Data on the acrosome reaction have recently been reviewed by Dan (1956), Colwin and Colwin (1957) and Franzén (1958).

As yet, no homologue of the acrosome filament has been described in mammalian spermatozoa, but a change that is roughly analogous to the breakdown of the invertebrate acrosome has been seen in some rodent spermatozoa as a probable outcome of capacitation (*see* p. 323). It can be argued that the jelly coat of the invertebrate egg, and its derivative the egg water, correspond in the mammal to secretions of the Fallopian tube and therefore that the alteration of the mammalian acrosome in capacitation and its removal on contact with the zona are equivalent to acrosome breakdown and release of acrosomal material in sea-urchin spermatozoa in the presence of egg water.

The Fertilisation Membrane

Fol (1879) found that in the starfish, *Asterias*, the spermatozoon came in contact with the gelatinous layer surrounding the egg, entered this " jelly " and reached the membrane of the egg in a few seconds. The head of the spermatozoon then passed through the membrane and at the point of entry the membrane was elevated from the surface of the egg, the elevation spreading rapidly round the surface until it appeared as though the egg were completely surrounded by a clear space. In the sea-urchin, this membrane elevation is a very striking phenomenon and is generally accepted as a reliable index of fertilisation. In the polychete worm, *Nereis*, penetration is a much slower process than in the sea-urchin and the details can be followed more easily (Lillie, 1923). The egg of *Nereis* is provided with a tough vitelline membrane beneath which is an alveolar cortical layer. When spermatozoa are added to a dish containing eggs, a large number of spermatozoa become attached to each egg. In about two or three minutes, all spermatozoa, with the exception of the one that is concerned with fertilisation, are normally carried away from the surface of the egg by the elevation of the fertilisation membrane. The formation of the fertilisation membrane in the sea-urchin has been the subject of particular attention since Fol described its elevation as a mechanism preventing polyspermy. Elevation certainly carries away from the surface of the egg superflous spermatozoa, but its rate of formation is not sufficiently rapid to prevent spermatozoa from adhering to the surface of the egg before elevation has been completed (Just, 1919). Furthermore, elevation of the membrane is not present in all eggs that undergo normal monospermic fertilisation. Observations on refertilisation (p. 390) support the conclusion that though membrane elevation is not the mechanism primarily responsible for preventing polyspermy it provides a more lasting barrier to spermatozoon entry. The fertilisation membrane is not essential for the survival of the embryo since normal development can ensue even if its formation is inhibited or the membrane is removed after its elevation (Tyler, 1937 ; Tyler and Scheer, 1937).

Formation of the fertilisation membrane appears to involve changes in, or actual disappearance of, certain granular elements that lie in the cortical region of the egg, just beneath the vitelline membrane. Rothschild (1956) points out that the existence of cortical granules in sea-urchin eggs and their probable implication in membrane formation were reported many years ago by Harvey (1911). Recently, however, interest in these structures has been renewed and the present state of knowledge is largely attributable to the work of Motomura (1936, 1941), Moser (1939), Runnström (1944), Runnström, Monné and Wicklund (1944, 1946), Runnström and Wicklund (1950), Endo (1952) and Colwin and Colwin (1954). Briefly, the current theory is that, as a result of spermatozoon attachment, the cortical granules unite with the vitelline membrane. In so doing, the granules lose their identity, apparently by "exploding," and bring about a hardening of the vitelline membrane, thus converting it into a fertilisation membrane. Elevation of this membrane is ascribed to the osmotic effect of colloids lying between it and the vitellus and possibly released in the disintegration of the cortical granules (Fig. 10. 9). After membrane elevation, the vitellus is bounded by a plasma membrane, which is covered by a homogeneous hyaline layer. In the egg of *Nereis* and in certain fish and lamprey eggs, the numerous alveoli displayed by the cortex evidently correspond to sea-urchin cortical granules. When the egg is activated, the alveoli break down releasing substances that are believed to be responsible for modifying the vitelline membrane or the chorion that closely invests the vitellus and for causing the elevation of these structures from the egg surface. Like cortical granules, cortical alveoli contain mucopolysaccharides (*see* Rothschild, 1958).

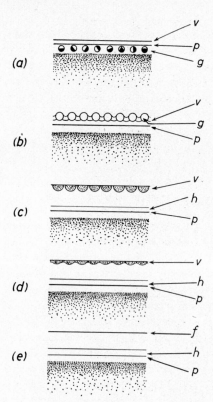

Fig. *10*. 9—Diagrams illustrating the mechanism by which elevation of the fertilisation membrane may occur in the sea-urchin egg. The cortical granules (" g ") apparently swell, pass through the plasma membrane (" p ") and unite with the vitelline membrane (" v ") converting the latter into the fertilisation membrane (" f "). " h " is the hyaline layer. (From Rothschild, 1956, after Endo, 1952.)

Fertilisation membranes are known in the eggs of sea-urchins, the starfish, the lancelet, *Branchiostoma* (= *Amphioxus*), the trout, the frog, and the prototherian mammals (*see* Rothschild, 1956). Such a structure is not known to exist in the eggs of any major group of metatherian or eutherian mammals. There are, however, reports that a fertilisation membrane is developed in the golden hamster (Graves, 1945 ; Venable, 1946) and it has been demonstrated that the hamster egg possesses cortical granules that disappear upon spermatozoon attachment

(Fig. *10.* 10) (Austin, 1956c). Samuel and Hamilton (1942) and Hamilton and Samuel (1956), however, make no mention of a fertilisation membrane, though they examined numerous hamster eggs, and even a specific search for it with the aid of the phase-contrast microscope was unsuccessful (Austin, 1956d). The hamster cortical granules may possibly play a role in the " zona reaction " described below.

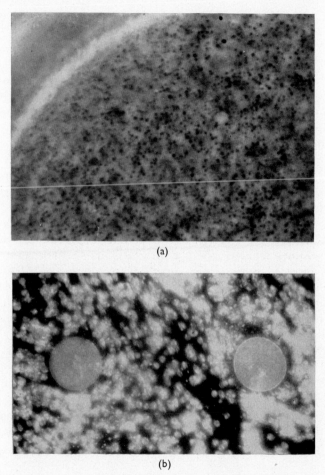

(a)

(b)

Fig. *10.* 10—(a) Cortical granules in a hamster egg. (b) Showing the difference in cortical light-refraction by penetrated (*left*) and unpenetrated (*right*) hamster eggs. (From Austin, 1956c.)

The Block to Polyspermy

It has long been recognised that the penetration of more than one spermatozoon into the vitellus of the egg is rare in some animals and common in others (*see* Boveri, 1891), and the phenomena were distinguished by the terms pathological polyspermy and physiological polyspermy, respectively. Polyspermy, however, can be regarded as potentially detrimental in any species and two devices have been evolved that generally avert the danger. One is a change induced in the surface of the egg by the first spermatozoon that penetrates it, a change that renders the egg surface impermeable to subsequent spermatozoa. Rothschild (1954) refers to this as Type I Inhibition, but it is more commonly known as the " block to polyspermy." It is only with this mechanism that we are here concerned. The second device, which acts upon extra spermatozoa that have entered the vitellus, is discussed later (p. 372) together with other cytological aspects of polyspermy.

It is a striking fact that when sea-urchin eggs are placed in comparatively dense spermatozoon suspensions, wherein they must be bombarded by large numbers of spermatozoa, they nevertheless generally undergo monospermic fertilisation. At first sight, it looks as though an extremely fast block to polyspermy must be involved, and Gray (1931) compared the supposed rate of the reaction to that of excitation in smooth muscle. On this basis, the block would take about 10^{-5} sec. to complete its circuit over a sea-urchin egg, which would implicate biophysical phenomena rather than biochemical or enzymic reactions. Measurements of resistance, capacitance, and potential across the egg membrane before and after fertilisation have been attempted by several investigators (Gelfan, 1931 ; Peterfi and Rothschild, 1935 ; Kamada and Kinosita, 1940 ; Rothschild, 1938, 1946, 1956 ; Scheer, Monroy, Santangelo and Riccobono, 1954 ; Tyler, Monroy, Kao and Grundfest, 1955, 1956) ; alterations of electrical properties were sometimes observed to follow spermatozoon penetration, but there was no certainty that they were directly related to the passage of the block to polyspermy. On the other hand, changes in the light-refracting property of the cortex (Runnström, 1928 ; Runnström, Monné and Broman, 1944 ; Rothschild and Swann, 1949) and in the state of the cortical granules (see above) have been thought to be the visible manifestations accompanying the passage of the block to polyspermy, though the difficulty arises that the changes evidently pass around the cortex at a much slower rate than that just considered. Runnström's (1928) estimate was 4 to 6 seconds and Rothschild and Swann's (1949) about 20 seconds. This difficulty is removed by further observations of Rothschild and Swann (1950 ; 1951a, b ; 1952) and Rothschild (1953), which indicate that estimates of the frequency of spermatozoon-egg collisions, based on the concentration and rate of movement of the spermatozoa, are misleading because the great majority of encounters would not necessarily lead to penetration. Their data also show that the block to polyspermy is in the nature of a diphasic change : a fast component conferring partial protection sweeps over the egg in one or two seconds and is followed by a slow component conferring full protection which takes approximately 60 seconds to complete the circuit (Fig. 10. 11). It is with the slower component that visible cortical changes may be associated.

Protection of the sea-urchin egg against polyspermy is probably not vested exclusively in the cortical modifications just described. The jelly coat may well contribute by impeding the approach of spermatozoa. The fertilisation membrane, though initially lacking complete impermeability, is an effective barrier once it has hardened. Finally, the hyaline layer, which can be seen to cover the vitelline surface when membrane elevation occurs, is reported to be capable of excluding spermatozoa (see Sugiyama, 1951 ; Hagström, 1956a, b, c ; Hagström and Runnström, 1959).

Less is known about the block to polyspermy in mammals. Evidence for the operation of a block is provided by the presence of spermatozoa within the perivitelline space in eggs into the vitellus of which a spermatozoon has already penetrated ; it is inferred that the spermatozoa in the perivitelline space have succeeded in passing through the zona pellucida but have been debarred from entering the vitellus. Such " supplementary " spermatozoa are commonly found in the eggs of the rabbit, mole, pocket gopher, rat, mouse, and guinea-pig, but are unknown or extremely rare in the eggs of the dog, sheep, hamster and vole. In the eggs of the latter group, the "zona reaction" is held to be responsible for excluding extra spermatozoa—this is discussed in the next sub-section. The observations of Amoroso and Parkes (1947) suggest that X-irradiation can destroy that property of the spermatozoon head that is normally responsible for evoking the block to polyspermy.

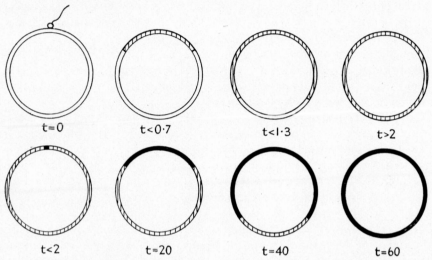

Fig. *10. 11*—The development of the block to polyspermy in the sea-urchin egg. Grey: rapid partial block. Black: slow complete block. *t* : time in seconds. (Redrawn slightly modified from Rothschild, 1956.)

Studies on invertebrate eggs have shown that, while polyspermy can be brought about by semination with very concentrated suspension of spermatozoa, it may also be produced by treatments that presumably slow down or interfere with the rate of the block to polyspermy. If eggs of the sea urchin are allowed to become stale in sea-water before fertilisation, many polyspermic eggs may be obtained (Goldforb, 1918 ; Smith and Clowes, 1924). O. and R. Hertwig (1887) noted that certain drugs, such as nicotine, strychnine and morphine, induce polyspermy, and Smith and Clowes (1924) found that within a narrow range of hydrogen-ion concentration centred about pH 7·2 nearly all the eggs of the sea-urchin, *Arbacia*, were polyspermic. In the starfish, *Asterias*, the range was wider, extending from pH 7·2 to pH 9·8. Studies have been made on experimentally induced poly-spermy in mammalian eggs also. Thus, Austin and Braden (1953a, b) reported that, whilst only 1·2 per cent of eggs were polyspermic in rats that had copulated at the normal time (about 10 hours before ovulation), nearly 8 per cent were poly-spermic when coitus was not permitted until the end of the 4-hour ovulation period. Odor and Blandau (1956), also, have found more polyspermic rat eggs after delayed coitus (3·3 per cent) than after coitus at the usual time (0·3 per cent).

The same effect has been noted in rabbits ; when coitus occurred at the time of artificially induced ovulation, the incidence of polyspermy was at least 8 per cent, compared with a normal incidence of less than 2 per cent (Austin and Braden, 1953b). From these data it appears that mammalian eggs, like those of the sea-urchin, start to age very shortly after ovulation, the change being recognisable through the loss in efficiency of the block to polyspermy. After the local application of heat to eggs in the Fallopian tube of the rat, about 16 per cent were found to be polyspermic (Austin and Braden, 1954b). The same procedure used in mice raised the frequency from 0·3 to 3·8 per cent (Braden and Austin, 1954b). In rats, induced hyperthermia was equally effective, giving about 20 per cent polyspermy in a group of animals (Austin, 1955a, 1956b)—when these results were examined more closely it became apparent that the age of the animal was important : whilst the incidence in 100–130-g. rats was only 13 per cent, that in 170–200-g. rats was 34 per cent.

From the data presented, the following tentative conclusions can be drawn : that in mammals the efficiency of the block to polyspermy diminishes with age, that eggs begin to age very shortly after ovulation, that heat accelerates ageing, and that eggs age more rapidly in older animals.

Hancock (personal communication, 1959) reports that in pigs, too, the eggs seem to become much more prone to polyspermy as they age. Thus, of 34 eggs recovered from sows mated at the onset of oestrus all were undergoing apparently normal fertilisation, but when mating occurred 24, 30 and 48 hours after the onset of heat an increasing proportion of the eggs, namely 1/29, 7/56 and 12/29 respectively, showed abnormalities of fertilisation almost certainly due in the majority to polyspermy.

There are, however, certain complications. Delayed coitus did not increase the incidence of polyspermy in mice (Braden and Austin, 1954b), so species differences obviously exist and, in view of the different results obtained with rats, by Austin and Braden (1953a, b) and Odor and Blandau (1956), it would seem that there may also be strain differences within a species. More recently, Braden (1958) has in fact found a significantly different incidence in polyspermy after delayed coitus (3·6 and 8·4 per cent) between two strains of rats tested under the same conditions. Pikó (1958) has observed differences in the incidence of poly-spermy between three strains of rats mated normally (0·0, 3·2, 0·9 per cent.) ; the difference between the figures for the first and third strains was significant. There was an increase in incidence in all three strains (up to 4·5, 6·6, 7·1 per cent. respectively) when the animals were mated after ovulation, but the differences between the strains were not now significant. (Further information on the incidence of polyspermy is given on p. 376.)

The Zona Reaction

It has long been known that rat eggs often contain one or more spermatozoa in the perivitelline space in addition to the fertilising spermatozoon in the vitellus (Sobotta and Burckhard, 1910). The perivitelline spermatozoa have frequently been referred to as " supernumerary," but it seems best to restrict this term to the extra spermatozoa in the vitellus of a polyspermic egg—a well-established use in descriptions of non-mammalian eggs—and to call the perivitelline spermatozoa "supplementary." Such a distinction is advisable because, at least in mammalian eggs, supernumerary spermatozoa generally take part in pronucleus formation and syngamy, whereas supplementary spermatozoa do not. In describing both classes of spermatozoa together it is convenient to refer simply to "extra spermatozoa." Supplementary spermatozoa commonly remain unchanged until they are released from the perivitelline space by loss of the zona pellucida in the uterus and it seems probable that they play no role in the development of the embryo, though contrary claims have been made (*see* p. 377).

Odor and Blandau (1949) examined the eggs from 43 mated rats and found that 23 per cent of them contained 1–5 supplementary spermatozoa. Of these eggs 67 per cent contained one supplementary spermatozoon, 24 per cent two, 6 per cent three, 2 per cent four, and 1 per cent five. Essentially similar results were obtained in mice as well as in rats by Braden, Austin and David (1954), who noticed, however, that the frequency distribution of eggs with extra spermatozoa differed from that which would be expected if chance alone had controlled the number of spermatozoa that penetrated the zona pellucida. This is well shown by the data from groups of 10 rats and 6 mice that were killed in the course of single experiments (Table II), and it is clear that with both animals the observed

TABLE II

OBSERVED AND EXPECTED FREQUENCIES OF RAT AND MOUSE EGGS CONTAINING VARIOUS
NUMBERS OF SPERMS

(Braden, Austin and David, 1954)

Species	Frequency	Number of eggs containing i sperms						Total eggs
		$i =$ 0	1	2	3	4	$\geqslant 5$	
Rats	Observed	5	68	15	1	2	0	91
	Expected	26·8	33·1	20·7	7·8	2·1	0·6	91·1
Mice	Observed	3	42	10	0	1	0	56
	Expected	15·3	22·4	12·8	4·4	1·0	0·2	56·1

frequency distribution differs widely from the expected or chance distribution. The important point is that a much greater proportion of eggs contained only the fertilising spermatozoon than would be expected from chance alone. Evidently, something changes after the entry of the first spermatozoon—either the egg becomes less attractive to spermatozoa or the zona pellucida becomes more difficult to penetrate. Because it is uncertain that mammalian eggs are ever attractive to spermatozoa (*see* discussion on "Chemotaxis" above) it would be illogical to ascribe the change to a loss of attractiveness. Moreover, Smithberg (1952) and Chang and Hunt (1956) have shown that the zona is removed by proteolytic enzymes more easily from fertilised than from unfertilised mouse and rat eggs ; they, too, concluded that the zona changes after fertilisation. The results are therefore interpreted to mean that the zona pellucida becomes less permeable to spermatozoa after the passage of the first spermatozoon, and the change is called the "zona reaction."

Mammalian eggs can thus be regarded as having two real or potential protective mechanisms against the danger of polyspermy—the block to polyspermy in the surface of the vitellus and the zona reaction (Fig. 10. 29). In any one species, however, both mechanisms may not normally be operative. In the rabbit, there

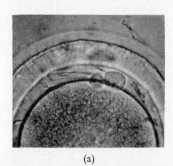

(a)

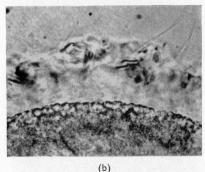

(b)

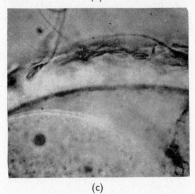

(c)

Fig. 10. 12—Illustrating the admission of supplementary spermatozoa to the perivitelline space of the rabbit egg (a), and their exclusion by the zona pellucida in dog (b) and sheep (c) eggs. (From Braden, Austin and David, 1954.)

appears to be no zona reaction, for spermatozoa continue to penetrate into the perivitelline space, often in large numbers, until the mucoprotein coat starts to be deposited (Fig. 10. 12a) (Van Beneden, 1875 ; Hensen, 1876 ; Moricard and Bossu, 1949b ; Chang, 1951b ; Braden, Austin and David, 1954 ; Adams, 1955, 1956b). The vitelline block to polyspermy, then, is the only one of these protective devices operative in the rabbit egg. Similarly, mole eggs have been reported to have numerous supplementary spermatozoa (Heape, 1886) and presumably also lack a reactive zona pellucida. On the other hand, supplementary spermatozoa have not been seen in eggs of the sheep and dog (Figs. 10. 12b and c) (Braden et al., 1954), and field vole (Austin, 1957c) ; in these eggs, therefore, it appears that there is a very rapid zona reaction and that the block to polyspermy is normally redundant. Hamster eggs may also belong to this group, for among 519 penetrated eggs none was found with supplementary spermatozoa and yet five instances of polyspermy were encountered (Austin, 1956d). In a later report, however, one apparently normal hamster egg was seen (amongst approximately another 500 penetrated eggs) that contained a supplementary spermatozoon (Austin and Bishop, 1958c). This finding suggests that in the eggs of the hamster, and perhaps also in those of the sheep, dog and vole, the vitellus is always capable of exhibiting a block to polyspermy but that the block is established no more rapidly than the zona reaction and consequently very rarely provides evidence of its occurrence. Rat and mouse eggs occupy an intermediate position, possessing, it would seem, only a moderately rapid zona reaction so that the block to polyspermy frequently subserves its specific function. Recently, Harvey (1958) observed that the egg of the pika (Ochotona princeps), like the rabbit egg, accumulates numerous spermatozoa in the perivitelline space; presumably, it lacks a zona reaction.

Early evidence suggested that the zona reaction was initiated in the substance of the zona pellucida and was propagated around the egg in this membrane. In eggs containing two spermatozoa, the points of entry were found more commonly in opposite hemispheres than in the same hemisphere, an observation that could be interpreted to mean that the reaction spread out through the zona from the point of entry of the first spermatozoon (Braden *et al.*, 1954). This conclusion was questioned by Rothschild (personal communication), who suggested that the actual reaction is propagated through the vitelline cortex but is associated with the release of some agent that passes across the perivitelline space and alters the nature of the zona pellucida. The zona reaction could thus be considered analogous in certain respects to the elevation of the fertilisation membrane. Some of the available data appeared to conflict with this theory (*see* Rothschild, 1956), but subsequently Austin and Braden (1956) provided data in support of it. In particular, they adduced evidence that the zona reaction in the mouse egg is evoked by passage of the spermatozoon into the vitellus but not by passage through the zona pellucida. Consistent also with Rothschild's suggestion is the observation that the hamster egg exhibits cortical granules that resemble those of the sea-urchin egg and disappear after spermatozoon contact with the vitelline surface (Fig. *10*. 10) (Austin, 1956c). It is reasonable to suppose that the hamster cortical granules could behave similarly to sea-urchin cortical granules except that their products would modify the zona pellucida instead of converting a vitelline membrane into a fertilisation membrane. Unlike the response shown by sea-urchin cortical granules, however, the disappearance of hamster cortical granules was not found to be associated with artificial activation of the eggs. It may, therefore, be inferred that the zona reaction is not necessarily evoked by artificial activation and the validity of this deduction has already been demonstrated for rat eggs (Austin and Braden, 1954b).

If the zona reaction is indeed mediated through the vitellus we should expect it to be influenced by the same factors that were observed to reduce the efficiency of the block to polyspermy. This has been found to be so : more spermatozoa pass through the zona in ageing eggs (Austin and Braden, 1953b), in eggs subjected to heat (Austin and Braden, 1954b), and in eggs recovered from animals that had been rendered hyperthermic (Austin, 1956b). In addition, equivalent strain differences are evident in the efficiency of the two mechanisms (Braden, 1958; Piko, 1959).

Penetration of the Vitellus

It is generally agreed that the spermatozoon of non-mammalian animals becomes motionless soon after attachment to the vitellus (*see* Wilson, 1928 ; Tyler, 1955). The spermatozoon head then progresses steadily into the egg cytoplasm, drawing the tail after it, and the motive force for this action is supposedly supplied by the egg. The process somewhat resembles phagocytosis (Loeb, 1917).

Observations on rat, mouse and hamster eggs show that the spermatozoon head makes contact with the vitelline surface very shortly after traversing the zona pellucida. The motility of the spermatozoon is gradually lost but nevertheless persists for a comparatively long time. The head becomes attached to the surface and is not dislodged by the residual movements of the spermatozoon tail. After lying on the vitelline surface for about half an hour the head seems simply to sink into the vitellus. The spermatozoon tail, which projects for a while through the penetration slit in the zona pellucida, progressively follows the head into the vitellus (Austin and Braden, 1956). Unlike fertilising spermatozoa, supplementary spermatozoa do not become attached to the vitellus but remain freely suspended in the perivitelline fluid. This is evidently true also for the rabbit egg (Pincus, 1939a). After passage of the block to polyspermy, therefore, the vitellus appears to lose its ability to form attachment with the spermatozoon head. Loss of this ability may also be induced experimentally, by subjecting unfertilised eggs to heat or cold treatment *in vitro* (Chang, 1952a). There is even evidence that suggests that the property of the spermatozoon head responsible for evoking attachment may be destroyed : eggs recovered from rabbits inseminated with semen that had been treated with an enzyme inhibitor were frequently found to contain a free spermatozoon in the perivitelline space although there was no spermatozoon within the vitellus (Fig. *10*. 13) (Parkes, Rogers and Spensley, 1954).

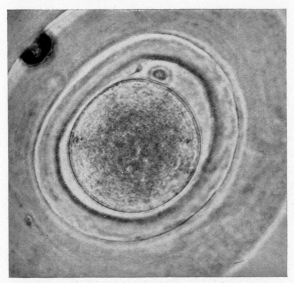

Fig. *10*. 13—Rabbit egg with spermatozoon that had been treated with an enzyme inhibitor whilst in the semen and which had subsequently failed to enter the vitellus. (From Parkes, Rogers and Spensley, 1954).

Associated with spermatozoon entry into the vitellus is the development of an elevation of the egg cytoplasm that has been termed an attraction cone, entrance cone or fertilisation cone (Fig. *10*. 8, 14 and 20). The form and duration of the cone vary widely between species (Chambers, 1930, 1933). It may appear as a rather thick filament, as in the starfish, or as a broader flame-shaped structure which develops a ragged surface, as in the sea-urchins. Hörstadius (1939a, b) described the cone as a hollow cylinder, which is consistent with the observations of Colwin and Clowin (1955) that the cone forms a kind of sleeve about the acrosome filament. The cone may disappear as the spermatozoon enters or persist for some time thereafter. In those species in which the spermatozoon extrudes an acrosome filament, the formation of the cone is probably initiated by contact of the filament with the egg cortex. In the rat and mouse, an elevation of the egg cytoplasm, which presumably corresponds to the entrance cone of the invertebrate, becomes evident while the spermatozoon head lies attached to the vitelline surface and seems to achieve its maximum size after the head has passed through the surface. The rodent cone persists for quite a long time and may still be seen when the spermatozoon head has been partially transformed into a pronucleus (Figs. *10*. 18 and 29). In freshly ovulated rodent eggs, a similar elevation is found above the second maturation spindle ; the significance of this particular structure is discussed later (p. 351).

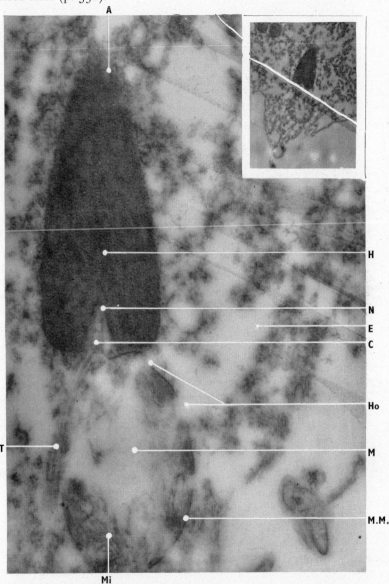

Fig. *10*. 14—Sea-urchin spermatozoon shortly after entry into the vitellus. A, site of acrosome. C, centriole. E, substance of egg. H, head. Ho, holes in mid-piece membrane. M, mid-piece. Mi, mitochondria in mid-piece. M.M, mid-piece membrane. N, remains of nuclear membrane. T, tail. (From Rothschild, 1957.)

Fate of Spermatozoon Components

As a general rule, the spermatozoon tail passes into the vitellus with the head at the beginning of fertilisation. The only regular exception in non-mammalian species appears to be in the polychete worm, *Nereis*, in which the tail (both mid-piece and main-piece) is left outside the bounds of the vitellus (Wilson, 1928). In other animals, such as the sea-urchin, the tail is known commonly to enter the vitellus, though it may not invariably do so (Fig. *10*. 14). Among the mammals, failure of entry of the tail in a fairly high proportion of eggs (about 40 per cent) has been recorded in the field vole, *Microtus agrestis* (Fig. *10*. 15b) (Austin, 1957c). More remarkable is the finding for the Chinese hamster, *Cricetulus griseus*: among 44 eggs recovered whilst undergoing fertilisation or early cleavage, only one had the spermatozoon tail within the vitellus (Fig. *10*. 15a) (unpublished data, C.R.A.). Nihoul (1927) believed that in the rabbit egg the tail did not always enter, but passage of the tail into the vitellus appears to be the normal occurrence. The spermatozoon tail has been observed within the vitellus in the following mammals: mouse (Lams and Doorme, 1908, who also cite Gerlach, 1906; Gresson, 1940, 1941), guinea-pig (Rubaschkin, 1905; Lams and Doorme, 1908; Lams, 1913), rat (Fig. *10*. 24 and 30e) (Sobotta and Burckhard, 1910; O. Van der Stricht, 1923; Kremer, 1924; Gilchrist and Pincus, 1932; Macdonald and Long, 1934; Austin and Smiles, 1948; Odor and Blandau, 1951b; Blandau and Odor, 1952), bat (O. Van der Stricht, 1902; Levi, 1915), dog (O. Van der Stricht, 1923), rabbit (Nihoul, 1927; Pincus, 1930; Austin and Bishop, 1957b), ferret (Main-

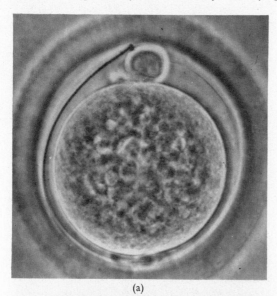

(a)

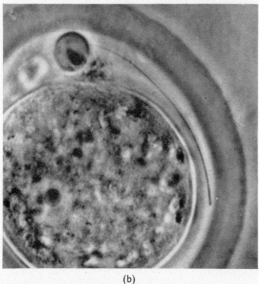

(b)

Fig. *10*. 15—Illustrating the failure of the spermatozoon tail to enter the vitellus in the eggs of the Chinese hamster (*a*), and the field vole (*b*).

land, 1930), pig (Fig. *10*. 35) (Pitkjanen, 1955; Hancock, 1958), golden hamster (Fig. *10*.21) (Austin, 1956d; Hamilton and Samuel, 1956), field vole (Austin, 1957c), multimammate rat and Libyan jird (unpublished data).

When the spermatozoon has passed into the vitellus of the egg, it undergoes gradual disintegration. The perforatorium disappears early (Fig. *10*. 21), except for the " rod " of some rodent spermatozoa, which tends to persist through the period of fertilisation. The mitochondria become detached from the mid-piece and are apparently incorporated in the embryo. Meves (1911, 1916) traced mitochondria from *Ascaris* and *Filaria* spermatozoa into the blastomeres of the 2-cell stage. In *Echinus*, however, the intact mid-piece was reported to be recognisable in one of the blastomeres of the 32-cell embryo (Meves, 1914). Gresson (1942, 1951) studied the break-up of the mid-piece in the mouse egg, noting that the mitochondria become detached during the course of fertilisation, mingle with the egg mitochondria and so presumably pass, in about equal numbers, to each of the first two blastomeres. The fate of the mid-piece mitochondria is apparently similar in the eggs of the field vole (Austin, 1957c), but in the rat (Blandau and Odor, 1952), guinea-pig (Lams, 1913), hamster (Austin, 1956d), and bat (O. Van der Stricht, 1909 ; Levi, 1915) their release is incomplete at the time of the first cleavage and the more or less intact spermatozoon mid-piece can still be seen in the 2-cell egg. The axial filaments of the spermatozoon persist for much longer and, in the rat, have been recognised even in the implanting blastocyst (Blandau and Odor, 1952).

Shortly after the spermatozoon has entered the echinoderm egg, the head rotates about 180 degrees so that the base becomes orientated towards the centre of the egg (Fig. *10*. 20). At the base of the head, an aster arises which, by division of the centrosome, gives rise to the first cleavage spindle. The origin of the centrosome was the subject of much discussion (*see* Wilson, 1928). Boveri postulated that the spermatozoon introduces the centrosome (Fig. *10*. 14, 20), which serves the egg as an essential kinetic centre for cell cleavage. Lillie (1923) showed, however, that the centrosome of the pronucleus can arise *de novo* since, in *Nereis*, only the nucleus of the spermatozoon enters the egg and the whole of the mid-piece is left outside. Furthermore, if eggs that have been seminated are centrifuged at a time when the spermatozoon has only partially entered the egg, the rest of the spermatozoon is washed away and only a small portion of its tip actually enters. In spite of this, an aster forms, though of diminished size. Rigid proof, however, that the introduction of a centrosome by the spermatozoon is not essential for the formation of a mitotic amphiaster is obtained from the results of artificial parthenogenesis in which cleavage and development proceed without any spermatozoon (*see* p. 387). In the higher plants, also, centrosomes have not been clearly demonstrated, although inability to find them may be due to their small size, or failure to react suitably to fixing and staining (Darlington, 1937). It is presumed that the spermatozoon centrosome in animals comes originally from the proximal of the two centrioles visible in the early spermatid (*see* Chapter 7). Spermatozoon centrosomes and the associated asters have occasionally been described in mamalian eggs (O. Van der Stricht, 1909, 1923 ; Sobotta and Burckhard, 1910 ; Lams, 1913) (*see* Fig. *10*. 30e), but are difficult to discern.

IV. ACTIVATION OF THE EGG

The Activating Stimulus

When the spermatozoon enters the egg, profound changes are induced in both the structure and function of the egg which mark the beginning of development of a new individual. The sudden assumption by the seemingly static or even deteriorating egg of this new kind of life is recognised to be the result of activation. As a feature of fertilisation, activation is associated with spermatozoon entry, but other forms of stimulus are known and there are even circumstances in which no external excitation appears necessary and some little understood internal modification of metabolism evidently initiates development. Fuller consideration is given to these matters later (Section VII), our present concern being with activation in fertilisation.

Activation follows contact of the spermatozoon with the vitelline surface. In many invertebrates, this is effected by the acrosome filament, but in mammals by the spermatozoon head. Recent work on rodent spermatozoa indicates that the acrosome is no longer present when contact occurs (Austin and Bishop, 1958a, c), so that the activating region may well be the surface of the perforatorium. Since attachment of the spermatozoon head to the surface of the vitellus is evidently a necessary preliminary to penetration into the cytoplasm, it is reasonable to suppose that attachment and not merely contact is required for activation. On the other hand, actual penetration of the vitelline surface is evidently unnecessary, for signs of activation may be seen whilst the supermatozoon head is still essentially within the perivitelline space (Austin, 1951c ; Austin and Braden, 1956). Just how attachment can lead to activation is not at all clear : possibly a chemical agent of some kind passes from the spermatozoon to exert its influence upon the egg. Whatever the nature of the stimulus may be, the observations of Edwards (1957a) suggest that it can be specifically destroyed—X-irradiated spermatozoa have been seen within some mouse eggs that showed no sign of activation. (As already noted (p. 335), X-irradiation can apparently destroy also the property of the spermatozoon that evokes the block to polyspermy.)

Many observations have been made on mechanical, physical and chemical processes in the egg that seem to characterise the immediate response to the activating stimulus. The principal changes that have been studied include alteration in shape and volume of the vitellus, rearrangements of cytoplasmic structures, modifications in metabolism, and, in most animals, occurrence or resumption of maturation, leading to extrusion of polar bodies.

General Structural Changes

Various structural changes have been described that are associated with the phenomenon of activation. Streaming movements of the cytoplasm have been observed in many invertebrate eggs, and in mammalian eggs changes have been noted in the form and distribution of cytoplasmic elements (*see* Chapter 14). Flynn and Hill (1939) observed that the germinal disc in the spiny anteater, *Tachyglossus* (= *Echidna*), is originally circular in outline but becomes elliptical after fertilisation and one end of the disc becomes superficially charged with fine yolk granules. They remarked that such a change of shape seems to be fairly general in the Sauropsida also. Changes in overall shape are known to occur in a number of invertebrate species, the egg often becoming spherical after having displayed an oval or irregular contour in the unfertilised state (Wilson, 1928 ; Rothschild, 1956). These changes probably denote alterations in surface elasticity of the cytoplasm and in the viscosity of its substance (Tyler, 1932 ; Runnström,

1949). Properties of the egg surface have been investigated by Heilbrunn and Wilson (1948) and Wilson (1951) employing centrifugation, and by Mitchison and Swann (1954a, b ; 1955) using a specially developed instrument known as a " cell elastimeter." Variations in surface rigidity were observed to follow fertilisation but the degree and direction of these changes differed—partly because of species differences in the eggs investigated and partly because different methods probably measured different properties. The results of Mitchison and Swann were in good accord with Heilbrunn's theory (Heilbrunn, 1952), which is that the significant response to activation, whether by spermatozoon penetration or by parthenogenetic agents, is a gelation of the cytoplasm (see p. 388). Mitchison and Swann conclude that the egg probably has no internal pressure and no membrane tension, and they compare the egg to a tennis ball, wherein the shape is maintained by the stiffness of the cortex, rather than to a rubber balloon or a fluid droplet, which owe their shapes to internal pressure or surface tension.

The occurrence of structural changes is also implied by changes in the light-scattering property of the egg cortex, which has been observed in invertebrate eggs by a number of workers (Runnström, 1928 ; Moser, 1939 ; Öhman, 1945 ; Monroy and Montalenti, 1947 ; Rothschild and Swann, 1952), and also in hamster eggs (Austin, 1956c). Some, however, reported an increase in refractility on spermatozoon penetration and others a decrease. The lack of agreement is almost certainly due to differences in the methods of examining the eggs ; in dark-ground illumination, the incident light may be directed at various angles from 180 to 60 degrees in respect of the observed beam of refracted light, according to the particular optical equipment selected. Mitchison and Swann (1952) explain the discrepancy in the interpretations of previous workers by concluding that, at spermatozoon penetration, there is a decrease in light scattered at large angles and an increase in light scattered at small angles. They cite Oster's (1950) data as showing that these changes signify an increase in particle size of cortical elements. Oster worked with protein solutions, so that this statement would presumably apply particularly to ultra-microscopic elements in the cortex, but it is reasonable to infer that changes in refractility are also associated with the " explosion " of cortical granules which has been described in connection with the formation of the fertilisation membrane (p. 332). As already noted, changes in light refraction seem to be associated with the slow component of the block to polyspermy, but the block is not necessarily evoked at activation when this occurs through non-specific stimulation—if the fertilisation membrane is mechanically removed from artificially activated sea-urchin eggs, spermatozoon penetration can occur (Loeb, 1913 ; Moore, 1916, 1917), though this may equally be owing to the transient nature of the block to polyspermy (see p. 390); in rat eggs, artificial activation does not preclude spermatozoon penetration (Austin and Braden, 1954b).

Another structural change induced by activation is the contraction of the vitellus, which may sometimes involve quite a large loss in cytoplasmic volume. Rothschild (1958) records the following reported estimates of the degree of shrinkage shown by the vitellus of fish and lamprey eggs : 7 per cent in the killifish, *Oryzias latipes* ; 25 per cent in the goldfish ; 2–9 per cent in the trout ; and 13 per cent in the lamprey.

Among mammals, it has been observed in several species that the vitellus of the egg contracts following spermatozoon penetration : rabbit (Gregory, 1930 ;

Pincus and Enzmann, 1932 ; Thibault, 1947a and 1949), mouse (Sobotta, 1895), guinea-pig (Lams and Doorme, 1908), dog, cat and bat (Van der Stricht, 1923), rat (Gilchrist and Pincus, 1932 ; Pincus and Enzmann, 1934 ; Pincus, 1936a ; Austin and Braden, 1954b), cow (Hamilton and Laing, 1946), hamster (Austin, 1956d), pig (Pitkjanen and Sheglov, 1958). Contraction incurs loss of fluid so that the perivitelline space becomes more conspicuous. A vitelline contraction, accompanied by expulsion of fluid, evidently occurs also at the time of formation of the first polar body (Van Beneden, 1875) and is responsible for the initial pro- duction of a true though small perivitelline space. Gilchrist and Pincus found that the reduction in vitelline volume of the rat egg after activation is 13–17 per cent and a similar finding was reported by Austin and Braden. In the hamster egg, the shrinkage is about 9 per cent. In the diminutive egg of the field vole, no significant reduction was detected (Austin, 1957c). Contraction of the vitellus should be regarded as a feature of activation rather than of spermatozoon penetra- tion, for vitelline shrinkage also occurs with experimentally induced activation (Pincus and Enzmann, 1934 ; Thibault 1947b, 1949) and, in the rat, may often involve a reduction equal to that seen after spermatozoon penetration (Austin and Braden, 1954b).

Changes in Metabolism

Loeb was the first to advance the view that the process of fertilisation was one mainly concerned with oxidations taking place in the egg, initiated by the entrance of the spermatozoon. This hypothesis was supported by measurements of oxygen consumption of the eggs of *Arbacia*, before and after fertilisation (Warburg, 1908) and measurements of heat production of *Strongylocentrotus* eggs (Meyerhof, 1911). Owing to technical limitations of the methods used, however, the results were equivocal. With the introduction of the Barcroft differential manometer, greater accuracy in measurement of oxygen uptake was obtained. Warburg (1915), using this instrument, found that the oxygen consumption of *Strongylocentrotus* eggs increased about six times after fertilisation. Shearer (1922) carried the investiga- tion a step further by the employment of a manometer in which it was possible to bring about the fertilisation of the eggs within the closed chamber of the apparatus. With *Echinus microtuberculatus* eggs and spermatozoa, he found an immediate increase in the oxygen consumption of the eggs on fertilisation. Although this method gives comparable measurements before and immediately after fertilisation, the results may be obscured because of the simultaneous release of CO_2 from bicarbonates present in the sea-water, caused by acid liberated from the eggs, or the retention of CO_2 by the eggs themselves and by the egg jelly. Laser and Rothschild (1939) pointed out that a true picture of the metabolism of the eggs during the fertilisation reaction can only be obtained if O_2 consumption and total CO_2 production and retention are measured. They found that, during the first 5 minutes after activation, the eggs of the sea-urchin, *Psammechinus miliaris*, show a sudden increase in O_2 consumption and in acid production. Neither of these effects persists ; the O_2 consumption falls to a low value, sometimes below the pre-fertilisation rate, but increases again about 10 minutes later. Similar findings were made by other investigators which tended to add further support to Loeb's hypothesis. New light was thrown on the problem, however, by the work of

Whitaker (1933), who showed that an increase of respiratory activity on fertilisation is by no means general, and that in some forms there may be no change or even a decrease depending upon the pre-fertilisation rate of O_2 consumption. Then it was found that, in any one species, the rate could be shown to increase, remain constant, or decrease, according to the condition of the eggs (Tyler and Humason, 1937), that the metabolic activity of the egg exhibited changes associated with maturation (Lindahl and Holter, 1941), and that a progressive decrease with time after removal from the ovary occurred in the respiratory processes of eggs (Holter and Zeuthen, 1944). These observations were extended by the studies of Borei (1948, 1949) and it is now acknowledged that Loeb's hypothesis cannot be sustained. Evidently, the rate of O_2 consumption in the unfertilised egg, though initially high, declines steadily, and the occurrence of a rise or fall in rate, or the lack of change, will depend upon the stage of maturation or of ageing of the egg at the time of fertilisation.

With the object of identifying the nature and degree of metabolic change associated with activation, numerous metabolic studies have been made on invertebrate eggs and a wealth of data, often conflicting and usually difficult of interpretation, has been accumulated. It has been established, largely through the work of Krahl, Keltch, Neubeck and Clowes (1941), Robbie (1946), Rothschild (1949) and Brachet (1950), that invertebrate eggs possess the cytochrome–cytochrome oxidase system; however, this is already present and functioning in unfertilised eggs. Particular attention has been given to carbohydrate metabolism and there is sufficient evidence for the conclusion that the enzymes required for both oxidative and glycolytic metabolic paths are available—before as well as after activation. Many other observations on chemical changes associated with fertilisation are discussed by Runnström (1949, 1956), Rothschild (1956), and Monroy (1957a, b, c). There seems to be general agreement that several quantitative and perhaps qualitative differences in the materials undergoing metabolism exist between unfertilised and fertilised eggs, but we still lack a comprehensive theory of the biochemical mechanisms of activation and, therefore, of fertilisation.

Because it is difficult to obtain mammalian eggs in sufficient numbers and because these eggs are not easy to maintain *in vitro*, the metabolic study of mammalian fertilisation has received scant attention. Attempts have been made to estimate the O_2 uptake in the eggs of the cow (Dragoiu, Benetato and Opreanu, 1937), rat (Boell and Nicholas, 1939, 1948) and rabbit (Smith and Kleiber, 1950; Fridhandler, Hafez and Pincus, 1956a, b, 1957); the results for the rat and rabbit suggest an uptake of $0\cdot5$–$1\cdot0$ mμl. O_2 per hour for each egg. There was little indication that the O_2 consumption was altered by activation or by fertilisation. Fridhandler *et al.* (1956a) found some evidence that the cytochrome system exists in mammalian eggs, as in those of marine invertebrates.

Extrusion of Polar Bodies

It has already been noted that the relationship between spermatozoon penetration and the maturation of the egg varies greatly among animals (*see* p. 313 and Fig. *10*. 2). Where maturation pauses at one or other phase of meiosis, the response to spermatozoon penetration, namely activation, is apparent through the resumption of maturation. In the sea-urchin type of fertilisation, however, maturation is already complete and evidence of activation is seen in cytoplasmic changes, the occurrence of syngamy and cell cleavage.

The mechanism of polar-body formation appears to be basically the same in all animal groups, but the size of polar bodies, relative to the size of the vitellus, is by no means constant. In the large, megalecithal eggs of fishes, reptiles and birds, the polar bodies are extremely small in comparison to the egg, whereas among the placental mammals, relatively large polar bodies are seen, especially in the rodents (Fig. *10*. 19). Occasionally, an abnormality of the meiotic process will produce a giant polar body, which may be as large as the rest of the egg. This has been observed in platyhelminths and gastropods (Wilson, 1928), the dog

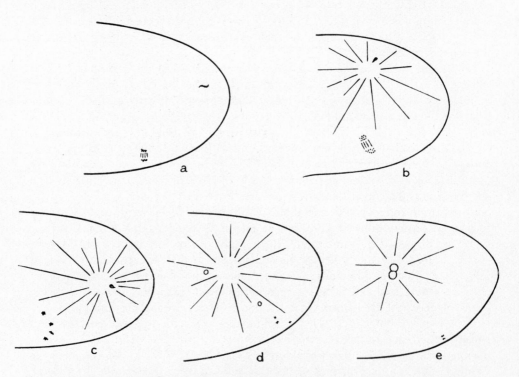

Fig. *10*. 16—Fertilisation in the egg of the parasitic wasp, *Habrobracon*. (Redrawn slightly modified from Speicher, 1936.) (By permission of the publisher, from *J. Morph.*, 1936, **59**, 419.)

(Grosser, 1927), and the mouse (Pesonen, 1946a, b; Braden, 1957). It has also been induced artificially in the mouse by subjecting eggs to heat (Fig. *10*. 40c) (Braden and Austin, 1954b, c, and *see* p. 384). In some insects and crustaceans, polar bodies are not extruded; instead, three of the four chromosomes groups produced by the two meiotic divisions are relegated to the superficial region of the egg and ultimately disappear (Fig. *10*.16) (*see* Wilson, 1928; Speicher 1936). Sometimes, in mammals, extrusion of first or second polar bodies is suppressed, spontaneously or under experimental conditions; the consequences are discussed on p. 380 and by Beatty (1957).

Among many invertebrates, the first polar body commonly undergoes division so that three polar bodies are finally produced. This is rare in mammals, but

can occur (in mouse, Sobotta, 1895 ; in guinea-pig, Rubaschkin, 1905)—more
often an abnormal and abortive spindle develops or else the chromosomes degenerate
or scatter.   In some mammalian species, the first polar body itself is short-lived
and breaks up before ovulation.   Thus, in the rat, only 1·3 per cent of eggs were
found to possess a first polar body, when examined shortly after ovulation (Austin
and Braden, 1954b).   Persistence of the first polar body was infrequently recorded

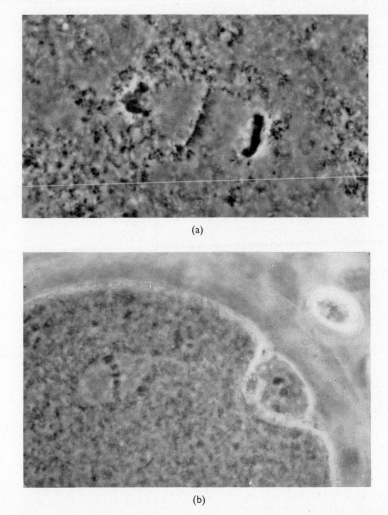

(a)

(b)

Fig. *10. 17*—(*a*) Telophase first-maturation spindle in a rat egg.   (From
Austin and Smiles, 1948.)   (*b*) First polar body and metaphase second-
maturation spindle in hamster egg.   (From Austin, 1956d.)

in some strains of mice (in about 9 per cent of eggs), but commonly in others
(54 per cent) (Braden, personal communication).   By contrast, the first polar
body was seen in 88 per cent of freshly ovulated eggs in the rabbit and in all eggs in
the hamster (Fig. *10.* 17b) (Austin, 1956d) and field vole (Austin, 1957c).   Ward
(1948) never saw nuclear reconstitution in the first polar body in the hamster

though it did occur in the second and Braden (1957) reports that this usually holds true also for the mouse.

Isolated stages in the formation of first and second polar bodies, generally as seen in histological preparations, have been described in detail, by Van Durme (1914) in birds, by Olsen (1942), Olsen and Fraps (1950) and Bekhtina (1958) in the hen, by Olsen and Fraps (1944) in the turkey, by Flynn and Hill (1939) in monotremes, by Hill (1910, 1918) and Hartman (1916, 1919) in marsupials, by Sobotta (1893, 1895), Lams and Doorme (1908) and Long and Mark (1911) in the mouse, by Sobotta and Burckhard (1910), Huber (1915), Blandau (1945), and Odor (1955) in the rat, by Rubaschkin (1905) and Lams (1913) in the guinea-pig, by Ward (1948) in the hamster, by Van Beneden and Julin (1880) in the bat, by Newman (1912) in the armadillo, by O. Van der Stricht (1909, 1923) in the bat, dog and cat,

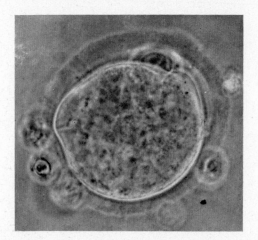 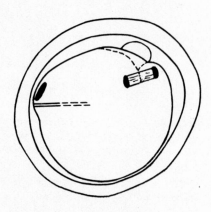

Fig. *10*. 18—Rat egg showing first polar body, second polar spindle involved in formation of second polar body, anterior end of the spermatozoon mid-piece, and the spermatozoon head undergoing transformation. Diagram depicts structures seen in several different focal planes. The spermatozoon tail passed out of the vitellus approximately where lines cease. (Compare with Fig. *10*. 29f.)

by Longley (1911), R. Van der Stricht (1911) and Dawson and Friedgood (1940) in the cat, by Van Beneden (1875) and Pincus and Enzmann (1935) in the rabbit, by Spalding, Berry and Moffit (1955) in the pig, and by Berry and Savery (1958) in the sheep. Phase-contrast microscopy has made possible the close study of living cells and by this means stages of polar-body extrusion were observed by Austin and Smiles (1948), Odor and Blandau (1951a) and Austin (1956d). If rat eggs are kept surrounded by the fluid accompanying them on recovery from the Fallopian tube, they may remain alive for several hours even though somewhat compressed beneath a coverslip. By this expedient, phases of maturation and fertilisation have been studied as continuous processes (Austin, 1950a, 1951b).

Maturation of the primary oöcyte starts with the movement of the germinal vesicle to a position just below the surface of the vitellus and with the loss of its nuclear membrane and nucleolus. As the nucleolus disappears, a group of chromosomes becomes visible (initially on the inner surface of the nuclear membrane—Makino, 1941) and these arrange themselves on the first polar spindle. At first, the spindle lies paratangentially in the superficial cytoplasm, and the surface of the vitellus is elevated above it. The raised mass of cytoplasm largely represents the material that will go to form the polar body. Meiosis proceeds through metaphase and anaphase to telophase (Fig. *10*. 17a). The centre of the spindle is now seen to be occupied by a thin disc of granular material which lies at right angles to the axis of the spindle and which is termed the central body. The surface of the vitellus becomes indented at one side of the elevation at a point immediately peripheral to the central body and a cleft develops from the indentation towards the central body. The spindle rotates about one pole through an angle of 90 degrees, eventually assuming a radial orientation, and, in this way, the chromosome group at what is now the more peripheral pole is carried into the

developing polar body. Simultaneously, the cleft extends inwards, following in the wake of the central body as if it were induced by this structure, and also laterally about the peripheral pole of the spindle (Fig. *10*. 18 and 29). By extension through a hemispherical course, the cleft finally cuts off the portion of cytoplasm containing the external pole of the spindle and so the extrusion of the first polar body is completed. For a while, the polar body remains attached to the vitellus by the spindle, which, though by now much elongated, still retains appreciable tensile strength. When the polar body is finally freed, the cleft is found to have passed just medially to the central body which is thus left within the polar body. In the vitellus, the residue of the spindle releases the chromosome group at its medial pole and disappears.

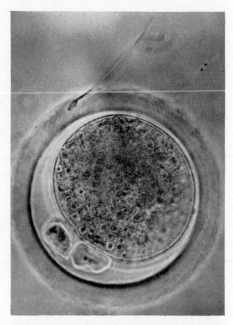

Fig. *10*. 19—Guinea-pig egg, showing polar bodies and spermatozoon head, lacking acrosome, embedded in zona pellucida.

Instead of giving rise to a resting nucleus, the chromosome group left within the egg after the extrusion of the first polar body immediately proceeds to take part in the formation of the second polar spindle (Fig. *10*. 17b). The second meiotic division and the extrusion of the second polar body takes place in essentially the same manner as the first. In the rabbit, the second polar body is formed about 12 hour after coitus (Yamane, 1930 ; Pincus and Enzmann, 1932 ; Chang, 1955e) or approximately 2 hours after spermatozoon penetration. Most rat eggs were found with a second polar body at the end of the fourth hour after spermatozoon penetration (Odor and Blandau, 1951a). *In vitro*, the second maturation spindle of the rat egg completed its rotation 2–3 hours after the initiation of meiosis (Austin, 1951b). Extrusion of the second polar body in the guinea-pig is reported to occur at $13\frac{1}{2}$ hours after coitus, and in the mouse at 5–7 hours (*see* Beatty, 1956).

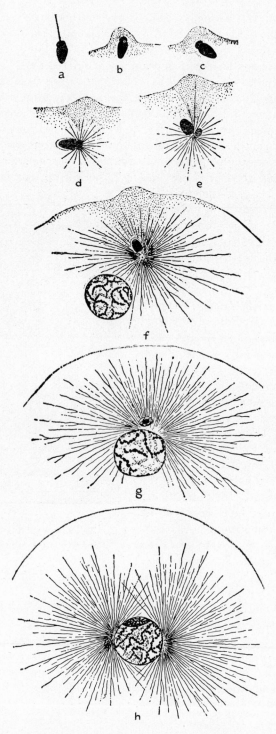

Fig. *10*. *20*—Fertilisation in the sea-urchin,
Toxopneustes. (From Wilson, 1928.)

V. THE PRONUCLEI

General Morphology of Pronuclear Development

Mammalian pronuclei seem to be known in greater detail than are the pronuclei of other animal's eggs. Most observations have been made on rat eggs (Sobotta and Burckhard, 1910 ; Huber, 1915 ; Kremer, 1924 ; Austin and Smiles,

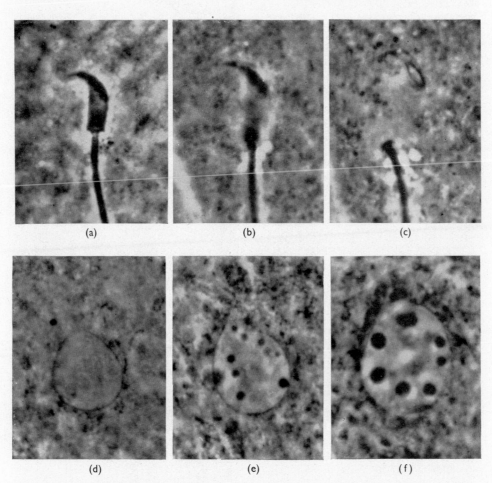

(a)   (b)   (c)

(d)   (e)   (f)

Fig. *10.* 21—Transformation of the hamster spermatozoon head into a male pronucleus. (a, b, c, from Austin and Bishop, 1958c.)

1948 ; Austin, 1950a, 1951b, 1952a ; Blandau and Odor, 1950 ; Odor and Blandau, 1951b ; Austin and Braden, 1953c, 1955 ; Braden and Austin, 1953a ; Ludwig, 1953, 1954 ; Dalcq, 1955a, b ; Izquierdo, 1955), and the description that follows is based chiefly on this species.

Shortly after the spermatozoon head has passed through the vitelline surface, it begins to swell, as if by hydration, and to lose its characteristic shape. The perforatorium and the spermatozoon tail become detached from the nucleus which

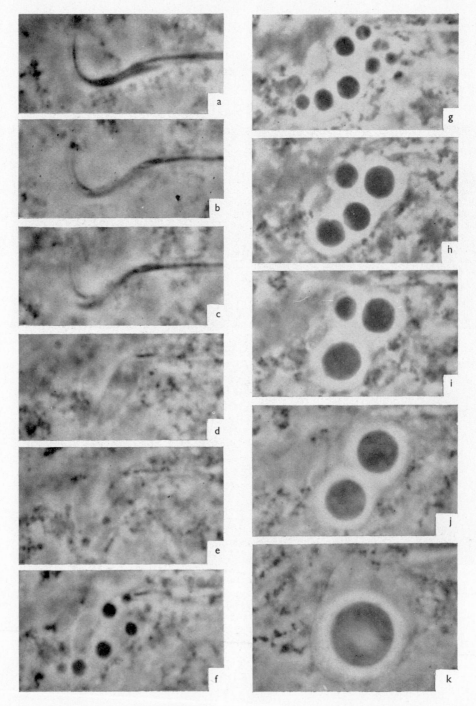

Fig. *10.22*—Transformation of a rat spermatozoon head into a male pronucleus. (From Austin, 1951b.)

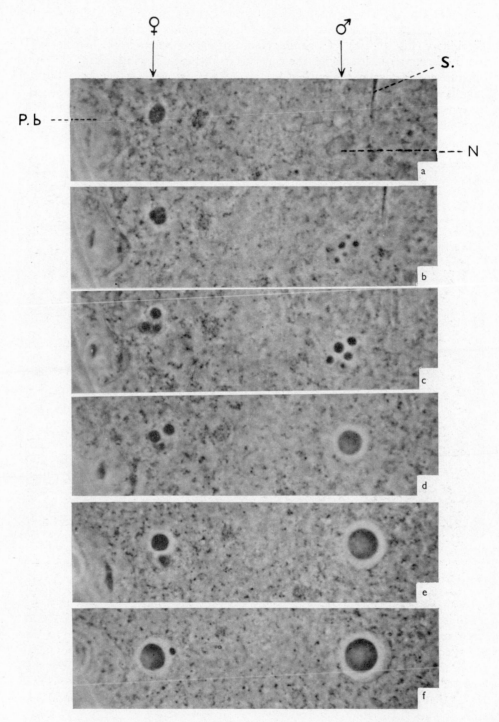

Fig. *10*. 23—Early development of male and female pronuclei. P.b., second polar body; S, spermatozoon tail; N, transforming spermatozoon head. (From Austin, 1951b.)

assumes an oval or somewhat rounded form. Soon, minute nucleoli make their appearance within the nucleus and a nuclear membrane develops around the periphery (Fig. *10*. 22). (A similar course of events occurs in the hamster egg— *see* Fig. *10*. 21.) Meanwhile, the consistency of the nucleus has changed ; in the mature spermatozoon, the nucleus is a compact structure (*see* Chapter 7), but as it swells within the egg it acquires the consistency of a gel. In turn, the gel becomes a typically fluid nucleoplasm. The male pronucleus thus formed now closely resembles a somatic nucleus except that it has initially a larger number of nucleoli

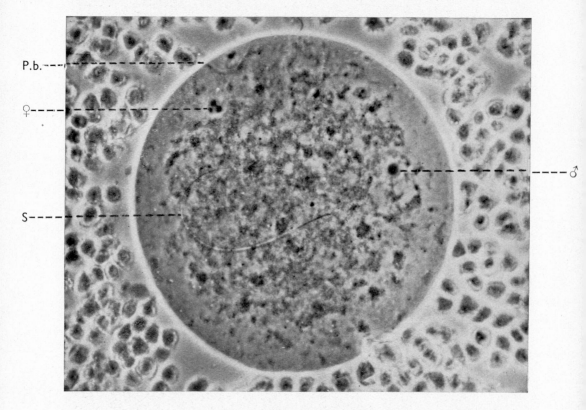

Fig. *10*. 24—Rat egg, showing early male and female pronuclei, spermatozoon tail (S), and second polar body (P.b.). (From Austin, 1949b.)

than is generally seen in somatic cells. As the nucleoli increase in size, however, they undergo coalescence and thus their number is soon reduced (Fig. *10*. 22). Coalescence is assisted by the relatively slower rate of expansion of the pronucleus compared to that of the nucleoli in the early stages and the nucleoli become crowded together as they tend to outgrow the available space. Later, the pronucleus grows faster than the nucleoli and, at full development, accommodates a large number of these bodies (Figs. *10*. 25f and 29k).

Development of the male pronucleus in the rat egg may be divided into six arbitrary stages (Austin, 1952a). The stage in which the nucleoli first appear and begin to grow and coalesce is referred to as the early primary stage (Fig. *10*. 22e, f, g). Crowding of the nucleoli, coalescence and decrease in number occur chiefly in the late primary stage (Fig. _10_. 22 h, i, j). Commonly, the number of nucleoli is reduced to one and this characterises the single-nucleolus stage (Figs. _10_. 22, 23, 24, 25), which also encompasses the beginning of accelerated pronuclear enlargement. New nucleoli are now seen to form and these differ from the earlier nucleoli in that they are found in contact with, and even apparently embedded in, the nuclear membrane whereas the early nucleoli all lay freely within the nucleus. The new or secondary nucleoli form, grow and apparently become detached from the nuclear membrane during the early secondary stage of pronuclear development (Fig. _10_. 25d). This appears to be the principal way in which the number of nucleoli is increased, but new nucleoli may possibly also be generated at points removed from the nuclear membrane. The primary nucleolus that distinguished the single-nucleolus stage diminishes in size as the other nucleoli grow. In the late secondary stage (Fig. _10_. 25e,), the pronucleus, now fully expanded, contains numerous nucleoli that are widely distributed through the nucleoplasm, some still in apposition with the nuclear membrane and others disposed at varying distances from it. Finally, the nucleoli gather more towards the central region of the pronucleus, leaving a free area near the nuclear membrane, and this is called the stage of maximum development (Fig. _10_. 25f). By now, the primary nucleolus has been reduced considerably in size but is probably identifiable still as the largest of the nucleoli. For a while, nothing more appears to happen, and then the stage of maximum development is terminated by the shrinkage of the pronucleus which marks the beginning of the process of syngamy.

The female pronucleus is formed at about the same time as the male pronucleus (Fig. _10_. 23). When the second polar body is extruded, a group of chromosomes is left within the egg and these shortly become aggregated so as to form an irregularly shaped mass. As with the spermatozoon nucleus, nucleoli become visible within the mass and a nuclear membrane forms. The development of the female pronucleus follows much the same course as that described above for the male except that fewer nucleoli are formed, the stages are not so distinct and the ultimate size of the pronucleus is smaller. In addition, nucleoli are found attached to the nuclear membrane during the primary stages as well as during the early and late secondary stages.

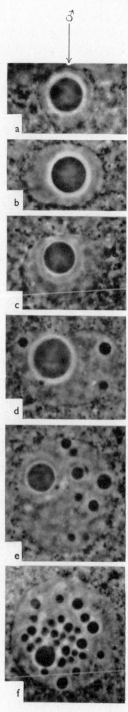

Fig. _10_. 25—Stages in the growth of the male pronucleus in the rat egg. (From Austin, 1951b.)

The generation of pronuclei from spermatozoon head or egg chromosomes is more or less synchronous, their growth proceeds *pari passu*, and, at the approach of syngamy, they show corresponding changes almost simultaneously. These observations strongly suggest that the development of the two pronuclei is directly correlated throughout their life span. Such a conclusion is supported by data gained from the study of eggs in which fertilisation has been interfered with in

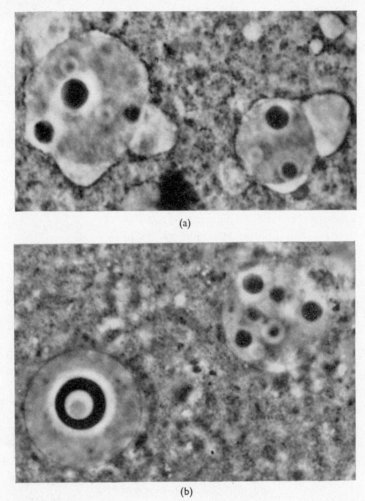

(a)

(b)

Fig. *10. 26*—Pronuclei in the eggs of (a) the Chinese hamster, and (b) the field vole.

various ways. Thus, if the events leading up to the formation of the female pronucleus are favoured by the artificial activation of the egg before spermatozoon penetration, the two pronuclei still appear at about the same time—the progress of the female element seems to be delayed until the normal relationship is restored (Austin and Braden, 1954b). Conversely, if the formation of the female pronucleus is temporarily inhibited, the development of the male element appears to be arrested and, again, pronuclear generation is synchronous. Further evidence of a correlating mechanism is to be found in observations made on mouse eggs undergoing fertilisation with spermatozoa that had been subjected to X-irradiation whilst in the male tract (Bruce and Austin, 1956). Some of the eggs contained pronuclei that seemed to have reached maximum development in a normal way, but fertilisation had evidently been held up at this stage, for these eggs were recovered from mice killed at times when eggs in control mice had reached the 4- to 8-cell stages of cleavage. It was surmised that X-irradiation had so affected the spermatozoon nucleus that the male pronucleus was unable to proceed to syngamy. Since development involving only the female pronucleus is quite possible (as in gynogenesis and parthenogenesis), failure of the female pronucleus also to proceed further must presumably, therefore, have been connected with the inability of the male pronucleus to do so.

Although there is thus good evidence for the existence of a correlating mechanism, its nature is unknown ; perhaps the biochemical processes in the two pronuclei are in some way interdependent. The existence of inter-pronuclear influences is shown also by Fankhauser's (1948) observations on the polyspermic eggs of the urodele, *Triturus helveticus*, in which the supernumerary pronuclei degenerate when syngamy occurs (*see* p. 372).

Pronuclear development in the eggs of other mammals appears to follow the same general plan as that just described for the rat. A noticeable difference in some species is the persistence of a single nucleolus throughout the second half of pronuclear development. This may mean that secondary nucleoli unite with the large nucleolus immediately after their formation or that increase in size of the single nucleolus replaces genesis of secondary nucleoli.

As seen by phase-contrast microscopy, the only bodies visible within the pronucleus of the living rat egg are the spherical nucleoli, the nucleoplasm being apparently homogeneous. No structure can generally be discerned within the nucleolus, but occasionally a spherical inclusion is seen to be present. The inclusion may be so small that its diameter is no more than about one-tenth that of the nucleolus, or it may be so large that it accounts for seven-eighths the diameter of the nucleolus. Sometimes, whilst the egg is under observation, the nucleolus appears to break, releasing the inclusion which mixes intimately with the nucleoplasm. The nucleolar material then immediately assumes the form of a solid sphere. In the egg of the field vole, pronuclear nucleoli were seen quite often to contain a small spherical body, possibly composed of nucleolar material, within the fluid inclusion (Austin, 1957c ; Fig. *10*. 26b).

If an egg is ruptured during examination, an entire pronucleus may pass into the surrounding medium. After a short time, vesicles develop within the nuclear membrane, suggesting a bilaminar structure. If the nucleus is broken, the nucleoplasm mixes freely with the surrounding medium (0·9 per cent saline solution), but the nucleoli seem to be insoluble and behave rather like oil droplets. A nucleolus constrained to pass through a narrow space is immediately altered in shape and may break up into smaller droplets which then assume the spherical form.

Quantitative Relations

Measurements have been made on rat pronuclei at the various stages described in the previous Section, and thus estimates can be given for the volumes of the pronuclei and for the number, total volume and total surface area of the nucleoli (Austin, 1952a). Approximate estimates were also derived for the relative duration of each stage. The early and late primary and the single-nucleolus stages were all brief and each occupied rather less than one-tenth the total period of pronuclear development. If the duration of pronuclear life is accepted as 15 hours (*see* p. 370), the stages just mentioned would occupy about $1\frac{1}{2}$ hours each. The early and late secondary stages were longer, each taking about one-sixth the total period, namely about $2\frac{1}{2}$ hours. The stage of maximum development was the longest—it lasted between one-third and one-half the total period, or 5–$7\frac{1}{2}$ hours.

The volumes of male and female pronuclei increased more than twenty times during the course of their development to final volumes of 5700 cu.µ and 2300 cu.µ respectively. Both pronuclei reached their greatest volume during the late secondary stage so that pronuclear enlargement all occurs in the first half of the pronuclear life span. The nucleoli grew rather more rapidly to reach maxima of 550 cu.µ and 220 cu.µ for male and female pronuclei, respectively. Maximum nucleolar volume was reached at about the end of the single-nucleolus stage, namely, within the first third of pronuclear life. It will be noticed that the male pronucleus was about two and a half times the size of the female pronucleus, both in pronuclear volume and total nucleolar volume. A further point of interest is that, in both pronuclei, the total nucleolar volume is about 10 per cent of the nuclear volume ; this is a much larger proportion than that represented by the nucleoli of rat somatic nuclei, which rarely exceed 1 per cent of the nuclear volume (Vincent, 1955).

In both pronuclei, the number of nucleoli continued to increase after the nucleolar volume became constant. The effect of this was that the total nucleolar surface area also continued to increase for at least half the period of pronuclear life. Since surfaces are important sites for synthetic processes, it seems possible that the increased nucleolar surface area is involved in some synthetic activity within the pronuclei—this is discussed later (page 369).

In polyspermic rat eggs at the stage of maximum pronuclear development, it was found that the sum of the volumes of the female and the two male pronuclei (7341 cu.µ) did not exceed the sum of the volumes of normal pronuclei (Austin and Braden, 1953b). Similarly, the sum of the total nucleolar volumes of polyspermic eggs (793 cu.µ) did not significantly exceed that of normal eggs. Measurements of the same kind were made in rat eggs that were undergoing early parthenogenetic development and that displayed well-formed single nuclei (Austin and Braden, 1955). The single nucleus had a much larger volume (4188 cu.µ) than a normal female pronucleus but fell far short of the sum of the volumes of normal male and female pronuclei. The same relationship held true also for the total nucleolar volume of the single nucleus (620 cu.µ). Similar findings were made in mouse eggs undergoing early parthenogenesis (Austin and Braden, 1955) and in hamster eggs in early gynogenesis (Austin, 1956d). Austin and Braden concluded that both pronuclear and nucleolar volumes are normally limited by the amount of certain cytoplasmic materials that are involved in their formation. Evidently, there is partition between the male and female pronuclei of formative material, so that a nucleus developing alone is able to achieve a larger size. However, there must also be some inherent factor limiting the growth of the pronucleus since single nuclei never reached the size theoretically possible. The feasibility of obtaining

more precise information on the nature of the formative substrate is indicated by
the observations of Edwards and Sirlin (1956, 1958) on the passage of radioactive
tracers from the cytoplasm to the pronuclei of the mouse egg.

According to the figures given above, the male pronucleus in the rat egg
evidently has a much greater affinity for cytoplasmic substrate than the female
pronucleus.   The preponderance of the male pronucleus in the rat egg is accepted
by other recent investigators (Odor and Blandau, 1951b ; Dalcq, 1955b), and pronuclear disparity has also been reported in the eggs of the guinea-pig (O. Van der
Stricht, 1923), rabbit (Amoroso and Parkes, 1947), multimammate rat (Austin
and Bishop, 1957b) and Chinese hamster (*see* Fig. *10*. 26a).   Inequality of pronuclear dimensions is, however, by no means universal, for pronuclei of very
similar size have been described in the eggs of the spiny anteater, *Echidna* (Flynn
and Hill, 1939, and *see* Fig. *14*. 6), the opossum, *Didelphis* (Hartman, 1916) the
native cat, *Dasyurus* (Hill, 1910), the armadillo (Newman, 1912), the bat (Van
Beneden and Julin, 1880 ; Škreb, 1957), the ferret (Hamilton, 1934), the pig
(Pitkjanen, 1955), the hamster (Austin, 1956d ; Hamilton and Samuel, 1956), and
in occasional eggs of the rabbit (Austin and Braden, 1953b) and field vole (Austin,
1957c).   Differences between individual eggs or perhaps between the eggs of
different strains of animals may account for some apparent contradictions : mouse
and cat pronuclei have been reported to exhibit distinct disparity by some workers
(Sobotta, 1895 ; Austin and Braden, 1955 ; Edwards and Sirlin, 1956 ; Hill and
Tribe, 1924) but not by others (Lams and Doorme, 1908 ; Gresson, 1941 ; R. Van
der Stricht, 1911).   In many invertebrates, such as the sea-urchins, the female
pronucleus is much larger than the male (*see* Fig. *10*. 20), whereas in others, as in
the round-worm, *Ascaris* (Makarov, 1953), and in certain insects (*see* Fig. *10*. 16),
the pronuclei are of about the same size ; in some nematodes the male pronucleus
is the larger.   In the flagellate, *Trichonympha*, the female pronucleus is slightly
larger (Cleveland, 1958a, b).

Mammalian eggs also vary somewhat in the structure and general proportions
of their pronuclei.   The relatively large rabbit egg with a diameter of about 140μ
has pronuclear volumes of 6200 and 4100 cu.μ for the larger and smaller pronuclei,
respectively (Austin and Bishop, 1957b).   These are big pronuclei compared with
those of rodent eggs, but owing to the larger volume of the cytoplasm the nucleocytoplasmic ratio in the rabbit is only about 1 : 88, whereas in the eggs of the rat,
mouse, hamster and field vole it is about 1 : 25, 1 : 34, 1 : 35 and 1 : 31, respectively.
The difference between the two groups is probably attributable to the greater
proportion of yolk material in rabbit eggs.   By contrast, the total nucleolar
volumes in the rabbit, 50 and 40 cu.μ, are much less than in rodent eggs.   A
possible reason for these differences between rabbit and rodent eggs is discussed
on p. 369.

Movements of Pronuclei

In the eggs of many invertebrates, the spermatozoon head passes into the
vitellus and then rotates through 180 degrees.   Thus, the anterior part of the head
comes to point towards the surface of the egg, and the spermatozoon aster, developing at the posterior pole of the head, is directed towards the centre of the egg.
In those forms in which maturation of the egg is not completed until after spermatozoon entry, the spermatozoon nucleus may move a short distance into the egg and

N*

then remain stationary until the end of maturation. Where maturation occurs before fertilisation, there is no delay and the egg and spermatozoon nuclei proceed at once to meet each other. In the frog, W. Roux observed that the path of the spermatozoon nucleus is marked by a trail of pigment granules carried in from the cortex. The path is curved and was said to have two components : the " penetration path " and the " copulation path." After passing a short distance along the penetration path, which is radially orientated, the course of the spermatozoon nucleus alters and is directed along the copulation path towards the point at which subsequently the nuclei meet. The egg nucleus does not move until the spermatozoon nucleus has altered its course along the copulation path ; it then begins to move slowly towards the copulation point. These observations have been confirmed by the study of other species and are probably general. The mechanism governing the movements of the nuclei is still obscure. Undoubtedly, the movements are the result of the interaction of forces between nucleus and cytoplasm, and perhaps between each nucleus, but the nature of these forces is as yet unknown (*see* Wilson, 1928 ; Gray, 1931). Chambers (1939) believed that the male pronucleus is brought to the middle of the egg by the growth of the aster ("a gelated body "), and that the female pronucleus is carried in a cytoplasmic current to the centre of the aster, the rays of which direct the course of movement in the final stages. Rothschild (1956) points out, however, that in sea-urchin eggs undergoing gynogenesis the female pronucleus still migrates to the centre of the egg although no male pronucleus is present. The same thing happens in the parthenogenetic egg of the parasitic wasp, *Habrobracon* (Speicher, 1936). According to Rothschild, observations on sea-urchin eggs leave no doubt that the male pronucleus " attracts " the female pronucleus ; on the other hand, male pronuclei in polyspermic eggs are pushed apart by their growing asters. This explanation is inappropriate in certain other species, for male pronuclei are known to come into close contact with each other in the polyspermic eggs of the round-worm, *Ascaris* (Makarov, 1957) the sturgeon (Ginsberg, 1957), and the rat (*see* Figs. *10*. 31 and 32, and p. 376).

Pronuclear movements in mammalian eggs are less easily followed because they take place very much more slowly than do those in invertebrate eggs and because of the difficulty of keeping the eggs in a normal state whilst under observation. The male and female pronuclei are generally first seen in contact during the stage of maximum development and they then occupy the central region of the egg. Sometimes, however, pronuclei may be found together at earlier stages of development and in more peripheral parts of the cytoplasm.

Morphology of Syngamy

Syngamy is the culmination of the fertilisation process—it is the phase during which the paternal and maternal chromosomes are brought together, preparatory to being shared equally between the two daughter cells into which the egg divides. Aggregation of the chromosomes may involve, in some animals, a preliminary fusion and intermingling of the male and female pronuclei ; in other animals the paternal and maternal complements retain their independence to varying degrees (*see* Wilson, 1928). In the sea-urchin (and *Trichonympha*: Cleveland, 1958a, b), a single cleavage nucleus forms (Fig. *10*. 20)—when this gives place to the visible

chromosomes, the paternal and maternal complements cannot readily be distinguished from
one another.   In the round-worm, *Ascaris*, the
pronuclei come into contact but do not fuse ; the
nuclear membranes persist until after the visible
chromosomes have been formed and the two
chromosome groups retain their individuality,
though arranged on the same spindle.   The eggs
of the crustacean, *Cyclops*, present a more extreme
condition, in that two separate cleavage spindles
are formed.   Among mammals, fusion possibly
occurs in the spiny anteater, *Tachyglossus* (=
Echidna), but though the intervening membranes
are said to disappear the component parts of the
zygote nucleus seem to retain their identity
(Flynn and Hill, 1939).   Observations indicate
that events in placental mammals are intermediate between those occurring in the sea-urchin
egg and the *Ascaris* egg : the pronuclei maintain
their individuality and give rise to two separate
chromosome groups but intermingling of chromosomes occurs in the prophase of the first mitosis.

The male and female pronuclei of the rat egg
generally come into contact at some time during
the stage of maximum development and they
stay thus for a while without showing obvious
change.   Then the pronuclei begin simultaneously
to diminish in volume and as this happens the
nucleoli tend to be brought together and so to
coalesce.   Total nucleolar volume evidently decreases also, and, as time passes, both processes
continue more rapidly.   When the pronuclei have
been reduced approximately to half their maximum volume, they contain noticeably fewer
nucleoli, and, at about this time, the nuclear
membrane becomes irregular and disappears.
Cytoplasmic granules invade the regions of the
pronuclei as the nucleoli dwindle and disappear.
These changes were observed in living eggs by
phase-contrast microscopy (Figs. *10*. 27 and 28)
(Austin, 1950a, 1951b).

After the nucleoli have disappeared, no trace
of the pronuclei can be discerned for a while in
the egg.   The pronuclei have apparently been
reduced to small bodies, having a gel-like
consistency and containing a number of cytoplasmic granules.   Odor and Blandau (1951b)
have shown that these bodies may be isolated from

♂   ♀
↓   ↓

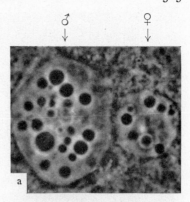

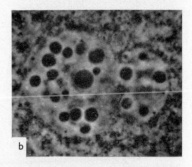

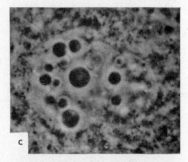

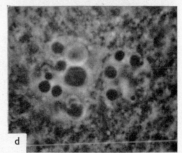

Fig. *10*. 27—Male and female pronuclei in the rat egg showing
reduction in volume and in
number of nucleoli that constitutes the early phase of
syngamy. (From Austin, 1951b.)

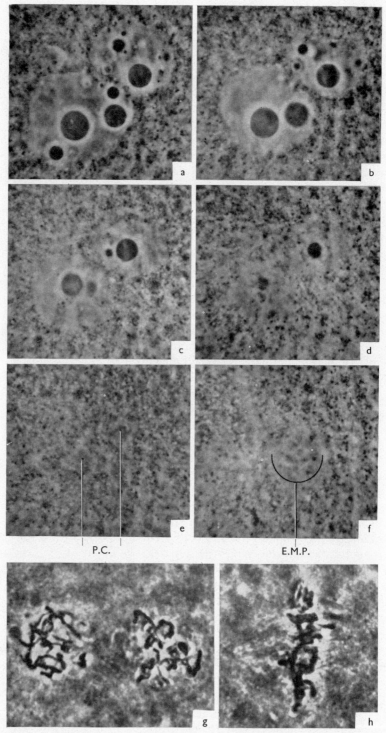

Fig. *10*. 28—(a) to (f) Completion of syngamy in the rat egg. P.C., prophase
chromosome groups; E.M.P., early metaphase plate. (g) Chromosome
groups that have replaced the pronuclei in a hamster egg. (h) Metaphase of
the first cleavage spindle in a hamster egg. (Eggs in (g) and (h) fixed with
acetic-alcohol, stained with toluidine blue; phase-contrast).

the cytoplasm by rupturing the egg, and they have thus demonstrated that the pronuclei have preserved their individuality, despite the absence of a visible nuclear membrane.

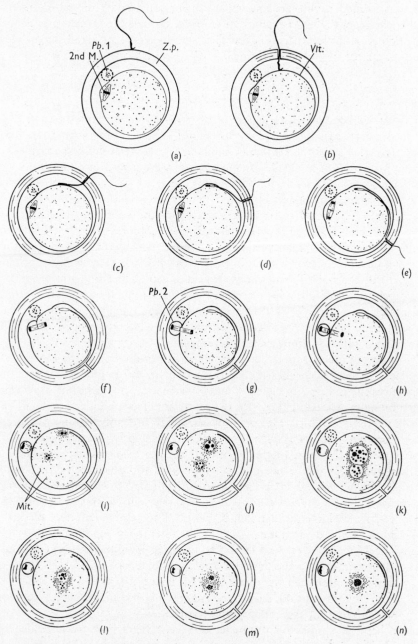

Fig. *10*. 29—Fertilisation of the rat egg. (From Austin and Bishop, 1957b.)

Gradually, chromosome groups become visible in the regions of the pronuclei in the bodies just described (Fig. *10*. 28 e, g). The chromosome groups draw together and unite, the single mass representing the prophase of the first cleavage mitosis. This marks the end of the process of fertilisation. The cleavage spindle now forms, chromosomes arrange themselves on it and split longitudinally ; with the progress of mitosis, the halves of each are separated towards opposing poles of the spindle. As mitosis is completed, cytoplasmic division occurs, the daughter cells thus formed having an equal share of maternal and paternal chromosomes. By this cleavage, the egg becomes an embryo, though the term egg is commonly used throughout at least the first few cleavage divisions. (Details of the cleavage processes appear in Chapter 14).

Histochemistry of Pronuclei

Earlier workers on mammalian fertilisation, notably Sobotta (1895), Lams and Doorme (1908), Sobotta and Burckhard (1910), Lams (1913), O. Van der Stricht (1923), Kremer (1924) and Mainland (1930), recorded peculiarities in the staining properties of nucleoli. Some nucleoli were deeply and uniformly stained with haematoxylin (" nucleinic " nucleoli), whereas others were hardly stained at all with haematoxylin but exhibited neutral or acidophilic properties (" plasmatic " nucleoli) (Fig. *10* 30d). Others again took the haematoxylin stain throughout a peripheral region but were neutral or acidophilic within. Haematoxylin staining was thought to denote basophilia and was considered to characterise a proportion of the nucleoli, particularly in early pronuclei. In later stages of pronuclear development, the nucleoli was variously said to lose their chromatic properties, to break up into coarse granules or to pass out of the nucleus into the cytoplasm. Explanations were put forward to account for these phenomena (though there is no doubt that some were artefactual in nature) and Kremer developed a theory of pronuclear function from such observations (*see* p. 370).

More recent investigations have provided little support for these observations and ideas. It has been shown that the use of haematoxylin is apt to produce appearances suggesting " nucleinic " and " plasmatic " nucleoli, but when eggs are stained by more refined methods for demonstrating basophilia and acidophilia, the nucleoli regularly exhibit strong acidophilia, which probably signifies the presence of basic protein (Braden and Austin, 1953a). Evidently, haematoxylin staining, when applied by the usual methods, denotes the possession of some property other than basophilia but the nature of this property is still obscure. Examination of living rat eggs by phase-contrast microscopy has failed to show that nucleoli disintegrate at any time—they were found to disappear only during syngamy (Austin, 1951b, 1952a ; Odor and Blandau, 1951b). The passage of nucleoli into the cytoplasm is a more contentious issue ; it has often been reported in invertebrate oöcytes (*see* Vincent, 1955) and is said to occur in mammalian oöcytes (Makino, 1941). There is even some modern evidence that such migration takes place from mammalian pronuclei (Izquierdo, 1955 ; Dalcq, 1955a). Odor and Blandau (1951b) and Austin (1952a), however, did not observe anything to suggest its occurrence in living rat eggs undergoing fertilisation.

Histochemical studies on pronuclei in recent years have been made chiefly with the object of revealing the distribution of nucleic acids. Application of the Feulgen staining technique permits the conclusion that high concentrations of deoxyribonucleic acid (DNA) exist in the spermatozoon head and in the group of egg chromosomes from which the female pronucleus springs. As the pronuclei form, the intensity of staining with the Feulgen reagent diminishes but detectable

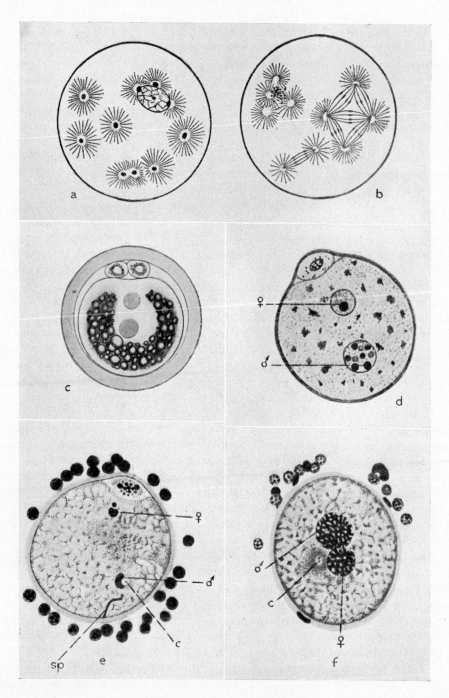

Fig. *10*. 30—(a) and (b) Nicotine-induced polyspermy in the sea-urchin egg (From Wilson, 1928, after O. and R. Hertwig.) (c) Bat egg showing polar bodies and pronuclei (From Van Beneden and Julin, 1880.) (d) Mouse egg showing polar body and male and female pronuclei (From Sobotta, 1895.) (e) and (f) Rat eggs showing early and late pronuclei, centrioles " c " with surrounding asters, and part of spermatozoon tail " sp." (From Sobotta and Burckhard, 1910.) (In the original Figures of (d) and (f) the larger pronuclei were marked as female.)

amounts of DNA tend to persist for a short time, particularly around the nucleoli and at the periphery of the pronuclei (Alfert, 1950 ; Braden and Austin, 1953a). Pyronine-methyl green staining also shows the presence of DNA about the early nucleoli but not the later ones (Ludwig, 1953, 1954). The nucleoli themselves are pyroninophilic (Odor and Blandau, 1951b ; Ludwig, 1953, 1954), and Odor and Blandau, accepting the views of Kurnick (1950), believe that this denotes the presence of ribonucleic acid (RNA). When the pronuclei enter upon the process of syngamy, DNA can again be detected, especially near the nuclear membrane and later, very clearly, in the chromosomes.

The ultra-violet absorption of pronuclei at 260 mμ indicates that high concentrations of nucleic acids are uniformly distributed in the nucleoplasm of the nascent pronuclei and in diminishing concentrations through the early and late primary stages of pronuclear development (Austin and Braden, 1953c). During the early and late secondary stages and at maximum development, no significant absorption of ultra-violet radiation was detected. The pronuclei thus stand in striking contrast to the nuclei of cleaved eggs, particularly those in the 4-cell and later stages, wherein regions of strong absorption are evident immediately about the nucleoli (Austin, 1953a). At no stage of pronuclear development or early cleavage do the nucleoli show significant ultra-violet absorption and it is concluded that they are virtually free of nucleic acids.

Recent experiments on living rat eggs stained with acridine orange and examined by ultra-violet radiation have yielded results that also testify to the uniform distribution of DNA in the nucleoplasm of early pronuclei and to the absence of nucleic acids from nucleoli (Austin and Bishop, 1959b ; Austin and Amoroso, 1959).

Histological tests have shown that pronuclear nucleoli stain orthochromatically with toluidine blue but often contain small metachromatic inclusions (Izquierdo, 1955). The inclusions also give a positive reaction to the periodic acid-Schiff test (Dalcq, 1955a). Both results indicate the presence of polysaccharides, probably as mucopolysaccharides. Positive reactions have been reported in nucleoli after treatment by Baker's test for phospholipids (Dalcq, 1954a, b) and with Gomori's reagent for alkaline phosphatases (Mulnard, 1955). Compared with other constituents of the nucleus, the nucleoli have a high specific gravity (Dalcq, 1951, 1952a).

From the evidence cited, the following conclusions are drawn : The DNA of the spermatozoon head and of the group of egg chromosomes becomes incorporated in the respective pronuclei. Appearances suggest that the nucleic acid is disposed particularly on the surface of the nucleoli and around the walls of the pronuclei, but this effect may be attributable to fixation artefact, as such a distribution is not indicated in studies on living eggs, wherein nucleic acid appears to be uniformly spread throughout the nucleoplasm. The amount of DNA does not seem to be augmented during pronuclear growth, for as the pronucleus enlarges, the concentration drops. The total amount, apparently haploid, may remain constant, which would be consistent with current ideas on the significance of DNA. Just before syngamy, however, the DNA concentration is evidently raised. Throughout pronuclear development, the nucleoli are virtually free of RNA : they are chiefly composed of basic proteins with some phospholipids, and they contain acid phosphatases and inclusions of mucopolysaccharides.

Pronuclear Function

Current ideas on nuclear function relate chiefly to the synthesis of proteins and nucleic acids. In somatic cells, synthetic processes are believed to take place especially in the system composed of the nucleolus and the nucleoprotein aggregate (containing DNA) that is characteristically associated with the nucleolus. The occurrence of synthesis is said to be marked by the accumulation of RNA within the nucleolus, and in the juxta-nuclear cytoplasm.

Much attention has also been given to cytoplasmic structures in recent years and two principal kinds are recognised, namely, the mitochondria and the microsomes. The mitchondria are known to contain complex enzyme systems and are thought to function by making available " high-energy " compounds, derived from the cell substrate, in a form suitable for synthetic processes. The microsomes are rich in RNA which may have originated in the nucleus and then have diffused into the cytoplasm or which may have been synthesised in the cytoplasm under the control of the nucleus. The microsomes are believed to catalyse the synthesis of specific proteins. To some extent, these cytoplasmic systems are independent of the nucleus, but there is good reason to believe that, under normal circumstances, the mitochondrial-microsomal system can supply material for synthetic processes within the nucleus and is influenced in its activities by the products of this synthesis.

There is some evidence indicating that cytoplasmic granular structures are involved in the genesis of the pronuclei. Polar bodies are commonly deficient in these structures and the chromosome groups included in the polar bodies often fail to show any transformation into vesicular nuclei. That such chromosome groups are inherently capable of transformation is shown by the development of two virtually identical female pronuclei when meiosis is completed without polar-body extrusion (*see* p. 379 and Fig. *10*. 36). Accordingly, an association can reasonably be assumed to exist between the activities of the pronuclei and those of the particulate elements of the cytoplasm, and so in some ways the functional interrelationship between nucleus and cytoplasm may well be the same in eggs as in somatic cells. But, in several other respects, the biochemical architecture of pronucleate eggs appears to be unique.

Pronuclei differ from cleavage and somatic nuclei in lacking the distinctive aggregate of DNA associated with the nucleolus, although the pronucleus demonstrably contains DNA, at least during early development. In addition, pronuclear nucleoli are apparently free of nucleic acid and, though the presence of moderate concentrations of nucleic acid in the cytoplasm, especially in association with the granular elements, is shown by the use of physical and histochemical methods, the concentrations immediately about the pronuclei are not regularly higher than in other parts of the cytoplasm. A synthesising system of the kind described above appears therefore to be lacking during fertilisation. Nevertheless, other systems presumably exist and a major significance of the nucleoli may still reside in the fact that they provide extra surfaces at which synthetic processes could take place.

If it is assumed that the internal surface of the pronucleus can have the same significance for synthesis as the nucleolar surface, this would explain why large pronuclei, such as those of the rabbit, need have but few and small nucleoli, whereas small pronuclei, such as those of the rat and mouse, have relatively large nucleoli. Perhaps, in addition, the nucleoli represent sites in which material, that also exists in the nucleoplasm, can be stored in higher concentration.

Kremer (1924) suggested that material synthesised in the pronuclei from cytoplasmic substrate was there subjected to the influence of hereditary agents. The material thus specifically modified was then thought to pass into the cytoplasm and so provide a mechanism for the transmission of hereditary qualities to the future embryo. What seems in fact to have been envisaged by Kremer is the production of templates that would later be involved in protein synthesis. The particular significance of pronuclei in this connection could be that the templates formed in them would have been fashioned exclusively under the influence of either paternal or maternal genes, whereas during cleavage and later, when the genes from the two sources are accommodated within the same nucleus, the templates may possibly represent the resultant of differing genic effects.

Dalcq (1955a, 1956, 1957) believes that substances in the nature of mucopolysaccharides are synthesised in nucleoli, forming inclusions, and passed into the cytoplasm where they accumulate—metachromasia was detected in the cytoplasm, especially near the later pronuclei. Additionally, he has produced evidence that acetalphosphatides and related compounds (" plasmalogene ") are elaborated in the cytoplasm under the influence of the nucleus. According to Dalcq's concept, these two groups of substances represent the substrate from which extra DNA is synthesised shortly before the first cleavage mitosis. Dalcq and Pasteels (1955) have shown that the doubling of the DNA content that occurs with each cellular division takes place during the preceding interphase. Thus, for Dalcq, the function of pronuclei is essentially the same as that of interphase nuclei in general.

Time Relations of Pronuclear Development and Syngamy

In invertebrate eggs, fertilisation is completed quite quickly. In the sea-urchin, *Arbacia punctulata*, for example, the pronuclei unite about 10 minutes after spermatozoon penetration, and the prophase of the first cleavage mitosis is evident about 25 minutes later (Harvey, 1956). In the egg of the parasitic wasp, *Habrobracon*, spermatozoon penetration occurs very shortly after oviposition and the two maturation divisions are completed and the pronuclei formed within the next 40–50 minutes. Syngamy takes place at about 55 minutes after spermatozoon entry and the first mitosis at about 60 minutes (Speicher, 1936).

Though less detailed information is available for mammalian fertilisation, the pronuclear life-span obviously lasts much longer than in the invertebrate egg. From the data of Sobotta (1895) and Gresson (1941), it seems that pronuclei are present in the mouse egg for roughly 15 hours. Gresson found the first cleavage spindle in eggs recovered between 21 and 28 hours after coitus. Calculations based upon the times of coitus, ovulation, pronucleus formation, and cleavage, lead to the conclusion that, in the rat egg also, pronuclear life extends over a period of about 15 hours (Boling, Blandau, Soderwall and Young, 1941 ; Odor and Blandau, 1951a, b ; Austin and Braden, 1954a). The interval between coitus, or the beginning of oestrus, and the first cleavage is about 30–35 hours (Huber, 1915 ; Odor and Blandau, 1951b). In the rabbit, the interval between coitus and the first cleavage of the egg is about 21–24 hours (Pincus, 1930, 1939a ; Pincus and

Enzmann, 1932 ; Chang, 1955e).   Since ovulation in this species is induced by coitus and occurs about 10 hours later (Barry, 1839 ; Bischoff, 1842), and since the pronuclei are formed about 3 hours after ovulation (Pincus and Enzmann, 1932 ; Chang, 1955e), the pronuclear life-span must last a little less than 9 or 10 hours.   In the hamster, pronucleus formation occurs at about 9 hours after coitus and cleavage at about 24 hours (Graves, 1945 ; Venable, 1946 ; Austin, 1956d ; Hamilton and Samuel, 1956) ; the duration of pronuclear life would thus be rather less than 15 hours.   From the data recorded by Beatty (1956), it can be calculated that the pronuclear life-span would be of the order of 11 hours in the guinea-pig and 15 hours in the ferret.   Ovulation in the field vole, *Microtus agretis,* under the usual laboratory conditions, evidently requires the stimulus of coitus (Chitty and Austin 1957), which is the normal mechanism in *Microtus californicus* (Greenwald, 1956b).   Since artificially induced ovulation occurred in 9–12 hours and fertilised eggs passed through the first cleavage division 24 hours after coitus (Austin, 1957a), it can be inferred that the entire process of fertilisation in the field vole would take about 14 hours and that pronuclear life would be about 9 or 10 hours.

The progress of syngamy has been studied in living rat eggs, maintained *in vitro* (Austin, 1951b).   Reduction of pronuclei to approximately half their volume took about 4 hours and final disappearance of pronuclei occurred about 1 hour later.   After an interval of about 40 minutes, the chromosome groups could be discerned and these came together in the succeeding 30 minutes.   These times, however, may well be longer than those for eggs developing *in vivo.*

VI. Atypical Forms of Fertilisation

Fertilisation is a complex process and is theoretically subject to numerous possible aberrations.   Many of these have in fact been observed as spontaneous events and, in addition, studies have been made involving their experimental production.   Analysis of the modifications exhibited has often yielded useful information.

One of the commonest variants is polyspermy—the entry of more than one spermatozoon into the cytoplasm of the egg, and the development of more than one male pronucleus (for data on the block to polyspermy, *see* p. 333).   The complementary state, namely the monospermic fertilisation of an egg containing two female pronuclei, is also known.   In both these conditions, the pronuclei themselves develop in a manner that is apparently normal except for the final size achieved.   Failure of pronucleus development, however, has also been described and this may involve either the male or the female pronucleus.   If embryogenesis proceeds without the proper participation of the male pronucleus, the phenomenon is referred to as gynogenesis : if without the female pronucleus, it is called androgenesis.   In the condition known as partial fertilisation, the participation of the male pronucleus is delayed until a stage of early cleavage and the cells of the embryo consequently do not all have a share of paternal chromosomes.   Other forms of atypical fertilisation have also been described (Wilson, 1928).   The effects of atypical fertilisation upon the chromosomal status of the embryo is discussed in detail by Beatty (1957).

Polyspermy

The penetration of more than one spermatozoon and the formation of more than one male pronucleus is a normal occurrence in some animal eggs, notably those laden with yolk. Only one of the male pronuclei undergoes syngamy with the female pronucleus and the others apparently offer no interference to normal development. The condition is referred to as physiological polyspermy; it has been known for a long time and has been recorded in many insects, the Polyzoa, some molluscs, the earthworm, the lamprey, elasmobranchs, urodeles, reptiles and birds (*see* Boveri, 1891; Marshall, 1922; Wilson, 1928; Hamilton, 1952; Rothschild, 1954). In other species, the presence of supernumerary pronuclei precludes normal development and constitutes the state of pathological polyspermy. From the study of a single egg, Gatenby and Hill (1924) suggested that polyspermy was physiological in the platypus, *Ornithorhynchus*, but Flynn and Hill (1939), who conducted a much more extensive investigation, concluded that fertilisation is normally monospermic in the Monotremata. There is little doubt that, throughout the Mammalia, polyspermy is pathological.

The subdivision of polyspermy into two categories reflects the operation of two mechanisms that exist in the animal egg and that normally prevent polyandrous syngamy, the admixture of two or more complements of paternal chromosomes to the maternal complement. The first mechanism, Rothschild's (1954) Type I Inhibition, is the block to polyspermy in the vitelline surface (p. 333), which in mammalian eggs may be assisted or supplanted by the zona reaction (p. 336). The second mechanism, Type II Inhibition, is less clearly defined; in some way, it prevents the approach and syngamy of more than one male pronucleus with the female pronucleus. Eggs in which pathological polyspermy may occur have the first mechanism and those in which physiological polyspermy may occur have the second. Neither mechanism is fully efficient, so that polyandrous syngamy is possible in any species.

The processes involved in physiological polyspermy are well exemplified in the urodele, *Triturus helveticus*. All the male pronuclei are maintained in a normal fashion until one of them comes into contact with the female pronucleus and fuses with it. The supernumerary male pronuclei then degenerate, the change starting first in the nearer pronuclei, and later involving the others (Fankhauser, 1932, 1948). This is, however, not the course of events in another urodele, *Diemictylus viridescens*, in which all supernumerary pronuclei degenerate simultaneously. If the egg of the former species is tied with a fine thread so as almost to bisect it and so as to include a lone supernumerary pronucleus in one half, this will degenerate when fusion occurs in the other half. If, however, bisection is complete, degeneration does not occur and both halves of the egg proceed to develop, the one with the lone male pronucleus undergoing andromerogony (androgenesis of an egg fragment) (Fankhauser, 1934; and *see* p. 380). At least for the events occurring in the egg of *Triturus helveticus*, a reasonable interpretation is that an inhibitory substance diffuses from the fusion nucleus, or its immediate surrounds, and progessively suppresses the supernumerary pronuclei. Similarly, in the parasitic wasp, *Habrobracon*, and the honeybee, *Apis mellifera*, there is reason to believe that a substance diffuses very rapidly from the zygote nucleus which prevents supernumerary spermatozoon nuclei from dividing (*see* von Borstel, 1957).

In the hen's egg, polyspermy is normal : from 3 or 4 to as many as 25 spermatozoa have been observed in a single egg (Patterson, 1910 ; Olsen, 1942 ;

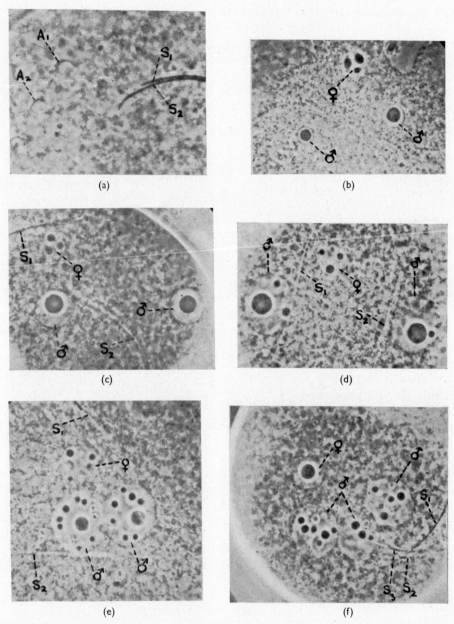

Fig. *10*. 31—(a) to (e) Polyspermic (dispermic) rat eggs at different stages in the formation and development of pronuclei. (f) A trispermic rat egg. A_1, A_2 = portions of the perforatoria of the two spermatozoa. S_1, S_2, S_3 = spermatozoon tails. (From Austin and Braden, 1953b.)

Bekhtina, 1955, 1958). Only one spermatozoon nucleus joins the egg nucleus and the supernumary ones distribute themselves near the margins of the blastodisc where they remain during the later phases of fertilisation and the first stages of

cleavage.   They undergo a certain amount of division, forming small groups of
daughter nuclei, and these divisions are frequently accompanied by partial cleavage
of the surrounding cytoplasm on the margin of the blastodisc.   At a later period,
when the egg has reached the 32-cell stage, they have usually undergone degenera-

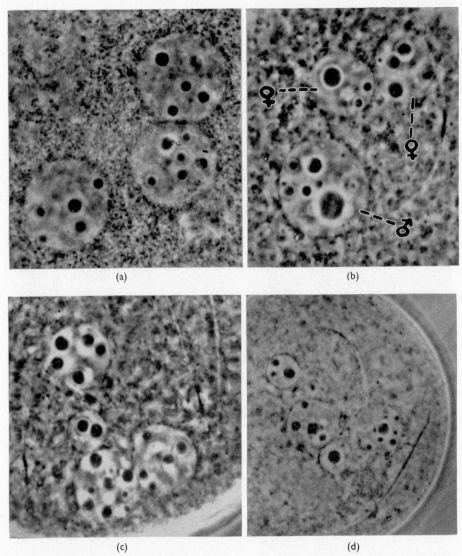

(a)   (b)

(c)   (d)

Fig. *10*. 32—(a) Polyspermic hamster egg.   (b) Rat egg with a male and two female pronuclei.
   (c) A polyspermic rat egg with a female and three male pronuclei.   (d) A polysperimc rat egg
   with two male and two female pronuclei.   (a, from Austin, 1956d; b, from Austin and Braden,
   1953b.)

tion and have disappeared.   For similar phenomena in the pigeon and turkey,
see Harper (1904), Blount (1909), and Olsen and Fraps (1944).   Evidence that
the supernumerary spermatozoon nuclei may sometimes persist and exert an effect
in the mature individual has been brought forward by Hollander (1949) and

Lebedev (1951), who attribute certain instances of mosaicism in pigeons and hens to this cause. Fowl mosaics have also been described by Greenwood and Blyth (1951) and Blyth (1954) which may have arisen through polyspermic fertilisation.

Investigation of pathological polyspermy has been extensively pursued in the sea-urchin egg. Here, several, but not necessarily all, the male pronuclei come into syngamy with the female pronucleus and a multipolar spindle eventuates (Figs. 10. 30a, b). The male pronuclei may also effect syngamy with each other. As a result, the first cleavage of the egg is multiple and complete disorganisation of the embryo soon ensues. In the frog egg, Type II Inhibition evidently operates and only one male pronucleus fuses with the female, but the asters that form in conjunction with the supernumerary male pronuclei cause a multiple first-cleavage division. Embryogenesis proceeds for a while but the animal dies before maturity (*see* Wilson, 1928).

Established instances of polyspermy in mammalian eggs are rare in the earlier literature, but there are several recent reports. The occurrence in eggs of two spermatozoa undergoing the early fertilisation changes has been observed by Austin and Braden (1953b) in the rat, and by Ludwig (1954) and Austin (1956d) in the hamster. Spermatozoon tails, however, are not always easily seen in the vitellus and so it is mostly eggs with three pronuclei that have excited attention. Trinucleate eggs have been recorded in the rat by Tafani (1889), Austin (1951b), Austin and Braden (1953b), Ludwig (1954), Odor and Blandau (1956), Braden (1958), and Pikó (1958); in the mouse by

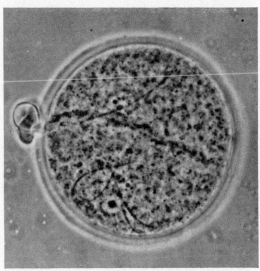

Fig. 10. 33—A polyspermic rat egg with five spermatozoon tails in the cytoplasm. On the left, some of the vitelline material is passing out through a slit made by one of the spermatozoa.

Kremer (1924), Pesonen (1949), Braden, Austin and David (1954) and Edwards and Sirlin (1956); in the cat by R. van der Stricht (1911) and Hill and Tribe (1924); in the ferret by Mainland (1930); in the rabbit by Amoroso and Parkes (1947) and Austin and Braden (1953b); in the pig by Pitkjanen (1955); in the cow by Pitkjanen and Ivankov (1956); in the hamster by Austin (1956d) and Hamilton and Samuel (1956); in the field vole by Austin (1957c); and in the sheep by Pitkjanen (1958). But the trinucleate state is sometimes attributable to the monospermic fertilisation of an egg bearing two female pronuclei. Confirmatory evidence of polyspermy, the presence of two spermatozoon tails, was provided in the reports of some observers, as indicated in Table III; *see also* Figs. 10. 31, 35. Confirmatory evidence of a different nature was obtained by Edwards and Sirlin: they had labelled the mouse spermatozoa with ^{14}C by appropriate treatment of the male and found that two of the three pronuclei gave auto-radiographs.

TABLE III

REPORTED INCIDENCE OF SPONTANEOUS POLYSPERMY

(Where the presence of two spermatozoon tails in the vitellus permitted or aided recognition of polyspermy, the figures are printed **bold**)

Animal	Total penetrated eggs	Presumptive polyspermic eggs	Incidence (per cent)	Reference
Cat	36	1	3	R. Van der Stricht (1911)
	11	2	18	Hill and Tribe (1924)
Ferret	71	1	1·4	Mainland (1930)
Rat	810	**10**	1·2	Austin and Braden (1953b)
	76	2	2·6	Ludwig (1954)
	326	**6**	1·8	Austin (1956b)
	336	1	0·3	Odor and Blandau (1956)
	165[1]	0	0	⎫
	126[2]	**4**	3·2	⎬ Pikó (1958)
	114[3]	1	0·9	⎭
Rabbit	69	1	1·4	Austin and Braden (1953b)
Mouse	169	**2**	1·2	Braden, Austin and David (1954)
	3377	**30**	0·89	Braden (1957)
Hamster	26	1	4	Ludwig (1954)
	725	**10**	1·4	Austin and Braden (1956)
Field vole	59	1	2	Austin (1957c)
Pig	50	5	10	Pitkjanen (1955)

[1,2,3] The females were of inbred strains " Jouy ", WAG and Wistar CF, respectively.

Trispermic fertilisation in rats has also been reported, both as a spontaneous phenomenon (Figs. *10.* 31 and 32) (Austin, 1951b ; Austin and Braden, 1953b) and as a result of experimental heat treatment (Austin and Braden, 1954b ; Austin, 1955a, 1956b). Eggs subjected to heat have also exhibited the tetra- and penta-spermic states, but the nuclear condition was very irregular (Fig. *10.*33). More recently, Pikó (1958) has recovered a tetraspermic rat egg from an untreated animal ; the five pronuclei were described as showing no major abnormality.

Detailed study of polyspermic rat eggs has shown that, at least in dispermic eggs, the male pronuclei are remarkably similar in size and form at all stages of pronuclear development (Fig. *10.* 31) (Austin and Braden, 1953b). This close correspondence testifies to the rapidity of the block to polyspermy—evidently the second spermatozoon must become attached to the vitellus very soon after the first if polyspermy is to supervene. The pronuclei of polyspermic eggs closely resemble those of normal monospermic eggs in several particulars, but they do not achieve the same size at full development (*see* p. 360).

At the approach of syngamy, the pronuclei come together and it is notable that male pronuclei are just as prone to make contact with each other as with the female

pronucleus.   Seen at later stages, dispermic rat eggs exhibited three, approximately equidistant, chromosome groups and, later still, a single chromosome
group (Fig. *10*. 34).   In some fortunate preparations, it has been possible to
demonstrate the presence of a triploid, or near-triploid, number of chromosomes
in such a group.   An approximately triploid chromosome number has also been
recorded in a polyspermic hamster egg (Austin, 1956a).   First-cleavage spindles
in most dispermic rat eggs were observed to be bipolar, and only on one occasion
was the spindle tripolar.   Pikó's (1958) observations add further support for the
belief that both paternal chromosome complements in dispermic eggs unite with
the maternal complement to form the chromosome group that is divided in the
first-cleavage mitosis.

Dispermic 2-cell, 4-cell, and 8-cell rat eggs have been recognised by the presence of two spermatozoon tails in the cytoplasm ; otherwise they were quite
normal in appearance.   The full extent to which polyspermic eggs will develop

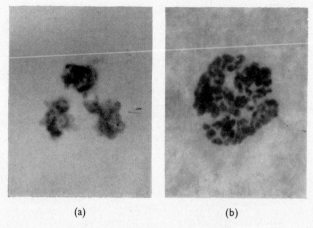

(a)   (b)

Fig. *10*. 34—Chromosome groups in polyspermic rat eggs.
(From Austin and Bishop, 1957b.)

is as yet unknown.   The identifying feature, the presence of two spermatozoon
tails, is lost in later stages of cleavage.   However, the evidence cited indicates that
dispermic embryos are almost certainly triploid and, according to Beatty (1951,
1957), triploid embryos are most unlikely to survive to birth.   On the other hand,
there are claims that polyspermy in mammals is actually beneficial to the embryo,
particularly if, through double mating, the spermatozoa are derived from different
sires (*see* Arakeljan, 1950 ; Kaminski and Marchlewski, 1952 ; Zibina, 1953 ;
Dokunin and Bashkaev, 1954 ; Kushner, 1954 ; Merkurjeva, 1954 ; Korobova,
1955 ; Milovanov and Sokolovskaja, 1955 ; Pitkjanen, 1955 ; *see* also review by
Thibault, 1956).   For these authors, however, the term " polyspermy " has a
wider meaning than that adopted in this chapter, and the phenomena it denotes
include not only those in which spermatozoa are involved in polyandrous syngamy,
but also those in which spermatozoa remain in the perivitelline space (namely,
supplementary spermatozoa) or in which extra spermatozoa enter the vitellus but
remain unchanged and take no part directly in the fertilisation process.   Except
in some of the reports just cited, the last condition has been described only by

Lams (1913) in a degenerate guinea-pig egg, by Amoroso and Parkes (1947), who used X-irradiated spermatozoa, and by some of the investigators who claim to have observed fertilisation *in vitro* (p. 393).

The unique feature of polyspermy in mammalian eggs, as inferred chiefly from observations on rat eggs, is that though polyandrous syngamy occurs it does not usually result in the formation of a multipolar spindle. Consequently, the early cleavage of the egg is seemingly normal. This suggests that the spermatozoon aster is of less importance in cleavage in mammals than in non-mammalian forms. A further point of interest is that the nuclei of polyspermic 2-cell rat and mouse eggs are not significantly larger than those of normal 2-cell eggs (Austin and Braden, 1955). Either some compensatory mechanism maintains a normal nucleocytoplasmic ratio or one set of paternal chromosomes is eliminated and the 2-cell nuclei are not in fact triploid. Observations on syngamy and the first cleavage mitosis in polyspermic eggs do not suggest any way in which a

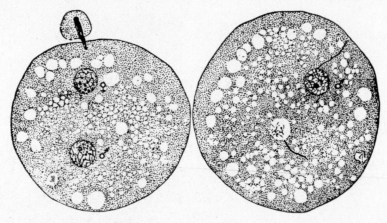

Fig. *10*. 35—Two sections of a polyspermic pig egg showing the three pronuclei and the two spermatozoon tails in the vitellus. (From Pitkjanen, 1955.)

complete chromosome complement could be eliminated or in which one rather than the other paternal complement could be selected for elimination. We believe, therefore, that the polyspermic 2-cell nucleus is triploid.

Fertilisation involving two Female Pronuclei

Eggs may have two female pronuclei because they originate from binucleate oöcytes or because either the first or the second meiotic division is completed without polar-body extrusion, the chromosome groups at both poles of the spindle giving rise to nuclei within the vitellus (Fig. *10*.36).

Binucleate primary oöcytes have been noted in ovaries in various species (Hartman, 1926), in the mouse (Engle, 1927), cat (Dederer, 1934), man (Pankratz, 1938 ; Bacsich, 1949), rat (Lane, 1938), goat (Harrison, 1948), and hamster (Skowron, 1956). They seem to be prone to early degeneration and it has yet to be established that they can undergo maturation and ovulation. Dempsey (1939), however, describes a guinea-pig ovarian egg that had two maturation spindles, possibly of the first division. The presence of two second-maturation spindles has been recorded in eggs of the rabbit (Vara and Pesonen, 1947), mouse (Pesonen, 1946a, b ; Braden and Austin, 1954b) and rat (Austin and Bishop, 1957b), but the possibility could not be ruled out that this condition had arisen through failure of first polar-body extrusion.   The rat egg referred to was a

" giant " egg and the possession of two female pronuclei
has been noted for another rat
giant egg (Austin and Braden,
1954c).   Giant eggs have been
described in several groups of
animals (*see* Wilson, 1928,
p. 972).   They are said to
arise in some instances by
fusion, but other ways are
possible, such as by failure of
cytoplasmic cleavage in the
final oögonial division.   Fusion may also involve the
nucleus, so that giant eggs
may contain two haploid
nuclei or a single diploid
nucleus.   Uninucleate rat
giant eggs have indeed been
recorded (Fig. *10.* 37), but so
far no estimate has been possible of their chromosome
number.   Sea-urchin giant
eggs, when fertilised, develop
into triploid embryos.

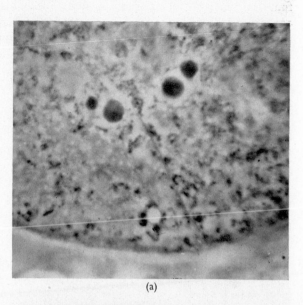

(a)

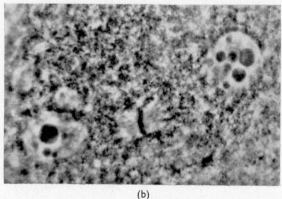

(b)

The development of two
female pronuclei in *Triturus*
eggs has been observed following the experimental
inhibition of second polar-
body extrusion by heat treatment (Fankhauser and God-
win, 1948).   The treatment
caused the second polar
spindle to move away from
the surface of the egg so that,
when meiosis took place, both
chromosome groups were left
within the vitellus and both
gave rise to female pronuclei.

Fig. *10.* 36—(a) Portion of a rat egg showing incomplete fissure lying between two nuclei that have developed from the chromosome groups of the second matura-tion spindle. Normally, the fissure extends to cut off the polar body, but this was evidently prevented by compression exerted by the overlying coverslip. (b) Two nuclei that have developed from the second maturation spindle in a hamster egg. The central body of the spindle can be seen between the nuclei.

In the fertilisation of such an egg, the male and both the female pronuclei con-jugated and the fusion nucleus thus contained a triploid chromosome complement. Subsequent embryonic development was apparently normal but degeneration occurred before maturity.

Polar-body extrusion may fail spontaneously in mammalian eggs (Pesonen, 1946a, b ; Bacsich and Wyburn, 1945 ; Vara and Pesonen, 1947), but this is difficult to establish because in many animals the first polar body often breaks up. Rat and mouse eggs of normal size but with two female pronuclei have been found and may owe their origin to such a mechanism (Austin and Braden, 1953b, 1954c), and Pesonen (1949) believed that his trinucleate mouse egg arose in this way. On the other hand, polar-body extrusion may be inhibited in mammalian eggs as in *Triturus* eggs, and this was found to be followed sometimes by the production of two female pronuclei (Thibault, 1949 ; Austin and Braden, 1954b). Colchicine injected into the female rat had a similar effect, but with both heat shock and colchicine the more common result was a fragmentation of the nuclear material. When rats were artifi-

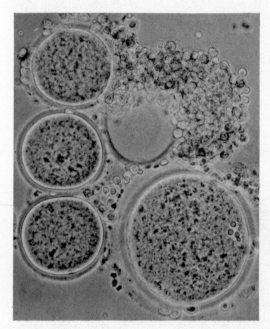

cially inseminated after ovulation, eggs with two female pronuclei were often recovered (Blandau, 1952 ; C.R.A., unpublished data). Braden (1957) examined large numbers of eggs undergoing fertilisation in four inbred strains of mice (CBA, C57, A, RIII) and in two outbred stocks (J and V). First polar-body suppression was very rare, except in one of the outbred stocks (V) in which the condition was detected in 14 eggs out of 596 (2·3 per cent). Suppression of the second polar body was detected in 20 eggs out of 3,377 (0·59 per cent) from the inbred strains, in 4 eggs out of 1,556 (0·26 per cent) from one of the outbred stocks (J) and in 11 eggs out of 260 (4·2 per cent) from the other (V). When V-stock females were mated with CBA males the incidence was found to be 15 out of 336 (4·5 per cent). Analysis

Fig. 10. 37—A rat " giant " egg and three eggs of normal size recovered from the Fallopian tube. The giant egg contains a single nucleus that had developed spontaneously.

of the results supported the conclusion that the susceptibility of eggs to polar-body suppression is controlled by the genotype of the female.

Monospermic fertilisation of eggs after failure of second polar-body extrusion may reasonably be held to give rise to triploid embryos, and indeed Fischberg and Beatty (1952) and Gates and Beatty (1954) believe that this is the chief mode of origin of spontaneous and induced triploidy in the mouse.

Gynogenesis and Androgenesis

The term gynogenesis implies that the egg has been activated by a spermatozoon which then fails to take any further part in fertilisation. The nuclei of the resulting embryo thus carry only the maternal chromosomes. Gynogenesis differs from parthenogenesis simply in the fact that, in the latter, activation is not effected by a spermatozoon. Androgenesis on the other hand is said to occur when the egg is activated by a spermatozoon, the egg nucleus fails to participate in any way, and the paternal chromosomes alone are involved in the first and subsequent mitoses. In most instances, both gynogenetic and androgenetic embryos are haploid.

Naturally occurring gynogenesis has been described in certain nematodes in which the spermatozoon activates the egg on penetration but takes no further part in fertilisation (Krüger, 1913 ; Hertwig, 1920 ; Peacock, 1944). Even in mammals, eggs sometimes show failure of development of the male pronucleus which could represent the beginning of gynogenesis. Two probable instances among 7,284 rat eggs were noted by Austin and Braden (1954c), and a much higher proportion, namely 4 eggs out of 318, was recorded in the hamster (Austin, 1956a). Each of the four hamster eggs contained a single large nucleus and a spermatozoon tail, and in two of them a small vesicular structure that was considered to be the partially transformed spermatozoon head could be discerned. Five possible, but not fully substantiated, cases of early spontaneous androgenesis (Fig. 10. 38) have been recorded in rat and mouse eggs (Austin and Braden, 1954c ; Austin and Bruce, 1956). Beatty (1954) has reported the occurrence of spontaneous haploidy in some blastocysts recovered from strains of mice giving a high incidence of heteroploid embryos. These blastocysts could have developed gynogenetically, androgenetically or even parthenogenetically. Braden (1957) observed a total of 85 uninucleate mouse

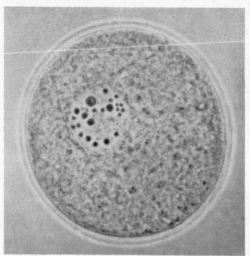

Fig. 10. 38—A possible androgenetic rat egg, containing single large nucleus and spermatozoon tail.

eggs each containing a spermatozoon tail. Indirect evidence suggested that some of these eggs were undergoing gynogenesis and others androgenesis. The incidence of the uninucleate eggs was comparatively low (0·2 to 0·9 per cent) in the females of inbred strains and comparatively high (2·0 to 7·8 per cent) in the females of outbred stocks.

Both gynogenesis and androgenesis have been obtained in non-mammalian animals by mechanical removal of the appropriate pronucleus during fertilisation. If a substantial portion of the cytoplasm is removed at the same time, development of the remainder of the egg is termed gynomerogeny or andromerogeny, respectively. Variations of these procedures have also been used (see Fankhauser, 1955).

Gynogenesis often results from attempts at hybridisation (see Wilson, 1928 ; Baltzer, 1952 ; Fankhauser, 1955). Thus, the eggs of the sea-urchin, Parechinus, may be entered and activated by spermatozoa of the mussel, Mytilus, or the annelid,

Adouinia, but the spermatozoon chromatin degenerates just before syngamy and the first and subsequent cleavages involve mitosis of only the maternal chromosomes. Similarly, when the eggs of the frog, *Hyla*, are seminated with the spermatozoa of the toad, *Bufo*, the resulting embryo develops gynogenetically to form a haploid tadpole. In this connection, the work of Moore, Woodroffe and Sanderson (1956) is of particular interest, for it indicates that hybrid gynogenesis is probably the normal mode of reproduction in certain spider beetles. *Ptinus hirtellus* and *P. latro* apparently compose a single polymorphic species in which male *P. latro* are lacking. *P. hirtellus* is diploid and *P. latro* triploid. Female *P. latro* yield no progeny unless inseminated by male *P. hirtellus*; all eggs then develop gynogenetically into female *P. latro* larvae which mature normally and can in their turn be bred from in the same way.

In other investigations, involving homologous gametes, the spermatozoon nucleus was specifically damaged without destroying the ability of the spermatozoon to enter and activate the egg. One of the earliest workers in this field was O. Hertwig (1911). He subjected frog spermatozoa to radium emanations and then added them to the eggs. In the lower dose range, the embryos developing from the eggs suffered degeneration and death, and this effect was intensified as the dosage increased. When a sufficiently high dosage was applied, however, apparently normal young were produced. Hertwig believed that at a low dosage the damaged spermatozoon nucleus effected syngamy with the egg nucleus and vitiated the embryo's chances of survival by contributing abnormal chromosomes. The high dose level was thought to prevent syngamy and thus enable the eggs to develop gynogenetically. Essentially similar results were later obtained by Rugh (1939), who employed X-irradiation. Confirmation both of the results and the interpretation was provided by G. Hertwig (1913) and Rugh and Exner (1940) in experiments on inter-generic crosses in Amphibia (*see* p. 205).

The complementary experiment, namely the irradiation of eggs which are then penetrated by normal spermatozoa, was first carried out by G. Hertwig (1913), who subjected the eggs of frogs and toads to radium emanations. Subsequent development was androgenetic owing to early regression of the egg nucleus. Similar results were obtained by Packard (1918) with eggs of the annelid worm, *Chaetopterus*.

Ultra-violet radiation, various dyes and radiomimetic agents have also been used successfully on urodele and anuran spermatozoa to produce the effects obtained by X-irradiation (*see* Dalcq and Simon, 1931, 1932; Fankhauser, 1945; Briggs, 1952; Brachet, 1953).

Attempts to reproduce the " Hertwig phenomenon " in mammals have been described in Chapter 9, p. 205, but the experiments of R. G. Edwards are especially relevant here. Mouse spermatozoa, treated *in vitro* with trypaflavine, toluidine blue, colchicine, or nitrogen mustard, or with ultra-violet or X-irradiation, were used for artificial insemination. X-irradiation damaged the spermatozoon chromosomes, which were probably responsible for the formation of the sub-nuclei that were seen later, during cleavage of the embryo. Ultra-violet irradiation was the most efficient agent for the induction of haploidy, the paternal chromatin in some eggs either failing to develop into a normal pronucleus or failing to take part in syngamy. After both forms of irradiation, the haploid and near-haploid embryos were found to be degenerate at $3\frac{1}{2}$ days of gestation. The haploids were thought to be of gynogenetic origin, and it was concluded that haploid gynogenesis in mice following these treatments is highly abnormal and probably restricted to the first few cleavage stages (Edwards, 1954a, b; 1957a, b; 1958a).

In other experiments, eggs were treated with colchicine by injection of the solution into the uterus before artificial insemination. The colchicine evidently destroyed the second-maturation spindle. After spermatozoon penetration, many eggs contained a single (male ?) pronucleus, and a few haploid blastocysts were found at $3\frac{1}{2}$ days' gestation. These haploids, and two haploid blastocysts found in the trypaflavine and toluidine-blue experiments described above, were believed to be androgenetic in origin, and Edwards suggests that haploid androgenones produced by these methods are likely to be more successful than the gynogenones (Edwards, 1954a, 1958b).

A rudimentary form of androgenesis may result from certain experiments involving deteriorating eggs. Thus, Blandau (1952) noted that when rats were artificially inseminated after ovulation, and consequently when ageing eggs were penetrated by spermatozoa, fertilisation was often characterised by the normal development of only the male pronucleus. Somewhat similar results were found to occur when rat eggs were subjected to heat treatment and other measures before fertilisation (Austin and Braden, 1954b).

Both gynogenesis and androgenesis, when uncomplicated by irregularities of chromosome division, lead to the production of haploid embryos. In urodeles, such embryos are capable of protracted development, but exhibit retarded growth and differentiation, and generally also a characteristic oedema that is associated with subnormal viability (see Fankhauser, 1945, 1955). Cell size is noticeably smaller and cell number a little higher than in the diploid individual. This supports the idea that the complex processes of embryonic development are independent of a constant relationship between cell size, cell number and rate of cell division. The rearrangement of cell size and cell number is thought to reflect the importance of the nucleocytoplasmic ratio in the metabolic processes of the cell, notably the nucleoprotein and enzyme syntheses. Failure to survive is, in many instances, probably attributable basically to the presence of unopposed lethal or low-viability genes in the haploid set of chromosomes. The special feature of androgenesis is that the embryo contains a maternal cytoplasm and paternal chromosomes. The characters of such embryos, however, are not always patriclinous and evidence is thus adduced for the persistence in the cytoplasm of a maternal genetic influence.

Partial Fertilisation

The term " partial fertilisation " was introduced by Boveri to describe a process he had observed in some sea-urchin eggs (see Wilson, 1928). After penetration, the spermatozoon nucleus lags behind and the spermatozoon aster becomes associated only with the egg nucleus. The first cleavage thus occurs without participation of the spermatozoon nucleus which ultimately effects syngamy with one of the nuclei of the 2-cell, 4-cell or 8-cell egg. Some of the cells of the resulting embryo therefore contain both paternal and maternal chromosomes, whereas others, usually the majority, contain only maternal chromosomes. Humphrey and Fankhauser (1943) suggest partial fertilisation as one mode of origin of certain haploid-diploid mosaic hybrids of the salamander, *Amblystoma*.

Unfertilised mouse eggs have been observed in some instances to undergo a precocious form of cleavage after being subjected to heat (Fig. *10*. 40c) (Braden and Austin, 1954c). They were found to have reached the 2-cell stage within a few hours of treatment, at which time most of the other eggs in the same animals had passed little further than extrusion of the second polar body. These 2-cell eggs were considered to have arisen through submergence of the second maturation spindle to a position near the centre of the egg so that completion of meiosis caused actual bisection of the egg. The process was termed " immediate cleavage." Similar eggs were seen in mated mice, and in two eggs spermatozoon penetration had occurred ; each exhibited a spermatozoon tail and two nuclei in one blasto-mere, and one nucleus in the other (Braden and Austin, 1954b). Of the two nuclei that were together it seemed likely that one was the male pronucleus. Later, Braden (1957), in an extensive investigation on fertilisation in inbred strains of mice, obtained evidence of spontaneous immediate cleavage in 8 eggs out of 910 (0·9 per cent) from mice of the A strain, but in none of the 2,467 eggs from mice of the CBA, C57 or RIII strains. In one outbred stock of mice (J), 7 examples (0·4 per cent) were found among 1,556 eggs undergoing fertilisation, and, in another outbred stock (V), one example among 336 eggs. Analysis of the data suggested that the genotype of the female determined the tendency of eggs to exhibit immediate cleavage. In all the eggs showing the phenomenon a spermato-zoon had entered and a male pronucleus could be seen. The possibility of a form of partial fertilisation in a mammalian egg was thus demonstrated ; if development continued, the embryo would presumably be a haploid-diploid mosaic. If both blastomeres were to undergo fertilisation with two separate spermatozoa, the resulting embryo could be a diploid hermaphrodite and such a process may possibly have been responsible for the development of some of the mammalian hermaphro-dites reported by Danforth (1927), Witschi (1932), Fekete (1937), Wells (1937), Asdell (1946), Klein (1955) and Hollander, Gowen and Stadler (1956).

VII. Parthenogenesis

Parthenogenesis is the development of a new individual from a male or female germ cell without the participation of a germ cell of the opposite sex. Development from male gametes is restricted to certain algae in which the germ cells of the two sexes are very similar. In animals, parthenogenesis involves only the maternal gametes, and may occur apparently spontaneously, when it is known as natural parthenogenesis, or it may be induced by experimental means and is then referred to as artificial parthenogenesis. Observations on parthenogenesis and associated phenomena and their effects on the chromosomal status of the mammalian embryo have recently been reviewed in detail by Beatty (1957).

Natural Parthenogenesis

Most of the known forms of natural parthenogenesis occur among the inverte-brates, especially the insects (*see* Peacock, 1944, 1952 ; Suomalainen, 1950). Development may lead to the production of males (arrhenotoky) or of females (thelytoky) or sometimes of both (amphotoky or deuterotoky). Arrhenotoky is well exhibited in the saw-flies, honeybees, wasps and ichneumon flies : unfertilised eggs develop into haploid males while fertilised eggs give rise to diploid females.   Several variations of thelytoky have been described, including cyclic parthenogenesis, paedogenesis, nematode pseudogamy, and geographical parthenogenesis.   Cyclic parthenogenesis occurs in the gall wasps, water fleas, plant lice and wheel animalcules.   It is characterised by the periodic alternation of bisexual reproduction and parthenogenesis, the change-over evidently being associated with season or with favourable or unfavourable environmental conditions.   In paedogenesis as seen in gall-flies and midges, parthenogenesis occurs in a cyclic manner but is exhibited by the larvae which produce other larvae within them.   This process may be repeated for several generations, until, owing to a change in environmental conditions, metamorphosis takes place and gives rise to the males and females of the sexual generation.   Larvae hatching from the eggs of these females are again capable of paedogenesis.   Nematode pseudogamy is simply another name for naturally occurring gynogenesis in nematodes (*see* p. 381). The term geographical parthenogenesis is used in circumstances in which one of two closely allied species or strains of animals reproduces parthenogenetically while the other, usually inhabiting a different geographical area, reproduces by normal bisexual means.   The phenomenon in different forms is known among molluscs, crustaceans, myriapods, and insects.   It is thought to represent a feature of adaptation.

A commonly occurring but abortive spontaneous activation (rudimentary parthenogenesis) and the rare protracted development of individuals are phenomena that are distributed widely among the vertebrate classes—only in reptiles is parthenogenesis unknown (Peacock, 1952).   Parthenogenesis is frequent in turkey eggs and often goes further than in the eggs of the domestic fowl and the pigeon (Kosin, 1945 ; Olsen and Marsden, 1953, 1954a, b ; Yao and Olsen, 1955 ; Kosin and Nagra, 1956 ; Olsen, 1956 ; Poole and Olsen, 1957).   In unfertilised turkey eggs examined before incubation, as many as 80 per cent showed some signs of cleavage.   Protracted development was much less common and was slower than in fertilised eggs, but sometimes reached stages equivalent to those normal for 26 to 27 days of incubation.   The embryos were found to be diploid and, in every one of 67 embryos in which the gonads were histologically examined, the sex was found to be male.   Incidence of parthenogenetic development varied with individual birds and with variety, and was possibly influenced also by environmental conditions.   There was evidence that the incidence was significantly increased merely by the proximity of male birds, which had no opportunity of coitus.

In mammals, it has long been known that oöcytes in regressing ovarian follicles often show stages of meiosis, and the apparent cleavage of ovarian eggs and of unfertilised tubal eggs has been a source of interest for many investigators.   Kampmeier (1929) attributes the first report to Pflüger (1863) ; since then numerous studies have been made on material from rats, mice, guinea-pigs, hamsters, ferrets, voles, rabbits, bats, armadillos, opossums, and man, and many instances of structures resembling 2-, 3-, 4- and 8-cell eggs, morulae and even blastocysts, have been described (Janosik, 1896 ; Bonnet, 1899 ; O. Van der Stricht, 1901 ; Rubaschkin, 1906 ; Athias, 1909 ; Newman, 1913 ; Kingery, 1914 ; Charlton, 1917 ; Hartman, 1919 ; Sansom, 1920 ; Champy, 1923 ; Courrier, 1923 ;

Courrier and Oberling, 1923 ; Mann, 1924 ; Lelièvre, Peyron and Corsy, 1927 ;
Pincus, 1930 ; Loeb, 1932 ; Harman and Kirgis, 1938 ; Dempsey, 1939 ; Krafka,
1939 ; Bacsich and Wyburn, 1945 ; Austin, 1949b ; Strassman, 1949 ; Thibault,
1949; Chang, 1950; Shettles, 1956; Skowron, 1956). Some authors considered the
changes to be early parthogenesis but most have pronounced in favour of degenerative fragmentation (*see also* p. 316). Nevertheless, it would seem that, in several
species of mammals, eggs have a tendency towards spontaneous development.
This is particularly noticeable in the hamster, in which nearly 80 per cent of the
tubal eggs were found to undergo spontaneous activation, extruding the second
polar body within 24 hours of ovulation and often showing one, and sometimes
two, large well-formed nuclei (Fig. *10*. 39) and normal-looking cleavage spindles,
though very few eggs passed through a regular first-cleavage division (Fig. *10*. 40a)

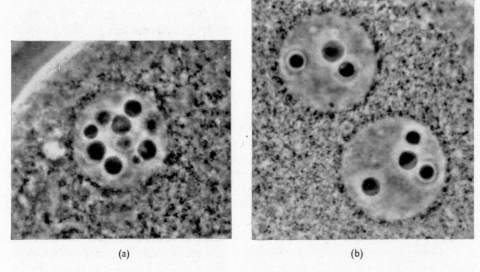

(a)   (b)

Fig. *10*. 39—Nuclei in unfertilised hamster eggs. (a, from Austin, 1956a.)

(Austin, 1956a). There is at least a possibility that spontaneously parthenogenetic
individuals might be born and survive. As Beatty (1957) points out, such animals
would be difficult to recognise and would probably have been overlooked in the
past ; chromosome number would not be a reliable guide as survival may well have
depended upon " regulation to diploidy " (*see* p. 388). Mammalian eggs may
indeed show one of the methods of regulation to diploidy that are known to permit
successful diploid parthenogenesis in non-mammalian forms, namely the utilisation
of the first polar spindle for the first cleavage of the egg. This has been reported
by Grosser (1927) in the dog, and Pesonen (1946a, b) and Braden (1957) in the
mouse. The possible survival of parthenogenones has been investigated in human
subjects (Balfour-Lynn, 1956). As a result of wide publicity in the press, eight
pairs of mothers and daughters were found in which there was reason to believe
that the daughter represented the product of parthenogenesis. Blood-group
studies and several other tests were carried out, and for one of the daughters
parthenogenesis could not be excluded as her mode or origin.

Artificial Parthenogenesis

The earlier work on artificial parthenogenesis has been described by Loeb (1913) and Morgan (1927) and special reference should also be made to the works of Wilson (1928), Dalcq (1928), Gray (1931), Tyler (1941) and Brachet (1950).

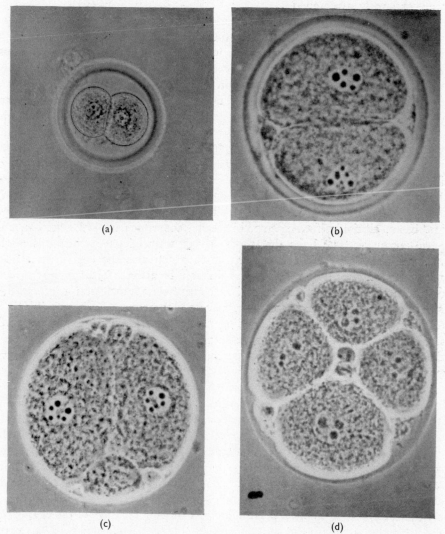

(a)　　　　　(b)

(c)　　　　　(d)

Fig. *10*. 40—(a) Apparently normal 2-cell hamster egg arising by spontaneous activation.　(b) Apparently normal 2-cell rat egg recovered after cold treatment.　(c) A 2-cell mouse egg with well-formed nuclei, recovered after heat treatment.　Division was believed to have occurred by " immediate cleavage."　(d) A 4-cell mouse egg recovered after heat treatment.　(a, from Austin, 1956a; b, from Austin and Braden, 1954d.)

Although R. Hertwig (1892) and Morgan (1896) succeeded in producing certain stages in the activation of the egg, Loeb (1899) was the first definitely to obtain viable plutei from the unfertilised eggs of the sea-urchin.　Loeb achieved most success with his " double method " in which eggs were first treated with butyric acid and then with a hypertonic solution (*see* Loeb, 1913). He believed that the first agent induced a required state of " superficial cytolysis " and that the second, which he termed the " corrective " factor, limited the spread of cytolysis which otherwise might involve the whole egg. Loeb's theory had a profound influence on early ideas of the mechanism of parthenogenetic activation but has since been largely superseded.

Investigations on parthenogenesis were further stimulated when it was found that calcium activated the eggs of many different animals (*see* Dalcq, 1928 ; Heilbrunn, 1952) and subsequent work has left little doubt that calcium is at least closely concerned with the activation process. Other activating agents would then have their effect by causing the liberation of calcium from the cortex, whence it would pass into the interior of the egg. Dalcq's conception was that calcium was involved in the redistribution of salts in the cortex and that this change altered the state of the vitelline colloids. Heilbrunn's theory gave a more central position to calcium : he believed that the changes induced in the egg were analogous to the clotting of blood, and further that protoplasmic coagulation led to the formation of spindles and asters.

A large variety of parthenogenetic agents has been identified, including hypo- and hypertonic salt solutions, cold, heat, ultra-violet radiation, radium emanations, acids, bases, alkaloids, fat solvents, bile salts, soaps, mechanical agitation, and electric currents. The hope that the study of artificial parthenogenesis might reveal the method by which the spermatozoon activates the egg has not been realised, and indeed no adequate explanation is as yet forthcoming for the mechanism of artificial parthenogenesis. Nevertheless, much useful information has been obtained on several aspects of early development.

The eggs of many animals, including nemertine and polychete worms, molluscs, sea-urchins, starfish, moths, fishes, newts, toads and frogs, have been artificially activated and have shown extensive development. The frequency of apparently normal development is usually low with any method, probably because of irregularities associated with the chromosomes, such as the occurrence of haploidy and abnormalities of chromosome distribution and of the mechanics of the mitotic process. Most successful instances are of animals that were subsequently found to be diploid and it would seem that " regulation to diploidy " is of the highest importance for the protracted development of a parthenogenetic animal. Diploidy may result in several ways : failure of the second meiotic division leading directly to the formation of a diploid nucleus, failure of second polar-body extrusion followed by union of the egg chromosomes with the presumptive polar chromosomes, participation of the first polar spindle in the first cleavage of the egg, participation of the second polar spindle in this way but associated with an extra division of the chromosomes, activation of a diploid egg arising from a tetraploid primary oöcyte, occurrence of an abortive first cleavage involving division of chromosomes but not of the cytoplasm.

The induction of early parthenogenesis in mammals appears to have been observed first by Champy (1923), who recorded an apparently normal 8-cell egg in a rabbit ovary that had been cultured *in vitro*. Pincus (1930) remarked on the frequency with which unfertilised rabbit eggs broke up in culture, sometimes in a way that suggested normal cleavage. This led to an extensive investigation of methods and consequences of artificial activation in the rabbit egg (Pincus, 1936a, b,

1939a, c ; Pincus and Enzmann, 1935, 1936 ; Pincus and Shapiro, 1940a, b). It was found that both tubal eggs and oöcytes recovered from follicles could be activated *in vitro* and would develop when kept in culture or transferred to the Fallopian tubes of rabbit hosts. Successful parthenogenetic agents were butyric acid with hypertonic solutions, hypertonic solutions alone, heating to 45–46° C. for short periods of time, and cooling to 6° C. for 10–85 minutes. Eggs could also be activated *in situ* by applying cold to the Fallopian tubes. Varying degrees of embryogenesis were observed and four rabbits were born that were considered to have been the product of parthenogenetic development. Shapiro (1942) recovered three cleaved eggs from a rabbit subjected to hypothermia. Later, it was estimated that the chances against the birth of parthenogenetic young in mammals is about 2,000 to 1 (Chang and Pincus, 1951).

A detailed investigation of artificial activation was also made by Thibault (1947a, b, 1948, 1949) and Thibault and Ortavant (1949), who worked with rabbit, rat and sheep eggs. It was confirmed that cold was an effective agent in the rabbit egg. A higher incidence of activation (88 per cent) was obtained with a temperature of about 0° C., achieved by applying ice to the Fallopian tube in the region of the eggs for three or four minutes, than by subjecting the eggs to a temperature of 6° C. *in vitro* (62 per cent) or *in situ* (65 per cent). Some of the eggs developed *in vivo* to the blastocyst stage and one blastocyst implanted. Thibault concluded that development occurs if the second polar-body extrusion is inhibited and a diploid nucleus formed, but if two nuclei arise, following central migration of the spindle, the egg fails to develop. In the rat, activation by cold (application of ice to the Fallopian tube) was effective in all eggs, which invariably extruded the second polar body. No nucleus was formed, however ; the chromosomes scattered and the eggs degenerated. Ether anaesthesia and barbiturate narcosis were also found to cause activation of a proportion of the eggs ; this was ascribed to the drop in body temperature induced and to a direct action of the ether upon the eggs. Sheep eggs behaved similarly to rabbit eggs after cold treatment *in situ* : polar-body extrusion was generally inhibited, whereupon a single diploid nucleus could form and the egg commence cleavage.

Chang (1954, 1957c) kept unfertilised rabbit eggs in a mixture of serum and Ringer solution at 10° C. or at 0° C. for 1 day and then transferred them to the Fallopian tubes of rabbits in which ovulation had been induced artificially 12 hours previously. After 6 days, the recipient rabbits were killed and the eggs examined. About 19 per cent of eggs that had been kept at 10° C., and about 4 per cent of those kept at 0° C., were found to have undergone development. Degeneration was common, however, and only 5·5 per cent of the former group, and none of the latter group, had grown into normal-looking blastocytes. The parthenogenetic blastocysts were smaller than normal but, in the four instances examined, exhibited a diploid chromosome number. Regulation to diploidy evidently involved inhibition of the second meiotic division, whereby the spindle degenerated, the polar body was not extruded and the chromosomes divided but did not properly separate. Thus, a single diploid nucleus was formed. In another experiment, 230 eggs, previously kept at 10° C. for 1 day, were transferred to recipient rabbits which were examined by laparotomy 13 to 28 days later ; there was no evidence of implantation.

The efficiency of cold as an activating agent for rat eggs was confirmed by

Austin and Braden (1954b) : virtually all treated eggs extruded the second pola body. Ether anaesthesia caused activation in more than half the eggs and this effect was attributed to the anaesthetic and not at all to the drop in body temperature, as a similar temperature fall with no activation was seen after subcutaneous administration of nembutal. Some other anaesthetics activated eggs, notably chloroform, paraldehyde and nitrous oxide, as also did nembutal when administered intraperitoneally. It was concluded that the effect of anaesthetics may have been due to the production of a local anoxia, an explanation that later received some support when hypoxia was found to activate rat eggs (Austin, 1956a). In contrast to Thibault's observations, about 10 per cent of rat eggs showed nucleus formation and cleavage after activation by cold (Fig. *10.* 40b) (Austin and Braden, 1954d). Mouse eggs were found to differ from rat eggs in that they showed little response to cold but were often activated by heat or ether anaesthesia (Braden and Austin, 1954b). After treatment by the latter methods, mouse eggs often showed extrusion of the second polar body, nucleus formation, and cleavage (Fig. *10.* 40d). In both rat and mouse eggs, the single nucleus formed is larger than either a normal male or female pronucleus—the significance of this point has been discussed earlier (*see* p. 360). An interesting additional effect of heat on mouse eggs was the production of immediate cleavage (p. 384).

The possible subsequent development of parthenogenetic rat and mouse eggs has not been investigated, but the low incidence at which cleavage stages beyond 2-cell eggs were seen suggests that extensive development is most unlikely. Beatty (1954) reported finding 7 haploid mouse blastocysts among a total of some 927 blastocysts in which chromosome numbers could be determined. Presumably, these embryos could have been gynogenetic, androgenetic or parthenogenetic, but they do represent the latest known stage to which haploid development may advance in mammals.

As noted previously (p. 386), hamster eggs have a pronounced tendency towards spontaneous development. Treatment intended to increase the incidence of activation (hypothermia) did not succeed, though it somewhat hastened its appearance (Austin, 1956a). In the ferret, the application of ice to the Fallopian tube also failed to increase the incidence of spontaneous development but apparently enabled it to proceed further—two morulae and a small blastocyst were recovered 7–9 days later (Chang, 1957b).

VIII. Refertilisation and Somatic Fertilisation

Tyler and Schultz (1932) found that, if the eggs of the echiuroid worm, *Urechis caupo*, were treated with acidified sea-water after spermatozoon entry but before the fertilisation membrane was thrown off, development was stopped and the eggs resumed their unfertilised appearance. The eggs could now be fertilised a second time and if no further treatment was applied development would continue. The course of development was not normal because the eggs now contained two fertilising spermatozoa. If the treatment was repeated a second time, the same thing happened and the entry of a third fertilising spermatozoon took place on semination. Sugiyama (1951) reported that he was able to obtain refertilisation of sea-urchin eggs at a later time by removing the membrane mechanically and treating the eggs for a short time with calcium-free or magnesium-free sea-water or with isosmotic urea solution.   Refertilisation could occur even in 2-cell eggs if they had been treated in this way.   Alternatively, the elevation of the fertilisation membrane could be reversed by placing the eggs, before membrane formation, in calcium-free or magnesium-free solutions and then returning them to fresh sea-water.   Under these circumstances, the membrane did not develop properly and returned to the egg surface, whereupon spermatozoon penetration could recur.   Sugiyama's observations were confirmed by Hagström and Hagström (1954a, b).   Recently, Tyler, Monroy and Metz (1956) found that in the eggs of two species of the sea-urchin, *Lytechinus*, refertilisation could be brought about simply by removing the fertilisation membrane, although a somewhat higher concentration of spermatozoa was required than for the original fertilisation.   Demembranation could be effected either mechanically or enzymatically.   Denuded eggs are commonly entered by a number of spermatozoa on re-semination.   These observations suggest that the block to polyspermy occurs in a surface structure that becomes incorporated in the fertilisation membrane.   Consequently, after membrane elevation the vitellus would lack a block to polyspermy and protection against the entry of extra spermatozoa would then reside in the fertilisation membrane (and perhaps to some degree in the hyaline layer if left intact—*see* p. 334).   Additionally, it is evident that the vitelline surface regains its capacity to form attachment with, and engulf, a spermatozoon.

In most mammals, the zona pellucida, after it has been modified in the zona reaction, resembles the fertilisation membrane in that it is impermeable to spermatozoa, so that the possible transience of the block to polyspermy is normally concealed.   In the rabbit egg, which is apparently incapable of evincing a zona reaction, the added mucin layer would have the same effect.   Supplementary spermatozoa, however, are known to retain motility in the perivitelline space for several hours, so that under normal circumstances the block to polyspermy must presumably last for at least as long as supplementary spermatozoa survive.   Nevertheless, there are observations on record that suggest that neither the block to polyspermy nor the zona reaction are permanent and that refertilisation may sometimes occur.   Sobotta (1895) stated that mice will sometimes mate a second time, 24 hours after the first mating, and in the cytoplasm of a few of the 2-cell eggs recovered from these animals there were objects resembling spermatozoon heads undergoing transformation, or even early pronuclei.   Rubaschkin (1905) remarked with some diffidence that guinea-pig eggs, exhibiting late pronuclei or a cleavage spindle, occasionally showed objects like early male pronuclei that could have arisen through a second and later spermatozoon penetration.   Essentially similar findings were reported by Kremer (1924) in rat and mouse eggs.   Kohlbrugge (1910a, 1913) claimed that spermatozoa may enter the developing embryo at even later stages.   He described morulae and blastocysts containing numerous spermatozoa, distributed inter- as well as intracellularly.   Kohlbrugge maintained that the influence of the male upon the future offspring was not restricted to fertilisation but was also exerted in this way upon the developing embryo.   A similar function has been attributed by several recent investigators to extra spermatozoa that are said to enter the egg at fertilisation as well as during cleavage (*see* p. 377).

If spermatozoa are capable of penetrating into the developing embryo, it is perhaps reasonable to believe that they may even penetrate the tissue of the Fallopian tube and uterus, and this Kohlbrugge (1910b, 1913) also described, in

elasmobranchs, the hen, the rabbit and the bat. He maintained that somatic
fertilisation thus effected would modify the functions of the genital tract and

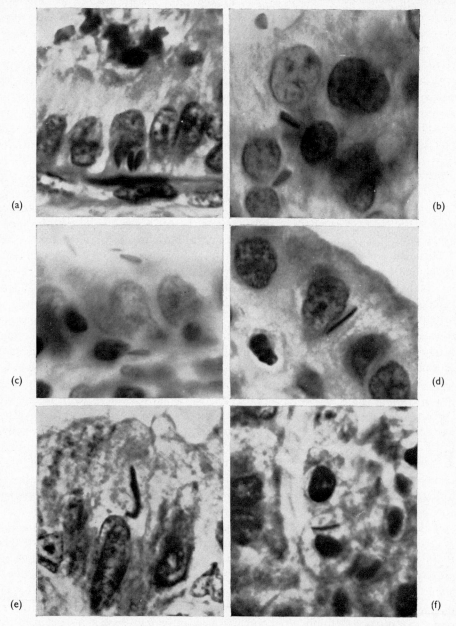

(a)

(b)

(c)

(d)

(e)

(f)

Fig. 10. 41—Spermatozoa in the Fallopian-tube mucosa in five different Orders
of mammals.   (a) Greater horseshoe bat.   (b) Common pipistrelle bat.
(c) Hedgehog.   (d) Rabbit.   (e) Rat. (f) Stoat.

thus influence the development of the foetus. Such modifications of the genital
tract were held to persist and so Kohlbrugge considered that his observations
provided an explanation of the mechanism of telegony, by which one male parent

was thought to influence the offspring sired subsequently by a different male parent. Belief in somatic fertilisation has received support in recent times (*see* Genin, 1951, 1953 ; Kushner, 1954 ; Borzedovska, 1955 ; Vojtiskova, 1955) ; it has indeed been maintained that the principal effect upon the embryo is beneficial, particularly if the spermatozoa come from different and unrelated sires. Lately, however, the alleged entry of spermatozoa into the maternal tissues has been critically re-examined by Vojtiskova (1956), who concludes that the results reported earlier by other investigators and by herself were attributable to artefacts and that the spermatozoa had been transferred during the processing of the histological material. A similar conclusion has been reached by Pósalaky and Törö (1957), Austin (1957b) and Edwards and Sirlin (1958) who were unable to find any evidence for the entry of spermatozoa into the uterine wall in the rat and mouse.

More recently, however, the identification of spermatozoa, at least in the mucous membrane of the Fallopian tube, has again been claimed (Austin and Bishop, 1959a ; Austin, 1959a). Spermatozoon heads were seen at various levels in the mucosa (Fig. *10.* 41), but not beyond the basement membrane nor in any other tissue. Mucosal-cell nuclei were often characteristically indented when spermatozoon heads lay nearby. The findings were made in bats of two species, the rat, the rabbit, the stoat, the mole and the hedgehog, and reasons were given for believing that the presence of the spermatozoa could not be ascribed to artefact. Except in the bats, the numbers of spermatozoa involved appeared to be quite small and it has yet to be determined whether there is any detectable antigenic or genetic effect, either locally or systemically.

On the other hand, data from several sources appear to support the idea that soluble proteins in the seminal plasma, or breakdown products of the spermatozoa, may be absorbed from the female tract after coitus and evoke the production of antibodies. It is at least conceivable that an influence could thus be exerted upon the functions of the genital tract and hence upon the embryos or upon the spermatozoa of later matings (*see* Hartman, 1939 ; Bengtsson, 1949 ; Batty, Brambell, Hemmings and Oakley, 1954 ; Austin and Bishop, 1957a ; Hemmings, 1958).

IX. Fertilisation *in Vitro*

The advancement of knowledge on mammalian fertilisation would undoubtedly be aided if the process could be studied *in vitro* with the ease that it can with the eggs of some marine invertebrates. For this purpose, it is necessary to have experimental conditions that permit the gametes to be maintained in a fully functional state *in vitro* and in which early development can be initiated and continued in a normal manner. Progress has been made in this direction but some difficulties remain to be overcome.

Many investigators have claimed to have observed the fertilisation of mammalian eggs *in vitro* but the evidence advanced in support of the claims was often unconvincing. Schenk (1878) treated guinea-pig and rabbit eggs with spermatozoa and reported the extrusion of a polar body and cleavage on subsequent culture. Onanoff (1893), using the eggs of the same species, transferred them after treatment to the peritoneal cavity and stated that embryos developed there. Long

o*

(1912) used rat eggs and found that addition of spermatozoa *in vitro* led to denudation of the eggs and the extrusion of a polar body. Frommolt (1934) placed spermatozoa with rabbit eggs *in vitro* and noted only a shrinkage of the vitellus. Krasovskaja and her colleagues also worked with rabbit eggs, which were obtained 17 hours after coitus with a vasectomised male ; they were treated with spermatozoa and subsequently examined by histological methods (Krasovskaja, 1934, 1935 ; Krasovskaja and Diomidova, 1934 ; Diomidova and Kusnezova, 1935). These authors described what they believed to be the presence of spermatozoa within the eggs, the development of pronuclei and the occurrence of cleavage. Yamane (1935) observed the denudation of rabbit eggs after treatment with spermatozoa and said that in histological sections spermatozoa could be seen within the eggs. The most extensive experiments are those of Pincus (1930, 1936a, 1939a), and Pincus and Enzmann (1934, 1935), who treated rabbit eggs with spermatozoa and maintained them in culture. It was reported that on two occasions a spermatozoon was seen to enter an egg and that several eggs underwent cleavage. Spermatozoa and male and female pronuclei were said to be demonstrable in histological preparations of the eggs. Eggs treated with spermatozoa were also transferred to the Fallopian tubes of rabbits in which ovulation had been induced and the subsequent birth of young (of unstated sex) was recorded. Rock and Menkin (1944) and Menkin and Rock (1948) were the first to use human eggs ; these were recovered from the ovary and were held in culture to permit maturation. When spermatozoa were added and the eggs cultured, some of the eggs underwent division. Examined in histological preparation, some eggs were said to contain spermatozoa. Moricard and Bossu removed the Fallopian tubes of rabbits after artificially induced ovulation, injected spermatozoa into the isthmus and maintained the tubes under liquid paraffin in an incubator (Moricard, 1949, 1950a, b, 1953, 1954a, b, c, d, 1955 ; Moricard and Bossu, 1949a). They also studied eggs that had been treated with spermatozoa whilst in culture in tubal, uterine or vaginal mucous secretions. They noted shrinkage of the vitellus and stated that spermatozoa and pronuclei could be seen within eggs in histological preparations. Smith (1951, 1953) recovered rabbit eggs from the tubes at 37° C. to avoid the danger of artificial activation and incubated them with spermatozoa in a medium containing tubal mucosal mash. The eggs were then transferred to a culture medium. After varying periods, the eggs were removed and examined by phase-contrast microscopy. Smith reported that she saw the spermatozoon go through the zona pellucida and into the vitellus, that spermatozoon heads and male and female pronuclei could be discerned in the vitellus, and that one egg was observed in several cleavage stages until it was 8-celled. Venge (1953) obtained rabbit eggs from ovarian follicles or from the Fallopian tube. The eggs were treated with spermatozoa, incubated for varying periods, and transferred to the Fallopian tubes of females mated earlier with vasectomised males. The birth of eight young (including at least three males) was recorded. Shettles (1953) maintained human ovarian and tubal eggs in culture with added spermatozoa. Some of the eggs, examined in the fresh state, were said to have a spermatozoon in the perivitelline space or in the vitellus. Dauzier and his associates used ovulated rabbit eggs recovered at 38–39° C. ; these were cultured in media containing suspensions of spermatozoa prepared by flushing the vagina, uterus or Fallopian tubes of rabbits mated 12 hours previously (Dauzier, Thibault and Wintenberger,

1954 ; Thibault, Dauzier and Wintenberger, 1954 ; Dauzier and Thibault, 1956). Histological sections of the eggs were later prepared and examined. Spermatozoa were reported to be visible within the eggs and the contraction of the egg, the emission of polar bodies, and stages of pronucleus development and of cleavage were described.

Provided that certain precautions are taken, the best criterion of the occurrence of fertilisation *in vitro* would undoubtedly be the birth of normal young of both sexes from eggs transferred to a host animal after treatment with spermatozoa *in vitro*. Precautions are necessary chiefly to exclude the following possibilities : (i) that parthenogenetic development is inadvertently initiated, (ii) that fertilisation actually occurs after the eggs, together with some adherent spermatozoa, have been transferred to the host, (iii) that the host's own eggs are fertilised by the adventitious spermatozoa introduced with the supposedly fertilised eggs. The first and third possibilities can be excluded by the use of suitable genetic markers, and the second can probably be avoided best by keeping the eggs *in vitro* for long enough before transfer to permit cleavage to occur or at least to allow fertilisation to reach a clearly recognisable stage.

The birth of young was reported by Pincus and Enzmann and by Venge, but their experiments are not conclusive because they did not exclude one or other of the possibilities given above.

Failure to replace eggs in the Fallopian tube and allow them the opportunity to give rise to living young, makes it much more difficult to establish conclusively that fertilisation *in vitro* has occurred. The cleavage of eggs in culture after treatment with spermatozoa cannot in itself be unequivocal evidence of fertilisation, for development may have occurred parthenogenetically. In view of the known variety of activating agents, parthenogenetic development must always be considered a possible outcome of experiments on eggs *in vitro* even when the attempt is made specifically to avoid activating the eggs. Similarly, when two nuclei are described within an egg it does not necessarily follow that they are male and female pronuclei—it has often been shown that artificially activated eggs may develop two nuclei. Dauzier and his colleagues believe, however, that they can distinguish between male and female pronuclei by the distribution of chromatic material as seen in histological preparations. Male and female pronuclei do often differ in size and may well have different structural or staining characteristics—there is some support for this in the observations of Pitkjanen (1955) and Hamilton and Samuel (1956) on the pronuclei of polyspermic pig and hamster eggs—but such a distinction cannot as yet be said to be fully established.

Evidence that the nuclei in binucleate eggs are indeed male and female pronuclei, or that cleaving eggs have been fertilised, is provided by the observation that spermatozoa were seen within eggs at an earlier stage, and such an observation greatly strengthens the claims made by Pincus and Enzmann, Rock and Menkin, Moricard *et al.*, Smith and Dauzier *et al.* It does not, however, completely exclude the possibility that parthenogenesis has occurred, since artificial activation need not prevent spermatozoon penetration. Again, it is hard to demonstrate convincingly that spermatozoa have entered an egg. The published illustrations that purport to show the presence of spermatozoa in the perivitelline space leave much to be desired. The objects indicated could indeed be spermatozoa but in the photographs they cannot be seen sufficiently clearly to leave no doubt in the mind of the impartial reader. Similarly, the small basophilic bodies shown in histological sections of eggs may be spermatozoon heads but they may also be of the nature of the " corps enigmatiques " and similar objects described by Rubaschkin (1905), Lams and Doorme (1908), O. van der Stricht (1909), Kremer (1924) and others. Sometimes, appearances in egg sections strongly suggest that the heads of spermatozoa immediately about the eggs have become dislodged during the cutting of the sections and have come to overlie the region of the vitellus. This kind of artefact has been admitted to occur in histological preparations (*see* Vojtiskova, 1956 ; Posalaky and Törő, 1957).

It would seem therefore that none of the accounts published so far conclusively demonstrates that mammalian eggs can be fertilised *in vitro*. Some of the claims made, notably those of Pincus and Enzmann, Smith, Venge, and Dauzier and his associates, are especially difficult to refute and may well point the way for future investigations.

Bibliography

Adams, C. E. (1954). The experimental shortening of the generation interval. *Proc. Brit. Soc. Anim. Prod.*, p. 97.
—— (1955). The frequency of occurrence of supernumerary spermatozoa in rabbit ova. *Proc. Soc. Stud. Fert.*, **7**, 130.
—— (1956a). Rate of sperm transport in the female reproductive tract of the rabbit. *J. Endocrin.*, **13**, xxi (proc.).
—— (1956b). A study of fertilization in the rabbit : the effect of post-coital ligation of the Fallopian tube or uterine horn. *J. Endocrin.*, **13**, 296.
Albrecht, M (1895). Künstliche Befruchtung. *Wschr. Thierheilk. Viehz.*, **39**, 205.
—— (1899). Ueber die Telegonie. *Dtsch. tierärztl. Wschr.*, **7**, 33.
Alfert, M. (1950). A cytochemical study of oogenesis and cleavage in the mouse. *J. cell. comp. Physiol.*, **36**, 381.
Allen, T. E., and Grigg, G. W. (1957). Sperm transport in the fowl. *Aust. J. agric. Res.*, **8**, 788.
Amoroso, E. C., and Parkes, A. S. (1947). Effects on embryonic development of X-irradiation of rabbit spermatozoa *in vitro*. *Proc. roy. Soc. B*, **134**, 57.
Arakeljan, M. A. (1950). The biological role of semen as an excitant in animals (trans. title). *Sovietsk. Zootech.*, (9) 68. (*Anim. Breed. Abstr.*, (1951), **19**, 231).
Asdell, S. A. (1946). *Patterns of mammalian reproduction.* Comstock Publishing Co., Ithaca, N.Y.
Athias, — (1909). Les phénomènes de division de l'ovule dans les follicles de De Graaf en voie d'atrésie chez le lérot (*Eliomys quercinus*). *Anat. Anz.*, **34**, 1.
Austin, C. R. (1948a). Function of hyaluronidase in fertilization. *Nature, Lond.*, **162**, 63.
—— (1948b). Number of sperm required for fertilisation. *Nature, Lond.*, **162**, 534.
—— (1949a). Fertilization and the transport of gametes in the pseudopregnant rabbit. *J. Endocrin.*, **6**, 63.
—— (1949b). The fragmentation of eggs following induced ovulation in immature rats. *J. Endocrin.*, **6**, 104.
—— (1950a). Fertilization of the rat egg. *Nature, Lond.*, **166**, 407.
—— (1950b). The fecundity of the immature rat following induced superovulation. *J. Endocrin.*, **6**, 293.
—— (1951a). Observations on the penetration of the sperm into the mammalian egg. *Aust. J. sci. Res.*, B, **4**, 581.
—— (1951b). The formation, growth, and conjugation of the pronuclei in the rat egg. *J. R. micr. Soc.*, **71**, 295.
—— (1951c). Activation and the correlation between male and female elements in fertilization. *Nature, Lond.*, **168**, 558.

AUSTIN, C. R. (1952a). The development of pronuclei in the rat egg, with particular reference to quantitative relations. *Aust. J. sci. Res.* B, **5**, 354.

—— (1952b). The " capacitation " of the mammalian sperm. *Nature, Lond.*, **170**, 326.

—— (1953a). Nucleic acids associated with the nucleoli of living segmented rat eggs. *Exp. Cell Res.*, **4**, 249.

—— (1953b). The growth of knowledge on mammalian fertilization. *Aust. vet. J.*, **29**, 191.

—— (1955a). Polyspermy after induced hyperthermia in rats. *Nature, Lond.*, **175**, 1038.

—— (1955b). Acquisition de la capacité fertilisatrice des spermatazoides (" capacitation ") dans les voies génitales femelles. In *La Fonction Tubaire et ses Troubles*, Masson et Cie, Paris, pp. 22–27.

—— (1956a). Activation of eggs by hypothermia in rats and hamsters. *J. exp. Biol.*, **33**, 338.

—— (1956b). Effects of hypothermia and hyperthermia on fertilization in rat eggs. *J. exp. Biol.*, **33**, 348.

—— (1956c). Cortical granules in hamster eggs. *Exp. Cell Res.*, **10**, 533.

—— (1956d). Ovulation, fertilization and early cleavage in the hamster (*Mesocricetus auratus*). *J. R. micr. Soc.*, **75**, 141.

—— (1957a). Oestrus and ovulation in the field vole (*Microtus agrestis*). *J. Endocrin.*, **15**, iv.

—— (1957b). Fate of spermatozoa in the uterus of the mouse and rat. *J. Endocrin.*, **14**, 335.

—— (1957c). Fertilization, early cleavage and associated phenomena in the field vole (*Microtus agrestis*). *J. Anat.*, **91**, 1.

—— (1959a). Entry of spermatozoa into the Fallopian-tube mucosa. *Nature, Lond.*, **183**, 908.

—— (1959b). The role of fertilization. *Perspectives Biol. Med.*, **3**, 44.

—— and AMOROSO, E. C. (1959). The mammalian egg. *Endeavour*, **18**, 130.

—— & BISHOP, M. W. H. (1957a). Preliminaries to fertilization in mammals. In *The beginnings of embryonic development*, ed. : A. Tyler, C. B. Metz and R. C. von Borstel, pp. 71–107. American Association for the Advancement of Science, Washington.

—— —— (1957b). Fertilization in mammals. *Biol. Rev.*, **32**, 296.

—— —— (1958a). Capacitation of mammalian spermatozoa. *Nature, Lond.*, **181**, 851.

—— —— (1958)b. Some features of the acrosome and perforatorium in mammalian spermatozoa. *Proc. roy. Soc.*, B, **149**, 234.

—— —— (1958c). Role of the rodent acrosome and perforatorium in fertilization. *Proc. roy. Soc.*, B. **149**, 241.

—— —— (1959a). Presence of spermatozoa in the uterine-tube mucosa of bats. *J. Endocrin.*, **18**, viii.

—— —— (1959b). Differential fluorescence in living rat eggs treated with acridine orange. *Exp. Cell Res.*, **17**, 35.

—— & BRADEN, A. W. H. (1952). Passage of the sperm and the penetration of the egg in mammals. *Nature, Lond.*, **170**, 919.

—— —— (1953a). Polyspermy in mammals. *Nature, Lond.*, **172**, 82.

—— —— (1953b). An investigation of polyspermy in the rat and rabbit. *Aust. J. biol. Sci.*, **6**, 674.

—— —— (1953c). The distribution of nucleic acids in rat eggs in fertilization and early segmentation. I : Studies on living eggs by ultraviolet microscopy. *Aust. J. biol. Sci.*, **6**, 324.

—— —— (1954a). Time relations and their significance in the ovulation and penetration of eggs in rats and rabbits. *Aust. J. biol. Sci.*, **7**, 179.

—— —— (1954b). Induction and inhibition of the second polar division in the rat egg and subsequent fertilization. *Aust. J. biol. Sci.*, **7**, 195.

—— —— (1954c). Anomalies in rat, mouse and rabbit eggs. *Aust. J. biol. Sci.*, **7**, 537.

—— —— (1954d). Nucleus formation and cleavage induced in unfertilized rat eggs. *Nature, Lond.*, **173**, 999.

—— —— (1955). Observations on nuclear size and form in living rat and mouse eggs. *Exp. Cell Res.*, **8**, 163.

AUSTIN, C. R. & BRADEN, A. W. H. (1956). Early reactions of the rodent egg to sperma-tozoon penetration. *J. exp. Biol.*, **33**, 358.

—— & BRUCE, H. M. (1956). Effect of continuous oestrogen administration on oestrus, ovulation and fertilization in rats and mice. *J. Endocrin.*, **13**, 376.

—— & SMILES, J. (1948). Phase-contrast microscopy in the study of fertilization and early development of the rat egg. *J. R. micr. Soc.*, **68**, 13.

BACSICH, P. (1949). Multinuclear ova and multiovular follicles in the young human ovary and their probable endocrinological significance. *J. Endocrin.*, **6**, i.

—— & HAMILTON, W. J. (1954). Some observations on vitally stained rabbit ova with special reference to their albuminous coat. *J. Embryol. exp. Morph.*, **2**, 81.

—— & WYBURN, G. M. (1945). Parthenogenesis of atretic ova in the rodent ovary. *J. Anat.*, **79**, 177.

BAER, K. E. VON (1927). *De ovi mammalium et hominis genesi*, Lipsiae.

BALFOUR-LYNN, S. (1956). Parthenogenesis in human beings. *Lancet*, **270**, 1071.

BALTZER, F. (1952). The behaviour of nuclei and cytoplasm in amphibian interspecific crosses. *Symp. Soc. exp. Biol.*, **6**, 230.

BARRY, M. (1839). Researches in embryology—second series. *Phil. Trans.*, pt. 2, 307.

—— (1843). Spermatozoa observed within the mammiferous ovum. *Phil. Trans.*, **133**, 33.

BATTY, I., BRAMBELL, F. W. R., HEMMINGS, W. A., & OAKLEY, C. L. (1954). Selection of antitoxins by the foetal membranes of rabbits. *Proc. roy. Soc. B.*, **142**, 452.

BEATTY, R. A. (1951). Heteroploidy in mammals. *Anim. Breed. Abstr.*, **19**, 283.

—— (1954). Haploid rodent eggs. *Caryologia*, **6**, (Suppl. Pt. 2), 784.

—— (1956). Ovum characteristics : mammals. In *Handbook of biological data*, ed. W. S. Spector, p. 124. W. B. Saunders Co., Philadelphia.

—— (1957). *Parthenogenesis and polyploidy in mammalian development.* Cambridge University Press.

BEKHTINA, V. G. (1955). Contribution to the fertilisation and early embryonic develop-ment in the hen (trans. title). *Trudy Pushkinskoi Labor.*, **7**, 198.

—— (1958). Morphology of fertilisation in the hen (trans. title). *Trudy Pushkinskoi Labor.*, **8**, 214.

BENGTSSON, L. (1949). Sperm absorption in rabbits (trans. title). *K. fysiogr. Sällsk. Lund Förh.*, **19**, 188. (*Anim. Breed. Abstr.* (1951), **19**, 510.)

BERG, W. E. (1950). Lytic effects of sperm extracts on the eggs of *Mytilus edulis*. *Biol. Bull.*, **98**, 128.

BERRY, R. O. and SAVERY, H. P. (1958). A cytological study of the maturation process of the ovum of the ewe during normal and induced ovulation. In *Reproduction and Infertility*, III. Symposium, ed. F. X. Gassner, pp. 75–82. Pergamon Press, London.

BIELIG, H. J., & MEDEM, F. (1949). Wirkstoffe der tierischen Befruchtung. *Experientia*, **5**, 11.

BISCHOFF, T. L. W. (1842). *Entwicklungsgeschichte des Kanincheneies.* Braunschweig.

—— (1854). *Bestätigung des von Dr. Newport bei den Batrachiern und Dr. Barry bei den Kaninchen behaupteten Eindringens der Spermatozoïden in das Ei.* Giessen.

BISHOP, D. W., & TYLER, A. (1956). Fertilizin of mammalian eggs. *J. exp. Zool.*, **132**, 575.

BLANDAU, R. J. (1945). The first maturation division of the rat ovum. *Anat. Rec.*, **92**, 449.

—— (1952). The female factor in fertility and infertility. I : Effects of delayed fertiliza-tion on the development of the pronuclei in rat ova. *Fertil. Steril.*, **3**, 349.

—— (1954). The effects on development when eggs and sperm are aged before fertiliza-tion. *Ann. N.Y. Acad. Sci.*, **57**, 526.

—— & JORDAN, E. S. (1941). The effect of delayed fertilization on the development of the rat ovum. *Amer. J. Anat.*, **68**, 275.

—— & MONEY, W. L. (1944). Observations on the rate of transport of spermatozoa in the female genital tract of the rat. *Anat. Rec.*, **90**, 255.

—— & ODOR, D. L. (1948). The number of spermatozoa reaching various segments of the oviduct of the rat, 12, 24 and 36 hr. after mating. *Anat. Rec.*, **100**, 733 (proc.)

BLANDAU, R. J. & ODOR, D. L. (1949). The total number of spermatozoa reaching various segments of the reproductive tract in the female albino rat at intervals after insemination. *Anat. Rec.*, **103**, 93.

—— —— (1950). Observations on fertilization of rat ova. *Anat. Rec.*, **106**, 177.

—— —— (1952). Observations on sperm penetration into the oöplasm and changes in the cytoplasmic components of the fertilizing spermatozoon in rat ova. *Fertil. Steril.*, **3**, 13.

—— & YOUNG, W. C. (1939). The effects of delayed fertilization on the development of the guinea-pig ovum. *Amer. J. Anat.*, **64**, 303.

BLOUNT, M. (1909). The early development of the pigeon's egg with special reference to polyspermy and the origin of the periblast nuclei. *J. Morph.*, **20**, 1.

BLUNTSCHLI, H. (1938). Le développement primaire et l'implantation chez un centetiné (Hemicentetes). *C. R. Ass. Anat. Bâle*, **1**, 39.

BLYTH, J. S. S. (1954). The mosaic daughter of a mosaic cock. *Poult. Sci.*, **33**, 310.

BOELL, E. J., & NICHOLAS, J. S. (1939). Respiratory metabolism of mammalian eggs and embryos. *Science*, **90**, 411.

—— —— (1948). Respiratory metabolism of the mammalian egg. *J. exp. Zool.*, **109**, 267.

BOLING, J. L., BLANDAU, R. J., SODERWALL, A. L., & YOUNG, W. C. (1941). Growth of the Graafian follicle and the time of ovulation in the albino rat. *Anat. Rec.*, **79**, 313.

BONNET, —— (1899). Giebt es bei Wirbeltieren Parthenogenesis ? *Ergebn. Anat. Entw-Gesch.*, **9**, 820.

BOREI, H. (1948). Respiration of oöcytes, unfertilized eggs and fertilized eggs from *Psammechinus* and *Asterias*. *Biol. Bull.*, **95**, 124.

—— (1949). Independence of post-fertilization respiration in the sea-urchin egg from the level of respiration before fertilization. *Biol. Bull.*, **96**, 117.

BORSTEL, R. C. VON (1957). Nucleocytoplasmic relations in early insect development. In *The beginnings of embryonic development*, ed. A. Tyler, C. B. Metz and R. C. von Borstel, pp. 175–199. Amer. Assoc. Advanc. Sci., Washington.

BORZEDOVSKA, B. (1955). Uterus impregnation in the white mouse by sperm penetration into the mucous membrane. *Pam. Inst. zootech. Polsce.*, 1955, p. 39 (*Anim. Breed. Abstr.*, (1956) **24**, 284.

BOVERI, T. (1891). Befruchtung. *Ergebn. Anat. EntwGesch.*, **1**, 386.

BOWMAN, R. H. (1951). Fertilization of undenuded rat ova. *Proc. Soc. exp. Biol., N.Y.*, **76**, 129.

BRACHET, J. (1950). *Chemical embryology*. Interscience Publ. Inc., N.Y.

—— (1953). Les acides nucléiques des oeufs de grenouille fécondés par des spermatozoïdes irradiés ou traités par une chloréthylamine (nitrogen mustard). *Experientia*, **9**, 182.

—— (1957). *Biochemical cytology*. Academic Press, N.Y.

BRADEN, A. W. H. (1952). Properties of the membranes of rat and rabbit eggs. *Aust. J. sci. Res. B.*, **5**, 460.

—— (1953). Distribution of sperms in the genital tract of the female rabbit after coitus. *Aust. J. biol. Sci.*, **6**, 693.

—— (1955). The reactions of isolated mucopolysaccharides to several histochemical tests. *Stain Tech.*, **30**, 19.

—— (1957). Variation between strains in the incidence of various abnormalities of egg maturation and fertilization in the mouse. *J. Genetics*, **55**, 476.

—— (1958). Strain differences in the incidence of polyspermia in rats after delayed mating. *Fertil. Steril.*, **9**, 243.

—— & AUSTIN, C. R. (1953a). The distribution of nucleic acids in rat eggs in fertilization and early segmentation. II : Histochemical studies. *Aust. J. biol. Sci.*, **6**, 665.

—— —— (1953b). Fertilization and fertility in mammals. *Aust. vet. J.*, **29**, 129.

—— —— (1954a). The number of sperms about the eggs in mammals and its significance for normal fertilization. *Aust. J. biol. Sci.*, **7**, 543.

—— —— (1954b). Fertilization of the mouse egg and the effect of delayed coitus and of hot-shock treatment. *Aust. J. biol. Sci.*, **7**, 552.

BRADEN, A. W. H. & AUSTIN, C. R. (1954c). Reaction of unfertilized mouse eggs to some experimental stimuli. *Exp. Cell Res.*, **7,** 277.

—— —— (1954d). The fertile life of mouse and rat eggs. *Science*, **120,** 361.

—— —— & DAVID, H. A. (1954). The reaction of the zona pellucida to sperm penetration. *Austr. J. biol. Sci.*, **7,** 391.

BRIGGS, R. (1952). An analysis of the inactivation of the frog sperm nucleus by toluidine blue. *J. gen. Physiol.*, **35,** 761.

BROKAW, C. J. (1957). " Electro-chemical " orientation of bracken spermatozoids. *Nature, Lond.*, **179,** 525.

—— (1958a). Chemotaxis of bracken spermatozoids. The role of bimalate ions. *J. exp. Biol.*, **35,** 192.

—— (1958b). Chemotaxis of bracken spermatozoids. Implications of electrochemical orientation. *J. exp. Biol.*, **35,** 197.

BRUCE, H. M., & AUSTIN, C. R. (1956). An attempt to produce the Hertwig effect by X-irradiation of male mice. *Proc. Soc. Study Fertil.*, **8,** 121.

BULLER, A. H. R. (1902). Is chemotaxis a factor in the fertilization of the eggs of mammals ? *Quart. J. micr. Sci.*, **46,** 145.

CALDWELL, W. H. (1887). The embryology of Monotremata and Marsupialia. I. *Phil. Trans. B*, **178,** 463.

CHAMBERS, E. L. (1939). The movement of the egg nucleus in relation to the sperm aster in the echinoderm egg. *J. exp. Biol.*, **16,** 409.

CHAMBERS, R. (1923). The mechanism of sperm entrance into the starfish egg. *J. gen. Physiol.*, **5,** 821.

—— (1930). The manner of sperm entry in the starfish egg. *Biol. Bull.*, **58,** 344.

—— (1933). The manner of sperm entry in various marine ova. *J. exp. Biol.*, **10,** 130.

CHAMPY, C. (1923). Parthénogénsè expérimentale chez le lapin. *C. R. Soc. Biol., Paris*, **96,** 1108.

CHANG, M. C. (1950). Cleavage of unfertilized ova in immature ferrets. *Anat. Rec.*, **108,** 31.

—— (1951a). Fertilizing capacity of spermatozoa deposited into the Fallopian tubes. *Nature, Lond.*, **168,** 697.

—— (1951b). Fertilization in relation to the number of spermatozoa in the Fallopian tubes of rabbits. *Ann. Ostet. Ginec. Milano*, **73,** 918.

—— (1951c). Fertility and sterility as revealed in the study of fertilization and development of rabbit eggs. *Fertil. Steril.*, **2,** 205.

—— (1952a). Fertilizability of rabbit ova and the effects of temperature *in vitro* on their subsequent fertilization and activation *in vivo*. *J. exp. Zool.*, **121,** 351.

—— (1952b). Effects of delayed fertilization on segmenting ova, blastocysts and fetuses in rabbit. *Fed. Proc.*, **11,** 24.

—— (1952c). An experimental analysis of female sterility in the rabbit. *Fertil. Steril.*, **3,** 251.

—— (1953a). Storage of unfertilized rabbit ova : subsequent fertilization and the probability of normal development. *Nature, Lond.*, **172,** 353.

—— (1953b). Fertilizability of rabbit germ cells. In *Mammalian germ cells*, ed. G. E. W. Wolstenholme, pp. 226–42. J. & A. Churchill Ltd., London.

—— (1954). Development of parthenogenetic rabbit blastocysts induced by low temperature storage of unfertilized ova. *J. exp. Zool.*, **125,** 127.

—— (1955a). Développement de la capacité fertilisatrice des spermatozoides du lapin a l'intérieur du tractus génital et fécondabilité des oeufs de lapine. In *La Fonction Tubaire et ses Troubles*, pp. 40–52. Masson et Cie, Paris.

—— (1955b). Development of fertilizing capacity of rabbit spermatozoa in the uterus. *Nature, Lond.*, **175,** 1036.

—— (1955c). Fertilization and normal development of follicular oöcytes in the rabbit. *Science*, **121,** 867.

—— (1955d). The maturation of rabbit oöcytes in culture and their maturation, activation, fertilization and subsequent development in the fallopian tubes. *J. exp. Zool.*, **128,** 379.

—— (1955e). Vital stain rabbit of eggs *in vitro* during fertilization. *Anat. Rec.*, **121,** 427.

CHANG, M. C. (1957a). A detrimental effect of seminal plasma on the fertilizing capacity of sperm. *Nature, Lond.*, **179**, 258.

—— (1957b). Natural occurrence and artificial induction of parthenogenetic cleavage of ferret ova. *Anat. Rec.*, **128**, 187.

—— (1957c). Some aspects of mammalian fertilization. In *The beginnings of embryonic development*, ed. A. Tyler, C. B. Metz and R. C. von Borstel, pp. 109–134. American Association for the Advancement of Science, Washington.

—— (1958) Capacitation of rabbit spermatozoa in the uterus with special reference to the reproductive phase of the female. *Endocrinology*, **63**, 619.

—— & HUNT, D. M. (1956). Effects of proteolytic enzymes on the zona pellucida of fertilized and unfertilized mammalian eggs. *Exp. Cell Res.*, **11**, 497.

—— & PINCUS, G. (1951). Physiology of fertilization in mammals. *Phys. Rev.*, **31**, 1.

—— —— (1953). Does phosphorylated hesperidin affect fertility ? *Science*, **117**, 274.

CHARLTON, H. H. (1917). The fate of unfertilized eggs in the white mouse. *Biol. Bull.*, **33**, 321.

CHITTY, H., & AUSTIN, C. R. (1957). Environmental modification of oestrus in the vole. *Nature, Lond.*, **179**, 592.

CLEVELAND, L. R. (1958a). Photographs of fertilization in the smaller species of *Trichonympha*. *J. Protozool.*, **5**, 105.

—— (1958b). Photographs of fertilization in *Trichonympha grandis*. *J. Protozool.*, **5**, 115.

COLWIN, A. L., & COLWIN, L. H. (1955). Sperm entry and the acrosome filament (*Holothuria atra* and *Asterias amurensis*). *J. Morph.*, **97**, 543.

—— —— (1957). Morphology of fertilization : acrosome filament formation and sperm entry. In *The Beginnings of embryonic development*, ed. A. Tyler, R. C. von Borstel and C. B. Metz, p. 135. Amer. Assoc. Advan. Sci., Washington.

—— —— & PHILPOTT, D. E. (1957). Electron microscope studies of early stages of sperm penetration in *Hydroides hexagonus* (Annelida) and *Saccoglossus kowalevskii* (Enteropneusta). *J. biophys. biochem. Cytol.*, **3**, 489.

COLWIN, L. H., & COLWIN, A. L. (1954). Sperm penetration and the fertilization cone in the egg of *Saccoglossus kowalevskii* (Enteropneusta). *J. Morph.*, **95**, 351.

—— —— (1956). The acrosome filament and sperm entry in *Thyone briarius* (*Holothuria*) and *Asterias*. *Biol. Bull.*, **110**, 243.

CORNER, G. W. (1923). The problem of embryonic pathology in mammals, with observations upon intrauterine mortality in the pig. *Amer. J. Anat.*, **31**, 523.

—— (1933). The discovery of the mammalian ovum. Lectures on the history of medicine, 1926–32. *Mayo Foundation Lectures, Philadelphia.*

CORNMAN, I. (1941). Sperm activation by Arbacia egg extracts, with special reference to echinochrome. *Biol. Bull.*, **80**, 202.

CORRIAS, L., and NOVARINI, L. (1950). Attivazione e agglutinazione dispermi di toro ad opera del liquido folliculare. *Monit. Zool. ital.*, **57**, 94.

COURRIER, R. (1923). Vésicule blastodermique parthénogénétique dans un ovaire de cobaye impubère. *Arch. Anat., Strasbourg*, **2**, 455.

—— & OBERLING, G. (1923). Parthénogénèse spontanée dans l'ovaire du cobaye. *Bull. Soc. anat. Paris*, **93**, 724.

CREW, F. A. E. (1926). On fertility in the domestic fowl. *Proc. roy. Soc. Edinb.*, **46**, 230.

CRUICKSHANK, W. (1797). Experiments in which, on the third day after impregnation, the ova of rabbits were found in the fallopian tubes ; and on the fourth day after impregnation in the uterus itself ; with the first appearances of the foetus. *Phil. Trans.*, pt. 1, 197.

DAKIN, W. J., & FORDHAM, M. G. C. (1924). The chemotaxis of spermatozoa and its questioned occurrence in the animal kingdom. *Brit. J. exp. Biol.*, **1**, 183.

DALCQ, A. M. (1928). *Les bases physiologiques de la fécondation et de la parthénogénèse.* Presses Univ., Paris.

—— (1951). New descriptive and experimental data concerning the mammalian egg, principally of the rat. I, IIa, b. *Proc. Acad. Sci. Amst.*, C, **54**, 351., 364, 469.

—— (1952a). Effets de la centrifugation sur l'oöcyte de 2ᵉ ordre et l'œuf fécondé indivis du rat. *Arch. Anat., Histol., Embryol.*, **34**, 157.

—— (1952b). *Initiation à l'embryologie générale.* Masson et Cie, Paris.

Dalcq, A. M. (1954a). Nouvelles données structurales et cytochimiques sur l'œuf des mammifères. *Rev. gén. Sci.*, **61**, 19.

—— (1954b). Fonctions cellulaires et cytochimie structurale dans l'œuf de quelques rongeurs. *C. R. Soc. Biol., Paris*, **148**, 1332.

—— (1955a). Processes of synthesis during early development of rodents' eggs and embryos. *Proc. Soc. Stud. Fert.*, **7**, 113.

—— (1955b). Sur la prévalence du pronucléus mâle chez le rat. *Arch. Anat. Histol. Embryol.*, **37**, 61.

—— (1956). Effets du réactif de Schiff sur les oeufs en segmentation du rat et de la souris. *Exp. Cell Res.*, **10**, 99.

—— (1957). *Introduction to general embryology*. Oxford University Press.

—— & Pasteels, J. (1955). Détermination photométrique de la teneur relative en DNA des noyaux dans les oeufs en segmentation du rat et de la souris. *Exp. Cell Res.*, Suppl. 3, 72.

—— & Simon, S. (1931). Contribution à l'analyse des fonctions nucléaires dans l'onto-génèse de la grenouille. III. Etude statistique et cytologique des effets de l'irra-diation d'un des gamètes sur la gestrulation chez *Rana fusca*. *Arch. Biol., Paris*, **42**, 107.

—— —— (1932). Contribution à l'analyse des fonctions nuclèaires dans l'ontogénèse de la grenouille. II. Le rôle dynamique des chromosomes mis en évidence par lésion mécanique ou irradiation des gamètes. *Protoplasma*, **14**, 497.

Dan, J. C. (1952). Studies on the acrosome. I. Reaction to egg-water and other stimuli. *Biol. Bull.*, **103**, 54.

—— (1954a). Studies on the acrosome. II. Acrosome reaction in starfish spermatozoa. *Biol. Bull.*, **107**, 203.

—— (1954b). Studies on the acrosome. III: Effect of calcium deficiency. *Biol. Bull.*, **107**, 335.

—— (1956). The acrosome reaction. *Int. Rev. Cytol.*, **5**, 365.

—— & Wada, S. K. (1955). Studies on the acrosome. IV: The acrosome reaction in some bivalve spermatozoa. *Biol. Bull.*, **109**, 40.

Danforth, C. H. (1927). A gynandromorph mouse. *Anat. Rec.*, **35**, 32.

Darlington, C. D. (1937). *Recent advances in cytology* (2nd ed.). J. & A. Churchill, London.

Dauzier, L., & Thibault, C. (1956). Recherches expérimentale sur la maturation des gamètes mâles chez les mammifères, par l'etude de la fécondation " in vitro " de l'œuf de lapine. *IIIrd Internat. Congr. Anim. Reprod., Cambridge*.

—— —— & Wintenberger, S. (1954). La fécondation *in vitro* de l'œuf de la lapine. *C. R. Acad. Sci., Paris*, **238**, 844.

Dawson, A. B., & Friedgood, A. B. (1940). The time and sequence of pre-ovulatory changes in the cat ovary after mating or mechanical stimulation of the cervix uteri. *Anat. Rec.*, **76**, 411.

Dederer, P. H. (1934). Polyovular follicles in the cat. *Anat. Rec.*, **60**, 391.

Dempsey, E. W. (1939). Maturation and cleavage figures in ovarian ova. *Anat. Rec.*, **75**, 223.

De Robertis, E. D. P., Nowinski, W. W. & Saez, F. A. (1954). *General cytology* (2nd edit.). W. B. Saunders Co., Philadelphia.

Diomidova, H. A., & Kusnetzova, N. A. (1935). Semination of rabbit eggs *in vitro* (trans. title). *Biol. Zh., Moscow*, **4**, 243.

Dokunin, A. V., & Bashkaev, I. S. (1954). On physiological polyspermy in mammals. (trans. title). *Bull. Biol. Méd. exp. URSS*, **37**, 62.

Dragoiu, I., Benetato, G. & Opreanu, R. (1937). Recherches sur la respiration des ovocytes des mammifères. *C. R. Soc. Biol., Paris*, **126**, 1044.

Dunn, L. C. (1927). Selective fertilization in fowls. *Poult. Sci.*, **6**, 201.

Edwards, R. G. (1954a). Colchicine-induced heteroploidy in early mouse embryos. *Nature, Lond.*, **174**, 276.

—— (1954b). The experimental induction of pseudogamy in early mouse embryos. *Experientia*, **10**, 499.

—— (1957a). The experimental induction of gynogenesis in the mouse. I: Irradiation of the sperm by X-rays. *Proc. roy. Soc.* B, **146**, 469.

EDWARDS, R. G. (1957b). The experimental induction of gynogenesis in the mouse. II : Ultra-violet irradiation of the sperm. *Proc. roy. Soc.* B, **146**, 488.

—— (1958a). Colchicine-induced heteroploidy in the mouse. I. *J. exp. Zool.*, **137**, 317.

—— (1958b). The experimental induction of gynogenesis in the mouse. III. *Proc. Roy. Soc.* B, **149**, 117.

—— & SIRLIN, J. L. (1956). Labelled pronuclei in mouse eggs fertilized by labelled sperm. *Nature, Lond.*, **177**, 429.

—— —— (1958). Radioactive tracers and fertilization in mammals. *Endeavour*, **17**, 42.

ENDO, Y. (1952). The role of the cortical granules in the formation of the fertilization membrane in eggs from Japanese sea urchins. *Exp. Cell Res.*, **3**, 406.

ENGLE, E. T. (1927). Polyovular follicles and polynuclear ova in the mouse. *Anat. Rec.*, **35**, 341.

EVANS, H. M., & COLE, H. H. (1931). An introduction to the study of the oestrous cycle in the dog. *Mem. Univ. Calif.*, **9**.

FANKHAUSER, G. (1932). Cytological studies on egg fragments of the salamander *Triton*. II. *J. exp. Zool.*, **62**, 185.

—— (1934). Cytological studies on the egg fragments of the salamander *Triton*. III : The early development of the sperm nuclei in egg fragments without the egg nucleus. *J. exp. Zool.*, **67**, 159.

—— (1945). The effects of changes in chromosome number on amphibian development. *Quart. Rev. Biol.*, **20**, 20.

—— (1948). The organization of the amphibian egg during fertilization and cleavage. *Ann. N.Y. Acad. Sci.*, **49**, 684.

—— (1955). The role of nucleus and cytoplasm. In *Analysis of development*, ed. B. H. Willier, P. A. Weiss and V. Hamburger, pp. 126–150. W. B. Saunders Co., Philadelphia.

—— & GODWIN, D. (1948). The cytological mechanism of the triploidy-inducing effect of heat on eggs of the newt, *Triturus viridescens*. *Proc. nat. Acad. Sci., Wash*, **34**, 544.

FEKETE, E. (1937). A case of lateral hermaphroditism in *Mus musculus*. *Anat. Rec.*, **69**, 151.

—— & DURAN-REYNALS, F. (1943). Hyaluronidase in the fertilization of mammalian ova. *Proc. Soc. exp. Biol., N.Y.*, **52**, 119.

FISCHBERG, M., & BEATTY, R. A. (1952). Heteroploidy in mammals. II : Induction of triploidy in pre-implantation mouse eggs. *J. Genet.*, **50**, 455.

FLOREY, H., & WALTON, A. (1932). Uterine fistula used to determine the mechanism of ascent of the spermatozoon in the female genital tract. *J. Physiol.*, **74**, 5 P.

FLYNN, T. T., & HILL, J. P. (1939). The development of the *Monotremata*. IV : Growth of the ovarian ovum, maturation, fertilization and early cleavage. *Trans. zool. Soc., Lond.*, **24**, 445.

FOL, H. (1877a). Sur les phénomènes intimes de la fecondation. *C. R. Acad. Sci., Paris*, **84**, 268.

—— (1877b). Sur le premier développement d'une Étiole der Mer. *C. R. Soc. Biol., Paris*, **84**, 357.

—— (1879). Recherches sur la fécondation et la commencement de l'hénogénie chez divers animaux. *Mem. Soc. Phys. Genève*, **26**, 89.

FRANZÉN, Å. (1958). On sperm morphology and acrosome filament formation in some Annelida, Echiuroidea and Tunicata. *Zool. Bidrag, Uppsala*, **33**, 1.

FRIDHANDLER, L., HAFEZ, E. S. E., & PINCUS, G. (1956a). O_2 uptake of rabbit ova. *IIIrd Internat. Congr. Anim. Reprod., Cambridge*.

—— —— —— (1956b). Respiratory metabolism of mammalian eggs. *Proc. Soc. exp. Biol., N.Y.*, **92**, 127.

—— —— —— (1957). Developmental changes in the respiratory activity of rabbit ova. *Exp. Cell Res.*, **13**, 132.

FROMMOLT, G. (1934). Die Befruchtung und Furchung des Kanincheneies im Film. *Zbl. Gynäk.*, **58**, 7.

GATENBY, J. B., & HILL, J. P. (1924). On an ovum of Ornithorhynchus exhibiting polar bodies and polyspermy. *Quart. J. micr. Sci.*, **68**, 229.

Gates, A. H. (1956). Viability and developmental capacity of eggs from immature mice treated with gonadotrophins. *Nature, Lond.*, **177,** 754.

—— & Beatty, R. A. (1954). Independence of delayed fertilization and spontaneous triploidy in mouse embryos. *Nature, Lond.*, **174,** 356.

Gelfan, S. (1931). Electrical potential difference across the nuclear membrane of the starfish egg. *Proc. Soc. exp. Biol., N.Y.*, **29,** 58.

Genin, D. I. (1951). The role of the large number of spermatozoa in the sexual process (trans. title). *Ž. obšč. Biol.*, **12,** 108. (*Anim. Breed. Abstr.* (1953), **21,** 178.)

—— (1953). The interaction between spermatozoa and animal tissues (trans. title). *Ž. obšč. Biol.*, **14,** 441 (*Anim. Breed. Abstr.* (1954), **22,** 382.)

Gilchrist, F., & Pincus, G. (1932). Living rat eggs. *Anat. Rec.*, **54,** 275.

Ginsburg, A. S. (1957). Monospermy in sturgeons in normal fertilisation and the consequences of penetration into the egg of supernumery spermatozoa (trans. title). *Dokl. Acad. Nauk S.S.S.R.*, **144,** 445.

Goldforb, A. J. (1918). Effects of ageing upon germ cells and upon early development. Part III : Changes in very aged eggs. *Biol. Bull.*, **35,** 1.

Graaf, R. de (1672). *De mulierum organis generatione inservientibus. Tractus novus.* Lugdoni Batav.

Graves, A. P. (1945). Development of the golden hamster, *Cricetus auratus* Waterhouse, during the first nine days. *Amer. J. Anat.*, **77,** 219.

Gray, J. (1931). *Experimental cytology.* Cambridge University Press.

Green, W. W., & Winters, L. M. (1935). Studies on the physiology of reproduction in the sheep. III : The time of ovulation and the rate of sperm travel. *Anat. Rec.*, **61,** 457.

Greenwald, G. S. (1956a). Sperm transport in the reproductive tract of the female rabbit. *Science*, **124,** 586.

—— (1956b). The reproductive cycle of the field mouse, *Microtus californicus.* *J. Mamm.*, **37,** 213.

—— (1957). Interruption of pregnancy in the rabbit by the administration of estrogen. *J. exp. Zool.*, **135,** 461.

Greenwood, A. W., & Blyth, J. S. S. (1951). Genetic and somatic aberrations in two asymmetrically marked fowls from sex-linked crosses. *Heredity*, **5,** 215.

Gregory, P. W. (1930). The early embryology of the rabbit. *Carneg. Inst. Wash. Contrib. Embryol.*, **21,** 141.

Gresson, R. A. R. (1940). Presence of the sperm middle-piece in the fertilised egg of the mouse (*Mus musculus*). *Nature, Lond.*, **145,** 425.

—— (1941). A study of the cytoplasmic inclusions during the maturation, fertilization and the first cleavage division of the egg of the mouse. *Quart. J. micr. Sci.*, **83,** 35.

—— (1942). A study of the cytoplasmic inclusions during maturation, fertilization and the first cleavage division of the egg of the mouse. *Quart. J. micr. Sci.*, **83,** 35.

—— (1951). The structure and formation of the mammalian spermatozoon. *Cellule*, **54,** 82.

Grosser, O. (1927). Frühentwicklung, Eihautbildung und Placentation des Menschen und der Säugetiere. *Dtsch. Frauenheilkunde*, **5,** 454 pp. (Bergmann).

Hagström, B. E. (1956a). The effect of removal of the jelly coat on fertilization in sea urchins. *Exp. Cell Res.*, **10,** 740.

—— (1956b). The influence of the jelly coat *in situ* and in solution on cross fertilisation in sea urchins. *Exp. Cell Res.*, **11,** 306.

—— (1956c). Studies on polyspermy in sea urchins. *Arch. Zool.*, **10,** 307.

Hagström, B., & Hagström, Br. (1954a). Refertilization of the sea-urchin egg. *Exp. Cell Res.*, **6,** 491.

—— —— (1954b). The action of trypsin and chymotrypsin on the sea-urchin egg. *Exp. Cell Res.*, **6,** 532.

—— & Runnström, J. (1959). Refertilization of partially fertilized sea-urchin eggs. *Exp. Cell Res.*, **16,** 309.

Haldane, J. B. S. (1955). Some alternatives to sex. *New Biology*, no. 19, 7.

Hamilton, H. H. (1952). *Lillie's development of the chick.* Henry Holt & Co., N.Y.

HAMILTON, W. J. (1934). The early stages in the development of the ferret. Fertilization to the formation of the prochordal plate. *Trans. roy. Soc. Edinb.*, **58**, 251.

—— & DAY, F. T. (1945). Cleavage stages of the ova of the horse, with notes on ovulation. *J. Anat.*, **79**, 127.

—— & LAING, J. A. (1946). Development of the egg of the cow up to the stage of blastocyst formation. *J. Anat.*, **80**, 194.

—— & SAMUEL, D. M. (1956). The early development of the golden hamster (*Cricetus auratus*). *J. Anat.*, **90**, 395.

HAMMOND, J. (1925). *Reproduction in the rabbit.* Oliver & Boyd, Edinburgh and London.

—— (1934). The fertilization of rabbit ova in relation to time. A method of controlling the litter size, the duration of pregnancy and the weight of the young at birth. *J. exp. Biol.*, **11**, 140.

—— & WALTON, A. (1934). Notes on ovulation and fertilisation in the ferret. *J. exp. Biol.*, **11**, 307.

HANCOCK, J. L. (1958). The examination of pig ova. *Vet. Rec.* **70**, 1200.

HARMAN, M. T., & KIRGIS, H. D. (1938). The development and atresia of the graafian follicle and the division of intra-ovarian ova in the guinea-pig. *Amer. J. Anat.*, **63**, 79.

HARPER, E. H. (1904). The fertilization and early development of the pigeon's egg. *Amer. J. Anat.*, **3**, 349.

HARRISON, R. J. (1948). The changes occurring in the ovary of the goat during the estrous cycle and in early pregnancy. *J. Anat.*, **82**, 21.

HARTMAN, C. G. (1916). Studies in the development of the opossum *Didelphis virginiana* L. I, II. *J. Morph.*, **27**, 1.

—— (1919). Studies in the development of the opossum *Didelphis virginiana* L. III, IV. *J. Morph.*, **32**, 1.

—— (1924). Observations on the viability of the mammalian ovum. *Amer. J. Obstet. Gynec.*, **7**, 40.

—— (1926). Polynuclear ova and polyovular follicles in the opossum and other mammals, with special reference to the problem of fecundity. *Amer. J. Anat.*, **37**, 1.

—— (1928). The breeding season of the opossum, *Didelphis virginiana*, and the rate of intra-uterine and postnatal development. *J. Morph.*, **46**, 143.

—— (1937). The hen's egg not fertilized in the ovary. *Science*, **85**, 218.

—— (1939). Ovulation, fertilization and the transport and viability of eggs and spermatozoa. In *Sex and Internal Secretions* (ed. E. Allen), 2nd ed., pp. 630–719. Baillière, Tindall and Cox, London.

—— (1953). Early death of the mammalian ovum with special reference to the aplacental opossum. In *Mammalian germ cells* (ed. G. E. W. Wolstenholme), pp. 253–261. J. & A. Churchill Ltd., London.

HARTMANN, M., & SCHARTAU, O. (1939). Untersuchungen uber die Befruchtungstoffe der Seeigel. *Biol. Zbl.*, **59**, 571.

HARVEY, ELMER B. (1958). Tubal ovum in Ochotonidae (Lagomorpha). *Anat. Rec.*, **132**, 113.

HARVEY, ETHEL B. (1956). *The American Arbacia and other sea-urchins.* Princeton University Press, New Jersey.

HARVEY, E. N. (1911). Studies on the permeability of cells. *J. exp. Zool.*, **10**, 507.

HARVEY, W. (1651). *Exercitationes de generatione animalium.* Amstelodami, and Londini.

HEAPE, W. (1886). The development of the mole (*Talpa europea*), the ovarian ovum, and segmentation of the ovum. *Quart. J. micr. Sci.*, **26**, 157.

—— (1905). Ovulation and degeneration of ova in the rabbit. *Proc. roy. Soc. B.*, **76**, 260.

HECHTER, O., & HADIDIAN, Z. (1947). Hyaluronidase activity of spermatozoa. *Endocrinology*, **41**, 204.

HEILBRUNN, L. V. (1952). *An outline of general physiology.* W. B. Saunders, Philadelphia.

—— & WILSON, W. L. (1948). Protoplasmic viscosity changes during mitosis in the egg of *Chaetopterus*. *Biol. Bull.*, **95**, 57.

HEMMINGS, W. A. (1958). Protein selection in the yolk-sac splanchnopleur of the rabbit : the total uptake estimated as loss from the uterus. *Proc. roy. Soc., B.*, **148**, 76.

HENSEN, V. (1876). Beobachtungen über die Befruchtung und Entwicklung des Kaninchens und Meerschweinchens. *Z. Anat. EntwGesch.*, **1**, 213.

HERTWIG, G. (1913). Parthenogenesis bei Wirbeltieren, hervorgerufen durch artfremden radiumbestrahlten Samen. *Arch. mikr. Anat.*, **81**, 87.

HERTWIG, O. (1876). Beiträge zur Kenntniss der Bildung, Befruchtung und Theilung des tierischen Eies. *Morph. Jb.*, **1**, 347.

—— (1911). Die Radiumkrankheit tierischer Keimzellen. *Arch. mikr. Anat.*, **77**, 97.

—— & HERTWIG, R. (1887). Über die Befruchtungs- und Teilungsvorgang des tierischen Eies unter dem Einfluss äusserer Argentien. *Jena. Z. Naturw.*, **20**, 120.

HERTWIG, P. (1920). Haploid and diploid parthenogenesis. *Biol. Zbl.*, **40**, 145.

HERTWIG, R. (1892). Ueber Befruchtung und Conjugation. *Verh. dtsch. Zool. Ges.*, **2**, 95.

HIBBARD, H. (1928). Contribution á l'étude de l'ovogénèse, de la fécondation et de l'histogénèse chez *Discoglossus pictus* Otth. *Arch. Biol.*, **38**, 251.

HILL, J. P. (1910). The early development of the marsupialia, with special reference to the native cat (*Dasyurus viverrinus*). *Quart. J. micr. Sci.*, **56**, 1.

—— (1918). Some observations on the early development of *Didelphis aurata*. *Quart. J. micr. Sci.*, **63**, 91.

—— & TRIBE, M. (1924). The early development of the cat (*Felis domestica*). *Quart. J. micr. Sci.*, **68**, 513.

HOLLANDER, W. F. (1949). Bipaternity in pigeons. *J. Hered.*, **40**, 271.

—— GOWEN, J. W., & STADLER, J. (1956). A study of 25 gynandromorphic mice of the Bagg albino strain. *Anat. Rec.*, **124**, 223.

HOLTER, H., & ZEUTHEN, E. (1944). The respiration of the egg and embryo of the Ascidian, *Ciona intestinalis* L. *C. R. Lab. Carlsberg*, **25**, 33.

HÖRSTADIUS, S. (1939a). Über die Entwicklung von *Astropecten aranciacus* L. *Publ. Staz. zool. Napoli*, **17**, 221.

—— (1939b). Über die larve von *Holothuria poli delle Chiaje*. *Arch. Zool.*, **31**, A, No. 14.

HUBER, G. C. (1915). The development of the albino rat, *Mus norvegicus albinus*. *J. Morph.*, **26**, 1.

HUMPHREY, R. R., & FANKHAUSER, G. (1943). Two unusual haploid-diploid mosaics of mixed *Amblystoma mexicanum* and *Amblystoma tigrinum* ancestry. *Anat. Rec.*, **87**, 23.

IVANOV, E. (1924). Recherches experimentale à propos du processus de la fécondation chez les poules. *C. R. Soc. Biol., Paris*, **91**, 54.

IZQUIERDO, L. (1955). Fixation des oeufs de rat colorés vitalement par le bleu de toluidine. Technique et observations cytologiques. *Arch. Biol.*, **66**, 403.

JANOSIK, J. (1896). Die Atrophie der Follikel. *Arch. mikr. Anat.*, **48**, 169.

JUST, E. E. (1919). The fertilization reaction in *Echinarachnius parma*. I, II, III. *Biol. Bull.*, **36**, 1.

—— (1929). The production of filaments by echinoderm ova as a response to insemination, with special reference to the phenomenon as exhibited by ova of the genus *Asterias*. *Biol. Bull.*, **57**, 311.

KAMADA, T., & KINOSITA, H. (1940). Membrane potential of sea-urchin eggs. *Proc. imp. Acad. Japan*, **16**, 149.

KAMINSKI, Z., & MARCHLEWSKI, M. (1952). Polispermic influences in canine breed formation. *Bull. int. Acad. Cracovie (Acad. pol. Sci.), Cl. Sci. math. nat.*, B. (II), 1951 : 285. (*Anim. Breed. Abstr.*, (1955), **23**, 71.)

KAMPMEIER, O. F. (1929). On the problem of " parthenogenesis " in the mammalian ovary. *Amer. J. Anat.*, **43**, 45.

KINGERY, H. M. (1914). So-called parthenogenesis in the white mouse. *Biol. Bull.*, **27**, 240.

KIRKHAM, W. B., & BURR, H. S. (1913). The breeding habits, maturation of eggs and ovulation of the albino rat. *Amer. J. Anat.*, **15**, 291.

KLEIN, M. (1955). Unilateral hermaphroditism in the mouse. *Anat. Rec.*, **122**, 341.

KOHLBRUGGE, J. H. F. (1910a). Der Einfluss der Spermatozoiden auf die Blastula. *Arch. mikr. Anat.*, **75**, 519.

—— (1910b). Der Einfluss der Spermatozoiden auf dem Uterus. *Z. Morph. Anthr.*, **12**, 359.

KOHLBRUGGE, J. H. F. (1913). Die Verbreitung der Spermatozoiden im weiblichen Körper und im befruchteten Ei. *Arch. Entw. Mech. Org.*, **35**, 165.

KOROBOVA, T. B. (1955). Contribution on fertilization in mammals (trans title). *Bull. Biol. Méd. exp. URSS.*, **39**, 54.

KOSIN, I. L. (1945). Abortive parthenogenesis in the domestic chicken. *Anat. Rec.*, **91**, 245.

—— & NAGRA, H. (1956). Frequency of abortive parthenogenesis in domestic turkey. *Proc. Soc. exp. Biol. N.Y.*, **93**, 605.

KRAFKA, J. (1939). Parthenogenetic cleavage in the human ovary. *Anat. Rec.*, **75**, 19.

KRAHL, M. E., KELTCH, A. K., NEUBECK, C. E., & CLOWES, G. H. A. (1941). Studies on cell metabolism and cell division. V. Cytochrome oxidase activity in the eggs of *Arbacia punctulata*. *J. gen. Physiol.*, **24**, 597.

KRASOVSKAJA, O. V. (1934). Fertilization of the rabbit egg outside the organism. II. *Arch. russ. Anat. Histol. Embryol.*, **13**, 415.

—— (1935). Cytological study of the heterogeneous fertilization of the egg of rabbit outside the organism. *Acta Zool.*, **16**, 449.

—— & DIOMIDOVA, H. A. (1934). Fertilization of the egg of the rabbit *in vitro*. I (trans. title). *Biol. Zh., Moscow*, **3**, 19.

KREMER, J. (1924). Das Verhalten der Vorkerne im befruchteten Ei der Ratte und der Maus mit besonderer Berücksichtigung ihrer Nucleolen. *Z. mikr.-anat. Forsch.*, **1**, 353.

KRÜGER, E. (1913). Fortpflänzung und Keimzellenbildung von *Rhabditis aberrans*. *Z. wiss. Zool.*, **105**, 87.

KURNICK, N. B. (1950). Methyl green-pyronin. I. Basis of selective staining of nucleic acids. *J. gen. Physiol.*, **33**, 243.

KUSHNER, K. F. (1954). The effect of heterospermic insemination in animals and its biological nature (trans. title). *Izv. Akad. Nauk S.S.S.R.*, ser. B., No. 1, 32.

LAING, J. A. (1957). Female fertility. Chap. 17 in *Progress in the physiology of farm animals*, Vol. 3, ed. J. Hammond. Butterworth's Scientific Publications.

LAMS, H. (1913). Etude de l'œuf de cobaye aux premiers stades de l'embryogenèse. *Arch. Biol., Paris*, **28**, 229.

—— & DOORME, J. (1908). Nouvelles recherches sur la maturation et la fécondation de l'œuf des mammifères. *Arch. Biol., Paris*, **23**, 259.

LANE, C. E. (1938). Aberrant ovarian follicles in the immature rat. *Anat. Rec.*, **71**, 243.

LASER, H., & ROTHSCHILD, LORD (1939). The metabolism of the eggs of *Psammechinus miliaris* during the fertilization reaction. *Proc. roy. Soc. B.*, **126**, 539.

LEBEDEV, M. M. (1951). Polyspermy in animals (trans. title). *Izv. Akad. Nauk S.S.S.R.*, Ser. biol., No. 3, 63. (*Anim. Breed. Abstr.*, **19**, 388 [1951].)

LEEUWENHOEK, A. VAN (1677). Observationes de natis e semine genitali animalculis. *Phil. Trans.*, **12**, 1040.

LELIVÈRE, — PEYRON, —, & CORSY, F. (1927). La parthénogénèse dans l'ovaire des mammifères et le problème de l'origine des embryones. *Bull. Ass. franç. Cancer*, **16**, 711.

LEONARD, S. L., PERLMAN, P. L., & KURZROK, R. (1947). Relation between time of fertilization and follicle cell dispersal in rat ova. *Proc. Soc. exp. Biol., N.Y.*, **66**, 517.

LEVI, G. (1915). Il comportamento dei condriosomi durante i più precoci periodi dello svillupo dei mammiferi. *Arch. Zellforsch.*, **13**, 471.

LEWIS, W. H., & WRIGHT, E. S. (1935). On the early development of the mouse egg. *Carnegie Inst. Contrib. Embryol.*, **25**, 113.

LILLIE, F. R. (1912). The production of sperm iso-agglutinins by ova. *Science*, **36**, 527.

—— (1913a). Studies on fertilization. V. The behavior of the spermatozoa of Nereis and Arbacia with special reference to egg extractives. *J. exp. Zool.*, **14**, 515.

—— (1913b). The mechanism of fertilization. *Science*, **38**, 524.

—— (1923). *Problems of fertilization*. Chicago University Press.

—— & JUST, E. E. (1924). Fertilization. *Cowdry's General Cytology*, pp. 451–536.

LINDAHL, P. E., & HOLTER, H. (1941). Über die Atmung der Ovozyten erster Ordnung von *Paracentrotus lividus* und ihre Veränderung während der Reifung. *C. R. Lab. Carlsberg*, **24**, No. 2, 49.

LOEB, J. (1899). On the nature of the process of fertilization and the artificial production of normal larvae (Plutei) from the unfertilized eggs of the sea-urchin. *Amer. J. Physiol.*, **3**, 135.

—— (1913). *Artificial parthenogenesis and fertilization.* Chicago University Press.

—— (1917). Fécondation et phagocytose. *Ann. Inst. Pasteur*, **31**, 437.

LOEB, L. (1932). The parthenogenetic development of eggs in the ovary of the guinea-pig. *Anat. Rec.*, **51**, 373.

LONG, J. A. (1912). The living eggs of rats and mice with a description of apparatus for obtaining and observing them. *Univ. Calif. Publ. Zool.*, **9**, 105.

—— & MARK, E. L. (1911). The maturation of the egg of the mouse. *Contr. Embryol. Carneg. Instn.*, **142**, 1.

LONGLEY, W. H. (1911). The maturation of the egg and ovulation in the domestic cat. *Amer. J. Anat.*, **12**, 139.

LUDWIG, K. S. (1953). Sur quelques aspects cytologique et cytochimique de la fécondation chez les Rongeurs. *C. R. Acad. Sci., Paris*, **237**, 496.

—— (1954). Das Verhalten der Thymonukleinsäure (D.N.A.) während der Befruchtung und den ersten Segmentationsstadien bei der Ratte und dem Goldhamster. *Arch. Biol., Paris*, **65**, 135.

MCCLEAN, D., & ROWLANDS, I. W. (1942). The role of hyaluronidase in fertilization. *Nature, Lond.*, **150**, 627.

MCCRADY, E. (1938). The embryology of the opossum. *Amer. anat. Mem.*, No. 16.

MACDONALD, E., & LONG, J. A. (1934). Some features of cleavage in the living egg of the rat. *Amer. J. Anat.*, **55**, 343.

MCDONALD, L. E., & SAMPSON, J. (1957). Intraperitoneal insemination of the heifer. *Proc. Soc. exp. Biol., N.Y.*, **95**, 815.

MCLAREN, A., & MICHIE, D. (1956). Studies on the transfer of fertilized mouse eggs to uterine foster-mothers. I : Factors affecting the implantation and survival of native and transferred eggs. *J. exp. Biol.*, **33**, 394.

MAKINO, S. (1941). Studies on the murine chromosomes. I. Cytological investigations of mice, included in the genus *Mus*. *J. Fac. Sci. Hokkaido Univ.*, **7**, 305.

MAINLAND, D. (1930). The early development of the ferret : the pronuclei. *J. Anat.*, **64**, 262.

MAKAROV, P. V. (1953). Cytological processes of fertilization in the equine *Ascaris* (trans. title). *Izv. Akad. Nauk S.S.S.R.*, Ser. Biol., No. 1, 46.

—— (1957). Über ungelöste Probleme der gegenwärtigen Zytologie. *Wiss. Z. Martin-Luther-Univ., Halle, Math-Nat.*, **6**, 549.

MANN, M. C. (1924). Cytological changes in the unfertilized tubal eggs of the rat. *Biol. Bull.*, **46**, 316.

MARSHALL, F. H. A. (1922). *Physiology of reproduction.* Longmans, Green & Co., London.

MEDEM, F. G. VON (1942). Beiträge zur Frage der Befruchtungsstoffe bei marinen Mollusken. *Biol. Zbl.*, **62**, 431.

MEISSNER, G. (1855). Beobachtungen über das Eindringen der Samenelemente in den Dotter. *Z. wiss. Zool.*, **6**, 208.

MENKIN, M. F., & ROCK, J. (1948). *In vitro* fertilization and cleavage of human ovarian eggs. *Amer. J. Obstet. Gynec.*, **55**, 440.

MERKURJEVA, E. K. (1954). Polyspermy in rabbits (trans. title). *Agrobiologija* (4), 92. (*Anim. Breed. Abstr.* (1956), **24**, 179.)

METZ, C. B. (1957). Specific egg and sperm substances and activation of the egg. In *The beginnings of embryonic development*, ed. A. Tyler, R. C. von Borstel, and C. B. Metz, pp. 23–69. Amer. Assoc. Advanc. Sci., Washington.

MEVES, F. (1911). Ueber die Beteiligung der Plastochondrien an der Befruchtung des Eies von *Ascaris megalocephala*. *Arch. mikr. Anat.*, **76**, 683.

—— (1914). Verfolgung des Mittelstückes des Echinidenspermiens durch die ersten Zellgenerationen des befruchteten Eies. *Arch. mikr. Anat.*, **85**, 1.

—— (1916). Ueber die Befruchtungsvorgang bei der Meismuschel (*Mytilus edulis* L.). *Arch. mikr. Anat.*, **87**, 47.

MEYERHOF, O. (1911). Untersuchungen über die Wärmetönung der vitalen Oxydationsvorgänge in Eiern. *Biochem. Z.*, **35**, 246.

MILOVANOV, V. K., & SOKOLOVSKAYA, I. I. (1955). The present status of the problems of fertilization in farm animals (trans. title). *Ž. obšč. Biol.*, **5**, 383.

MITCHISON, J. M., & SWANN, M. M. (1952). Optical changes in the membranes of the sea-urchin egg at fertilization, mitosis and cleavage. *J. exp. Biol.*, **29**, 357.

—— —— (1954a). The mechanical properties of the cell surface. I : The cell elastimeter. *J. exp. Biol.*, **31**, 443.

—— —— (1954b). The mechanical properties of the cell surface. II : The unfertilised sea-urchin egg. *J. exp. Biol.*, **31**, 461.

—— —— (1955). The mechanical properties of the cell surface. III. The sea-urchin egg from fertilization to cleavage. *J. exp. Biol.*, **32**, 734.

MONROY, A. (1948). A preliminary approach to the physiology of fertilization in *Pomatoceros triqueter* L. *Ark. Zool.*, 40A, No. 21.

—— (1957a). Studies of proteins of sea-urchin egg and of their changes following fertilization. In *The beginnings of embryonic development*, ed. A. Tyler, R. C. von Borstel and C. B. Metz., pp. 169–174. Amer. Assoc. Advan. Sci., Washington.

—— (1957b). An analysis of the process of fertilization and activation of the egg. *Int. Rev. Cytol.*, **6**, 107.

—— (1957c). Adenosinetriphosphatase in the mitochondria of unfertilized and newly fertilized sea-urchin eggs. *J. cell. comp. Physiol.*, **50**, 73.

—— & MONTALENTI, G. (1947). Variations of the submicroscopic structure of the cortical layer of fertilized and parthenogenetic sea-urchin eggs. *Biol. Bull.*, **92**, 151.

MOORE, B. P., WOODROFFE, G. E., & SANDERSON, A. R. (1956). Polymorphism and parthenogenesis in a Ptinid beetle. *Nature, Lond.*, **177**, 847.

MOORE, C. R. (1916). On the superposition of fertilization on parthenogenesis. *Biol. Bull.*, **31**, 137.

—— (1917). On the capacity for fertilization after the initiation of development. *Biol. Bull.*, **33**, 258.

MORGAN, T. H. (1896). The production of artificial astrospheres. *Arch. EntwMech. Org.*, **3**, 339.

—— (1927). *Experimental embryology*. Columbia University Press, N.Y.

MORICARD, R. (1949). Pénétration *in vitro* du spermatozoïde dans l'ovule des mammifères et niveau du potentiel d'oxydoréduction tubaire. *C. R. Soc. franç. Gynéc.*, **19**, 226.

—— (1950a). Penetration of the spermatozoon into the mammalian ovum oxydo potential level. *Nature, Lond.*, **165**, 763.

—— (1950b). Premières observations de la pénétration du spermatozoide dans la membrane pellucide d'ovocytes de lapine fécondés *in vitro* niveau de potential d'oxydo réduction de la sécrétion tubaire. *C. R. Ass. Anat., Louvain*, No. 63, 337.

—— (1953). Research on the formation of the second polar body in the tube after entrance of the sperm into the oöcyte. (Comparative studies *in vivo* and *in vitro*). In *Mammalian germ cells*, ed. G. E. W. Wolstenholme, pp. 187–97. J. & A. Churchill, London.

—— (1954a). Observation of *in vitro* fertilization in the rabbit. *Nature, Lond.*, **173**, 1140.

—— (1954b). Méiosis et fécondation ; étude *in vivo* et *in vitro* sur l'ovule des mammifères. *Gynaecologia*, **138**, 310.

—— (1954c). Pénétration spermatique obtenue *in vitro* au travers de la membrane pellucide d'ovocytes de lapine cultivés dans les liquides de sécrétion utéro-tubaire. *C. R. Soc. Biol., Paris*, **148**, 423.

—— (1954d). Etude cinematographique de la fécondation réussie *in vitro* de l'ovule de lapine. *Bull. Féd. Soc. Gynéc. Obst.*, **6**, 271.

—— (1955). La fonction fertilisatrice des sécrétions utérotubaires (étude microcinematographique *in vitro* de la fécondation *in vitro* de l'ovocyte de lapine). In *La fonction tubaire et ses troubles*. Masson et Cie, Paris.

—— & BOSSU, J. (1949a). Premières études du passage du spermatozoïde au travers de la membrane pellucide d'ovocytes de lapine fécondés " *in vitro.*" *C. R. Acad. Méd.*, **33**, 659.

MORICARD, R. & BOSSU, J. (1949b). Numération des spermatozoides au voisinage de l'ovocyte de lapine. Inexistence d'un essain de spermatozoides provoquant l'effritement des cellules granuleuses au moment de la fécondation. *Bull. Ass. Gynécol. Lang. franç.*, **1**, 30.

—— —— (1951). Arrival of fertilizing sperm at the follicular cell of the secondary oöcyte. A study of the rat. *Fertil. Steril.*, **2**, 260.

MOSER, F. (1939). Studies on a cortical layer response to stimulating agents in the Arbacia egg. I. Response to insemination. *J. exp. Zool.*, **80**, 423.

MOTOMURA, I. (1936). Notes on the cytoplasmic structure of the egg of a sea-urchin. *Strongylocentrotus pulcherrimus*. *Zool. Mag., Tokyo*, **48**, 753.

—— (1941). Materials of the fertilization membrane in the eggs of echinoderms. *Sci. Rep. Tôhoku Univ.*, 4th Ser., **16**, 345.

MULNARD, J. (1955). Contribution à la connaissance des enzymes dans l'ontogénèse. Les phosphomonoestérases acide et alcaline dans la développement du rat et de la souris. *Arch. Biol., Paris*, **66**, 525.

NELSON, H. (1851). On the reproduction of *Ascaris mystax*. *Proc. roy. Soc. B*, **6**, 86.

NEWMAN, H. H. (1912). The ovum of the nine-banded armadillo. Growth of the ovocytes, maturation and fertilization. *Biol. Bull.*, **23**, 100.

—— (1913). Parthenogenetic cleavage of the armadillo ovum. *Biol. Bull.*, **25**, 59.

NEWPORT, G. (1853). On the impregnation of the ovum in the Amphibia (2nd Ser.) and in the direct agency of the spermatozoon. *Phil. Trans.*, **143**, 233.

NIHOUL, J. (1927). Recherches sur l'appareil endocellulaire de Golgi dans les premiers stades du développement des mammifères. *Cellule*, **37**, 23.

NOYES, R. W. (1952). Fertilization of follicular ova. *Fertil. Steril.*, **3**, 1.

—— (1953). The fertilizing capacity of spermatozoa. *West. J. Surg.*, **61**, 342.

—— WALTON, A., & ADAMS, C. E. (1958a). Capacitation of rabbit spermatozoa. *Nature, Lond.*, **181**, 1209.

—— —— —— (1958b). Capacitation of rabbit spermatozoa. *J. Endocrin.*, **17**, 374.

ODOR, D. L. (1955). The temporal relationship of the first maturation division of rat ova to the onset of heat. *Amer. J. Anat.*, **97**, 461.

—— & BLANDAU, R. J. (1949). The frequency of occurrence of supernumerary sperm in rat ova. *Anat. Rec.*, **104**, 1.

—— —— (1951a). Observations on the formation of the second polar body in the rat ovum. *Anat. Rec.*, **110**, 329.

—— —— (1951b). Observations on fertilization and the first segmentation division in rat ova. *Amer. J. Anat.*, **89**, 29.

—— —— (1956). Incidence of polyspermy in normal and delayed matings in rats of the Wistar strain. *Fertil. Steril.*, **7**, 456.

ÖHMAN, L. O. (1945). On the lipids of the sea-urchin egg. *Arch. Zool.*, 36A, No. 7, 1.

OLSEN, M. W. (1942). Maturation, fertilization, and early cleavage in the hen's egg. *J. Morph.*, **70**, 513.

—— (1956). Fowl pox vaccine associated with parthenogenesis in chicken and turkey eggs. *Science*, **124**, 1078.

—— & FRAPS, R. M. (1944). Maturation, fertilization, and early cleavage of the egg of the domestic turkey. *J. Morph.*, **74**, 297.

—— —— (1950). Maturation changes in the hen's ovum. *J. exp. Zool.*, **114**, 475.

—— & MARSDEN, S. J. (1953). Embryonic development in turkey eggs laid 60–224 days following removal of males. *Proc. Soc. exp. Biol., N.Y.*, **82**, 638.

—— —— (1954a). Natural parthenogenesis in turkey eggs. *Science*, **120**, 545.

—— —— (1954b). Development in unfertilized turkey eggs. *J. exp. Zool.*, **126**, 337.

ONANOFF, J. (1893). Recherches sur la fécondation et la gestation des mammifères. *C. R. Soc. Biol., Paris*, **45**, 719.

OSTER, G. (1950). Scattering of visible light and X-rays by solutions of proteins. *Progr. Biophys.*, **1**, 73.

OTT, D. v. (1882). Über künstliche Befruchtung durch die Peritonealhöhle. *Zbl. Gynäk.*, **6**, 573.

PACKARD, C. (1918). The effect of radium radiations on the development of *Chaetopterus*. *Biol. Bull.*, **35**, 50.

PANKRATZ, D. S. (1938). Some observations on the graafian follicles in an adult human ovary. *Anat. Rec.*, **71**, 211.

PARAT, M. (1933). Nomenclature, genèse, structure et fonction de quelques éléments cytoplasmique des cellules sexuelles males. *C.R. Soc. Biol., Paris*, **112**, 1131.

PARKER, G. H. (1931). The passage of sperms and eggs through the oviduct in terrestrial vertebrates. *Phil. Trans.*, **219**, 381.

PARKES, A. S. (1953). Prevention of fertilization by a hyaluronidase inhibitor. *Lancet*, **ii**, 1285.

—— ROGERS, H. J., & SPENSLEY, P. C. (1954). Biological and biochemical aspects of the prevention of fertilization by enzyme inhibitors. *Proc. Soc. Stud. Fertil.*, **6**, 65.

PATTERSON, J. T. (1910). Studies on the early development of the hen's egg. *J. Morph.*, **21**, 101.

PEACOCK, A. D. (1944). Animal parthenogenesis, natural and artificial. *Proc. R. phil. Soc. Glasg.*, **68**, 99.

—— (1952). Some problems of parthenogenesis. *Advanc. Sci., Lond.*, **9**, 134.

PEARSON, O. P. (1944). Reproduction in the shrew (*Blarina brevicorda* Say). *Amer. J. Anat.*, **75**, 39.

—— & ENDERS, R. K. (1943). Ovulation, maturation and fertilization in the fox. *Anat. Rec.*, **85**, 69.

PESONEN, S. (1946a). Abortive egg cells in the mouse. *Hereditas*, **32**, 93.

—— (1946b). Über Abortiveier. I. *Acta obstet. gynec. Scand.* (suppl. II), 152.

—— (1949). On abortive eggs. III : On the cytology of fertilized ova in the mouse. *Ann. Chir. Gyn. Fenn.*, **38**, (Suppl. 3), 337.

PÉTERFI, T., & ROTHSCHILD, LORD (1935). Bio-electric transients during fertilization. *Nature, Lond.*, **135**, 874.

PFLÜGER, F. (1863). *Über die Eierstöcke der Säugetiere und des Menschen.* Leipzig.

PIKÓ, L. (1958). Etude de la polyspermie chez le rat. *C.R. Soc. Biol. Paris*, **152**, 1356.

PINCUS, G. (1930). Observations on the living eggs of the rabbit. *Proc. roy. Soc. B.* **107**, 132.

—— (1936a). *The eggs of mammals.* Exper. Biol. Monographs, Macmillan Co., New York.

—— (1936b). The parthenogenetic activation of rabbit eggs. *Anat. Rec.*, **67**, (Suppl. 1), 34.

—— (1939a). The comparative behaviour of mammalian eggs *in vivo* and *in vitro*. IV : The development of fertilized and artificially activated rabbit eggs. *J. exp. Zool.*, **82**, 85.

—— (1939b). The maturation of explanted human ovarian ova. *Amer. J. Physiol.*, **126**, 600.

—— (1939c). The breeding of some rabbits produced by recipients of artificially activated ova. *Proc. nat. Acad. Sci., Wash.*, **25**, 557.

—— & ENZMANN, E. V. (1932). Fertilization in the rabbit. *J. exp. Biol.*, **9**, 403.

—— —— (1934). Can mammalian eggs undergo normal development *in vitro* ? *Proc. nat. Acad. Sci., Wash.*, **20**, 121.

—— —— (1935). The comparative behaviour of mammalian eggs *in vivo* and *in vitro*. I. The activation of ovarian eggs. *J. exp. Med.*, **62**, 665.

—— —— (1936). The comparative behaviour of mammalian eggs *in vivo* and *in vitro*. II : The activation of the tubal eggs of the rabbit. *J. exp. Zool.*, **73**, 195.

—— & SHAPIRO, H. (1940a). The comparative behaviour of mammalian eggs *in vivo* and *in vitro*. VII : Further studies on the activation of rabbit eggs. *Proc. Amer. phil. Soc.*, **83**, 631.

—— —— (1940b). Further studies on the parthenogenetic activation of rabbit eggs. *Proc. nat. Acad. Sci., Wash.*, **26**, 163.

—— PIRIE, N. W., & CHANG, M. C. (1948). The effects of hyaluronidase inhibitors on fertilization in the rabbit. *Arch. Biochem.*, **19**, 388.

PITKJANEN, I. G. (1955). Ovulation, fertilization and early embryonic development in the pig (trans. title). *Izv. Acad. Nauk S.S.S.R.*, Ser. Biol., No. 3, p. 120.

—— (1958). Fertilization and early stages of embryonic development in the sheep (trans. title). *Izv. Acad. Nauk S.S.S.R.*, Ser. Biol., No. 3, p. 291.

PITKJANEN, I. G. & IVANKOV, M. F. (1956).   Fertilisation and early stages of embryonic development in the cow (trans. title).   *Izv. Acad. Nauk S.S.S.R.*, Ser. Biol., No. 3, p. 77.

—— & SHEGLOV, O. V. (1958).   Dimensions of sow eggs (trans. title).   *Trudy Pushkinskoi Labor.*, **8**, 116.

POLGE, C. (1956).   The development of an artificial insemination service for pigs.   *Anim. Breed Abstr.*, **24**, 209.

POOLE, H. K., & OLSEN, M. W. (1957).   The sex of parthenogenetic turkey embryos.   *J. Hered.*, **48**, 217.

POPA, G. T. (1927).   A lipo-gel reaction exerted by follicular fluid upon spermatozoa and its significance (Lillie's reaction).   *Biol. Bull.*, **52**, 223.

PÓSALAKY, Z., & TÖRŐ, I. (1957).   Fate of spermatozoa not participating in the fertilization process.   *Nature, Lond.*, **179**, 150.

PRÉVOST, J. L., & DUMAS, J. B. A. (1824).   De la génération dans les mammifères, et des premiers indices du developpement de l'embryon.   *Ann. Sci. nat.*, **3**, 113.

QUINLAN, J., MARE, G. S., & ROUX, L. L. (1932).   The vitality of the spermatozoa in the genital tract of the Merino ewe, with special reference to its practical application in breeding.   *18th. Rep. Div. Vet. Serv. Animal Ind., Union of S.A.*, pp. 831–70.

RIS, H. (1955).   Cell division.   In *Analysis of development*, ed. B. H. Willier, P. A. Weiss and V. Hamburger, pp. 91–125.   W. B. Saunders Co., Philadelphia.

ROBBIE, W. A. (1946).   The effect of cyanide on the oxygen consumption and cleavage of the sea urchin egg.   *J. cell. comp. Physiol.*, **28**, 305.

ROCK, J., & MENKIN, M. F. (1944).   *In vitro* fertilization and cleavage of human ovarian eggs.   *Science*, **100**, 105.

RÖDEL, L., & KARG, H. (1955).   Beitrag zum Mechanismus des Befruchtungsvorganges bei Säugetieren.   *Dtsch. tierärztl. Wschr.*, **62**, 25.

ROTHSCHILD, LORD (1938).   The biophysics of the egg surface of *Echinus esculentus* during fertilization and cytolysis.   *J. exp. Biol.*, **15**, 209.

—— (1946).   Physiology of fertilization.   *Nature, Lond.*, **157**, 720.

—— (1949).   The metabolism of fertilized and unfertilized sea-urchin eggs : the action of light and carbon monoxide.   *J. exp. Biol.*, **26**, 100.

—— (1953).   The fertilization reaction in the sea-urchin.   The induction of polyspermy by nicotine.   *J. exp. Biol.*, **30**, 57.

—— (1954).   Polyspermy.   *Quart. Rev. Biol.*, **29**, 332.

—— (1956).   *Fertilization*.   Methuen & Co., London.

—— (1957).   The fertilizing spermatozoon.   *Discovery*, **18**, 64.

—— (1958).   Fertilization of fish and lamprey eggs.   *Biol. Rev.*, **33**, 372.

—— & SWANN, M. M. (1949).   The fertilization reaction in the sea-urchin egg.   A propagated response to sperm attachment.   *J. exp. Biol.*, **26**, 164.

—— —— (1950).   The fertilization reaction in the sea-urchin egg.   The effect of nicotine.   *J. exp. Biol.*, **27**, 400.

—— —— (1951a).   The conduction time of the block to polyspermy in the sea-urchin egg.   *Exp. Cell Res.*, **2**, 137.

—— —— (1951b).   The fertilization reaction in the sea-urchin.   The probability of a successful sperm-egg collision.   *J. exp. Biol.*, **28**, 403.

—— —— (1952).   The fertilization reaction in the sea-urchin.   The block to polyspermy.   *J. exp. Biol.*, **29**, 469.

—— & TYLER, A. (1955).   Acrosome filaments in spermatozoa.   *Exp. Cell Res.*, Supp. 3, 304.

ROWLANDS, I. W. (1957a).   Insemination of the guinea-pig by intraperitoneal injection.   *J. Endocrin.*, **15**, iii.

—— (1957b).   Insemination of the guinea-pig by intraperitoneal injection.   *J. Endocrin.*, **16**, 98.

—— (1958).   Insemination by intraperitoneal injection.   *Proc. Soc. Study Fertil.*, **10**, 150.

RUBASCHKIN, W. (1905).   Über die Reifungs- und Befruchtungs-prozesse des Meerschweincheneies.   *Anat. Hefte*, **29**, 509.

—— (1906).   Über die Veränderungen den Eier in den Zugrunde gehenden Graafschen Follikeln.   *Anat. Hefte*, **32**, 255.

RUGH, R. (1939). Developmental effects resulting from exposure to X-rays. I : Effect on the embryo of irradiation of frog sperm. *Proc. Amer. phil. Soc.*, **81**, 447.

—— & EXNER, F. (1940). Developmental effects resulting from exposure to X-rays. II : Development of leopard frog eggs activated by bull-frog sperm. *Proc. Amer. phil. Soc.*, **83**, 607.

RUNNER, M. N., & PALM, J. (1953). Transplantation and survival of unfertilized ova of the mouse in relation to postovulatory age. *J. exp. Zool.*, **124**, 303.

RUNNSTRÖM, J. (1928). Die Veränderung der Plasmakolloide bei der Entwicklungserregung des Seeigeleies. *Protoplasma*, **4**, 388.

—— (1944). Notes on the formation of the fertilization membrane and some other features of the development of the Asterias egg. *Acta Zool.*, **25**, 159.

—— (1949). The mechanism of fertilization in metazoa. *Advanc. Enzymol.*, **9**, 241.

—— (1956). Some considerations on metabolic changes occurring at fertilization and during early development of the sea-urchin egg. *Publ. Staz. Zool., Napoli*, **28**, 315.

—— & WICKLUND, E. (1950). Formation mechanism of the fertilization membrane in the sea-urchin egg. Inhibitory effect of heparin and jelly substance on clotting of the vitelline membrane. *Arch. Zool.*, **1** (Nr. 13), 179.

—— MONNÉ, L., & BROMAN, L. (1944). On some properties of the surface layers in the sea-urchin egg and their changes upon activation. *Ark. Zool.*, 35A., No. 3, 1.

—— —— & WICKLUND, E. (1944). Mechanism of formation of the fertilization membrane in sea-urchin eggs. *Nature, Lond.*, **153**, 313.

—— —— —— (1946). Studies on the surface layers and the formation of the fertilization membrane in sea-urchin eggs. *J. Colloid Sci.*, **1**, 421.

—— TISELIUS, A., & LINDWALL, S. (1945). The action of Androgamone III on the sea-urchin egg. *Ark. Zool.*, 36A, No. 22. 1.

SAMUEL, D. M., & HAMILTON, W. J. (1942). Living eggs of the golden hamster (*Cricetus auratus*). *J. Anat.*, **76**, 204.

SAN MARTIN, F. M. (1951). Algunos aspectos experimentales sobre la actividad reproductiva. *Tesis Fac. Med., Univ. Nac. Mayor San Marcos, Lima*. 66 pp. (Abstr. in *Anim. Breed. Abstr.* (1952), **20**, 257.)

—— & FERNANDEZ, L. (1949). Viabilidad del ovulo de la coneja. *Rev. Fac. Med. vet., Lima*, **4**, 16.

SANSOM, G. S. (1920). Parthenogenesis in the water vole, *Microtus amphibius*. *J. Anat.*, **55**, 68.

SCHEER, B. T., MONROY, A., SANTANGELO, M., & RICCOBONO, G. (1954). Action potentials in sea-urchin eggs at fertilization. *Exp. Cell Res.*, **7**, 284.

SCHENK, S. L. (1878). Das Säugethierei künstlich befruchtet ausserhalb des Mutterthieres. *Mitt. Embr. Inst. K. K. Univ. Wien.*, **1**, 107.

SHAPIRO, H. (1942). Parthenogenetic activation of rabbit eggs. *Nature, Lond.*, **149**, 304. (Editorial summary.)

SHARMAN, G. B. (1955a). Studies on marsupial reproduction. II : The oestrous cycle of *Setonix brachyurus*. *Aust. J. Zool.*, **3**, 44.

—— (1955b). Studies on marsupial reproduction. III : Normal and delayed pregnancy in *Setonix brachyurus*. *Aust. J. Zool.*, **3**, 56.

SHEARER, C. (1922). On the oxidation process of the Echinoderm egg during fertilization. *Proc. roy. Soc. B*, **93**, 213.

SHETTLES, L. B. (1953). Observations on human follicular and tubal ova. *Amer. J. Obstet. Gynec.*, **66**, 235.

—— (1956). Intrafollicular cleavage of human ovum. *Nature*, **178**, 1131.

SKJERVEN, O. (1955). Conception in a heifer after deposition of semen in the abdominal cavity. *Fertil. Steril.*, **6**, 66.

SKOWRON, S. (1956). The development of the oöcytes in Graafian follicles of the golden hamster " Mesocricetus auratus " (trans. title). *Folia Biologica*, **4**, 23.

ŠKREB, N. (1957). Etudes cytologiques sur l'œuf de quelques cheiroptères. *Arch. Biol., Paris*, **68**, 381.

SMITH, A. H., & KLEIBER, M. (1950). Size and oxygen consumption in fertilized eggs. *J. cell. comp. Physiol.*, **35**, 131.

SMITH, A. U. (1951). Fertilization *in vitro* of the mammalian egg. *Biochem. Soc. Symp.*, No. 7, 3.

—— (1953). In Discussion after paper by Venge (1953).

SMITH, H. W., & CLOWES, G. H. A. (1924). The influence of hydrogen-ion concentration on unfertilized Arbacia, Asterias and Chaetopterus eggs. *Biol. Bull.*, **47**, 304.

SMITHBERG, M. (1952). The effect of different proteolytic enzymes on the zona pellucida of mouse ova. *Anat. Rec.*, **117**, 554 (proc.).

SOBOTTA, J. (1893). Mitteilungen über die vorgänge bei der Reifung, Befruchtung und ersten Furchung des Eies der Maus. *Anat. Anz.*, **7**, 111.

—— (1895). Die Befruchtung und Furchung des Eies der Maus. *Arch. mikr. Anat.*, **45**, 15.

—— & BURCKHARD, G. (1910). Reifung und Befruchtung des Eies der weissen Ratte. *Anat. Hefte*, **42**, 433.

SPALDING, J. F., BERRY, R. O., & MOFFIT, J. G. (1955). The maturation process of the ovum of swine during normal and induced ovulations. *J. anim. Sci.*, **14**, 609.

SPEICHER, B. R. (1936). Oogenesis, fertilization and early cleavage in *Hobrobracon*. *J. Morph.*, **59**, 401.

STRASSMANN, E. O. (1949). Parthenogenetic development of the ovum as observed by vital staining. *Amer. J. Obstet. Gynec.*, **58**, 237.

STRAUSS, F. (1938). Die Befruchtung und der Vorgang der Ovulation bei Ericulus aus der Familie der centetiden. *Biomorphosis*, **1**, 281.

—— (1950). Ripe follicles without antra and fertilization within the follicle ; a normal situation in a mammal. *Anat. Rec.*, **106**, 251 (proc.).

—— (1954). Das Problem des Befruchtungsortes des Säugetiereies. *Bull. schweiz. Akad. med. Wiss.*, **10**, 239.

—— (1956). The time and place of fertilization of the golden hamster egg. *J. Embryol. exp. Morph.*, **4**, 42.

SUGIYAMA, M. (1951). Re-fertilization of the fertilized eggs of the sea-urchin. *Biol. Bull.*, **101**, 335.

SUOMALAINEN, E. (1950). Parthenogenesis in animals. *Advanc. Genet.*, **3**, 193.

SWANN, M. M. (1952). The nucleus in fertilization, mitosis and cell division. *Symp. Soc. exp. Biol.*, **6**, 89.

SWYER, G. I. M. (1947a). The release of hyaluronidase from spermatozoa. *Biochem. J.*, **41**, 413.

—— (1947b). A tubal factor concerned in the denudation of rabbit ova. *Nature, Lond.*, **159**, 873.

TAFANI, A. (1889). La fécondation et la segmentation étudiées dans les oeufs des rats. *Arch. ital. Biol.*, **11**, 112.

THIBAULT, C. (1947a). La parthénogénèse expérimentale chez le lapin. *C. R. Acad. Sci.*, *Paris*, **224**, 297.

—— (1947b). Essai de parthénogénèse expérimentale chez le rat. *C. R. Soc. Biol.*, *Paris*, **141**, 607.

—— (1948). L'activation et la régulation de l'ovocyte parthénogénètique de lapine. *C. R. Soc. Biol., Paris*, **142**, 495.

—— (1949). L'œuf des mammifères. Son développement parthénogénètique. *Ann. Sci. nat. Zool.*, **11**, 136.

—— (1956). Quelques considerations sur la physiologie de la reproduction en rapport avec l'insemination artificielle. *IIIrd Internat. Congr. Anim. Reprod., Camb.* Plenary papers, pp. 89–104.

—— DAUZIER, L., & WINTENBERGER, S. (1954). Etude cytologique de la fécondation *in vitro* de l'œuf de la lapine. *C. R. Soc. Biol., Paris*, **148**, 789.

—— & ORTAVANT, R. (1949). Parthénogénèse expérimentale chez le brebis. *C. R. Acad. Sci., Paris*, **228**, 510.

TRIMBERGER, G. W., & DAVIS, H. P. (1943). Conception rate in dairy cattle by artificial insemination at various stages of estrus. *Res. Bull. Neb. agric. Exp. Sta.*, No. 129, p. 14.

TYLER, A. (1932). Changes in volume and surface of *Urechis* eggs upon fertilization. *J. exp. Zool.*, **63**, 155.

Tyler, A. (1937). On the energetics of differentiation. V : Comparison of the rates of development and of oxygen consumption of tight membrane and normal echinoderm eggs. *J. exp. Zool.*, **76**, 395.

—— (1939). Extraction of an egg membrane-lysin from sperm of the giant keyhole limpet (*Megathura crenulata*). *Proc. nat. Acad. Sci., Wash.*, **25**, 317.

—— (1941). Artificial parthenogenesis. *Biol. Rev.*, **16**, 291.

—— (1948). Fertilization and immunity. *Phys. rev.*, **28**, 180.

—— (1949). Properties of fertilizin and related substances of eggs and sperm of marine animals. *Amer. Nat.*, **83**, 195.

—— (1954). Fertilization and antibodies. *Sci. Amer.*, **190**, 70.

—— (1955). Gametogenesis, fertilization and parthenogenesis. In *Analysis of development*, ed. B. H. Willier, P. A. Weiss and V. Hamburger, pp. 170–212. W. B. Saunders Company, Philadelphia.

—— & Humason, W. D. (1937). On the energetics of differentiation. VI : Comparison of the temperature coefficients of the respiratory rates of unfertilized and fertilized eggs. *Biol. Bull.*, **73**, 261.

—— & Scheer, B. T. (1937). Inhibition of fertilization in eggs of marine animals by means of acid. *J. exp. Zool.*, **75**, 179.

—— & Schultz, J. (1932). Inhibition and reversal of fertilization in the eggs of the echiuroid worm, *Urechis caupo*. *J. exp. Zool.*, **63**, 509.

—— Monroy, A., & Metz, C. B. (1956). Fertilization of fertilized sea-urchin eggs. *Biol. Bull.*, **110**, 184.

—— —— Kao, C. Y., & Grundfest, H. (1955). Electrical potential changes upon fertilization of the starfish egg. *Biol. Bull.*, **109**, 352.

—— —— —— —— (1956). Membrane potential and resistance of the starfish egg before and after fertilization. *Biol. Bull.*, **111**, 153.

Van Beneden, E. (1875). La maturation de l'œuf, la fécondation et les premières phases du developpement embryonnaire des mammifères d'après des recherches faites chez le lapin. *Bull. Acad. Belg. Cl. Sci.*, **40**, 686.

—— & Julin, C. (1880). Observations sur la maturation, la fécondation et la segmentation de l'œuf chez les chiroptères. *Arch. Biol., Paris*, **1**, 551.

Van der Horst, C. J., & Gillman, J. (1941). The number of eggs and surviving embryos in *Elephantulus*. *Anat. Rec.*, **80**, 443.

Van der Stricht, O. (1901). L'atrésie ovulaire et l'atrésie folliculaire du follicule de De Graaf dans l'ovaire de chauve-souris. *Verh. anat. Ges.*, 15 Versamml. Bonn.

—— (1902). Le spermatozoïde dans l'œuf de chauve-souris (*V. noctula*). *Verh. anat. Ges.*, 16 Versamml., Halle, p. 163.

—— (1909). La structure de l'œuf des mammifères (Chauvesouris, Vesperugo noctula). Troisième partie. L'oöcyte à la fin du stade d'accroissement, au stade de la maturation, au stade de la fécondation et au début de la segmentation. *Mém. Acad. R. Belg. Cl. Sci.*, 2me Ser., **2**, 1.

—— (1923). Etude comparée des ovules des mammifères aux différentes périodes de l'ovogenèsis, d'après les travaux du Laboratoire d'Histologie et d' Embryologie de l'Université de Gand. *Arch. Biol., Paris*, **33**, 229.

Van der Stricht, R. (1911). Vitellogenèse dans l'ovule de chatte. *Arch. Biol., Paris*, **26**, 365.

Van Drimmelen, G. C. (1951). Artificial insemination of birds by the intraperitoneal route. A study in sex physiology of pigeons and fowls with reports upon a modified technique of semen collection, and a new technique of insemination, and observations on the spermatozoa in the genital organs of the fowl hen. *Onderstepoort J. vet. Research*, Suppl. No. 1, 200 pp.

Van Durme, M. (1914). Nouvelles recherches sur la vitallogenèse des oeufs d'oiseaux aux stades d'accroissement, de maturation, de fécondation et du début de la segmentation. *Arch. Biol., Paris*, **29**, 71.

Vara, P., & Pesonen, S. (1947). Über Abortiveier. II : Untersuchungen über die im Chromosomensatz der Säugetiereizelle während der Reifeteilungen sich abspielenden abnormen Erscheinnungen. *Acta obstet. gynec. scand.*, **27**, 215.

VENABLE, J. H. (1946). Pre-implantation stages in the golden hamster (*Cricetus auratus*). *Anat. Rec.*, **94**, 105.

VENGE, O. (1953). Experiments on fertilization of rabbit ova *in vitro* with subsequent transfer to alien does. In *Mammalian germ cells*, ed. G. E. W. Wolstenholme. J. & A. Churchill Ltd., London.

VINCENT, W. S. (1955). Structure and chemistry of nucleoli. In *Int. Rev. Cytol.* **4**, 269.

VOJTISKOVA, M. (1955). Spermatozoal behaviour in the reproductive tract of the hen. (trans. title). *Csl. Biol.*, **4**, (3) 141. (*Anim. Breed. Abstr.* (1957), **25**, 206.)

—— (1956). The question of the participation of non-fertilising sperms in the sexual process. *Folia Biol.*, **2**, 245.

WADA, S. K., COLLIER, J. R., & DAN, J. C. (1956). Studies on the acrosome. V: An egg-membrane lysin from the acrosomes of *Mytilis edulis* spermatozoa. *Exp. Cell Res.*, **10**, 168.

WALTON, A. (1952). Flow orientation as a possible explanation of " wave-motion " and " rheotaxis " of spermatozoa. *J. exp. Biol.*, **29**, 520.

—— & HAMMOND, J. (1928). Observations on ovulation in the rabbit. *Brit. J. exp. Biol.*, **6**, 190.

—— & WHETHAM, E. O. (1933). The survival of spermatozoa in the domestic fowl. *J. exp. Biol.*, **10**, 204.

WARBURG, O. (1908). Beobachtungen über die Oxydationsprozesse im Seeigelei. *Z. phys. Chem.*, **57**, 1.

—— (1915). Notizen zur Entwicklungsphysiologie des Seeigeleies. *Pflügr. Arch. ges. Physiol.*, **160**, 324.

WARD, M. C. (1948). The maturation divisions of the ova of the golden hamster *Cricetus auratus*. *Anat. Rec.*, **101**, 663 (proc.).

WARREN, D. C., & KILPATRICK, L. (1929). Fertilization in the domestic fowl. *Poult. Sci.*, **8**, 237.

WELLS, L. J. (1937). Reproductive organs of two mammalian hermaphrodites and their response to injections of pregnant mare serum. *Anat. Rec.*, **67**, 233.

WHITAKER, D. M. (1933). On the rate of oxygen consumption by fertilized and unfertilized eggs. V: Comparisons and interpretation. *J. gen. Physiol.*, **16**, 497.

WHITE, M. J. D. (1954). *Animal cytology and evolution* (2nd Edit.). Cambridge.

WHITNEY, L. F. (1927). The mating cycle of the dog. *Chase Mag.*

WILSON, E. B. (1928). *The cell in development and heredity*. The Macmillan Co., N.Y.

WILSON, W. L. (1951). The rigidity of the cell cortex during cell division. *J. cell. comp. Physiol.*, **38**, 409.

WINTREBERT, P. (1929). La digestion de l'enveloppe tubaire interne de l'œuf par des ferments issus des spermatozoides, et de l'ovule, chez *Discoglossus pictus* Otth. *C. R. Acad. Sci.*, Paris, **188**, 97.

WITSCHI, E. (1932). Sex deviations, inversions, and parabiosis. Chap. 5. in *Sex and internal secretions*, ed. E. Allen.

YAMANE, J. (1930). The proteolytic action of mammalian spermatozoa and its bearing upon the second maturation division of ova. *Cytologia*, **1**, 394.

—— (1935). Kausal-analytische Studien über die Befruchtung des Kanincheneies. I : Die Dispersion der Follikelzellen und die Ablosung der Zellen der Corona radiata des Eies durch Spermatozoen. *Cytologia*, **6**, 233.

YAO, T. S., & OLSEN, M. W. (1955). Microscopic observations of parthenogenetic embryonic tissues from virgin turkey eggs. *J. Hered.*, **46**, 133.

YOUNG, W. C. (1937). The vaginal smear picture, sexual receptivity and the time of ovulation in the guinea pig. *Anat. Rec.*, **67**, 305.

—— (1953). Gamete-age at the time of fertilization and the course of gestation in mammals. In *Pregnancy Wastage*, ed. E. T. Engle. Springfield, Illinois, U.S.A.

—— & BLANDAU, R. J. (1936). Ovum age and the course of gestation in the guinea-pig. *Science*, **84**, 270.

ZIBINA, E. V. (1953). Cytological study of fertilization and different stages of development of rabbit eggs (trans. title). *Dokl. Acad. Nauk S.S.S.R.*, **88**, 917.

CHAPTER 11

GONADAL AND GONADOTROPHIC HORMONES
IN LOWER VERTEBRATES

By J. M. Dodd

I. Introduction

The reproductive apparatus of vertebrates consists fundamentally of gonads which produce germ-cells, and ducts which lead these germ-cells to the exterior. Evolutionary modifications of this basic plan appear to have taken the form of morphological refinement of the ducts, associated with secretion, copulation and viviparity; physiological refinements of the gonads, associated with the control of cyclical rhythms; and psychological refinements, as a result of which mere congregation of the two sexes at breeding time has been superseded by more or less complex behaviour patterns associated with mating and brooding.

The reproductive system appears to have retained a degree of plasticity unknown in the other organ-systems of the body. This is no doubt due to the special relationship between it and the rest of the body. As Hisaw (1959) has expressed it: " . . . any part or all of the structures directly concerned with reproduction may fail to function or be surgically removed without affecting general health or life expectancy. Therefore, reproduction is essential only for the propagation of the species, while as to the individual it is merely a privilege which may or may not be indulged." Thus modification of the reproductive system can occur without greatly affecting other parts of the organism, and this must account for the apparent ease with which, for example, a wide and discontinuous selection of vertebrate species has become modified for viviparity.

Internal control of the reproductive system is almost exclusively hormonal and is vested mainly in the pituitary gland and in specialised regions of the gonads. Hisaw (1959) has also pointed out that the hormones of the reproductive tract are not vitally essential for the well-being of the individual and this may be extended to include also the gonadotrophic hormones of the pituitary gland. Thus, here again, there is an unusual degree of freedom to evolve without unduly affecting the rest of the body. This must certainly be reflected in the evolutionary history of the hormonal controlling mechanisms and may well have resulted in a greater degree of variability than might otherwise be expected. These concepts have special relevance to the present chapter, the main function of which is to examine the nature of the mechanisms which control sex and reproduction in cold-blooded vertebrates.

There is no justification for treating the cold-blooded vertebrates as a unit, other than convenience and the fact that their bodies are all designed to operate over a wide and varying range of temperature. Apart from this, the group is one of extreme diversity, both between the various classes and within the classes themselves. There are probably some 25,000 species of cold-blooded vertebrates, most of which existed millions of years before mammals first appeared. In view of this and of the striking differences already discovered within the mammals, it would be surprising indeed if there were not some fairly pronounced differences, both in the chemical nature of the reproductive hormones, and in their functions, in this heterogeneous collection of organisms. Such differences are beginning to emerge, though there is still a marked tendency to emphasise the similarities which exist between mammals and cold-blooded vertebrates, and to treat apparent differences as something which future work will bring into line.

Structures associated with sex and reproduction in vertebrate animals are the gonads, reproductive ducts, copulatory structures, other secondary sexual characters, morphological, physiological and psychological, and the pituitary gland. Other endocrine organs, and a variety of external factors, are no doubt also concerned in the inception and maintenance of reproductive rhythms, though these are not considered here, since little is known of the part played by the other glands in reproduction, and reproductive rhythms have been considered in an earlier volume (Volume 1, Part 1, Chapters 1 and 3).

The descriptions of gonads, reproductive ducts and secondary sexual characters which follow are intended to be read in conjunction with certain sections of Volume 1, Part 1 of this treatise, especially Chapters 2, 3 and 5, in which the basic histology of the vertebrate gonad, and the cyclical changes characteristic of gonads and secondary sex characters have already been dealt with. In addition, a detailed treatment of various aspects of viviparity in lower vertebrates is to be found in Volume 2, Chapter 15. The present account is therefore limited to a consideration of those aspects of gonads, reproductive ducts and other secondary sexual characters which have received attention in studies on endocrine physiology.

A great deal has been written on the morphology and histology of the pituitary gland of lower vertebrates; much less is known of its physiology. Hypophysectomy has been achieved in a fairly wide range of species, but the evidence it has yielded has rarely been supplemented by physiological and pharmacological researches. It does not appear to have been generally realised that several of the cold-blooded vertebrates, because of the fact that their pituitaries are usually less compact than in the mammals, offer unusually good possibilities for partial hypophysectomy, as a result of which more precise localisation of hormone production may be possible. The morphological and histological descriptions of pituitary glands which follow are concerned almost entirely with those regions of the pituitary which have been claimed to control reproductive processes; no attempt has been made to deal with other regions of the gland in anything other than general terms.

The main function of the present chapter is to survey the work which has been carried out on the endocrinological control of reproduction and associated sexual phenomena in the lower vertebrate groups. Techniques similar to those used in mammalian endocrinology have been employed in this work, and the effects of hypophysectomy, gonadectomy and replacement therapy have been described for a considerable number of species. However, it must be admitted that there are difficulties inherent in the material which make synthesis difficult and generalisations hazardous. The groups are large, ancient and diverse; body temperature

is variable and this factor has not always been adequately controlled in experimental work; there are usually no criteria on which to establish dosage, and as a
result the physiological significance of a good deal of the work is difficult to assess;
hormone specificity has undoubtedly been encountered, though the data are too
few to show whether this specificity obeys any laws; the length of the breeding
cycle and the importance of environmental conditions in its control have also made
it much more difficult to assess discordant results. Yet, as the following survey
shows, in spite of these difficulties, a great deal has been done towards establishing
the nature and degree of the control exerted by the hormones of pituitary and
gonads on reproductive structures and processes in the lower vertebrates.

II. Cyclostomata

Little is known about the endocrinology of sex and reproduction in cyclostomes
and much of the available information is contradictory or difficult to interpret in
the light of what is accepted for the higher vertebrate groups. Only two species
have been investigated experimentally, namely *Lampetra* (*Petromyzon*) *planeri* and
L. fluviatilis. So far as it is possible to diagnose ammocoete species accurately in
these animals, it appears that both ammocoete and adult stages have been investigated in *L. planeri*, whereas in the case of *L. fluviatilis* only adults have been
studied. Towards the end of larval life in non-parasitic lampreys, the gonad
starts to develop, though spermatogenesis and growth of the oöcytes does not
normally occur until after metamorphosis. However, Zanandrea (1956, 1957)
has described neoteny in females of *L. planeri Zanandreai*, in which fairly mature
eggs are visible through the transparent body wall of the larvae, and the secondary
sexual characters of the sexually mature adult are present. Furthermore, most
workers who have investigated the effects of hormones on lampreys have reported
occasional precocious sexual maturity in saline-injected controls as well as in
experimental animals. These examples illustrate the variability which can occur
in the time of onset of sexual maturity in this group and which has undoubtedly
been responsible for some of the discordant results reported below. It seems that
experiments on endocrine physiology in lampreys must be carried out well prior
to the normal time of onset of sexual maturity.

Gonads

The gonad of cyclostomes is unpaired in both sexes, has no connection with
the kidneys, and is ductless. Okkelberg (1921) has shown that in *Entosphenus
wilderi* the gonadal stroma originates as a single primordium in which the germinal
elements differentiate without regard to their relative position. In all other
vertebrates, with the exception of teleost fish, the gonadal stroma is a double
structure, consisting of a cortex which originates from a localised area of peritoneum, and a medulla which originates from the mesonephric, or interrenal
blastema.

Early workers believed that *Myxine* was a functional hermaphrodite showing
protandry. However, Schreiner (1904) and Conel (1917) demonstrated that this
is not the case; the sexes are separate but there are heterosexual progonads which
are non-functional and degenerate prior to the formation of the definitive gonad,
However, degeneration of the heterosexual elements in genetic males is usually

incomplete, so that Schreiner (1904) found only 19 pure males in 2,500 individuals.

The mature testis in cyclostomes is made up of a number of more or less isolated units which are divided into lobules by well-vascularised connective tissue. The lobules are lined by germinal epithelium undergoing typical spermatogenesis. When the germ-cells are ripe, the testis breaks down and the spermatozoa are liberated into the body cavity. They reach the outside through two pores which develop in the urinary sinus at sexual maturity and communicate with the duct of the urino-genital papilla.

The ovary is an elongated organ which contains large numbers of developing eggs. Ripe eggs are shed into the body cavity and reach the exterior through a temporary pore which, in *Myxine*, enters the urinary duct and opens with it into the cloaca. In *Petromyzon*, two pores enter the urinary ducts which then fuse and traverse a short urino-genital papilla to open at its tip.

Secondary Sexual Characters

Well-defined secondary sexual characters, which appear only when sexual maturity is imminent, are a characteristic feature of the cyclostomes (*see* Volume 1, Part 1, p. 15). In the male these consist of greatly enlarged cloacal labia and an enlarged erectile " penis ": in the female, the cloacal region becomes similarly swollen and hyperaemic (*see* Fig. 11. 2). These changes occur immediately prior to spawning but they are preceded by the development of other features which serve to differentiate the sexes. All the fins enlarge, especially the posterior dorsal fin, and the gap between the two dorsal fins, present in immature lampreys, disappears. A swelling, more conspicuous in the female than in the male, develops at the base of the posterior dorsal fin and a small ventral fin appears immediately behind the cloaca in the female. In addition to these changes the entire post-cloacal region of the male becomes sharply curved downwards, whereas that of the mature female curves upwards. Various internal changes also occur which involve the relationship between kidney ducts and cloaca. In the ammocoete, the kindey ducts (mesonephric ducts) joint the rectum to form a urino-rectal sinus which opens into the cloaca. In the adult, the rectum opens separately into the cloaca, the kidney ducts fusing to form a urinary sinus which discharges on a urinary papilla. At maturity, as has already been described, the latter becomes a urino-genital papilla. All these morphological characters have been studied in relation to the hormones of the pituitary and gonads.

The Pituitary Gland

The cyclostome pituitary gland (Fig. 11. 1), except in the case of *Myxine*, is a well-developed structure in which all the zones characteristic of the pituitary of higher vertebrates are probably represented. The morphology of the gland is, however, unusual in that the various regions do not form a compact structure but are serially arranged. The extensive hypophyseal cavity is also aberrant in that it lies, not between pars anterior and pars intermedia, but below the pituitary, between it and the mouth cavity, and opens to the exterior by a median pore. The structure and development of the cyclostome pituitary have been reviewed by de Beer (1923, 1926), and the glands of *Petromyzon marinus* (Tilney, 1937) and *Ichthyomyzon fossor* (Leach, 1951) have been described in detail.

The anterior glandular lobe of the adenohypophysis is comparatively small and consists of basophil and acidophil cells arranged in vertical columns. It passes abruptly into the transitional lobe (*ubergangsteil*), which is the largest part of the gland and is composed mainly of basophil cells. Beyond the transitional lobe lies the intermediate lobe which underlies the neurohypophysis. Several authors have attempted to homologise the various parts of the adenohypophysis with similar regions of this lobe in the higher vertebrates, but since the histology of the cyclostome pituitary is not well known, and since there are no histochemical or

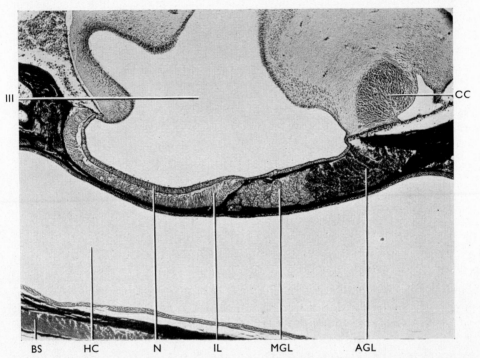

Fig. *11. 1—Petromyzon fluviatilis:* Parasagittal section through pituitary region (× 50) (right is anterior). AGL, anterior glandular region; BS, base of skull; HC, hypophyseal cavity; IL, posterior glandular region (intermediate lobe); MGL, middle glandular region (übergangsteil); N, neurohypophysis; OC, optic chiasma; III, third ventricle. (Preparation and photomicrograph by Mr. P. J. Evennett.)

experimental studies on which to base a judgment, it is unwise to attempt to establish functional analogies with other pituitaries. So far as concerns sex and reproduction, it is not known whether the pituitary gland, or any part of it, controls these aspects of cyclostome physiology.

The neurohypophysis is a very reduced structure, being merely a thickened part of the infundibulum.

The pituitary homologue in *Myxine* is extremely reduced; the hypophyseal and neural elements do not come into intimate contact, and it has been suggested by Herlant (1954) that this fact accounts for the failure of the adenohypophysis to differentiate. The hypophyseal rudiment is composed of a number of nests of cells separated from each other by connective tissue; the cells are of a uniform type and there is no subdivision of the adenohypophysis into separate parts. De Beer (1926) inclines to the view that the pituitary homologue in *Myxine* is degenerate rather than primitive.

Nothing is known regarding the function of the large glandular accessory olfactory organ which was believed to be the homologue of the pars tuberalis by Woerdeman (1914). The possibility that it might be connected with gonad development is briefly mentioned by Leach (1951). This suggestion receives some support from the fact that the accessory olfactory organ is glandular and is much better developed at metamorphosis in the non-parasitic lampreys which become sexually mature immediately, than in the parasitic species which remain immature during their parasitic phase.

Hypophysectomy and Gonadectomy

Hypophysectomy of adults and larvae of *Lampetra fluviatilis* and *L. planeri* has been carried out by Young (1935), and Knowles (1941) hypophysectomised ammocoete larvae of a species which was probably *L. planeri*. However, neither of these authors examined the gonads or secondary sexual characters for possible effects of pituitary removal. So far as concerns gonadectomy, Knowles (1939) states that it is impossible in *L. fluviatilis* because of the position of the gonads, and there are no records in the literature of gonadectomy having been performed in other species. This is unfortunate since hypophysectomy and gonadectomy might reasonably be expected to establish the extent and nature of pituitary and gonadal control of reproductive physiology in a manner which the injection of mammalian pituitary hormones and synthetic steroids can never do.

Effects of Mammalian Gonadotrophins and Sex Steroids

Calvet (1932) was the first to investigate endocrine physiology in Cyclostomes. He injected a number of ammocoetes of *L. planeri* with human pregnancy urine. Mortality as a result of the injection was extremely high and only one specimen survived. This was kept for three days, having received, on the two previous days, an injection of 0·2 ml. pregnancy urine. Calvet noted numerous oöcytes in the posterior region of the coelom which were much larger than those of the normal ammocoete. The excessive mortality encountered in the injection experiment led him to try immersion as a method of administration of the hormone. Ammocoete larvae were immersed in diluted pregnancy urine for 8 to 10 minutes per day for 10 days and were sacrificed 5 or 6 days later. As a result of this treatment, the cloaca seemed profoundly altered and the gonads showed an almost complete disappearance of connective tissue and a marked increase in size of the oöcytes, which had abundant cytoplasm and a large nucleus. Calvet recognised that ammocoetes in nature have ripe or ripening gonads from October to April of the last year of their lives and carried out his experiments in August, at which time the ovaries of these larvae prior to injection contained only a few small oöcytes. However, few animals survived the treatment, and most subsequent workers have reported that pregnancy urine, mammalian anterior lobe pituitary extract and steroid hormones have no stimulatory effect on the gonads of either ammocoetes or adult lampreys.

Damas (1933) gave details of the onset of sexual maturity in *L. fluviatilis* and described experimental attempts to induce precocious sexual development in maturing adults by the injection of human pregnancy urine.   Some thirty lampreys were injected during this work, and in most cases the secondary sexual characters and gonads were strikingly stimulated.   Some eggs were obtained from injected females by stripping, and successful artificial fertilisations were made.   Additional experiments were carried out using mammalian anterior pituitary extracts and these also resulted in the stimulation of secondary sexual characters and gonads. However, it should be noted that these experiments were carried out towards the time when sexual maturity is attained in untreated animals, few animals were injected, and there is no mention of controls.   In the light of a more recent paper by Damas (1951) in which he was unable to repeat this work, these results are of doubtful significance.

Young and Bellerby (1935) attempted to accelerate metamorphosis in larvae of *L. planeri* by the injection of extracts of anterior lobe of ox pituitary gland.   The extracts were prepared in two different ways; in the first case the extract was

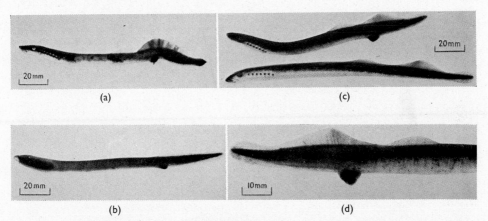

(a)   (c)

(b)   (d)

Fig. *11.2*—(a) Normal adult male *Lampetra planeri*, about to spawn.   (b) Ammocoete.   Male. Received six daily injections each equivalent to 0·85 g. of anterior lobe tissue.   (c) Below, normal immature male; above, male which had received twenty-four injections on alternate days, each equivalent to 0·15 g. of anterior lobe tissue.   (d) Same animal as in (c), to show details of the cloacal swelling.   (From Young and Bellerby, 1935.)

found to stimulate metamorphosis in axolotls, and in both extracts a gonad-stimulating activity was present, as demonstrated by the action of the extract on the amphibian ovary.   In an extensive series of injections carried out between September and January, no signs of metamorphosis were produced and mortality was high.   However, a striking change was seen in the cloacal region in nearly all the ammocoetes which received the injection (Fig. *11.* 2).   This change was entirely similar to that which occurs at sexual maturity.   Injection of a more concentrated extract gave similar results, but in some cases the effect was noticeable after the second daily injection, whereas with the less concentrated extract no effect was noticeable for about 12 days.   Injection of an acid extract of Ox anterior lobe tissue into metamorphosed but sexually immature lampreys produced an even more marked effect on the cloacal region, and also caused the characteristic change in shape of tail and caudal fin which accompanies sexual maturity.   A further effect of the injection on both larvae and metamorphosed immature adults was a change in shape to the swollen body form characteristic of sexually mature adults.

Although the secondary sexual characters were undoubtedly stimulated, histological examination of the ammocoete gonads of both sexes showed that the injection had produced no significant effect on either oögenesis or spermatogenesis, although the extract had already been shown to have gonad-stimulating properties in Amphibia. Young and Bellerby (1935) were unable to decide whether the effects on the secondary sex characters were direct, or indirect, and there is still no evidence to enable us to choose between these possibilities, since similar experiments have never been carried out on gonadectomised animals.

Injection of sex hormones might be expected to throw further light on this problem, and Knowles (1939) investigated the effect of injecting testosterone, oestrone and mammalian anterior lobe pituitary extract into immature adults of *L. fluviatilis* and ammocoete larvae. Injections were carried out in January and throughout February.

TABLE I

The Effect of Anterior-Pituitary, Testicular, and Ovarian Hormones on the Adult *L. fluviatilis*

(From Knowles, 1939)

No. of animals	Details of injection	Date of last injection	External effect
	Anterior-pituitary preparation A.P. 6B [1]		
8	1 mg./day (14 injections)	5 Jan.	No effect
6	10 mg./day (8 injections)	29 Jan.	5 animals had swollen cloacal labia
	Testosterone		
5	1 mg. (1 injection)	4 Feb.	4 animals had very swollen cloacal labia
5	1 mg. (1 injection)	15 Feb.	All animals had very swollen cloacal labia
	Oestrone		
5	50 i.u./day (5 injections)	9 Feb.	3 animals had swollen labia

[1] An alcohol precipitate from an N/20 NaOH extract of acetone-dried ox anterior lobe pituitary tissue.

The nature and results of these experiments are seen in Tables I and II. Metamorphosis of the fins was not observed, even in those animals which showed swollen cloacal labia. Subsequent histological examination showed that swelling of the labia was entirely due to an influx of blood into the tissues: there was no cellular hypertrophy.

Injection of boiled pituitary extract, aqueous oestrone, or water, had no effect on the cloacal region, though pitressin produced hyperaemia but no swelling of the cloacal lips.

Injection of steroids into ammocoete larvae gave results which were similar to those obtained on adults. This can be seen by reference to Table II.

TABLE II

THE EFFECT OF ANTERIOR-PITUITARY AND TESTICULAR HORMONES ON AMMOCOETE LARVAE

(From Knowles, 1939)

No. of animals	Details of injection	Response
	Testosterone	
10	1 mg. (1 injection)	2 animals had slightly swollen cloacal labia
	1 mg./day (3 injections)	3 animals had swollen cloacal labia
	A.P. 6B	
10	1 mg./day (5 injections)	6 animals had swollen cloacal labia
	A.P. 15B [1]	
20	1 mg. (1 injection)	16 animals had swollen cloacal labia
	A.P. 32D (thyrotrophic) [2]	
20	½ mg./day (32 injections)	No response

[1] An alcohol precipitate from a 50 per cent pyridine extract of acetone-dried ox anterior lobe pituitary tissue.

[2] Purified thyrotrophic extract of mammalian anterior lobe pituitary tissue.

An interesting difference between the two series of experiments lies in the fact that sex steroids were more effective in the adults than anterior pituitary extracts in inducing the changes, whereas in the ammocoetes the reverse was true, testosterone producing only occasional and slight effects. It was also noted that larger larvae responded more frequently to pituitary extracts than did larvae less than 110 mm. in length.

Histological examination of the posterior coelomic regions of the injected immature adults at the end of January showed a further interesting effect of the pituitary extracts and sex steroids: a connection had appeared between the coelom and mesonephric duct; this is a feature of the sexually mature animal which does not normally appear until March (Fig. *11*. 3). A comparable effect was produced in the ammocoete as a result of injecting anterior pituitary extract.

Histological examination of the gonads of both sexes in ammocoetes and immature adults yielded no unequivocal evidence of stimulation by any of the materials injected. In a few of the experimental animals a precocious ripening appeared to have occurred, but this phenomenon was also encountered in several of the controls.

P*

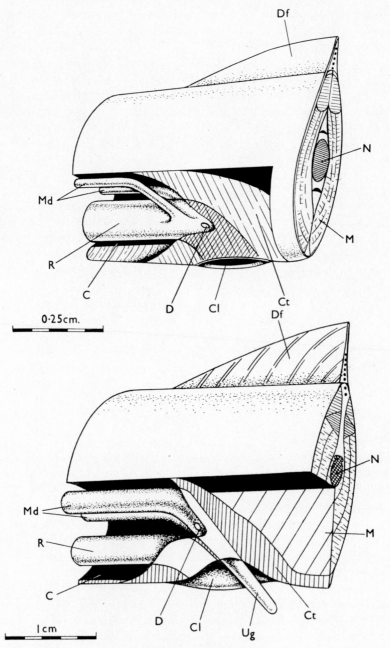

Fig. *11.* 3—*Lampetra (Petromyzon)* sp.

Upper figure: View of the cloacal region of an ammocoete larva which has been dissected from the left side to show the relations of the excretory ducts to the cloaca. C, coelom; Cl, cloacal labium; Ct, connective tissue; D, duct formed by the injection of a mammalian pituitary preparation (this duct is not normally present in the ammocoete); Df, dorsal fin; M, muscle; Md, Mesonephric duct; N, notochord; R, rectum.

Lower figure: View of the cloacal region of an adult *Lampetra fluviatilis* which has been dissected from the left side, to show the relations of the excretory and genital ducts to the cloaca. C, coelom; Cl, cloacal labium; Ct, connective tissue; D, duct leading from the coelom to the mesonephric duct; Df, dorsal fin; M, muscle; Md, mesonephric duct; N, notochord; R, rectum; Ug, urino-genital papilla.

(Redrawn from Knowles, 1939.)

It therefore appears that the findings of Calvet must be discounted, and that neither mammalian anterior lobe pituitary extracts nor sex steroids can, under the conditions of the experiments reported above, exert any effect on gametogenesis in ammocoetes or lampreys of either sex.   New investigations using extracts of cyclostome pituitaries are needed, and these might also throw interesting light on the problem of specificity of pituitary hormones.   There is no doubt, however, that injection of anterior pituitary extracts and steroid hormones has a marked stimulatory effect on the secondary sexual characters of ammocoetes and cyclostomes; hyperaemia of the cloaca and urinogenital papilla, fusion of fins, change in body form, and perforation of the urinary sinus have all been encountered as a result of treating larval and immature cyclostomes, and these features characterise the sexually mature animal.

In the absence of evidence which can only be obtained by castration, it is impossible to judge whether the pituitary extracts were acting directly on the secondary sexual characters or indirectly through the gonads.   Considering the latter possibility, it seems likely that the steroid secreting areas of the gonad, if such exist, are capable of stimulation by pituitary hormones from mammalian sources before the time at which the genital products are completely ripe, and this would account for the precocious appearance of secondary sexual characters.   It seems significant that testosterone propionate will stimulate the secondary sexual characters of immature adults, whereas it is much less active in ammocoetes, and it may well be that testosterone propionate is not the most active steroid in lampreys, though effective in the final stages of maturation at relatively high dose levels.

III. ELASMOBRANCHII

As has been pointed out elsewhere (Dodd, 1955), elasmobranch fish afford special opportunities for studying reproductive physiology.   The Order contains closely related species which are oviparous, ovoviviparous and viviparous, and post-ovulatory corpora lutea are a common feature of the elasmobranch ovary.   In contrast to the teleosts, well-developed genital ducts are present and the primordial gonad is a double structure; in these two features the elasmobranchs resemble the higher vertebrates.   External secondary sexual characters in the form of claspers are present in the males and a well defined breeding cycle is characteristic of many species.   In spite of these attractive features little was known of the endocrinology of reproduction in elasmobranchs until relatively recently.

Gonads and Reproductive Ducts
Male

Elasmobranch testes are paired sub-cylindrical or flattened structures the relative size of which varies considerably in different species.   They are attached to the dorsal body wall by mesorchia.   Closely applied to each testis along its outer border and forming a fairly extensive prolongation at its posterior end is the mass of lymphomyeloid tissue which constitutes the epigonal organ, of unknown function.   The early literature on testis, epididymis and epigonal organ has been well summarised by Matthews (1950), and this author has given a detailed description of these structures in the basking shark, *Cetorhinus maximus*.

Histological examination of the elasmobranch testis shows it to have a zonate structure quite unlike that of most other vertebrates (see Fig. 11. 9). It consists of concentric zones of ampullae, each ampulla having a central cavity and containing germ-cells at an identical stage of differentiation. Along the medio-ventral border of each testis runs the so-called " germ-line ", or " tubulogenic zone "

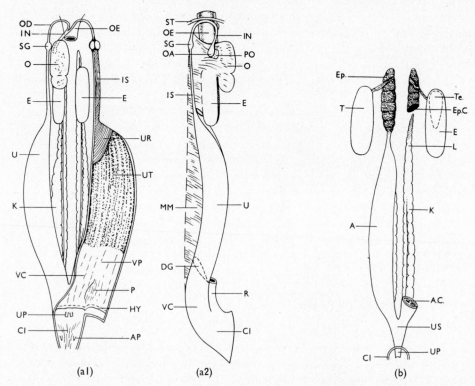

(a1)   (a2)   (b)

Fig. 11. 4—*Cetorhinus maximus* (the basking shark): Internal reproductive organs. (a1) Female reproductive system from the ventral surface, left oviduct opened longitudinally. (a2) Lateral view of female reproductive system from the right side. (b) Male reproductive system from the ventral surface. Most of the left ampulla ductus deferentis has been removed to expose the kidney. A, ampulla ductus deferentis; A.C., cut end of ampulla; AP, abdominal pores; Cl, cloaca; DG, digitiform gland; E, epigonal organ; Ep, epididymis; Ep.C, cut end of epididymis; HY, hymen; IN, oviduct (unpaired region); IS, isthmus; K, kidney; L, Leydig's gland; MM, mesometrium; O, ovary; OA, ostium abdominale; OD, oviduct (paired region); OE, oesophagus; P, pad in lateral wall of common vagina; PO, pocket in right side of ovary; R, rectum; SG, shell gland; ST, septum transversum; T, testis and epigonal organ; Te, testis; U, uterus; UP, urinary papilla; UR, uterus lined with folds; US, urinogenital sinus; UT, uterus lined with trophonemata; VC, common vagina; VP, paired vagina of the left side. (Redrawn from Harrison Matthews, 1950.) (*Phil. Trans.* B, 1950, **234,** 247.)

(Fratini, 1953). It is from this zone that new seminiferous ampullae arise; these lie in an arc around the cells of the germ-line and contain spermatogonia, and Sertoli cells in process of migration from the centre of each ampulla to its periphery. The region of spermatogonial ampullae passes distally into the zone of primary spermatocytes in which the germ-cells have large nuclei which are usually seen in the prophase of the first meiotic division. Distal to this are similar well-marked concentric bands of ampullae containing secondary spermatocytes, spermatids and finally mature spermatozoa, this last zone being the largest in mature fish.

Inter-ampullar connective tissue is scarce in the elasmobranch testis; it consists of scanty connective tissue fibres among which are scattered a few small, fusiform cells. There has been some argument as to whether these are the true interstitial cell homologues (*see* Matthews, 1950). Stephan (1902a) believed they were not; he held that the Sertoli cells constitute the secretory element of the testis. Battaglia (1925) studied the interstitial cells in four elasmobranch species and concluded that they were derived from connective tissue. His view that these cells had an endocrine function was based solely on the fact that they contained lipid. Marshall and Lofts (1956) state that they have identified interstitial cells of the inter-tubular variety in two widely separated chondrichthyan genera, *Scyliorhinus* and *Chimaera*. However, it has not yet been demonstrated that the elasmobranch testis secretes androgen, and no recent histochemical studies are available, so the function of the interstitial cells still remains to be established.

The testis is enclosed in a thick capsule with which the inter-ampullar connective tissue appears to be continuous.

The reproductive ducts in the male comprise the vasa efferentia and vasa deferentia which connect the testis with the urinogenital papilla. They vary throughout the group mainly in the nature of the specialisation of the distal region of the vas deferens (Borcea, 1906). Matthews (1950) has described these structures in detail for *Cetorhinus maximus* in which the most striking feature of the vas deferens is the enormous ampulla deferentis into which it expands distally. In one shark this structure measured 1·8 m. and was 25 cm. in its greatest diameter. Matthews estimated that the average ampulla deferentis contained five or six gallons of spermatophores. It appears to be concerned with the preparation and storage of spermatophores (Fig. *11*. 4).

Female

The elasmobranch ovary originates as a paired structure, but early in development one member of the pair, usually the left, atrophies and the other enlarges to become the definitive gonad. It is suspended from the dorsal body wall by the mesovarium and, as in the case of the testis, the germinal tissue is associated with a varying amount of epigonal tissue. Matthews (1950) has described the ovary of the basking shark in considerable detail. It is a large structure, some 50 cm. long, of soft pulpy consistency and invested in a fibrous tunic. There is an anterior opening or pocket through which the ovarian tissue communicates with the abdominal cavity. The ovary proper consists of a loose stroma filled with an immense number of small ova and pierced by ramifying tubes which open eventually at the pocket. The larger ova are spherical, reach 4 or 5 mm. in diameter and are semi-translucent and pale yellowish-white in colour. It is not known with certainty whether *Cetorhinus* is viviparous, though this is believed to be the case, and since nothing is known of its life history, it is impossible to assess the degree of maturity of these larger eggs. In the oviparous dogfish *Scyliorhinus caniculus*, the ovary retains traces of a sac-like structure, though the large yolk-laden eggs are ovulated directly into the body cavity. The mature ovary also contains large numbers of small whitish translucent eggs and a variable number of eggs in different stages of vitellogenesis. Corpora lutea and corpora atretica are also usually found; these are discussed below.

The ovary of skates and rays is very similar to that of sharks, though it is a more flattened structure; it is also relatively smaller and contains fewer large eggs than does the ovary of oviparous sharks.

The structure of the ovarian follicle in the skate *Rhinobatus granulatus* has been described by Samuel (1943). An inner epithelium, the homologue of the mammalian granulosa, surrounds the egg and is itself enclosed in a theca consisting of two distinct layers. The granulosa appears to play a part in the deposition of yolk in the developing egg, in its removal during atresia and in the formation of the post-ovulation corpus luteum.

Structures associated with sex in the female elasmobranch are few and simple (Borcea, 1906). The paired oviducts are modified Müllerian ducts and, as Thiebold (1952a, 1953a) has shown, they are derived by longitudinal division of the mesonephric ducts. The oviducts share an anterior median osteum abdominale and a localised anterior segment of each duct is differentiated into a large nidamental gland (Prasad, 1948), which secretes albumen, mucus and horny egg case material (Fig. *11*. 4).

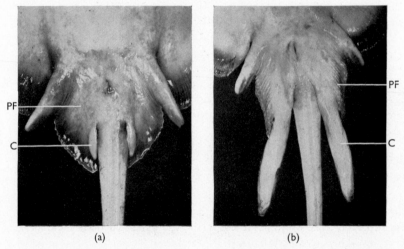

(a)   (b)

Fig. *11*. 5—*Raia clavata:* Claspers. (a) Sexually immature male, disc width 32 cm. (b) Sexually mature male, disc width 57 cm. C, Clasper; PF, pelvic fin. (Photograph by Dr. D. B. Carlisle.)

Secondary Sexual Characters

Male

External secondary sexual characters take the form of copulatory structures which consist of articulated cartilaginous rods. These are the claspers and they are associated in the performance of their function with muscular sacs or siphons. These structures have been described in great detail by several previous authors (Jungersen, 1899; Leigh-Sharpe, 1920, 1921, 1922; Matthews, 1950). In the selachoid elasmobranchs they are rod-like appendages which do not project far beyond the posterior margin of the pelvic fins even at maturity, but in the mature batoid they may be grossly swollen and elongated structures (Fig. *11*. 5). Clasper growth and differentiation are closely correlated with the onset of sexual maturity; the evidence that these processes are controlled by sex steroids is considered below.

Female

There are no obvious external secondary sexual characters in the female, though the cloacal region differentiates at puberty and the hymen, which closes each oviduct in the immature fish, breaks down.

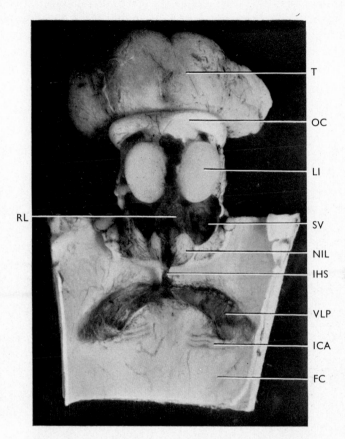

Fig. *11. 6*—*Raia clavata:* Pituitary region of adult male. Brain deflected upward and backward to show ventral lobe of pituitary attached to floor of cranium (× 3). T, telencephalon; OC, optic chiasma; LI, lobi inferiores; SV, saccus vasculosus; NIL, neuro-intermediate lobe pituitary; IHS, inter-hypophyseal stalk; VL, ventral lobe pituitary; ICA, internal carotid artery; FC, floor of cranium; RL, rostral lobe pituitary. (From Goddard and Dodd, in the press.)

The Pituitary Gland

The pituitary gland of elasmobranchs (Figs. *11.* 6 and *11.* 7) consists of three distinct and well-defined lobes. The neuro-intermediate lobe is the posterodorsal moiety and consists of interdigitated neural and intermediate lobe tissue which forms a bulbous and somewhat bilobed structure. It has been variously called the " posterior part " (Herring, 1911), the " distal epithelial portion " (Tilney, 1911), and the " superior lobe " (Baumgartner, 1915).

Intimately associated with the median ventral region of the neuro-intermediate lobe, and lying between it and the optic chiasma, is the delicate tongue-like rostral lobe. This shows two more or less well marked regions in most species. It has been called the " juxta-neural portion " (Tilney, 1911), the " superior sac " (Charipper, 1937), and the " pars anterior " or " anterior lobe " (most workers). The term " rostral lobe " was proposed by Sterzi (1909). The third region of the elasmobranch pituitary is a unique feature. It lies ventral to the other two and is either firmly attached to the endocranium or embedded in the cartilaginous floor of the cranium. It is connected by an " interhypophyseal stalk " to the caudal

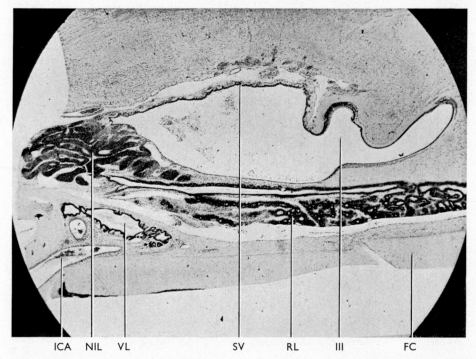

ICA   NIL   VL   SV   RL   III   FC

Fig. *11. 7*—*Scyliorhinus caniculus:* Parasagittal section through pituitary gland (× 25). (Right is anterior). ICA, internal carotid artery; NIL, neuro-intermediate lobe pituitary; VL, ventral lobe pituitary; SV, saccus vasculosus; RL, rostral lobe pituitary; III, third ventricle; FC, floor of cranium. (From Goddard and Dodd, in the press.)

end of the rostral lobe (Baumgartner, 1915; Norris, 1941), with which it shares a common lumen. It has been referred to as the " inferior lobes " (Baumgartner, 1915), the " pars ventralis " (Howes, 1936; Hogben, 1936), and the " inferior sac " (Charipper, 1937).

The saccus vasculosus, a thin-walled bilobed structure which lies lateral to the neuro-intermediate lobe, has often been considered to be part of the pituitary, but there is no evidence of any kind that it has an endocrine function.

The morphology of the elasmobranch pituitary was extensively studied by Norris (1941). He examined the pituitary glands of fifty-one genera and distinguished two main types, a selachoid gland and a batoid gland, mainly differentiated by the form of the ventral lobe. In the selachoid type (Fig. *11.* 8) the ventral lobe is deeply embedded in the cartilage of the endocranium and its connection with the rostral lobe is a tenuous cord of cells, whereas in the batoid type, the ventral lobe is merely attached to the endocranium and the lumina of the rostral and ventral lobes are continuous. Norris says of the ventral lobe: " It is frequently functionless and in some instances reduced to little more than a thin membranous sac. But in other forms its size, vesicular histological structure and abundant blood supply indicate an important function." Recent work of Goddard and Dodd (in the press) throws doubt on the statement that the ventral lobe is frequently functionless and suggests that this idea may have arisen through the examination of glands from sexually immature fish. These workers have noted that the size of the ventral lobe of the dogfish pituitary increases considerably at sexual maturity and that this size increase is relatively greater than that shown by the rest of the pituitary. In view of this, and because of the striking effects of

Fig. *11*. 8—*Scyliorhinus caniculus:* Parasagittal section through ventral lobe of pituitary (× 125). (From Goddard and Dodd, in the press.)

ablation of the ventral lobe on the gonads, Goddard and Dodd are led to the view that this lobe is probably the seat of gonadotrophin production.

The histological structure of the dogfish pituitary is illustrated in Fig. *11*. 7. Few histological studies have been made on the elasmobranch pituitary gland and relatively little is known of its fine structure. Consequently it is difficult to establish the homologies of the various regions with any degree of confidence. Scharrer (1952) studied the neural component of the pituitary and its relationship with the hypothalamus. Working with *Scyllium (Scyliorhinus) stellare*, he found that the fibres entering the pars neuralis originate in the nucleus praeopticus of the hypothalamus. The axons of the cells comprising this nucleus enter the neuro-intermediate lobe of the pituitary. They do not form a discrete pars nervosa as in other vertebrate groups, but become distributed among the cells of the pars intermedia, and it is these nerve-endings which constitute the pars nervosa. Van de Kamer and Verhagen (1954) studied the cytology of the neuro-hypophysis, the saccus vasculosus and recessus anterior in *Scyliorhinus caniculus*. They state that the neuro-hypophysis is built mainly of nerve fibres forming a narrow layer within the neuro-intermediate lobe. The fibres penetrate between the cells of the intermediate tissue in the form of strands.

The histology of the adenohypophysis is much less well known and it has not yet been investigated by the histochemical reactions which are said to identify certain of the cell types usually present in the adenohypophysis, notably the gonadotrophs and thyrotrophs.

De Beer (1926) described the histology of the elasmobranch pituitary and stated that the cells which surrounded the blood vessels were eosinophilic, whereas the others were basophilic. In the blood vessels he found a substance which he identified as the product of eosinophils. De Beer took the view that both eosinophils and basophils belong to the same cell type, the difference in staining reaction indicating merely different stages in a functional cycle. He made no suggestions as to the nature of the hormones produced by the cells at different stages of the cycle. Comes (1935) investigated the female *Torpedo* and stated that the acini of the rostral lobe contained both chromophobe and eosinophil cells. Comes held that the colloid found in the lumina of the tubules is secreted by the chromophobes which border them. He noted that the amount of colloid increases at gestation, and concluded that the chromophobes are concerned in the production of gonadotrophin. Ranzi (1936a, b) studied histological changes during gestation in the pituitaries of female *Torpedo* and *Trygon*, both of which are ovoviviparous, and of *Mustelus*, which is viviparous. He found that as gestation proceeds, the rostral and neuro-intermediate lobes show a general hyperaemia; he did not mention the ventral lobe. There is an increase in the amount of colloid in the acini of the rostral lobe whilst the peripheral cells show decreased eosinophilia. Howes (1936) described the morphology and histology of the pituitary in three species of *Raia*. He divided the rostral lobe into three regions on the basis of staining reactions: an anterior, strongly basophil region; a middle, faintly basophil region; and a posterior, mainly acidophil region. He suggests that these regions are the homologues of the pars tuberalis and the basophil and acidophil areas respectively of the mammalian pars anterior. Howes also suggests that the ventral lobe may be the homologue of part of the mammalian pars tuberalis. However, these homologies are based only on tinctorial reactions and must be treated with reserve.

Butcher (1936) separated the rostral lobe of the dogfish pituitary into anterior and posterior regions, which he called respectively pars distalis and pars medialis. Lewis and Butcher (1936) working with *Squalus* and *Raia* claimed that the pituitary could be separated into six lobes, namely, pars distalis and pars medialis (rostral lobe), pars intermedia and pars neuralis (neuro-intermediate lobe), pars ventralis, and saccus vasculosus.

In spite of the considerable amount of research into the morphology and histology of the elasmobranch pituitary, no histochemical studies have been reported and the existing work offers no clue as to the origin of the gonadotrophic hormones if, in fact, these exist in the elasmobranch gland. In particular, statements relating to the ventral lobe have been superficial and often misleading.

The Effects of Hypophysectomy

Hypophysectomy has been carried out on elasmobranchs with varying success, by a number of workers: Lundstrom and Bard (1932), Orias (1932), Hogben

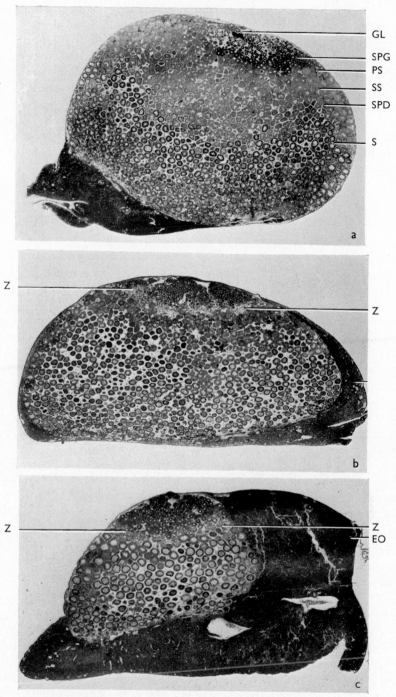

Fig. *11.9*—*Scyliorhinus caniculus* T.S. testes (all × 6.) (a) T.S. normal testis. (b) T.S. testis 6 weeks after removal of ventral lobe pituitary. Note zone of degeneration lying between spermatogonial zone and zone of primary spermatocytes. (c) T.S. testis 22 months after removal of ventral lobe pituitary. Note zone of degeneration and absence of spermatocytes and spermatids. All large ampullae contain only spermatozoa. EO, epigonal organ; GL, tubulogenic zone; SPG, zone of spermatogonia; PS, zone of primary spermatocytes; SS, zone of secondary spermatocytes; SP, zone of spermatozoa; SPD, zone of spermatids; Z, degenerate zone. (From Goddard and Dodd, in the press.)

(1936), Waring (1936, 1938), Abramowitz, Hisaw, Boettiger and Papandrea (1940), Hisaw and Abramowitz (1938), Vivien (1940, 1941), Hisaw and Albert (1947), Goddard and Dodd (in the press). However, few of these workers have investigated the influence of hypophysectomy on the reproductive organs and reproduction. The operation is relatively easy and it is possible to remove all three lobes, or any combination of them, though the ventral lobe is difficult to remove since it is relatively inaccessible and embedded either in tough connective tissue or cartilage. Post-operative survival has been poor, except in the cases reported by Vivien (1940, 1941) and Goddard and Dodd (in the press), who resorted to force-feeding. The latter authors report survival up to 20 months after the operation.

Males

Vivien (1940, 1941) demonstrated that total hypophysectomy resulted in a decrease in weight of the testes in *Scyliorhinus caniculus*. The ratio of weight of gonad to weight of body in male fish 300 days after operation was 0·005, whereas in controls it was 0.042. No appreciable fall in testicular weight was recorded until some 25 weeks after the operation. Unfortunately, Vivien's work was never completed and all his material was destroyed before it could be examined histologically.

Goddard and Dodd (in the press) have shown that the testes of mature male dogfish are apparently under the control of the ventral lobe of the pituitary. These workers removed the ventral lobe and left the remainder of the pituitary intact; they obtained breakdown of a highly localised region of the testis, the effect being well marked by 6 weeks after the operation (Fig. *11*. 9). The affected region of the testis was located between spermatogonia and primary spermatocytes and the degenerative changes consisted of cytolysis of the germ cells and abnormalities in nuclear division (Fig. *11*. 10). These effects were never obtained when the rostral and neuro-intermediate lobes of the pituitary were removed. This precise localisation of the effect of ventral-lobectomy is an interesting phenomenon and the zone of breakdown appears to correspond closely with that found by most workers in other vertebrates after hypophysectomy. " Replacement therapy " has not yet been carried out, nor have elasmobranch gonadotrophins been identified and measured by biological assay.

Females

The ventral lobe of the pituitary plays a similarly important role in the maintenance of the dogfish ovary. Ventral lobectomy results in atrophy of all eggs in which vitellogenesis has started, the eggs being converted into corpora atretica (Fig. *11*.11). Effects are first noticed about 6 weeks after hypophysectomy; follicles containing large eggs become hyperaemic and change colour to orange-yellow. They also lose their spherical shape and become flaccid. The process of atresia continues during the succeeding weeks and considerable folding of the egg surface and removal of broken down contents produces marked shrinkage. One specimen of *S. caniculus*, 11 months after removal of the ventral lobe, had an ovary containing twelve small but easily recognisable corpora atretica and many small white eggs none of which had a diameter greater than 2 mm. (Fig. *11*.11).

Hisaw and Albert (quoted by Dodd, 1955) have shown that removal of the pituitary gland during ovulation in the smooth dogfish (*Mustelus canis*) stops the process, but it can be re-initiated by implantation of homoplastic pituitary material. No attempt was made to localise the region of the pituitary responsible for controlling ovulation. However, Dodd and Goddard (unpublished) have shown that ovulation in *Scyliorhinus caniculus* is controlled by the ventral lobe of the pituitary. They have noted that ablation of the ventral lobe immediately stops ovulation whereas females from which the rostral lobe had been removed were still ovulating as long as nine months after the operation.

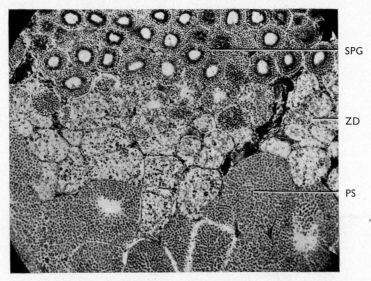

SPG

ZD

PS

Fig. *11. 10*—*Scyliorhinus caniculus:* Effect of ventral lobectomy. T.S. part of testis to show zone of degeneration lying between zone of spermatogonial ampullae and zone of ampullae containing primary spermatocytes (× 60). SPG, testicular ampullae containing spermatogonia; ZD, degenerate zone; PS, testicular ampullae containing primary spermatocytes. (From Goddard and Dodd, in the press.)

Injection of Mammalian Gonadotrophic Hormones

Elasmobranchs might be expected to yield information of considerable interest on the question of hormone specificity, but there are few data available as yet on this aspect of the problem. Carlisle (1954), using the male dogfish, has investigated the effects of certain mammalian hormones on the spermiation reaction. Freshly caught mature dogfish can be made to yield spermatozoa at the urinogenital papilla by lightly stimulating the belly region, whereas this reaction can no longer be elicited from males which have been starved for some time. However, Carlisle found that the spermiation reaction could be re-initiated in such fish by certain mammalian hormones. Chorionic gonadotrophin induced spermiation at a dose level of 1–2 mg. per fish, but was inactive at 0·5 mg.; luteotrophic hormone, extracted from human post-partum urine, was effective at 2 mg. per fish, and anterior lobe pituitary gonadotrophin (Praephyson) stimulated spermiation when 105 i.u. were injected into each fish, but was ineffective at a dose level of 35 i.u. Dodd (1955) has reported that serum gonadotrophin (Gestyl, Organon) caused a small, though significant increase in the weight of ovary and oviducts of immature specimens of *Raia radiata*. These results are of interest, but their

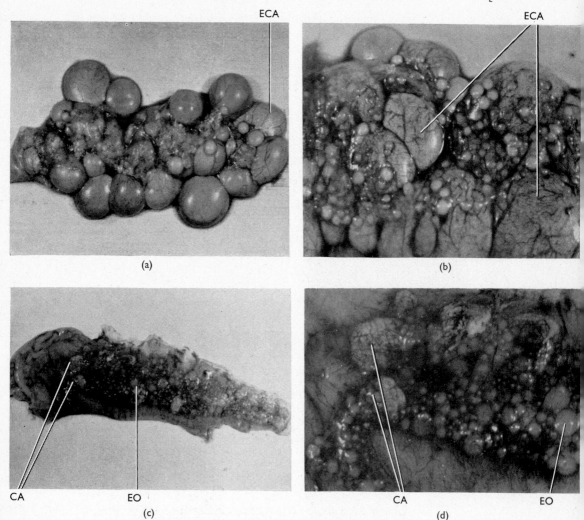

Fig. *11. 11*—*Scyliorhinus caniculus:* Ovaries in various stages of atresia following removal of ventral lobe pituitary.   Note corpora atretica, and small oöcytes which are apparently normal. (a) Ovary in early atresia, 3 weeks after ventral lobe removal.   Some large oöcytes (far right and top left) already flaccid and hyperaemic (× 1).   (b) Part of ovary 8 weeks after ventral lobe removal.   Large oöcytes atretic; note folding of surface and hyperaemia.   Several normal looking early oöcytes also visible (× 5).   (c) Ovary in late atresia, 11 months after ventral lobe removal.   Several corpora atretica visible, also large numbers of normal-looking early oöcytes (× 1).   (d) Enlarged view of part of (c) (× 5).   ECA, early corpora atretica; CA, corpora atretica; EO, early oöcytes.   (Dodd and Goddard, unpublished.

significance is difficult to assess since nothing is known of the potency of elasmo-branch gonadotrophins under similar experimental conditions.

Gonadal Hormones

Little work appears to have been carried out on the nature and occurrence of sex steroids in the elasmobranch ovary or testis, and neither castration nor ovari-ectomy has been reported in any elasmobranch fish.   However, recent work of Wotiz, Boticelli, Hisaw and Ringler (1957) has demonstrated the existence of 17βoestradiol in the ovaries of the dogfish *Squalus suckleyi*. This is a most interesting and significant finding and it is virtually the only example of the chemical identification of a sex hormone in the cold-blooded vertebrates.

Injection and implantation of androgens

Hisaw and Abramowitz (1938) investigated the effect of testosterone on growth of the claspers in *Mustelus canis*: they obtained a definite though small growth increment from the implantation of pellets of this androgen. Goddard and Dodd (in Dodd, 1955) have shown that intramuscular injections of testosterone propionate in ethyl oleate produce a slight stimulation of the claspers of immature specimens of *R. radiata*, though very large amounts were injected, and the average growth increment was less than 1 cm. The results of these experiments, considered in conjunction with the striking enlargement which occurs in the claspers of skates and rays at sexual maturity, suggests strongly that these structures are, in fact, under steroid control.

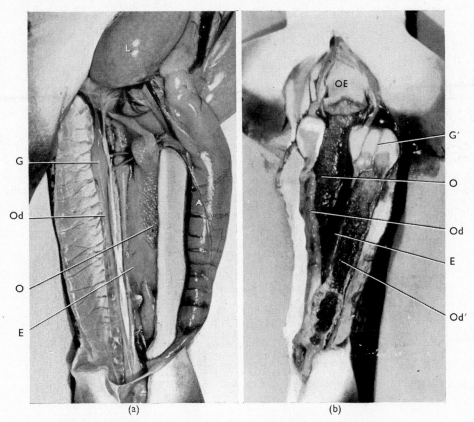

Fig. *11*. *12—Scyliorhinus caniculus:* Effects of implanting oestradiol. (a) Immature female, control. Note immature ovary, large epigonal organ and immature oviducts. (b) Immature female, 159 days after implantation of a pellet of oestradiol weighing 25 mg. Note immature ovary, large epigonal organ, well-developed oviducts distended with horny "tendril" material. (Left oviduct opened, alimentary canal removed.) (Both × ½.) A, alimentary canal; E, epigonal organ; G, shell gland; G′, shell gland opened; L, liver; O, ovary; Od, oviduct; Od′, horny secretion; OE, oesophagus. (From Dodd and Goddard, in the press.)

Injection and implantation of oestrogens

Hisaw and Abramowitz (1938) have reported that implantation of oestrogen pellets had a stimulating effect on the reproductive tract of the female smooth dogfish (*M. canis*).   Dodd and Goddard (in the press) have obtained similar results for the spotted dogfish (*S. caniculus*).   Pellets of oestradiol weighing 25 mg. were implanted intramuscularly and it was found 6 months later that the oviducts of certain fish with immature ovaries were greatly stimulated, and full of the horny threadlike secretion by means of which the egg-cases of these fish are attached to various objects in the sea (Fig. *11.12*).   Absorption from the oestradiol pellets was satisfactorily low; in the most-stimulated fish, less than 3 mg. had been absorbed in nearly 7 months.   A few very immature females were implanted and a few animals which were mature and laying eggs: the steroid implants had no observable action in either of these groups.   It seems likely that the peritoneal ciliation of the mature female, and the hymen-like membranes which seal the oviducts at the cloacal end in immature specimens, are also under steroid control, but there are no experimental data to support these claims.

Effects of Steroids on Primary Sex Differentiation

Chieffi (1950, 1951, 1952a) has shown that the process of sex-differentiation in *Torpedo ocellata* and *Scyliorhinus caniculus* is closely similar to this process in Amphibia and Amniota; it therefore differs markedly from what is found in cyclostomes and teleosts.   The gonadal rudiment is a double structure both in origin and in morphology, consisting of cortex and medulla.   As in the higher groups, the cortex develops from peritoneum whilst the medulla originates from cells of the interrenal blastema (Chieffi, 1951, 1952a).   Further development in the female sense is characterised by the persistence of gonia in the cortex of the gonad and the regression of the medulla.   In genetic males, primitive germ-cells migrate from cortex into medulla; the cortex ultimately disappears and the medulla becomes organised into a testis.

Vivien (1954) has shown that developmental stages of the dogfish *Scyliorhinus caniculus* are excellent experimental material for a variety of investigations; injections of hormones into the yolk-sac of the embryos can be made easily at any stage in the long incubation period and the horny case is transparent enough to enable any gross changes to be seen through it.   By this method of intra-vitelline injection, the effects of certain sex hormones and other steroids on the gonads and developing secondary sex structures has been studied.   A good deal is also known of the origin and development of these structures before they come under the influence of hormones.   Chieffi (1951, 1952a, 1954a, b, 1955) has dealt with gonadal development and shown by histochemical methods that the medulla of the gonad originates from cells of the interrenal blastema, and Thiebold (1952a, 1954) has demonstrated that the primary ureter in embryos of both sexes divides longitudinally, giving rise to the Müllerian and Wolffian ducts.

So far as concerns the action of sex steroids on primary sex-differentiation in elasmobranchs, Chieffi (1952b, 1953a, b, 1954a) and Thiebold (1952b) have demonstrated that testosterone propionate can inhibit the gonadal medulla of genetic males.   Chieffi (1954a) finds, however, that gonad development is unaffected by a single injection of 10 µg. testosterone propionate, or by high doses of hormone when the injections are made before the stage of normal sexual differentiation (embryo length 29–30 mm.).   Thiebold (1954) has also reported that testosterone propionate stimulates the Wolffian ducts and mesonephroi, and produces hypertrophy of the anterior segment of the Müllerian duct, whereas in untreated males this shows early regression.

The action of oestradiol benzoate has also been studied.   Thiebold (1953b, 1954) injected 50 μg oestradiol benzoate into the vitelline sac of dogfish embryos measuring 9–15 mm.   The gonads of genetic males were feminised; they were smaller than control gonads and had numerous gonia in the prominent cortex. The embryonic Müllerian ducts, which atrophy at an early stage in genetic male embryos, persisted.   Genetic females showed a precocious differentiation of the shell gland region, and an acceleration in the regression of the left gonad as a result of oestradiol treatment.   Stimulation of the Wolffian ducts by oestradiol was an interesting feature of these experiments, though not, perhaps, a surprising one since Wolffian and Müllerian ducts originate in the embryo by longitudinal splitting of a common duct.

Chieffi (1954a) has investigated the effects of progesterone and desoxycorticosterone acetate on sex structures in the embryo of *S. caniculus* and found a feminising action on gonads and genital ducts.   A similar investigation by Thiebold (1955) showed that anhydroxyprogesterone (ethinyl testosterone) feminises the gonads of genetic males, as does oestradiol, yet its actions on the other sexual structures are similar to those produced by androgens.   Thiebold points out that Gallien (1950) recorded an identical reaction pattern when the anuran *Discoglossus pictus* was treated with anhydroxyprogesterone.

Viviparity in Elasmobranchs

It is generally accepted that viviparity has arisen independently and many times in various animal groups and nowhere is this better illustrated than in the elasmobranchs.   It occurs sporadically throughout the Order and may exist in several different grades, depending on the degree to which the embryo is indebted to the mother for nutriment.   In the genus *Mustelus*, *M. vulgaris* is ovoviviparous whilst *M. laevis* and *M. canis* are both truly viviparous.   The eggs of the ovoviviparous species are usually some eight to ten times heavier than those of viviparous species, and the relationship between dry weight and ash content of newly ovulated eggs and developing embryos reflects the higher proportion of nutriment contributed by the mother in viviparous species.   Detailed consideration has already been given to histological aspects of viviparity in elasmobranchs (Volume 2, Chapter 15).

Gestation is a lengthy process in those elasmobranchs for which the information exists; in *M. canis* it appears to occupy about 11 months, and in *Squalus acanthias* it may last for nearly 2 years.   Hisaw and Albert (quoted by Dodd, 1955) have shown that the pituitary appears to play no part in maintaining pregnancy in *M. canis* during the first 3 months, though they have no information concerning the later stages and parturition.

Corpora lutea have been described in several elasmobranchs (Samuel, 1943, in *Rhinobatus granulatus*; Hisaw and Albert, 1947, in *Squalus acanthias*; Matthews, 1950, in *Cetorhinus maximus*: see also Volume 1, Part 1, Chapter 5).   In *Rhinobatus*, the luteal cells are formed by hypertrophy of the cells of the granulosa and theca interna whilst the theca externa gives rise to the sheath and supporting frame-work.   In *Squalus*, on the other hand, the luteal tissue originates entirely from granulosa, the connective-tissue framework being derived from theca interna. Matthews (1950) has described the occurrence of large numbers of corpora lutea in the basking shark.   He believes that most, if not all, of these bodies arise by atresia of large eggs.   However, two types of corpora lutea are encountered in this species; these differ in histological appearance and in size.   The small number of large ones reach a diameter of 4 or 5 cm. and consist of a mass of large cells with small rounded nuclei and lipid-containing cytoplasm.   These bodies shrink with age and the central cavity disappears; it seems possible that they are true post-ovulatory corpora lutea.   The large numbers of small corpora lutea which are a striking feature of the *Cetorhinus* ovary are believed to result from atresia of follicles which have reached a diameter of about 1·0 mm.   Their central cavity is small and is bounded by a clear structureless region which probably represents the vitelline membrane.   This is surrounded by two concentric zones of cells, an inner zone in which the cells are rich in lipid and a peripheral zone which consists of clumps of cells and which increases in size with age.   These bodies reach a more or less static condition at a diameter of 500–600 μ and appear to per-sist unchanged for a long time.

Hisaw and Albert (quoted by Dodd, 1955) have shown by hypophysectomy that neither formation nor maintenance of corpora lutea appears to be under pituitary control in *M. canis*.   This is a very significant finding from the point of view of comparative endocrinology: it appears to indicate that at this evolutionary level, the influence of pituitary gonadotrophins on the follicle ends with ovulation. Extension of pituitary influence to include control of the corpus luteum appears to have arisen later.

Corpora atretica occur in the elasmobranch gonad and it is difficult to dif-ferentiate between these structures and corpora lutea.   It has been shown that corpora atretica can arise as a result of hypophysectomy and it may be that their presence in the ovary of an intact fish indicates that the circulating gonadotrophin has fallen below the level required for maintaining the large eggs.   Corpora atretica have been called pre-ovulation corpora lutea (Bretschneider and Duyvené de Wit, 1947), but this seems unwise in view of the little which is known about them.   Indeed, until some function has been ascribed to the corpora lutea them-selves, and until it is known whether they secrete progesterone, the physiological status of both corpora atretica and corpora lutea in elasmobranchs must remain in doubt.

IV. Actinopterygii

The Actinopterygii is by far the largest class of vertebrates: it comprises the bony fish, and much the most numerically important section of the class is the order Teleostei.   The account which follows deals almost exclusively with teleosts, though the commercial importance of the sturgeons (Chondrostei) has encouraged various workers to pay considerable attention to their reproductive processes, and a good deal is known of the hormonal control of reproduction in these fish.

There are some 20,000 species of teleosts and, as Hoar (1957) has pointed out, they "exhibit almost every type of sexual reproductive mechanism found in the

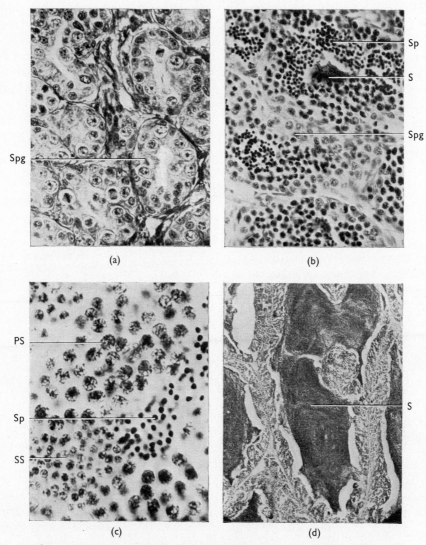

Fig. *11. 13—Salmo gairdnerii* (Rainbow trout). (a) T.S. testis of fish aged 11
months, showing cysts of spermatogonia: several are dividing by mitosis
(× 500). (b) T.S. testis of fish aged 16 months, showing cysts of germ-
cells in active spermatogenesis. Single clump of spermatozoa. Note that
each cyst contains cells at one stage of development (× 500). (c) T.S.
testis of fish aged 18 months, showing primary and secondary spermatocytes
and spermatids, no spermatogonia (× 1050). (d) T.S. mature testis.
Lobules greatly enlarged and filled with masses of fully developed spermatozoa. Cysts in lobule walls contain primary and secondary spermatocytes
and spermatids. PS, primary spermatocytes; S, spermatozoa; Sp, spermatids; Spg, spermatogonia; SS, secondary spermatocytes. (From Robertson, 1958.)

Animal Kingdom, and several specialisations have appeared which are without
parallel elsewhere among vertebrate animals." In spite of this, and although a
great deal of work has been reported in the literature, knowledge of the physiological control of these diverse adaptations is limited to a handful of species, most

of which come from the three families Cyprinidae, Poeciliidae and Cyprinodontidae. Similarly, little is known concerning the effects of hormones on the
embryonic gonads and sex structures, though this has a special interest in view of
the origin of the teleost gonad from a single anlage (Dodd, 1960).

Several recent reviews exist, and these cover most aspects of reproductive
endocrinology in fish (Hoar, 1951, 1955, 1957; Olivereau, 1954; Dodd, 1955).
There is also the excellent monograph of Pickford and Atz on the physiology of
the pituitary gland of fishes, in which all aspects of the subject are discussed
exhaustively, and of which free use has been made in compiling the present
account.

The Gonads and Reproductive Ducts

Male

The structure of the testis has been described in a number of teleosts (Turner,
1919; James, 1946; Weisel, 1949; Cooper, 1952; Hoar, 1957; Marshall and
Lofts, 1957; Robertson, 1958), and it has been shown to vary considerably in
complexity and in the arrangement of its constituent parts. The maturing testis
consists usually of lobules bound together by an investing *tunica albuginea*. Each
lobule is an elongated blind-ended structure which may be considerably branched.
There is no permanent germinal epithelium, primary germ-cells migrate into the
lobule walls after spawning and a new wave of spermatogenesis is initiated. The
primary germ-cells occupy cysts in which all the cells divide at one time and ultimately become spermatozoa (Fig. *11*.13). When this stage is reached, the cysts
rupture and their contents are shed into the lobule lumen, which is in communication with the deferent duct of the testis.

The early literature on the occurrence of interstitial tissue in the teleost testis
is contradictory (*see* reviews by Craig-Bennett, 1931; Hoar, 1955). Craig-Bennett
(1931) found easily recognisable Leydig cells in the stickleback, *Gasterosteus
aculeatus* and these showed cyclical behaviour which could be correlated closely
with the sexual activity of the fish. Potter and Hoar (1954) likewise have reported the
presence of typical interstitial cells in the testes of Pacific salmon (*Oncorhynchus
keta*); these seem to resemble closely the Leydig cells of the mammal testis. However, other workers were unable to locate interstitial tissue in fish with well-marked
secondary sexual characters and it was doubted whether it was, in fact, present.
Recent work of Marshall and Lofts (1956, 1957) may well have resolved the
controversy. These workers have shown that some teleosts (*Esox lucius, Salvelinus
Willughbii, Labeo* sp.) lack a true interstitium. However, they have described
certain cells lying at the periphery of the testis lobules and have suggested that

---

Fig. *11*. 14—*Esox lucius:* Cyclical changes in the testis. (1) Testis in October showing lobules
    becoming swollen with cysts of spermatocytes, spermatids and free spermatozoa. (2) Testis
    in March. The lobules are full of spermatozoa and the boundary cells of the lobule wall are
    charged with cholesterol-positive lipids. (3) Part of the lobule wall showing lobule boundary
    cells from which lipids have been dissolved, leaving a series of small vacuoles in the cyto-
    plasm. (4) Testis in March (immediately prior to spawning) showing lobules at maximum
    size. Lobule boundary cells are heavily lipoidal, but lobules are lipid-free. (5) Testis in
    May (immediately after spawning) showing great decrease in size and lobule steatogenesis.
    (6) Primary germ cells migrating into the lobule lumen of a " spent " testis in May. S, sperma-
    tozoa; Sp, spermatids; SS, secondary spermatocytes; PS, primary spermatocytes; PGS,
    primary germ cells; LL, lobule lumen. (From Lofts and Marshall, 1957.)

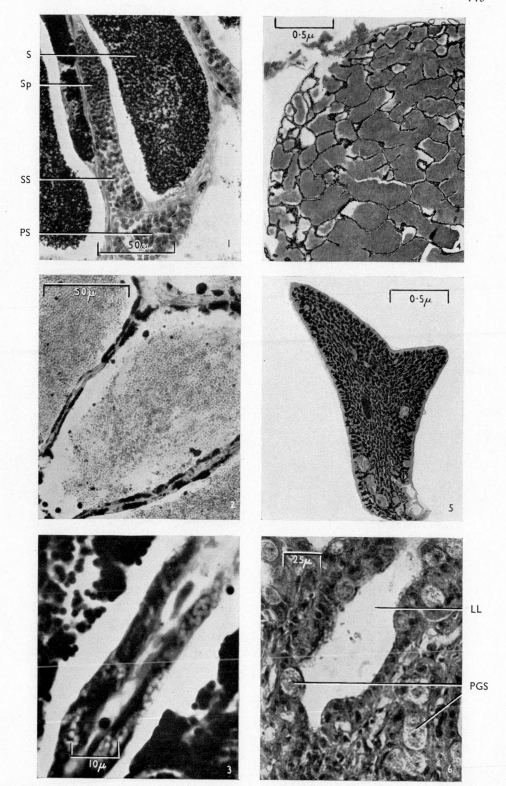

these are the Leydig-cell homologues. These " lobule boundary cells " (Fig. *11.14*) originate as fibroblasts which, as the lobules grow, accumulate cholesterol-positive lipids, believed to be the precursors of the male hormone. Other teleosts (*Gasterosteus aculeatus; Tilapia* spp.; *Clupea sprattus; Oncorhynchus keta*) have Leydig cells which conform in appearance and position much more closely to the more usual vertebrate arrangement, whilst, according to Robertson (1958), both lobule boundary cells and interstitial cells are present in the testis of the rainbow trout *Salmo gairdnerii* (Fig. *11.15*).

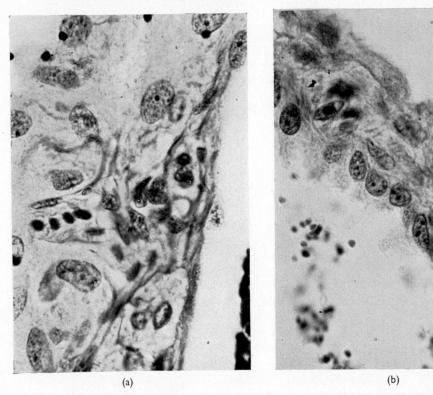

(a)   (b)

Fig. *11.15—Salmo gairdnerii:* (a) T.S. testis of spent fish showing Leydig-like cells in the interstitial tissues (× 1050). (b) T.S. lobule wall of spawning fish showing lobule boundary cells (× 1050). (From Robertson, 1958.)

Sertoli cells have been described in the mature testis of the stickleback (Craig-Bennett, 1931; Follenius, 1953); their function is unknown.

The vas deferens in teleost fish, unlike this structure in most lower vertebrates, has no connection with the kidney at maturity, though most workers believe it to be derived from the posterior part of the mesonephros and its duct. The testicular lobules discharge into a common cavity which connects directly with a deferent duct at the posterior pole of the testis. The duct runs parallel with the ureter and opens to the exterior between it and the anus. In eels, as in cyclostomes, the testis discharges into the body cavity, and sperms reach the exterior through a short duct.

In the Chondrostei (*Acipenser*), there is a well-developed network of anterior mesonephric tubules which constitute the vasa efferentia and these connect with the mesonephric duct in typical vertebrate fashion.   In the Dipnoi, the contribution of the kidney to the genital system is more limited, the vasa efferentia being formed from posterior kidney tubules only.   The sperms traverse this region of the kidney and reach the exterior via the mesonephric duct.

In some teleosts, notably blennies and gobies, the posterior region of each sperm duct is modified to form a " seminal vesicle." These structures are so named merely by analogy with the mammalian seminal vesicle; they are different both in origin and function.   They do not store sperm, though, like their mammalian counterparts, they secrete a viscous liquid which is ejected at the time of sperm discharge.   Several suggestions have been made as to their function, most of which involve some kind of protective and nutritive role relative to the sperms (Weisel, 1949; Rasquin and Hafter, 1951).   Coujard (1941) believes that the adhesive secretion of the seminal vesicles of the male blenny may be of importance in the nest-making and brooding operations which it performs.   A somewhat similar function is known to be discharged by the sticky secretion which is produced by certain modified tubules of the posterior end of the kidney in the stickleback.

Female

The teleost ovary consists of a mass of follicles embedded in a connective-tissue stroma and limited by a thin tunic.   It may be either compact or hollow; in the latter case, the cavity is a part of the coelom which has become segregated from the remainder during development.   The ovarian follicles are embedded in connective tissue and their arrangement varies considerably; Brock (1878) examined the ovaries of fifty-seven teleost species and subdivided them into eight morphological types.   There is usually a large number of follicles containing small yolkless oöcytes, and a crop of growing eggs undergoing vitellogenesis from which the eggs of the current breeding season are recruited.

Bretschneider and Duyvené de Wit (1947) have described the ovarian follicle of the bitterling, *Rhodeus amarus* which has an internal granulosa and outer theca; these two layers are by no means always easy to identify, and the wall of the follicle seems often to be made up of a single fibrous investment.   However, Brock (1878) concluded that a granulosa is always present, and Hoar (1957) has suggested that an inner granulosa and an outer theca are potentially present whether or not they are clearly marked.

The teleost ovary, in common with that of all cold-blooded vertebrates so far described, contains a number of corpora atretica.   Various authors have ascribed a secretory function to these structures, but there is no unequivocal evidence that they are anything other than unovulated eggs in process of resorption.

The oviducts of teleosts, unlike those of the majority of cold-blooded vertebrates, are not modified Müllerian ducts.   In most cases they appear to be merely posterior continuations of the ovarian tunic and their lumina are continuous with the ovarian cavity when one is present.   In several teleost families, including the Salmonidae, the oviducts have degenerated to a greater or lesser degree; the ova in these cases are shed into the body cavity and reach the exterior through the persistent posterior parts of the oviducts, which are sometimes reduced to mere pores.

In the Dipnoi, Chondrostei and in *Amia* among Holostei, the oviduct is a modified Müllerian duct and the relationships of the various parts of the reproductive system are exactly as in elasmobranchs (Fig. *11*.16).

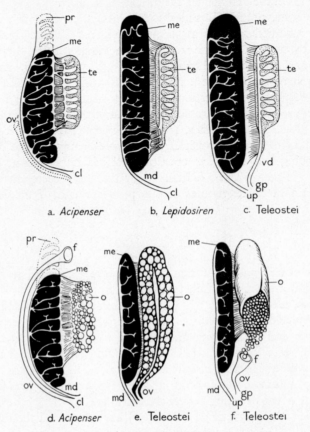

a. *Acipenser* b. *Lepidosiren* c. *Teleostei*

d. *Acipenser* e. *Teleostei* f. *Teleostei*

Fig. *11*. 16—Actinopterygii: Representative types of urinogenital systems. Upper series: males. Lower series: females. cl, cloaca; f, funnel of oviduct; gp, genital papilla and pore; md, mesonephric duct; me, mesonephros; o, ovary; ov, oviduct; ov′, rudimentary Müllerian duct; pr, pronephros; te, testis; up, urinary pore; vd, vas deferens. (Redrawn from Hoar, 1957.)

Secondary Sexual Characters

Some remarkable secondary sexual characters occur in fish, though in the majority of cases the two sexes are identical. Sexual dimorphism in body size is sometimes encountered and in extreme cases the male may be a dwarf, parasitic on the female and having an atrophic digestive tract (*Edriolychus*) (Fig. *11*.17). However, less extreme size dimorphism is more common and in most cases the female is larger than the male; the mature female eel, for instance, is more than twice as long as the male. There are some exceptions to this general rule, however; in the genera *Callionymus*, *Cepola*, *Polyacanthus* and *Amia* (Holostei), the male is larger than the female.

Dimorphic fin differentiation is frequently encountered in teleosts; the characteristic fin shape is altered and several of the rays of selected fins differentiate in various ways and may become greatly elongated. Such modified fins are frequently, though not always, used in copulation. The gonopodium of poeciliid fishes is an example of such a structure. In *Gambusia affinis*, the third, fourth, fifth and sixth rays of the anal fin of males elongate and differentiations such as hooks, spines, serrae and plates develop, the whole structure forming a complicated intromittent organ, or gonopodium. A similar structure develops in sexually mature males of *Xiphophorus* spp. and, in addition, the lower margin of the caudal fin is strikingly modified to form the " sword " (Fig. *11*.18). In *Callionymus*, the two dorsal fins of the male are enlarged, the anterior one being especially tall and sail-like. Frequently the modification affects single fin rays, as in *Tinca tinca* where the second ray of the pelvic fin is thickened, and in *Cobitis taenia* in which the second ray of the pectoral fin is enlarged and expanded into a plate at its base.

Intromittent organs not associated with fins are found in the males of several teleost species; they are usually merely papillar outgrowths of the vas deferens.

The remarkably elongated ovipositor of the mature female bitterling is a secondary sexual character which has received a great deal of attention from endocrinologists. It appears to be unusually labile since it has been stimulated to develop by such a variety of substances.

Modifications of the head of male fish are commonly encountered. Elongation of the lower jaw during the breeding season of the salmon is well known and the teeth of male blennies and gobies become longer and stronger at this time. Excrescences of different kinds are commonly developed; for example, the male minnow and many carps are distinguished by warts on the head during the breeding season, whilst males of the bitterling (*Acheilognathus*) develop pearl organs which are horny growths on head and operculum.

Colour differences between the sexes is not common, but several striking instances do exist. Thus, the stickleback male is distinguished during the breeding season by red colouration of the belly region and blue colouration of the dorsal surface and iris of the eye. *Lebistes* also shows a marked sex dimorphism, the male being much more brightly coloured than the female. Perhaps the most striking sex differences in colouration are shown by two marine teleosts. The male of *Labrus mixtus* is orange with bright blue horizontal stripes, whereas the female is uniformly red with a few postero-dorsal black spots, and the two sexes of *Callionymus lyra* are so different, both in their colouration and in their fins, that they were first described as two different species.

The secondary sexual characters of the bow-fin *Amia calva* (Holostei) have been well described by Zahl and Davis (1932), who also considered the endocrine mechanism by which they are produced (*see below*). The pectoral, pelvic and anal fins of the male change colour to a vivid moss-green during the breeding season and the belly region becomes pale green, whereas, in the female, it is white. Another striking feature of the male in full breeding dress is the ocellus, which lies on the antero-dorsal region of the caudal fin and consists of a black central area surrounded by a brilliant yellow-orange corona.

Secondary sexual characters of a rather different kind are shown by many teleosts; these concern the behaviour pattern characteristic of the breeding season and are manifested in the fighting which usually accompanies courting,

nest-building activities, courting behaviour, and care of the young (Fig. *11.17*).
Usually, though not always, the male takes the active role in these operations.

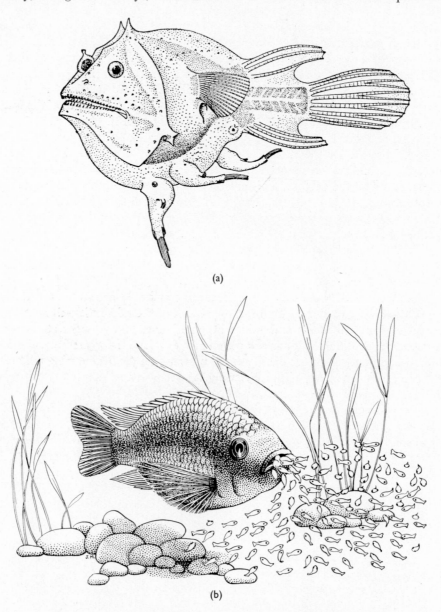

(a)

(b)

Fig. *11*. 17—Teleostei: Sexual dimorphism. (a) Size dimorphism. Female specimen of
Edriolychus schmidti, an angler fish, with three attached dwarf males.   (b) Brooding
behaviour. Female of *Tilapia mossambica* with young. In this mouth-brooding
species, the young take refuge in the buccal cavity of the female parent in times of
danger. (From Parker and Haswell, Vol. 2, 7th ed.)

Hoar (1955) has dealt in detail with reproductive behaviour in fish and discussed
its endocrine control.

There has been a good deal of experimental work on the part played by the

gonads in the initiation and maintenance of these secondary sexual characters; this
work is discussed below in the appropriate section.

(a)

(b)

Fig. *11. 18—Xiphophorus helleri:* Sex dimorphism.   (a) Mature male, note gonopodium (G),
and sword (s) ($\times$ 1½). (b) Mature female ($\times$ 1½). (Photographby Mr. K. M. Ferguson.)

The Pituitary Gland

The pituitary gland of bony fish shows considerable morphological diversity,
though the homologies of the various regions are relatively easy to interpret
within the group.   The " anterior lobe " of the other vertebrate classes is usually
represented by a structure which can be differentiated into three regions or zones
by various staining techniques.   The middle region of the three is usually accepted
as the site of gonadotrophin production, though this view is not universally held.
The function of the anterior region is not well understood, but the posterior region
appears undoubtedly to be the homologue of the pars intermedia of the other
vertebrates.

Most of our knowledge concerning the pituitary of bony fish comes from a study
of teleost glands, though a certain amount is known about the pituitaries of other
actinopterygians.   The following account deals in a general way with pituitary
morphology and histology throughout the group; it is detailed only in its treatment
of the relationship between pituitary histology and reproduction.

Teleostei

The teleost pituitary gland (Fig. *11*.19) is a highly characteristic organ which is relatively uniform in basic structure in those species in which it has been examined.

The neurohypophysis and adenohypophysis are always present and easily recognisable, though the neurohypophysis usually takes the form of anastomising strands rather than a discrete lobe; these strands penetrate deeply into the tissues of the adenohypophysis. The adenohypophysis itself is the largest part of the gland and it is usually possible to identify three more or less distinct regions. Unfortunately there is little agreement between different workers as to the homologies of the various parts and this is reflected in the chaotic condition of the terminology. Pickford and Atz (1957) have reviewed the position and have suggested

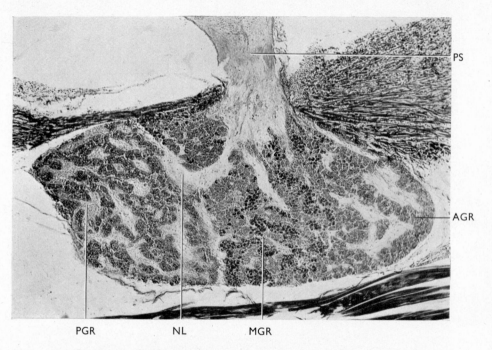

Fig. *11*. 19—*Leuciscus rutilis* (the Roach): Longitudinal section of pituitary gland (× 110). AGR, anterior glandular region; MGR, middle glandular region; PGR, posterior glandular region; NL, branch of neural lobe; PS, pituitary stalk. (From Kerr, 1948.)

the terms pro-, meso- and meta-adenohypophysis for the various regions of the " anterior " lobe. However, such a scheme is premature and may be positively misleading if by extension to other groups its use suggests homologies for which there is no good evidence. The older terminology in which the adenohypophysis is subdivided into anterior glandular region, middle glandular region (transitional zone or *übergangsteil*) and posterior glandular region will be used here.

A typical hypophyseal cavity is never present in the teleost pituitary, though the anterior glandular region communicates with the pharynx by an open hypophyseal duct in the young milk fish, *Chanos chanos* (Tampi, 1951), and in the herring, *Clupea harengus*, up to the time of metamorphosis (Buchmann, 1940). It has been suggested that the follicular cavities so characteristic of the anterior glandular zone in certain fish, notably the herring and salmon, may represent the hypophyseal cavity in the pituitary of the adult teleost.

The homologies of the anterior glandular lobe are not clear, though it has been suggested that it may be the homologue of the pars tuberalis. However, there is no physiological evidence for this suggestion and it seems wise to reserve judgment until such evidence is forthcoming (Olivereau, 1954). Virtually nothing is known of the functions of the anterior glandular region. Bock (1928a) found no changes in it during the annual sexual cycle of *Gasterosteus aculeatus*, though Buchmann (1940) stated that there is great secretory activity in the follicles of the anterior glandular region of the herring at spawning time.

The middle glandular region appears to be the functional homologue of the mammalian pars distalis. Evidence for this is largely based on tinctorial and histochemical investigations, but the amount of such evidence is striking. Most authors are of the opinion that the source of gonadotrophin in the teleost pituitary is one of the so-called basophil (cyanophil) cells of the middle glandular region. The main evidence on which this view is based is the observation that this cell type increases in number and activity during the phase of maturation of the gonads. Such a correlation has now been recorded for several genera of teleost fish: *Clupea harengus* (Buchmann, 1940); *Salmo salar* (Fontaine and Olivereau, 1949; Olivereau, 1954); *Anguilla anguilla* (Bernardi 1948); *Leuciscus rutilus* (Kerr, 1948); *Rhodeus amarus* (Bretschneider and Duyvené de Wit, 1947; Verhoeven and van Oordt, 1955); *Carassius auratus* and *Cyprinus carpio* (Scruggs, 1951); *Astyanax mexicanus* (Rasquin, 1949); *Fundulus heteroclitus* (Matthews, 1936; Sokol, 1953); and *Xiphias gladus* (Lee, 1942).

The difficulties inherent in tinctorial methods for localising cell types are well known and results obtained by such methods are often of doubtful value. To overcome this, recent workers have turned to histochemical reactions which are said to demonstrate in cells the presence of chemical substances which can to some degree be identified with the various hormones.

Gonadotrophins and thyrotrophins are known to be glycoproteins, and the periodic acid Schiff (PAS) reaction (Pearse, 1952, 1953) has been used with success to locate such substances in cells of the pituitary. Another histochemical reaction, the aldehyde-fuchsin (AF) technique of Gomori (Halmi, 1952), has been considered by some workers (Purves and Griesbach, 1951; Barrington and Matty, 1955) to differentiate between thyrotrophs and gonadotrophs, since both are PAS-positive, but only the thyrotrophs are AF-positive. Barrington and Matty (1955) demonstrated that the middle glandular zone of the adenohypophysis of the minnow (*Phoxinus phoxinus*) contains two types of basophil cells, both of which are PAS-positive, whilst only one of the two types is AF-positive. These workers were mainly concerned with localising thyrotrophs, but they provisionally recognised the PAS-positive, AF-negative cells as gonadotrophs, noting that in animals that had been artificially illuminated and in which the reproductive system had in consequence been activated, these cells were enlarged.

Atz (1953), working with *Astyanax*, was able to distinguish two types of basophil and, by experimental treatment and the use of the PAS reaction, to demonstrate that one of these cell types was a gonadotroph. Unlike Barrington and Matty, Atz was unable to differentiate between thyrotrophs and gonadotrophs by using the AF reaction.

Sokol (1955) distinguished marked changes in granulation of the basophil cells of the adenohypophysis of *Lebistes reticulatus* during gestation.   In addition, she demonstrated two populations of basophils in the middle glandular zone by treating one group of fish with thiourea, and castrating another group and subsequently applying a modification of Halmi's AF reaction to the pituitary glands of both groups.   In this way the putative gonadotrophs were located in the middle glandular zone of the adenohypophysis.

These tinctorial and histochemical reactions appear to demonstrate that the gonadotrophs in fish pituitaries are basophil, PAS-positive cells usually located in the middle glandular region.   Physiological evidence in support of the view comes from the work of Kazanskii and Persov (1948), who dissected carp pituitaries into two parts, one part consisting of the posterior glandular region and more distal part of the neurohypophysis, the other consisting mainly of anterior and middle glandular regions and the more proximal part of the neurohypophysis.   These parts were extracted, and injected into female vy'un (*Misgurnus fossilis*).   Only the latter fraction caused stimulation of the ovaries.

The above evidence is supplemented by certain other investigations.   Kerr (1948) has studied changes in the middle glandular region of the roach (*Leuciscus rutilus*), parasitised with the plerocercoid of the tapeworm *Ligula*.   In parasitised fish he found that the basophils of the middle glandular zone were markedly reduced in size and granulation whilst other cell types were not affected.   At the same time the gonads showed a very reduced condition with all the later maturation stages missing.   Stolk (1953) has added a small piece of circumstantial evidence that the middle glandular region of the adenohypophysis is the seat of gonadotrophin production.   He describes a chromophobe adenoma which was localised in this region in *Lebistes reticulatus* and the fish had the appearance of an intersex.   Unfortunately, no details are given as to the structure of the gonads.   Finally, Verhoeven and van Oordt (1955) showed that when the female *Rhodeus* is sexually stimulated by exposure to increased light there is an increase in the number of basophils in the pituitary gland.

Palaeoniscoidei

The pituitary gland of *Polypterus* has been studied by Gérard and Cordier (1937).   There is a persistent hypophyseal duct which remains open even in the adult and which leads from the mouth into the anterior region of the adenohypophysis.   Such a structure is unusual, though not unique; it has led these workers to suggest that the anterior region of the pituitary is an exocrine gland.   There are no details available as to cyclical changes in the gland which might give a clue to the location of the gonadotrophin-secreting cells.

Chondrostei; Holostei

The pituitary glands of *Acipenser*, *Amia* and *Lepisosteus* are similar in all important respects to those of teleosts.   The typical nervous and glandular components of the vertebrate pituitary are present, and the glandular portion is divided into three main regions as in teleosts.   In *Acipenser*, the hypophyseal cavity is retained in the adult, though this is never the case in the teleosts, but in *Amia* and *Lepisosteus* the cavity disappears during development.

The morphology and histology of the pituitary glands of *Amia calva*, *Lepidosteus*

(*Lepisosteus*) *osseus* and *Acipenser pulvescens* have been described by Kerr (1949). Two types of basophil cell are found in the middle glandular region of *Amia*: in the case of *Lepisosteus* only a single type of basophil has been identified and this is confined to the middle glandular region. Basophil cells are found in all three regions of the glandular zone of the *Acipenser* pituitary. Unfortunately no details are available as to the sexual condition of the fish or the time of year at which the pituitaries were fixed. Hence it is not possible to assess the significance of the cell types in relation to reproduction.

However, the pituitary glands of several species of sturgeon have been studied by certain Russian workers in an attempt to establish a relationship between pituitary gland histology and reproduction. Barannikova (1949a, b, 1950) studied *Acipenser stellatus* and *A. guldenstadti*, and Ivanova (1953) studied *A. ruthenus*. Both authors have noted important seasonal changes in the middle glandular region of the adenohypophysis which appear to be correlated with the reproductive cycle. Barannikova also described a ventral basophilic zone which was termed the gonadotrophic zone. It undergoes striking changes at the time of the spawning migration and spawning.

Barannikova (1949b) carried this work further and obtained evidence that the ventral basophilic zone of the sturgeon pituitary does, in fact, contain gonadotrophin. Pituitaries of *Acipenser stellatus* were divided into three parts and injected into female vy'un. The posterior glandular lobe was found to be inactive. The anterior and middle glandular regions were divided into dorsal and ventral parts and it was found on injection that both caused the ovaries of test fish to mature, though the ventral region was slightly more effective than the dorsal region.

Crossopterygii

Dipnoi; Coelacanthini

The pituitary glands of all three living genera of Dipnoi have been studied (*Neoceratodus*, Griffiths, 1938; *Protopterus*, Dawson, 1940; Wingstrand, 1956; *Lepidosiren*, Kerr, 1933). The morphology and histology of the dipnoan pituitary is strongly reminiscent of the Amphibian gland, in fact, Wingstrand (1956) has shown that the pituitary of *Protopterus* is almost identical to that of the urodele *Necturus*. Dawson (1940) was able to differentiate three types of chromophil cells in the pituitary of *Protopterus*, namely cyanophils (basophils), fuchsinophils, and Orange-G cells. However, no studies have been made which attempt to relate the disposition and number of these cells to any stage in the sexual cycle.

Millot and Anthony (1955) have reported briefly on the pituitary gland of *Latimeria* (Crossopterygii, Coelacanthini). This appears to be a remarkable structure consisting of a long cord approximately 10 cm. in length. The glandular region is said to be composed of two parts, the posterior of which lies beneath the telencephalon and corresponds to the classical hypophysis. The anterior part forms a long cylinder and is stated by Millot and Anthony to be without counterpart in other vertebrates, except perhaps in a reduced form in *Polypterus*. Nothing is known of the physiology of the gland and no histochemical studies have yet been made.

It can be seen from the above review that the pituitary has been studied in a considerable variety of bony fish. The gland shows a striking uniformity within the group, but is markedly different from its counterpart in other vertebrates, though the lungfish pituitary bears a strong resemblance to that of the Amphibia.

Less is known about the physiology of the gland, partly because the intimate interdigitation of the constituent parts makes their separate removal impossible. Consequently, the relatively few data which are reported below on the effects of pituitary removal refer in all cases to total hypophysectomy.

Effects of Hypophysectomy

Hypophysectomy has been carried out on some twenty species of teleost fish, but in only seven of these have its effects on reproductive structures been studied (Pickford and Atz, 1957). Among the direct effects of hypophysectomy which have been reported are gross and microscopic changes in the gonads ; these in turn lead to indirect effects on secondary sexual characters and behaviour. Most workers have reported a marked seasonal variability in response to the operation and this is a feature common to animals in which the gonads and secondary sexual characters show limited seasonal activity.

Hypophysectomy in the male

Vivien (1938, 1941) has described the effects of pituitary removal on adult males of *Gobius paganellus* L. The colouration associated with sexual development failed to appear and the testes became atrophic. Two glands on the ejaculatory duct of the vas deferens were also greatly reduced in size. Regression of gonads and accessory sexual structures started approximately 3 months after the operation, and after 5½ months the testes appeared immature, the tubules had collapsed and their lining was reduced to a simple undifferentiated epithelium

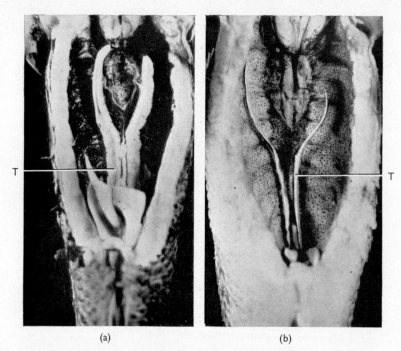

(a)   (b)

Fig. *11.20*—*Gobius paganellus*. (a) Normal male at end of reproductive period. (b) Male hypophysectomised at end of reproductive period and autopsied 94 days later. T=testis. (From Vivien, 1941.)

(Fig. *11.20*).   Pituitary removal shortly before the natural reproductive climax caused a retention of sperm in 70 per cent of the operated fish.   When the pituitary was removed during winter, there was a rapid cessation of spermatogenesis, though testicular involution was relatively slow to appear.   Ultimately the testes became greatly reduced in size and all stages in spermatogenesis other than spermatogonia had disappeared (*see* Fig. *11.21*, illustrating similar results in *Xiphophorus* (Vivien, 1952, 1952a)).   Vivien (1941) extended his work on *Gobius* to include immature fish and he found that the gonads were unaffected by hypophysectomy.   Pickford (1953a) reported essentially similar results in *Fundulus*.   She found a marked decrease in size of the testes 5 months after the operation.   They were reduced to half the size of those of adults in the non-breeding season, and to one-twentieth of the size of ripe testes.   Nuptial colouration was lost 2 weeks after the operation

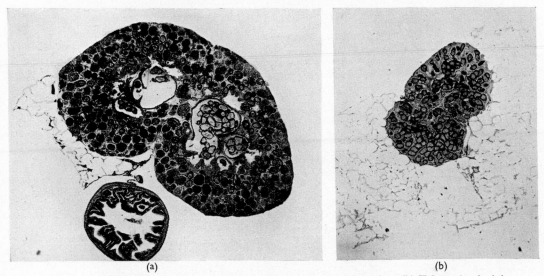

(a)   (b)

Fig. *11.21*—*Xiphophorus helleri*.   (a) T.S. testis of normal adult male.   (b) T.S. testis of adult male 90 days after hypophysectomy.   (From Vivien, 1941.)

(*see also* Matthews, 1939; Burger, 1941, 1942).   Other species in which hypophysectomy has been reported are *Gobius cobitis* and *Ameiurus nebulosus* (Buser-Lahaye, 1953) and *Bathygobius soporator* (Tavolga, 1955); the results are in excellent agreement with those already described.   In addition, Tavolga noted that pituitary removal abolishes courtship and fighting behaviour and diminishes territorial behaviour in *Bathygobius*.

It is important to identify the precise stage in spermatogenesis which is affected by hypophysectomy; some data exist on this point.   Matthews (1939) found that in *Fundulus* it was inhibited beyond the spermatogonial stage about 10 days after hypophysectomy in autumn and in about 26 days in spring.   Pickford (1953a), also working with *Fundulus*, reports essentially similar results.   She found that spermatogonia were unaffected, but there were few spermatocytes or spermatids and no spermatozoa 5 months after the operation.

There are few data available on the effects of hypophysectomy on the interstitial cells of the teleost testis, though Buser-Lahaye (1953) found that they showed histological signs of atrophy in *Gobius cobitis* and *Ameiurus nebulosus*.

Hypophysectomy in the female

Follicular atresia and some degree of ovarian involution have been recorded in all teleost species from which the pituitary gland has been removed. Vivien (1939a) hypophysectomised female specimens of *Gobius* before and after spawning. He reported that the ovaries of the first group showed little reduction in size

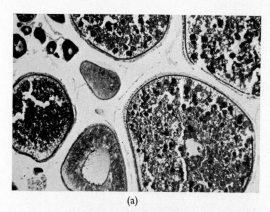

(a)

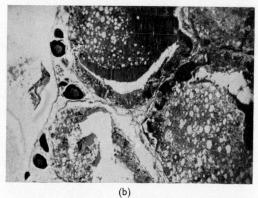

(b)

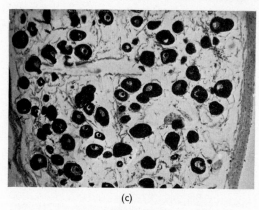

(c)

Fig. *11.22*—*Gobius paganellus*. (a) T.S. normal ovary of mature adult female. (b) T.S. ovary showing regression following hypophysectomy. (c) T.S. ovary of female hypophysectomised 295 days previously. (From Vivien, 1958.)

2 months after the operation, though all the large eggs were atretic and the ovary was milky white in colour. Young oöcytes, less than 60 μ in diameter, remained apparently unaffected, but their further development was inhibited. Specimens from the post-spawning series, autopsied between 62 and 86 days after the operation, had smaller ovaries than the controls and fewer young oöcytes. The diameter of the oöcytes was usually less than 60 μ, and only rarely exceeded 80 μ. Vitellogenesis was not seen even though abundant food reserves were present (Fig. *11.22*). Vivien (1941) showed as a result of later work on immature and mature females of *Gobius* that pituitary removal left the ovaries of immature females unaffected, though it completely blocked ovulation in mature females, and caused involution of the gonads as in the earlier work (*see also* Vivien, 1939b, 1939c). Closely similar results have been reported for *Xiphophorus helleri* (Régnier, 1938; Vivien, 1952a).

The time elapsing before the effect of hypophysectomy becomes apparent is relatively short. Buser-Lahaye (1953) reports that marked involution is seen some 6 weeks after hypophysectomy in *Gobius cobitis* and *Ameiurus nebulosus*. Matthews (1939) similarly reported a considerable decline in ovary–body weight ratio in three female specimens of *Fundulus* which survived hypophysectomy for more than 30 days.

It is clear then, from the results discussed above, that the gonads of both sexes of teleosts are under pituitary control.   In the male, all stages of spermatogenesis other than spermatogonia are affected by hypophysectomy, though the nature of the effect is not clear.   In the female, eggs below a certain size can apparently persist indefinitely in the absence of the pituitary, and oöcyte development appears to come under its control from the onset of vitellogenesis.   In the few cases in which the secondary sexual characters have been studied after hypophysectomy, these also appear to be affected, presumably indirectly, by pituitary removal.

Injection and Implantation of Fish Pituitary Glands

Injection

This facet of fish endocrinology has received more attention than any other, perhaps mainly because of its important commercial aspects.   Pickford and Atz (1957) have reviewed the extensive Russian literature on injection of pituitary extracts into fish and this is not dealt with in detail here, though key references are given.

Some fifty genera of fish have been investigated in this context and the usual method has been to inject saline or glycerine suspensions of homoplastic or hetero-plastic pituitary material collected from fish at different stages of the reproductive cycle and dried in either acetone or ethyl alcohol.   Such material has been found to possess fairly stable gonadotrophic properties ; Hasler, Meyer and Wisby (1950) have reported that acetone-dried carp pituitary was still effective 10 years after collection.

The work of Houssay (1931) pioneered this aspect of reproductive physiology. He showed that injection of pituitary extracts from *Micropogon opercularis* and *Luciopimelodus pati* into *Cnesterodon decemmaculatus* caused egg-laying before the normal spawning time.   Pereira and Cardoso (1934) injected *Prochilodus* sp. daily with five homoplastic pituitaries and obtained ovulation and spermiation; two in a group of ten ovulated 24 hours after the first injection, five specimens ovulated after two injections and a further specimen after three injections.   In the same year, Cardoso (1934) obtained a 370 per cent augmentation in weight of the ovary and a 60 per cent increase in weight of the testis of *Pimelodas clarias* by injecting eight heteroplastic fish pituitaries per day for 10 days into fish well prior to the natural spawning season.   Von Ihering (1935) induced spawning and mating activity in female specimens of two species of *Astyanax* by injecting suspensions of pituitary gland material from *Hoplias malabaricus* and he obtained genital products from both sexes of *Prochilodus* sp. by similar treatment.

Gerbilskii and Kaschenko (1937) injected homoplastic pituitary suspensions intra-cranially into females of *Osmerus eperlanus*, *Lucioperca lucioperca* and *Abramis brama*, and found that the injection of two fresh hypophyses resulted in ovulation between 12 hours and 4 days later, though it was not obtained in *Lucioperca* when pituitaries from spent fish were used.   De Azevedo and Canale (1938) injected pituitary suspensions into ten species of fish of both sexes which were closely related to the donor species.   They obtained premature ovulation in 104 out of 134 treated females and premature ripening in 113 of 144 treated males.   Butler (1940) injected homoplastic pituitary material into *Carassius auratus* 4 months after spawning and obtained a histological picture in the testes which was re-miniscent of that seen about one month prior to spawning.

The results reported in the literature on the effects of gonadotrophin treatment in eels have been unusually discordant. Van Oordt and Bretschneider (1942) obtained appreciable stimulation of the gonad in male eels; they administered pituitary extracts from carp and reported enlargement of the testes and, as a result of the highest dosages, stimulation of spermatogenesis as far as the spermatid stage.

Pliszka (1951) treated males of *Vimba vimba* with homoplastic pituitary material 5 months before the spawning season and showed a striking stimulation of spermatogenesis, and Rasquin (1951) reported stimulation of both spermatogenesis and oögenesis in *Astyanax mexicanus* by pituitary material from carp.

Implantation

Implantation of homoplastic pituitary glands into fish produces effects which are closely similar to those already reported for injection. Vivien (1939a) showed that specimens of *Gobius paganellus*, 15 days after normal spawning, could be induced to lay more eggs by the intramuscular or intraperitoneal implantation of between ten and fifteen homoplastic pituitaries. He also found that the same effect was produced by only two glands if these were placed in the cranial cavity. This method of intracranial implantation was developed by Gerbilskii and Kaschenko (1937), and by Gerbilskii (1938a), and was based on earlier work of Florentin (1934a, b).

Landgrebe (1941) reported the results of implantation experiments in *Anguilla* which were unsuccesful, in contrast to those of van Oordt and Bretschneider already reported. He found that implantation of eighteen fresh homoplastic glands over a period of 3 weeks had no effect on the gonads 6 weeks after the start of treatment, though most of the glands were established. Since, under natural conditions, the eel becomes sexually mature only once, and that late in life, its reactions to pituitary stimulation might be expected to vary a good deal depending on the time at which treatment is given. This no doubt accounts for the conflicting results which have been obtained with this animal (*see also below*).

The work of Robertson and Rinfret

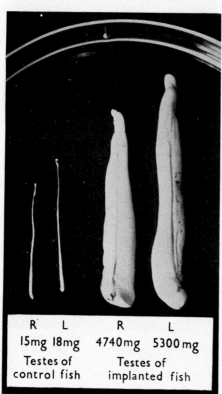

R   L   R   L
15mg 18mg   4740mg 5300mg
Testes of   Testes of
control fish   implanted fish

Fig. *11.23*—*Salmo gairdnerii* (Rainbow trout). Testes of juvenile trout (*right*) 2 months after intramuscular implantation of pellet containing 5 mg. gonadotrophic fraction of salmon pituitary. Control testes from a similar fish on the left (× 3/4). (From Robertson and Rinfret, 1957.)

(1957) is particularly significant since they have improved on previously reported techniques in two important ways; they have used purified gonadotrophic fractions of fish pituitary material, and have administered it in cholesterol pellets.

Thus the purity of the hormone and the amount administered can be much more carefully controlled. Implantation of pellets containing the gonadotrophic fraction of pituitary glands of *Oncorhynchus* sp. into immature males of *Salmo gairdnerii* produced full maturation of the testes, with shedding of motile spermatozoa, 2 months after treatment had started (Fig. *11. 23*).

There are several records showing that the gonads are insensitive to gonadotrophins until near the onset of puberty, and they are relatively insensitive at certain periods of the breeding cycle (de Azevedo, Vianna Dias and Borges Vieira, 1938 ; Bacon, 1951 ; Gerbilskii and Kaschenko, 1937 ; Kazanskii, 1939, 1950, 1952 ; de Menezes, 1944, 1945).

The stimulating effect on the gonads of both sexes by implantation and injecttion of fish pituitary material is well established. The few early results which appear to cast doubt on this can easily be explained by taking into account such important variables as state of maturity, state of ripeness, condition of the fish under the experimental régime, source and subsequent treatment of the pituitary material and amount of pituitary administered.

Specificity of Gonadotrophic Hormones of Fish

There is a certain amount of evidence available on the specificity of fish gonadotrophins and this has been analysed by Pickford and Atz (1957). This evidence relates both to specificity among fish themselves and also between fish and other vertebrate groups. Gerbilskii (1938c) concluded that pituitary injections were effective in gonad stimulation when both donor and recipient belonged to the same family. Subsequent work has shown this to be an oversimplification. Kazanskii (1940) has concluded that there is little inter-generic specificity, but a much greater degree of specificity at the ordinal level. His results are summarised in Table III.

TABLE III

REACTION OF BONY FISHES TO TREATMENT WITH GONADOTROPHIN FROM DONORS OF VARIOUS TAXONOMIC RELATIONS

(From Pickford and Atz, 1957 ; based on data of Kazanskii, 1940)

Relationship of donor and recipient	Number of species or species combinations[1]	Number of fish treated	Number of fish positive	Percentage of fish positive
Intraspecific	5	874	651	74
Intergeneric–intra-familial	7	69	48	70
Inter-ordinal–intra-class	9	163	15	9

[1] Reciprocal relationships counted separately.

However, it is clear that the matter is a good deal more complicated than this table indicates. For example, whereas Kazanskii obtained only 9 per cent successful injections at the inter-ordinal level, Pickford and Atz have computed that other workers, even when their results are combined with those of Kazanskii, have reported 55 per cent success.

It seems that certain orders of teleosts have a greater ability as pituitary donors than others. For example, of 332 fish from various orders, other than the Ostariophysii, which were treated with pituitaries from ostariophysiids, 72 per cent reacted positively, whilst only 34 per cent of 319 fish treated with pituitaries from non-ostariophysiid orders showed stimulation.

Many more data are required, from a much greater variety of species, before it can be decided with any confidence whether the degree of specificity which undoubtedly exists is related to phylogeny, or whether it is largely haphazard.

EFFECTS OF INJECTING PITUITARY GONADOTROPHINS FROM VERTEBRATES OTHER THAN FISH

Mammalian pituitary gonadotrophins

Mammals have been the main donor species in work on the effects of " foreign " pituitary extracts on fish, with amphibians, mainly frogs, taking second place. Bird and reptile pituitaries have been relatively little used.

Craig-Bennett was one of the first investigators to inject mammalian anterior lobe pituitary (ALP) extract into fish. He used sticklebacks which had previously been castrated by X-rays and found that the pituitary material resulted in the redevelopment of interstitial tissue. Schreiber (1935a, b) investigated the action of a commercial ALP preparation (Prolan) on the testes of the male silver eel and reported an increase in size, and stimulation of all stages of spermatogenesis up to and including the production of mature spermatozoa. The same preparation when injected into both sexes of the perch, *Perca fluviatilis*, induced maturation of the gonads, spermiation and ovulation (Morosova, 1936).

Castelnuovo (1937) reported acceleration of spermatogenesis in the male carp as a result of injecting an aqueous extract of mammalian ALP, and Régnier (1938) found that mammalian ALP powder, when administered in the aquarium water, reduced the time between successive parturitions in *Xiphophorus*. Cantilo and Gonzalez-Regalado (1942) treated female *Salvelinus fontinalis* in a similar manner to Régnier for 8 months, and found that the ovaries matured 1 year earlier than those of the controls. More recently Tchechovitch (1952) has reported a variable but appreciable degree of stimulation of the gonads of both sexes in *Perca fluviatilis* and in females of *Esox lucius* and *Salmo gairdnerii* by mammalian pituitary extracts.

Human pituitary material has also been shown to be active in fish. Kirschenblat (1949) induced ovulation in females of *Misgurnus fossilis* by intramuscular injection of half a human pituitary, and Ramaswami and Hasler (1955) found that two intraperitoneal injections of 0·05 mg. human pituitary gland induced the production of a full complement of breeding tubercles in males of *Hyborhynchus notatus*.

In contrast to these findings, many workers who have investigated the action of mammalian ALP on fish have reported completely negative results (Koch and Scheuring, 1936 ; von Ihering, 1937; von Ihering and de Azevedo, 1937 ; de

Azevedo and Canale, 1938 ; Creaser and Gorbman, 1939 ; Hasler, Meyer and Field, 1939 ; Johnson and Riddle, 1939 ; Veil, 1940 ; Hasler and Meyer, 1941, 1942 ; Landgrebe, 1941 ; Bernardi, 1948 ; Hoar, 1951).

No doubt hormone specificity and seasonal unresponsiveness of the target organs are responsible for some of these discordant results, though there are probably real differences between the abilities of different species to respond to one and the same gonadotrophin. The position can be clarified only by the use of graded doses of fractionated pituitary material at the time of year when homoplastic gonadotrophins are known to be active in the experimental fish. A certain amount of such work has been carried out and it may be significant that the most recent workers have achieved considerable success and have reported interesting findings on the relative effectiveness of mammalian FSH and LH fractions in fish.

Hasler, Meyer and Field (1939) reported that female rainbow trout did not spawn as a result of injection with mammalian FSH, and Hasler and Meyer (1942) found that goldfish did not spawn when injected with mammalian LH. However, Pickford (1953b, and in Pickford and Atz, 1957) injected FSH and LH fractions of swine pituitaries into hypophysectomised male *Fundulus* and found their testes increased in weight. She gave thrice-weekly injections of FSH varying between 10 μg. and o·1 μg. per gm. body weight for the last month of a 2-month hypophysectomy period, and similar injections of LH varying between 1 μg. and o·o1 μg. per gm. body weight. The FSH preparation was only one-fifth to one-tenth as active as the LH preparation in increasing the gonosomatic index (weight of gonad × 100 ÷ total weight of body). Moreover, as Pickford points out, the former contains some 3–4 per cent LH, which is probably sufficient to account for the degree of stimulation produced by the FSH fraction.

Sundararaj (1957), quoted by Ramaswami and Lakshman (1958), found that both LH and FSH (Armour) were effective in inducing spawning in intact catfish (*Heteropneustes*). They state : " The response of the fish to the follicle-stimulating hormone is obviously due to the small amount of luteinising hormone present in it." There are therefore some indications that mammalian LH is an effective gonadotrophin in fish, whereas FSH is either much less effective, or completely ineffective.

There have been suggestions that a luteotrophin, or luteotrophin-like substance is present in the fish pituitary. This suggestion stems from the work of Leblond and Noble (1937), who found that when they implanted large numbers of fish pituitaries (between 30 and 100), intra-dermally over the crop gland of pigeons, the gland reacted, though in a manner which was far from typical of the response produced by injection of luteotrophin (prolactin). Moreover, similar reactions could be produced by extracts of the livers of pigeon, turtle, catfish and sunfish, and also by brain of sunfish and catfish. Indeed, Leblond and Noble themselves concluded that the prolactin-like reaction produced by all the pituitaries they tested probably does not imply the presence of prolactin. Similarly, the work of Fonseca-Ribeiro and Tabarelli-Neto (1943), in which the pituitaries of *Prochilodus* sp. were shown to cause secretion of the oviducal glands of *Bufo arenarum*, cannot be accepted as evidence that the pituitaries contained prolactin.

However, Pickford and Atz (1957) report unpublished work of Lehrman in which it is claimed that fractionated pituitaries of *Pollachius virens* have given definite indications of the presence of prolactin by the pigeon-crop method of assay.

Apart from the undocumented statement of Carlisle (Medawar, 1953) that pituitaries of the dogfish stimulate lactation in the mammary gland, no one appears to have tested fish pituitaries for prolactin by direct injection into the mammary gland ; there is an obvious need for such an approach.

In contrast to the fragmentary evidence concerning the occurrence of prolactin in the fish pituitary, there are several records of its diverse effects on fish themselves. Noble, Kumpf and Billings (1936, 1938) investigated the effect of prolactin on brooding behaviour in the cichlid " mouth brooder " *Hemichromis bimaculatus*. In this species eggs and young are brooded, the eggs being guarded and fanned, and the young protected, usually in the mouths of the parents ; straying young are retrieved and the young fish are " called " by abrupt fin movements. Noble *et al.* reported that brooding behaviour was induced by prolactin in adult fish which had spawned at least once, but a great variety of substances other than pro-lactin, including phenol and, especially, corpus luteum extract, were also found to be effective in inducing parental care. Such results are difficult to interpret and, as Noble *et al.* realised, they do not substantiate the claim that prolactin is responsible for inducing broodiness in these fish. Pickford (*see* Pickford and Atz, 1957) injected hypophysectomised male and female *Fundulus* with prolactin (10 μg. per gm. body weight), and obtained no observable gonadotrophic effect, though Carlisle (1954) found that crude prolactin induced spermiation in starved male dogfish.

Thus the evidence that prolactin exists in fish, or that mammalian prolactin has any effect on reproductive function in these animals is extremely meagre. Pickford and Kosto (1957) have recently shown prolactin to be extremely effective in in-creasing the degree of melanism, in *Fundulus*, but an appraisal of this work is beyond the scope of the present chapter.

It is evident from this survey that much of the work on pituitary gonado-trophins and their effects in fish has been characterised by an attempt to interpret experimental results in the light of what is known for mammals. The success of this attempt has been limited, yet there is little doubt that fish gonadotrophin(s) perform similar, if not identical, functions to their counterparts in mammals. For example, they undoubtedly stimulate the germinal tissue, and are concerned in spermiation and ovulation, and, to this extent, there is evidence for the presence of an LH-like gonadotrophin in the fish pituitary. Moreover, although the evidence available from injection experiments in fish, in which LH from mam-malian sources has been injected, is discordant, there are many records of the effectiveness of mammalian LH in fish ; not only has it been found to induce spermiation and ovulation, but it also appears to have an FSH-like effect on the germinal tissue. Corroborative evidence from experiments with chorionic gonadotrophin, which has an LH-mimetic action in mammals, is discussed below.

There is little direct evidence for the existence of an FSH-like gonadotrophin in fish, though the germinal epithelium is undoubtedly under the influence of the pituitary; it therefore seems reasonable to postulate the existence of a follicle-stimulating substance. The questions which remain unanswered concerning it are: the nature of its relationship to LH, since mammalian LH appears to be able to mediate the effects it would be expected to produce; the degree to which it is similar to mammalian FSH and the manner in which it acts.

Witschi (1955), on the basis of the vaginal cornification test in rats and the feather reaction in weaver-finches, attempted to compare the relative amounts of FSH and LH in mammalian and fish pituitaries. He concluded that the fish pituitary is low in FSH, but contains an amount of LH similar to that found in mammals, and suggests that this indicates that the fish pituitary holds a store of LH where as it produces FSH only for immediate release. Witschi also suggests that LH may be of greater importance than FSH in the lower vertebrates, and that in the female, induction of ovulation is both a more general and a more ancient function than its role in corpus luteum formation. These suggestions are both interesting and challenging, but it cannot be said that the existing data, based as they are on the measurement of chemically diverse hormones by biological assays on mammals and birds, do more than hint at them.

Thus, in spite of a considerable amount of work, it is not yet possible to say whether more than one gonadotrophin exists in fish. As Pickford and Atz (1957) have pointed out, the position concerning the nature and occurrence of gonadotrophins in mammals is far from clear, and it is not surprising that in fish it is even more obscure. Like many similar problems in comparative endocrinology, the final answer must await the chemical characterisation of the hormones. On the evidence already available, it is safe to predict that not only will there be differences between the gonadotrophins of fish and mammals, but also between those of fish themselves, but the nature and magnitude of these differences are as yet unknown.

Mammalian gonadotrophins of extra-pituitary origin

Several species of fish have been treated with chorionic gonadotrophin (CG) and serum gonadotrophin (PMS). Results of administering CG have varied, but there are many records of stimulation both of gonads and of accessory reproductive structures. Boucher, Boucher and Fontaine (1934) showed that both sexes of the eel (*Anguilla anguilla*), which usually matures late in life and therefore might be expected to be somewhat refractory to stimulation, responded to treatment with CG. Seven intramuscular injections of pregnancy urine totalling 10 ml. were given between December and March and resulted in an increase in ovarian size. Fontaine (1936) injected two silver eels between January and February with four intramuscular injections of early pregnancy urine. Fifteen days after the last injection, well-marked secondary sexual characters were present and both specimens emitted sperm. Bruun and Møller-Christensen (1941) and Bruun, Hemmingsen and Møller-Christensen (1949) were also successful in producing maturation or partial maturation in both male and female silver eels by injections of commercial preparations of CG. In the treated females, increase in size of the eggs was greater when weekly injections of 1 mg. hexoestrol were given in addition to the gonadotrophin. However, large amounts of both hormones were administered (up to 12,500 i.u. chorionic gonadotrophin and 25 mg. hexoestrol in 42 weeks), and mortality was high.

It is evident from a survey of the literature that CG has a stimulatory effect on the gonads of a wide variety of bony fish. Furthermore, many species have been induced to spawn as a result of treatment with CG : *Perca fluviatilis* (Morosova, 1936 ; Skadovskii and Parfenova, 1937) ; *Carassius auratus* (Butler, 1940) ; *Lebistes reticulatus* (Berkowitz, 1941a ; Jaski, 1946) ; *Xiphophorus helleri* (Baldwin and Li, 1942), *Cyprinus carpio* (Ichikawa and Kawakami, 1944) ; *Salmo irideus*

(Nishino, 1948); *Misgurnus fossilis* (Kirshenblat, 1949, 1953); *Misgurnus anguillicaudatus* (Egami, 1954a); *Conger conger* and other teleost species (Carlisle, 1955); *Heteropneustes fossilis, Clarias batrachus* (Ramaswami and Sundararaj, 1957a, b; Ramaswami and Lakshman, 1958). Response of the fish ovary to CG varies with its state of maturity, but there are several records of immature ovaries being stimulated (*Carassius auratus*, Butler, 1940), and of immature eggs being laid (*Acipenser* spp., Morosova, 1937; *Misgurnus fossilis*, Kirshenblat, 1952, 1953).

Several of the early workers reported negative results from treatment of a variety of fish species with CG (*Salmo irideus*, Koch and Scheuring, 1936; *Prochilodus argenteus*, von Ihering and de Azevedo, 1937, de Azevedo and Canale, 1938; *Acipenser stellatus*, Gerbilskii, 1938b; *Anguilla anguilla*, Hansen, 1939, Landgrebe, 1941).

There is no doubt, however, that at certain dose levels, and under good experimental conditions, chorionic gonadotrophin is capable of stimulating both germinal tissue and interstitial cells of a wide range of teleosts of both sexes, and of inducing spawning. In certain fish species, notably the eel *Anguilla anguilla*, the state of ripeness of the experimental fish is undoubtedly of great importance. It seems reasonably certain that the use of very immature specimens accounts for the fact that Hansen (1939) and Landgrebe (1941) were unable to stimulate the gonads of their experimental fish with CG and crude pregnancy urine respectively, whereas Tuzet and Fontaine (1937), using more-mature silver eels, obtained testis enlargement and some motile sperm with only five injections of 2 ml. pregnancy urine. Ramaswami and Sundararaj (1957b) found also that timing of the experiments relative to the spawning season was all-important. Injections of CG into gravid specimens of *Clarias batrachus* in the pre-spawning period (May and June) were ineffective. Similar injections during July yielded viable eggs.

Fewer data are available on the effects of pregnant mare serum gonadotrophin (PMS) on fish gonads, and the results are again somewhat contradictory. However, it seems that in some species, both testes and ovaries can be stimulated by PMS whilst others appear to be refractory even in the breeding season. Hasler, Meyer and Field (1939) found that female specimens of *Salmo trutta* were insensitive to PMS until near the end of the spawning season, but that at this time certain normally refractive specimens could be made to spawn by injecting PMS. Johnson and Riddle (1939) and Berkowitz (1941a) found female specimens of *Salmo gairdnerii* and *Lebistes reticulatus* more refractive to PMS than males. Egami (1954a) showed that the ovaries of *Misgurnus anguillicaudatus* responded to injections of PMS. Eight injections of 50 i.u. PMS given two to three months before the spawning season produced a significant increase in ovarian weight. Vivien (1950b), however, reported no visible effect of PMS on the ovaries of *Xiphophorus helleri*, and Ramaswami and Sundararaj (1957a, b) and Ramaswami and Lakshman (1958) have reported a similar lack of success in the catfish *Clarias* and *Heteropneustes*.

Pituitary gonadotrophins from non-mammalian vertebrates

Gonadotrophins from a considerable variety of non-mammalian vertebrates have been injected into fish though, except in those cases in which amphibians have been donors, the recorded data are too few for generalisation.

Kawamura and Otsuka (1950) were unable to induce ovulation in the goldfish *Carassius auratus* during the breeding season by injecting half to one pituitary gland of the fowl, but Otsuka (1952) was more successful in the same species using " crude " FSH and " crude " LH fractions of hen pituitaries. However, in no experiment were more than half the experimental fish induced to ovulate.

Reptile pituitary material appears to have been injected into fish on only two occasions. Kazanskii (1940) injected twenty female specimens of *Vimba vimba* with single glands of the turtle (*Emys orbicularis*) and reported no effects. However, Watanabe, Yamada and Matsushima (1950) obtained a moderate ovulation response from female *Misgurnus anguillicaudatus* by injecting 6 mg. of pituitary material from the lizard *Takydromus tachydromoides*.

Many investigators have injected amphibian pituitary material into fish ; most of it appears to have come from frogs (genus *Rana*), and in a high proportion of cases it has produced stimulation of gonads, ovulation and spermiation. Gallien (1941) injected both sexes of the minnow *Phoxinus phoxinus* with eleven pituitaries of *Rana temporaria* over 3 days. The fish were mature, but were injected 2 months prior to the spawning season. The males assumed breeding dress 3 hours after the first injection and sperm could be expressed on the second day. Three treated females laid eggs spontaneously during, and immediately after, the injection period. However, when female minnows were given three injections totalling seventeen glands, 3 months before the spawning season, although there was marked enlargement of oöcytes, there was no ovulation (Gallien, 1942). Kawamura and Motanaga (1950) report a long series of experiments on *Misgurnus anguillicaudatus* and *Cobitis* spp. Females received injections of *Rana nigromaculatus* and *R. catesbiana* pituitary material in varying amounts. As a result of treatment virtually all injected females ovulated and eggs were also obtained when excised ovaries were treated with frog pituitary material. Similar work by Kawamura and Otsuka (1950), in which *Carassius auratus* was treated with bullfrog pituitary material, yielded comparable results. Otsuka (1952) fractionated frog pituitaries and injected " crude FSH " fraction and " crude ICSH " fraction into female goldfish ; a high percentage of these ovulated to both fractions within 3 days.

Effects of Gonadotrophins on Secondary Sexual Characters

Possible changes in the Leydig-cell homologues of the fish testis consequent upon treatment with gonadotrophins have been virtually ignored by workers in this field, but there are several records of the effect of gonadotrophin treatment, presumably indirect, on the secondary sexual characters of fish. Butler (1940) showed that the " pearl " organs of *Carassius auratus* developed 4 months after the spawning season as a result of intraperitoneal injection of six pituitary glands. Burrows, Palmer and Newman (1952) found that spawning colouration was intensified in *Oncorhynchus nerka* by intra-muscular injection of pituitary material from *O. tshawytscha*, in spite of the fact that maturation of the gonads was unaffected, indeed, lowered fertility was recorded. In further work on salmon, Palmer, Burrows, Robertson and Newman (1954) induced the appearance of spawning colouration in *O. nerka* 15 days before it appeared in the controls by injection of pituitary material from *O. keta*. Pliszka (1951) obtained similar effects in *Vimba*

vimba by injecting homoplastic pituitary material 4 months prior to the spawning season. Male secondary sex characters in the form of breeding tubercles occur in the minnow, *Hyborhynchus notatus*, and Ramaswami and Hasler (1955) have shown that the full array of tubercles will appear 2 days after injecting pituitary material from *Cyprinus carpio*.

There are a few reports in the literature concerning the influence of pituitary hormones on behaviour patterns associated with reproduction. Hubbs and Hubbs (1933) showed that nuptial behaviour, including courting and nest-building, could be induced in sunfish hybrids by injection of homoplastic pituitary material into males even if they were treated before seminal fluid could be expressed by stripping. Pickford (1952) described artificially induced spawning reflexes in *Fundulus heteroclitus* as a result of injecting pituitary material collected from various gadids. There is also the report of Ramaswami and Hasler (1955) that male specimens of *Hyborhynchus notatus* showed territorial and display behaviour when injected with pituitary material from *Cyprinus carpio*.

There is no evidence to suggest that these effects of gonadotrophin injections on the secondary sexual characters are direct ones. The possibility has already been considered in a similar situation in cyclostomes when it was pointed out that critical evidence would be forthcoming only when castrated animals were injected with gonadotrophins. The same applies in the present case. However, there is excellent evidence that secondary sexual characters and reproductive behaviour in most fish are controlled by sex hormones, and it seems reasonable to suggest that the stimulation of these characters by gonadotrophins is in most cases indirect.

Hormones of the Testis

A great deal is known of the origin, functions and chemical identity of the hormones secreted by the mammalian testis and of the manner in which their secretion is controlled by the pituitary gland. Much less is known about these hormones in teleosts. Indeed, the only evidence for their existence is indirect. It comes from castration, testis-implantation, the injection of fish testis extracts into fish and other vertebrates and the injection of sex steroids into fish.

Castration

Surgical castration is not an easy operation in teleosts and it usually entails a high mortality. Because of this, early work was largely inconclusive (Champy, 1923 ; van Oordt and van der Maas, 1926). Castration by X-rays has been attempted by several workers (Champy, 1923 ; Craig-Bennett, 1931 ; Vivien, 1950a ; Follenius, 1953), but regeneration of testes, incomplete destruction of interstitial tissue and the possibility of deleterious side effects combine to make this method unsatisfactory. Vivien (1952b), however, has used it in conjunction with surgical castration and with interesting results. He has shown that surgical castration of *Xiphophorus* results in the absence of secondary sexual characters, whereas castration by irradiation has a hardly significant effect on them, and this appears to be correlated with the fact that the interstitial cells of the testis are not affected by X-rays. This author (Vivien, 1953a, b, c) has also shown that it is possible to achieve complete castration of *Xiphophorus* and *Lebistes* by immersing them in radioactive phosphorus, though here again, the interstitial cells are not affected, and the secondary sexual characters develop in the normal way.

In most cases, surgical castration has resulted in a modification of the secondary sexual characters and the castrated male comes to resemble the female, or reverts to the condition found in immature animals of both sexes. A considerable range of structures appears to be under testicular control in teleosts. One of the most striking of these is the nuptial colouration or breeding dress which is fully developed only at the height of the breeding season. This has been shown to regress as a result of castration in several species : *Gasterosteus* (Bock, 1928b ; Ikeda, 1933) ; *Amia* (Zahl and Davis, 1932) ; *Oryzias* (Niwa, 1955). Non-seasonal sexually dimorphic colouration is also profoundly affected by castration in : *Halichoeres* (Kinoshita, 1935) ; *Oryzias* (Okada and Yamashita, 1944a ; Masuda, 1952) ; *Tilapia* (Aronson, 1948, 1951 ; Levy and Aronson, 1955). In fact, virtually all the external secondary sexual characters described earlier have been shown to be under testicular control. Among these are : pearl organs in *Carassius* (Tozawa, 1923) and in *Acheilognathus* (Tozawa, 1929) ; modified pectoral fins in *Misgurnus* (Kobayashi, 1951) ; modified anal fin in *Oryzias* (Okada and Yamashita, 1944a ; Masuda, 1952) ; gonopodium in *Gambusia* (St. Amant, 1941 ; Okada and Yamashita, 1944b ; Turner, 1947a), in *Xiphophorus* (Grobstein, 1947) and in *Lebistes* (Hopper, 1949a, 1951) ; the genital papilla in *Tilapia* (Aronson, 1948, 1951 ; Levy and Aronson, (1955), and in *Oryzias* (Yamamoto and Suzuki, 1955).

Certain internal secondary sexual characters are also under hormonal control and these become atrophic after castration. This applies to the segment of the male kidney which produces a secretion used in nest-building by *Gasterosteus* (Ikeda, 1933), and also to the seminal vesicles of *Bathygobius* (Tavolga, 1955).

So far as concerns the control of reproductive behaviour, castration has yielded somewhat equivocal results. Noble and Borne (1940) have shown that castrates of *Xiphophorus helleri* lose their position in the social hierarchy. Several workers have shown for other species that sexual behaviour in the male is largely dependent on the hormones of the testis (*Salmo salar*, Jones and King, 1952 ; *Gasterosteus aculeatus*, Bock, 1928a ; Ikeda, 1933). However, it seems that most workers in this field have encountered some species in which the testis plays little, if any, part in conditioning sexual behaviour. Noble and Kumpf (1936) working with *Hemichromis bimaculatus* found that the castrated male is completely normal with regard to courtship, fertilisation behaviour, secondary sex-characters and brooding for as long as 202 days after the operation. Moreover, in *Hemichromis*, they detected signs of heightened awareness in the castrates. Aronson (1951) found a similar state of affairs in castrated male *Tilapia*, and Tavolga (1955) encountered an increased sexual activity in castrated *Bathygobius*, although hypophysectomy in the latter species stopped all courtship behaviour. It should be noted, however, that these workers do not state whether the gonad regions of the castrates were serially sectioned, and since St. Amant (1941 ; quoted by Turner, 1942b) has found that in *Gambusia affinis* as little as one-fifth of a testis is sufficient to induce development of a normal gonopodium, their results must be accepted with caution. They must not be ignored, however, because they interfere with generalisations ; indeed, there is no reason to expect that a group of animals as old and diversified as the teleosts will fit into any unified scheme as far as hormonal control of behaviour is concerned.

Effects of unilateral castration

Several workers have investigated the effects of unilateral castration and all have reported some degree of compensatory hypertrophy in the remaining testis (Bock, 1928b, and Craig-Bennett, 1931, in sticklebacks ; Wunder, 1955, in carp). Robertson (1958), in a detailed study of this phenomenon, has found that unilateral castration of the rainbow trout (*Salmo gairdnerii*) results in stimulation of growth and maturation of the remaining testis. He found that stimulation was greatest in fish castrated between 13 and 17 months of age; below this, stimulation was slight, and above it, gonads of control fish grew just as quickly as the undisturbed testis in the partial castrates. He concludes that the lack of response to the operation in fish less than 13 months old is due to absence of gonadotrophin in their pituitary; evidence for this view comes from two sources: Robertson has shown that the infantile testis can be stimulated by intramuscular implantation of pituitaries from mature fish, and he has been unable to demonstrate gonadotrophins in the pituitary glands of immature fish.

Implantation of testes and administration of crude testicular extracts

Castration has provided a good deal of information on the role of the testis in initiating and maintaining the secondary sexual characters ; implantation of testes and administration of testicular extracts into castrated and intact animals have supplemented these data. Owen (1937) showed that nuptial colouration could be produced in the male Japanese bitterling *Acheilognathus intermedium* by feeding fresh or dried testicular material, or by adding an oily extract of testes to the aquarium water in which the fish were living. Similarly, Bretschneider, Duyvené de Wit and Goedewaagen (1941) found that growth of the ovipositor of female *Rhodeus amarus* was stimulated by an ether extract of the ovaries of the angler fish *Lophius piscatorius*. Nagata (1936) and Okada and Yamashita (1944a) have found that testes of *Oryzias latipes*, when transplanted into ovariectomised female hosts, remained fully functional through two breeding seasons and stimulated the development of male secondary sexual characters in the host fish.

Further evidence for the stimulatory role of the testis *vis-à-vis* secondary sexual characters has come from a somewhat unusual source. Ovariectomy of *Betta splendens* (Noble and Kumpf, 1937 ; Kaiser and Schmidt, 1951) produced a surprising result in a few of the fish in which regeneration of the gonads occurred ; testes appeared in place of the ovaries which had been removed. Noble and Kumpf found that the testis was regenerated from the cut end of the oviduct and such an abnormal regenerate was obtained seven times in 150 ovariectomised fish. Three months after the operation the fish began to develop typical male fins. Three sacrificed at this time showed active spermatogenesis and some mature sperm. Four sex-reversed fish, retained 149 to 163 days after the operation, showed full development of the male fins, and when placed with normal females, three of them spawned normally and fertilised the eggs of the females. The fourth showed typical male behaviour in nine successive spawnings, but although eggs were laid by the accompanying females, he did not fertilise them. At autopsy the first three fish were found to have typical testes whereas the last had an organ resembling a testis but showing no signs of spermatogenesis.

It seems well established therefore that the fish testis manufactures a substance or substances capable of repairing the effects of castration on the secondary sexual characters, though its site of production has not yet been established ; interstitial cells, lobule boundary cells and Sertoli cells have all been put forward as sites of origin. The chemical nature of the fish sex hormones is not known, though it has been shown that extracts of fish testis have a testosterone-like action in several other vertebrates. D'Ancona and Sabbadin (1952) showed that vacuum-dried testicular substance from *Mugil*, *Sparus*, and *Gobius* when fed to *Rana* tadpoles had a masculinising effect on their gonads. So far as the action of the fish testis extract on birds is concerned, Hazleton and Goodrich (1937) have reported that an alcohol-benzene extract of the testes of Pacific salmon produced comb growth in capons. Similarly, Potter and Hoar (1954) have shown that a testosterone-like material (which will stimulate comb growth in chicks) can be obtained from the testes of chum salmon by alcohol-ether extraction. The yield of this substance measured by its biological activity is comparable weight for weight to that obtained from mammalian testes. It may be hoped that the increasing availability of chromatographic techniques for steroid identification will enable the teleost testicular hormones to be identified both qualitatively and quantitatively. Such a step would yield information of great interest from a comparative biochemical point of view and at the same time would make possible an evaulation of the existing experimental work on sex hormones and point the way to other, more critical experiments.

The Effects of Androgens

The effects of several different androgens have been investigated in teleosts : testosterone, testosterone propionate, methyl testosterone and testosterone acetate. In addition, ethinyl testosterone, which is always androgenic in fish, has yielded results of considerable interest. They have been administered either by injection in oil, or by adding them to the aquarium water. The physiological significance of some of these experiments is extremely difficult to assess since high concentrations of steroid have often been used and many investigators have experimented with intact animals. It is clear that the presence of the pituitary and gonads is a complicating influence in work of this kind because of the interactions which are known to take place between them and exogenous sex hormones.

Fish of the families Poeciliidae and Cyprinodontidae have been widely used in studies on sex steroids because of their well-developed secondary sexual characters. A good deal of detailed work has been reported on the effects of androgens on the gonads and secondary sexual characters of both sexes in a variety of species.

Effects of androgens on the testis.—There are two records in the literature on the effects of androgens on the testes of hypophysectomised fish. Burger (1942) obtained slight stimulation of the testes of *Fundulus* by injecting testosterone propionate at a dose level of 8 mg. administered over 42 days ; at the end of the experiment, the testes of the treated animals were one-fifth heavier than those of the hypophysectomised control males. This effect had been brought about by some degree of stimulation of spermatogenesis though Burger points out that the testes were greatly regressed by comparison with the intact controls. He also reported that injection of testosterone propionate into intact sexually inactive males had no effect on spermatogenesis. On the other hand, Pickford (1957), as a result of her extensive work on hypophysectomised *Fundulus*, believes that

androgens may well stimulate gametogenesis in the fish testis, though the histological evidence on which this view is based is not reported. She found that
twelve intraperitoneal injections of methyl testosterone at a level of 2 µg. per gm.
body weight given over the second month of a 2-month hypophysectomy period
had a pronounced stimulatory effect on the testes, which was reflected in the
increased gonosomatic index.

There have been several reports of stimulation of the testes of intact fish by
androgens. Eversole (1941), working with *Lebistes*, found that ethinyl testosterone induced stimulation of the testes, and ultimately produced signs of
exhaustion in them.   On the other hand, in a similar investigation on *Xiphophorus*,
Tavolga (1949) reported stimulation by ethinyl testosterone of all spermatogenetic
stages, but no exhaustion.   No doubt this is merely a difference in degree of
response and can be accounted for by dosage and time differences.   In addition
to these results, several other workers have reported testicular stimulation by
androgens administered to intact fish. (*Xiphophorus*, Régnier, 1938, Laskowski,
1953 ; *Lebistes*, Svärdson, 1943 ; *Phoxinus*, Bullough, 1942 ; *Oryzias latipes*,
Okada and Yamashita, 1944a).   Vallowe (1957), the most recent worker in this
field, treated sexually immature specimens of *Xiphophorus helleri* (49–55 days old)
with nine weekly injections of androgen each consisting of 0·25 mg. testosterone
propionate.   He noted that the testes were greatly stimulated, the testicular
tubules being filled with all stages of spermatogenesis including well-formed spermatophores and closely resembling those of mature males.   The epithelium
lining the sperm ducts was markedly hypertrophied.

It seems then from this survey that the later stages of spermatogenesis are dif-
ferentially stimulated in intact animals and this probably accounts for the signs
of exhaustion which have been observed in the testes of treated fish.   The picture
in hypophysectomised fish is less clear, though there are indications that androgens
have a gametogenic effect in them also.   Clearly, detailed investigations on the
precise effect of androgens on the testis of hypophysectomised fish are required,
especially in view of the fact that they are now known to exert a stimulatory effect
on spermatogenesis in mammals (Greep and Chester Jones, 1950 ; Ludwig, 1950 ;
Leathem and Wolf, 1955).

Effects of androgens on the ovary.—In female teleosts, androgens have been
found to exert an entirely masculinising effect on the ovary.   The degree of masculinisation produced by them varies a good deal, and it may well be controlled by the
stability of the sex-determining mechanism.   Their first effects on the ovary is the
inhibition of oögenesis and vitellogenesis, and this is followed by degenerative
changes.   Witschi and Crown (1937) found that addition of testosterone propionate
to the water in which pregnant females of *Xiphophorus helleri* were living caused
abortion or resorption of embryos within one or two days.   Resorption of all
large eggs in non-pregnant adult females was also observed and the ovaries came
to resemble testes though spermatogenesis was not observed.   Régnier (1938)
and Baldwin and Goldin (1939), also working with *Xiphophorus*, corroborate these
findings.   Eversole (1939) found, as a result of treating *Lebistes* with testosterone
propionate, that gametogenetic activity was inhibited in mature females and large
eggs and embryos were resorbed.   In 3 fish out of the 100 which were treated,
ovotestes were observed.   Mohsen (1958) has recently obtained similar results
by treating genetic males of *Lebistes* with ethinyl testosterone.   Of 55 treated

animals, 37 were males, 15 were hermaphrodite with ovotestes, and only 2 were females and these had a gonopodium.   He claims that the failure of previous workers to obtain striking signs of masculinisation and the production of ovo-testes is due to too short a period of treatment and too high a concentration of steroid.

Bullough (1940) reported degeneration of the ovary of *Phoxinus laevis* as a result of injecting testosterone propionate, and Okada and Yamashita (1944b) showed that methyldihydro-testosterone arrests ovarian growth in *Gambusia affinis*.   They also showed that although testosterone masculinised females of *Oryzias* both in appearance and sexual behaviour, nevertheless, they continued to lay eggs (Okada and Yamashita, 1944a).

The effects of androgens on the fish ovary are therefore uniformly inhibitory ; the degree to which masculinisation is induced is, however, variable.   As we have seen, Eversole (1941) obtained ovotestes in a small proportion of his androgen-treated *Lebistes*, and Okada and Yamashita (1944b) and Hamon (1945a) reported spermatogenesis in ovaries of similarly treated *Gambusia affinis*.   More recently, Vallowe (1957) has obtained a high degree of masculinisation in the much more sexually labile poeciliid *Xiphophorus helleri*.   He administered nine intraperi-toneal injections of testosterone propionate at weekly intervals to sexually immature fish (49–55 days old) ; each fish received a total of 2·25 mg. steroid over the injec-tion period.   As a result, the young fish took on the appearance of sexually mature adult males.   The ovaries of the treated immature females contained no ova ; follicles were present, but these were filled with a loose collection of cells. In other follicles, primary spermatocytes, spermatids and spermatophores were observed.   The ovarian cavity was obscured and the altered gonad showed an unusual amount of stroma.   Vallowe also treated sexually mature fish, and found inhibition of the ovaries, but no masculinisation even when treatment was con-tinued for 18 weeks at a weekly dose level of 0·5 mg. testosterone per fish.   Histo-logical examination showed all the large ova to be in various stages of disintegra-tion, though the hormone appeared to have had little effect on the smaller ova which were still firm and surrounded by a well-organised follicle.   This investiga-tion illustrates the importance of the state of sexual maturity in experiments of this kind ; it appears that the immature gonads of *Xiphophorus* retain a high degree of lability, but that the ovary of sexually mature females is relatively little affected by a high dosage of testosterone propionate over a protracted period.

Effects of androgens on the secondary sexual characters.—There are many records dealing with the effect of androgens on the secondary sexual characters of fish and there is complete agreement that they stimulate the appearance of all the secondary sexual characters proper to the male.   Unfortunately, there is no information concerning the action of androgens on gonadectomised fish.

Witschi and Crown (1937), in their work on *Xiphophorus helleri*, found that all females treated with testosterone propionate, assumed gradually but completely the male secondary sexual characters, colouration, gonopodium and sword.   Sub-sequent workers on this species have reported similar results (Régnier, 1938; Baldwin and Goldin, 1939 ; Noble and Borne, 1940 ; Okada and Yamashita, 1944b ; Cohen, 1946 ; Grobstein, 1947, 1948 ; Sangster, 1948 ; Tavolga, 1949 ; Vivien, 1952b ; Vivien and Mohsen, 1952 ; Rubin and Gordon, 1953 ; Laskowski, 1953 ; Vallowe, 1957).

Owen (1937) found that testosterone acetate caused all male specimens of *Acheilognathus intermedium* to develop precocious nuptial colouration with total doses as low as 0·04 i.u., and 66 per cent of female fish were masculinised by doses of 35 i.u.   Eversole (1941) studied the effects of ethinyl testosterone, and other steroids on sexual differentiation in *Lebistes*.   He reported several interesting findings : ethinyl testosterone functioned solely as an androgen ; none of the fifty-one fish treated from birth showed any female secondary sexual characters, and all of them, regardless of age, sex and dosage, showed transformation of the anal fin into a gonopodium.   Eversole also found that the extent to which female sex characters were suppressed depended on the age at which treatment was started.   Other workers on *Lebistes* have recorded identical findings (Régnier, 1941, 1942 ; Svärdson, 1943 ; Scott, 1944 ; Okada and Yamashita, 1944b ; Goodrich, Hine and Lesher, 1947 ; Gallien, 1949a ; Hopper, 1949b, 1951 ; Mohsen, 1958).

Turner (1942a, b) studied the chronology of gonopodial differentiation in *Gambusia affinis* as affected by androgen treatment.   He established that a concentration of 1 mg. methyl testosterone in 25,000,000 ml. water would induce development of the first stage of the gonopodium ; ethinyl testosterone was approximately half as potent.   Each successive stage required an increased concentration of the hormone, and abnormalities in growth pattern occurred if too high a concentration was used for any particular stage.   Thus optimal development of the third, fourth and fifth fin rays was found to occur at a concentration of 1 mg. methyl testosterone in 5,000,000 ml. water.   Turner has suggested, in explanation of these results, that the direction of development and level of tissue susceptibility in each differentiating area of the gonopodium is under genetical control, and the developing testes secrete increasing amounts of androgen with time.   A similar study has been carried out by Grobstein (1948) on *Xiphophorus*.

In general, reproductive behaviour in the male appears to be conditioned by androgens, though there are data which appear to indicate that, in some instances, it may be conditioned directly by pituitary hormones.   However, as we have seen above, castration usually results in the disappearance of behaviour patterns associated with reproduction, and the injection of androgens has the effect of causing such behaviour to reappear (*Xiphophorus*, Noble and Borne, 1940 ; *Lebistes*, Eversole, 1941, Svärdson, 1943 ; *Oryzias*, Okada and Yamashita, 1944a, Cohen, 1946, Tavolga, 1949, Laskowski, 1953).

Most of the other secondary sexual characters which are encountered in fish have been studied, and their responses to exogenous androgens have supplemented the information already reported from castration experiments (*Hyborhynchus*, Ramaswami and Hasler, 1955 ; *Rhodeus*, Brantner, 1956 ; *Carassius*, Ghadially and Whiteley, 1952 ; *Tilapia*, Aronson, 1948, Levy and Aronson, 1955 ; *Oryzias*, Okada and Yamashita, 1944a ; Egami, 1954c, d ; Yamamoto and Suzuki, 1955 ; *Thalassoma*, Stoll, 1955).

Pickford and Atz (1957) have reviewed the evidence on the nature of the male sex hormone in fish, and have concluded with Hoar (1955) that it is probably the same as in mammals.   However, they draw attention to the fact that fish react very differently from birds and mammals to ethinyl testosterone.   In these, it has mild androgenic, oestrogenic and progestational actions, whereas in fish it has powerful androgenic effects, and is probably some twenty-five times as potent as testosterone propionate. The most powerful androgen in fish, namely methyl testosterone, is only about twice as potent as ethinyl testosterone.

Hormones of the Ovary

Evidence for the existence of hormones in the fish ovary comes from several sources, of which ovariectomy is the most direct. Data from this source have been supplemented by injection of extracts of fish ovaries into fish and other test animals, and by injection of a variety of oestrogenic steroids into intact, castrated and hypophysectomised fish.

Ovariectomy

Ovariectomy in teleosts, like castration, often results in a high mortality. In consequence, the information available on the endocrine effects of the ovaries in fish is scanty. In 'the bowfin, *Amia calva* (Ganoidei), there is a caudal ocellus which is potentially present in both sexes, but under normal conditions is sex limited and found only in males. Zahl and Davis (1932) ovariectomised several specimens of *Amia*, and found that the ocellus began to appear in 3–5 weeks, and in 3 months it was clearly defined though the corona was absent. The nuptial colouration of the male *Amia* has already been described and has been shown to be conditioned by androgens ; none of this striking colouration appeared after castration. It seems clear that inhibition of the ocellus in the female is due to an ovarian secretion, whereas the nuptial colouration of the male is stimulated by a testicular secretion. Interesting corroborative evidence for the inhibitory role of the ovary is provided by several females having abnormal ovaries ; in these specimens the caudal ocellus was present.

Most workers have reported, however, that ovariectomy has no effect on the external characters of the female (*Halichoeres poecilopterus*, Kinoshita, 1935 ; *Oryzias latipes*, Okada and Yamashita, 1944b, Niwa 1955 ; *Gambusia*, Okada and Yamashita, 1944b ; *Lebistes*, Hopper, 1949a ; *Misgurnus*, Kobayashi, 1951). This is no doubt due to the fact that the body form and colouration of the mature female is usually that of the immature animal of both sexes and it undergoes no special metamorphosis at the time of sexual maturity. It is also in direct contrast to the effects produced by testis removal, as a result of which the male comes to resemble the female, or, rather, loses those characteristics which differentiate him from immature males and females. On the other hand, in cases in which the female does possess secondary sexual characters, they have usually been shown to be under ovarian control. For example, Aronson (1948) showed that ovariectomy in *Tilapia* entailed a rapid decrease in length of the genital tube and a return of the opercular colouration to that of the immature fish.

It has already been reported that castration frequently modifies reproductive behaviour in the male ; the same is usually, though not always, true of the female after ovariectomy. Noble and Kumpf (1936) ovariectomised females of *Xiphophorus helleri*, *Betta splendens* and *Hemichromis bimaculatus* and found that neither *Betta* nor *Hemichromis* showed the characteristic breeding behaviour of the female, though ovariectomised *Xiphophorus* females were still sexually attractive to males of their own species.

Effects of ovarian extracts and oestrogens

There are no reports in the literature on the effects of ovarian transplantation in fish and few on the injection of ovarian extracts. Bretschneider, Duyvené de Wit and Goedewaagen (1941) extracted the ovaries of *Lophius* with ether and administered the extract to female bitterling and found that it stimulated growth of the ovipositor but, apart from this record, most of the information available on the effects of sex steroids comes from the injection of synthetic material.

Effects of oestrogens on the testis.—Oestrogens have usually been found to have an inhibitory effect on the male gonad. Berkowitz (1937, 1938, 1941b) showed that oestrone and oestradiol administered in the aquarium water to *Lebistes reticulatus* suppressed spermatogenesis and caused partial involution of the testis ; in some cases definite ovotestes were produced, even in specimens in which sex-differentiation was already complete. Cohen (1946) reported that α oestradiol benzoate had a pronounced feminising action on the gonads of immature genetic males of *Xiphophorus maculatus* ; the gonads were smaller than in the controls and contained large ova in addition to early spermatogenetic stages. But after 20 weeks the gonads of treated fish were much more like those of controls ; spermatids and spermatophores were present and there were no ova. This is strongly reminiscent of the position in frogs among Amphibia, in which the early feminisation exerted by oestradiol does not persist after metamorphosis even if treatment is continued. *Xiphophorus* hybrids were treated with oestradiol by Taylor (1948), who found that the testes showed pronounced effects of the treatment. Only the cortex with its cysts of primary spermatogonia remained relatively undisturbed. Okada and Yamashita (1944a, b) found that oestradiol and diethyl stilboestrol produced ovotestes in young males of *Gambusia affinis* whilst in mature males degeneration of the gonad is a more usual effect, though ova have been seen in such cases also. Hamon (1946), on the other hand, found that oestradiol feminises males of all ages in *G. holbrooki*. The work of Tavolga (1949) illustrates a striking and interesting difference between the response of the fish *Xiphophorus maculatus* to oestradiol on the one hand and oestradiol benzoate on the other. In mammals, these two oestrogens have identical actions, but in *Xiphophorus* the ester has a marked inhibitory effect on both testes and ovaries, whereas oestradiol strongly stimulates the testes of males over 19 mm. in length and induces the formation of large, well-differentiated gonopodia. In the male of *Misgurnus anguillicaudatus*, Egami (1954b) found that the testes are but little affected by oestrone or oestrone benzoate though the secondary sex characters are suppressed and testicular grafts are unable to establish themselves. Thus, so far as concerns the testis, oestrogens are mainly inhibitory and spermatogenesis is usually suppppressed (*Salmo irideus*, Padoa, 1937; *Phoxinus laevis*, Bullough, 1940; *Lebistes reticulatus*, Berkowitz, 1941b; *Xiphophorus maculatus*, Cohen, 1946; *Misgurnus fossilis* and *Oryzias latipes*, Egami, 1954b, 1955a, b). In some cases ovotestes have been induced (*Salmo irideus*, Padoa, 1937; *Lebistes reticulatus*, Berkowitz, 1941b, Svärdson, 1943; *Oryzias latipes*, Okada and Yamashita, 1944a, b, Egami, 1955a; *Xiphophorus helleri*, Baldwin and Li, 1945; *Xiphophorus maculatus*, Cohen, 1946).

Effects of oestrogens on the ovary.—Oestrogens have usually been reported to have an inhibiting or regressive action on the fish ovary. Tavolga (1949) found that oestradiol-treated *Xiphophorus* females showed ovarian degeneration, and

Berkowitz (1941b) and Egami (1954e, 1955b) reported similar findings in *Lebistes* and *Oryzias* respectively. Egami (1954a) also found that both oestrone and oestrone benzoate inhibit the ovaries of *Misgurnus anguillicaudatus*. However, some workers have reported oestrogen stimulation of fish ovaries (Bullough, 1942 ; Svärdson, 1943 ; Kawamoto, 1950), but Bullough found that although oestrone stimulated the production of small oögonia in *Phoxinus*, development of primary oöcytes was inhibited and they finally disintegrated.

Effects of oestrogens on the secondary sexual characters.—Berkowitz (1937, 1941b) was one of the first workers to demonstrate the feminising action of oestrogens on the secondary sexual characters of fish. Of sixty immature *Lebistes* treated with Progynon for from 1 to 5 months, none showed male secondary sexual characters and all had the size and body form of the female. Berkowitz also demonstrated that age at the start of treatment was of great importance ; Progynon had no effect on the secondary sexual characters of adult males even after 4 months. The gonopodium of *Xiphophorus maculatus* was found by Cohen (1946) to be suppressed by oestradiol benzoate, but only when spermatogenesis was completely inhibited. Taylor (1948), as already reported, found that oestradiol had a pronounced adverse effect on the testes of *Xiphophorus* hybrids and yet there were no external signs of sex reversal. Most workers have reported that adult fish show few external effects of oestrogen treatment whilst young fish are much more labile, but Hamon (1946) has found that oestradiol benzoate feminises males of all ages in *Gambusia holbrooki*. Scott (1944) reported a feminising influence of α oestradiol on the anal fin structure of *Lebistes*. A similar feminising action was reported by Egami (1954b), who treated *Misgurnus* with oestrone and oestrone benzoate and found that the male secondary sexual characters were completely suppressed. It may also be noted that Noble and Borne (1940) showed that oestradiol had no effect on the social hierarchy of female *Xiphophorus helleri*.

The amount of work carried out on the effects of oestrogens on fish is less than that reported for androgens and the results are more discordant. Oestrogens are predominantly feminising in action, though, as Tavolga has shown, closely related oestrogens may have a completely different effect from each other and from that which they show in mammals. As Pickford and Atz (1957) have pointed out, the literature on the effects of sex steroids in fish is extensive, but it lacks the critical quality experiments on castrate animals would have. We may also note that much of it would be easier to interpret if the pituitary had not been present at the time of treatment.

Effects of Hormones on Embryonic Gonads

As in cyclostomes, but unlike all other vertebrates, the embryonic gonad in teleosts is a single structure which is probably homologous with the gonadal cortex of other vertebrate groups (D'Ancona, 1952). Auxocytes (early oöcytes) are usually the most prominent cells in the primordial gonad of teleosts and this has led several workers to postulate a protogynous condition. However, D'Ancona (1950) states that both types of gonia are present from the start, though the spermatogonia are smaller and less obvious. Genetically mediated inductor substances are believed to be secreted by certain cells of the gonadal stroma ; in the male these favour development of the spermatogonia and regression of the auxocytes, whereas in the female the reverse is the case.

The chemical nature of the inductor substances is unknown, though they are thought by some workers to be identical with the sex steroids. Whether this be the case or not, exogenous androgens and oestrogens can, under certain experimental conditions, exert an effect on sex differentiation. The small amount of work on this subject in teleosts has been reviewed by Ashby (1952, 1957), who also reported his own work on alevins of *Salmo trutta* in which he investigated the effects of oestradiol (50 and 300 μg/.l.) and testosterone (60 μg./l.) on the developing gonads. Both substances had a strong inhibitory action on gonadal development, but there was no evidence of sex-inversion. Progesterone and desoxycorticosterone acetate had a similar effect.

Viviparity in Bony Fish

Viviparity in lower organisms has already been discussed (Volume 2, Chapter 15) and recent reviews on this aspect of fish reproduction have been published by Turner (1947b) and Hoar (1955). In general, gestation takes place either in the ovarian cavity or within the follicle. In the latter case, sperm penetrates the ovarian wall (Dulzetto, 1937; Turner, 1947b), and Turner has reported finding active sperm in the ovary of *Heterandria formosa* as long as 10 months after copulation. It seems that the stored sperm is capable of fertilising eggs as they become ripe, and this can lead to the development of several broods of different ages in any one ovary. This phenomenon has been called " superfetation " by Turner (1937); it is a characteristic feature of many poeciliid fish. It has reached its greatest development in *Heterandria*, where as many as nine broods may be developing simultaneously.

Viviparity has almost certainly evolved separately in the different families in which it occurs, and may well have evolved more than once in several of the families. It is found in all or many of the following families : Poeciliidae, Anablepidae, Fitzroyiidae, Goodeidae, Hemiramphidae, Embiosocidae, Clinidae, Zoarcidae, Brotulidae, Scorpaenidae, and Comephoridae, and ranges between ovoviviparity and true viviparity in which the young are dependent upon the mother for food as well as for respiratory and excretory needs.

Turner (1942b, 1947b) has discussed the endocrinological basis of viviparity in teleosts and it is apparent from his account that little indeed is known about this most interesting specialisation in teleost reproductive physiology.

For example, it would be very interesting to know whether, in those forms in which the young develop within the follicle, liberation of the embryos is brought about by the same agencies which effect ovulation in oviparous species. Also, whether pseudo-placentae are under hormonal control and whether they themselves function as endocrine organs. Further, is the cyclical nature of viviparous breeding controlled by the pituitary, and, if so, what modification takes place to permit superfetation ? Are there functional corpora lutea in follicle-breeding species ? and are the muscular contractions of the ovarian wall by means of which the young are born controlled by hormones ? These and many other questions await an answer.

Hypophysectomy might be expected to yield results of interest, but it does not appear to have been carried out on any of the viviparous species during gestation. Experiments in which pituitary extracts have been administered have yielded equivocal results : Houssay (1930, 1931) and Haempel (1950) have reported premature release of young in *Cnesterodon* and *Lebistes* respectively ; Régnier (1938) and Haempel (1950) in *Xiphophorus* and *Lebistes*, respectively, obtained viable young and the interval between broods appeared to be reduced. In some cases Haempel obtained protracted gestation and still-births at parturition.

Administration of testosterone propionate caused premature parturition or resorption of young in *Xiphophorus helleri* within one or two days of the injection (Witschi and Crown, 1937). Hamon (1945a) also observed premature parturition in *Gambusia*, and Régnier (1937, 1938) and Eversole (1941) reported resorption of embryos in *Xiphophorus* and *Lebistes*, all as a result of treatment with androgens.

Changes in pituitary histology have been reported in several live-bearing fish, and this work, which has already been discussed, seems to suggest that the pituitary gland is implicated in gestation (Sokol, 1955 ; Stolk, 1951).

The corpus luteum is closely associated with viviparity in mammals, and structures which have been given this name have been reported from all vertebrate classes (Volume 1, Part 1, Chapter 5). In the placental mammals, the corpus luteum is essential for implantation, placentation and the maintenance of the early stages of pregnancy. Further, the pituitary is necessary for the development and functioning of the corpus luteum ; two pituitary hormones appear to be implicated, namely, luteinising hormone (LH) and luteotrophic hormone (LTH). However, in fishes, as indeed in all cold-blooded vertebrates, there is no evidence that the so-called corpora lutea are in any way controlled by the pituitary ; equally, there is no critical evidence that they are secretory, or, indeed, that they have any physiological function. The position is further complicated by the fact that corpora lutea are frequently confused with corpora atretica, from which they are at certain stages indistinguishable. These structures originate by atresia of mature follicles and are found in all vertebrate groups and may be more numerous than are corpora lutea. They are frequently called " pre-ovulation corpora lutea ", but this is probably undesirable. In fact, the use of the term " corpus luteum " in any group other than the mammals may well be unjustified on physiological grounds and has already given rise to a great deal of confusion.

Wallace (1903) reported that the ruptured follicle of the viviparous blenny (*Zoarces viviparus*) had little resemblance at any stage to a mammalian corpus luteum, and the same view was expressed by Mendoza (1943), who studied the fate of the evacuated follicles of *Neotoca* during the time the developing young were lying in the ovarian lumen. In *Xiphophorus helleri*, the embryos develop within the follicle, and Bailey (1933) has observed hypertrophy and signs of secretory activity in the collapsed follicles after release of the embryos. It is difficult to assign a function to such an activity, since it appears to take place too late to be of any significance in gestation. Matthews (1938) observed marked activity of the follicular epithelium of *Fundulus* after ovulation and reported that corpora lutea were developed. Unfortunately, data are available on the fate of the follicle cells after ovulation for only a few fish, and it is known that, in some cases at least, ovulation is followed by rapid disintegration and disappearance of what remains of the folicular epithelium (Cunningham, 1898, for the plaice). An extended comparative study of this subject in fish having a variety of post-ovulation histories might well offer clues as to the possible significance of corpus luteum-like structures. A method of deluteinisation is unfortunately not easily available in the viviparous species since the young are incubated either in the cavity of the ovary or in the follicles themselves so that ovaries cannot be removed without terminating pregnancy.

The so-called pre-ovulation corpus luteum is of widespread occurrence in fish, and most of our knowledge as to its formation and possible functions comes from the work of Bretschneider and Duyvené de Wit (1947), who studied these structures in the bitterling (*Rhodeus amarus*), and described their occurrence in a variety of teleosts, both oviparous and viviparous. They believe that pre-ovulation corpora lutea are the only secretory glands in the fish ovary. Hoar (1955) also inclines towards this view, as does d'Ancona (1950), who studied seven species of Sparid fish and found modified atretic follicles in four of them. He states that these structures are identical to the pre-ovulation corpora lutea described by Bretschneider and Duyvené de Wit, and believes them to have a secretory function.

The nature and possible functions of these pre-ovulatory corpora lutea constitutes one of the many unsolved problems in comparative endocrinology. Smith (1955) concludes that they are identical to the corpora atretica of the amphibian ovary, and Pickford and Atz (1957) have reviewed the contradictory and often unsatisfactory evidence concerning them. The latter authors agree with Dodd (1955) that the physiological status of fish corpora lutea in general must remain in doubt until it has been demonstrated whether or not they produce progesterone and play a part in the maintenance of pregnancy.

V. AMPHIBIA

There are some 2,000 species of living Amphibia, and these belong to three sharply separated subclasses : Urodela (newts and salamanders), Anura (frogs and toads), and Apoda (a small tropical group of limbless, blind, burrowing amphibians). Little is known concerning the reproductive physiology of the Apoda ; in consequence, the present account is limited to Urodela and Anura, about which a good deal is known. In fact, the reproductive endocrinology of certain Anura, namely the frogs and toads which are used in the diagnosis of human pregnancy, has received an unusual degree of attention.

Although most Amphibia are land-living vertebrates for the greater part of their lives, they have not accepted the challenge that dry land offers to reproductive adaptability. The majority are still dependent on a return to water at breeding time, fertilisation is usually external, the eggs never acquire a shell, and any degree of parental care is the exception rather than the rule. Several urodeles lay their eggs on dry land and some others are ovoviviparous, but the modifications associated with these specialisations are slight. Some Anura are similarly independent of water at the breeding time ; *Protopipa* and *Pipa* incubate their eggs in individual chambers on the back of the females. In *Phyllobates* and *Dendrobates*, the male acts as nurse, and in the marsupial tree frogs the eggs are carried in a pouch or marsupium on the female's back. There are, in addition, a few ovoviviparous anuran species, though the degree to which the developing young are dependent on the mother in these cases is extremely slight.

Endocrinological studies on Amphibia have therefore been limited almost entirely to the hormonal control of gonads, reproductive ducts and accessory sexual organs in oviparous species. It is unfortunate that the few amphibian species which have developed special adaptations for reproduction on dry land are often rare and usually difficult to obtain, since it would be interesting to know the nature and degree of control, if any, exerted by pituitary and gonads on these adaptations and on viviparity. However, there is no doubt that the reproductive system has lagged behind the rest of the body in adapting itself to life on dry land, and because of this, investigations on amphibian reproduction are likely to make only a small contribution towards the important comparative study of viviparity.

Gonads and Reproductive Ducts

The gonads and reproductive ducts of the two main amphibian orders are fundamentally similar in structure. They are paired in both sexes and consist of testes, vasa efferentia and vasa deferentia (Wolffian ducts) in the male, and of ovaries, and oviducts (Müllerian ducts) in the female. The gonad primordia are double structures, the cortex originating from peritoneum, and the medulla from the interrenal blastema. In genetic males, the medulla acts as host to the primordial germ-cells and a testis develops, whereas, in genetic females, the medulla more or less disappears and the cortex develops into the ovary.

The amphibian kidney is a mesonephros. In urodeles it is elongated and retains more of its primitive segmental arrangement than in anurans. It is also markedly subdivided into an anterior genital kidney and a posterior urinary kidney. Both segments are drained by the Wolffian duct, which is therefore both a urinary duct and a vas deferens. Vasa efferentia are formed by outgrowths from the genital segment of the kidney.

The Müllerian duct, which serves as an oviduct in the female, arises from the Wolffian duct anlage in urodeles, whereas in anurans it develops from a separate primordium.

The morphology of the amphibian urinogenital system has been described by many authors, of whom the following are representative: Spengel, 1876; Champy, 1913; Aron, 1924; de Beaumont, 1929; McCurdy, 1931; Rodgers and Risley, 1938; Adams, 1940; Houssay, 1947.

The male (Fig. 11. 24a, b)

The testes of mature urodeles usually consist of several well-marked lobes which are joined together by thread-like segments. The histological appearance varies with time of year, but, in winter, each lobe consists of two zones, visible to the naked eye. One is large and white, the other much smaller and hyaline. The former consists of a mass of ampullae, each surrounded by connective tissue and having an efferent ductule which communicates ultimately with the vasa efferentia. Each ampulla contains a mass of spermatozoa held together in bundles by Sertoli cells. The hyaline area contains nests of primary and secondary spermatogonia. It is in these nests of cells that the succeeding wave of spermatogenesis starts.

The anuran testis (Champy, 1913), consists of a mass of seminiferous ampullae, each limited by a distinct basement membrane and bound together to form the ovoid testis by an investing tunic of elastic tissue. The testis contains several nests of cells called spermatocysts, each covered with a membrane of flattened follicular cells. Each spermatocyst matures independently, so that any one ampulla may contain spermatocysts at very different stages of maturation. The mother-cell of each cyst is a primary spermatogonium which lays down the investing membrane

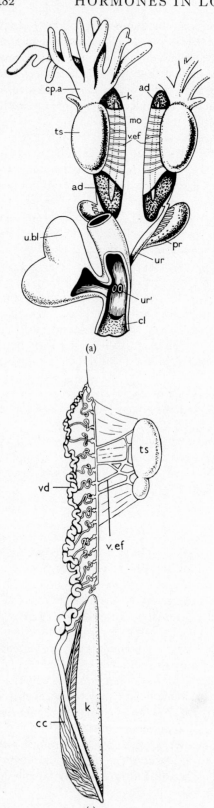

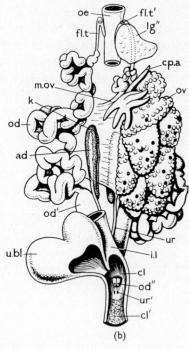

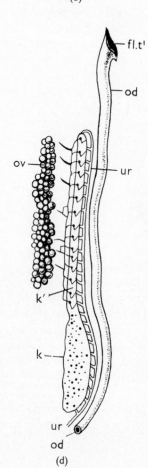

and becomes transformed into many secondary spermatogonia; these undergo maturation divisions and ultimately give rise to spermatozoa. When this point has been reached, the cyst membranes vanish, the heads of the spermatozoa become inserted in Sertoli cells and their tails project into the lumen of the ampulla. The histological picture offered by the anuran testis differs profoundly at different times of the year. The annual cycle in *Rana temporaria* has been excellently described by van Oordt (1956).

The male reproductive ducts are essentially similar in urodeles and anurans. They consist of the vasa efferentia which communicate on one side with the efferent ducts of the testicular ampullae, and on the other side with the genital segment of the kidney. The entire kidney is drained by the Wolffian duct, which is therefore both ureter and vas deferens and carries urine and spermatozoa to the cloaca. In some frogs, a vesicula seminalis differentiates on the lower segment of the vas deferens. It is usually a highly secretory structure, which, at maturity, communicates by several small channels with the vas deferens.

The female (Fig. *11*. 24 c,d)

The ovaries are sac-like structures which are mere folds of the peritoneum. The abundant stroma characteristic of the mammalian ovary is absent. The eggs lie in the cortical region, the appearance of which varies greatly throughout the year as in all seasonal breeders. Immediately after spawning, three populations of cells may be recognised in the ovary : young follicles from which the next batch of eggs will be recruited ; numerous cell nests which will provide eggs for the subsequent spawning, and primary germ-cells (Smith, 1955).

Each follicle consists of an investing epithelium of cells enclosed in a vascular network and containing the oöcyte. The latter is contained in a thin vitelline membrane which is said by Smith, (1916) to be double in *Cryptobranchus* and to consist of an outer zona pellucida, produced by the follicle cells, and an inner zona radiata, secreted by the egg itself.

All authors have been unanimous in describing atretic follicles in the amphibian ovary. Burns (1932) and Tuchmann-Duplessis (1945) have described their mode of formation and it closely resembles that outlined for pre-ovulation corpora lutea in the bitterling by Bretschneider and Duyvené de Wit (1947). Corpora atretica have already been discussed in the teleost section above and the views expressed there apply here also.

The ovary-like Bidder's organ, found in all bufonids so far examined, though not in other Amphibia, is described below.

The genital ducts in the female are modified Müllerian ducts. They extend from the anterior end of the body cavity on each side of the middle line to the cloaca and hang from the dorsal body wall by a mesentery. Adams (1940) has recognised

Fig. *11*. 24—Amphibian urinogenital systems. (a) and (b), Anura. (c) and (d), Urodela. (a) *Rana temporaria*, male (redrawn from Howes, 1902). (b) *R. temporaria*, female, right ovary removed (redrawn from Howes, 1902). (c) *Triturus* sp., male (redrawn from de Beaumont, 1929). (d) *Triturus* sp., female (redrawn from Wiedersheim, 1883). ad, adrenal; cl, cl', cloaca; cp.a, fat body; cc, urinary collecting tubules; fl.t, anterior region of oviduct; fl.t', anterior oviducal opening; i.l, rectum; k, kidney (mesonephros); k', kidney (pronephros); lg'', lung; mo, mesor-chium; mov, mesovarium; od, od', segments of oviduct; od'', oviducal opening; oe, oesophagus; ov, ovary; pr, *vesicula seminalis*; ts, testis; u.bl, urinary bladder; ur, ureter; ur', openings of ureters; v.d, vas deferens; v.ef, vasa efferentia.

six regions in the mature oviduct of *Triturus viridescens*; three of these lie in front of the kidney. The infundibular region opens into the body cavity by the osteum abdominale, and leads into a transparent sector of the tube with a watery secretion; this is followed by an opaque region, the cells of which contain eosinophilic granules. The first of the three regions parallel to and posterior to the kidney is transparent and wide; it is followed by an opaque chalky-white zone, and finally there is a straight section with few internal folds which leads into the cloaca. The oviducts at full maturity are convoluted and glandular and part, or all, of their lumen is ciliated. In *Rana*, where the lower third of the oviduct is distinctly wider than the rest and forms the so-called " uterus " in which the ovulated eggs lodge

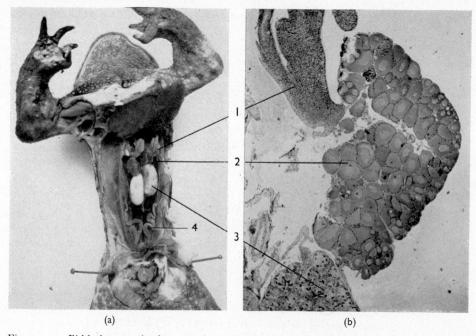

(a)   (b)

Fig. *11*. *25*—Bidder's organ in the normal male toad. (a) Anatomical relationships. (b) Sagittal section through fat body, Bidder's organ and rostral end of testis. 1, fat body; 2, Bidder's organ; 3, mature, testis; 4, rudimentary oviduct. (From Ponse, 1949.)

for days or weeks before oviposition, only the upper two-thirds of the duct are ciliated, whereas in *Xenopus*, the entire duct is ciliated and ovulation is followed automatically by oviposition (Waring, Landgrebe and Neill, 1941).

Bidder's organ (Fig. *11*. *25*)

Bidder, more than 100 years ago, described a structure lying at the rostral end of the gonad in both sexes of *Bufo vulgaris*, between fat body and definitive gonad, which has the appearance of a rudimentary ovary, and which normally remains in an undeveloped condition, taking no part in reproduction. It consists of a compact mass of small oöcytes which never evolve beyond an early stage of development and which surround a vestigial ovarian cavity (Fig. *11.25*). Chang (1955) points out that from both the histological and physiological points of view the term " Bidder's organ " seems inappropriate. The structure in question is not an independent organ and it has no obvious function; it is merely a cortical (ovarian) lobe of the gonad.   Moreover, it was first described by Roesel von Rosenhof some 88 years before Bidder's publication.   However, in spite of these reservations it seems unlikely that the term " Bidder's organ " will disappear from literature since it is so firmly entrenched by long usage.

The occurrence of Bidder's organ in bufonid anura has been the subject of several publications ; Ponse (1924), Stohler (1931), Witschi (1933), Koch (1934), de Vos (1935) and Davis (1936).   It has been found to occur in all adult male bufonids and in some adult females.   The position was reviewed by Dubois (1947), who added several new genera to the list of bufonids known to possess a Bidder's organ.

Ponse (1924) removed Bidder's organ from male toads and showed that it plays no part in the maintenance of the sexual characters of the normal male.   It does, however, react to castration, ovariectomy and the injection of certain steroids, and these reactions are described below.

Fig. 11. 26—*Bufo vulgaris:* Hermaphrodite specimen. O, ovary; T, testis; OD, oviduct. (From Ponse, 1924.)

Hermaphroditism in Amphibia

Hermaphroditism in *Rana temporaria* is a common phenomenon which has often been observed since the original record of Pflüger (1882).   It is much less common in other Amphibia, though Ponse (1949) mentions eighty-seven known cases of *Bufo vulgaris* in which the external appearance was that of a male, whilst the internal organs showed varying degrees of hermaphroditism. One of these specimens is illustrated in Fig. *11.26*. Ponse (1949) has shown that at the time of metamorphosis the gonad of male *B. vulgaris* is a tripartite structure, consisting of

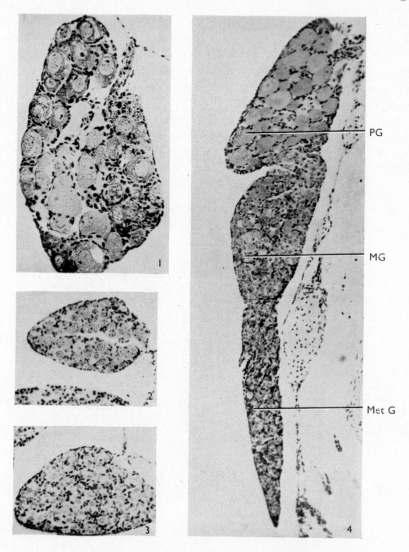

Fig. *11.27*—*Bufo vulgaris:* Histology of gonad of male at metamorphosis. (1) T.S. progonad, i.e. larval Bidder's organ; note pseudovocytes. (2) T.S. mesogonad; predominantly ovarian. (3) T.S. metagonad; testis anlage; note spermatogonia. (4) L.S. gonad showing all regions. PG, progonad; MG, mesogonad; MetG, metagonad. (From Ponse, 1949.)

an anterior progonad which contains only pseudovocytes and is the larval Bidder's organ, a mesogonad which is predominantly ovarian, and a metagonad which is the definitive testis and contains spermatogonia (Fig. *11.27*). In genetic males, under normal circumstances, the mesogonad quickly disappears, but it is obvious that a well-developed anatomical basis exists for hermaphroditism in this animal.

Hermaphroditism in *R. temporaria* was widely accepted as an aberrant manifestation of sexuality in a species which was basically gonochoristic, until Witschi
(1923) studied the condition in different races. He showed that hermaphroditism
was not a feature of all races and that hermaphrodites were usually individuals in
process of sex-change. Witschi showed that in some races of *R. temporaria*, the
so-called " undifferentiated " races, all individuals were females at the time of
metamorphosis; it was only at some subsequent time, often after functional female
phase, that the genetic males became functional males. Other races were said to
be " differentiated "; these had a very short hermaphrodite phase and already
showed their genetic sex at the time of metamorphosis.

Secondary Sexual Characters

The Amphibia possess a great diversity of dimorphic characters associated
with sex, the development of many of which has been shown to depend on hormones of the gonads. The characters, as a whole, are usually classified as pre-
pubertal or post-pubertal, that is, those which make a gradual appearance as the
animal grows, and those, such as the newt's nuptial dress, which appear suddenly
at the first breeding season and thereafter undergo regression and make a cyclic
annual appearance. It is, of course, the post-pubertal characters with which we
are most concerned here.

(a)

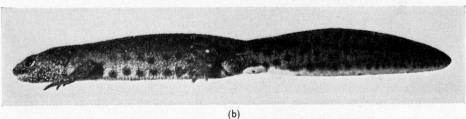

(b)

Fig. *11.* 28—*Triturus cristatus carnifex:* Sex dimorphism. (a) Male in nuptial dress. Note dorsal
crest on head and body, enlarged tail fins, and swollen cloaca at base of tail. (b) Sexually ripe
female. (Natural size.)

Urodela (Fig. *11. 28*)

The striking colouration adopted by many newts at the breeding season is one
of the best-known amphibian secondary sexual characters. The bizarre colour
patterns appear to give added emphasis to the display behaviour in which the male

indulges, and which induces a state of sexual excitement in the female so that she will accept the spermatophore when it is deposited by the male.

Bright colouration is often accompanied by a dorsal crest, webbing of the toes and a terminal caudal filament. The crest varies a good deal in aspect; in *Triturus cristatus*, it is a high serrated ridge which is distinct from the non-serrated tail fin. In other newts, the crest is usually not serrated, but may be tall and wavy (*T. punctatum*) or low and continuous along both body and tail (*T. alpestris*). Webbing and pigmentation of the hind feet are especially prominent in *T. palmatus* and a long caudal filament of uncertain function is present in both sexes of this species.

The so-called " hedonic " glands of certain urodeles appear to play a part in courtship behaviour, and their distribution is usually such that they are brought into full use during the courtship antics characteristic of the species. They appear to be modified mucous glands which produce a granular secretion which, though apparently odourless, appears to hold the attention of the female during courtship (Noble, 1931). In *Triturus viridescens* they are situated on the cheeks of the male, and according to Rogoff (1927) they serve to quiet the female and induce her to follow the male and accept the spermatophore. In the plethodontid salamanders, however, the hedonic glands are much more widely distributed, being found on cheeks, body and tail of the male ; their secretion apparently stimulates the female during courtship.

Other glandular structures which have a different appearance and function in the two sexes, though they are similarly distributed, are the glands associated with the cloaca. These are the pelvic glands, and the cloacal glands proper, which together manufacture the spermatophore in the male, and the abdominal glands which may or may not open into the cloaca and are probably hedonic glands. All three sets may be present in the female though they have different functions here. The pelvic glands serve as reservoirs for the spermatozoa (spermathecae) after their liberation from the spermatophore, and the cloacal glands may play a part in forming the egg capsule. In some urodeles this complement of glands is potentially present though it does not normally develop, and in all cases the development of the glands seems to be largely controlled by the sex hormones (*see below*).

Certain other miscellaneous sex-dimorphic characters have been described in urodeles, these are the cloacal papillae of some newts (Nakamura, 1927), and the elongated monocuspid teeth of male plethodontids, such as *Eurycea bislineata*, which develop at sexual maturity from the short bicuspid teeth normal to the species.

Although internal fertilisation is the rule in urodeles other than in the two most primitive families Hynobiidae and Cryptobranchidae, no intromittent organs have been developed. Sperms are deposited in spermatophores by the males, and these are picked up by the cloacal lips of the females and stored in the cloaca until they are required for fertilisation.

Anura (Fig. *11*. 29, 30)

Devices to facilitate amplexus are found in considerable profusion in the Anura, the best known being the nuptial pads or thumb pads of the common frog. These structures show pronounced differences in morphology and position in different species. The nuptial pad usually consists of a cluster of black epidermal spines which cover a glandular swelling formed by closely grouped acinous glands. In some forms the glands are absent (*Bufo vulgaris*), in others the spines are absent

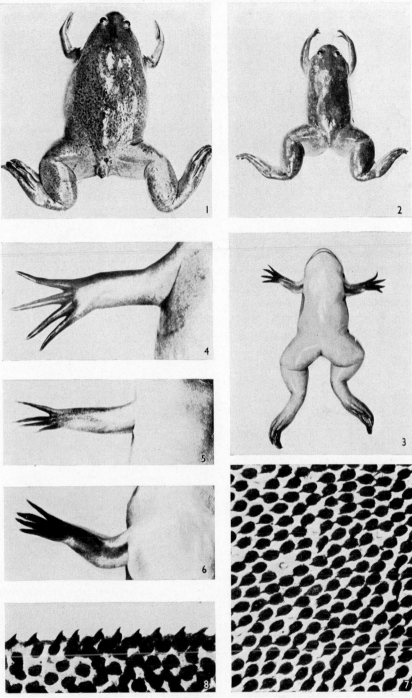

Fig. *11. 29—Xenopus laevis:* Sex dimorphism. (1) Dorsal view of mature female; note prominent cloacal lips ($\times$ $\frac{1}{2}$). (2) Dorsal view of mature male; note size dimorphism between sexes ($\times$ $\frac{1}{2}$). (3) Ventral view of mature male; note "gloving" of anterior surfaces of hands and arms ($\times$ $\frac{1}{2}$). (4) Anterior surface of hand and arm of mature female ($\times$ $1\frac{1}{2}$). (5) Anterior surface of hand and arm of immature male ($\times$ $1\frac{1}{2}$). (6) Anterior surface of hand and arm of mature male ($\times$ $1\frac{1}{2}$). (7) Photomicrograph of desquamated epidermis from "gloved" region of forearm of mature male; note pigmented spines ($\times$ 180). (8) Profile view of pigmented spines ($\times$ 180).

Hyla arborea), and the distribution of glandular areas over the body differs a good deal throughout the group. In *Rana temporaria*, the male has a single glandular pad on each thumb, whereas, in *Xenopus laevis*, an extensive sheet of pigmented

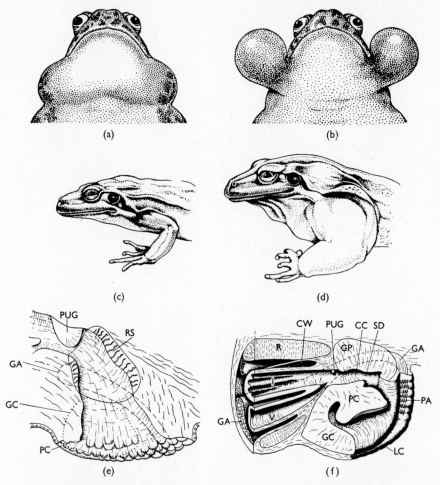

Fig. *11*. 30—*Amphibia:* Sexual dimorphism. (a) and (b) Vocal apparatus. (a): *Rana temporaria* croaking with distended *internal* vocal sacs; (b): *R. ridibunda* croaking with distended *external* vocal sacs. (From Parker and Haswell, Vol. 2, 7th ed.) (c) and (d) Brachial skeleton and musculature. *Leptodactylus ocellatus,* showing sexual dimorphism of the forelimbs. (c): female; (d): male. (From Noble, 1931.) (e) and (f) Cloacal regions. (e): *Triturus* sp., male, sagittal section, semi-diagrammatic; (f): *Triturus* sp., female, sagittal section, semi-diagrammatic. (From de Beaumont, 1929.) CC, cloacal canal; CW, Wolffian duct; GA, abdominal glands; GC, glands of the cloacal lips; GP, pelvic glands; I, rectum; LC, cloacal lips; PA, papillae on which the abdominal glands open; PC, cloacal papillae; PUG, urinogenital papilla; R, kidney; RS, *receptaculum seminis*; V, bladder. ((d) from *Biology of the Amphibia*, by G. K. Noble, reprinted by permission of Dover Publications, Inc., New York.)

spines appears on the ventral surfaces of the digits and forearms, and in its full development extends as a narrow band as far as the axilla (Fig. *11*.29). A number of modifications associated with the clasp-reflex of frogs and toads may occur in the forearm of the male. These usually consist of greater muscular development and corresponding skeletal changes during the breeding season (Fig. *11*.30).

A device which is apparently associated with egg-laying is found in the female *X. laevis*. It consists of a pair of prominent glandular cloacal lips which become very hyperaemic at the time of amplexus (Fig. *11.29*). The function of these structures is not fully understood.

In most, though not all, anurans, the females are either voiceless or produce a mere grunt, whereas the males in many species have strongly developed vocal sacs. Thus, the male *Rana esculenta* croaks loudly, whilst the female is virtually dumb. In association with his louder voice and greater activity, the male has more powerful abdominal muscles and larger lungs.

Most Anura, unlike reptiles and birds, show little or no colour dimorphism, and Noble and Farris, (1929) have claimed that sight plays almost no part in sex-recognition in those Amphibia which have been investigated. In Anura which do exhibit colour dimorphism, notably *Bufo canorus* and *Arthroleptella lightfooti*, there is a pronounced difference in colour and pattern between the two sexes, and it seems unlikely that such marked differences are unassociated with sex, though there are other, much less striking, colour differences which do appear to be merely incidental. For example, the changes in pigmentation of the throat region in the cricket frog, *Acris gryllus*, appear to be due entirely to the enormous expansion of this region during the breeding season and the concomitant increase in surface area and number of melanophores.

Certain other anuran secondary sexual characters are associated with protection of the developing eggs and young ; such devices are the cheek pouches of the male *Rhinoderma darwinii*, the honeycomb of chambers which develop on the backs of female *Pipa pipa*, and the " marsupium " of *Gastrotheca marsupiatum*.

Fertilisation is external in most Anura, but in the African genus *Nectophrynoides* which is ovoviviparous, it is internal, though there are no intromittent organs. The " tailed " American frog *Ascaphus* appears to be exceptional in developing an extension of the cloaca, the so-called tail, which serves as an intromittent organ.

The entire question of secondary sexual characters in Amphibia, their evolution and interrelationships, and the part they play in the reproductive biology of these animals, has been considered in detail by Noble (1931). The role of the gonads in their development and maintenance is discussed below.

The Pituitary Gland

The amphibian pituitary gland is a highly characteristic organ which shows a much greater uniformity of structure than is usual in the other cold-blooded vertebrate groups (Fig. *11.31*). It projects backwards from the mesencephalon so that the adenohypophysis is the most posterior component of the gland ; it cannot therefore, with any justification, be called the " anterior " lobe and is probably best termed " pars distalis ". The pars distalis is a well-developed lobe, rich in sinusoids which subdivide its cells into cord-like aggregations and give them an exceptionally rich blood supply. The pars intermedia partially invests the antero-dorsal margin of the pars distalis and frequently shows enlargement of its lateral regions. The pars nervosa lies antero-dorsal in position and varies a good deal in the extent to which it is developed; in most urodeles it consists merely of a thin plate of cells.

A pars tuberalis is probably always present in the amphibian pituitary. In the

Anura it usually consists of two small plaques lying on the ventral surface of the tuber cinereum. They are connected with the pars distalis by a layer of flattened cells which may be reduced to a virtual membrane. The pars tuberalis in urodele amphibia retains a more obvious connection with the pars distalis, being represented by a pair of processes continuous with the pars distalis and extending forward under the tuber cinereum.

The pars tuberalis consists of small cells with large nuclei and correspondingly little cytoplasm which is chromophobic or weakly basophilic. In *Triturus viridescens*, it appears to reach its peak of development, both in number and size of cells, at about the middle of the red eft stage. It then regresses, and attains its

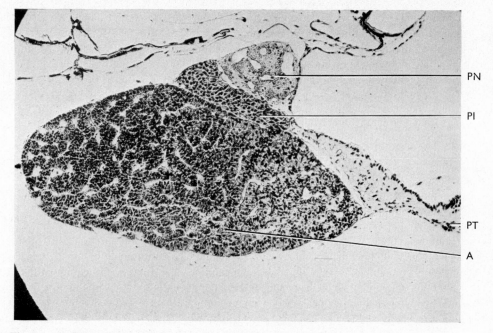

PN
PI
PT
A

Fig. *11*. 31—*Rana temporaria:* Pituitary gland in parasagittal section. A, adenohypophysis; PI, pars intermedia; PN, pars nervosa; PT, pars tuberalis. (From a preparation by Dr. J. C. van de Kamer.)

adult size by the time of final metamorphosis. There is no definite activity or cycle of changes associated with the tuberalis which might give a clue to its function (Copeland, 1943).

The histology of a variety of amphibian pituitaries has been described and attempts have been made to establish the functions of the various cells of the different regions (*Anura*: Atwell, 1918, 1938, 1941; Cordier, 1948, 1953; Zuber-Vogeli, 1952. *Urodela*: Atwell, 1921; Sumi, 1924; Charipper, 1931; Roofe, 1937; Klose, 1941; Copeland, 1943; Mazzi, 1949, 1952; Mazzi and Pieri, 1949; Leghissa, 1953; Miller and Robbins, 1955. *Apoda*: Stendell, 1914). Copeland (1943), using a modification of Heidenhain's Azan technique, distinguished four cell types in the pars distalis of *Triturus viridescens*, two of which were basophilic in reaction and two acidophilic. One of the basophils had a greater affinity for aniline blue than the other and contained no inclusions. The other, the so-called " globular basophil ", contained acidophilic secretion in the form of spheres; the majority of these cells were located away from sinusoids. The acidophilic cells were also of two kinds, one of which, the carmine acidophil, showed an affinity for azocarmine, whilst the other took up the orange-G component of the stain. Zuber-Vogeli (1952) has studied pituitary histology in *Bufo vulgaris* and her findings agree closely with those of Copeland. In addition to the two types of acidophils and basophils, however, a cell type which stains mauve or violet by the Azan technique, is described. These cells are said to be localised round the sinusoids at the anterior pole of the pars distalis and were found in all the toads examined.

Miller and Robbins (1955) have found the pituitary gland of the newt *Taricha* (*Triturus*) *torosa* to be very similar to that of other urodeles, and have described four zones in the pars distalis : an anterior dorsal area of basophilic cells, a median area with largely chromophobic cells, a ventral acidophilic area, and a ventral peripheral zone of basophils which had different cytological characteristics from the dorsal basophils.

Several workers have examined the cyclical changes which occur in the amphibian pituitary and attempted to relate them to phases in the reproductive cycle. Zahl (1935, 1937) examined the pituitary glands of *Rana pipiens* throughout the year, following especially the changes which occurred in the proportions of acidophil and basophil cells in the pars distalis. He noted a gradual increase in acidophilic granules during the sexually quiescent phase (winter), whereas in spring, at the time of sexual activity, a sudden degranulation of acidophils occurred. Immediately after ovulation, the granular basophils showed a marked increase in number and this was maintained until July, at which time they regressed, and by September had reached the level characteristic of the sexually quiescent phase. Zahl supplemented these data by implantation of pituitaries and castration and concluded from all this work that the acidophil secretion is concerned with ovulation, whilst the basophil cells are related to development of the ovarian follicles.

Tuchmann-Duplessis (1945) came to very similar conclusions as a result of studying the pituitaries of various species of *Triturus*. He suggested that the acidophils, which were most plentiful at the time of spawning, produced an LH-like gonadotrophin, whilst the basophils were concerned with the maturation of the gonads and produced an FSH-like hormone.

Most other workers have found a less-marked correlation between the acidophils and the reproductive cycle, though they are unanimous in reporting marked changes in the basophil cells of the adenohypophysis which appear to correspond closely with phases of reproductive activity. Severinghaus (1939) reviewed the existing literature and concluded that increased basophilia is the commonest post-castration phenomenon in the pituitary. Kerr (1939) studied pituitary cytology during and following metamorphosis in *Rana temporaria*, and found that the basophil cells increased markedly after metamorphosis, at which time the gonads were starting to grow. Aplington (1942) studied the reproductive rhythms and pituitary cytology in males of *Necturus maculosus*, the mud puppy. He found that the testis is involuted between December and April ; it then embarks on a period of rapid growth and maturation which lasts until August ; spermatozoa are formed during the latter part of August and September, and are shed in late August, September and early October : a phase of testicular regression lasts from October to December. During the period of testicular growth, two types of basophil cells, one of which is granular, and one agranular, increase in number in the pars distalis. During the breeding season these cells remain constant. Aplington believes that the correlation is striking enough to warrant the conclusion that these basophils are responsible for growth and maturation of the testes in *Necturus*. Copeland (1943), working with *Triturus viridescens*, has arrived at a similar con- clusion ; he believes that his " globular basophils " are the homologues of the " granular basophils " described by Aplington and that they are the seat of gonado- trophin production. In *Triturus*, the globular basophils first appear at the time when the rudimentary gonads begin to grow. Further, in the mature male these cells are smallest during the phase of gonadal exhaustion. When the testes begin to grow and spermatogenesis starts, the basophils multiply and increase in size and globule content. As the testes become mature, the globules are discharged and the cytoplasm of the exhausted globular basophils becomes chromophobic. Copeland also obtained evidence of the gonadotrophic function of these basophilic cells from castration experiments. Newts which had been castrated for $3\frac{1}{2}$–6 months showed an increase in the number of such basophils in the pars distalis.

Zuber-Vogeli (1952) has obtained results for male *Bufo vulgaris* which are in close agreement with those of Aplington and Copeland in that they strongly impli- cate the pituitary basophil in the control of the gonadal cycle. Basophils are the predominant cell type in the pituitary from March to May, that is at the time of maximal sexual activity, whereas the acidophils are least in evidence at this time. The importance of the basophils in the reproductive cycle is also indicated by castration studies, though the effects of gonad removal on the pituitary are not evident until about a year after the operation. By this time, the large basophils are markedly reduced in size, have lost their spheres and have become vacuolated and more or less chromophobic.

Miller and Robbins (1955) are in close agreement with the earlier workers who have found that increase in the basophil cells of the pituitary goes hand in hand with heightened reproductive activity. They consider that increased basophilia in spring and autumn in the pituitary of *Taricha torosa* is probably related to gametogenesis and final maturation of the gonads respectively. Miller and Robbins believe, like Zahl (1937) and Mazzi and Pieri (1949), that the rapid degranulation of the acidophils during breeding may also be associated with gonadotrophin production.

There is some corroborative evidence from other types of investigation that basophilia of the pituitary and gonadotrophic activity are correlated. The evidence from castration has already been considered. Grant (1940) investigated the ovulation-inducing potency of the pituitary of *Rana pipiens* at different seasons, and found that the glands of animals which had recently ovulated were less than half as potent in inducing ovulation *in vitro* as glands taken from hibernating animals. Novelli (1942) showed that the pituitary of *Bufo arenarum* can induce ovulation and spermiation throughout the year, though there are two maxima, one in July and one in September, and these coincide with the times of the year at which the basophils are most plentiful. Additional evidence was provided by Zuber-Vogeli, who made subcutaneous testicular autografts in *Bufo vulgaris*, and reported a close relationship between the state of the autografts and the degree of basophilia of the pituitary.

Thus it appears to have been established that certain of the basophil cells of the amphibian pars distalis, which are also PAS-positive (Mazzi, 1952 ; Miller and Robbins, 1955), are associated with gonadotrophin production, though there is less agreement as to the nature and functions of the hormone or hormones they produce.   Some workers feel that acidophil cells are also implicated in the control of reproduction by the pituitary gland, though there is less unanimity on this point.

The Pituitary and Reproduction

Effects of hypophysectomy

The pioneer work of Adler (1914), Smith (1916) and Allen (1916) on hypophysectomy of the embryonic stages of Amphibia, although it was mainly con-

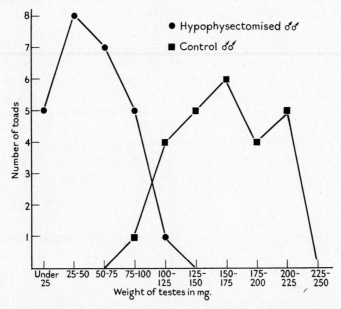

Fig. *11*. 32—*Xenopus laevis:* Effect of hypophysectomy on the testis. Frequency distribution of testicular weights in hypophysectomised and control male toads. (From Bellerby and Hogben, 1938.)

cerned with metamorphosis and other aspects of pituitary-thyroid relationships, established for the first time the diverse and remarkable effects of pituitary removal in Amphibia.   These workers found that hypophysectomy had no effect on the amphibian gonad in early developmental stages, but there is abundant evidence from later work that gonadal development and maturation are under pituitary control in the Amphibia as in all other vertebrates.

Hypophysectomy in the mature male.—The effects of total hypophysectomy and of removing only the adenohypophysis, have been studied in a variety of male Amphibia since Giusti and Houssay (1923, 1924) established that the testes of *Bufo arenarum* suffer slow though progressive involution if the pituitary gland is removed.   This effect is reflected in the marked loss in weight suffered by the testes of hypophysectomised Amphibia (Fig. *11*.32).   Similar findings of testicular regression have since been reported for a variety of Amphibia : *Xenopus laevis*, Hogben (1930), Shapiro and Shapiro (1934), Bellerby and Hogben (1938); *Ambystoma* sp., *Pleurodeles waltlii*, *Triturus cristatus*, Woronzowa and Blacher (1930); *A. tigrinum*, Burns and Buyse (1932) ; *Rana temporaria*, Gallien (1938, 1940), Sluiter, van Oordt and Grasveld (1950), van Oordt, 1956 ; *Bufo vulgaris*, Rey (1939) ; *Triturus* spp., Tuchmann-Duplessis (1945) ; *Rana esculenta*, Sluiter, van Oordt and Mighorst (1950) ; *Bufo arenarum*, Burgos (1949), Penhos and Cardeza (1952). In fact, the only workers who have reported an inability to discover a pituitary-gonad liaison in the Amphibia are Derevici, Derevici and Dornescu (1940). They worked with *Rana esculenta*, but since they do not give the time elapsing between hypophysectomy and autopsy, and since several investigators have emphasised the slowness of the testicular response, this result is difficult to evaluate.

One of the most fascinating problems of reproductive endocrinology is the nature of pituitary control over the gonad at the cell level. It is difficult to obtain any information on this aspect from the early literature on hypophysectomy, but later workers have given it a good deal of attention.

Tuchmann-Duplessis (1945), in a comprehensive study of reproduction in three European newts (*Triturus palmatus*, *T. alpestris* and *T. marmoratus*), found that removal of the hypophysis had striking and rapid effects on the testis. By the end of 1 week, the cysts of spermatozoa were showing agglutination, and this was followed by phagocytosis ; finally the lobules of this region of the testis were replaced by connective tissue. Atrophic changes in the gonial lobe of the testis were not evident, however, until some 2 weeks after hypophysectomy, when the secondary spermatogonia showed signs of both nuclear and cytoplasmic degeneration. Mitotic activity of the germinal elements was much reduced over that of the controls.

Burgos (1950) has studied the effects of removal of the pars distalis in *Bufo arenarum* and has supplemented the information available for this toad. He carried out adenohypophysectomy in each of the four seasons of the year and examined the testes after 30, 50, 60 and 75 days. Involution was found in this case to be slow and progressive, becoming well marked by 50–75 days. Burgos found, as might be expected, that the nature of the changes was conditioned by the state of the testis at the particular time of year when the operation was performed. Spermatozoa and spermatids were the first elements to be affected and they were followed by spermatocytes and finally spermatogonia. Interstitial tissue was found to atrophy in a very marked fashion as a result of hypophysectomy in Autumn and spring.

The most recent and much the most detailed study on the interrelationships between pituitary and testis is that of van Oordt (1956) on *Rana temporaria*. After describing the histological picture in the testis throughout the year, van Oordt deals in detail with the effects of hypophysectomy in winter, spring, summer and autumn. Removal of the adenohypophysis in November, that is during hibernation, when the testis picture is largely unchanging, has no effect on the weight of the testis, or on the average diameter of its tubules. The majority of sperm-cells are completely normal and the initial stages of spermiation are not affected. On the other hand, in the operated animals, unlike the controls, spermatogenesis is not initiated and the number of primary spermatogonia seems lower. Van Oordt believes that these results indicate that hypophysectomy affects the testis even during the resting season, the primary spermatogonia being deprived of their mitotic capacity. Sluiter, van Oordt and Mighorst (1950) reported similar findings for *Rana esculenta*, and it may be noted that Burgos (1955) identified histochemical changes in the testes of hypophysectomised *R. pipiens* during the resting period.

Hypophysectomy in August, when the testes were in the final stages of spermatogenesis, had no effect on the late stages of spermatogenesis : the testis tubules of all the operated frogs were filled with numerous sperm bundles. On the other hand, there was no increase in the number of primary spermatogonia, although such an increase was a marked feature of the control testes.

Van Oordt draws several important conclusions from this work concerning the part played by the pars distalis of the frog pituitary in controlling the histological changes which go on in the testis throughout the annual cycle. Primary spermatogonia are believed to be unable to divide in the absence of the pituitary, and control of mitotic cell division in these cells appears to be its main role, though it seems also to exert a stimulatory effect on the intermediate stages of spermatogenesis. Neither the final stages of spermatogenesis, nor the initiation of spermiation appear to be affected by pituitary removal. The result concerning spermiation is a surprising one considering the fact that this process is known to be induced by injections of pituitary gland material and of purified gonadotrophins ; it clearly requires further study.

Burgos (1955) investigated histological and histochemical changes in the testis of *R. pipiens* following hypophysectomy. He reports atrophic changes in the Sertoli cells, Leydig cells and spermatogonia in the testes of hibernating frogs on removal of the pituitary. Liberation of mature spermatozoa from the Sertoli cells was also encountered and pronounced histochemical changes were described. Glycogen, normally present in the Sertoli cells, disappeared as a result of hypophysectomy, and the cholesterol-content of the Leydig cells appeared to increase. Moreover, enzymatic activity declined in the Sertoli cells following pituitary removal.

There seems to be a fair measure of agreement between different workers that the spermatogonia are more profoundly affected by hypophysectomy than are the other spermatogenetic stages, though there is still room for a careful cytological study of the affected region of the testis following pituitary removal. The degree to which spermiation is controlled by pituitary gonadotrophins must remain an open question, and no doubt it will be difficult to solve, since a variety of possibly non-physiological changes in the Sertoli cells appear to result in release of the spermatozoa. The nature and degree of control of the intermediate stages of spermatogenesis by the pituitary must also receive further study.

The effect of hypophysectomy on interstitial tissue, thumb pads and Wolffian ducts in *Rana esculenta* has been considered in some detail by Sluiter, van Oordt and Mighorst (1950). They found that in hypophysectomised animals the number of interstitial cells increases markedly, but the histological signs suggest that both the secretory and the storage capacity of these cells are diminished. Sluiter *et al.* conclude from this that the pituitary promotes and maintains the functional activity of the interstitial tissue, but not the capacity of the cells to divide. Gallien (1940) showed that the thumb pads of *Rana temporaria* regressed very quickly after hypophysectomy ; Sluiter *et al.* obtained similarly rapid effects in

R. esculenta. Two weeks after the operation, the cuticle of the thumb pads was thin and smooth, and the epidermal glands were small, with low cells and large lumen (Fig. *11*.33). This is a much more speedy response than that evident in the interstitial cells, and Sluiter *et al.* therefore question whether this regression can possibly be caused by decreased secretion of androgens.

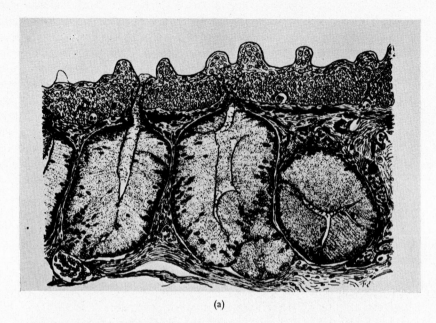

(a)

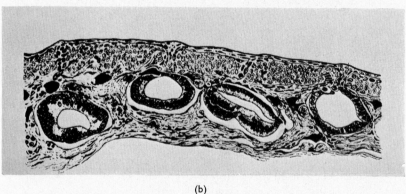

(b)

Fig. *11*. 33—*Rana esculenta.* (a) Section through a thumb-pad of a control frog (× 100). (b) Section through a thumb-pad of a frog hypophysectomised 14 days previously (× 100). (From Sluiter, van Oordt and Mighorst, 1950.)

A similar quick regression was noticed in the Wolffian ducts following hypophysectomy ; this took the form of a decrease in diameter of the ducts and of the cell heights of the lining epithelium (Fig. *11*.34).

Hypophysectomy in the immature male.—Larval amphibians have been hypophysectomised by removing the pituitary anlage and the effects of the operation on gonads and reproductive ducts are substantially uniform. Witschi (1930) showed that this operation on larvae of *Taricha* (*Triturus*) *torosa* produces a distinct underdevelopment of the testes, the difference between control and hypophysecto-mised animals being obvious a few months after the controls have metamorphosed. However, retardation of the ovaries does not become noticeable until about a year after the time of normal metamorphosis.

Chang and Witschi (1955) have investigated the effects of hypophysectomy on larval *Rana pipiens* and found that the gonads are affected somewhat earlier than in urodeles. One year after metamorphosis, the testes of intact specimens of *R. pipiens* are large and contain all stages of spermatogenesis, including mature sperms, whilst hypophysectomised larvae of the same age still have testes of the size and degree of differentiation of controls at the time of metamorphosis, that is, they contain only spermatogonia (Fig. *11*.35).

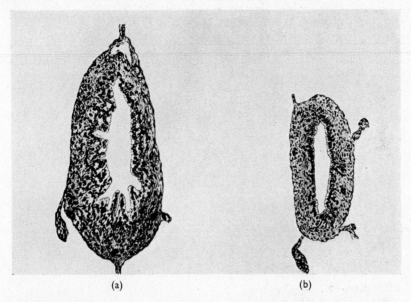

(a)   (b)

Fig. *11*. 34—*Rana esculenta*. (a) Cross-section through Wolffian duct of a control frog (× 100). (b) Cross-section through Wolffian duct of frog hypophysec-tomised 9 months previously (× 100). (From Sluiter, van Oordt and Mig-horst, 1950.)

Chang (1955) reported similar findings in *Bufo americanus*. He found that the initial differentiation of the testes remained unaffected, but in the advanced juvenile stages, starting at about 3 months after metamorphosis, a gradual retarda-tion in growth of the gonads and differentiation of the germ-cells was observed.

Hypophysectomy in the female.—Woronzowa and Blacher (1930) hypophy-sectomised three species of adult and developing urodeles (*Ambystoma* sp. ; *Pleurodeles waltlii* ; *Triturus cristatus*). They examined the immature specimens between 6 and 16 months after the operation and found that they showed no de-velopment of either ovaries or secondary sex characters. In the mature adults regressive changes were seen in the ovaries though these were not described in detail. Pronounced degeneration of secondary sexual characters was encountered between the end of the first and third years following pituitary removal. Burns and Buyse (1932) obtained very similar effects in developing and adult specimens of *Ambystoma trigrinum*. In the hypophysectomised immature animals, although somatic growth was not permanently affected, no further development occurred in the ovaries, though there was no degeneration of ovarian tissue already present at

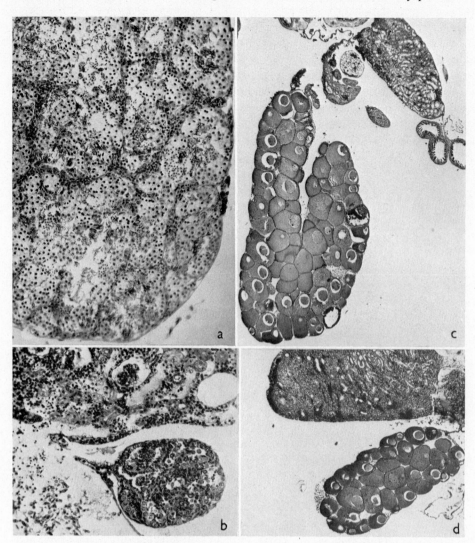

Fig. *11.35—Rana pipiens:* Effects of removal of pituitary anlage. (a) Male frog (control), 485 days old. T.S. testis showing all stages of spermatogenesis ($\times$ 100). (b) Male frog (hypophysectomised), 472 days old. T.S. testis showing only primary spermatogonia ($\times$ 100). (c) Female frog (control), 485 days old. T.S. ovary, mesonephros and oviduct ($\times$ 30). (d) Female frog (hypophysectomised), 472 days old. Note smaller ovary and absence of oviduct ($\times$ 30). (From Chang and Witschi, 1955.)

the time of operation. Older animals, studied 6 months after hypophysectomy, showed undoubted regressive changes is their ovaries. Follicles were seen in various stages of resorption and there were several corpora atretica. Follicles below a certain size seemed unaffected but they showed no signs of growth or vitellogenesis. Appreciable atrophy of the oviducts was also reported, though there was no return

to the larval condition. Burns (1932) studied hypophysectomy in relation to follicular atresia and yolk formation in the ovaries of *A. tigrinum*. He found that atresia
was limited to follicles in which yolk deposition had already started and that the
largest surviving follicles were all small and of uniform size, namely, some 400 μ.
Burns suggests that small follicles can grow to this critical size even in the absence
of the pituitary. Tuchmann-Duplessis (1945) obtained essentially similar results
in *Triturus palmatus*, *T. alpestris* and *T. marmoratus*, though much more quickly.
Fourteen days after hypophysectomy of mature specimens, ovarian weight had
decreased by 25 per cent compared with that of control animals. By the end of a
month this figure had reached 75–80 per cent. The main macroscopic change in
the ovaries was the appearance of atresia in all eggs having a diameter greater than
300 μ. Histological examination of these atretic eggs showed rapidly dividing
thecal cells which were invading and engulfing the yolk. Oöcytes less than 300 μ
in diameter were only affected a considerable time after pituitary removal and the
manner of their atresia was different ; the nucleus was affected first and later, the
yolky cytoplasm degenerated. These results led Tuchmann-Duplessis to postulate that the first stages of maturation entirely escape hypophyseal hormonal
control, but that, as in mammals, pituitary hormones are implicated in maturation
of the oöcytes.

So far as concerns female Anura, the results of hypophysectomy are essentially
similar to those already described for Urodela. Giusti and Houssay (1922, 1924)
investigated *Bufo arenarum* and reported premature ovulation by females hypophysectomised in September ; the eggs were evacuated a few days after the operation. This is the only record of such a sequel to hypophysectomy. It is probably
best explained by assuming that the toads were on the threshold of ovulation at
the time of operation, and the response was a non-specific one.

Hogben (1930) and Hogben, Charles and Slome (1931) described ovarian
involution in female *Xenopus laevis* which had been hypophysectomised ; in most
of the operated animals there were no macroscopically visible eggs, and in general
the ovaries were embryonic in appearance. Shapiro and Shapiro (1934) confirmed these results. They observed that by 4½ months after total hypophysectomy
or adenohypophysectomy, the characteristic large yolky ova could no longer be
seen in the ovary of *Xenopus*. Histological effects of the operation seemed to be
limited to the large mature eggs of the ovary, the peripherally placed immature
eggs appeared unaffected. Bellerby and Hogben (1938) expressed the effects of
pituitary removal in *X. laevis* graphically by comparing the weight distribution
of the ovaries of control females with that of hypophysectomised females
(Fig. *11*.36).

Christensen (1931) hypophysectomised mature females of *R. pipiens* and found
that the oviducts degenerated ; 8 months after the operation they were comparable
with the oviducts of the pre-pubertal female. This would normally be considered
an indirect effect of hypophysectomy, mediated through the ovaries ; however,
there is some evidence, which is considered below, which suggests that the pars
distalis may also play a direct role in controlling the oviducts.

Gallien (1939, 1940) removed the adenohypophysis from female *R. temporaria*
at different times of the year and reported effects which were closely correlated
with the state of the ovary at the time of the operation. Frogs hypophysectomised
in April or May, and autopsied in September, showed complete inhibition of

vitellogenesis in those oöcytes which would have matured during the summer. However, in animals hypophysectomised in November or December, the period of sexual quiescence, neither the ovaries nor the oviducts showed any signs of atrophy when examined in the following February.   A few of these frogs were kept for 10 months after the operation, and it was found that the ovary was a mass of atretic follicles, there being no new crop of eggs such as was found in the controls. However, Gallien also reported a size-threshold of 350–400 μ below which oöcytes appeared to be unaffected by hypophysectomy.   In common with other authors,

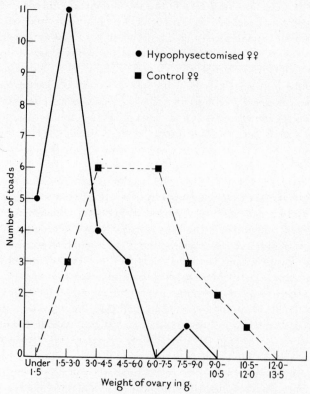

Fig. *11. 36—Xenopus laevis:* Effect of hypophysectomy on the
ovary.   Frequency distribution of ovarian weights in hypophysectomised and control female toads.   (From Bellerby and
Hogben, 1938.)

Gallien found a relatively slight reduction in size of the oviducts ; it seems that they involute only slowly after pituitary removal, though rate of involution varies with the time of year at which the operation is carried out. Bellerby and Hogben (1938) found the tubular glands of the oviducal mucosa reduced in size in the hypophysectomised *Xenopus*, and the lumen of the oviducts more obvious in consequence.   A very characteristic difference between experimental and control animals concerned the nuclei ; in the controls they were flattened and peripheral in position, whereas in the experimental group they were central, spheroidal and stained more deeply.   It was further noted that the two groups showed no noticeable difference in content of secretory granules.

Weisman and Coates (1944) have considered the effects of pituitary removal

on breeding behaviour in female *X. laevis*. They have found that hypophysectomised females are no longer clasped by sexually active males, and have assumed
that this is due to the marked regression which the ovaries undergo as a result of
the operation.

Hypophysectomy in the immature female.—The work of Witschi (1930) on hypophysectomy of male larval Amphibia has already been considered. He also
investigated pituitary removal in female larvae of *Taricha* (*Triturus*) *torosa* at the
same time and found that the inhibitory effect on the ovaries was just as marked,
though it was not noticeable until about a year after metamorphosis. A similar
state of affairs exists in *Rana pipiens* from which the pituitary anlage has been
removed (Chang and Witschi, 1955). The ovaries of such animals at 18 months
are nearly twice the size normally attained at metamorphosis, though they are
appreciably smaller than the ovaries of control females of the same age (Fig. *11*.35).
Chang and Witschi draw specal attention to the remarkable absence of oviducts
in the hypophysectomised larvae, whereas in intact animals they are well formed,
convoluted and partly distended.

It seems clear, therefore, from the considerable amount of work which has
been done on the effects of hypophysectomy on the ovaries of a variety of Amphibia,
that marked regression follows removal of the pituitary gland, or of its pars distalis.
Rather little is known as to the precise processes in ovarian metabolism which
are affected, though they appear to be connected with growth of the follicles and
perhaps vitellogenesis. Whether or not direct nuclear changes are involved is not
known, and in the present state of knowledge it is not possible to compare in any
detail the nature of the effects shown by the ovary, as a result of pituitary removal,
with those shown by the testis. The solution to this intriguing problem must
await the results of careful cytological and histochemical investigations.

It has usually been assumed that the effects of hypophysectomy on secondary
sexual characters is an indirect one, due primarily to regressive changes in the
gonad. However, there is some evidence, which is discussed below, that the
pituitary may in some cases be directly implicated in the control of certain accessory
sexual characters, especially the oviducts.

Hypophysectomy and Bidder's organ.—Bidder's organ has been found to atrophy
in the absence of the pituitary, just as does the definitive ovary. Moreover, the
hypertrophy of Bidder's organ which follows castration is annulled by hypophysectomy (Houssay and Lascano-Gonzalez, 1931, 1935).

Implantation and injection of amphibian pituitary gland material

Hypophysectomy has yielded incontrovertible evidence that the pituitary
gland largely controls development and growth of the gonads in Amphibia and
this work has already been considered. Another approach to the same problem
has been made by implanting and injecting pituitary gland material from a variety
of organisms into intact and hypophysectomised Amphibia.

Implantation.—Houssay and Lascano-Gonzalez (1929) removed the pars
distalis from a large number of male *Bufo arenarum* at the height of summer and
placed homoplastic pituitary glands under the skin of the back of the operated
animals. Glands were implanted nine times during the succeeding 34 days. Not
only did this treatment abolish the testicular atrophy which follows hypophysectomy, but hypertrophy of the testes and strong stimulation of the germinal

epithelium were produced. Simultaneously, but independently, Wolf (1929a, b) had obtained similar results in *Rana pipiens*, and later in the same year, Houssay, Giusti and Lascano-Gonzalez (1929) extended the work to include *Bufo d'Orbigniyi* and *Leptodactylus ocellatus* and showed that, in these species also, implanted homoplastic pituitaries were capable of preventing the damage inflicted on the testis by hypophysectomy. Similar results have been reported by subsequent workers for a variety of amphibian species. Schreiber and Rugh (1945) implanted pituitary glands of adult pre-ovulating specimens of *Rana pipiens* into newly metamorphosed frogs of the same species. As a result, the testes became five to ten times larger than those of the control animals. Histological examination showed undoubted spermatogenic stimulation in treated males ; primary and secondary spermatocytes and spermatids were abundant and the seminiferous tubules were large and well formed.

Female Amphibia have received a greater share of attention so far as implantation of pituitary glands is concerned. Wolf (1929a, b) and Houssay and Lascano-Gonzalez (1929) were again pioneers. Wolf, using *Rana pipiens*, implanted one pituitary per day in September and October and obtained ovulation in 3–4 days. Rugh (1935a) reviewed the literature for the 5 years following the original work and showed that nine species of Amphibia had responded by ovulation to implanted homoplastic pituitary glands, and twelve species had responded to glands from other species of Amphibia. However, Rugh makes the point that absorption of gonadotrophin is more rapid and more complete when pituitary suspensions are injected into the body cavity than when whole glands are implanted, and this technique has been more widely adopted.

Injection.—Injection is both a more convenient and a more easily controlled method of administering pituitary material and it has been used by most subsequent workers. The results have been remarkably uniform so far as concerns the injection of amphibian pituitary material into other amphibia ; gonad stimulation has usually been observed in both sexes, in addition to spermiation in males and ovulation in females, provided the injected animals were not suffering from inanition, and the physical conditions, especially temperature, were satisfactory.

The early work was concerned with merely establishing the gonad-stimulating potency of the amphibian pars distalis. This soon led to an investigation of different variables which might be of significance in modifying either the potency of the pituitary material, or the response of the injected animal.

Rugh (1934) showed that ovulation could be induced in *Rana pipiens* by injection of a suspension of homoplastic pituitary material. He claimed that pituitary glands from female frogs were more potent than those from males, and found that daily intraperitoneal injections of two female pituitaries or four male pituitaries induced ovulation in 2–4 days.

Rugh (1935a) showed that the minimum amount of pars distalis effective in inducing ovulation in *Rana pipiens* during the hibernation period is one female, or two male glands, though the hormone is not sex-specific. The amount required during late summer and early autumn is greater ; this is clearly correlated with the fact that the gonads are less mature at this time than during the winter hibernation period. Bardeen (1932), unlike Rugh, found no difference in ovulation-producing potency between male and female *R. pipiens*, though Rostand's findings for *R. temporaria* and *R. esculenta* were similar to those of Rugh (Rostand, 1935).

Houssay, Giusti and Lascano-Gonzalez (1929) tested the pituitaries of normal males, castrated males, normal females and spawning females of *Bufo arenarum* with regard to their ability to induce ovulation and found no appreciable differences. Novelli (1932) obtained similar results when he compared the pituitaries of intact *B. arenarum* with those castrated for 30, 60 and 90 days. Adams and Mayo (1936), in similar work on *Triturus viridescens*, reported a slightly greater ovulation-inducing potency in pituitaries of castrates, but the difference is of doubtful significance.

Creaser and Gorbman (1939) reviewed the literature on injection and implantation of Amphibia with amphibian pituitary material and showed that there were remarkable differences in sensitivity to pituitary treatment between species and between males and females of the same species. The female of *R. pipiens* is highly refractory to pituitary material; Creaser and Shcolnek (1939) were unable to induce ovulation even when eighteen pituitaries of *Necturus maculosus* were injected, and Adams and Granger (1938) were successful only when they administered between forty and ninety glands from *Triturus viridescens*. On the other hand, the male *R. pipiens* is said to be so labile with regard to spermiation that misleading positive results are all too easy to obtain. In other species, the male is more refractive to pituitary treatment than the female (*Bufo arenarum* : Houssay, Giusti and Lascano-Gonzalez, 1929 ; various salamanders : Noble and Evans, 1932 ; Noble and Richards, 1930, 1932). *Bufo vulgaris* is one of the most resistant species studied ; it will ovulate to homoplastic pituitary material, but not to the pituitaries of another anuran, *Rana vulgaris*. It is clear, however, that this is highly unusual and that most amphibians respond readily to amphibian pituitary material from a wide range of donors.

Recent work on induced ovulation in Amphibia (Chang and Witschi, 1957, on *Rana pipiens* ; Ramaswami and Lakshman, 1958, on *Rana cyanophlyctis*) suggests that the endocrine basis of ovulation may be more complicated than is generally believed. Cortisone was found by Chang and Witschi to have a facilitating role in ovulation under certain conditions in *R. pipiens*, and Ramaswami and Lakshman report that a considerable range of hormones, both proteins and steroids, appear to have a similar effect on ovulation in *R. cyanophlyctis*. Future work will demonstrate how far these effects are implicated in the normal physiology of ovulation.

Some interesting work has been reported on ovulation *in vitro* in *Rana pipiens*. Heilbrunn, Daugherty and Wilbur (1939) suspended an entire ovary of *Rana pipiens* in 30 ml. Ringer's solution containing one macerated homoplastic pituitary; this resulted in ovulation. Ryan and Grant (1940) carried out similar work on *R. pipiens* and found that effective concentrations of homoplastic pituitary material ranged between 1/32nd of a gland and 4 glands (pars distalis). These workers noted a seasonal variability ; their successful experiments were carried out in spring, when the ovaries are ripe; identical treatment in October yielded negative results. Wright (1945, 1950) has extended this work. He verified the marked seasonal variation in sensitivity of the *R. pipiens* ovary to gonadotrophins, which had been encountered by earlier workers; he found that ovulation of a few eggs could be induced as early as the end of August, there was a gradual increase during the winter, and nearly complete ovulation was achieved in March and April. Wright experimented with amounts of homoplastic pituitary material (pars distalis) varying between 1/512th pituitary gland and 2 glands and found that as the concentration was increased, there was a progressive increase in the percentage of eggs ovulated until one-sixteenth or one-eighth of a pituitary gland was reached, after which there was a decline in the number of eggs ovulated. Wright suggests that the ovulation percentage decreases when the concentration of pituitary suspension rises above a certain level, because the content of LH in the suspension becomes excessive. He quotes the work of Foster, Foster and Hisaw (1937) on experimental ovulation in mammals, in which ovulation could not be induced by the administration of large doses of an unfractionated preparation because of an excess of LH.

Nadamitsu (1953) has shown that three Japanese species of *Rana*, and *Triturus pyrrhogaster* can be induced to ovulate *in vitro*, using a similar technique to that practised by Wright, and by administering homoplastic pituitaries.

So far as concerns male Amphibia, Houssay (1954) has summarised the extensive and detailed work of his school on the effects of endogeneous pituitary gonado-trophins on the male *Bufo arenarum*. He concludes that they are responsible for the initation of spermiation, that is, liberation of sperm from the testicular ampullae and their expulsion from the testis and appearance in the urine, the maintenance and stimulation of spermatogenesis and of the interstitial tissue, the initiation of amplexus in the intact animal, and the development and maintenance of the secondary sexual characters, both in the intact and castrate animal. On the other hand, van Oordt (1956), working with *Rana temporaria*, holds that the final stages of spermatogenesis, and spermiation, may be independent of the presence of gonadotrophic hormones. Van Oordt is also inclined to ascribe considerable importance in the spermatogenetic processes to an inherent rhythm in the sensi-tivity of the germinal epithelium to gonadotrophic hormones. There is no doubt that several extra-pituitary factors, both internal and external, are of importance in vertebrate sexual cycles, and van Oordt reports new work on these aspects of the subject and summarises the existing literature.

Injection of gonadotrophins from vertebrates other than Amphibia

Effects of gonadotrophins from mammals.—It is clear from the fact that Amphibia of both sexes are now so widely used in human pregnancy diagnosis, that they are sensitive to at least some gonadotrophins from mammalian sources.

Houssay, Giusti and Lascano-Gonzalez (1929) administered pituitaries from rat, guinea-pig, dog and ox to *Bufo arenarum* without effect ; they ascribed this to species specificity. However, several other early workers were successful in inducing ovulation in a variety of female Amphibia by injecting gonadotrophins from mammalian sources (mainly sheep and cattle) : *Discoglossus pictus* (Kehl, 1930a); *Ambystoma tigrinum* (Buyse and Burns, 1931; Ogilvie, 1933); *Triturus pyrrhogaster* (Ogilvie, 1933) ; *Rana vulgaris* (Adams, 1931) ; *Rana temporaria* (Bellerby, 1933b) ; *Rana catesbiana* (Rugh, 1935b) ; *Bufo fowleri* (Rugh, 1935b) ; *Xenopus laevis* (Bellerby, 1933a, 1934).

The obvious interest, both theoretical and practical, of this aspect of amphibian reproductive biology stimulated a great amount of similar work and the results were highly contradictory. The field was reviewed by Creaser and Gorbman (1939), who concluded from their own work on *Rana pipiens* (Creaser and Gorbman, 1935, 1936), and a review of the extensive literature on the subject, that a qualitative species variation exists in gonadotrophic hormones. This sometimes manifests itself in the excessively high doses of hormone which are necessary to produce an effect, and quite frequently the difference is great enough between widely separated species to lead to a complete ineffectiveness of the hormone in the recipient species.

Creaser and Gorbman concluded that qualitative hormone variation between amphibia and mammals is of sufficient value to reduce greatly the efficiency of action of the hormones in reciprocal exchange. This view was based largely on the reactions of female *Rana pipiens* to mammalian gonadotrophins, and this species has been found by all workers to be highly refractive to anything other than amphibian pituitary material. The great amount of work which has been carried out in the search for amphibian species suitable for use in pregnancy diagnosis has yielded other examples of refractory species.

In general, however, both male and female Amphibia are sensitive to gonado-trophins from mammalian sources. The literature concerning the effects of chorionic gonadotrophin and pregnant mare's serum gonadotrophin on various amphibians of both sexes is voluminous and will not be dealt with here except in so far as it illustrates fundamental aspects of the actions of gonadotrophins in the Amphibia. Several excellent reviews are available (Cowie, 1948 ; Bhaduri, 1951 ; Lanza, 1951a, b ; Houssay, 1954).

Hogben (1930) showed that injection of extracts of the anterior lobe of the ox pituitary stimulated ovulation and oviposition in *Xenopus laevis*. Bellerby (1934) described the use of *Xenopus* as a test animal for assaying anterior-lobe pituitary materials and other gonad-stimulating substances. This gave rise to a mass of research on induced ovulation in female Amphibia with a view to using suitable species for the diagnosis of human pregnancy. Galli Mainini (1947) was similarly responsible for initiating work on spermiation in male Amphibia by his discovery that human pregnancy urine induced spermiation in the male *Bufo arenarum*. Houssay (1954) has reviewed this work and concludes that this test animal responds only to pituitary and placental gonadotrophins. The intact *Xenopus* female, on the other hand, ovulates to at least twelve steroids in addition to these gonado-trophins (Shapiro, 1936b), and the *Xenopus* male is known to respond by spermia-tion to International Standard ALP powder, PMS, CG, DOCA, methyl testo-sterone and ethinyl oestradiol (Hobson, 1952).

Less is known of the ability of purified gonadotrophic fractions of mammalian pituitary glands to affect the gonads of Amphibia, though most of the anuran species which are used in pregnancy diagnosis have been investigated from this point of view.

Wright and Hisaw (1946) extended the work of Wright (1945) on *in vitro* ovulation in *Rana pipiens* to include the effects of mammalian pituitary gonado-trophins. They fractionated sheep pituitary glands and obtained a " fairly pure " FSH fraction and three mixed fractions containing FSH and LH in known pro-portions. It may be noted that previous workers had reported that *R. pipiens* was refractive to all mammalian preparations tested. However, Wright and Hisaw found that the FSH fraction induced ovulation in the intact animal during January, February and March, though it was ineffective both in the hypophysectomised frog and on the excised ovary. However, they found that the FSH preparation exerted a marked sensitising effect on the ovary of hypophysectomised *R. pipiens* which could then respond much more readily to injected frog pituitary glands. The experiments in which combined FSH-LH fractions were injected yielded ovulation in both intact and hypophysectomised frogs and also in the excised ovary. Wright and Hisaw postulate, on the basis of these experiments, that the chief function of FSH in ovulation in *R. pipiens* is to sensitise the ovarian follicles. Thus, although FSH and LH have not been isolated as such from amphibian pituitaries, Wright and Hisaw believe they are likely to be present and to have similar functions to those they have in mammals. They further suggest that there is a continuous slow secretion of FSH from the amphibian pituitary during hibernation, and that this sensitises the follicles to either the existing level of LH, or to a raised concentration at the normal time of ovulation.

Several workers have investigated the effects of purified FSH, LH and luteo-trophic hormone (Prolactin, LTH) on intact and hypophysectomised male frogs and toads, and the results have been apparently contradictory, though the dis-cordance can be resolved by postulating specific differences and, in some cases it may be due to the use of impure hormone fractions. Crézé (1949) reported that spermiation can be induced in *Rana esculenta* by injecting mammalian LH. Bhaduri (1951) obtained a similar result in *Bufo melanostictus* by injecting either LH or FSH, and Houssay (1954) states that the same applies in the case of *Bufo arenarum*. Robbins (1951) and Robbins and Parker (1952), working with male specimens of *Rana pipiens*, found that FSH induces spermiation, and Hobson (1952) reported that the male *Xenopus laevis* is very sensitive to the FSH in the urine of menopausal and castrate subjects. On the other hand, Thorborg and Hansen (1951) found that males of *Bufo bufo* were not stimulated by high doses of FSH, and this has been the experience of subsequent workers. For example, Atz and Pickford (1954) tested purified LH and FSH fractions of mammalian pituitary on *R. pipiens* and found the LH preparation to be between 40 and 100 times more potent than the FSH fraction in eliciting spermiation. These workers interpret their results by assuming that only the LH fraction was active, any activity shown by the FSH fraction being due to its known contamination with LH.

Burgos and Ladman (1957) have also investigated the effects of purified FSH and LH fractions of mammalian pituitary material on male *Rana pipiens*, using both intact and hypophysectomised specimens. In both groups, LH induced spermiation, whereas FSH was ineffective, except where the dose was so large that LH contamination was probably responsible for the positive result. On the other hand, FSH significantly increased the number of primary spermatogonia in both intact and hypophysectomised animals. Burgos and Ladman also noted that LH exerted a stimulatory effect on the interstitial cells.

LTH has also been administered and the results are equally contradictory. Greenblatt, Clark and West (1949) induced spermiation in *R. pipiens* by injecting LTH, whereas Atz and Pickford (1954) and Burgos and Ladman (1957) obtained negative results in this species, and Houssay, Penhos and Burgos (1953) found that LTH was ineffective in *B. arenarum*.

A great deal of the work carried out in connection with pregnancy diagnosis is concerned with the action of mammalian gonadotrophins of extra-pituitary origin, mainly chorionic gonadotrophin (CG) and pregnant mare serum gonadotrophin (PMS). As already mentioned, many amphibian species have been tested and most of them respond to CG by ovulation in the female and spermiation in the male.   Whether or not ovulation is followed by oviposition depends on the nature of the oviposition process (Waring, Landgrebe and Neill, 1941).

Tuchmann-Duplessis (1945) attempted to annul the effects of hypophysectomy on the ovaries of newts (" *Triton* ") by injecting PMS.   Success was limited even though each animal received 10 mouse units PMS three times per week.   Animals autopsied 35 days after pituitary removal showed marked atrophic changes in their ovaries.   Greater success has been reported as a result of injecting PMS into male Amphibia: Burgos and Rufino (1952) found that PMS initiated spermiation in the intact *B. arenarum* and stimulated spermatogenesis; it was also said to produce marked proliferation of interstitial cells without, however, inducing secretory activity.   Houssay (1954) states that similar results have been obtained in hypophysectomised toads.   Sluiter, van Oordt and Grasveld (1950) and van Oordt (1956) have also reported that PMS accelerates spermatogenesis and, at certain times of the year, produces a weight increase in the testes of intact and hypophysectomised *Rana esculenta* and *R. temporaria*.

Burgos and Mancini (1947) have shown that in *Bufo arenarum* spermiation and spermatogenesis can be stimulated *in vitro* by a variety of gonadotrophins.   Addition of aqueous extracts of homoplastic anterior lobe pituitary material results in spermiation within half an hour; it also has a marked stimulatory effect on the germinal epithelium.   CG and PMS are also effective in bringing about these changes, though PMS is less potent than CG.   It is unfortunately difficult to assess the physiological significance of this work since a hypotonic medium and a variety of non-specific agents have been shown to produce spermiation under *in vitro* conditions.

CG has been found to induce spermiation and ovulation in a considerable variety of Amphibia and reference has already been made to the literature dealing with pregnancy diagnosis, in which this work is reported.   Houssay (1954) has summarised the extensive work of his school on the male *B. arenarum*, and it appears that in this toad, as in most other Amphibia, the effects of CG are LH-mimetic : it induces spermiation and marked hypertrophy and hyperplasia of the interstitial cells, with signs of enhanced secretory activity.   Burgos and Rufino (1952) have reported that simultaneous administration of CG and PMS to hypophysectomised toads (*B. arenarum*) produces an effect which is comparable with that obtained by injections of pituitary extracts.   Thus there is a good deal of evidence which tends to indicate that in the Amphibia, as in the mammals, the pituitary gland produces two gonadotrophins, the main functions of which appear to be closely similar in the two groups.   Future work will show to what extent the differences reported between species are real, and to what extent they can be resolved.

Effects of gonadotrophins from non-mammalian vertebrates.—Wills, Riley and Stubbs (1933) obtained ovulation in a single specimen of *Rana pipiens* by implantation of four pituitaries per day from the garfish *Lepisosteus platystoma* and *L. osseus* ; eggs were obtained on the fourth day.   In a similar investigation, using *Bufo americanus*, between two and four pituitaries of *Lepisosteus platystoma* were implanted and ovulation was obtained between 2 and 6 days later.   This work was questioned by Creaser and Gorbman (1939) because of the small number of animals used and the absence of adequate controls.   However, Stroganov and Alpatov (1951) obtained spermiation in three different species of frog as a result of injecting suspensions of sturgeon pituitaries, though Atz and Pickford (1954) were only partially successful even when large amounts of teleost glands were injected, and Houssay (1947a) was completely unsuccessful. Pickford and Atz (1957) have reviewed the literature on the administration of fish pituitary material to Amphibia and have found that of 79 amphibians treated with fish pituitary material, only 27 per cent responded positively. It may be significant from a phylogenetic point of view that most of the positive records have been obtained by injecting pituitary material from ganoid fish such as *Lepisosteus* and *Acipenser*, but more data are required before any generalisations can be made with confidence in connection with phylogenetic specificity.

Hormones of the Testis

The literature shows a good deal of discordance concerning the site of hormone production by the testis. Germ-cells, Sertoli cells and interstitial tissue have all been put forward as candidates and, since the evidence is mainly histological, and, to a lesser extent, histochemical, several interpretations are usually possible. Friedman (1898) and Mazzetti (1911), working with *Rana fusca* and *R. esculenta* respectively, described an increase in the amount of interstitial tissue after mating, at a time when the secondary sexual characters are reduced. Champy (1921) has presented evidence which he interprets in favour of a parallelism between development of spermatozoa and maturation of the secondary sex characters. Humphrey (1925) analysed comparative data for several urodeles (*Salamandra, Necturus, Desmognathus* and *Cryptobranchus*), and concluded that interstitial cell development is associated with regressive changes in the seminiferous tubules following discharge of spermatozoa, and that either the germ-cells or the Sertoli cells are responsible for the development of the secondary sex characters. Adams (1940) arrives at similar conclusions for *Triturus viridescens*. On the other hand, several workers have reported a close correlation between interstitial cell development and secondary sex characters. Aron (1926) and Smith (1938) found this to be the case in *Rana temporaria*, and Glass and Rugh (1944), using the thumb pad as an index, reported that volume of interstitial tissue was directly correlated with degree of development of the thumb pads in *R. pipiens*.

Sluiter, van Oordt and Mighorst (1950) studied the effects of hypophysectomy on the interstitial cells and secondary sex characters of *R. esculenta*. They found that although thumb pads and Wolffian ducts show marked regressive changes after hypophysectomy and spermatogenetic activity declines, yet the number of interstitial cells increases. However, they have much less cytoplasm, and Sluiter *et al.* point out that the physiological state of the cells is the criterion which must be applied when attempting to demonstrate a relationship between interstitial tissue and secondary sex characters ; cell number and volume of tissue considered in isolation can be misleading. The evidence obtained from intact frogs was equally difficult to interpret. The rapid development of the thumb pads in autumn was found to coincide with the presence of active interstitial cells, and yet control (captive) frogs were found to have fully developed thumb pads as late as July, whereas secretory activity of the interstitial cells ends in the spring.

Thus, although there is abundant evidence for testicular control of accessory sexual characters, it is not known with certainty which testicular elements are implicated.   Nor have the other lines of attack, about to be considered, resolved the difficulty.

Castration

The general principle that the secondary sexual characters and the sexual instincts are dependent on the presence of the testis in Amphibia, as in other vertebrates, has been elaborated by many workers.   Prior to 1935, when synthetic sex hormones became generally available, castration and implantation or injection of testis material were the methods most widely used in these studies.

Urodela.—A great deal of work has been carried out on the effects of castration in urodeles ; this is no doubt correlated with the fact that the secondary sexual characters are so much more striking than in the Anura.   Bresca (1910) noted that castration of newts is followed by the loss of some of the sex dimorphic characters. Aron (1924), in extensive researches on *Triturus cristatus*, found that, following castration, the secondary sexual characters such as nuptial colouration and dorsal crest, as well as vas deferens, sexual segment of the kidney and cloacal glands, fail to develop, or atrophy, depending on the phase of the reproductive cycle at which castration takes place.   Champy (1933) studied the effects of castration in newts, and found that it resulted in the suppression of caudal filaments, crest, toe webs and cloacal swelling.   Adams and Kirkwood (1928) made similar observations on *Triturus viridescens*.   De Beaumont (1933) has described the effect of early castration on the urinogenital system and other potentially dimorphic characters present in sexually immature *Triturus cristatus* of both sexes.   Castration was carried out after differentiation of the gonads, but before differentiation of the genital tract. He found that an asexual morphology was produced, similar to that resulting from ovariectomy of the female.   This asexual type is more or less intermediate between the two sexes as judged by the state of the internal organs, cloacal characters and crest.   De Beaumont also reported complete cessation of secretory activity in the Wolffian ducts, the sexual segment of the kidney and the cloacal glands.   In short, he found that castration resulted in complete regression of the post-pubertal sexual characters, whilst the pre-pubertal characters remained intact even after 2 years.   Castration also prevents the seasonal change in the eye colour of *T. alpestris* (Champy, 1922), and results in loss of the characteristic teeth found in male *Desmognathus fuscus carolinensis* (Noble and Pope, 1929).

Aron (1924) exposed males of *T. cristatus* in full nuptial dress to radium.   The results were somewhat equivocal, but he concluded that it was possible to effect physiological castration by exposing newts to radioactive substances.

Tuchmann-Duplessis (1945) studied the effects of castration in the male *T. palmatus* by removing the testes at the start of sexual activity and observing the effects for 2 months.   By the end of the first month after castration, the secondary sexual characters all showed some slight regression.   This consisted of relatively slight changes in the crest and cloaca ; and internally, the chromatophores of the Wolffian duct were seen to contract and the prostate or internal cloacal gland, a gland of unknown function, characteristic of newts, showed signs of early atrophy, due mainly to partial resorption of its secretion.   By the end of 2 months, all these characters were reduced to the non-breeding condition.   They were found to regress at different rates ; cloaca, dorsal crest and Wolffian ducts showed the effects of castration relatively early ; reduction of the palmation of the feet and virtual disappearance of the tail filament followed somewhat later. The striking pigmentation associated with sexual activity in the male became subdued from the fifth week onwards.

Anura.—Steinach (1894), was one of the first to demonstrate the dependence of the secondary sexual characters of male Anura on the gonads. Nussbaum (1905) showed that the thumb pad, and the associated hypertrophy of the muscles of the forearm, failed to appear in the castrated frog (*Rana temporaria*). Pflüger (1907) confirmed this observation, and further concluded that the internal secretion of the testis directly stimulates the development of the thumb pad and the muscles associated with the clasping reflex. Several other workers confirmed the existence of a functional relationship between the testes and various secondary sexual characters in a variety of Anura : *Rana temporaria*, Harms, 1910, Meyns, 1910, 1911, Meisenheimer, 1911 ; *Rana esculenta*, Aron, 1926 ; *Bufo vulgaris*, Ponse, 1922, 1924. Welti, 1928; *Bombinator* spp., Moszkowska, 1932; *Xenopus laevis*, Shapiro, 1937; *Discoglossus pictus*, Kehl, 1944. (*See* Ponse (1924) for an excellent review of the early literature on the effects of castration and implantation in Anura).

Of the secondary sexual characters in Anura, thumb pads and the sexual embrace have been most fully investigated. Kehl (1944) found that castration of *Discoglossus* was followed by regressional changes which were well marked 3 weeks after the operation. There is substantial agreement on this point in all species tested. However, the position concerning the effect of castration on the sexual clasp in Anura is less clear. Goltz (1869) found that castration of *Rana temporaria* during the breeding season did not prevent the male from approaching and clasping the female, and Tarchanoff (1887) reported similarly that removal of the testis had no immediate effect upon clasping in the frog. Steinach (1894) also claimed that the clasping reflex appears in male frogs during the breeding season despite castration a few months earlier. He found, however, (Steinach 1910), that with longer post-operative intervals the response is greatly reduced or completely lost, and concluded that the clasp is, in fact, conditioned by a hormone produced by the testis. Houssay and Giusti (1930) believe the sexual embrace to be mainly a nervous phenomenon since it is observed in animals which have been hypophy-sectomised or castrated. Nevertheless, these workers found that injection of large amounts of testicular tissue provoked the sexual embrace in castrates.

There are several reports in the literature to the effect that castration eliminates clasping. Schrader (1887) found that the male frog fails to clasp if castration is performed before the annual breeding season, and Nussbaum (1905) and Edinger (1913) reported substantially similar findings.

Aron (1926) exposed *Rana temporaria* and *R. esculenta* to X-rays with a view to destroying their testes, and he found that, contrary to results obtained on mammals, the spermatic tubules were highly resistant to irradiation, whereas there were clear signs of degeneration in the interstitial tissue. In consequence, the thumb pads atrophied even though the testis tubules appeared unaffected and showed normal spermatogenesis.

The most recent investigation on castration is that of Burgos (1950), who found that it caused a gradual and complete regression of clasping and of the other secondary sexual characters ; these results were appreciable at 20 days, obvious at 30 days, and striking at 60 days. The croaking reflex was not affected. Burgos further reported that although clasping behaviour could not be re-initiated in the castrate by testosterone alone, success was achieved by simultaneous injection of pars distalis and testosterone. This obviously requires further investigation.

The discrepancies in these results are no doubt partly resolved by the finding of Steinach (1910) that where the post-operative interval is short, clasping may still be encountered. There are several similar cases from other vertebrate species in which behavioural responses which are demonstrably dependent upon hormones may persist apparently unchanged for a varying length of time after the source of the hormone has been removed. The existing evidence is probably best interpreted by postulating a basic nervous mechanism which is conditioned by testicular secretion.

Transplantation of testes

The evolution of testis grafts in gonadectomised Amphibia is the same in the female host as in the male and follows the same course in successful graftings whether the transplantation is intra-specific or inter-specific. Initially there is a phase of degeneration followed usually by a revival of spermatogenesis in localised regions of the graft (Ponse, 1924; Welti, 1928; de Beaumont, 1929; Moszkowska, 1932).

Into castrated males.—The experiments of Nussbaum (1909) on the effects of transplantation of testicular tissue into the lymphatic sacs of castrated mature frogs provides a good example of early work on the endocrinology of the testis. Nussbaum found that if a second transplantation was made before the first piece of testis had entirely degenerated, the stimulus provided was adequate in strength and duration to cause the development of the nuptial pads and seminal vesicles. There is little doubt, however, that the engrafted testes never became functional; presumably sex hormones were liberated as a result of cytolysis of the tissue. Meisenheimer (1911) obtained results similar to those of Nussbaum, but Smith and Schuster (1912) were unable to repeat these findings.

Ponse (1922, 1924) grafted testes into castrated toads and obtained restoration of the sex characters; the grafts became established and, in some cases, maintained the normal complement of sex characters for several years. Aron (1924) grafted testis tissue into castrated newts (*T. cristatus*), but found that it degenerated after a short time. De Beaumont (1929) was more successful; he found that autografts of testis in castrates of *T. cristatus* resulted in a reappearance of the secondary sex characters, though the effects were delayed until a new testis had developed from the degenerate remains of the graft. Welti (1928) has reported an extended study of gonadal homografts and heterografts in *Bufo vulgaris*, in which testes were implanted into intact and gonadectomised toads of both sexes. Although the report is mainly concerned with detailed descriptions of the fate of the grafts, there are frequent references to the positive effects which successful grafts exerted on the secondary sexual characters.

Into ovariectomised females.—Secondary sexual characters which are controlled by autosomal genes are potentially present in both sexes. The factor which limits the phenotypic expression of such genes to one sex is the internal environment provided by the sex hormones. It follows from this that gonadectomised animals into which the gonads of the opposite sex are grafted might be expected to show at least some of the secondary sex characters proper to the donor sex. This principle has been well illustrated in the Amphibia by grafting testicular tissue into ovariectomised females.   Thus Ponse (1923) induced the development of nuptial pads in immature female toads, though she failed to produce any effect in adult females.   Welti (1925, 1928), however, by means of successful testis grafts, caused both immature and adult females of *Bufo vulgaris* to acquire male sex characters, including thumb pads, sex-call and mating behaviour.   Noble and Pope (1929) found that a testis grafted into a female *Desmognathus fuscus* resulted in replacement of the blunt bicuspid premaxillary teeth characteristic of the female by the elongated monocuspid teeth found in the male.   In addition, the male behaviour pattern was induced, as were the pelvic, abdominal and cloacal glands characteristic of the male.

The fact that the various glands associated with the urodele cloaca are homologous in the two sexes of *Triturus cristatus* has been established by transplanting a testis into the body of the ovariectomised female (de Beaumont, 1928).   The spermatheca then changes into a pelvic gland and the rudimentary abdominal glands become functional.   Noble and Pope (1929) have shown by a similar technique that in *Desmognathus*, where neither abdominal nor cloacal glands are present even as rudiments in the female, they can be made to develop *de novo* from the undifferentiated epithelium of the female cloaca.

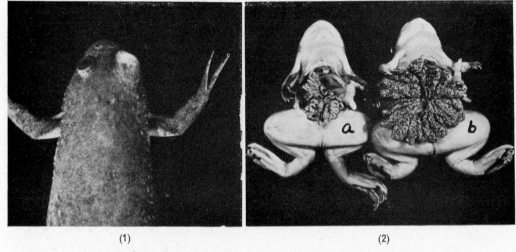

(1)   (2)

Fig. *11. 37*—*Xenopus laevis:* Transplantation of adult testes into adult females. (1) Host 167 days after metamorphosis, with testis graft behind right eye ($\times$ 2). (2a) Female host with testis graft in body cavity. Note reduced size of ovary and reduction of other secondary sexual characters compared with normal female (b). (From Chang, 1953.) (By permission of the publisher from *J. exp. Zool.*, 1953, **123,** 1.)

Into intact females.—Chang (1953) has described the effects of transplanting testicular tissue into developing female larvae and adult females of *Xenopus laevis*. He studied the effects of this procedure on both gonads and accessory sexual characters.   Grafts were made either into the body cavity or behind the eye (Fig. *11*.37).   He found that testes of immature metamorphosed males cause complete sex-reversal if implanted into female tadpoles during the first half of the larval period.   The formation of small testicular nodules was induced in the gonads of such female hosts.   On the other hand, heterosexual combinations of hosts and donors of the same age retard general ovarian development but do not result in

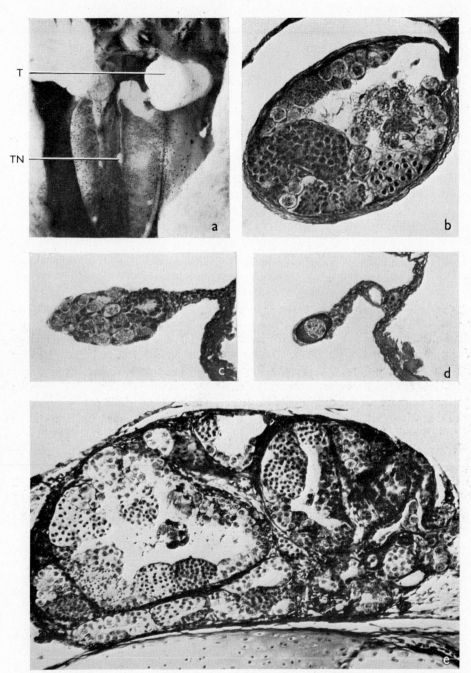

Fig. *11*. 38—*Xenopus laevis:* The effects of gonad grafting. (a) Female host with testis graft in body cavity. Note development of testicular nodules in severely inhibited ovaries (× 6). (b) T.S. testicular nodule shown in (a) (× 250). (c) T.S. upper part of left ovary of (a) (× 250). (d) T.S. left ovary of (a) in another region. Ovarian cortex is represented by a single oöcyte (× 250). (e) T.S. adult testicular graft behind eye of female host. Note normal testicular tubules (× 150). T, engrafted testis; TN, testicular nodule. (From Chang, 1953.) (By permission of the publisher from *J. exp. Zool.*, 1953, **123**, 1.)

sex-reversal. An engrafted mature testis has a marked effect on the host's ovary which becomes greatly reduced in size through continuous degeneration of large oöcytes (Fig. 11.38). It also causes some regression of the oviducts, reduction in size of the cloacal lips, development of the arm and hand spicules (gloving) characteristic of the mature male, and enlargement of the larynx. These results are a striking demonstration of the degree to which the male secondary sexual characters are under testicular control ; they also demonstrate *inter alia* the sex-limited mode of inheritance of these characters.

The effects of injecting testis extracts and androgens

Testicular extracts and androgens have a direct action both on the gonads and on the secondary sexual characters of animals into which they are injected. The fact that the affected gonads may in turn react on the secondary sexual characters makes it difficult to evaluate the results of such work on intact animals. A further complication is introduced by the fact that sex hormones are known to affect the pituitary and this in turn reacts on the other target organs. It follows from this that critical experiments on the effects of sex hormones must usually be carried out on animals which are hypophysectomised and gonadectomised.

Injection of testicular extracts.— Some of the earliest attempts to demonstrate endocrine activity of the testis were made on frogs (Steinach, 1910 ; Harms, 1910 ; Meisenheimer, 1911). These workers administered crude extracts or suspensions of testes, using the thumb pad or the clasp reflex as an index of activity. Houssay and Giusti (1930) found that it was necessary to inject extracts of one or two whole testes into *Bufo arenarum* in order to elicit the sexual embrace. The results obtained in these early experiments must be regarded with some doubt, but later work has demonstrated unequivocally the effect of androgens on amphibian secondary sexual characters.

Steinach described certain frogs which did not show the clasping reflex ; these he described as " impotent ". However, he claimed that the reflex could be induced in these animals by injecting an extract of testes from frogs which themselves showed the reflex. Brossard and Gley (1929) repeated this work, using extracts of bull testis, and found that the reflex appeared the day following the injection and persisted for one or two days.

*Injection of androgens.—*A good deal of consideration has been given to the effects of sex steroids on both the gonads and the secondary sex characters of Amphibia. Greenberg (1942) found that the testes of male specimens of the cricket frog (*Acris gryllus*) when treated with testosterone propionate differed little from those of untreated controls ; the ovary of the female was similarly unaffected. On the other hand, Cei and Acosta (1953) reported profound inhibition of the testes of *Leptodactylus chaquensis* by testosterone propionate. There was degeneration of spermatogonia and spermatocytes, alteration of the mitotic rhythm of the spermatogonia and a suppression of growth of the secondary spermatogonia. Cei and Acosta take these findings to indicate that secretion of FSH by the pituitary is seriously reduced by the administered androgen. Evidence that this is a reasonable explanation was obtained from an experiment in which testosterone propionate (20 mg. given over 15 days) and serum gonadotrophin (800 i.u. over 15 days) were injected simultaneously. This treatment resulted in an enlargement of the testes and stimulation of more active spermatogenesis than that found in the controls. In addition, primary spermatogonia were in full mitosis, secondary spermatogonia and primary spermatocytes were more abundant than in the controls, and the seminiferous tubules were wider. Puckett (1939), on the other hand, reported that injection of testosterone propionate into male *Rana pipiens* over a 30-day period had no effect on the testes, though female specimens treated similarly showed marked degeneration of the ovaries. Blair (1946) injected testosterone propionate into juvenile specimens of *Bufo fowleri* and noted that it accelerated spermatogenesis, but damaged the tubules and slightly reduced the size of the testes. Ovaries and Bidder's organs were adversely affected (Fig. *11*.39).

Most of the work concerning steroid hormones in amphibian reproductive physiology has dealt with their effects on the secondary sexual characters. Thus

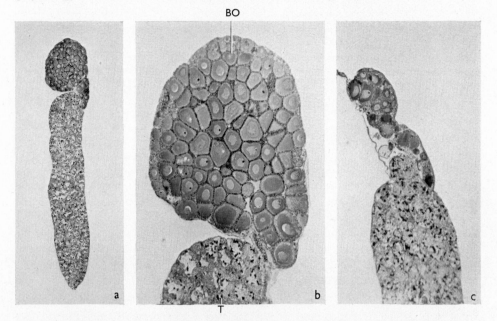

Fig. *11.* 39—*Bufo fowleri:* L.S. Bidder's organ and part of testis from male toad. (a) Typical relationship of Bidder's organ and testis (× 9). (b) Bidder's organ of control male (× 30). (c) Bidder's organ of testosterone-treated male (× 30). B.O., Bidder's organ; T, testis. (From Blair, 1946.) (By permission of the publisher from *J. exp. Zool.*, 1946, **103**, 365.)

Champy, Coujard and Coujard (1939) found that the glands of the thumb pad in *Rana temporaria* are stimulated by injection of testosterone. Many male anurans have vocal sacs and highly pigmented throats during the breeding season and these characters are not present in the immature animal. Greenberg (1942) treated males and females of the cricket frog *Acris gryllus* with testosterone propionate and noted as the most outstanding effect of steroid treatment, the appearance of black pigmentation in the throat region of both sexes. This was due to a great increase in the number of melanophores, and these became expanded to produce the characteristic interlacing pattern. He also found that the vocal sacs were stimulated in both sexes, but they never became as large as in the ripe male. Greenberg also quotes unpublished work on *Hyla cinerea* in which similar treatment induced the development of black pigment, vocal sacs, and even the sex-call.

Tuchmann-Duplessis (1945) investigated the effects of androgens on the secondary sexual characters of three species of newts. The experiments were carried out 4–6 weeks after subsidence of breeding dress, and testosterone propionate was injected at a dose level of 1 μg. per 3 days until a total of 10 μg. had been injected. This treatment produced stimulation of the cloacal region and of the dorsal crest; the secondary sexual characters in general were reminiscent of those of the sexually active animal. Tuchmann-Duplessis also investigated the ability of testosterone propionate to repair castration atrophy. He found a weekly dose of 100 μg. to be an adequate replacement for the first 5 weeks following castration, but after this time certain of the secondary sexual characters began to show atrophic changes. He found that in general those characters which were associated with secretory processes were more satisfactorily maintained by testosterone propionate than the others. Blair (1946) was able to stimulate the mating-calls by testosterone propionate, to increase the size of the larynx, and to stimulate development of thumb pads and throat pigmentation in juvenile *Bufo fowleri* of both sexes.

The effects of androgens on Wolffian ducts and Müllerian ducts have also been investigated by several workers. Puckett (1939) found that injections of small amounts of testosterone propionate over a 30-day period induced great hypertrophy of both Wolffian and rudimentary Müllerian ducts in the male *Rana pipiens*. In a similar series of experiments on the toad *Bufo americanus*, Puckett found again that both sets of reproductive ducts showed marked hypertrophy. Greenberg (1942) described important changes in the Wolffian ducts of male specimens of *Acris gryllus*. In this frog, as in other male Hylids, the terminal region of the Wolffian duct is expanded to form a sperm reservoir or primitive seminal vesicle. As a result of testosterone injections, this structure becomes hypertrophied, its diameter being twice that of the controls. Striking histological changes are also produced so that the epithelium lining the duct in animals injected during the sexually quiescent season comes to resemble that found in control animals at the height of the breeding season. The oviducts of the treated females similarly showed striking hypertrophy; they increased in length and diameter and consequently became coiled and flattened. The jelly-secreting glands took on the aspect of those found in breeding animals.

Blair (1946) obtained a small though significant stimulatory effect on the Müllerian ducts of juvenile *Bufo fowleri* of both sexes by the injection of testosterone propionate. On the other hand, Gallien (1944) found that testosterone propionate caused total involution of the Müllerian ducts if administered to *Rana temporaria* after metamorphosis.

Cei and Acosta (1953) found an appreciable stimulation of the Wolffian ducts of male *Leptodactylus chaquensis* under testosterone propionate treatment, though they obtained no effects on either the interstitial tissue or external secondary sexual characters.

Ethynyl testosterone usually behaves as an androgen in the lower vertebrates and there are several records of its androgenic effects on various sex structures. Eversole and D'Angelo (1943) found that it had a pronounced stimulatory effect on the seminal vesicle region of the Wolffian ducts in both sexes of recently metamorphosed *Rana pipiens*, and Gallien (1949b) has reported similar findings in *Discoglossus pictus*. Eversole and D'Angelo also encountered stimulation of the oviducts. It may be noted here that, although several workers have reported a stimulatory effect of androgens on the secretory activities of the oviducts, Galli-Mainini (1951) was unable to discover such an effect in *Bufo arenarum* ; this was also true of oestrogens, though a variety of other substances, including progesterone, were active.

The work of Tuchmann-Duplessis (1945) on the effects of very small doses of testosterone propionate on the external accessory sexual characters of newts has already been described. In the course of his work he also noted that the so-called prostate glands and the Wolffian ducts were stimulated though they were less developed than at the height of the breeding season. A marked stimulatory effect of testosterone on the Müllerian ducts of female *Triturus viridescens* was obtained by Adams, Gay and Terzian (1941), and such an effect has now been obtained by many workers both for anurans and urodeles. *Bufo arenarum* is the outstanding exception, and it may well be that there are specific differences in reactivity of the Müllerian duct, examples of which may become more numerous as a result of further work.

Hormones of the Ovary

Ovariectomy

It has already been pointed out that the female anuran has few secondary sexual characters. Consequently, the small amount of work on the effects of ovariectomy deals mainly with its effects on the oviducts. It has long been known that early differentiation of the accessory sexual structures is independent of the gonads, and regression of these structures after removal of the ovaries proceeds only as far as the condition they had reached at the end of this stage of self-differentiation. Regressive changes are therefore least marked in those species in which the second sexual characters undergo the greatest degree of self-differentiation.

Urodela.—Bresca (1910) found that ovariectomy produced little change in the external appearance of the female *Triturus cristatus*, though he noted that when the cloaca was swollen at the time of operation, it regressed afterwards. Other workers have also found that the post-pubertal development of the oviducts is under ovarian control (*Triturus viridescens*, Adams and Kirkwood, 1928 ; *T. cristatus*, de Beaumont, 1929 ; *Bufo arenarum*, Houssay, 1947b).

As in the Anura, most of the evidence for ovarian control of the secondary sexual characters is indirect, and comes from hypophysectomy. The results of this work have already been considered above ; they reinforce the conclusion that all the cyclical secondary sexual characters are under some degree of hormonal control. The majority of workers believe that this control comes from the gonads, but Tuchmann-Duplessis (1945) claims that the pituitary exerts a direct control over some, at least, of the secondary sexual characters of newts (*Triturus* spp.). He finds that regression in the hypophysectomised newt is more than twice as fast as in the gonadectomised animal and the various characters regress at different rates and times as a result of the two operations. The prostate gland and sexual colouration regress more quickly after hypophysectomy, whereas the genital ducts respond much more to castration. Tuchmann-Duplessis believes that the gonadal hormones control especially the phenomena of secretion whilst the pituitary controls tissue hypertrophy, so that neither the gonad nor the pituitary alone is capable of producing the complete development of secondary sexual characters.

Anura.—Christensen (1931) ovariectomised mature females of *Rana pipiens* and found that the oviducts degenerated. Atrophic changes were first evident at about 3 months, and by 8 months after the operation the oviducts resembled those of the pre-pubertal female.

Shapiro (1937) found that ovariectomy in *Xenopus laevis* is followed by the loss of all mating reflexes. This appears to be the only direct evidence that sexual behaviour in the female is under ovarian control, though there is, of course, some indirect evidence both from hypophysectomy, which has already been described, and from the injection of sex hormones which is described below. It would be interesting to know whether the tendency of females of certain species of *Bufo* and *Hyla* to approach croaking males (*see* Noble and Aronson, 1942) is abolished by ovariectomy.

The main effect of ovariectomy in female Anura is undoubtedly that shown by the oviducts. Wolf (1928) found that ovariectomy of *Rana pipiens* in September resulted in marked degeneration of the oviducts by December; the glandular cells lining them were small and had vacuolated cytoplasm and few secretion granules. Atrophy of the oviduct was slower in frogs ovariectomised in December. Gitlin (1939), working with *Xenopus*, obtained a similar degeneration and decrease in weight of the oviducts after ovariectomy. Pomerat (1940) has shown that ovariectomy in *B. arenarum* does not interfere with the development of oviducal glands in young toads, though Houssay (1947b) has shown that it causes a marked atrophy of these glands in older animals.

It seems from these results that the seasonal growth-cycle of the oviducts of female Amphibia is controlled by ovarian hormones, though there is less agreement concerning control of secretion of the oviduct. Many workers believe that it also is controlled by the ovaries, but Houssay and his colleagues have brought forward a good deal of evidence for direct control of oviducal secretion by the pars distalis, (Houssay, 1949, 1950). Galli-Mainini (1951), however, as a result of more recent work, has shown that the ovaries, at least under certain experimental conditions, are also implicated. For example, chorionic gonadotrophin induces the oviducts to secrete, but only in the presence of the ovaries. Furthermore, implantation of pituitaries will cause the appearance of a substance in the host's ovaries within an hour, which causes the oviducts to secrete. The chemical nature of this substance is not known. Galli-Mainini, as a result of this and the earlier work, concludes that secretion in the oviducts in *B. arenarum* is controlled both by the direct action of an anterior pituitary hormone, and also indirectly by an ovarian hormone which does not appear to be an oestrogen, but may be a progesterone-like substance.

Transplantation of ovaries into castrated males

Adams (1930) remarks that vertebrates with rudiments of the sexual apparatus of one sex remaining in the other are common. Some of the most familiar examples of this condition are the mammary glands in male mammals, the clitoris in female mammals, rudimentary Wolffian ducts in female birds, and rudimentary Müllerian ducts in males of some Anura and Urodela. With a view to inducing development of the Müllerian duct rudiment in castrated males of *Triturus viridescens*, Adams transplanted ovaries into such males and autopsied the engrafted animals 200–292 days later.   She found the ovaries to be in good condition at autopsy and reported hypertrophy of the Müllerian ducts to a degree which appeared to correlate well with the number of large yolky oöcytes.   Regression in activity of pelvic and abdominal glands of the cloaca, characteristic of castrates, appeared to be reduced when ovarian grafts were present, and the Wolffian duct and collecting ducts of the kidney also seemed more dilated than in the typical castrates.

Welti (1925) implanted ovarian grafts into castrated male toads (*B. vulgaris*) and found that they stimulated growth of the rudimentary Müllerian ducts.   De Beaumont (1929) induced hypertrophy of these ducts in castrated male *Triturus cristatus* by the same means, and later (de Beaumont, 1933) obtained complete feminisation of genetic male newts by early castration and ovarian grafting.

There can be no doubt that the results of successful gonad grafting experiments demonstrate beyond doubt the important part played by the gonads in the development and maintenance of the accessory sexual characters.   They also show that the gonads of one sex inhibit the gonads and secondary sexual characters of the other sex.

The effects of injecting oestrogens

The effects of injecting oestrogens into animals having an intact pituitary are difficult to interpret.   This applies especially to effects on the gonads, yet virtually all workers in this field have used intact animals and it is impossible to say whether the effects they obtained are direct ones, or mediated via the pituitary.

Puckett (1939) injected oestrone (Theelin) into males of *Rana pipiens* and *Bufo americanus* and found that it had no effect on the testes of either species, or on Bidder's organ in the case of the toad.   Similar results were obtained by Schreiber and Rugh (1945), who injected 0·03 mg. oestradiol in sesame oil into newly metamorphosed *R. pipiens*, and by Mintz, Foote and Witschi (1945), who found ovogenesis and spermatogenesis in larval *Rana clamitans* to be unaffected by oestradiol.

On the other hand, Adams (1946) treated intact males of *Triturus viridescens* with diethyl stilboestrol, the total amounts administered varying between 0·2 mg. and 6·0 mg. in sesame oil, distilled water, or gelatine pellets.   Marked atrophy of the testes resulted.   After 77–94 days only a few spermatogonia and a small amount of connective tissue remained.   Similar work was carried out on intact female *T. viridescens* (Adams, 1950).   The ovaries first increased in weight due largely to the formation of atypical corpora atretica.   However, the atretic follicles soon decreased in size and the ovaries regressed.   Adams is unable to say whether these gonadal changes are due to a direct effect of the steroid, or are mediated through the pituitary.   Work on mammals has shown that stilboestrol usually results in enlargement of the pars anterior, a decrease in the proportion of chromophilic elements and a depletion in gonadotrophic content.   The work of Burgos (1953) appears to indicate that oestrogens may have a similar effect in Amphibia.   He treated male *Bufo arenarum* with large doses of oestradiol benzoate for 58–83 days and reported pronounced pituitary changes ; the basophils of the pars distalis decreased in number and size and their cytoplasm became degranulated.   These changes were accompanied by profound involution of the gonads.   Testicular weight decreased and all stages in spermatogenesis were adversely affected.   The Sertoli cells decreased in size and sperms were freed

s*

from them.   Also, there was marked atrophy of the interstitial cells, and Bidder's organ became involuted.

Burgos (1953) obtained similar inhibitory effects in *Bufo arenarum*.   He found that large doses of oestradiol benzoate induced profound modification of the testes, weight diminished and all phases of spermatogenesis were altered.   Marked atrophy of interstitial cells, and pycnosis of the Sertoli cells with liberation of spermatozoa into the tubule lumina were observed, and Bidder's organ showed a great degree of involution.   However, such results may well have no physiological significance since there is a good deal of evidence that steroids, especially oestrogens, at high dosage have a profoundly damaging effect on gonadal tissue.   Indeed, as a study of the paradoxal effect of sex steroids on amphibian sex-determination shows, steroids can exert marked selective inhibition on the developing gonad at concentrations a good deal lower than those used in much of the experimental work on sexual physiology.

Female Amphibia have few accessory sexual characters and little is known of the effects of oestrogens on them.   Ciliation of large areas of peritoneum in the female amphibian is an interesting example of a sex-limited secondary sexual character.   It has been shown by Donahue (1934) that some degree of ciliation can be induced in male specimens of *Rana pipiens* by injecting oestrone.   Several specimens were given daily intraperitoneal injections of 5 r.u. oestrone (Theelin) and it was found that patches of active cilia were induced between 15 and 31 days after treatment started, though in no case was the degree of ciliation comparable with that found in the normal female.

The importance of the ovariectomised animal in studies of this kind is illustrated by the work of Shapiro and Zwarenstein (1937) on the cloacal lips of the spayed *Xenopus laevis*.   Injection of up to 1 mg. oestrone and up to 1·2 mg. oestradiol are ineffective in inducing hyperaemia of the cloacal lips of the spayed animal, though such treatment is invariably successful in the intact female. Shapiro and Zwarenstein conclude that stimulation of these structures is therefore due to some substance different from known mammalian sex-hormones, which is secreted by the ovary when stimulated.

A good deal more is known concerning the action of oestrogens on the sex-ducts of both males and females.   Wolf (1928) showed that castration-atrophy of the oviduct of female *Rana pipiens* can be prevented by daily injections of 2 r.u. " Mammalian follicular hormone ".   In later work (Wolf, 1939), she injected α oestradiol benzoate into ovariectomised *R. pipiens* and obtained, in 8 days, a 47·1 per cent increase in oviduct–body-weight ratio.   Puckett (1939) injected oestrone into intact females of *Rana pipiens* and obtained hypertrophy of the Müllerian ducts.   These investigations were concerned with adult frogs ; the action of oestradiol on newly metamorphosed specimens of *R. pipiens* has been investigated by Schreiber and Rugh (1945).   These workers found that a single injection of 0·03 mg. oestradiol caused marked hypertrophy of the oviducts of the female and Müllerian ducts of the male, 8–10 days after treatment ; stimulation of the distal ends was especially marked.   At 4 weeks the epithelial lining was columnar and ciliated, whereas, in the controls, the ducts were undifferentiated and hardly visible.   On the other hand, de Allende (1939) reported that oestrone in amounts varying between 480 i.u. and 10,000 i.u. and acting for 3–10 days produced no histological stimulation in the oviducts of *Bufo arenarum*.   At the highest dosage there was a slight stimulation of secretion, but de Allende agrees that this is unlikely to be a physiological effect (*see also* Galli-Mainini, 1951). Somewhat similar findings have been reported by Ponse (1941), who injected oestrone into ovariectomised specimens of *Bufo vulgaris*. This had no action on the atrophic oviducts, whereas implantation of *Bufo* ovaries resulted in their regeneration. Ponse therefore concludes that the toad ovary produces a hormone which is different from oestrogens of mammalian origin.

Adams (1946) treated adult intact and castrated males of *Triturus viridescens* with diethylstilboestrol. The atrophic effect of this treatment on the testes has already been described ; concomitant effects were produced on the Wolffian and Müllerian ducts. The former were caused to shrink until they were similar in appearance to the Wolffian ducts of castrates. The Müllerian ducts, on the other hand, became hypertrophied and showed active ciliation and secretory activity of the lining epithelium. The changes induced in the Wolffian ducts are believed by Adams to be indirect results mediated through testicular atrophy, whilst, since the Müllerian ducts were stimulated both in intact and castrated animals, this is believed to be a direct effect of the stilboestrol. Adams (1950) repeated this work on intact and ovariectomised females and found a moderate though positive action of the steroid on the oviducts ; both size and secretory activity were increased.

Hormonal Effects on Embryonic Gonads and Sex Structures

Much more is known about primary sex-differentiation in Amphibia than in any other cold-blooded vertebrate group. The process has been experimentally modified by treatment of embryonic stages with a variety of steroids, by parabiosis and by grafting. So far as this work concerns sex-determination, it has already been considered (Volume 2, Chapter 22) and detailed reviews are available (Humphrey, 1942 ; Ponse, 1949; Gallien, 1954; Witschi, 1957; Dodd, 1960; papers and discussions in " Colloque sur la différenciation sexuelle chez les Vertébrés (Colloque, 1950)). However, much of this work throws interesting light on the influence exerted by sex steroids on the embryonic gonads and other reproductive structures of the Amphibia and it therefore calls for further consideration here.

Effects of parabiosis and other grafting techniques on gonads and reproductive ducts

The work of Lillie (1916) and Keller and Tandler (1916) on the " freemartin " phenomenon in cattle led several workers to investigate, by artificial parabiosis, the action of the circulating hormones of one sex on the gonads and reproductive structures of the other. This technique was employed with great success in the Amphibia. Burns (1925) was the first worker to study the effects of parabiosis in these animals. He united early embryos of the salamander *Amblystoma punctatum* and reared them until well past the time at which sex was fully differentiated. It is, of course, impossible to determine the sex of these embryos, but assuming that he started with an equal number of embryos of both sexes, chance pairing would be expected to produce the following arrangement and proportion of sex pairs : 1 ♂♂ : 2 ♂♀ : 1 ♀♀. In the event, Burns obtained 44 ♂♂ pairs, and 36 ♀♀ pairs, and he interpreted this result by assuming that sex-reversal had occurred in one of the gonads of each heterosexual pair. There were no gonads intermediate in structure, and hence no clue as to how sex-inversion had taken place.

These results of Burns remain unexplained since all subsequent parabiotic unions of *A. punctatum* have yielded approximately 50 per cent of recognisably heterosexual pairs, and, in these, the ovaries of the females have usually shown marked masculinisation. The results of interaction between larval gonads of different sexes have now been studied by parabiosis in several amphibian species. In most cases, the heterosexual pairs have shown sex-inversion of the ovaries of the female members (*Rana sylvatica*, Witschi, 1927 ; *Amblystoma tigrinum*, Burns, 1930 ; *Triturus torosus*, Witschi and McCurdy, 1929; *A. tigrinum*, Humphrey, 1936a; *A. punctatum*, Humphrey, 1936b; *Rana esculenta*, Montalenti and Calisti, 1936). However, a slight initial retardation in development of the testes of the male co-twin has usually also been reported.

Although nothing is known as to the nature of the inductor substance which is produced by the embryonic testis and which exerts such a marked effect on the structure of the co-twin's ovary, several peculiarities in its mode of action have emerged which have been interpreted by certain workers to indicate that the substance is not a steroid. Montalenti *et al.* (1936), working with *Rana esculenta*, and Witschi (1927, 1931, 1939), working with *R. sylvatica*, *R. aurora* and *Hyla regilla*, have shown that, although the ovaries of heterosexual pairs are masculinised by the testes of the male partner, the degree of masculinisation is usually a function of distance between the two interacting gonads, so that frequently only that part of the ovary nearest to the co-twin's testis is masculinised. Moreover, in *Bufo americanus*, heterosexual parabiosis results in no gonadal changes in either partner unless testis and ovary are in physical contact (Witschi, 1939).

In contrast to the strict localisation of the effect of parabiosis characteristic of frogs and toads, newts show widespread diffusion of the male inductor substance, so that, even in chains of parabionts, the testes of a single male can produce a substance which diffuses freely and quickly reduces the ovaries of all females in the chain to sterile rudiments (Witschi and McCurdy, 1929).

Thus male parabionts appear to be dominant over females, and testes inhibit ovaries or masculinise them, and this is the general rule in Amphibia. However, several cases are on record in which the testes of the male partner have been inhibited by the ovaries of the female. In these cases, the female has invariably been the larger or faster growing of the partners. For example, Witschi (1937) found that in heterosexual pairs consisting of female *A. tigrinum* and male *A. jeffersonianum*, the latter being a dwarf species, the ovary of the female remained normal, whereas the testes of the male were first transformed into atypical ovaries and later into ovotestes.

The most recent worker to investigate amphibian reproductive structures by parabiosis is Chang (1953), who joined early tailbud embryos of *Xenopus laevis* (Fig. *11*.40) and obtained viable adults in the following sex combinations : 5 ♂♂ : 11♂♀ : 7 ♀♀, a result which agrees closely with the expected random distribution. Chang found that in heterosexual pairs, initial differentiation of the gonads always followed the inherited sex pattern, but later, ovarial development became progressively inhibited, and in the most advanced cases observed, there were signs of sex inversion of the ovaries consisting of reduction of the ovarian cortex, degeneration of oöcytes and medullary hypertrophy (Fig. *11*.40).

Parabiosis as an experimental tool suffers from the disadvantage that the partners are often difficult to rear, once they begin to move actively. Chang (1953) makes

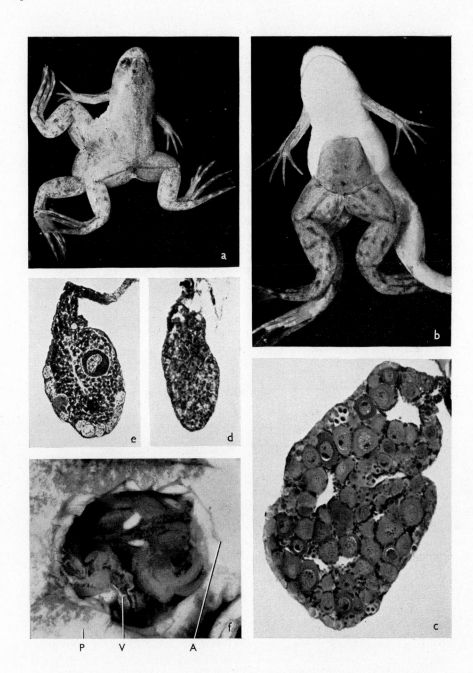

Fig. *11.* 40—*Xenopus laevis:* Parabiosis experiments.   (a) Parasite joined to left flank of
autosite, 90 days after metamorphosis ($\times$ 2).   (b) Parasite joined to ventral body wall
of autosite, 107 days after metamorphosis ($\times$ 2).   (c) T.S. normal ovary at metamorphosis ($\times$ 150).   (d) T.S. testis of parasite at metamorphosis ($\times$ 150).   (e) T.S.
gonad of female parasite, showing advanced stage in sex transformation.   Ovarian
cortex reduced, medullary cords hypertrophied ($\times$ 250).   (f) Male autosite inhibits
normal development of ovaries in parasite; note vestigeal ovaries ($\times$ 4).   A, autosite;
P, parasite; V, Inhibited ovaries.   (From Chang, 1953.)   (By permission of the publisher from *J. exp. Zool.,* 1953, **123,** 1.)

special mention of this in *Xenopus* in which the tadpoles are pelagic throughout larval life and they must be united in such a way that the swimming movements of the partners are not antagonistic. In order to overcome such difficulties, Humphrey (1928, 1929), introduced the technique of grafting gonadal primordia into embryonic stages of various urodele amphibia. In the earliest work, the engrafted gonad merely replaced one of the animal's own gonads (orthotopic grafting). In later work Humphrey also resorted to ectopic grafting and pre-orthotopic grafting. As would be expected, in approximately half of the cases,

(a)   (b

Fig. *11.*41—*Amblystoma tigrinum.* (a) Gonadal primordium from a female embryo grafted into female host.
Note normal structure of ovary derived from graft (on
the left) ($\times$ 4). (b) Gonadal primordium from a
female grafted into a male host. Note the slender
inhibited ovary derived from the graft (on the left), and
compare with graft ovary in (a) ($\times$ 4). (From
Humphrey, 1931.) (By permission of the publisher
from *J. exp. Zool.*)

heterosexual combinations are made, so that testis and ovary are brought into contact with each other and their mutual interactions can be studied.

The results are similar to those encountered in parabiotic grafting. When host gonad and engrafted gonad are of the same sex, each develops normally, but in heterosexual combinations the host's ovary is dominated by the foreign testis (Fig. *11.*41). Such inhibited ovaries become long and ribbon-like and have an irregularly thickened free edge. The growing oöcytes degenerate and the ovarian cortex is reduced to a few indifferent gonia. The ovarial sacs disappear and the ovary shrinks. Humphrey (1942) emphasises that this ovarian inhibition is effected by the testis directly, rather than through the pituitary, since it takes place before the gonad comes under pituitary stimulation ; it is also a different and more severe effect than that which results from hypophysectomy.

Although in most cases the host ovary is inhibited by the testis which develops from the engrafted gonad preprimordium, Humphrey (1935) has shown that, as in parabiosis, under certain conditions, the reverse change can occur. For example, if a gonadal preprimordium from a genetic male *A. punctatum* is orthotopically grafted into a genetic female embryo of *A. tigrinum*, the ovary is the dominant gonad. *A. tigrinum* is a faster-growing species than *A. punctatum*, so that the discrepancy in size between donor and host which resulted in male-to-female transformations in parabiosis obtains here also.

The reproductive ducts are also involved to a greater or lesser degree in the sex-change encountered in parabiosis and grafting experiments. In the normal female amphibian, the Wolffian duct is the urinary duct, whereas in the male it is also the vas deferens. In females caused to undergo reversal the Wolffian duct (ureter) may become a functional vas deferens. In some axolotl males produced by sex reversal, the testis does not communicate with the vas deferens, but this is not due to any deficiency in the Wolffian duct, and in several cases genetic females have been transformed into anatomically typical males which were physiologically functional. As shown below, even in the adult female the Wolffian duct seems to retain its capacity to respond to androgens by transforming into a functional vas deferens.

The Müllerian ducts appear to be formed in the male as well as the female in the majority of Amphibia. In adult males of most frogs they disappear, though in *Rana pipiens*, toads and urodeles they persist in an undifferentiated functionless state. Grafting experiments have shown that the rudiments appear to respond to ovarian hormones, so that when a male embryo is united in parabiosis with a larger female, the Müllerian duct of the male develops into a typical oviduct.

The cloacal glands of urodeles, as has already been stated, are true secondary sexual characters, and it has been shown (Witschi, 1939) that these glands show the typical male structure in a female *Amblystoma* whose ovaries have been inhibited by a male parabiont. Conversely, when the male undergoes sex reversal, his glands change to the female type.

The earlier work on grafting was supplemented and greatly extended by the use of crystalline preparations of sex hormones once these became available. In those species which have been submitted to grafting techniques and also studied by treatment with steroid hormones, the results are in extremely close agreement, and it seems clear that if, as some workers believe, the sex steroids are not identical to the inductor substances, then they are at least strongly inductor-mimetic. The results of this work on sex and sex-determination in a variety of Amphibia have recently been considered in some detail (Dodd, 1960); the main conclusions may be briefly summarised. A variety of androgens (testosterone, methyl testosterone, ethinyl testosterone, testosterone propionate and androsterone) and oestrogens (oestrone, oestradiol, oestradiol benzoate, oestradiol-3-benzoate-17-N-butyrate and oestradiol dipropionate) have been used and they have been administered either by injection in oil, or by immersing the larvae in aqueous solutions of steroid. A considerable range of concentrations has been tried and it has been demonstrated beyond doubt that the nature of the reaction of the amphibian larva to these substances can be profoundly altered by merely changing the amount administered. It has also been shown that there is a pronounced taxonomic specificity in the response to the same hormone at the same concentration (Fig. *11*.42).

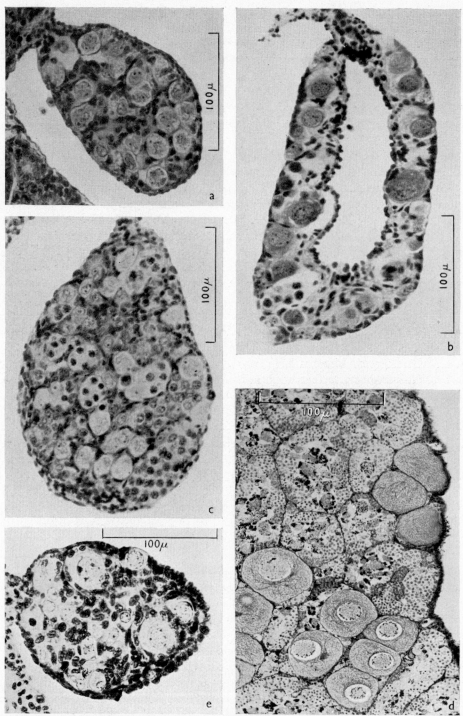

Fig. *11. 42*—*Xenopus laevis:* Sections through early gonad stages.   (a) T.S. gonad of control male, 1 month after metamorphosis.   (b) T.S. gonad of control female at metamorphosis.   (c) T.S. intersexual gonad (ovotestis) of larva treated with testosterone propionate.   (d) T.S. ovotestis of a toad aged 15 months treated with testosterone propionate—complete intermixing of testicular and ovarian tissue.   *Discoglossus pictus;* (e) T.S. intersexual gonad resulting from treatment of larva with testosterone propionate.   Fixed at time of metamorphosis.   (From Gallien, 1956 and 1950.)

The Ranidae amongst Anura show total and stable masculinisation of genetic females by androgens and are sensitive to extremely low concentrations. Thus, Witschi (1950) has shown that complete masculinisation of gonads of *Rana sylvatica* can be achieved by a concentration of methyl testosterone in the aquarium water as low as 1 in 10^{11}. Furthermore, genetic females of *R. agilis* (Vannini, 1941) and *R. temporaria* (Gallien, 1944) can be masculinised by androgen even when treatment is not started until after metamorphosis, and Mintz, Foote and Witschi (1945) have shown that *R. clamitans* can be masculinised after normal sex differentiation has taken place.

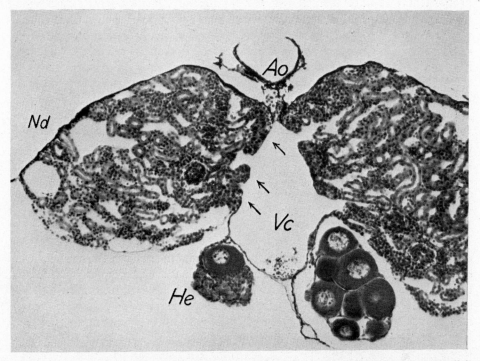

Fig. *II*. 43—*Rana pipiens*. Metamorphosing hermaphrodite (genetic male), raised in oestradiol, 50 μg/1. Adrenal lobules enlarged (arrows) (× 100). Ao, dorsal aorta; He, hermaphrodite gonad; Vc, vena cava. (From Witschi, 1953.)

The action of oestrogens on the higher Anura is variable. They have a limited feminising action on early genetic males at low concentrations, and gonads of treated animals may show hermaphroditism at metamorphosis (Fig. *II*.43). But even if treatment is continued indefinitely, the genetic sex sooner or later manifests itself. At high concentrations, however, oestrogens exert a paradoxal masculinisation, the aetiology of which is not clear, though it is always associated with a more or less abnormal-looking inhibition of the cortex of the gonad.

The urodeles and lower Anura (*Bufonidae, Xenopus, Alytes, Discoglossus*), so far as they have been studied, are uniform in their reaction to sex steroids and differ markedly from the Ranidae. They show total and stable feminisation to oestrogens and a paradoxal reaction to androgens. The latter seems to be achieved through a generalised inhibition of cells, especially those of the gonadal medulla, but the mesonephros is also affected.

VI. REPTILIA

Reptiles are the most primitive amniotes ; they therefore occupy a phylogenetic position of special importance. Moreover, since many of the features
which differentiate them from the anamnia are adaptations for reproduction on
dry land, reptiles may be presumed to have special relevance to any study on comparative reproductive physiology. Internal fertilisation is universal in the group ;
the developing eggs are now independent of water, and must, therefore, be protected from desiccation ; also, some degree of viviparity is encountered in a higher
proportion of reptiles than in fish and Amphibia. These adaptations have all
made new demands on the reproductive apparatus and, presumably, on the endocrine mechanisms associated with it. Thus internal fertilisation has involved the
development of copulatory organs and specialised mating behaviour ; shelled eggs
have necessitated further differentiation of the oviduct for the production of the
shell, and viviparity requires controlling mechanisms to ensure that the developing embryos are retained in the oviducts for the appropriate length of time, to
govern the interchanges which go on between the embryos and the mother, and to
ensure birth of the young at full term. It therefore becomes a matter of considerable
importance and interest to establish the degree to which the new secondary sexual
characters and pregnancy are under endocrine control. A good deal is known about
the former in reptiles, though much less is known with certainty of the mechanisms
controlling pregnancy. The available evidence, which is discussed below, tends
to show that although some controlling mechanisms must exist, they are likely to
differ from those which operate in mammals.

There are probably some 2,500 species of living reptiles, and these are classified into three distinct orders : the Chelonia, consisting of tortoises and turtles,
the Squamata, which includes lizards and snakes, and the Crocodilia. Reproductive endocrinology has received some attention in all three groups, though the
number of species investigated is very small, and in some cases only young stages
have been studied. There is undoubtedly a need for further work on this interesting group, especially on those members of it which have achieved true viviparity.

Gonads and Reproductive Ducts

The gonads and reproductive ducts are paired structures in both sexes ; they
differ only in detail in the various reptilian groups, the differences being relatively
slight even between oviparous and viviparous species (Mulaik, 1946). The following general description of these structures may be supplemented by reference
to detailed accounts of the morphology and histology of gonads and reproductive
tracts in a variety of individual species : *Lacerta agilis*, Regamey, 1935 ; *Emys
blandingii*, Nicholson and Risley, 1940 ; *Sceloporus spinosus floridanus*, Forbes,
1941 ; *Sceloporus* spp., Mulaik, 1946 ; *Vipera berus*, Volsoe, 1944, Marshall and
Woolf, 1957 ; *Terrapene carolina*, Altland, 1951 ; *Zootoca vivipara*, Panigel,
1956.

Male (Fig. *11.44*, a)

The testes have essentially the same structure as in the mammals ; they are
oval bodies, consisting of a compact mass of seminiferous tubules bound together
by an investing capsule of connective tissue. Each tubule consists of a typical

multi-layered germinal epithelium surrounding a central lumen.   Sertoli cells of unknown function lie around the periphery of each tubule and Leydig cells have been identified in the interstitium of the testis.   Marshall and Woolf (1957) speak of these cells as being prominent and glandular in the viper (*Vipera berus*).   They have described a depletion of the cholesterol-positive lipids in them with the onset of sexual maturity and the appearance of sexual behaviour, and assume that this indicates that the lipids are used to manufacture male sex hormone.

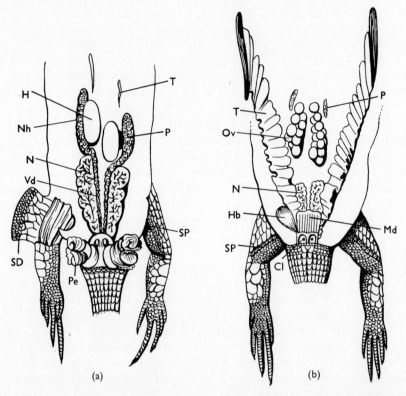

(a)   (b)

Fig. *11.*44—*Lacerta agilis:* Urinogenital system.   (1) Male; (2) Female.   Cl, cloaca; H, testis; Hb, urinary bladder; Md, rectum; N, kidney; Nh, epididymis; Ov, ovary; P, adrenal; Pe, penis; SD, femoral glands; SP, femoral pores; T, Müllerian ducts; Vd, vas deferens.   (Redrawn from *Lehrbuch der Zoologie;* Claus, Berlin, 1932.)

All reptiles are seasonal breeders, but the time of occurrence and duration of testicular activity varies (*see* Volume 1, Part 1, Chapter 3).   In the Lacertilia, about which most is known, and Ophidia, active spermatogenesis occurs throughout the year with only a short lull immediately after the breeding season.   Spermatogenesis in the Chelonia, however, is completed before the hibernation period starts, as in Amphibia.

The reproductive ducts of reptiles are similar in all main respects to those of the Amphibia.   In the male, the testes communicate with vasa efferentia which in turn merge with long coiled vasa deferentia ; these open on the genital papilla which communicates with the penis via the urinogenital groove.   Records of the occurrence of rudimentary Müllerian ducts in male reptiles have been reviewed by

Risley (1940). No fewer than seven of the seventeen males of the turtle *Emys blandingii* studied by this author had rudimentary Müllerian ducts. This finding, together with the known occurrence of more advanced hermaphroditism in reptiles also reviewed by Risley, serves to explain to some extent the relative ease with which the development of certain reptilian reproductive structures, notably the Müllerian ducts, can be influenced by hormones.

Female (Fig. *11*.44, b)

The ovaries of the viviparous lizard, *Xantusia vigilis*, have been described by Miller (1948), who has also reviewed the literature on the reptile ovary in general. Each ovary in *Xantusia* is an oval body lying postero-dorsally in the body cavity. It consists of a thin ovarian epithelium, scanty stromal tissue, female germ-cells in all stages of oögenesis, corpora lutea, corpora atretica, and contains an extensive cavity lined with squamous epithelium. It contains twelve to twenty whitish opaque ova varying in diameter between 0·1 and 1·3 mm., each enclosed in a follicle consisting of granulosa, theca interna and theca externa. One of the eggs in each ovary undergoes a period of rapid growth in the 2 months preceding ovulation and reaches a diameter of 7–8 mm. Immediately following ovulation the collapsed follicle develops into a corpus luteum which shows signs of secretory activity throughout pregnancy though its purpose is obscure. At the time of parturition the corpus luteum is undergoing obvious disintegration and within 3–4 weeks it has almost disappeared.

The ovaries of the turtle *Emys blandingii* are described by Nicholson and Risley (1940) as loose membranous organs which spread laterally and ventrally over the kidneys and posterior part of the lungs. They contain a large number of eggs at different stages of development. The detailed structure and development of the individual follicle has been described for several reptiles (Fraenkel and Martins, 1938 ; Boyd, 1940 ; Samuel, 1944 ; Bragdon, 1952 ; Panigel, 1956).

In female reptiles, Müllerian ducts function as oviducts. They are paired undulating muscular tubes which open at their anterior ends via the ostium abdominale and posteriorly into the cloaca. The anterior region of each oviduct is specialised for the secretion of albumen and shell, whilst the posterior region is thicker, more muscular, and ciliated when mature.

Various grades of viviparity are commonly met with in reptiles, and Mulaik (1946) has carried out a comparative study of the reproductive organs in three species of the genus *Sceloporus*, one of which was oviparous whilst two were ovoviviparous. She reported that the number of ripening ova in the oviparous species was somewhat greater than in the two ovoviviparous species. She also found that the oviducts of the oviparous species were markedly pleated and folded along their entire lengths, whereas in the viviparous species, apart from a few folds near the ostium, they were virtually unfolded. The cloacae of the ovoviviparous species were much more muscular than was the case in the oviparous species.

Secondary Sexual Characters

External sex dimorphism is usually poorly developed among reptiles. Thus, Cunningham and Smart (1934) point out that in the slow-worm (*Anguis fragilis*), for instance, the sexes are difficult to distinguish unless careful examination is

made for the copulatory organs.   In the class as a whole, however, there is a considerable variety of dimorphic characters, associated almost exclusively with the
male sex.

Remarkable head furnishings are found in the males of several species of
chamaeleon and other lizards ; these consist of dewlaps, gular fans and pouches,
as well as erectile dorsal crests.   These crests and throat pouches of lizards, like
the horns of ungulates, show every gradation from full presence in both sexes to
complete absence in one.

In many reptilian species, especially snakes, there is often a slight colour difference between the sexes, the males being more vivid, but the assumption of
special nuptial colouration by the male does not seem to be very common.   Femoral
pores, opening on specially modified yellowish scales, have also been reported in a
variety of lizards, and it has been shown that the dense wax-like substance exuded
from the femoral pores of the male during the mating season is associated with
mating activity (Smith, 1946).

The boid snake, *Enygrus clarinatus*, has vestigial hind-limbs which take the
form of large curved hooks or spurs in the male, whereas, in the female, they are
usually reduced to minute horny projections.   The spurs are used during court·
ship, the male scratching the body of the female with them in the region above
the cloaca (Stickel and Stickel, 1946).

Male chelonians also show a variety of secondary sexual characters.   Evans
(1951a) states that the male slider turtle (*Pseudemys scripta troostii*) becomes mature
in its fourth or fifth year and at this time the tail grows rapidly until it is noticeably
longer than that of the female of similar body size.   The tail is used in courtship,
and in copulation it serves to bring the two cloacae together ;   Evans identifies it
as a true secondary sexual character.   A sex-dimorphism also exists between the
three middle digits of both fore- and hind-feet, the second, third and fourth digits
of the fore-feet of the male being at least two and one-half times longer than those
of the female.   They are used in courtship to titillate the neck and jaws of the
female (Cagle, 1948).   The elongated rear claws of the male box-turtle (*Terrapene
carolina*) are also copulatory structures of some importance.   Evans (1952a),
describing copulation in this species, states: " In the preliminary phase, the male
bites at the carapace of the female, then mounts her.   He places his rear claws on the
posterior edge of her plastron.   The female closes the plastron tightly, thus holding
the male pinioned, often for two hours.   During this interval, the male snaps at the
nuchal plates and head of the female.   When she finally becomes receptive, her
plastron opens, permitting copulation to take place."   Other sex-dimorphic
characters encountered in the Chelonia are the concave plastron of the male box-
turtle and the red or pink iris of the mature male turtle.

In many reptiles, notably the land tortoises, the male utters cries during the
breeding season, and in some species of terrapins he produces characteristic sounds
by rubbing together horny tubercles on his hind-legs.   These tubercles are absent
in the female.   Mating behaviour associated with courtship may also be well
developed and this aspect of sex in reptiles has received considerable attention.
It is considered in some detail below together with the endocrine relationships of
reptilian secondary sexual characters in general.

The reptile cloaca is a well-developed structure which usually shows certain
sex-dimorphic characters.   Mulaik (1946) and Nicholson and Risley (1940) have

described it in detail in the lizard (*Sceloporus*) and in the turtle (*Emys blandingii*) respectively, in both of which differentiation reaches a high degree of complexity. In both sexes the cloaca is subdivided into three chambers : the coprodaeum, which is the largest of the three, and is antero-dorsal in position, the urodaeum, and the proctodaeum, which is postero-ventral and opens to the exterior by the vent. The urodaeum is the urinogenital sinus into which genital and urinary ducts open. From each of its lateral walls there arises a forwardly projecting papilla, at the base of which the ureters open whilst the vasa deferentia open at its posterior extremity. In the male, the genital papilla is a simple conical projection of the cloacal wall, whilst in the female it is a large expanded fleshy structure, the inner surface of which is markedly folded. In *Emys*, there arises from the floor of the cloaca in the male a heart-shaped glans penis which is composed of three concentric sheaths. The homologue of this structure in the female is the glans clitoris, a much smaller structure which, as in the male, arises near the end of the urinogenital groove. The body of the penis springs from the anterior extremity of the ventral cloacal wall ; it consists of corpora fibrosa and spongiosa which embrace the urinogenital groove. The penis acts as an intromittent organ which is erected by an influx of blood and retracted by the retractor penis muscle. In lizards and snakes, the penis is a markedly bifid structure ; each half is called a hemipenis and may function independently of the other.

In *Anolis*, and probably many other reptiles, the cloacal lining shows sex-dimorphism ; in females and out-of-season males, it is mucoid, whereas in ripe males it is intensely keratinised.

A further, most interesting sex-dimorphic character is found associated with the kidney of many male reptiles. This so-called sexual segment has already been considered in some detail (Volume 1, Part 1, Chapter 3). Several early workers described and figured a thick pre-terminal segment with high secretory activity in the uriniferous tubules of male lizards and snakes, but did not note that it was absent in females or that it showed seasonal activity in lizards. Regaud and Policard (1903) were the first to note that the unusual secretory activity of part of the uriniferous tubules in several genera of lizards and snakes was associated with sex. The diameter of the secretory region is greater than that of any other part of the tubule and the cells lining it are columnar filled with secretion granules whilst those lining the corresponding region in females are low, muciparous and never contain granules. In some species, hypertrophy and secretory activity is extended to include also the terminal segment of the kidney tubule, collecting canal and ureter.

In snakes, the sexual segment is maintained in an active state throughout the year, whilst in lizards it is active only during the breeding season. Endocrinological studies which are discussed below have shown conclusively that development and secretory activity of the sexual segment of the reptilian kidney are controlled by secretions of the testis.

Pituitary Gland

The morphology of the pituitary gland varies somewhat in the different groups of reptiles, though it resembles in general that of the Amphibia. All the regions are more variable in form and in their relationship to each other than in the Amphibia, but the differences are superficial. Rathke (1839) was the first to describe the development and structure of the reptilian pituitary gland ; his description has been followed during the succeeding years by many morphological studies on pituitaries from most of the reptilian Orders.   The literature has been reviewed by de Beer (1926), Charipper (1937), Gorbman (1941), Herlant (1954) and Wright (1956).

Baumgartner (1916) described the embryology and histology of various lizard and snake pituitary glands and was the first to differentiate between acidophilic, basophilic and chromophobic cells in the anterior lobe of reptiles.   He does not appear to have identified the posterior lobe in spite of the fact that Herring (1913) had previously described a posterior lobe in *Testudo* and *Lacerta*.   Reese (1931)

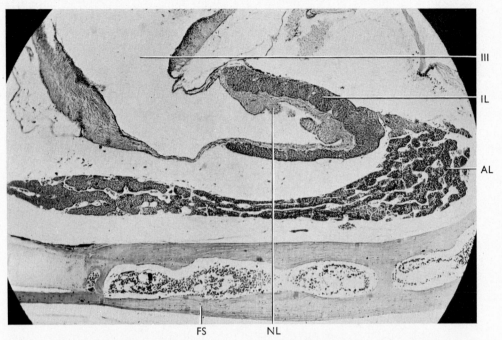

Fig. *11.45—Agama agama:* Parasagittal section of pituitary gland lying in shallow sella turcica.
A.L., anterior lobe; I.L., intermediate lobe; N.L., neural lobe; F.S., floor of sella turcica;
III, third ventricle (× 70). (From Wright, 1956.)

described the histology of the pituitary of the alligator, and this was followed by descriptions of the gland of *Thamnophis radix* by Siler (1936) and *Anolis carolinensis* by Poris and Charipper (1938).

Altland (1939) made a detailed study of the histology of the pituitary of the fence lizard *Sceloporus* and was the first to suggest a connection between cyclical histological changes and function.   He described numerous acidophilic cells surrounding the sinusoids of the pars distalis and suggested that variations in cell size were related to physiological activity.   Basophils were most abundant in May when the animals were at the height of their sexual activity : at all other times of year they were less numerous than the acidophils.   Hatta (1941) reported a similar state of affairs in the lizard *Tachydromus*.   He found an almost constant number of acidophils throughout the year in both sexes, whereas, in the breeding season, the basophils were increased in number by conversion of the chromophobe cells.

Gonadectomy resulted in an increase in the number of basophils and a decrease in the number of acidophils. Hatta concluded that the basophil cells were gonadotrophs. Miller (1948) studied the pituitary of the lizard *Xantusia vigilis* and carried out a detailed quantitative investigation into the relative abundance of different cell types at different phases of the reproductive cycle. The pituitary gland is asymmetrical in *Xantusia*, the posterior regions of partes nervosa and intermedia being displaced to the right of centre, whereas most of the pars distalis lies to the left of the median plane and the left side of the pars anterior is thicker than the right. The cells of the anterior lobe are arranged in anastomosing and branching cords separated from each other by blood sinuses. Four cell types were identified by the use of Heidenhain's azan technique : two types of acidophil, a basophil and a chromophobe. One type of acidophil was found to be restricted to the cranial half of the pars distalis whilst the other acidophil was restricted to the caudal half. Basophils and chromophobes were found throughout the pars distalis, but the former were more numerous in the peripheral zone. Miller found a close correlation between gonad growth and increase in the number of basophil cells. During winter, the testes regress and the basophil cell count decreases concomitantly. The basophils undergo a marked increase in number in February and March, just prior to the period of greatest testicular activity. The testis shows heightened spermatogenetic activity in late July and this is correlated with an increase in the number of basophils in the pars distalis of the male. However, there is no corresponding increase either in ovarian activity or in the number of basophils in the pars anterior of the female at this time. But later, following parturition in early September, the ovary shows a burst of activity and this is accompanied by a rise in the number of basophils. Thus at all stages of the reproductive cycle in both sexes, heightened gonad activity is closely correlated with an increase in the number of basophil cells in the pars distalis of the pituitary.

Xantusia is a viviparous lizard and well-marked corpora lutea are present throughout gestation. Miller states that if these corpora lutea are under hormonal control it would appear that the acidophils are implicated rather than the basophils.

Panigel (1956) studied the cytology of the pituitary gland of *Zootoca vivipara* throughout the year, but especially during gestation. He used the trichrome stains of Masson and Heidenhain and distinguished the three usual cell types : acidophils, basophils, and chromophobes. He found a marked increase in the number of acidophils during gestation, a fact which he was unable to explain, and an appreciable increase in the number of basophils in the weeks preceding ovulation. He interpreted this increase by assuming that the basophils were concerned in the maturation of the ovarian follicles. Similar close correlation between fluctuations of the basophil cells of the pars distalis and cyclical activity of the gonads has been reported by Hartmann (1944) and Cieslak (1945) in *Thamnophis sirtalis* and *T. radix*.

Gonadectomy, or the injection of sex-steroids into intact animals, with subsequent examination of the pituitary gland for concomitant changes, are recognised techniques for locating gonadotrophins in the pituitary. Poris (1941) has used both techniques to investigate pituitary cytology in the lizard *Anolis*. She injected either oestradiol propionate or oestradiol benzoate for periods up to 1 month and found that the basophils of the posterior region of the pars distalis appeared smaller, stained more faintly and had less definite cell outlines than those of the control lizards. Pituitary glands of animals castrated for from $7-10\frac{1}{2}$ weeks showed no obvious histological changes, but there was a slight increase in the percentage of basophils present. In three animals which had been castrated for $4\frac{1}{2}$ months, basophilic cells in the posterior region of the pars distalis differed from those in normal glands. These findings, and the observation that basophilia increases in spring when the gonads are most active, are in agreement with the view that the basophils are responsible for secreting gonadotrophic hormone in reptiles as in most other vertebrates.

The Effects of Hypophysectomy

Hypophysectomy varies a good deal in difficulty in the different reptilian orders. In snakes the pituitary is easily accessible from the mouth and the operation is simple, whereas in lizards it tends to lie rather deep in the skull, access is made difficult by muscle, and it is hard to avoid fatal haemorrhage.

The male

Schaefer (1933) was the first worker to report successful hypophysectomy in reptiles. He removed the pituitary glands of two species of garter snake, *Thamnophis sirtalis* and *T. radix*, and found that the testes of hypophysectomised animals became small and flaccid with degenerating spermatocytes in the atretic seminiferous tubules, while the size of the interstitial cells was less than normal. Subcutaneous implantation of a single hypophysis every other day for a period of 30 days stimulated germ-cell production, enlarged the tubules and increased the size of the interstitial cells. Cieslak (1945) studied the relationship between the reproductive cycle and the pituitary gland in *Thamnophis radix* and reported in detail on the effects of hypophysectomy. Male garter snakes were hypophysectomised, and autopsied 9 and 16 days later. The testes showed only a slight decrease in weight, but profound histological effects were noted. After 9 days, the germinal epithelium underwent a marked sloughing, so that desquamated cells completely filled the lumen of the tubules. Sixteen days after hypophysectomy the tubules were much shrunken and hyperaemic. Cytolysis of germinal cells and pycnosis of their nuclei were pronounced features of the atretic testes, whilst interstitial cells were small and compact and had irregular nuclei and vacuolated cytoplasm. Cieslak also dealt with the effects of long-term hypophysectomy, that is for 44 and 66 days respectively. This caused a marked reduction in testis volume and weight, so that testis weight in the operated animals was only one-tenth that of the normal controls. This represents a 50 per cent reduction below that which occurs during hibernation, at which time the gonads are normally minimal in size. The seminiferous tubules of hypophysectomised males were lined by only a single row of spermatogonia and Sertoli cells and their lumina contained cellular debris. Interstitial cells also showed signs of atresia and no seminal fluid was present in the vas deferens.

Cieslak also carried out replacement therapy with a view to repairing the effects of hypophysectomy. In July, fresh pituitary glands from male animals were macerated in distilled water and injected intraperitoneally. Each of five hypophysectomised males received a total of 10 pituitary glands in four injections. After 9 days, the testis weight was twice that of the controls and spermatogenesis was active and normal.   Cieslak summarised his results by saying that " The gonadotrophic potency of July male pituitaries was sufficient not only to maintain testicular activity and produce the normal increase in testis weight during this period but also, in the amount administered, to stimulate a further increase." Another group of hypophysectomised males was given five daily intraperitoneal injections of equine gonadotrophin.   Each received a total of 350 i.u. and was autopsied 16 days later.   This produced stimulation in excess of that normally found at the peak of the seasonal cycle.

Wright (1956) carried out adenohypophysectomy on male specimens of *Agama agama*, and obtained substantially similar results though some spermatocytes were still present 39 days after the operation (Fig. *11.46*).

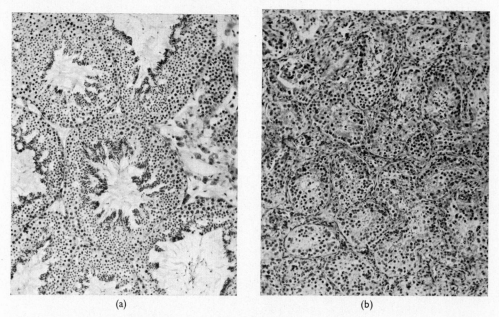

(a)   (b)

Fig. *11*.46—*Agama agama;* Effects of adenohypophysectomy on the testis.   (a) Control testis: Tubules are normal and all stages of spermatogenesis are represented.   Note tubule lumina containing spermatozoa (× 120).   (b) Testis from adenohypophysectomised animal.   Tubules are completely atretic and few normal stages in spermatogenesis can be seen.   Interstitial cells appear unaffected (× 120).   (From Wright, 1956.)

These results demonstrate beyond doubt the important role of the reptile pituitary in maintaining the testes in functional activity.   The work of Cieslak also shows that, as in the other cold-blooded vertebrates for which the information exists, spermatogonia appear to be relatively unaffected by hypophysectomy, though they appear to be unable to transform into primary spermatocytes.

The female

Hansen and Tabb (1941) hypophysectomised female box-turtles (*Terrapene carolina*) at the time of year when ovarian weights in normal animals were increasing The operation produced a marked regression of the ovaries.   At the time of hypophysectomy the right ovary was removed from both experimental animals and controls ; the average weight of these ovaries was 2·7 g.   Three months later, the left ovaries of the operated animals weighed only 0·61 g., whereas in the controls they averaged 6·0 g.

The reptiles show a variety of grades of viviparity and several workers have investigated the role of the pituitary in " pregnancy ". Clausen (1935, 1940) studied this problem in water-snakes (*Natrix*, 4 spp.), garter snakes (*Thamnophis*, 2 spp.) and brown snakes (*Storeria* sp.). He found that snakes hypophysectomised early in pregnancy resorbed their young, whereas when the operation was performed during the later stages of pregnancy, abortion occurred and all the young were delivered dead. Clausen concluded that the pituitary, or part of it, is essential for the maintenance of pregnancy at all stages of gestation, and he suggested that the pituitary also maintains the placenta-like structures. He also found that injections of 1 ml. of an extract of mammalian posterior-lobe pituitary, or extract of whole sheep pituitary, caused parturition within 48 hours of injection in late stages of gestation: in the early and the middle stages of gestation, 3–4 injections of 2 ml. had no effect.

However, subsequent workers have been unanimous in disagreeing with Clausen's findings. Bragdon (1950, 1951) hypophysectomised the common garter snake (*Thamnophis sirtalis*) and the water-snake (*Natrix sipedon*). He reports that hypophysectomy has no effect on young in the uteri of pregnant snakes ; they continue to develop to term. There is, however, interference with parturition and young are retained beyond full term. Bragdon also notes that if hypophysectomy is performed prior to ovulation, ovulation does not occur, but the operation does not appear to affect the capacity of the granulosa cells to digest yolk during follicular atresia.

Panigel (1956), in a study on the reproductive physiology of the ovoviviparous lizard *Zootoca vivipara*, has verified most of Bragdon's findings concerning the effects of hypophysectomy on gestation, though he disagrees with Bragdon's conclusions that corpora lutea are of no physiological importance in connection with gestation, and that the pituitary has no influence on their formation and survival. Panigel states that, in *Zootoca*, histological study of the corpora lutea, as well as histological modifications observed in the pituitary during gestation, lead him to believe that both these structures are of physiological importance and there may be a functional relationship between them. Further, both Bragdon (1952) and Panigel (1956) have reported an increased luteal cell density in the corpus luteum of hypophysectomised animals, caused by a decreased cytoplasm/nucleus ratio. Panigel also suggests that hypophysectomy, through its subsequent effect on the corpora lutea, is responsible for the abnormalities in parturition which both Bragdon and he noted in hypophysectomised animals. This work is considered in greater detail in the section below dealing with ovariectomy.

In summary, the pituitary of the female reptile has been shown to be essential for the maintenance of ovarian structure and function, though there are no histological data available on the nature of the ovarian degeneration which follows pituitary removal. But it certainly includes atresia of large eggs, and ovulation is inhibited. The evidence that the pituitary exerts control over the corpora lutea is contradictory, indirect and meagre. However, a point of such importance to comparative endocrinology must clearly be investigated further, bearing in mind the possibility that the degree of control involved may well be slight and difficult to demonstrate.

Implantation and Injection of Pituitary Material into Reptiles

Houssay (1931) was the first to investigate the effects of pituitary gonado-trophins in reptiles and he appears to be one of only two workers who have made use of reptile pituitaries for this purpose.   He implanted five homoplastic pituitaries into the snake *Xenodon merremi* and this resulted in eggs being laid 6 days later.   Presumably the implantations were made near the normal time of egg-laying, though this is not stated.   Herlant (1933) injected extract of mammalian anterior pituitary gland into several adult male *Lacerta* during the non-breeding period and induced active secretion in the previously quiescent sexual segment of the kidney.   However, Regamey (1932, 1935) was unable to stimulate the inter-stitial cells of *Lacerta agilis* as a result of injecting mammalian hypophyseal extracts, though this could well have been due to the injection of inadequate amounts of hormone over too short a time.   Other early workers who reported positive effects from pituitary injections were : Cunningham and Smart (1934), who induced ovulation in *Lacerta vivipara* and *Anguis fragilis* by injecting an acid extract of mammalian pituitary, and Kehl (1935), who administered mammalian pituitary extracts to male palm lizards (*Uromastix*) and induced spermatogenesis during the sexually inactive period.

Forbes (1934, 1937) extended the scope of this work to include immature as well as mature animals and studied the injected animals in greater detail.   He used the alligator (*Alligator mississippiensis*) ; two groups of animals were treated, one aged 4 months, the other aged 18 months.   The first group received intraperi-toneal injections of 0·5 ml. alkaline extract of whole sheep pituitary three times per week for 6 weeks (total 9 ml.).   The second group received 1 ml. whole gland extract six times per week until 39 ml. had been injected.   As a result of this treat-ment, both groups showed hypertrophy of the gonads, especially the testes, though spermatogenesis was not induced.   The oviducts of the female were hypertrophied and convoluted, though the vasa deferentia did not differ macro-scopically from those of the controls.   The main results of this work are presented in Table IV.

The work of Evans (1935a, b, c, d) on the effects of gonadotrophic injections in lizards extends the field still further to include changes in the behaviour of injected animals.   Evans (1935a, c) investigated the effects of extract of sheep pituitary on both sexes of the lizard *Anolis carolinensis*.   Twenty-five females and twenty-five males were injected, and fifty animals were kept as controls.   The males showed a marked response to the injection.   The testes were considerably hyper-trophied and often became two or three times the size of control testes.   Epidi-dymides and vasa efferentia were always greatly enlarged ; in an extreme case, a single loop of epididymis was found to be fourteen times the diameter of that of a control.   Sperms were found in the epididymides after the fourth daily injection and there was slight enlargement of the vasa efferentia.   External secondary sexual characters and courtship behaviour were also stimulated : the dorsal crest on the neck and back of the head was stimulated, the hemipenis could be everted, and fighting and courtship were common every sunny day during winter and early spring in the injected animals.   Evans (1935c) has also reported implantation of pituitary glands into female specimens of *Anolis carolinensis*.   One animal received four homoplastic pituitaries from male *Anolis* ; it failed to ovulate but the genital system was approximately twice as large as that of the controls at autopsy. Of three females which received five homoplastic pituitary implants, two, which died before ovulation, had hypertrophied genital systems, the remaining female laid two eggs. In other similar experiments (Evans, 1935b), injected females laid several eggs, all appreciably before the start of egg-laying by any of the controls.

Mellish (1936) has investigated the effects of temperature in conjunction with injections of hog pituitary extract, on the horned lizard *Phrynosoma cornutum* during the period of sexual quiescence. One group of animals was kept at 35° C. and divided into two lots, one of which received control injections whilst the other received 0·2 ml. hog anterior pituitary extract on alternate days until 3 ml. (said

TABLE IV

Alligator mississippiensis: EFFECTS OF PROLONGED ADMINISTRATION OF ALKALINE EXTRACTS OF WHOLE GLAND SHEEP PITUITARY TO IMMATURE SPECIMENS

(From Forbes, 1937)

Alligators aged 4 months	
	Ratios
Control testis : experimental testis	1 : 4·10
Control ovary : experimental ovary	1 : 2·39
Control testis : control ovary	1 : 1·53
Experimental testis : experimental ovary	1 : 0·89
Alligators aged 18 months	
	Ratios
Control testis : experimental testis	1 : 27·47
Control ovary : experimental ovary	1 : 2·65
Control testis : control ovary	1 : 4·14
Experimental testis : experimental ovary	1 : 0·39

to be equivalent to 60 r.u.) had been given. In the injected group, pronounced signs of stimulation were seen ; the gross diameter of the testis tubules was greater than in the control animals and many mitoses were seen. All stages of spermatogenesis were encountered, whereas in the control group spermatogenesis had not progressed beyond the prophase of the first maturation division. Although this experiment was carried out during the period of sexual quiescence, the testis picture is said to be comparable with that found in the sexually active animal in June. The epididymides were also stimulated, the lining epithelium being tall columnar and showing active secretion. The ovaries of the injected females also showed signs of stimulation ; the eggs did not appear to be increased in number, but the average diameter was 4–5 mm. as compared with 1 mm. in the control animals. Furthermore, the oviducts showed pronounced signs of precocious maturity in all regions.   Three males and three females, kept at 5° C., were injected in a similar manner to those just described.   Two of each sex died before the end of the experiment and the remainder showed no signs of stimulation. Mellish also demonstrated that increase of temperature without injected material is incapable of producing precocious activity in the reproductive system.

Mellish and Meyer (1937) continued this investigation on *Phrynosoma* using a variety of gonadotrophins : luteinizing hormone (LH) and follicle-stimulating hormone (FSH) of sheep pituitary and also pregnant mare serum (PMS).   Injections were made once daily for 8 days during the sexually quiescent period, and the animals were killed on the ninth day.   All these substances had a stimulating effect on the ovaries of the horned lizard.   Marked yolk deposition was recorded and the oviducts increased in vascularity and became wider : LH was less effective in stimulating the gonads and reproductive ducts than FSH and PMS.

Risley (1941) treated juvenile diamond-back terrapins (*Malaclemmys centrata*) with extract of sheep pituitary gland.   Each animal received 42·75 rat units over a 30-day period.   The testes of the treated males were hypertrophied, seminiferous tubules became patent, and there was distinct interstitial cell differentiation.   Wolffian ducts and the ureters of males showed signs of hypertrophy, presumably a concomitant change due to prior stimulation of the testes.   Signs of growth and differentiation were also evident in the glans penis and corpus fibrosum, but the Müllerian ducts showed no changes.   In the injected females only doubtful responses were obtained.

Panigel (1956) has reported that during gestation in the ovoviviparous lizard *Zootoca vivipara* several ovarian follicles undergo atresia, and vitellogenesis and maturation of other follicles almost cease.   He has also investigated whether exogenous gonadotrophin can initiate renewed maturation of follicles, ovulation, and the formation of corpora lutea in female lizards between the middle and end of gestation.   Each female received intraperitoneal injections of 5 mouse units of an anterior pituitary extract (Gonadormone, Byla) at 3-day intervals and this was sufficient to produce maturation of a small number of follicles, ovulation, and the formation of a new generation of corpora lutea.   The injection had no effect on the eggs which were already developing *in utero*.

Injection of the Gonadotrophins of Pregnancy

Chorionic gonadotrophin (CG) and PMS have been used less in the reptiles as sources of gonadotrophin than in the other groups.   They have in general yielded results closely similar to those produced by pituitary gonadotrophins.

Herlant (1933) injected human pregnancy urine into male blindworms (*Anguis fragilis*) and he obtained secretory activity of the sexual segment of the kidney and an increase in the amount of interstitial tissue in the testis.

Evans (1935b) injected Antuitrin-S (chorionic gonadotrophin) into female specimens of *Anolis carolinensis* and produced marked enlargement and convolution of the oviducts.   This was brought about mainly by great hypertrophy of the glands lying beneath the mucous lining of the lumen, though all regions showed some degree of stimulation and the duct became patent.   The ovaries of the injected animals increased in size to between two and four times that of the controls, but egg-laying was not induced.   This is in marked contrast to similar experiments in the same series in which injection of extracts of sheep pituitary glands resulted in precocious egg-laying.   However, it is difficult to arrive at any accurate assessment of the amounts of hormone administered in this work, and the relative amounts of LH-like substances in the two preparations are not known. It is therefore impossible to compare their ovulation-inducing potencies.

Serum gonadotrophin (PMS, Roussel) and chorionic gonadotrophin (CG, Roussel) were injected by Panigel (1956) into the lizard *Zootoca vivipara* during gestation and it was found that both had a marked effect on the ovaries.   Five intraperitoneal injections of PMS, each of 100 i.u., caused maturation of one to three follicles in each ovary.   Four injections of CG, each of 75–100 i.u., at intervals of 3 days, had a profound effect near the end of gestation.   Four follicles matured in the right ovary and this ovary was greatly hypertrophied : it weighed 370 mg., whereas the corresponding ovary of a control lizard weighed only 10–15 mg.

Hormones of the Gonads

Gonadectomy and gonad transplantation

Castration.—Castration has been carried out in a number of lizards and it has been established that its effects are identical to those already well known in other vertebrates.   Male genital ducts, copulatory structures, external secondary sexual characters, behaviour and, in those reptiles in which it is present, the sexual segment of the kidney, are all affected to some degree by removal of the testes.

Matthey (1929) described post-castration changes in *Lacerta agilis* ; he reported that 1 year after the operation the femoral glands of the male closely resembled those of the female and the typical male colouration had been replaced by a type which was much closer to that of the female.   Also, in the castrate, there is an accumulation of fat which gives the body a superficial resemblance to that of the female.   Matthey reported that castration had little effect on the copulatory structures of the mature animal.   Padoa (1933) confirmed Matthey's findings on the femoral gland and stated that castration caused suppression of the secretory activity in the epididymis in *Lacerta muralis*, and Herlant (1933) showed that castration of *Lacerta* and *Anguis* caused severe inhibition of the sex segment of the kidney.   Similar investigations by Regamey (1935) yielded additional data: the femoral glands, vasa deferentia and epididymides were all affected and the colouration of the castrated animals changed slowly towards that of the female.   A further demonstration that the sex segment of the kidney is under the control of gonadal hormones has been provided by Takewaki and Fukuda (1935), who castrated winter specimens of the lizard *Takydromus tachydromoides* and obtained pronounced inhibition of the sexual segment.   Castration of *Uromastix* by Kehl (1935) yielded results which were essentially similar.

Neeser (1940) has described in detail the so-called femoral glands of lizards (*Lacerta viridis*) which are usually well developed in males and which constitute the most constant sexual difference in these animals.   They are situated on the ventral surface of the thigh, where there is a special region of scales through which emerges the secretion of the gland.   These organs are best developed in May, at which time the secretion becomes abundant.   Later in the year regression sets in, so that in winter they are very slightly developed and there is no secretion visible at the exterior.   Neeser (1940) showed that castration caused marked degeneration of the femoral glands but was able to repair the damage by grafting small pieces of testis in the liver. Two months after castration and implantation, in those cases in which the grafts has taken, there were no external differences between the femoral glands of operated animals and controls.

Evans and Clapp (1940) castrated males of *Anolis carolinensis* and reported that this operation resulted in a 63 per cent reduction in diameter of the vas deferens compared with sexually ripe controls and a 37 per cent reduction compared with unripe controls. Castration also caused some reduction in the height of the epithelial cells lining the vas deferens. Injections of mammalian anterior pituitary

TABLE V

Eumeces fasciatus: Quantitative Histological Data on the Ductus Epididymis and Sexual Segment of the Kidney at Different Seasons, and as a Result of Castration, and Injection of Androgen

(From Reynolds, 1943)

	Epithelial cell height	Lumen diameter	Tubule diameter
Ductus Epididymis			
Mean of all normals in the non-breeding season . . .	19·7	28·5	50·4
Mean of all castrates . . .	15·3	18·4	47·9
Mean of all normals in the breeding season	40·0	61·7	143·0
Mean of all androgen-injected lizards	43·9	73·3	160·8
Sexual Segment of Kidney			
Mean of all normals in the non-breeding season . . .	17·9	15·9	49·5
Mean of all castrates . .	11·4	13·9	32·5
Mean of all normals in the breeding season	31·3	21·3	80·6
Mean of all androgen-injected lizards	49·9	22·6	119·0

extracts, as might be expected, had no ability to repair the atrophy resulting from castration. Reynolds (1943), in a detailed study of castration in the red-headed skink, *Eumeces fasciatus*, described perceptible regressive changes after a castrate period of 27 days, well-advanced changes at 47 days, and at 64 days involution was maximal. Quantitative data illustrating the effects of castration on various dimensions of the ductus epididymis and sexual segment of the kidney are reported in Table V. Castration also resulted in a decline in the secretory capacity of these structures. Vasa efferentia seemed little affected by castration but possibly their ciliation was a little less prominent. The intensity of the red head colouring in castrates was less marked and they were never seen to court or copulate even though kept with adult females during the breeding season. In a later paper

(Reynolds, 1947), it was shown that the hemipenes of *Eumeces* are markedly affected by castration. The hemipenis–body-weight ratio of males castrated at the breeding season (May–June) is closely similar to that of males at involution (October–January).

It seems from this survey that castration effects have been investigated in only a few reptiles species, all of which belong to the Lacertilia. The results, so far as they go, are completely in line with those obtained for other vertebrates, but there is a strong case for extending the work to include other reptile Orders.

Ovariectomy.—Ovariectomy has a special significance in reptiles since it can be used in many cases to investigate the physiology of gestation. In the viviparous elasmobranchs, ovariectomy is usually considered too drastic an operation and only poor survival rates have been achieved ; in viviparous teleosts, the ovary or its follicles are the incubatory chambers and therefore it cannot be removed without terminating gestation, and in Amphibia there are few viviparous species

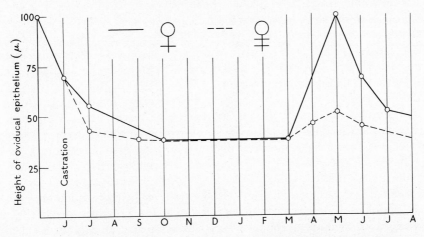

Fig. *11.47*—*Lacerta agilis:* Seasonal variations in height of oviducal epithelium in intact and ovariectomised (castrated) females. (From Regamey, 1935.)

and these have not as yet been studied. It should be noted in this connection that, whereas castration results in the removal of only germinal tissue and inter-stitial tissue, ovariectomy results also in the removal of corpora lutea and corpora atretica and, although no function has yet been convincingly demonstrated for these structures, it cannot be assumed that none exists.

Early work on ovariectomy in reptiles was largely concerned with its effects on aspects of reproductive physiology other than viviparity. Regamey (1932) failed at first to produce any external modifications in *Lacerta agilis* by ovariectomy, but in later work (Regamey, 1935) he recorded a slight increase in size of the head, and deposits of fat in the region of the abdomen. There was no colour change and only a slight inhibition of the femoral glands. The kidneys were unchanged, but the oviduct and urinogenital fossa showed marked atrophy. Ovariectomy during the nuptial season resulted in regression to the anoestrous condition more rapidly than in the controls and anoestrous was permanent. Regamey expressed the atrophic changes quantitatively by relating height of the oviducal epithelium to time of year and time after ovariectomy (Fig. *11.47*).

Takewaki and Fukuda (1935) showed that, in *Tachydromus*, ovariectomy does not affect the sexual segment of the kidney. Evans and Clapp (1940) ovariectomised several female specimens of *Anolis* and found that it produced striking effects on the oviducts. The oviducts of the summer controls weighed 68 per cent more than the oviducts of the spayed females. A histological examination showed that the epithelial cells of the oviducts in the spayed animals were 34 per cent lower than the summer controls and 10 per cent lower than in the mature winter controls. The cloaca also showed the effect of removal of the ovary; its mucosa was much less folded than in either the summer controls or the winter controls.

Evans (1936a, b, 1937) has reported an interesting series of investigations on the behaviour of ovariectomised specimens of *Anolis carolinensis*. He observed that the intact female lacks any observable tendency to express its dominance over other females which reside habitually in the same cage with it. The normal male, however, has a strong urge to dominate as well as to hold territory. Ovariectomised females resemble males, they show combativeness towards other females and smaller males in the same cage and tend to dominate them. They may also adopt the fighting postures of males. Evans concludes that the urge to fight in the normal female is probably inhibited by hormones secreted by the ovaries and that fighting takes place in ovariectomised females as soon as the ovarian hormone drops below the threshold of inhibition.

The work of Clausen (1935, 1940) on the effects of hypophysectomy on the gonads of viviparous snakes has already been considered. He also investigated the effects of ovariectomy on parturition in viviparous snakes (*Natrix, Thamnophis, Storeria*), and found that removal of the ovary in early gestation results in resorption of embryos and yolk masses by 6 weeks after the operation. Removal of the ovary during the middle period results in the birth of dead embryos near the end of the normal gestation period, growth of the embryos being retarded but not completely inhibited. Ovariectomy in late gestation has no effect on development, and parturition is quite normal. Clausen concluded that corpora lutea are of importance in the early stages of pregnancy and suggested that the " placenta " is their functional replacement in the later stages.

Similar work was carried out by Rahn (1939), who ovariectomised the snakes *Thamnophis* and *Natrix*. In one series, abortion followed the operation in two of six cases, whilst in the second, seventeen snakes were completely spayed, and autopsies up to 25 days later showed only living young. There is no doubt that the operation of ovariectomy is a severe one, and it may well be that abortion is an indirect effect, due to trauma associated with the operation. It may be significant that abortions were encountered by Rahn in his first series of operations though not in the subsequent series, and the same experience was reported later by Panigel (1956).

The work of Bragdon (1950, 1951) was designed to resolve the conflicting evidence on the part played by the ovaries and, more especially, the corpora lutea in the maintenance of pregnancy. He ovariectomised pregnant garter snakes and water-snakes during the middle third of pregnancy and found that normal development of the young continued in the absence of the ovary, but they were retained in the uterus past full term and parturition was distinctly abnormal. Bragdon concludes from these findings that since corpora lutea are known to occur in these snakes, and since the ovaries are not essential for the normal development of the embryos, " it seems from the standpoint of evolution that the morphological appearance of the corpora lutea antedated their utilisation as endocrine organs ".

Panigel (1956) reported results from ovariectomy of the ovoviviparous lizard, *Zootoca vivipara*, which were identical to those of Bragdon. Unilateral castration had no effects on either gestation or parturition, whereas, after bilateral ovariectomy, gestation was not affected, though parturition was abnormal.

Injection of sex hormones

Reptiles, in common with other amniotes and with elasmobranchs and Amphibia, have a primordial gonad consisting of two well-defined zones, cortex and medulla. In the process of sexual differentiation, these zones come under the influence of genetically mediated inductor substances which result in the development of one zone and the atrophy of the other. In several reptiles, especially Chelonians (Risley, 1933, 1934), a relatively long period of juvenile hermaphroditism is usual, when both medullary and cortical elements are present in the gonads of both sexes. Although relatively little work has been carried out on primary sex differentiation in reptiles, it is known that the fate of the gonadal zones can be altered by sex hormones (*see below*). Much more is known concerning the reactivity of gonoducts, copulatory structures and other secondary sex characters to exogenous sex steroids.

The fundamentally bisexual nature of reptiles allows of development of the sex structures common to one sex in the body of the other and, as might be expected, there are numerous records of naturally occurring hermaphroditism in various reptiles. Von Leydig (1872) described specimens of *Lacerta* and *Anguis* in which vestigial heterosexual gonoducts were present. Persistent Müllerian ducts have frequently been described in otherwise normal male *Lacerta* (Howes, 1886; Jacquet, 1895; Lantz, 1923; Regamey, 1931) and in two immature male alligators (Gaddow, 1887). Fantham (1905) reported a male *Testudo* having a left ovotestis and two well-formed oviducts, and Matthey (1927) recorded exactly similar abnormalities in a male *Emys*. Risley (1933) described the occurrence of oöcytes in the testes of two species of *Sternotherus adoratus*; he interpreted this as evidence of spontaneous sex-reversal from female to male. Evans (1939) reported that three females out of twenty-four adult specimens of *Chrysemis picta bellii* had rudiments of epididymides and vasa efferentia, whereas a fourth had a small rudiment of the vas efferens only. This degree of naturally occurring hermaphroditism suggests that the various sex structures might be relatively labile and easily influenced by exogenous sex hormones ; this is, in fact, the case.

Androgens.—Regamey (1935) studied the effect of injecting macerated homoplastic testis tissue into castrated male lizards, but obtained only dubious results. The study of the action of crystalline androgens on the reproductive system of reptiles began shortly afterwards.

Risley (1937, 1940) was the first worker to investigate the effects of androgens on sexual structures in developing reptiles. He injected eggs of *Chrysemys marginata bellii* at the gastrulation stage, with 250 µg. testosterone propionate in 0·05 ml. sesame oil. The eggs were incubated for 60 days, at which time the embryos were removed. The results of this work are difficult to assess because of the low survival rate of the embryos. However, the treated female gonads showed varying degrees of intersexuality never found in normal embryos at a similar developmental stage. In contrast to these effects on the gonads, the secondary sex structures, namely, oviducts, mesonephric ducts, penis and clitoris, showed no recognisable effects.

Hartley (1945) investigated the effects of testosterone propionate on primary sex-differentiation in the garter snake (*Thamnophis*). The hormone was administered either by injection into pregnant females each day during pregnancy, or directly into the amniotic cavity of the embryo whilst it was still in oviduct. Hartley found that the androgen had no marked effect on the sex of the gonad, although the cortical region of the gonad in both sexes was slightly retarded whilst the medullary regions were stimulated to the extent that early signs of seminiferous tubule formation were seen. Müllerian ducts also showed slight signs of stimulation by testosterone propionate. Hartley points out that the period of

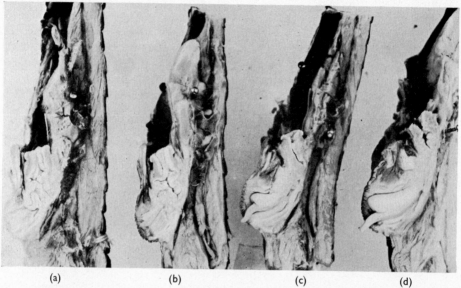

(a)   (b)   (c)   (d)

Fig. *11*. 48—*Alligator mississippiensis:* Photomicrographs of median sagittal sections through the cloacal regions of alligators. Note penis and clitoris in each case. (a) Control female. (b) Control male. (c) Female treated with testosterone propionate. (d) Male treated with testosterone propionate. (All × 1.) (From Forbes, 1939.) (By permission of the publisher from *Anat. Rec.*, 1939, **75,** 51.)

bisexuality which occurs in the development of the reptile gonad is very variable in length. It extends until hatching in the turtle and lizard and beyond the time of hatching in the alligator. Moreover, in the male turtle, and in both sexes in the alligator, well-defined gonadal remnants of the opposite sex are present throughout the first few years of life. In the garter snake, however, sexual differentiation occurs early, and in the male a definite cortex hardly develops, whilst in the female there is little evidence of an organised medulla. Thus, the period during which it might be expected that primary sex-differentiation could be altered by exogenous hormones is extremely short and this may well account for the fact that Hartley encountered such a slight effect on the embryonic gonad. These remarks have general relevance to all endocrine studies carried out on reptiles and may well account for some of the variability which has been encountered.

Experimental investigations on developmental stages have an obvious import-tance in the study of sex-determination, and the developing embryos of reptiles are ideal material for such work, yet no further studies on the effects of exogenous androgens on primary sex-differentiation appear to have been carried out.   However, several investigators have studied the effects of sex steroids on the gonads and reproductive structures in young reptiles.   Forbes (1938a) studied the action of testosterones on the accessory sex structures of recently hatched female alligators.   He found that a total of 10 mg. of testosterone injected over a 91-day period into each of 14 alligators (1 male, 13 females), 3 months old when the experiment began, had certain well-marked effects.   It resulted in a uniform and striking oviducal growth in the injected females and, in the single male, such a marked hypertrophy of the penis that this organ protruded from the cloaca.   The injections had no effect on the clitorides of females or on the Wolffian ducts or mesonephroi of either sex.   The absence of effect on the clitoris is in marked contrast to what is found in pre-pubertal mammals in which testosterone has a greater effect on the clitoris than on the penis.

Forbes (1939) extended his work to include older alligators (17 months); he found once again striking hypertrophy of the penes of the testosterone-treated males and the clitorides of the experimental females were larger than those of the controls.   In both cases the tips of these organs protruded from the cloaca (Fig. 11.48).   The gonads were not obviously affected by the steroid and this may be due to the fact that the ovarian medulla is highly regressed in animals of this age However, the oviducts showed considerable hypertrophy and their anterior ends were thrown into irregular folds.   Forbes (1941), working with immature males of *Sceloporus*, found that implants of testosterone stimulated spermatogenesis and produced some hypertrophy of the epididymides and vasa efferentia, though the cloaca and its associated structures were not affected (Fig. 11.49).   Kehl (1938) injected androsterone benzoate into adult female lizards (*Uromastix acanthinurus*) during sexual quiescence and produced a marked activation and development of the oviducal mucosa and the sexual segments of the kidneys.   These responses were similar to those seen in male lizards during the breeding period.   A further record of the stimulatory effect of testosterone propionate on lizard oviducts has been recorded by Gorbman (1939) for *Sceloporus occidentalis*.   Two dose levels were used (4·0 mg. given over 5 days, or 5 mg. given over 2 weeks) ; the results were almost identical.   A 57 per cent increase in the diameter of the oviduct was obtained and a 115 per cent increase in the thickness of its wall.   This is a slightly greater effect than was produced by oestrone (Theelin) injections (*see below*), though in the case of oestrone, the mucosa was stimulated as well as the mucous glands.

Panigel (1956) also obtained stimulation of the oviduct of a lizard by an androgen.   Working with *Zootoca vivipara*, he injected strong doses of testosterone acetate (six intraperitoneal injections of 1 mg. made at intervals of a week) and found that it produced a structural modification of the oviduct very similar to that observed after administration of oestradiol.   He suggests that the oviduct in *Z. vivipara*, as in other reptiles, must be regarded as ambisexual substrate.   In Panigel's experiments, all injected females were previously ovariectomised, so that there is no possibility that the testosterone acetate stimulated the ovaries to produce oestrogen which in turn acted on the oviducts.   Gonadectomy in these experiments is a precaution which is essential if the results are to be properly evaluated ; unfortunately it is a precaution which has rarely been taken.

Noble and Greenberg (1940) have dealt at length with the " bisexual " effects of testosterone propionate in the American chameleon (*Anolis carolinensis*). Pellets of the androgen were implanted subcutaneously into gonadectomised and intact immature and adult specimens of both sexes. Immature animals absorbed approximately 1·58 mg. testosterone in 24 days, whilst the adults absorbed 3·03 mg. in 30–36 days. As a result of this treatment, the oviducal mucosa of ovariectomised and intact immature and adult females showed marked glandular hypertrophy. Oviducts of adult ovariectomised controls averaged 6·79 mg. in weight, whilst those of treated females averaged 36·34 mg. The lining of the cloaca was also

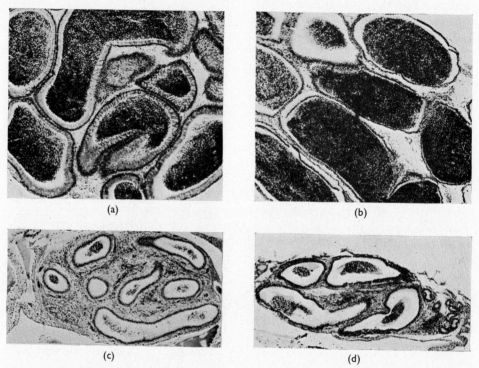

Fig. *11.49*—*Sceloporus spinosus floridanus:* Photomicrographs of sections from posterior region of epididymis. (a) Sperm-filled tubules of a control lizard. (b) Testosterone-treated animal showing dense sperm masses. (c) Oestrone-treated animal showing atrophy of tubules and virtual absence of sperm. (d) Immature, untreated animal. (All × 55.) (From Forbes, 1941.) (By permission of the publisher from *J. Morph.*, 1941, **68,** 31.)

affected ; in all testosterone-treated animals it showed intense keratinisation, whereas in the controls, as in spayed and out-of-season females, and in all males, it was mucoid.

The rudimentary Wolffian ducts of immature females were greatly hypertrophied by testosterone propionate, becoming as large as those treated immature males. Epididymides and vasa deferentia of male castrates were maintained by testosterone treatment and the sexual segment of the kidney was markedly hypertrophied in all treated lizards. The latter has no secretory activity in normal adult females, yet it secreted actively in treated specimens of both sexes.

Noble and Greenberg also found that testosterone propionate produced a striking enlargement of the ovaries of both immature and adult females. Ovarian weights in adult controls ranged between 3·35 and 65·63 mg., whereas ovaries of treated adult females ranged between 31·29 and 309 mg. in weight. Whether this is a direct effect on the ovary, or mediated via the pituitary, is not known, since parallel experiments were not performed on hypophysectomised animals.

Testosterone propionate treatment also had a profound effect on sexual behaviour. Full sex activity was induced in immature and adult castrated males, and male courtship and copulation behaviour was shown by immature and adult females, whether spayed or intact.

These results are more striking than any obtained before or since : they raise points of such interest that the work should certainly be repeated.

Risley (1941) reported the effects of injecting testosterone propionate into juvenile specimens of *Malaclemmys centrata* 2–2½ months after hatching. The hormone was injected in oil over a 48-day period (1,000 μg. total), or over a 38-day period (680 μg. total). The testes were slightly stimulated ; Wolffian ducts and ureters showed some hypertrophy in both sexes, whilst Müllerian ducts, glans penis, glans clitoris, and corpora fibrosa in both sexes were considerably stimulated, both in size and in histological differentiation.

Most of the more recent experimental work on the effects of androgens in reptiles has been concerned with secondary sexual characters and behaviour. Reynolds (1947) has studied the effect of testosterone propionate on the hemipenis of the red-headed skink, *Eumeces fasciatus*. This structure shows marked seasonal cycles of growth and regression, being involuted between October and January and hypertrophied in May and June. Reynolds showed that testosterone propionate had a pronounced stimulating effect on the hemipenis, both in the normal involute and also in the castrated male. Hemipenis weights in treated animals frequently exceeded those of intact animals at the peak of seasonal activity. Another external secondary sexual character which shows seasonal cyclical behaviour and which can be stimulated by androgens is the erectile dorso-nuchal crest in the male lizard *Anolis carolinensis* (Evans, 1948).

A good deal is known regarding the endocrine control of certain accessory sexual characters which are of importance in copulation in turtles. Evans (1951a) has shown that in the slider turtle, *Pseudemys scripta troostii*, the male uses his tail in preliminary courtship and copulation and it lengthens considerably at puberty. Pellets of testosterone propionate were implanted into juvenile sliders and 8 months later the males showed marked increase in tail length. The penis also became greatly enlarged so that it could not be retracted into its sheath.

Cagle (1950) has reported that the lengthened fore-claws in male slider turtles are used to titillate the neck and jaws of the female as part of courting behaviour. Evans (1952a) has shown that they behave as true secondary characters and are under the control of androgens. He implanted pellets of testosterone propionate weighing 4 mg. into immature specimens of *Pseudemys* and showed that by four and a half months after implantation, the second, third and fourth fore-claws were 33 per cent longer than in untreated specimens.

It is interesting to note that the very large abruptly curved rear claws of the male box-tortoise *Terrapene carolina carolina*, which are also of importance in copulation are likewise stimulated by androgen. Evans (1951b) implanted juvenile specimens of *T. c. carolina* with pellets of testosterone propionate and the rear claws of treated animals became some 38 per cent longer and correspondingly thicker than those of untreated juveniles, though it was more than a year and a half after the start of treatment before noticeable changes in the claws appeared. (Fig. *11.50*).

Other secondary sexual characters in male chelonians which can be stimulated by testosterone propionate, in addition to penis, tail and claws, are the iris, which changes colour to red or pink, and the plastron of the male box-turtle, which becomes concave at maturity (Evans, 1951c, 1952b).

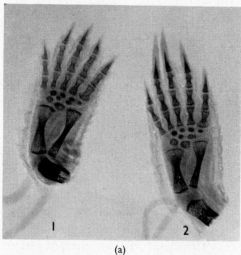

(a)

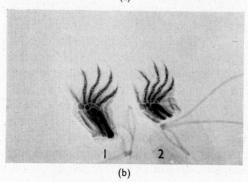

(b)

Fig. *11.50*—*Pseudemys scripta troostii:* Claw growth in normal and testosterone propion-ate-treated turtles. (a) 1, X-ray photograph of fore-foot of untreated turtle ($\times$ 2·3); 2, X-ray photograph of fore-foot of turtle treated with testosterone propionate ($\times$ 2·3). (b) 1, X-ray photograph of hind-foot of un-treated turtle ($\times$ 1); 2, X-ray photograph of hind-foot of turtle treated with testosterone propionate ($\times$ 1). (From Evans, 1952.) (By permission of the publisher from *Anat. Rec.*, 1952, **112**, 251.)

Oestrogens.—Several of the in-vestigators who studied the effects of androgens on reproductive morpho-logy and physiology considered also the role of oestrogens, so that some direct comparisons are possible. In general, however, they have re-ceived less attention than androgens. In particular, little is known of their effect on primary sex-differentiation. Dantchakoff (1937) was one of the earliest workers in this field. She injected 0·05 mg. oestrone in oil into the yolk sac of developing lizards and found that it stimulated both cortical and medullary regions of the female gonad, whereas the male gonads showed a poorly de-veloped cortical zone containing a few early oöcytes, and a very reduced medulla. Oestrone also stimulated the Müllerian duct rudiments so that at the time of hatching they were larger in embryos of both sexes than in control females. The cloacal region was also affected and the penial rudiments were absent in the oestrone-treated males.

Hartley (1945) investigated the effects of oestradiol dipropionate on early differentiation of the gonads and secondary sex structures of the garter snake (*Thamnophis* sp.) Injec-tions were made into pregnant females late in gestation on the assumption that the developing embryos would come under the influence of the hormone, and also into early embryos whilst still in the oviduct. The testes of injected males were completely differentiated at autopsy, though the tubules showed a small decrease in diameter. This slight inhibition of the medulla contrasts with the stimulation which was observed as a result of testosterone treatment. Neither the mesonephric tubules nor the Wolffian ducts were affected by the hormone. The ovaries were slightly stimulated ; there was an increased number of follicles and the cortical region of the gonad was somewhat thicker than in the controls. The Müllerian ducts were greatly stimulated ; they were longer and more convoluted, and showed a 177 per cent increase in thickness over the controls. This is a somewhat greater degree of stimulation than was reported when testosterone was used. All regions of these ducts were stimulated and there were signs of precocious ciliation in the posterior regions. There was a complete inhibition of parturition in the oestradiol-injected animals. Hartley suggested

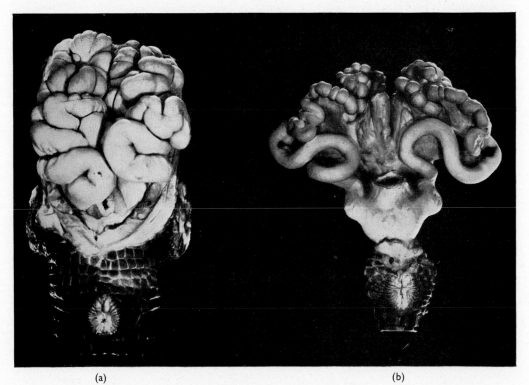

(a)   (b)

Fig. *11. 51*—*Alligator mississippiensis:* Reproductive tracts of immature female alligators after oestrone treatment. (a) Enormously hypertrophied oviducts of an injected female *in situ* following removal of ventral body wall and intestinal tract ($\times$ 1). (b) Entire reproductive system of an injected female when dissected free from the body; ovaries partly obscured. Note development of cloacal wall ($\times$ 1). (From Forbes, 1938.) (By permission of the publisher from *J. exp. Zool.*, 1938, **78**, 335.)

that this was due to maintenance of the corpora lutea, and therefore of pregnancy, by the steroid, but this may not be the case since the hormone was toxic and mortality was high. The toxicity of oestrogens has been mentioned by many of the workers who have injected them into cold-blooded vertebrates ; this must obviously be borne in mind when interpreting results in this field.

Kehl (1930b) appears to have been the first worker to investigate the effect of oestrogens on sexual structures in immature, as opposed to embryonic, reptiles. He injected young specimens of *Testudo iberica* with Folliculine at a dose level of 5 r.u. per 2 days for 3–4 weeks. Pronounced stimulation of the oviducts was obtained ; many of the cells of the mucosa were three or four times higher than

T*

in the controls and some were already ciliated.   Invaginations of the mucosa such as precede the formation of oviducal glands were also numerous.

Clapp (1937) studied the effects of oestrone (Theelin) on the reproductive system of male lizards (*Anolis carolinensis*).   He found, as a result of injecting $4\frac{1}{2}$–$11\frac{1}{2}$ r.u. aqueous Theelin, that the testes of treated males were inhibited. Their weight was only 40 per cent that of the controls and the seminal tubules were appreciably narrower.   On the other hand, vas deferens and cloaca were stimulated.

Forbes (1938b), as a result of prolonged injections of oestrone into immature alligators, before the appearance of external secondary sexual characters, obtained stimulation of both ovaries and secondary sexual structures (Fig. *11*.51).   Each experimental animal received 9,300 r.u. oestrone over an 80-day period.   Ovaries at the end of this period showed distinct stimulation, cortical volume having increased by 90 per cent, chiefly due to an increase in the number of oögonia ; medullary tissue was unaffected.   The oviducts showed remarkable hypertrophy, resulting in distension of the abdomen and displacement of the alimentary canal. All layers of the oviduct were stimulated and the mucosa of the posterior region was ciliated, a condition never found in the controls.   However, there were no shell glands or other secretory regions, and the oviducts were closed at their cloacal ends. The results are expressed quantitatively in Table VI.   The mesonephroi and Wolffian ducts of treated females were not affected.

TABLE VI

Alligator mississippiensis :   DIMENSIONS AND ESTIMATED VOLUME OF A TYPICAL CONTROL OVIDUCT, AND A TYPICAL EXPERIMENTAL OVIDUCT AFTER TREATMENT WITH OESTRONE

(From Forbes, 1938b)

	Length in cm.	Average diameter in cm.	Estimated volume in ml.	Volumes expressed as a ratio
Control . .	4·5	0·06	0·013	1·0
Experimental .	43·5	0·50	8·541	671·3

So far as concerns the injected males, their testes showed a significant though variable increase in amount of cortical tissue ; this variability was encountered also in the testes of control males.   The medullary regions of treated male gonads were not affected, nor were mesonephroi or Wolffian ducts.   In the control males, there was great variability concerning the survival of the Müllerian duct rudiments. However, in all experimental males, a well-developed segment of Müllerian duct was present at the level of the testes and it showed a significant though variable degree of stimulation.

It seems clear from these results that oestrone stimulates the cortical regions of both testes and ovaries, but fails to inhibit the medulla.   Moreover, it stimulates vestigial and definitive Müllerian duct rudiments, the latter showing profound stimulation of all layers and regions whilst Wolffian duct, penis and cloaca remain unaffected. The role, if any, played by the pituitary gland in this work cannot be assessed.

Forbes (1941) extended his study on the effects of oestrogens in reptiles to the lizard *Sceloporus spinosus floridanus*. Pellets of oestrone were implanted intra-peritoneally into lizards of both sexes and approximately 1·6 mg. was absorbed by each animal during the 44 days of experimental treatment. Mortality was very high, which makes the physiological significance of the marked inhibition

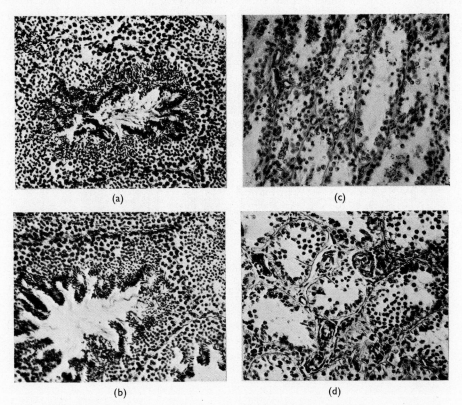

(a)

(c)

(b)

(d)

Fig. *11.* 52—*Sceloporus spinosus floridanus:* Photomicrographs of sections from representative testes. (a) Control testis. (b) Stimulation of spermatogenesis by testosterone. (c) and (d) Cessation of spermatogenesis and atrophy of seminiferous tubules as a result of administering oestrone. (All × 180.) (From Forbes, 1941.) (By permission of the publisher from *J. Morph.*, 1941, **68**, 31.)

suffered by testes, epididymides, vasa deferentia and femoral glands difficult to judge (Fig. *11.*52 ; Fig. *11.* 53). However, the striking hypertrophy of the per-sistent Müllerian duct segment in the single surviving animal in which it was present testifies to the stimulatory effect of oestrone on the reproductive duct proper to the female.

A closely related lizard, *Sceloporus occidentalis*, was investigated by Gorbman (1939). He injected Theelin (0·08 mg. given over 5 days, or 0·10 mg. given over 2 weeks) and found slight testicular inhibition and a 20 per cent reduction in the epididymis. On the other hand, the Müllerian ducts were greatly stimulated, especially their mucosa, and secretion was present in the lumina of the ducts.

The increase in cross-sectional diameter of the ducts was 40 per cent, and a greater than 100 per cent increase was recorded in the thickness of the wall. This degree of stimulation is slightly less than that recorded as a result of treatment with testosterone propionate in the work described above.

Dantchakoff and Kinderis (1938) studied the reactivity of gonads and oviducts of immature lizards to oestrone and found them remarkably sensitive to this steroid.

Dantchakoff (1938), in a further study, has described cornification of the cloacal epithelium in lizards under the influence of oestrogens and compared this reaction with the Allen and Doisy vaginal cornification test in mice. A similar effect was

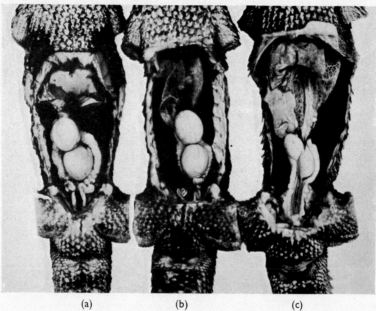

(a)   (b)   (c)

Fig. *11*. 53—*Sceloporus spinosus floridanus:* Ventral view of testes, epididymides
and vasa deferentia of 3 male specimens. (a) Testosterone-treated lizard;
note that epididymides and vasa deferentia show considerable hypertrophy.
(b) Control animal. (c) Oestrone-treated lizard; testes are markedly
atrophied and epididymal tubules and vasa deferentia are less convuluted
than those of the control (× 1·2). (From Forbes, 1941.) (By permission
of the publisher from *J. Morph.*, 1941, **68**, 31.)

obtained by Noble and Greenberg (1940) as a result of implantation of oestradiol dipropionate into gonadectomised male and female specimens of *Anolis carolinensis.* The cloacal lining in spayed and out-of-season females and all males is mucoid, whereas in spayed females treated with oestradiol it was intensely keratinised. Noble and Greenberg found also in this work that oestradiol dipropionate, unlike testosterone propionate, has no effect on the epididymis and vas deferens of adult castrate males, though oestrone is said to produce enlargement of the male ducts in intact adult *Eumeces* and young *Anolis.* The sexual segment of the kidney is unaffected, but, in common with all other reptiles investigated, the Müllerian ducts are strongly stimulated by the oestrogen.

Reynolds (1943) studied the effects of injecting oestradiol benzoate into intact and castrated specimens of the red-headed skink, *Eumeces fasciatus.* There were slight, but possibly not significant, signs of testicular regression, and the sexual segment of the kidney was unaffected. Reynolds (1947) later showed that the rudimentary hemipenes of the female *E. fasciatus* could be slightly stimulated by progynon, though the effect was variable and few animals were studied. He also encountered a marked increase in weight of the Müllerian ducts in the oestrogen-treated animals.

The importance of the specially modified middle fore-claws in the male slider turtle (*P. scripta troostii*) and of the real claws in the male box-tortoise *Terrapene carolina carolina* has been discussed above. Evans (1952a) implanted pellets of either oestradiol benzoate or diethyl stilboestrol into juvenile slider turtles and examined the reaction of the claws to these hormones. Oestradiol benzoate has a slight stimulating effect, but mainly on the first and fifth claws, whereas at sexual maturity it is the middle three which lengthen. Diethyl stilboestrol had a somewhat more selective action, though it was a good deal less effective in stimulating the third and fourth fore-claws than was testosterone propionate. The diethyl stilboestrol had a marked stimulatory effect on the rear claws also, an effect which is not normally seen in *P. scripta troostii* even at sexual maturity.

Viviparity in Reptiles

The majority of reptiles are oviparous and the young develop inside a shelled egg and receive no attention from the parents. Others, like *Zootoca vivipara*, are ovoviviparous and can develop normally even if removed from the oviduct at fertilisation (Panigel, 1956). The remainder are viviparous and a simple connection is established between the embryo and the uterine wall (*see* Volume 2, Chapter 15). Viviparity in the mammals is largely under the control of endocrine agencies, and it is obviously of great interest to discover how far the simple adaptations for viviparity and the course of gestation in reptiles are similarly controlled. The work of Clausen (1940), Bragdon (1951) and Panigel (1956) on ovoviviparous and viviparous species has already been considered in other contexts and the nature of the reptile corpus luteum has already been discussed.

In the mammals, the early stages of gestation are controlled by the corpora lutea which in turn are regulated by LH and luteotrophic hormone (LTH) from the pituitary. In the later stages, the placenta is largely responsible. We have already seen that the findings of Clausen (1940) have not been obtained by either of the two subsequent workers, both of whom have reported that hypophysectomy has no action on the course of gestation, though it appears to inhibit parturition. Bragdon (1953) has also shown that LH and LTH from mammalian sources have no recognisable effect on the lipids of the corpora lutea of *Natrix sipedon* during the latter half of pregnancy. This work is suggestive, but it must be repeated using reptilian pituitary extracts.

Although the corpora lutea of reptiles are well known from a histological point of view, little is known of their physiology. Porto (1942) has found that an alcohol extract of corpora lutea of two ovoviviparous snakes, *Crotalus terrificus* and *Bothrops jararaca*, has progestational activity in the spayed rat, and Fraenkel, Martins and Mello (1940) have reported that removal of corpora lutea in these snakes terminates gestation. However, the findings of Porto have not been confirmed, and the survival time in the experiments of Fraenkel *et al.* was only 10 days. There are good grounds for repeating this work and for extending it to include reptiles in which the yolk content of the eggs is obviously reduced and which have a well-developed allanto-placenta (Bragdon, 1951).

Bragdon (1951) has reported that ovariectomy and, consequently, deluteinisation of *Thamnophis sirtalis* and *Natrix sipedon* has no action on the developing embryos when performed in the middle third of pregnancy, though it interferes with parturition. Panigel (1956) found the same to be true in *Zootoca vivipara*. Bragdon therefore concludes that the corpora lutea are not essential for the maintenance of pregnancy, and the weight of evidence favours this view. However, Bragdon, Lazo-Wasem, Zarrow and Hisaw (1954) have shown that progesterone is present in the plasma of non-pregnant water-snakes, as demonstrated by the Hooker-Forbes technique, and that during pregnancy the titre rises, reaching a peak at full term. It is also present in male snakes at about the same level as in non-pregnant females. The physiological role and origin of this progesterone are unknown. It may also be noted that both Bragdon and Panigel have reported an increased luteal cell density in the corpora lutea as a result of hypophysectomy, and Panigel believes that the histological picture shown by the corpus luteum of *Zootoca* is one of active secretion.

It is difficult to interpret this evidence and there is an obvious need for more work. In general it seems that Bragdon's conclusion that the appearance of the corpus luteum antedated its endocrine function is well founded. However, the slight though suggestive evidence for the existence of a pituitary–corpus luteum interrelationship and a physiologically active corpus luteum in reptiles cannot be ignored.

Bibliography

ABRAMOWITZ, A. A., HISAW, F. L., BOETTIGER, F., & PAPANDREA, D. N. (1940). The origin of the diabetogenic hormone in the dogfish. *Biol. Bull. Wood's Hole*, **78**, 189.

ADAMS, A. E. (1930). Egg laying in *Triturus viridescens* following pituitary transplantation. *Proc. Soc. exp. Biol., N.Y.*, **27**, 433.

—— (1931). Induction of ovulation in frogs and toads. *Proc. Soc. exp. Biol., N.Y.*, **28**, 677.

—— (1940). Sexual conditions in *Triturus viridescens*. III: The reproductive cycle of the adult aquatic form of both sexes. *Amer. J. Anat.*, **66**, 235.

—— (1946). Sexual conditions in *Triturus viridescens*. IV: The effect of the administration of diethylstilbestrol on adult normal and castrated males. *J. exp. Zool.*, **101**, 1.

—— (1950). Sexual conditions in *Triturus viridescens*. V: The effect of the administration of diethylstilbestrol on adult normal and castrated females. *J. exp. Zool.*, **113**, 463.

—— GAY, H., & TERZIAN, A. (1941). The effect of injections of testosterone propionate in adult female newts. *Anat Rec.*, **79**, 67.

—— & GRANGER, B. (1938). Induction of ovulation in *Rana pipiens* by pituitaries of *Triturus viridescens*. *Proc. Soc. exp. Biol., N.Y.*, **38**, 552.

—— & KIRKWOOD, E. S. (1928). The effects of gonadectomy in *Triturus viridescens*. *Anat. Rec.*, **41**, 35.

—— & MAYO, V. (1936). The gonad-stimulating potency of the pars anterior in normal and castrated newts. *Proc. Soc. exp. Biol., N.Y.*, **35**, 227.

ADLER, L. (1914). Metamorphosenstudien auf Batrachierlarven. Extirpation endokriner Drüsen. Extirpation der Hypophyse. *Arch. Entw.Mech. Org.*, **39**, 21.

ALLEN, B. M. (1916). Extirpation experiments in *Rana pipiens* larvae. *Science*, **44**, 755.

ALLENDE, I. L. C. DE. (1939). Acción de la estrona sobre el oviducto del sapo *Bufo arenarum* Hensel. *Rev. Soc. argent. Biol.*, **15**, 185.

ALTLAND, P. D. (1939). Cytology of the hypophysis of the fence lizard. *Anat. Rec.*, **74**, 109.

—— (1951). Observations on the reproductive organs of the Box Turtle. *J. Morph.*, **89**, 599.

APLINGTON, H. W., JR. (1942). Correlative cyclical changes in the hypophysis and gonads of *Necturus maculosus* Rafinesque. I : The male. *Amer. J. Anat.*, **70**, 201.

ARON, M. (1924). Recherches morphologiques et expérimentales sur le déterminisme des caractères sexuels mâles chez les Urodèles. *Arch. Biol., Paris*, **34**, 1.

—— (1926). Recherches morphologiques et expérimentales sur le déterminisme des caractères sexuels mâles chez les Anoures. *Arch. Biol., Paris*, **36**, 3.

ARONSON, R. L. (1948). Problems in the behaviour and physiology of a species of African mouthbreeding fish. *Trans. N.Y. Acad. Sci.*, **11**, 33.

—— (1951). Factors influencing the spawning frequency in the female cichlid *Tilapia macrocephala*. *Amer. Mus. Novit.*, No. 1484, 1.

ASHBY, K. R. (1952). Sviluppo del sistema riproduttivo di *Salmo trutta* L., in condizioni normali e sotto l'influenza di ormoni steroidi. *Riv. Biol.*, **44**, 3.

—— (1957). The effect of steroid hormones on the Brown Trout (*Salmo trutta* L.) during the period of gonadal differentiation. *J. Embryol. exp. Morph.*, **5**, 225.

ATWELL, W. J. (1918). The development of the hypophysis of the Anura. *Anat. Rec.*, **15**, 73.

—— (1921). The morphogenesis of the hypophysis in the tailed amphibia. *Anat. Rec.*, **22**, 373.

—— (1938). The pars tuberalis of the hypophysis in toads. *Anat. Rec.*, **72**, 38.

—— (1941). The morphology of the hypophysis cerebri of toads. *Amer. J. Anat.*, **68**, 191.

ATZ, E. H. (1953). Experimental differentiation of basophil cell types in the transitional lobe of the pituitary of a teleost fish, *Astyanax Mexicanus*. *Bull. Bingham oceanogr. Coll.*, **14**, 94.

—— & PICKFORD, G. E. (1954). Failure to elicit the Galli-Mainini reaction in *Rana pipiens* with spawning reflex fractions and other teleostean pituitary preparations, and observations on the response to mammalian gonadotrophins. *Zoologica*, **39**, 117.

DE AZEVEDO, P., & CANALE, L. (1938). A hipófise e sua açao nas gonadas dos peixes neotropicos. *Arch. Inst. biol. (Def. agric. anim.), S. Paulo*, **9**, 165.

—— VIANNA DIAS, M., & BORGES, VIEIRA, B. (1938). Biologia do sagiurú (*Characidae, Curimatinae*). *Mem. Inst. Osw. Cruz.* **33**, 481.

BACON, E. H. (1951). Experimental use of carp pituitary in the production of fish. *Master's dissertation, Michigan State Coll. Agric. and Applied Sci.* (Quoted by Pickford & Atz, 1957.)

BAILEY, R. J. (1933). The ovarian cycle in the viviparous teleost *Xiphophorus helleri*. *Biol. Bull. Wood's Hole*, **64**, 206.

BALDWIN, F. J., & GOLDIN, H. S. (1939). The effects of testosterone propionate on the female viviparous teleost, *Xiphophorus helleri* Heckel. *Proc. Soc. exp. Biol., N.Y.*, **42**, 813.

BALDWIN, F. M., & LI, M. H. (1942). Effects of gonadotropic hormone in the fish, *Xiphophorus helleri* Heckel. *Proc. Soc. exp. Biol., N.Y.*, **49**, 601.

—— —— (1945). Induction of ovotestis in estrogen treated adult male teleost, *Xiphophorus helleri*. *Amer. Nat.*, **79**, 281.

BARANNIKOVA, I. A. (1949a). Concentration of the gonadotrophic hormone in the hypophysis of male and female sevriuga (*Acipenser stellatus*) in different stages of sexual cycle. *C. R. Acad. Sci. U.R.S.S.*, **68**, 1147. (Quoted by Pickford & Atz, 1957.)

—— (1949b). Localization of the gonadotrophic function in the hypophysis of sevriuga (*Acipenser stellatus*). *C. R. Acad. Sci. U.R.S.S.*, **69**, 117. (Quoted by Pickford & Atz, 1957.)

—— (1950). On the difference in the function of basophilic cells of the hypophysis of the Kura osetr (*Acipenser güldenstädti persicus* Borodin) of different biological groups. *C. R. Acad. Sci. U.R.S.S.*, **74**, 1033. (Quoted by Pickford & Atz, 1957.)

BARDEEN, H. W. (1932).   Sexual reactions of certain anurans after anterior lobe implants. *Proc. Soc. exp. Biol.*, *N.Y.*, **29**, 846.

BARRINGTON, E. J. W., & MATTY, A. J. (1955).   The identification of thyrotrophin-secreting cells in the pituitary gland of the minnow (*Phoxinus phoxinus*).   *Quart. J. micr. Sci.*, **96**, 193.

BATTAGLIA, F. (1925).   Ricerche istologische ed istochimiche sul testicolo dei Selaci con particolare reguardo alle cellule interstiziali.   *Riv. Biol.*, **7**, 283.

BAUMGARTNER, E. A. (1915).   The development of the hypophysis in *Squalus acanthias*. *J. Morph.*, **26**, 391.

—— (1916).   The development of the hypophysis in Reptiles.   *J. Morph.*, **28**, 209.

DE BEAUMONT, J. (1928).   Modifications de l'appareil uro-génital du *Triton cristatus* femelle aprés greffe de testicules.   *C. R. Soc. Biol.*, *Paris*, **98**, 655.

—— (1929).   Les caractères sexuels du Triton et leur déterminisme masculinisation et féminisation.   *Arch. Biol.*, *Paris*, **39**, 175.

—— (1933).   La différenciation sexuelle dans l'appareil uro-génital du Triton et son déterminisme.   *Arch. mikr. Anat.*, **129**, 120.

DE BEER, G. R. (1923).   Some observations on the hypophysis of *Petromyzon* and of *Amia*. *Quart. J. micr. Sci.*, **67**, 257.

—— (1926).   *The Comparative Anatomy, Histology and Development of the Pituitary Body.* London.

BELLERBY, C. W. (1933a).   The endocrine factors concerned in the control of the ovarian cycle.   I : *Xenopus laevis* as a test animal.   *Biochem. J.*, **27**, 615.

—— (1933b).   The endocrine factors concerned in the control of the ovarian cycle.   II : *Rana temporaria* as a test animal.   *Biochem. J.*, **27**, 2022.

—— (1934).   A rapid test for the diagnosis of pregnancy.   *Nature, Lond.*, **133**, 494.

—— & HOGBEN, L. (1938).   Experimental studies on the sexual cycle of the South African clawed toad (*Xenopus laevis*).   *J. exp. Biol.*, **15**, 91.

BERKOWITZ, P. (1937).   Effect of oestrogenic substances in *Lebistes reticulatus*.   *Proc. Soc. exp. Biol.*, *N.Y.*, **36**, 416.

—— (1938).   The effects of oestrogenic substances in *Lebistes reticulatus*.   *Anat. Rec.*, **71**, 161.

—— (1941a).   The response of fish (*Lebistes reticulatus*) to mammalian gonadotropins. *J. exp. Zool.*, **86**, 247.

—— (1941b).   The effect of estrogenic substances in the fish (*Lebistes reticulatus*).   *J. exp. Zool.*, **87**, 233.

BERNARDI, C. (1948).   Correlazioni dell'ipofisi e della tiroide con lo stato di maturazione delle gonadi nelle anguille gialle e argentine.   *Riv. Biol.*, **40**, 186.

BHADURI, J. L. (1951).   The role of Salientia in human and mammalian pregnancy tests. *Proc. 38th Indian Sci. Congress* (sect. zool. and entomol.), 1.

BLAIR, A. P. (1946).   The effects of various hormones on primary and secondary sex characters of juvenile *Bufo fowleri*.   *J. exp. Zool.*, **103**, 365.

BOCK, F. (1928a).   Die Hypophyse des Stichling (*Gasterosteus aculeatus* L.) unter besonderer Berucksichtigung der Jahrecyklischen Veranderungen.   *Z. wiss.*, *Zool.*, **131**, 645.

—— (1928b).   Kastration und sekundäre Geschlechtsmerkmale bei Teleostiern.   *Z. wiss. Zool.*, **130**, 455.

BORCEA, I. (1906).   Recherches sur le système urogénital des elasmobranches.   *Arch. Zool. exp. gén.*, **4**, 199.

BOUCHER, S., BOUCHER, M., & FONTAINE, M. (1934).   Sur la maturation provoquée des les organes génitaux de l'anguille.   *C. R. Soc. Biol.*, *Paris*, **116**, 1284.

BOYD, M. (1940).   The structure of the ovary and the formation of the corpus luteum in *Hoplodactylus maculatus* Gray.   *Quart. J. micr. Sci.*, **82**, 337.

BRAGDON, D. E. (1950).   Hormonal control of the reproductive cycle of ovoviviparous snakes as related to the evolution of viviparity.   *Virginia J. Sci.*, **1**, 391.

—— (1951).   The non-essentiality of the corpora lutea for the maintenance of gestation in certain live-bearing snakes.   *J. exp. Zool.*, **118**, 419.

—— (1952).   Corpus luteum formation and follicular atresia in the common Garter Snake, *Thamnophis sirtalis*.   *J. Morph.*, **91**, 413.

BRAGDON, D. E. (1953). A histochemical study of the lipids of the corpus luteum of pregnancy in the water snake *Natrix sipedon sipedon*. *Virginia J. Sci.*, **4**, 273.

—— LAZO-WASEM, E. A., ZARROW, M. X., & HISAW, F. L. (1954). Progesterone-like activity in the plasma of ovoviviparous snakes. *Proc. Soc. exp. Biol.*, *N.Y.*, **86**, 477.

BRANTNER, G. (1956). Die Unabhängigkeit des morphologischen Farbwechsels vom physiologischen Farbwechsel bei der Entstehung des Hochzeitkliedes des männlichen Bitterlings. *Z. vergl. Physiol.*, **33**, 324.

BRESCA, G. (1910). Experimentelle Untersuchungen ueber die Sekundären Sexualcharaktere der Tritonen. *Arch. Entw.Mech. Org.*, **29**, 403.

BRETSCHNEIDER, L. H., & DUYVENÉ DE WIT, J. J. (1947). *Sexual Endocrinology of Non-mammalian Vertebrates*. Amsterdam.

—— DUYVENÉ DE WIT, J. J., & GOEDEWAAGEN, M. A. (1941). Das Legeröhrenwachstum des Bitterlingweibchens (*Rhodeus amarus*), nach dem Prinzip der doppelten Sicherung. (Zugleich Skizze einer Histophysiologischen Analyse). *Acta neerl. morph.*, **4**, 79.

BROCK, J. (1878). Beiträge zur Anatomie und Histologie der Geschlechtsorgane der Knochenfische. *Morph. Jb.*, **4**, 505.

BROSSARD, C., & GLEY, P. (1929). Production expérimentale du réflexe d'embrassement de la grenouille. *C. R. Soc. Biol.*, *Paris*, **101**, 757.

BRUUN, A. F., HEMMINGSEN, A. M., & MØLLER-CHRISTENSEN, E. (1949). Attempts to induce experimentally maturation of the gonads of the European eel, *Anguilla anguilla* L. *Acta endocr.*, *Copenhagen*, **2**, 212.

—— & MØLLER-CHRISTENSEN, E. (1941). Om Virkningen paa den europaeiske Aal (*Anguilla anguilla* L.) of gonadotrope Hormonerog af det syntetiske östrogene Stof. Hexöstrol A B. *Soertryk af Naturhistorisk Tidende*, **6**, 89. (Quoted by Bruun, Hemmingsen & Møller-Christensen, 1949.)

BUCHMANN, H. (1940). Hypophyse und Thyroidea im Individualzyklus des Herings. *Zool. Jb.*, **66**, 191.

BULLOUGH, W. S. (1940). A study of sex reversal in the minnow (*Phoxinus laevis* L.). *J. exp. Zool.*, **85**, 475.

—— (1942). Gametogenesis and some endocrine factors affecting it in the adult minnow (*Phoxinus laevis* L.). *J. Endocrin.*, **3**, 211.

BURGER, J. W. (1941). Some experiments on the effects of hypophysectomy and pituitary implantation on the male *Fundulus heteroclitus*. *Biol. Bull. Wood's Hole*, **80**, 31.

—— (1942). Some effects of androgens on the adult male *Fundulus*. *Biol. Bull. Wood's Hole*, **82**, 233.

BURGOS, M. H. (1949). Estudio histológico del testículo del sapo hipofisoprivo. *Rev. Soc. argent. Biol.*, **25**, 206.

—— (1950). Regulación hormonal de los caracteres sexuales secondarios en el sapo macho. *Rev. Soc. argent. Biol.*, **26**, 359.

—— (1953). Acción de los estrógenos sobre el testículo, cuerpo de Bidder y glándulas endocrinas del sapo. *Rev. Soc. argent. Biol.*, **29**, 162.

—— (1955). Histochemistry of the testis in normal and experimentally treated frogs (*Rana pipiens*). *J. Morph.*, **96**, 283.

—— & LADMAN, A. J. (1957). The effects of purified gonadotrophins on the morphology of the testes and thumb pads of the normal and hypophysectomised autumn frog (*Rana pipiens*). *Endocrinology*, **61**, 20.

—— & MANCINI, R. E. (1947). Expulsión de espermatozoides por acción de las gonadotrofinas en el testículo de sapo *in vitro*. *Rev. Soc. argent. Biol.*, **23**, 165.

—— & RUFINO, M. A. (1952). Acción de las gonadotrofinas suérica y coriónica sobre el testículo de sapo. *Rev. Soc. argent. Biol.*, **28**, 159.

BURNS, R. K. (1925). The sex of parabiotic twins in Amphibia. *J. exp. Zool.*, **42**, 31.

—— (1930). The process of sex transformation in parabiotic *Amblystoma*. I : Transformation from female to male. *J. exp. Zool.*, **55**, 123.

—— (1932). Follicular atresia in the ovaries of hypophysectomised salamanders in relation to yolk formation. *J. exp. Zool.*, **63**, 309.

Burns, R. K., Jr., & Buyse, A. (1932). Effects of hypophysectomy on the reproductive system of salamanders. *Anat. Rec.*, **51**, 333.

Burrows, R. E., Palmer, D. D., & Newman, H. W. (1952). Effects of injected pituitary material upon spawning of blueblack salmon. *Progr. Fish-Cult.*, **14**, 113.

Buser-Lahaye, J. (1953). Étude expérimentale du déterminisme de la régénération des nageoires chez les poissons téléostéens. *Ann. Inst. océanogr. Monaco*, **28**, 1.

Butcher, E. O. (1936). Histology of the pituitaries of several fish. *Bull. Mt. Desert I. biol. Lab.*, 1936, 18.

Butler, P. A. (1940). Modification of the normal seasonal cycle by means of pituitary hormones in the common goldfish, *Carassius auratus* L. *Ph.D. Dissertation, Northwestern University.* (Quoted by Pickford & Atz, 1957.)

Buyse, A., & Burns, R. K., Jr. (1931). Ovulation in the neotenic *Amblystoma tigrinum* following administration of extracts of mammalian hypophysis. *Proc. Soc. exp. Biol.*, *N.Y.*, **29**, 80.

Cagle, F. R. (1948). Sexual maturity in the male turtle, *Pseudemys scripta troostii. Copeia*, **2**, 108.

—— (1950). The life history of the slider turtle, *Pseudemys scripta troostii. Ecol. Monogr.*, **20**, 32.

Calvet, J. (1932). Action du lobe antérieur d'hypophyse chez divers vertébrés (lamproies, oiseaux). *C. R. Soc. Biol., Paris*, **109**, 595.

Cantilo, E., & Gonzalez Regalado, T. (1942). Investigaciones realizadas con el extracto anterohipofisario en el dessarrollo des *Salvelinus fontinalis. Rev. Med. vet.*, *B. Aires*, **24**, 323.

Cardoso, D. M. (1934). Relations entre l'hypophyse et les organes sexuels chez les poissons. *C. R. Soc. Biol., Paris*, **115**, 1347.

Carlisle, D. B. (1954). The effect of mammalian lactogenic hormone on lower chordates. *J. mar. biol. Ass. U.K.*, **33**, 65.

—— (1955). In discussion of Dodd, 1955, *Mem. Soc. Endocrin.*, **4**, 185.

Castelnuovo, G. (1937). Effetti di alcuni ormoni sulla maturazione delle carpe. *Riv. Biol.*, **23**, 365.

Cei, G., & Acosta, D. I. (1953). Effet auxogène expérimental des gonadotrophines sériques dans l'interrelation gonado-hypophysaire du leptodactyle mâle (*Leptodactylus chaquensis*) traité par la testostérone. *C. R. Soc. Biol., Paris*, **147**, 250.

Champy, C. (1913). Recherches sur la spermatogenèse des Batraciens et les éléments accessoires du testicule. *Arch. Zool. exp. gén.*, **52**, 13.

—— (1921). Sur les correlations entre les caractères sexuels mâles et les divers éléments du testicule chez les Amphibiens. *C. R. Acad. Sci., Paris*, **172**, 482.

—— (1922). Étude expérimentale sur les différences sexuelles chez les Tritons. *Arch. morph. gén. exp.*, **8**, 1.

—— (1923). Observations sur les caractères sexuels chez les poissons. *C. R. Soc. Biol., Paris*, **88**, 414.

—— (1933). Étude du mécanisme de développement de quelques Caractères sexuels des Urodèles. *Arch. Zool. exp. gén.*, **76**, 59.

—— Coujard, R., & Coujard, C. (1939). Détail du déterminisme hormonal du coussinet du pouce de la Grenouille. *C. R. Soc. Biol., Paris*, **130**, 250.

Chang, C. Y. (1953). Parabiosis and gonad transplantation in *Xenopus laevis* Daudin. *J. exp. Zool.*, **123**, 1.

—— (1955). Hormonal influences on sex differentiation in the toad *Bufo americanus. Anat. Rec.*, **123**, 467.

—— & Witschi, E. (1955). Independence of adrenal hyperplasia and gonadal masculinization in the experimental andrenogenital syndrome of frogs. *Endocrinology*, **56**, 597.

—— —— (1957). Cortisone effect on ovulation in the frog. *Endocrinology*, **61**, 514.

Charipper, H. A. (1931). Studies on amphibian endocrines. II : The pituitary gland of *Necturus maculosus. Anat. Rec.*, **49**, 345.

—— (1937). The morphology of the hypophysis in lower vertebrates particularly Fish and Amphibia with some notes on the cytology of *Incarassius auratus* (the goldfish) and *Necturus maculosus* (the mud puppy). *Cold. Spr. Harb. Sym. quant. Biol.*, **5**, 151.

CHIEFFI, G. (1950). Il differenziamento dei sessi nei Selaci. *Experientia*, **6**, 465.

—— (1951). Sulla organogenesi della medulla della gonade in *Torpedo ocellata* e in *Scylliorhinus canicula*. *Boll. Zool.*, **18**, 183.

—— (1952a). Sull' organogenesi dell ' interrenale e della medulla della gonade in *Torpedo ocellata* e in *Scylliorhinus canicula*. *Pubbl. Staz. zool. Napoli*, **23**, 186.

—— (1952b). Azione del testosterone e della diidro follicolina sul differenziamento sessuale di *Scylliorhinus canicula*. *Boll. Zool.*, **19**, 117.

—— (1953a). Ulteriori osservazioni sull' azione degli ormoni steroidi sul differenziamento sessuale di *Scylliorhinus canicula*. *Atti Soc. ital. Anat.*, **15**, 1.

—— (1953b). Azione del testosterone sul differenziamento sessuale di *Scylliorhinus canicula*. *Ric. Sci.*, **23**, 111.

—— (1954a). L'inversione del sesso ottenuta con gli ormoni sessuali e corticosurrenale in *Scylliorhinus canicula*. *Pubbl. Staz. zool. Napoli*, **25**, 477.

—— (1954b). Ricerche istochimiche sull' organogenesi della medulla della gonade dei Vertebrati. *Boll. Zool.*, **21**, 147.

—— (1955). Nuove osservazioni sull' organogenesi della medulla della gonade nei Vertebrati : Ricerche istochimiche in *Rana esculenta*, *Bufo viridis* e *Scylliorhinus canicula*. *Publ. Staz. zool. Napoli*, **27**, 62.

CHRISTENSEN, K. L. (1931). Effect of castration on the secondary sex characters of males and females of *Rana pipiens*. *Anat. Rec.*, **48**, 241.

CIESLAK, E. S. (1945). Relations between the reproductive cycle and pituitary gland in the snake *Thamnophis radix*. *Physiol. Zoöl.*, **18**, 299.

CLAPP, M. L. (1937). Effect of Theelin upon the reproductive system of male *Anolis carolinensis*. *Anat. Rec.*, **70**, 97.

CLAUSEN, H. J. (1935). The effects of ovariotomy and hypophysectomy on parturition in Snakes. *Anat. Rec.*, **64**, 88.

—— (1940). Studies on the effect of ovariotomy and hypophysectomy on gestation in snakes. *Endocrinology*, **27**, 700.

COHEN, H. (1946). Effects of sex hormones on the development of the platyfish *Platypoecilus maculatus*. *Zoologica, N.Y.*, **31**, 121.

COLLOQUE (1950). Colloque sur la Différenciation sexuelle chez les Vertébrés. *Arch. Anat. micr.*, **39**, 180.

COMES, E. C. (1935). Ricerche istofisiologiche sull' ipofisi dei Selaci con particolare riguardo alle modificazioni gravidiche. *Pubbl. Staz. zool. Napoli*, **15**, 339.

CONEL, J. (1917). The urogenital system of Myxinoids. *J. Morph.*, **29**, 120.

COOPER, L. J. (1952). A histological study of the reproductive organs of crappies (*Pomoxis nigromaculatus* and *Pomoxis annularis*). *Trans. Amer. Micr. Soc.*, **71**, 393.

COPELAND, D. E. (1943). Cytology of the pituitary gland in developing and adult *Triturus viridescens*. *J. Morph.*, **72**, 379.

CORDIER, R. (1948). Sur l'aspect histologique et cytologique de l'hypophyse pendant la métamorphose chez *Xenopus laevis*. *C. R. Soc. Biol., Paris*, **142**, 845.

—— (1953). l'hypophyse de *Xenopus*, interprétation histophysiologique. *Ann. Soc. Roy. Zool. Belg.*, **84**, 5.

COUJARD, R. (1941). Sur l'existence d'une gland testiculaire et d'une glande Génitale annexe chez les Gobies. *C. R. Soc. Biol., Paris*, **135**, 570.

COWIE, A. T. (1948). Pregnancy diagnosis tests : a review. *Commonwealth Agricultural Bureaux Joint Publication* No. 13.

CRAIG-BENNETT, A. (1931). The reproductive cycle of the three-spined stickleback, *Gasterosteus aculeatus* Linn. *Phil. Trans. B.*, **219**, 197.

CREASER, C. W., & GORBMAN, A. (1935). Apparent specificity of the induced ovulation reaction in Amphibia. *Amer. J. Physiol.*, **113**, 32.

—— —— (1936). Specificity of pituitary gonadotropic factor as demonstrated in Amphibia. *Copeia*, no. 2, 91.

—— —— (1939). Species specificity of the gonadotropic factors in vertebrates. *Quart. Rev. Biol.*, **14**, 311.

—— & SHCOLNEK, M. (1939). Specificity within the Amphibia of pituitary gonadotropic factors derived from Amphibia. *Papers of Mich. Acad. Sci., Arts, Letters*, **24**, 85.

CRÉZÉ, J. (1949). Sensibilité du testicule des batraciens a l'hormone lutéinisante hypophysaire (LH). *C. R. Soc. Biol., Paris*, **143**, 1331.

CUNNINGHAM, J. T. (1898). On the histology of the ovary and of the ovarian ova in certain marine fishes. *Quart. J. micr. Sci.*, **40**, 101.

—— & SMART, W. A. (1934). The structure and origin of corpora lutea in some of the lower vertebrata. *Proc. Roy. Soc.* B, **116**, 258.

DAMAS, H. (1933). Note sur l'apparition naturelle et provoquée des caractères sexuels chez la lamproie. *Bull. Soc. Sci. Liège*, **2**, 94.

—— (1951). La ponte en aquarium des lamproies fluviatiles et de planer. *Ann. Soc. zool. Belg.*, **81**, 151.

D'ANCONA, U. (1950). Détermination et différenciation du sexe chez les poissons. *Arch. Anat. micr.*, **39**, 274.

—— (1952). Territorial sexualization in the gonads of teleosteans. *Anat. Rec.*, **114**, 666.

—— & SABBADIN, A. (1952). Tentativi di deviazione sessuale in larve di amfibi per mezzo di materiali gonadici adulti. *Arch. zool. (ital.), Napoli*, **37**, 405.

DANTCHAKOFF, V. (1937). Sur l'action de l'hormone femelle sexuelle chez les Reptiles. *C. R. Acad. Sci., Paris*, **205**, 424.

—— (1938). Über chemische Werkzeuge bei der Realisation normal bestimmter embryonaler geschlechtlicher Histogenese bei Reptilien. *Arch. EntwMech. Org.*, **138**, 465.

—— & KINDERIS, A. (1938). Sur les réactions que provoque la folliculine dans les ébauches des oviductes et les gonades chez le Lézard. *C. R. Soc. Biol., Paris*, **127**, 602.

DAVIS, D. D. (1936). The distribution of Bidder's organ in the Bufonidae. *Publ. Field Mus.* (f), **20**, 115.

DAWSON, A. B. (1940). The pituitary gland of the African lung-fish, *Protopterus aethiopicus*. *Biol. Bull. Wood's Hole*, **78**, 275.

DEREVICI, M., DEREVICI, A., & DORNESCU, G. T. (1940). Efectele hipofisectomiei asupra glandei genitale mascule de *Rana esculenta*. *Anal. Acad. romane*, **16**, 97. (Quoted by van Oordt, 1956.)

DODD, J. M. (1955). The hormones of sex and reproduction and their effects in fish and lower chordates. *Mem. Soc. Endocrin.*, **4**, 166.

—— (1960). Genetic and environmental aspects of sex-determination in cold-blooded vertebrates. *Mem. Soc. Endocrin.*, **7**.

—— & GODDARD, C. K. (1960). Some effects of oestradiol benzoate on the reproductive ducts of the female dogfish (*Scyliorhinus caniculus*). In the press.

DONAHUE, J. K. (1934). Sex-limitation of cilia in body cavity of the frog (*R. pipiens*). *Proc. Soc. exp. Biol., N.Y.*, **31**, 1166.

DUBOIS, R. (1947). On the distribution of Bidder's organ in Bufonids. *Zoöl. Meded.*, **28**, 275.

DULZETTO, F. (1937). Sulla struttura dell' apparato sessuale femminile di *Gambusia holbrookii* (Grd.). *Arch. Zool. (ital.), Napoli*, **24**, 275.

EDINGER, D. (1913). Die Leistungen des Zentralnervensystems bein Frosch dargestellt mit Ruecksicht auf die Lebensweise des Tieres. *Z. allg. Physiol.*, **15**, 15.

EGAMI, N. (1954a). Inhibitory effect of estrone benzoate on ovarian growth in the loach, *Misgurnus anguillicaudatus*. *J. Fac. Sci. Tokyo Univ.*, **7**, 113.

—— (1954b). Effects of estrogen on testis of the loach, *Misgurnus anguillicaudatus*. *J. Fac. Sci. Tokyo Univ.*, **7**, 121.

—— (1954c). Effects of hormonic steroids on the formation of male characteristics in females of the fish *Oryzias latipes*, kept in water containing testosterone propionate. *Annot. Zool. jap.*, **27**, 122.

—— (1954d). Influence of temperature on the appearance of male characters in females of the fish *Oryzias latipes*, following treatment with methyldihydrotestosterone. *J. Fac. Sci. Tokyo Univ.*, **7**, 281.

—— (1954e). Effects of hormonic steroids on ovarian growth of adult *Oryzias latipes* in sexually inactive seasons. *Endocrin. Japon.*, **1**, 75.

—— (1955a). Production of testis-ova in adult males of *Oryzias latipes*. I : Testis-ova in the fish receiving estrogens. *Jap. J. Zool.*, **11**, 21.

EGAMI, N. (1955b).   Effect of estrogen administration on oviposition of the fish *Oryzias latipes*. *Endocrin. Japon.*, **2**, 89.

EVANS, L. T. (1935a).   The effect of Antuitrin-S on the male lizard, *Anolis carolinensis*. *Anat. Rec.*, **62**, 213.

—— (1935b).   The effects of Antuitrin-S and sheep pituitary extracts on the female lizard, *Anolis carolinensis*. *Biol. Bull. Wood's Hole*, **68**, 355.

—— (1935c).   The effects of pituitary implants and extracts on the genital system of the lizard. *Science*, **81**, 468.

—— (1935d).   Winter mating and fighting behavior of *Anolis carolinensis* as induced by pituitary injections. *Copeia*, 1935, 3.

—— (1936a).   Behavior of castrated lizards. *J. Genet. Psychol.*, **48**, 217.

—— (1936b).   Territorial behavior of normal and castrated females of *Anolis carolinensis*. *J. Genet. Psychol.*, **49**, 49.

—— (1937).   Differential effects of the ovarian hormones on the territorial reaction time of female *Anolis carolinensis*. *Physiol. Zool.*, **10**, 456.

—— (1939).   Rudiments of epididymis and vas deferens in female turtles. *Anat. Rec.*, **75**, 76.

—— (1948).   The effects of gonadotropic and androgenic hormones upon the dorsonuchal crest of the lizard. *Anat. Rec.*, **100**, 25.

—— (1951a).   Effects of male hormone upon the tail of the slider turtle, *Pseudemys scripta troostii*. *Science*, **114**, 277.

—— (1951b).   Male hormone effects upon the claws of juvenile box tortoises. *Anat. Rec.*, **109**, 370.

—— (1951c).   Endocrines and secondary sex characters of the box tortoise, *Terrapene carolina*. *Anat. Rec.*, **111**, 555.

—— (1952a).   Endocrine relationships in turtles.   II : Claw growth in the slider, *Pseudemys scripta troostii*. *Anat. Rec.*, **112**, 251.

—— (1952b).   Endocrine relationships in turtles.   III : Some effects of male hormone in turtles. *Herpetologica*, **8**, 11.

—— & CLAPP, M. (1940).   Effects of ovarian hormones and seasons on *Anolis carolinensis*. *Anat. Rec.*, **77**, 57.

EVERSOLE, W. J. (1939).   The effects of androgens upon the fish *Lebistes reticulatus*. *Endocrinology*, **25**, 328.

—— (1941).   The effects of pregneninolone and related steroids on sexual development in fish (*Lebistes reticulatus*). *Endocrinology*, **28**, 603.

—— & D'ANGELO, S. A. (1943).   The effects of pregneninolone on the sexual development of *Rana pipiens*. *J. exp. Zool.*, **92**, 215.

FANTHAM, H. B. (1905).   On hermaphroditism and vestigeal structures in the reproductive organs of *Testudo graeca*. *Ann. Mag. nat. Hist.*, **16**, 120.

FLORENTIN, P. (1934a). Histophysiologie comparée de l'hypophyse. L'excrétion de la colloïde hypophysaire chez les téléostéens. *Ann. Physiol. Physicochim. biol.*, **10**, 963.

—— (1934b).   Les diverses voies d'excrétion des produits hypophysaires chez les téléostéens. *Rev. franç. Endocr.*, **12**, 271.

FOLLENIUS, E. (1953).   Contribution a l'étude du déterminisme de la différenciation des caractères sexuels chez les cyprinodontes.   Action des rayons X sur les gonades de *Lebistes reticulatus* Regan. *Bull. biol.*, **87**, 68.

FONSECA RIBEIRO, O., & TABARELLI NETO, J. F. (1943).   Ação de hipófise de peixe sôbre o oviduto do sapo, *Bufo marinus* L. *Rev. Fac. Med. Vet. S. Paulo*, **2**, 99.

FONTAINE, M. (1936).   Sur la maturation complète des organes génitaux de l'anguille mâle et l'émission spontanée de ses produits sexuels. *C. R. Acad. Sci., Paris*, **202**, 1312.

—— & OLIVEREAU, M. (1949).   L'hypophyse du saumon (*Salmo salar* L) à diverses étapes de sa migration. *C. R. Acad. Sci., Paris*, **228**, 772.

FORBES, R. T. (1934).   The effect of injections of pituitary whole gland extract on immature alligators. *Proc. Soc. exp. Biol., N.Y.*, **31**, 1129.

—— (1937).   Studies on the reproductive system of the alligator.   I : The effects of prolonged injections of pituitary whole gland extract in the immature alligator. *Anat. Rec.*, **70**, 113.

FORBES, R. T. (1938a). Studies on the reproductive system of the alligator. III : The action of testosterone on the accessory sex structures of recently hatched female alligators. *Anat. Rec.*, **72,** 87.

—— (1938b). Studies on the reproductive system of the alligator. II : The effects of prolonged injection of oestrone in the immature alligator. *J. exp. Zool.*, **78,** 335.

—— (1939). Studies on the reproductive system of the alligator. V : The effects of injections of testosterone propionate in immature alligators. *Anat. Rec.*, **75,** 51.

—— (1941). Observations on the urogenital anatomy of the adult male lizard *Sceloporus*, and on the action of implanted pellets of testosterone and of oestrone. *J. Morph.*, **68,** 31.

FOSTER, M. A., FOSTER, R. C., & HISAW, F. L. (1937). The interrelationship of the pituitary sex hormones in ovulation, corpus luteum formation, and corpus luteum secretion in the hypophysectomised rabbit. *Endocrinology*, **21,** 249.

FRAENKEL, L., & MARTINS, T. (1938). Sur le corps jaune des Serpents vivipares. *C. R. Soc. Biol., Paris*, **127,** 466.

—— —— & MELLO, R. F. (1940). Studies on the pregnancy of viviparous snakes. *Endocrinology*, **27,** 836.

FRATINI, L. (1953). Observations on spermatogenesis of *S. canicula*. *Pubbl. Staz. zool. Napoli*, **24,** 201.

FRIEDMAN, F. (1898). Beiträge zur Kenntniss der Anatomie und Physiologie der männlichen Geschlechtsorgane. *Arch. mikr. Anat.*, **52,** 856.

GADDOW, H. (1887). Remarks on the cloaca and on the copulatory organs of the Amniota. *Phil. Trans.* B, **178,** 5.

GALLIEN, L. (1938). Inhibition du cycle sexuel et involution testiculaire consécutives à l'hypophysectomie chez *Rana temporaria* L. *C. R. Soc. Biol., Paris*, **129,** 1043.

—— (1939). Hypophysectomie et cycle sexuel chez la Grenouille rousse (*Rana temporaria* L.). *C. R. Acad. Sci., Paris*, **208,** 766.

—— (1940). Recherches sur la physiologie hypophysaire dans ses relations avec les gonades et le cycle sexuel chez la Grenouille rousse, *Rana temporaria*. *Bull. biol.*, **74,** 1.

—— (1941). Ovulation provoquée chez le vairon par l'hypophyse de grenouille. *C. R. Soc. Biol., Paris*, **135,** 1567.

—— (1942). Action de l'hypophyse de grenouille sur le développement ovarien du *Phoxinus loevis*. *C. R. Soc. Biol., Paris*, **136,** 109.

—— (1944). Recherches expérimentales sur l'organogénèse sexuelle chez les Batraciens Anoures. *Bull. biol.*, **78,** 257.

—— (1949a). Analyse des facteurs endocriniens et génétiques controlant le phéno-type sexuel somatique chez *Lebistes reticulatus* Regan. *C. R. XIIIe Congr. int. Zool., Paris*, **168.**

—— (1949b). Effet androgène de la prégnéninolone sur le canal de Wolff entrainant la formation d'une vésicule séminale chez le têtard de *Discoglossus pictus* Otth. *C. R. Soc. Biol., Paris*, **143,** 343.

—— (1950). Étude de quelques facteurs intervenant dans l'action des hormones sexuelles au cours de la différenciation du sexe chez les Amphibiens Anoures. *Bull. biol.*, **84,** 341.

—— (1954). Hormones sexuelles et différentiation du sexe chez les Amphibiens. *Rev. suisse Zool.*, **61,** 349.

GALLI-MAININI, C. (1947). Pregnancy test using the male toad. *J. clin. Endocr.*, **7,** 653.

—— (1951). Action de l'ovaire et des oestrogènes sur l'oviducte du crapaud. *C. R. Soc. Biol., Paris*, **145,** 131.

GÉRARD, P., & CORDIER, P. (1937). Sur la persistance d'une continuité tissulaire entre hypophyse et épithélium buccale chez *Polypterus weeksi*. *Monit. zool. ital.*, **47,** 22.

GERBILSKII, N. L. (1938a). Effet des injections craniennes de suspension d'hypophyse chez les téléostéens. *C. R. Acad. Sci. U.R.S.S.*, **19,** 327.

—— (1938b). L'influence de l'agent gonadotrope de l'hypophyse sur l'état de la fraison chez l'*Acipenser stellatus*. *C. R. Acad. Sci. U.R.S.S.*, **19,** 333.

GERBILSKII, N. L. (1938c).   Data characterising the gonadotropic factor of the hypophysis in teleostei *Bull. Biol. Med. exp. U.R.S.S.*, **5**, 447.

—— & KASHCHENKO, L. A. (1937).   The effect of the hypophysis upon the gonads of teleostei.   *Bull. Biol. Med. exp. U.R.S.S.*, **3**, 158.

GHADIALLY, F. N., & WHITELEY, H. J. (1952).   Hormonally induced epithelial hyperplasia in the goldfish (*Carassius auratus*).   *Brit. J. Cancer*, **6**, 246.

GITLIN, G. (1939).   Gravimetric studies of certain organs of *Xenopus laevis* (the South African clawed toad) under normal and experimental conditions.   *S. Afr. J. med. Sci.*, **4**, 41.

GIUSTI, L., & HOUSSAY, B. A. (1922).   Le rôle de l'hypophyse et du cerveau dans la production des altérations cutanées chez le crapaud.   *C. R. Soc. Biol., Paris*, **86**, 1112.

—— —— (1923).   Altérations cutanées et génitales par lésion de l'hypophyse ou du cerveau chez le crapaud.   *C. R. Soc. Biol., Paris*, **89**, 739.

—— —— (1924).   Modifications cutanées et génitales produites chez le Crapaud par l'extirpation de l'hypophyse ou par lésion du cerveau.   *C. R. Soc. Biol., Paris*, **91**, 313.

GLASS, F. M., & RUGH, R. (1944).   Seasonal study of the normal and pituitary stimulated frog (*Rana pipiens*).   I : Testis and thumb pad.   *J. Morph.*, **74**, 409.

GODDARD, C. K., & DODD, J. M. (1960).   Gonadotrophic functions of the pituitary gland of the dogfish (*Scyliorhinus caniculus*).   In the press.

GOLTZ, F. (1869).   *Beiträge zur Lehre von den Functionen der Nervencentren des Frosches.* Berlin.

GOODRICH, N. B., HINE, R. L., & LESHER, H. M. (1947).   The interaction of genes in *Lebistes reticulatus*.   *Genetics*, **23**, 535.

GORBMAN, A. (1939).   Action of mammalian sex hormones in the lizard, *Sceloporus occidentalis*.   *Proc. Soc. exp. Biol., N.Y.*, **42**, 811.

—— (1941).   Comparative anatomy and physiology of the anterior pituitary.   *Quart. Rev. Biol.*, **16**, 294.

GRANT, R. (1940).   Seasonal changes in the weight and ovulation inducing potency of the glandular lobe of the pituitary in mature female *Rana pipiens*.   *Anat. Rec.*, **78**, 86.

GREENBERG, B. (1942).   Some effects of testosterone on the sexual pigmentation and other sex characters of the cricket frog (*Acris gryllus*).   *J. exp. Zool.*, **91**, 435.

GREENBLATT, R. B., CLARK, S., & WEST, R. M. (1949).   Hormonal factors producing the gametokinetic response in the male frog (*Rana pipiens*).   *J. clin. Endocrin.*, **9**, 668.

GREEP, R. O., & CHESTER JONES, I. (1950).   Steroids and pituitary hormones.   In *A Symposium on Steroid Hormones*.   Madison.

GRIFFITHS, M. (1938).   Studies on the pituitary body.   II. Observations on the pituitary in Dipnoi and speculations concerning the evolution of the pituitary.   *Proc. Linn. Soc. N.S.W.*, **63**, 88.

GROBSTEIN, C. (1947).   The role of androgen in declining regenerative capacity during morphogenesis of the *Platypoecilus maculatus* gonopodium.   *J. exp. Zool.*, **106**, 313.

—— (1948).   Optimal gonopodial morphogenesis in *Platypoecilus maculatus* with constant dosage of methyl testosterone.   *J. exp. Zool.*, **109**, 215.

HAEMPEL, O. (1950).   Untersuchungen über den Einfluss von Hormonen auf den Geschlechtszyklus von *Lebistes reticulatus* (Pet.).   *Z. Vitam.-Horm.-u-Fermentforsch.*, **3**, 261.

HALMI, N. S. (1952).   Differentiation of two types of basophils in the adenohypophysis of the rat and the mouse.   *Stain Tech.*, **27**, 61.

HAMON, M. (1945a).   Effets morphologiques du propionate de testostérone sur la femelle de *Gambusia holbrooki* Gir.   *C. R. Soc. Biol., Paris*, **139**, 110.

—— (1945b).   Action de l'hormone oestrogène sur la lignée germinale mâle de *Gambusia holbrooki* Gir.   *C. R. Soc. Biol., Paris*, **139**, 761.

—— (1946).   Action des hormones sexuelles de synthèse sur la morphologie externe de *Gambusia holbrooki* Gir.   *Bull. Soc. Hist. nat. Afr. N.*, **37**, 122.

HANSEN, I. B. (1939).   The experimental hormonal stimulation of the reproductive organs of the common eel.   *Bull. Mt. Desert I. biol. Lab.*, 1939, 25.

HANSEN, I. B., & TABB, M. L. (1941). Hypophysectomy in the box turtle *Terrapene carolina*. *Anat. Rec.*, **75**, 123.

HARMS, W. (1910). Hoden und Ovarialinjektionen bei *Rana fusca* Kastraten. *Pflüg. Arch. ges. Physiol.*, **133**, 27.

HARTLEY, R. T. (1945). Effects of sex hormones on the development of the urogenital system in the garter snake (*Thamnophis*). *J. Morph.*, **76**, 115.

HARTMANN, J. F. (1944). Seasonal cytological changes in the anterior hypophysis of the Garter Snake. *Amer. J. Anat.*, **75**, 121.

HASLER, A. F., & MEYER, R. K. (1941). Metabolic and reproductive responses to endocrine substances. In *A Symposium on Hydrobiology*. Madison.

—— —— (1942). Respiratory responses of normal and castrated goldfish to teleost and mammalian hormones. *J. exp. Zool.*, **91**, 391.

—— —— & FIELD, H. M. (1939). Spawning induced prematurely in trout with the aid of pituitary glands of the carp. *Endocrinology*, **25**, 978.

—— —— & WISBY, W. J. (1950). Hastening spawning in salmon with pituitary hormones. (Quoted by Pickford & Atz, 1957.)

HATTA, K. (1941). Seasonal variations and changes after gonadectomy in the anterior hypophysis of the Lizard (*Takydromus tachydromoides*). *Anat. zool. jap.*, **20**, 147.

HAZLETON, L. W., & GOODRICH, F. J. (1937). A note on the presence of male sex hormone in fish testes. *J. Amer. pharm. Ass.*, **26**, 420.

HEILBRUNN, L. V., DAUGHERTY, K., & WILBUR, K. M. (1939). Initiation of maturation in the frog egg. *Physiol. Zoöl.*, **12**, 97.

HERLANT, M. (1933). Recherches histologiques et expérimentales sur les variations cycliques du testicule et les caractères sexuels secondaires chez les reptiles. *Arch. Biol., Paris*, **44**, 347.

—— (1954). Anatomie et physiologie comparées de l'hypophyse dans la série des vertébrés. *Bull. Soc. zool. Fr.*, **79**, 256.

HERRING, P. T. (1911). The development of the elasmobranch pituitary. *Quart. J. exp Physiol.*, **4**, 183.

—— (1913). Further observations upon the comparative anatomy and physiology of the pituitary body. *Quart. J. exp. Physiol.*, **6**, 73.

HISAW, F. L. (1959). Endocrine adaptations of the mammalian estrous cycle and gestation. In *Comparative Endocrinology*. New York.

—— & ABRAMOWITZ, A. (1938). The physiology of reproduction in the dogfish *Mustelus canis*. *Rep. Wood's Hole oceanogr. Instn*, 1937, 21.

—— & ALBERT, A. (1947). Observations on the reproduction of the Spiny Dogfish, *Squalus acanthias*. *Biol. Bull. Wood's Hole*, **92**, 187.

HOAR, W. S. (1951). Some aspects of the physiology of fish : Hormones in fish. *Univ. Toronto Stud. biol.*, **59** ; *Publ. Ont. Fish. Res. Lab.*, **71**, 1.

—— (1955). Reproduction in teleost fishes. *Mem. Soc. Endocrin.*, **4**, 5.

—— (1957). In *The Physiology of Fishes*, vol. **1**. New York.

HOBSON, B. M. (1952). Conditions modifying the release of spermatozoa in male *Xenopus laevis* in response to chorionic gonadotrophin. *Quart. J. exp. Physiol.*, **37**, 191.

HOGBEN, L. (1930). Some remarks on the relation of the pituitary gland to ovulation and skin secretion in *Xenopus laevis*. In *Trans. roy. Soc. S. Afr.* **22**, xvii.

—— (1936). The pigmentary effector system. VII : The chromatic function in elasmobranch fishes. *Proc. roy. Soc. B*, **120**, 142.

—— CHARLES, E., & SLOME, D. (1931). Studies on the pituitary. VIII : The relation of the pituitary gland to calcium metabolism and ovarian function in *Xenopus*. *J. exp. Biol.*, **8**, 345.

HOPPER, A. F. (1949a). Development and regeneration of the anal fin of normal and castrate males and females of *Lebistes reticulatus*. *J. exp. Zool.*, **110**, 299.

—— (1949b). The effect of ethynyl testosterone on the intact and regenerating anal fins of normal and castrated females and normal males of *Lebistes reticulatus*. *J. exp. Zool.*, **111**, 393.

—— (1951). The effects of ethynyl testosterone and progynon on the regeneration of the gonopodium of normal and castrated males of *Lebistes reticulatus*. *Pap. Mich. Acad. Sci.*, **35**, 109.

Houssay, B. A. (1930). Acción sexual de la hipófisis en los peces y reptiles. *Rev. Soc. argent. Biol.*, **6**, 686.

—— (1931). Action sexuelle de l'hypophyse sur les poissons et les reptiles. *C. R. Soc. Biol., Paris*, **106**, 377.

—— (1947a). Expulsión de espermatozoides por acción hipofisaria en el sapo. *Rev. Soc. argent. Biol.*, **23**, 114.

—— (1947b). Ovulación y postura del sapo *Bufo arenarum* Hensel. V. Transporte de los óvulos por el oviducto y el útero. *Rev. Soc. argent. Biol.*, **23**, 275.

—— (1949). Hypophyseal functions in the toad *Bufo arenarum* Hensel. *Quart. Rev. Biol.*, **24**, 1.

—— (1950). Gobierno hormonal del oviducto. *Rev. Soc. argent. Biol.*, **26**, 185.

—— (1952). La Régulation hormonale des fonctions de l'oviducte du crapaud. *J. suisse Méd.* **82**, 119.

—— (1954). Hormonal regulation of the sexual function of the male toad. *Acta Physiol. Latinoamer.*, **4**, 2.

—— & Giusti, L. (1930). Fonction sexuelle, hypophyse et hypothalamus chez le crapaud. *C. R. Soc. Biol., Paris*, **104**, 1030.

—— —— & Lascano-Gonzalez, J. M. (1929). Implantation d'hypophyse et stimulation des glandes et des fonctions sexuelles du Crapaud. *C. R. Soc. Biol., Paris*, **102**, 864.

—— & Lascano-Gonzalez, J. M. (1929). L'hypophyse et le testicule chez le crapaud *Bufo marinus* (L.) Schneid. *C. R. Soc. Biol., Paris*, **101**, 938.

—— —— (1931). Hypophyse et corps de Bidder. *C. R. Soc. Biol., Paris*, **108**, 131.

—— —— (1935). Hypophyse et hypertrophie compensatrice du testicule chez le Crapaud. *C. R. Soc. Biol., Paris*, **120**, 362.

—— Penhos, J. C., & Burgos, M. H. (1953). Modificaciones de la espermiación producida por gonadotrofinas en el sapo. *Rev. Soc. argent. Biol.*, **29**, 108.

Howes, G. B. (1886). On the vestigeal structures of the reproductive apparatus in the male of the green lizard. *J. Anat., Lond.*, **21**, 185.

—— (1902). *Atlas of Practical Elementary Zootomy.* London.

Howes, N. H. (1936). A study of the histology of the pituitary gland of the skate. *Quart. J. micr. Sci.*, **78**, 637.

Hubbs, C. L., & Hubbs, L. C. (1933). The increased growth, predominant maleness, and apparent infertility of hybrid sunfishes. *Pap. Mich. Acad. Sci.*, **16**, 613.

Humphrey, R. R. (1925). The development of the temporary sexual characters in *Diemyctylus viridescens* in relation to changes within the testis. *Anat. Rec.*, **29**, 362.

—— (1928). The developmental potencies of the intermediate mesoderm of *Amblystoma* when transplanted into ventro-lateral sites in other embryos : The primordial germ cells of such grafts and their role in the development of a gonad. *Anat. Rec.*, **40**, 67.

—— (1929). The early position of the primordial germ cells in Urodeles. *Anat. Rec.*, **42**, 301.

—— (1935). Sex reversal in *Amblystoma*. VIII : Sex type of gonads developed from gonadic preprimordia of *A. punctatum* implanted in axolotl females. *Proc. Soc. exp. Biol., N.Y.*, **33**, 102.

—— (1936a). Studies on sex-reversal in *Amblystoma*. IX : Reversal of ovaries to testes in parabiotic *A. tigrinum*. *J. exp. Zool.*, **73**, 1.

—— (1936b). Studies on sex-reversal in *Amblystoma*. X : Sex reversal in parabiotic *A. punctatum* of various local races. *Amer. J. Anat.*, **59**, 347.

—— (1942). Sex inversion in the Amphibia. *Biol. Symp.*, **9**, 81.

Ichikawa, M., & Kawakami, I. (1944). Acceleration of spawning in the carp by means of pituitary hormones. *Rep. Hyogo Fish. Exp. Stn*, **5**, 1. (Quoted by Pickford & Atz, 1957.)

von Ihering, R. (1935). Die Wirkung von Hypophyseninjektion auf den Laichakt von Fischen. *Zool. Anz.*, **111**, 273.

—— (1937). A method for inducing fish to spawn. *Progr. Fish. Cult.*, **34**, 15.

—— & de Azevedo, P. (1937). Über die Wirkung des Säugetier-Hypophysenhormons auf den Laichakt der Fische. *Zool. Anz.*, **120**, 71.

IKEDA, K. (1933).   Effect of castration on the secondary sexual characters of anadromous three-spined stickleback, *Gasterosteus aculeatus aculeatus* (L.).   *Jap. J. Zool.*, **5**, 135.

IVANOVA, S. A. (1953).   A histological investigation of the gonad, thyroid gland and hypophysis of the sterlet *Acipenser ruthenus* when it is kept under natural-river and pond conditions.   *C. R. Acad. Sci. U.R.S.S.*, **91**, 651.   (Quoted by Pickford & Atz, 1957.)

JACQUET, M. (1895).   Note sur un cas d'hermophroditisme incomplet observé chez le *Lacerta agilis*.   *Bibliogr. anat.*, **3**, 273.

JAMES, M. F. (1946).   Histology of gonadal changes in the bluegill, *Lepomis macrochirus* Rafinesque, and the largemouth bass, *Huro salmoides* (Lacépède).   *J. Morph.*, **79**, 63.

JASKI, C. J. (1946).   A rapid test for pregnancy by means of the ovary of *Lebistes reticulatus* (Peters).   *Natuurk., Tijdschr. Ned.-Ind.*, **102**, 196.

JOHNSON, M. W., & RIDDLE, O.   (1939). Tests of mammalian gonad-stimulating hormones on gonads of fishes.   *Proc. Soc. exp. Biol., N.Y.*, **42**, 260.

JONES, J. M., & KING, G. M. (1952).   The spawning of the male salmon parr (*Salmo salar* Linn. juv.).   *Proc. zool. Soc. Lond.*, **122**, 615.

JUNGERSEN, J. F. E. (1899).   On the appendices genitales in the Greenland Shark *Somniosus microcephalus* (Bl. Schn.) and other selacians.   *Danish Ingolf-Expedition*, **2**, 1.

KAISER, P., & SCHMIDT, E. (1951).   Vollkommene Geschlechstumwandlung nach Kastration beim weiblichen siamesischen Kampffisch, *Betta splendens*.   *Zool. Anz.*, **146**, 66.

VAN DE KAMER, J. C., & VERHAGEN, T. G. (1954).   The cytology of the neurohypophysis, the saccus vasculosus and the recessus posterior in *Scylliorhinus caniculus*.   *Proc. Acad. Sci. Amst.*, C, **57**, 358.

KAWAMOTO, N.Y. (1950).   The influence of sex hormones on the reproductive organ of a Sôgyo *Ctenopharyngodon idellus*.   *Jap. J. Ichthyol.*, **1**, 8.

KAWAMURA, T., & MOTANAGA, T. (1950).   On artificial ovulation in the spinous loach.   *Jap. J. Ichthyol.*, **1**, 1.

—— & OTSUKA, S. (1950).   On acceleration of the ovulation in the goldfish.   *Jap. J. Ichthyol.*, **1**, 157.

KAZANSKII, B. N. (1939).   The sturgeon production station Veltianka on the river Volga.   *Rybnoe Khozialistvo*, **19**, (11), 21.   (Quoted by Pickford & Atz, 1957.)

—— (1940).   Zur Frage der systematischen Spezifität des gonadotropen Hormons der Hypophyse bei den fischen.   *C. R. Acad. Sci. U.R.S.S.*, **27**, 180.

—— (1950).   Effects of hypophysis on nuclear processes in the oöcytes of fish.   *C. R. Acad. Sci. U.R.S.S.*, **75**, 311.   (Quoted by Pickford & Atz, 1957.)

—— (1952).   Experimental analysis of intermittent spawning in fish.   *Zool. Zh.*, **31**, 883.   (Quoted by Pickford & Atz, 1957.)

—— & PERSOV, G. M. (1948).   The localization of the gonadotrophic factor in the hypophysis of bony fish.   *C. R. Acad. Sci. U.R.S.S.*, N.S., **61**, 169.   (Quoted by Pickford & Atz, 1957.)

KEHL, R. (1930a).   Action d'un extrait d'hypophyse antérieure de Mammifère sur la ponte des Batraciens.   *C. R. Soc. Biol.*, Paris, **103**, 744.

—— (1930b).   Action de la folliculine de mammifère sur l'oviducte de la tortue.   *C. R. Soc. Biol.*, Paris, **105**, 512.

—— (1935).   Note préliminaire sur le cycle génital chez quelques reptiles sahariens.   *C. R. Soc. Biol.*, Paris, **118**, 1077.

—— (1938).   Action de l'Androstérone sur le " segment sexuel " urinaire de l'Uromastix femelle.   *C. R. Soc. Biol.*, Paris, **127**, 142.

—— (1944).   Études de quelques problèmes d'endocrinologie génitale chez un batracien Nord-Africain (Discoglosse).   *Rev. canad. Biol.*, **3**, 29.

KELLER, K., & TANDLER, J. (1916).   Ueber das Verhalten der Eihaeute bei der Zwillingsträchtigkeit des Rindes.   *Wien. tierärztl. Mschr.*, **3**, 513.

KERR, T. (1933).   On the pituitary in *Lepidosiren* and its development.   *Proc. roy Soc. Edinb.*, **53**, 147.

—— (1939).   On the histology of the developing pituitary in the frog (*Rana temporaria*) and in the toad (*Bufo bufo*).   *Proc. zool. Soc. Lond.*, **109**, 167.

KERR, T. (1948). The pituitary in normal and parasitized roach (*Leuciscus rutilus* Flem.) *Quart. J. micr. Sci.*, **89**, 129.

—— (1949). The pituitaries of *Amia, Lepidosteus* and *Acipenser*. *Proc. zool. Soc. Lond.*, **118**, 973.

KINOSHITA, Y. (1935). Effects of gonadectomies on the secondary sexual characters in *Halichoeres poecilopterus* (Temminck & Schlegel). *J. Sci. Hiroshima Univ.*, **4**, 1.

KIRSHENBLAT, I. D. (1949). The action of gonadotrophic hormones of man on female fish. *Priroda*, **38**, 75. (Quoted by Pickford & Atz, 1957.)

—— (1952). The action of steroid hormones on female vy'un. *C. R. Acad. Sci. U.R.S.S.*, **83**, 629. (Quoted by Pickford & Atz, 1957.)

—— (1953). Influence of sympaticotropic and vagotropic substances on the maturation of oöcytes and ovulation in fish. *C.R. Acad. Sci., U.R.S.S.*, **93**, 373. (Quoted by Pickford & Atz, 1957.)

KLOSE, H. G. (1941). Ueber den einfluss der Kastration auf Schilddrüse, Hypophyse und Interrenalsystem der Urodelen. Beitrag zur Morphologie und Histologie dieser Drüsen bei *Triton vulgaris* Laur. und *Triton cristatus* Laur. *Z. wiss. Zool.*, **155**, 46.

KNOWLES, F. G. W. (1939). The influence of anterior-pituitary and testicular hormones on the sexual maturation of lampreys. *J. exp. Biol.*, **16**, 535.

—— (1941). The duration of larval life in ammocoetes and an attempt to accelerate metamorphosis by injections of anterior pituitary extract. *Proc. zool. Soc. Lond.*, **111A**, 101.

KOBAYASHI, H. (1951). Experimental studies on the sexual characters of the loach, *Misgurnus anguillicaudatus* (Cantor). *Annot. zool. jap.*, **24**, 212.

KOCH, M. (1934). Ueber das Urogenitalsystem der Bufoniden, im besonderen über die Histologie des Bidderschen Organs. *Z. Naturf.* **68**, 499.

KOCH, W., & SCHEURING, L. (1936). Die Wirkung von Hypophysenvorderlappenhormon auf den Laichakt von Fischen. *Zool. Anz.*, **116**, 62.

LANDGREBE, F. W. (1941). The role of the pituitary and the thyroid in the development of teleosts. *J. exp. Biol.*, **18**, 162.

LANTZ, L. A. (1923). Hermaphroditism partial chez *Lacerta saxicola*. *Bull. Soc. zool. Fr.*, **48**, 289.

LANZA, B. (1951a). Notizie e ricerche sul ciclo sessuale maschile degli amfibi europei in relazione al loro uso per le ricerca e il dosaggio delle gonadotrofine. Part I. *Arch. Fisiol.*, **51**, 54.

—— (1952b). Notizie e ricerche sul ciclo sessuale maschile degli amfibi europei in relazione al loro uso per la ricerca e il dosaggio delle gonadotrofine. Part II. *Arch. Fisiol.*, **51**, 127.

LASKOWSKI, W. (1953). Reaktionen der primären und sekundären Geschlechtsmerkmale von *Platypoecilus variatus* (♂ heterogamet) und *Platypoecilus maculatus* (♂ homogamet) auf Sexualhormone. *Arch. EntwMech. Org.*, **146**, 137.

LEACH, W. J. (1951). The hypophysis of lampreys in relation to the nasal apparatus. *J. Morph.*, **89**, 217.

LEATHEM, J. H., & WOLF, R. C. (1955). The varying effects of sex hormones in mammals. *Mem. Soc. Endocrin.*, **4**, 220.

LEBLOND, C. P., & NOBLE, G. K. (1937). Prolactin-like reaction produced by hypophysis of various vertebrates. *Proc. Soc. exp. Biol. Med., N.Y.*, **36**, 517.

LEE, R. E. (1942). The hypophysis of the broad-billed swordfish, *Xiphias gladius* L. *Biol. Bull. Wood's Hole*, **82**, 401.

LEGHISSA, S. (1953). Sull' anatomia microscopia e sull' istologia della parte anteriore della ipofisi di Axolotl. 2 : Citologia, secrezione e rigenerazione degli elementi ipofisari. *Ric. Morf.*, **22**, 409.

LEIGH-SHARPE, W. H. (1920). The comparative morphology of the secondary sexual characters of elasmobranch fishes. *J. Morph.*, **34**, 245.

—— (1921). The comparative morphology of the secondary sexual characters of elasmobranch fishes. *J. Morph.*, **35**, 359.

—— (1922). The comparative morphology of the secondary sexual characters of Holocephali and elasmobranch fishes. *J. Morph.*, **36**, 221.

Levy, M., & Aronson, L. R. (1955). Morphological effects of castration and hormone administration in the male cichlid fish *Tilapia macrocephala*. *Anat. Rec.*, **122**, 450.

Lewis, M. R., & Butcher, E. O. (1936). The separation of the hypophysis cerebri of certain selachians (*Squalus acanthias* and *Raja strabuliformis*) into six distinct lobes. *Bull. Mt. Desert I. Biol. Lab.*, 1936, p. 16.

Leydig, F. von (1872). *Die im Deutschland lebenden Arten der Saurien.* Tübingen.

Lillie, F. R. (1916). The theory of the free-martin. *Science*, **43**, 611.

Ludwig, D. J. (1950). The effect of androgen on spermatogenesis. *Endocrinology*, **46**, 453.

Lundstrom, H. M., & Bard, P. (1932). Hypophysial control of cutaneous pigmentation in an elasmobranch fish. *Biol. Bull. Wood's Hole*, **62**, 1.

Marshall, A. J., & Lofts, B. (1956). The Leydig-cell homologue in certain teleost fishes. *Nature, Lond.*, **177**, 704.

—— —— (1957). Cyclical changes in the distribution of the testis lipids of a teleost fish, *Esox lucinus*. *Quart. J. micr. Sci.*, **98**, 79.

—— & Woolf, F. M. (1957). Seasonal lipid changes in the sexual elements of a male snake, *Vipera berus*. *Quart. J. micr. Sci.*, **98**, 89.

Masuda, A. (1952). The experimental studies on the secondary sexual characters in *Oryzias latipes*. I : The relation between salinity and the disappearance of the secondary sexual characters. *Res. Rep. Kochi Univ.*, **1**, 1.

Matthews, L. H. (1950). Reproduction in the basking shark *Cetorhinus maximus* (Gunner). *Phil. Trans.* B, **234**, 247.

Matthews, S. A. (1936). The pituitary gland of *Fundulus*. *Anat. Rec.*, **65**, 357.

—— (1938). The seasonal cycle in the gonads of *Fundulus*. *Biol. Bull. Wood's Hole*, **75**, 66.

—— (1939). The relationship between the pituitary gland and the gonads in *Fundulus*. *Biol. Bull. Wood's Hole*, **76**, 241.

Matthey, R. (1927). Intersexualité chez un Tortue (*Emys europaea*). *C. R. Soc. Biol., Paris*, **97**, 369.

—— (1929). Caractères sexuels secondaires du Lézard mâle. *Bull. Soc. vaud. Sci. nat.*, **57**, 71.

Mazzetti, I. (1911). I caratteri sessuali secondari e le cellule interstiziale del testiculo. *Anat. Anz.*, **38**, 361.

Mazzi, V. (1949). La citologia dell' ipofise del Tritone crestato. *Arch. ital. Anat. Embriol.*, **54**, 1.

—— (1952). Nuove osservazione intorno alle cellule basofile nell' ipofisi del Tritone crestato. *R. C. Accad. Lincei*, **12**, 116.

—— & Pieri, M. (1949). Ciclo annuo e modificazioni spermentali della ipofisi nel Tritone crestato. *Riv. Biol.*, **41**, 271.

McCurdy, H. M. (1931). Development of the sex organs in *Triturus torosus*. *Amer. J. Anat.*, **47**, 367.

Medawar, P. B. (1953). Some immunological and endocrinological problems raised by the evolution of viviparity in vertebrates. *Symp. Soc. exp. Biol.*, **7**, 320.

Meisenheimer, J. (1911). Ueber die Wirkung von Hoden und Ovarialsubstanz auf die sekundären Geschlechtsmerkmale des Frosches. *Zool. Anz.*, **38**, 53.

Mellish, C. (1936). Effect of anterior pituitary extract and certain environmental conditions on the genital system of the horned lizard, *Phrynosoma cornutum*. *Anat. Rec.*, **67**, 22.

Mellish, C. H., & Meyer, R. K. (1937). The effects of various gonadotropic substances and thyroxine on the ovaries of horned lizards, *Phrynosoma cornutum*. *Anat. Rec.*, **69**, 179.

Mendoza, G. (1943). The reproductive cycle of the viviparous teleost, *Neotoca bilineata*, a member of the family Goodeidae. IV : The germinal tissue. *Biol. Bull. Wood's Hole*, **84**, 87.

de Menezes, R. S. (1944). Nota sôbre a hipofisção de peixes de rio Mogi-Guaçú com extrato glicerinado de hipófises de peixe. *Bol. Industr. anim.*, **7**, 36.

—— (1945). Ação de hipófises de peixes doadores em diestro sôbre peixes reprodutores em estro. *Rev. bras. Biol.*, **5**, 535.

MEYNS, R. (1910). Ueber Froschhodentransplantation. *Pflüg. Arch. ges. Physiol.*, **132,** 433.

—— (1912). Transplantationen embryonaler und jugendlicher Keimdrüsen auf erwachsene Individuen bei Anuren nebst einem Nachtrag über Transplantationen geschlechtsreifer Froschhoden. *Arch. mikr. Anat.*, **79,** 148.

MILLER, M. R. (1948). The gross and microscopic anatomy of the pituitary and the seasonal histological changes occurring in the pars anterior of the viviparous lizard, *Xantusia vigilis*. *Univ. Calif. Publ. Zool.*, **47,** 225.

—— & ROBBINS, M. E. (1955). Cyclic changes in the pituitary gland of the urodele amphibian, *Taricha torosa* (*Triturus torosus*). *Anat. Rec.*, **122,** 105.

MILLOT, J., & ANTHONY, J. (1955). Considérations physiomorphologiques sur la tête de *Latimeria* (Crossoptérygien coelacanthidé). *C. R. Acad. Sci., Paris*, **241,** 114.

MINTZ, B., FOOTE, C. L., & WITSCHI, E. (1945). Quantitative studies on response of sex characters of differentiated *Rana clamitans* larvae to injected androgens and oestrogens. *Endocrinology*, **37,** 286.

MOHSEN, T. (1958). Masculinising action of pregneninolone on female gonads in the Cyprinodont *Lebistes reticulatus* R. *Nature, Lond.*, **181,** 1074.

MONTALENTI, G., & CALISTI, M. (1936). Contributo allo studio dell'effetto " free martin " nei girini di *Rana esculenta* in parabiosi. *Arch. Zool. Ital.*, **23,** 397.

MOROSOVA, T. E. (1936). Die wirkung des Prolans und des unsterilisierten Harns schwangerer auf die Reifung des Geschlechtsprodukte des Barsches. *Zool. Zh.*, **15,** 169.

—— (1937). Effect of gravidan (sterilized urine of pregnant women) on the maturation of the sexual products of acipenserine fish. *Uchen. Zap. mosk. Univ.*, **9,** 156. (Quoted by Pickford & Atz, 1957.)

MOSZKOWSKA, L. (1932). Études endocrinologiques (testicule et hypophyse) chez le *Bombinator*. *Bull. biol.*, **66,** 503.

MULAIK, D. DE M. (1946). A comparative study of the urinogenital systems of an oviparous and two ovoviviparous species of the lizard genus *Sceloporus*. *Bull. Utah Univ. Biol., Ser.*, **9,** 1.

NADAMITSU, S. (1953). Ovulation *in vitro* in several species of amphibians. *J. Fac. Sci. Hiroshima Univ. (Zool.)*, **14,** 151.

NAGATA, Y. (1936). Transplantation of testis into ovariotomized *Oryzias latipes*. *Zool. Mag., Tokyo*, **48,** 102.

NAKAMURA, T. (1927). Étude anatomo-comparative embryologique et embryo-mécanique de la papille cloacale des Tritons. *Bull. biol.*, **61,** 333.

NEESER, V. (1940). Masculinisation des Lézards castrés en fonction des greffes testiculaires et des implantations d'hypophyses. *Rev. suisse Zool.*, **47,** 153.

NICHOLSON, F. A., & RISLEY, P. L. (1940). A study of the urogenital systems of *Emys blandingii*, with observations on the occurrence of Müllerian ducts in males. *Proc. Iowa Acad. Sci.*, **47,** 343.

NISHINO, K. (1948). On the acceleration of spawning in the rainbow trout, *Salmo irideus* Gibbon, with the aid of *Oncorhynchus keta* (Walbaum) pituitaries. *Sci. Rep. Hokkaido Fish Hatch.*, **3,** 23.

NIWA, H. (1955). Effects of castration and administration of methyl-testosterone on the nuptial coloration of the medaka, *Oryzias latipes*. *Jap. J. Ichthyol.*, **4,** 193.

NOBLE, G. K. (1931). *The Biology of the Amphibia*. New York.

—— & ARONSON, L. R. (1942). The sexual behaviour of Anura. V : The normal mating pattern of *Rana pipiens*. *Bull. Amer. Mus. Nat. Hist.*, **80,** 127.

—— & BORNE, R. (1940). The effect of sex hormones on the sexual hierarchy of *Xiphophorus helleri*. *Anat. Rec.*, **78,** 147.

—— & EVANS, G. (1932). Observations and experiments on the life history of the salamander, *Desmognathus fuscus fuscus* (Rafinesque). *Am. Mus. Novit.*, No. 533.

—— & FARRIS, E. J. (1929). The method of sex-recognition in the wood frog *Rana sylvatica* Le Conte. *Am. Mus. Novit.*, No. 363.

—— & GREENBERG, B. (1940). Testosterone propionate, a bisexual hormone in the American chameleon. *Proc. Soc. exp. Biol., N.Y.*, **44,** 460.

—— & KUMPF, K. F. (1936). The sexual behavior and secondary sexual characters of gonadectomized fish. *Anat. Rec.*, **67,** 113.

NOBLE, G. K. & KUMPF, K. F. (1937). Sex reversal in the fighting fish, *Betta splendens*. *Anat. Rec.*, **70**, 97.

—— —— & BILLINGS, V. N. (1936). The induction of brooding behavior in the jewel fish. *Anat. Rec.*, **67**, 50.

—— —— —— (1938). The induction of brooding behavior in the jewel fish. *Endocrinology*, **23**, 353.

—— & POPE, S. H. (1929). The modification of the cloaca and teeth of the adult salamander, *Desmognathus*, by testicular transplants and by castration. *Brit. J. exp. Biol.*, **6**, 399.

—— & RICHARDS, L. B. (1930). The induction of ovulation by anterior pituitary transplants. *Am. Mus. Novit.*, No. 396.

—— & RICHARDS, L. B. (1932). Experiments on the egg-laying of salamanders. *Am. Mus. Novit.*, No. 513.

NORRIS, H. W. (1941). *The Plagiostome Hypophysis, General Morphology and Types of Structure.* Grinnell, Iowa.

NOVELLI, A. (1932). Rôle de la castration sur l'action sexuelle de l'hypophyse du Crapaud. *C. R. Soc. Biol., Paris*, **111**, 476.

—— (1942). Variación estracional del poder gonadotrópico de la hipófisis del sapo *Bufo arenarum* Hensel. *Rev. Soc. argent. Biol.*, **18**, 238.

NUSSBAUM, M. (1905). Innere Sekretion und Nerveneinfluss. *Ergebn. Anat. EntsGesch,* **15**, 39.

—— (1909). Hoden und Brunstorgane des braunen Landfrosches. *Pflüg. Arch. ges. Physiol.*, **126**, 519.

OGILVIE, A. E. (1933). Induced ovulation in amphibians by injection of antuitrin-S. *Proc. Soc. exp. Biol., N.Y.*, **30**, 752.

OKADA, Y. K., & YAMASHITA, H. (1944a). Experimental investigation of the manifestation of secondary sexual characters in fish, using the medaka, *Oryzias latipes* (Temminck & Schlegel) as material. *J. Fac. Sci. Tokyo Univ.*, **6**, 383.

—— —— (1944b). Experimental investigation of the sexual characters of poeciliid fish. *J. Fac. Sci. Tokyo Univ.*, **6**, 589.

OKKELBERG, P. (1921). The early history of the germ-cells in the Brook-Lamprey *Entosphenus wilderi* (Gage) up to and including the period of sex differentiation. *J. Morph.*, **35**, 1.

OLIVEREAU, M. (1954). Hypophyse et gland thyroïde chez les poissons. Étude histophysiologique de quelques corrélations endocriniennes en particulier chez *Salmo salar* L. *Ann. Inst. océanogr. Monaco*, **29**, 95.

VAN OORDT, P. G. W. J. (1956). *Regulation of the Spermatogenetic Cycle in the Common Frog (Rana temporaria).* Arnhem.

VAN OORDT, G. J., & BRETSCHNEIDER, L. H. (1942). Über den Einfluss gonadotroper Stoffe auf die Entwicklung der Hoden des Aales, *Anguilla anguilla* L. *Arch. Entw.Mech. Org.*, **141**, 45.

—— & VAN DER MAAS, C. J. J. (1926). Castration and implantation of gonads in *Xiphophorus helleri* Heckel. *Proc. Acad. Sci. Amst.*, **29**, 1172.

ORIAS, O. (1932). Influence of hypophysectomy on the pancreatic diabetes of dogfish. *Biol. Bull. Wood's Hole*, **63**, 477.

OTSUKA, S. (1952). Acceleration of ovulation in the goldfish by injection of anterior pituitary extracts of domestic fowls and frogs. *Jap. J. Ichthyol.*, **2**, 45.

OWEN, S. E. (1937). The bitterling fish response to male sex hormones. *Endocrinology*, **21**, 689.

PADOA, E. (1933). Ricerche sperimentali su ipori femorali e sull' epididimo della lucertola. *Arch. ital. Anat. Embriol.*, **31**, 205.

—— (1937). Differenziazione e inversione sessuale (femminizzazione) di avanotti di trota (*Salmo irideus*) trattati con ormone follicolare. *Monit. zool. ital.*, **48**, 195.

PALMER, D. D., BURROWS, R. E., ROBERTSON, O. H., & NEWMAN, H. W. (1954). Further studies on the reactions of adult blueback salmon to injected salmon and mammalian gonadotrophins. *Progr. Fish-Cult.*, **16**, 99.

PANIGEL, M. (1956). Contribution a l'étude de l'ovoviviparité chez les reptiles : gestation et parturition chez le lézard vivipare *Zootoca vivipara*. *Ann. Sci. nat. (Zool.)*, **18**, 569.

PEARSE, A. G. E. (1952).   Cytochemical localization of the protein hormones of the anterior hypophysis.   *Ciba Found. Colloq. Endocrin.*, **4**, 1.

—— (1953).   *Histochemistry, Theoretical and Applied.*   London.

PENHOS, J. C., & CARDEZA, A. F. (1952).   Les glandes endocrines du crapaud hypophysoprive alimenté.   *C. R. Soc. Biol., Paris*, **146**, 132.

PEREIRA, J., & CARDOSO, D. M. (1934).   Hypophyse et ovulation chez les poissons.   *C. R. Soc. Biol., Paris*, **116**, 1133.

PFLÜGER, E. (1907).   Ob die Entwicklung der secundären Geschlechtscharaktere vom Nervensysteme abhängt.   *Pflüg. Arch. ges. Physiol.*, **116**, 375.

PICKFORD, G. E. (1952).   Induction of a spawning reflex in hypophysectomized killifish.   *Nature, Lond.*, **170**, 807.

—— (1953a).   A study of the hypophysectomised male killifish, *Fundulus heteroclitus* (Linn.).   *Bull. Bingham oceanogr. Coll.*, **14**, 5.

—— (1953b).   The response of hypophysectomised male Fundulus to injections of purified beef growth hormone.   *Bull. Bingham oceanogr. Coll.*, **14**, 46.

—— (1957).   In Pickford & Atz, 1957.

—— & ATZ, J. W. (1957).   *The Physiology of the Pituitary Gland of Fishes.*   New York.

—— & KOSTO, B. (1957).   Hormonal induction of melanogenesis in hypophysectomised killifish (*Fundulus heteroclitus*).   *Endocrinology*, **61**, 177.

PLISZKA, F. (1951).   Effect on the testicle of *V. vimba* of therapeutic injections of its hypophysis.   *Roczn. Nauk rol.*, **58**, 385.

POMERAT, C. M. (1940).   The development of oviducal glands in ovariectomised immature toads.   *J. Alabama Acad. Sci.*, **12**, 24.

PONSE, K. (1922).   Disparition et récupération des caractères sexuels secondaires mâles par castration et greffe chez *Bufo vulgaris*.   *C. R. Soc. Phys. Hist. nat. Genève*, **39**, 144.

—— (1923).   Masculinisation d'une femelle de crapaud.   *C. R. Soc. Phys. Hist. nat. Genève*, **40**, 150.

—— (1924).   L'organe de Bidder et le déterminisme des caractères sexuels secondaires du Crapaud (*Bufo vulgaris* L.).   *Rev. suisse Zool.*, **31**, 177.

—— (1941).   Sur la spécificité zoologique dans la réaction aux hormones.   *C. R. Soc. Phys. Hist. nat. Genève*, **58**, 211.

—— (1949).   *La Différenciation du sexe et l'intersexualité chez les Vertébrés.*   Lausanne.

PORIS, E. G. (1941).   Studies on the endocrines of reptiles.   II : Variations in the histology of the hypophysis of *Anolis carolinensis*, with a note on the Golgi configuration in cells of the pars anterior and pars intermedia.   *Anat. Rec.*, **80**, 99.

—— & CHARIPPER, H. A. (1938).   Studies on the endocrines of reptiles.   I : The morphology of the pituitary gland of the lizard (*Anolis carolinensis*) with special reference to certain cell types.   *Anat. Rec.*, **72**, 473.

PORTO, A. (1942).   Sobre a presença de progesterona no corpo amarelo de serpentes ovoviviparas.   *Mem. Inst. Butantan*, **15**, 27.

POTTER, G. D., & HOAR, W. S. (1954).   The presence of androgens in chum salmon (*Oncorhynchus keta* Walbaum).   *J. Fish. Res. Bd. Can.*, **11**, 63.

PRASAD, R. R. (1948).   Observations on the nidamental glands of *Hydrolagus colliei*, *Raja rhina* and *Platyrhinoidis triseriatus*.   *Copeia*, 1948, p. 54.

PUCKETT, W. O. (1939).   Some effects of crystalline sex hormones on the reproductive structures of several anurans.   *Anat. Rec.*, **75**, 127.

PURVES, H. D., & GRIESBACH, W. E. (1951).   The significance of the Gomori staining of the basophils of the rat pituitary.   *Endocrinology*, **49**, 652.

RAHN, H. (1939).   Structure and function of placenta and corpus luteum in viviparous snakes.   *Proc. Soc. exp. Biol., N.Y.*, **40**, 381.

RAMASWAMI, L. S., & HASLER, A. D. (1955).   Hormones and secondary sex characters in the minnow, *Hyborhynchus*.   *Physiol. Zoöl.*, **28**, 62.

—— & LAKSHMAN, A. B. (1958).   Spawning catfish with mammalian hormones.   *Nature, Lond.*, **182**, 122.

—— & SUNDARARAJ, B. I. (1957a).   Induced spawning in the catfish *Heteropneustes* with mammalian chorionic gonadotrophins.   *Acta. anat.*, **32**, 230.

—— —— (1957b).   Induced spawning in the catfish *Clarias*.   *Naturwissenschaften*, **44**, 384.

RANZI, S. (1936a). Ipofisi e gestazione nei selaci. *R. C. Accad. Lincei*, **23**, 365.

—— (1936b). Ghiandole endocrine, maturità sessuale e gestazione nei selaci. *R. C. Accad. Lincei*, 528, **24**.

RASQUIN, P. (1949). The influence of light and darkness on thyroid and pituitary activity of the characin, *Astyanax mexicanus*, and its cave derivatives. *Bull. Amer. Mus. nat. Hist.*, **93**, 497.

—— (1951). Effects of carp pituitary and mammalian ACTH on the endocrine and lymphoid systems of the teleost *Astyanax mexicanus*. *J. exp. Zool.*, **117**, 317.

—— & HAFTER, E. (1951). Age changes in the testis of the teleost, *Astyanax mexicanus*. *J. Morph.*, **89**, 397.

RATHKE, H. (1839). *Entwicklungsgeschichte der Natter*. Königsberg.

REESE, A. M. (1931). The ductless glands of *Alligator mississippiensis*. *Smithson. misc. Coll.*, **82**, 1.

REGAMEY, J. (1931). Un cas d'intersexualité chez le lézard vert (*Lacerta viridis* Daudin). *Bull. Soc. vaud. Sci. nat.*, **57**, 311.

—— (1932). Caractères sexuels secondaires du *Lacerta agilis*. *Bull. Soc. vaud. Sci. nat.*, **57**, 589.

—— (1935). Les caractères sexuels du Lézard (*Lacerta agilis* L.). *Rev. suisse Zool.*, **42**, 87.

REGAUD, C., & POLICARD, A. (1903). Variations sexuelles de structures dans le segment préterminal du tube urinifère de quelques Ophidiens. *C. R. Soc. Biol.*, *Paris*, **55**, 216.

RÉGNIER, M. T. (1937). Action des hormones sexuelles sur l'inversion du sexe chez *Xiphophorus helleri* Heckel. *C. R. Acad. Sci.*, *Paris*, **205**, 1451.

—— (1938). Contribution à l'étude de la sexualité des Cyprinodontes vivipares (*Xiphophorus helleri, Lebistes reticulatus*). *Bull. biol.*, **72**, 385.

—— (1941). Action androgène de la prégnéninolone sur les caractères sexuels secondaires du *Lebistes reticulatus*. *C. R. Acad. Sci.*, *Paris*, **213**, 537.

—— (1942). Masculinisation des femelles de *Lebistes reticulatus* sous l'influence de la prégnéninolone. *C. R. Soc. Biol.*, *Paris*, **136**, 202.

REY, P. (1939). Modifications du cycle annuel de l'ovaire après l'ablation du lobe principal de l'hypophyse chez *Bufo vulgaris*. *C. R. Soc. Biol.*, *Paris*, **130**, 957.

REYNOLDS, A. E. (1943). The normal seasonal reproductive cycle in the male *Eumeces fasciatus* together with some observations on the effects of castration and hormone administration. *J. Morph.*, **72**, 331.

—— (1947). Sex hormone response of the hemipenis of *Eumeces fasciatus* as reflected by organ weight. *Proc. Ind. Acad. Sci.*, **57**, 191.

RISLEY, P. L. (1933). Contributions on the development of the reproductive system in *Sternotherus odoratus* (Latreille). II : Gonadogenesis and sex differentiation. *Z. Zellforsch.*, **18**, 403.

—— (1934). An ovarian cystadenoma and its influence upon sex differentiation in an immature diamond-back terrapin. *Anat. Rec.*, **60**, 68.

—— (1937). A preliminary study of sex development in turtle embryos following administration of testosterone. *Anat. Rec.*, **70**, 103.

—— (1940). Intersexual gonads of turtle embryos following injection of male sex hormone. *J. Morph.*, **67**, 439.

—— (1941). A comparison of effects of gonadotropic and sex hormones on the urogenital systems of juvenile terrapins. *J. exp. Zool.*, **87**, 477.

ROBBINS, S. L. (1951). Observations on the use of the male North American frog (*Rana pipiens*) in pregnancy diagnosis. *J. clin. Endocr.*, **11**, 213.

—— & PARKER, F. (1952). Studies on the mechanism of the spermatic release of the male North American frog (*Rana pipiens*). *J. clin. Endocr.*, **12**, 354.

ROBERTSON, O. H. (1958). Accelerated development of testis after unilateral gonadectomy, with observations on normal testis of rainbow trout. *Fish. Bull.*, *W.S.*, **58**, 9.

—— & RINFRET, A. P. (1957). Maturation of the infantile testes in rainbow trout (*Salmo gairdnerii*) produced by salmon pituitary gonadotrophins administered in cholesterol pellets. *Endocrinology*, **60**, 559.

RODGERS, L. T., & RISLEY, P. L. (1938). Sexual differentiation of urogenital ducts of *Ambystoma tigrinum*. *J. Morph.*, **63**, 119.

ROGOFF, J. L. (1927). The hedonic glands of *Triturus viridescens* : a structural and functional study. *Anat. Rec.*, **34**, 132.

ROOFE, P. C. (1937). The morphology of the hypophysis of *Amblystoma*. *J. Morph.*, **61**, 485.

ROSTAND, J. (1935). Sur l'ovulation provoquée chez quelques Anoures. *C. R. Soc. Biol., Paris*, **119**, 697.

RUBIN, A. A., & GORDON, M. (1953). Effects of alpha-estradiol benzoate and methyl testosterone upon the platyfish *Xiphophorus maculatus* skeleton. *Proc. Soc. exp. Biol., N.Y.*, **83**, 646.

RUGH, R. (1934). Induced ovulation and artificial fertilisation in the frog. *Biol. Bull. Wood's Hole*, **66**, 22.

——(1935a). Ovulation in the frog. I : Pituitary relations in induced ovulations. *J. exp. Zool.*, **71**, 149.

——(1935b). Pituitary-induced sexual reactions in the Anura. *Biol. Bull. Wood's Hole*, **68**, 74.

RYAN, F. J., & GRANT, R. (1940). The stimulus for maturation and for ovulation of the frog's egg. *Physiol. Zoöl.*, **13**, 383.

ST. AMANT, L. (1941). Unpublished Ph.D. thesis, Northwestern University. (Quoted by Turner, C. L., 1942b.)

SAMUEL, M. (1943). Studies on the corpus luteum in *Rhinobatus granulatus* Cuv. *Proc. Indian Acad. Sci. B*, **18**, 133.

——(1944). Studies on the corpus luteum in *Enhydrina schistosa* and *Hydrophis cyanocinctus* of the Madras coast. *Proc. Indian Acad. Sci. B*, **20**, 143.

SANGSTER, W. (1948). A study of the quantitative effects of ethynyl testosterone upon the sword and gonopodium of *Xiphophorus helleri*. *Physiol. Zoöl.*, **21**, 134.

SCHAEFER, W. H. (1933). Hypophysectomy and thyroidectomy of snakes. *Proc. Soc. exp. Biol., N.Y.*, **30**, 1363.

SCHARRER, E. (1952). Das Hypophysen-zwischenhirnsystem von *Scyllium stellare*. *Z. Zellforsch.*, **37**, 196.

SCHRADER, M. E. G. (1887). Zur Physiologie des Froschgehirns. *Pflüg. Arch. ges. Physiol.*, **41**, 75.

SCHREIBER, B. (1935a). Tentativi di maturazione sperimentale dell'Anguilla con ormoni ipofisari. *R. C. Ist. lombardo*, **68**, 669.

——(1935b). Ulteriori osservazioni sull'azione di ormoni preipofisarii sul maschio di anguilla. *Boll. Soc. ital. Biol. sper.*, **10**, 818.

SCHREIBER, S. S., & RUGH, R. (1945). The effect of anterior pituitary implants and of estradiol benzoate on the gonads and gonaducts of newly metamorphosed frogs, *Rana pipiens*. *J. exp. Zool.*, **99**, 93.

SCHREINER, K. E. (1904). Ueber das Generationsorgan von *Myxine glutinosa*. *Biol. Zbl.*, **24**, 91.

SCOTT, J. L. (1944). The effects of steroids on the skeleton of the Poeciliid fish, *Lebistes reticulatus*. *Zoologica, N.Y.*, **29**, 49.

SCRUGGS, W. M. (1951). The epithelial components and their seasonal changes in the pituitary gland of the carp (*Cyprinus carpio*, L.) and goldfish (*Carassius auratus*, L.). *J. Morph.*, **88**, 441.

SEVERINGHAUS, A. E. (1939). Anterior hypophyseal cytology in relation to the reproductive hormones. In *Sex and Internal Secretions*, 2nd ed., Baltimore.

SHAPIRO, B. G., & SHAPIRO, H. A. (1934). Histological changes in the ovaries and ovarian blood vessels of *Xenopus laevis* associated with hypophysectomy, captivity and the normal reproductive cycle. *J. exp. Biol.*, **11**, 73.

SHAPIRO, H. A. (1936a). The biological basis of sexual behaviour in Amphibia. I : The experimental induction of the mating reflex (coupling) in *Xenopus laevis* (the South African clawed toad) by means of pregnancy urine and of anterior pituitary extracts with the production of fertilised ova. *J. exp. Biol.*, **13**, 48.

——(1936b). Induction of ovulation by testosterone and certain related compounds. *J. Soc. chem. Ind., Lond.*, **55**, 1031.

SHAPIRO, H. A. (1937).   The biological basis of sexual behaviour in Amphibia. IV. *J. exp. Biol.*, **14,** 38.

——— & ZWARENSTEIN, H. (1937).   Effects of progesterone and testosterone on *Xenopus* and on its excised ovary. *J. Physiol.*, **89,** 38 P.

SILER, K. A. (1936).   The cytological changes in the hypophysis cerebri of the garter snake (*Thamnophis radix*) following thyroidectomy. *J. Morph.*, **59,** 603.

SKADOVSKII, S. N., & PARFENOVA, O. J. (1937).   Die Wirkung des Harns der Schwangernden auf die Reifung der Eier und auf das Laichen beim Barsch. *Uchen. Zap. mosk. Univ. (Biol.*), **9,** 139.

SLUITER, J. W., OORDT, G. J. VAN, & GRASVELD, M. S. (1950).   Spermatogenesis in normal and hypophysectomized frogs (*Rana temporaria*), following gonadotrophin administration. I : Experiments with spring and summer frogs. *Acta endocr., Copenhagen,* **4,** 1.

——— ——— & MIGHORST, J. C. A. (1950).   A study of the testis tubules, interstitial tissue, and sex characters (thumb-pads and Wolffian ducts) of normal and hypophysectomized frogs (*Rana esculenta*). *Quart. J. micr. Sci.,* **91,** 131.

SMITH, B. G. (1916).   The process of ovulation in Amphibia. *Mich. Acad. Sci.,* 18th *Ann. Rep.,* 102.

SMITH, C. L. (1938).   The clasping reflex in frogs and toads and the seasonal variation in the development of the brachial musculature. *J. exp. Biol.,* **15,** 1.

——— (1955).   Reproduction in female Amphibia. *Mem. Soc. Endocrin.,* **4,** 39.

SMITH, G., & SCHUSTER, E. (1912).   Studies in the experimental analysis of sex. Pt. 8. On the effects of the removal and transplantation of the gonad in the frog. *Quart. J. micr. Sci.,* **57,** 439.

SMITH, H. M. (1946).   *Handbook of Lizards.* Ithaca, New York.

SMITH, P. E. (1916).   Experimental ablation of the hypophysis in the frog embryo. *Science,* **44,** 280.

SOKOL, H. W. (1953).   Selective staining of the pituitary gland of teleost fishes demonstrating at least six tinctorial cell types in the adenohypophysis. *Anat. Rec.,* **117,** 582.

——— (1955).   Experimental demonstration of thyrotropic and gonadotropic activity in the adenohypophysis of the guppy, *Lebistes reticulatus* (Peters). *Anat. Rec.,* **122,** 451.

SPENGEL, J. W. (1876).   Das urogenitalsystem der Amphibien. *Arb. Zool. Inst. Würzburg,* **3,** 1.

STEINACH, E. (1894).   Untersuchungen zur vergleichenden Physiologie der männlichen Geschlechtsorgane. III : Über den Geschlechtstrieb der vor und nach der Pubertat Kastrierten. Ratten und über das Schicksal der akzessorischen Geschlechtsdrüsen in Folge der Kastration. *Pflüg. Arch. ges. Physiol.,* **56,** 304.

——— (1910).   Geschlechtstrieb und echt sekundäre Geschlechtsmerkmale als Folge der innersekretorischen Funktion der Keimdrüsen. II : Über die Entstehung des Umklammerungsreflexes bei Froschen. *Zbl. Physiol.,* **24,** 551.

STENDELL, W. (1914).   Die Hypophysis cerebri. In *Lehrbuch der vergleichenden mikroskopischen Anatomie,* Pt. **8.**

STEPHAN, M. P. (1902a).   Sur la développement de la cellule de Sertoli chez les Sélaciens. *C. R. Soc. Biol., Paris,* **54,** 773.

——— (1902b).   L'évolution de la cellule de Sertoli des Sélaciens après la spermatogenèse. *C. R. Soc. Biol., Paris,* **54,** 775.

STERZI, G. (1909).   *Il sistema nervosa centrale dei Vertebrati,* Vol. 2. Padova.

STICKEL, W. H., & STICKEL, L. F. (1946).   Dimorphism of the pelvic spurs of *Enygrus. Copeia,* 1946, 10.

STOHLER, R. (1931).   Das Vorkommen des potentiellen Ovars bei den Bufoniden. *Verh. naturf. Ges. Basel,* **42,** 196.

STOLK, A. (1951).   Histo-endocrinological analysis of gestation phenomena in the cyprinodont *Lebistes reticulatus* Peters. III : Changes in the pituitary gland during pregnancy. *Proc. Acad. Sci., Amst.,* **54,** 566.

——— (1953).   Tumours of fishes. II : Chromophobe adenoma of the pituitary gland in the viviparous cyprinodont *Lebistes reticulatus* Peters. *Proc. Acad. Sci. Amst.,* **56,** 34.

STOLL, L. M. (1955). Hormonal control of the sexually dimorphic pigmentation of *Thalassoma bifasciatum*. *Zoologica, N.Y.*, **40**, 125.

STROGANOV, N. S., & ALPATOV, V. V. (1951). A new unit for determining the activity of the hypophysis in fish. *Rybnoe Khoziaiskvo*, **27**, 56. (Quoted by Pickford & Atz, 1957.)

SUMI, R. (1924). On the morphogenesis of the epithelial hypophysis of the tailed amphibia. *Folia anat. jap.*, **2**, 83.

SUNDARARAJ, B. I. (1957). Studies on the structural correlation of fish pituitary and gonads and experiments on inducing spawning in fishes. Ph.D. thesis, University of Mysore. (Quoted by Ramaswami & Lakshman, 1958.)

SVÄRDSON, G. (1943). Studien über den Zusammenhang zwischen Geschlechtsreife und Wachstum bei *Lebistes*. *Medd. UndersöknAnst. Sötvattensfisk. Stockh.*, (21) : 48.

TAKEWAKI, K., & FUKUDA, S. (1935). Effect of gonadectomy and testicular transplantation on the kidney and epididymis of a lizard *Takydromus tachydromoides*. *J. Fac. Sci. Tokyo Univ.*, **4**, 63.

TAMPI, P. R. S. (1951). Pituitary of *Chanos chanos* Forskål. *Nature, Lond.*, **167**, 686.

TARCHANOFF, J. R. (1887). Zur Physiologie des Geschlechtsapparatus des Frosches. *Pflüg. Arch. ges. Physiol.*, **40**, 330.

TAVOLGA, M. C. (1949). Differential effects of estradiol, estradiol benzoate and pregneninolone on *Platypoecilus maculatus*. *Zoologica, N.Y.*, **34**, 215.

TAVOLGA, W. N. (1955). Effects of gonadectomy and hypophysectomy on prespawning behavior in males of the gobiid fish, *Bathygobius soporator*. *Physiol. Zoöl.*, **28**, 218.

TAYLOR, A. B. (1948). Experimental sex-reversal in the red swordtail hybrid *Xiphophorus–Platypoecilus*. *Trans. Amer. micr. Soc.*, **67**, 155.

TCHECHOVITCH, G. (1952). La ponte artificielle chez quelques poissons d'eau douce provoqué par les hormones hypophysaires. *Arch. Sci. biol., Belgrade*, **4**, 27.

THIEBOLD, J. J. (1952a). Observations concernant l'évolution de l'uretère primaire chez les embryons de *Scylliorhinus canicula*. *Bull. Soc. zool. Fr.*, **77**, 470.

—— (1952b). Action du propionate de testostérone sur la différenciation sexuelle des embryons de *Scylliorhinus canicula*. *C. R. Acad. Sci., Paris*, **235**, 1551.

—— (1953a). Observations préliminaires concernant la différenciation des gonades et du tractus génital chez les embryons de *Scylliorhinus canicula* traités par le propionate de testostérone. *C. R. Soc. Biol., Paris*, **147**, 480.

—— (1953b). Action du benzoate d'oestradiol sur la différenciation sexuelle des embryons de *Scylliorhinus canicula*. *C. R. Acad. Sci., Paris*, **236**, 2174.

—— (1954). Étude préliminaire de l'action des hormones sexuelles sur la morphogénèse des voies génitales chez *Scylliorhinus canicula* L. *Bull. biol.*, **88**, 130.

—— (1955). Action de l'anhydrooxyprogestérone sur la morphogénèse sexuelle de *Scylliorhinus canicula* L. *C. R. Soc. Biol., Paris*, **149**, 1036.

THORBORG, J. V., & HANSEN, K. (1951). The use of *Xenopus laevis*, *Bufo bufo* and *Rana esculenta* as test animals for gonadotrophic hormones. III : Quantitative investigations on the sensitivity of the animals to chorionic gonadotrophin. *Acta Endocrinol.*, **6**, 51.

TILNEY, F. J. (1911). Comparative histology of the hypophysis. *Mem. Wistar Inst.*, **2**, 29.

—— (1937). The hypophysis cerebri of *Petromyzon marinus donatus*. *Bull. neurol. Inst. N.Y.*, **6**, 70.

TOZAWA, T. (1923). Studies on the pearl organ of the goldfish. *Annot. zool. jap.*, **10**, 253.

—— (1929). Experiments on the development of the nuptial coloration and pearl organs of the Japanese bitterling. *Folia anat. jap.*, **7**, 407.

TUCHMANN-DUPLESSIS, H. (1945). Corrélations hypophyso-endocrines chez le triton. Déterminisme hormonal des caractères sexuels secondaires. *Actualités sci. industr.*, No. 987, Paris.

TURNER, C. L. (1919). The seasonal cycle in the spermary of the perch. *J. Morph.*, **32**, 681.

—— (1937). Reproductive cycles and superfetation in poeciliid fishes. *Biol. Bull. Wood's Hole*, **72**, 145.

Turner, C. L. (1942a). A quantitative study of the effects of different concentrations of ethynyl testosterone and methyl testosterone in the production of gonopodia in females of *Gambusia affinis*. *Physiol. Zoöl.*, **15**, 263.

—— (1942b). Diversity of endocrine function in the reproduction of viviparous fishes. *Amer. Nat.*, **76**, 179.

—— (1947a). The rate of morphogenesis and regeneration of the gonopodium in normal and castrated males of *Gambusia affinis*. *J. exp. Zool.*, **106**, 125.

—— (1947b). Viviparity in teleost fishes. *Sci. Mon.*, N.Y., **65**, 508.

Tuzet, O., & Fontaine, M. (1937). Sur la spermatogénèse de l'anguille argentée (*Anguilla vulgaris* Cuv.). *Arch. Zool. exp. gén.*, **78**, 199.

Vallowe, H. H. (1957). Sexual differentiation in the teleost fish *Xiphophorus helleri*, as modified by experimental treatment. *Biol. Bull. Wood's Hole*, **112**, 422.

Vannini, E. (1941). Rapida azione mascolinizzante del testosterone sulla gonadi di girini di *Rana agilis* " in metamorfosi ". *Reale Accad. Ital.*, fasc. 8, sér. vii, 1.

Veil, C. (1940). Insensibilité saisonnière de la cellule pigmentaire de poisson à l'adrénaline. *C. R. Soc. Biol.*, Paris, **134**, 536.

Verhoeven, B., & Oordt, G. J. van. (1955). The influence of light and temperature on the sexual cycle of the bitterling, *Rhodeus amarus* (preliminary communication). *Proc. Acad. Sci. Amst.*, **58**, 628.

Vivien, J. H. (1938). Sur les effets de l'hypophysectomie chez un téléostéen marin, *Gobius paganellus* L. *C. R. Acad. Sci.*, Paris, **207**, 1452.

—— (1939a). Rôle de l'hypophyse dans le déterminisme du cycle genital femelle d'un téléostéen, *Gobius paganellus* L. *C. R. Acad. Sci.*, Paris, **208**, 948.

—— (1939b). Rôle de l'hypophyse dans le déterminisme du cycle sexuel chez les Poissons. *Bull. Soc. zool. Fr.*, **64**, 141.

—— (1939c). Relations hypophyso-génitales chez quelques téléostéens et sélaciens. *C. R. Soc. Biol.*, Paris, **131**, 1222.

—— (1940). Quelques résultats expérimentaux concernant les relations hypophysogénitales chez un sélacien. *C. R. Acad. Sci.*, Paris, **210**, 230.

—— (1941). Contribution a l'étude de la physiologie hypophysaire dans ses relations avec l'appareil génital, la thyroïde et les corps suprarénaux chez les poissons sélaciens et téléostéens. *Bull. biol.*, **75**, 257.

—— (1950a). Masculinisation des femelles de xiphophores par action des rayons X sur la gonade. *C. R. Acad. Sci.*, Paris, **231**, 1166.

—— (1950b). Morphologie comparée des formations gonopodiales obtenues chez les ♂ et les ♀ de *Xiphophores* traités par les rayons X. *C. R. Soc. Biol.*, Paris, **144**, 1551.

—— (1952a). Rôle de l'hypophyse dans le déterminisme de l'involution ovarienne et de l'inversion sexuelle chez les xiphophores. *J. Physiol.*, Paris, **44**, 349.

—— (1952b). Influence de la castration précoce et de l'irradiation par les rayons X sur la différenciation des caractères sexuels secondaires chez le Xiphophore. *C. R. Acad. Sci.*, Paris, **234**, 2394.

—— (1953a). Effets du radio-phosphore, 32P, sur les gonades des Cyprinodontes vivipares. *C. R. Acad. Sci.*, Paris, **236**, 535.

—— (1953b). Stérilisation totale des gonades après traitement par le phosphore radioactif, chez les Cyprinodontes: *Lebistes* et *Xiphophores*. *C. R. Acad. Sci.*, Paris, **236**, 2172.

—— (1953c). Action du phosphore radioactif sur les gonades des Cyprinodontes vivipares : *Lebistes* et *Xiphophores*. *C. R. Soc. Biol.*, Paris, **147**, 1459.

—— (1954). Quelques examples de l'utilisation du germe et de l'embryon de Sélacien dans les recherches expérimentales concernant la régulation, les paragénèses, l'organogénèse et la physiologie embryonnaire. *Arch. Anat. Strasbourg*, **37**, 163.

—— (1958). In *Traité de Zoologie*, Paris, **13**, fasc. 2.

—— & Mohsen, T. (1952). Action de l'anhydrooxyprogestérone sur les caractères sexuels squelettiques du xiphophore. *C. R. Soc. Biol.*, Paris, **146**, 773.

Volsøe, H. (1944). Structure and seasonal variation of the male reproductive organs of *Vipera berus* (L.). *Spolia Zool. Mus. Hauniensis*, **5**, 1.

DE VOS, C. M. (1935). Bidder's organ in South African species of *Bufo*. *S. Afr. J. Sci.*, **32,** 396.

WALLACE, W. (1903). Observations on ovarian ova and follicles in certain teleostean and elasmobranch fishes. *Quart. J. micr. Sci.*, **47,** 161.

WARING, H. (1936). Colour change in the dogfish (*Scyllium canicula*). *Proc. Lpool. biol. Soc.*, **49,** 17.

—— (1938). Chromatic behaviour of elasmobranchs. *Proc. Roy. Soc.* B, **125,** 264.

—— LANDGREBE, F. W., & NEILL, R. M. (1941). Ovulation and oviposition in Anura. *J. exp. Biol.*, **18,** 11.

WATANABE, M., YAMADA, A., & MATSUSHIMA, M. (1950). On the effects of the hormone of anterior lobe of hypophysis upon the loach. II : Salmon, catfish, snake, lizard, and praehormone. *Bull. Jap. Soc. sci. Fish*, **15,** 799.

WEISEL, G. F. (1949). The seminal vesicles and testes of *Gillichthys*, a marine teleost. *Copeia*, 1949, 101.

WEISMAN, A. I., & COATES, C. W. (1944). The South African Frog (*Xenopus laevis*) in pregnancy diagnosis. New York Biologic Research Foundation.

WELTI, E. (1925). Masculinisation et féminisation de Crapauds par greffe de glandes génitales hétérologues. *C. R. Soc. Biol.*, Paris, **93,** 1490.

—— (1928). Evolution des greffes de glandes génitales chez le Crapaud (*Bufo vulgaris*). *Rev. suisse Zool.*, **35,** 75.

WIEDERSHEIM, R. (1883). *Lehrbuch der vergleichenden Anatomie der Wirbelthiere*. Jena.

WILLS, I. A., RILEY, G. M., & STUBBS, E. M. (1933). Further experiments on the induction of ovulation in toads. *Proc. Soc. exp. Biol.*, N.Y., **30,** 784.

WINGSTRAND, K. G. (1956). The structure of the pituitary in the African lungfish *Protopterus annectens* (Owen). *Vidensk. Medd. dansk naturh. Foren. Kbh.*, **118,** 193.

WITSCHI, E. (1923). Ueber die genetische Konstitution der Froschzwitter. *Biol. Zbl.*, **43,** 83.

—— (1927). Sex-reversal in parabiotic twins of the American wood frog, *Rana sylvatica*. *Biol. Bull. Wood's Hole*, **52,** 137.

—— (1930). Sex development in parabiotic chains of the California newt. *Proc. Soc. exp. Biol.*, N.Y., **27,** 763.

—— (1931). Range of the cortex-medulla antagonism in parabiotic twins of Ranidae and Hylidae. *J. exp. Zool.*, **58,** 113.

—— (1933). Studies in sex differentiation and sex determination. VI : The nature of Bidder's organ in the toad. *Amer. J. Anat.*, **52,** 461.

—— (1937). Quantitative relationships in the induction of sex differentiation, and the problem of sex reversal in parabiotic salamanders. *J. exp. Zool.*, **75,** 313.

—— (1939). Sex deviations, inversions and parabiosis. In *Sex and Internal Secretions*. Baltimore.

—— (1950). Génétique et physiologie de la différenciation du sexe. *Arch. Anat. micr.*, **39,** 215.

—— (1955). Vertebrate gonadotrophins. *Mem. Soc. Endocrin.*, **4,** 149.

—— (1957). The inductor theory of sex differentiation. *J. Fac. Sci. Hokkaido Univ.*, **13,** 428.

—— & CROWN, E. N. (1937). Hormones and sex-determination in fishes and in frogs. *Anat. Rec.*, **70,** 121.

—— & MCCURDY, H. M. (1929). The free-martin effect in experimental parabiotic twins of *Triturus torosus*. *Proc. Soc. exp. Biol.*, N.Y., **26,** 655.

WOERDEMAN, M. W. (1914). Die vergleichende Anatomie der Hypophysis. *Arch. mikr. Anat.*, **86,** 198.

WOLF, O. M. (1928). The effect of mammalian follicular extract on the oviducts of the frog (*R. pipiens shreber*). *Anat. Rec.*, **41,** 41.

—— (1929a). Effect of daily transplants of the anterior lobe of the pituitary on reproduction of the frog. *Anat. Rec.*, **44,** 206.

—— (1929b). Effect of daily transplants of the anterior lobe of the pituitary on reproduction of the frog. *Proc. Soc. exp. Biol.*, N.Y., **26,** 692.

—— (1939). An effect of the injection of a solution of dihydroxyestrin into castrated female frogs, *Rana pipiens*. *Biol. Bull.*, **77,** 338.

Woronzowa, M. A., & Blacher, L. J. (1930). Die Hypophyse und die Geschlechts-drüsen der Amphibien. I : Der Einfluss des Hypophysenexstirpation auf die Geschlechtsdrüse bei Urodelen. *Arch. EntwMech. Org.*, **121**, 327.

Wotiz, H. H., Boticelli, C., Hisaw, F. L., Jr., & Ringler, I (1957). Identification of estradiol 17β from dogfish ova. *Fed. Proc.*, **16**, 274.

Wright, A. (1956). Studies on the adrenal gland of the Reptilia and Monotremata. Ph.D. Thesis, University of Liverpool.

Wright, P. A. (1945). Factors affecting *in vitro* ovulation in the frog. *J. exp. Zool.*, **100**, 565.

—— (1950). Time relationships in frog ovulation. *J. exp. Zool.*, **114**, 465.

—— & Hisaw, F. L. (1946). Effect of mammalian pituitary gonadotrophins on ovulation in the frog, *Rana pipiens*. *Endocrinology*, **39**, 247.

Wunder, W. (1955). Das verhalten von Loden, niere und leber nach entfernung von teilstücken beim karpfen. *Zool. Anz.*, **155**, 232.

Yamamoto, T., & Suzuki, H. (1955). The manifestation of the urinogenital papillae of the medaka (*Oryzias latipes*) by sex hormones. *Embryologia*, **2**, 133.

Young, J. Z. (1935). The photoreceptors of lampreys. II : The functions of the pineal complex. *J. exp. Biol.*, **12**, 254.

—— & Bellerby, C. W. (1935). The response of the lamprey to injection of anterior lobe pituitary extract. *J. exp. Biol.*, **12**, 246.

Zahl, P. A. (1935). Cytological changes in frog pituitary considered in reference to sexual periodicity. *Proc. Soc. exp. Biol., N.Y.*, **33**, 56.

—— (1937). Cytologische Untersuchungen über die Hypophysis cerebri des weiblichen Frosches. Unter besonderer Berüchsichtigung der Fortplanzungstätigkeit. *Z. mikr.-anat. Forsch.*, **42**, 303.

—— & Davis, D. D. (1932). Effects of gonadectomy on the secondary sexual characters in the ganoid fish, *Amia calva* L. *J. exp. Zool.*, **63**, 291.

Zanandrea, G. (1956). Neotenia in *Lampetra planeri Zanandreai* (Vladykov) e l'endocrin-ologia sperimentale dei Ciclostomi. *Boll. Zool.*, **23**, 413.

—— (1957). Neoteny in a lamprey. *Nature Lond.*, **179**, 925.

Zuber-Vogeli, M. (1953). L'histophysiologie de l'hypophyse de *Bufo vulgaris* L. *Arch. Anat., Strasbourg*, **35**, 77.

CHAPTER 12

THE REPRODUCTIVE HORMONES IN BIRDS

By A. S. Parkes and A. J. Marshall

I. Introduction

The reproductive physiology of birds is not only of intrinsic importance; it is of especial interest because its study laid the foundations of endocrinology. Many familiar species show emphatic seasonal and other sexual differences which led to speculation from early times and it is not surprising that birds attracted the experimental attention of such pioneers as John Hunter (1771) and A. A. Berthold (1849). Hunter was interested in transplants of various kinds and among other experiments exchanged the spurs and gonads of domestic cocks and hens. He autografted a testis among the abdominal viscera "where it has adhered, and has been nourished", and homografted to a hen with the same result He injected hepatic vessels and proved that the grafts established a vascular supply from the liver. In hens, at least some engrafted testes duly enlarged. Further, Hunter described the hypertrophy of a residual testicular fragment in a partially castrated cock, and thus made an early observation on the effects of gonadotrophins. However, according to Forbes (1947), there is no evidence that Hunter was aware of the existence of blood-borne secretions. The details of his work have never been published.

Berthold castrated six cockerels and in several birds reintroduced single testes among the intestines where they became vascularised, but did not re-establish nerve connections. As the recipients did not suffer the behavioural and anatomical changes characteristic of capons, Berthold concluded that the testes must contribute some sort of blood-borne substance essential to the maintenance of accessory sexual structures and behaviour. Apparently Berthold did not know of Hunter's work, and he did not indicate why his own investigation was undertaken. As is well known, however, he had the idea that each organ (including those now known to be endocrine) might make specific contributions to the blood and it may be that he thought and wished to demonstrate that the gonads, like other organs, as he believed, elaborated blood-borne substances (Forbes, 1949). Berthold's results caused no more comment in 1849 than did Mendel's fundamental genetical report some seventeen years later.

In any consideration of avian endocrinology, it must be remembered that a highly disproportionate amount of the available information refers to *Gallus bankiva*. By artificial selection for egg-production " the fowl " has become in one central respect quite atypical of Aves as a whole. This selection may perhaps have influenced events right along the neuro-endocrine chain between the environment and the production of young. However, to be balanced against this fact is the extraordinary morphological uniformity of the Aves. The whole class, including even flightless forms, exhibits fewer significant differences than many orders, or even families, of Reptilia and other lower groups.

II. Relation Between Sexuality and General Characters

Sex Dimorphism

As in the Mammalia, " general " characters such as body size and configuration, fat deposition, mineral metabolism, skeletal structure, temperament and behaviour patterns in birds are influenced directly or indirectly by the sex of the individual. It is still uncertain to what extent some of such characters are under gonadal control. There is, for example, no experimental evidence that sex hormones have any connection with the relatively large size of female birds-of-prey or the small size of the males. Furthermore, some " general " characters such as bone and fat deposition may become " special " characters when they arise in certain body regions in one or other sex during specific phases of the reproductive cycle (pp. 587, 635). As Riddle (1931a) said, " It is becoming logically impossible to disentangle secondary sex characters from anything else that pertains to sexuality."

Body size

In birds the male is often larger than the female, especially in game-fowl and many breeds of domestic poultry. The Old English Game Bantam cock is usually about twice as heavy as the hen. The poulard does not attain the size of the cock, so that the dimorphism may be genetic. Size dimorphism in which the male is the larger is marked also in the Great Bustard (*Otis tarda*), many of the pheasants Phasianidae, and the Peafowl (*Pavo cristatus*). Among the birds-of-prey (Falconiformes), on the other hand, the female is usually the larger. The female Sparrow Hawk (*Accipiter nisus*), for example, may attain a weight double that of the male.

Skeletal characters

There are a number of sex differences in the skeletal system quite apart from those associated with the greater size and musculature of the male. The pelvis of the female is apt to show special features associated with egg laying. Thus, in domestic fowl, and petrels (Procellariiformes) among other species, the gap between the pubic bones increases during the breeding season, and in fowl the degree of separation is commonly used to diagnose the imminence of laying. It is uncertain to what extent such seasonal variations are hormone controlled.

Detailed observations have been made on sex dimorphism in the size of bones of domestic fowl. Schneider and Dunn (1924) found a significant difference in length of the long bones in male and female White Leghorns, although overlap of the lower and upper extremes in each sex made it impossible to use any particular bone as a criterion of sex. Similar results were obtained on Leghorns by Hutt (1929), who found differences with a high degree of significance.

Differences in the internal structure of the bones of pigeons were recorded by Kyes and Potter (1934). Females possess relatively solid bones and this state is probably correlated with ovarian activity and egg-shell formation (Bloom, Bloom and McLean, 1941) and may therefore be considered as a " special " character.

Metabolism

Metabolism has long been regarded as closely connected with sexuality, and sex differences have been detected in the metabolic rates of birds. In young

Plymouth Rock fowl the males were found to have a B.M.R. higher than that of the females (Mitchell, Card and Haines, 1927). Concordant results have been obtained in doves.

Sex differences in erythrocyte count have also been established in fowl, pigeons and doves (Blacher, 1926 ; Riddle and Braucher, cited by Riddle, 1932). The amount of haemoglobin similarly differs between the sexes. Domm and Taber's figures (1946) are summarised in Table II. It has also been shown that the phosphorus content of the blood is higher in hen pigeons than cocks. The level of blood lipids is much higher in laying hens than in cocks or immature hens (Lorenz, Entenman and Chaikoff, 1938).

Effects of Gonadectomy on General Characters

The popular impression that capons grow larger than cocks was not substantiated by Waite (1920), who demonstrated that there was little difference until the cockerels began to reach puberty at which time the capons made slightly better gains. Horowitz (1934) concluded that the size difference between capons and cocks was due to the greater amount of fat on the capons. Juhn and Mitchell (1929) found no difference in body weights of cocks and capons. Domm's illustrations (1939a) show that the bilaterally ovariectomised poulard has a build and posture similar to that of a capon, although the large size of the capon is not attained.

There is some evidence that castration affects the length of the long bones, as in certain mammals (Chapter 29. *See* Volume III). Pirsche (1902) reported an increased length of the long bones in capons, together with delayed ossification, but his material was inadequate. Hutt (1929) found that there was a general increase in the length of the long bones of castrated domestic fowl and that there were gradients down the limbs. Huxley (1932) in discussing these results, emphasised that whereas the fore-limbs showed a gradient of decreasing effect passing proximally-distally, the hind-limbs showed a gradient of increasing effect

TABLE I

PERCENTAGE CHANGE IN SIZE IN PARTS OF THE LIMBS OF MALE FOWLS INDUCED BY CASTRATION. (From Huxley, 1932.)

	Humerus	Radius, Ulna	Carpo-metacarpus	Phalanges of digit 3 (mean)
Fore-limb	+ 2·6	+ 2·25	+ 2·2	− 0·1
Hind-limb	+ 3·0	+ 3·4	+ 3·9	+ 4·7
	Femur	Tibio-tarsus	Tarso-metatarsus	Phalanges of digit 3 (mean)

(Table I). Results obtained by Landauer (1937) were, however, negative and contradictory to those of Hutt. Effects of gonadectomy on the red cell count in fowl, as recorded by Domm and Taber (1946), are shown in Table II and indicate that the high count in the male is a positive male attribute.

U*

TABLE II

Erythrocyte Counts in Normal and Gonadectomised Fowl
(From Domm and Taber, 1946.)

Sex	No. of birds	No. of counts	Average red cell count*	Standard deviation
Male . . .	82	288	3.25	0.434
Female .	84	678	2.61	0.345
Capon . . .	89	401	2.48	0.295
Sinistrally . . ovariectomised poulard	30	134	3.00	0.331
Bilaterally . . ovariectomised poulard	16	67	2.60	0.257

* Expressed in millions per cubic millimeter.

Migration

Edward Jenner (1824) emphasised strongly the connection between sexuality and migration but the rôle of androgens and oestrogens in pre-nuptial migration remains in dispute. At a time when the fact of bird migration was " not being generally admitted by naturalists of celebrity," Jenner's long-forgotten paper presented arguments against the then current notion that many birds hibernated in winter. Jenner, a student of John Hunter, said that the *cause* (Jenner's italics) " which excites the migratory bird, at certain seasons of the year, to quit one country for another is the enlargement of the testes in the male and the ovaria in the female, and the need of a country where they can for awhile be better accommodated with succour for their infant brood than in that from which they depart."

Rôle of the gonadal hormones

The early photostimulation work of Rowan (p. 729) a century later was for some time generally believed to substantiate Jenner's conclusions that (leaving external factors out of consideration) the gonads are primarily influential in starting the migration to the breeding grounds. This traditional view, however, has been seriously challenged in later years. In one of the most recent reviews Aschoff (1955) says " admittedly there is no direct dependence [of migration] on the functional state of the gonads " (trs.), and Farner (1950, 1955) considers it improbable that the gonads are a " generally essential part of the stimulatory mechanism." In support of this view, Farner (1950) cited: (1) pre-nuptial migration of castrated birds; (2) the improbability of identical functions of hormones produced by ovaries and testes; and (3) the failure by Wolfson (1945) to provoke pre-migratory fat disposition with gonadtrophin, whereas an essentially somatotrophic preparation did so. All these, however, can be opposed by equally valid arguments and observations.

Some writers, too, have claimed that migrants arrive at their breeding grounds with " inactive " gonads, but this view is probably due to the use of outmoded histological techniques.   There is no valid evidence that any pre-nuptial migrant has left its " wintering " locality with truly inactive gonads, whereas there is much evidence that the reverse is true in both passerines and Charadriiformes (Rowan and Batrawi, 1939; Marshall and Williams, 1959; Marshall, Robinson and Serventy, unpublished observations).   Further, many species before leaving exhibit undeniable sexual behaviour (including pairing), and song during passage is commonly recorded.   Again, a number of species produce spermatozoa before they arrive at their distant breeding grounds (Marshall, 1952a).

Zugunruhe

Migratory birds come twice a year into *Zugunruhe*, a restless nocturnal pre-migratory activity which was described in caged birds early in the nineteenth century (*see* Farner, 1955).   It is probable, but not proved, that true *Zugunruhe* in cage-birds has the same physiological basis as migration.   It is accompanied in many, but apparently not in all migratory species (Nice, 1946), by the accumulation of depot fat in specific areas.   Measurement of *Zugunruhe* under various conditions by Schildmacher (1933, 1934a, b) and other authors suggested that sex hormones are the primary stimulus to the pre-nuptial movement and that oestrogen, administered when the gonads are reduced after reproduction, will depress contra-nuptial migration, i.e. movement away from the breeding ground.   Such experiments, however, were based on very few individuals and have been much criticised (Merkel, 1938; van Oordt, 1949; and others).

It has to be recognised that even if birds are proved to exhibit *Zugunruhe* in the absence of gonads, such activity might still be an androgenic influence, a view already stressed by Bullough (1945).   The androgenic influence of the adrenal cortex is well known and, in fact, virilism associated with a cortical tumour has been recorded in the domestic fowl (McGowan, 1936).   There is also evidence (Koch, 1939; Kar, 1947a, b) that the adrenal cortex enlarges after gonadectomy. Kar showed that in young capons the proportion of cortical tissue rose from about 40 per cent to 70 per cent of the total gland and there was hypertrophy of individual cells.   However, although glandular activity appeared considerable (Kar, 1947b) there was no comb-growth to suggest androgen secretion.   At the same time, castration-induced adrenal hypertrophy in cockerels can be avoided by treatment with testo-sterone propionate and diethylstilboestrol (Kar, 1947b).

Accumulation of depot fat

During recent years considerable attention has been paid to the possible rôle played in migration by the substantial subcutaneous and visceral fat-deposits that are accumulated in specific areas by migrating birds (*see*, e.g., Wolfson, 1945). McCreal and Farner (1956) found fifteen such regions in adults of the migratory White-crowned " Sparrow " (*Zono richia leucophrys*).   In this species there occurs a striking accumulation of depot fat during the last two weeks of April and preceding the pre-nuptial migration when, in natural populations, " mean lipid indices increase from about 5 per cent to more than 20 per cent " (King and Farner, 1956). This fat deposition is followed by the development of *Zugunruhe*.   Observations such as these have helped to establish the modern view that a " total physiological state " must be reached before migration can take place.

The factors initiating this pre-migratory fat deposition (which may provide metabolic water as well as energy *en route*) have not been determined with certainty. Wolfson (1945) has shown that photostimulation leading to gonad activation is followed by fat deposition in migratory birds. Schildmacher and Steubing (1952) obtained more definitive information that premature fat deposition in bramblings is induced not only by photostimulation and the administration of P.M.S. but by implantation of testosterone. However, an agent other than sex hormone may be responsible for fat deposition before the post-nuptial (autumn) migration. Lofts and Marshall (1957) found that fat deposition occurred in some contra-nuptial migrants that had not yet developed a functional interstitium, and some have held that whereas the pre-nuptial journey is initiated by sex hormones, movement away from the breeding territory is allowed essentially by their absence (*see* Bullough, 1945). The latter view has been criticised by Marshall and Coombs (1957) and Lofts and Marshall (1957), who showed that some migratory birds develop at least a potentially secretory interstitium before their autumn departure, and may exhibit pre-migratory sexual behaviour before the appearance of the apparently innate, neural drive to migrate towards the traditional " wintering " ground. It is of interest that Promptov (cited by Farner, 1955) showed, in a small number of Scarlet Grosbeaks (*Carpodacus ery hrinus*), that the contra-nuptial *Zugunruhe* started at a specific age and not at a particular time of the year.

Conclusion

Zugunruhe is a behaviour pattern that is undeniably activated by photostimulation and probably by testosterone. Fat deposition, which apparently does not occur in all migratory species (*see* Nice, 1946 ; Farner, 1955), can be induced by photostimulation, gonadotrophins and testosterone. A great deal has been written about " total physiological state " involving preliminary fat-deposition before migration, but it remains to do the experiment of keeping pre-migrants at a dietary level insufficient for the accumulation of depot fat and then measuring the nocturnal activity of castrated and non-castrated birds after photostimulation. On the balance of evidence, the most economical hypothesis for the time being is probably the traditional one, i.e. that androgens and oestrogens are the primary activating agents of the pre-nuptial migration, and possibly also for the fat deposition by which it is generally preceded.

The rôle of the internal rhythm in these events is considered on p. 675.

III. Relation Between the Gonads, the Special Characters and the Accessory and Other Organs

Sex Dimorphism in Special Characters

Secondary sexual characters in birds may include, in addition to specialised plumage, various highly coloured soft structures such as combs, wattles, facial and neck corunculations and pouches, as well as spurs on the wings or feet (Fig. *12.* 1). The female often has more or less developed rudiments of these characters, but usually they differ clearly from those of the male. Beak-colour and voice may provide further sex differences and there are often sharp contrasts in sexual and other behaviour. The few accessory reproductive organs of birds will also be considered in this section.

Plumage

Sex dimorphism in plumage has extraordinary variety and, in birds-of-paradise in particular, is extremely beautiful and complex. For example, display in *Lophorina superba* involves the erection of two tiny patches of shiny green feathers between the eyes. These patches are raised " in a manner so subtle that they catch the light and are transformed into scintillating green eyes, which, by their very brightness, mask the true eyes; they are so realistic that it is hard to believe that they are no more than tiny spots of feathers " (Stonor, 1940).

Colour effects in feathers may be achieved by simple pigmentation or frequently by " interference " (Auber, 1957). Thus, the basic pigment colour of the nuchal crest of certain bower-birds (*Chlamydera*) is revealed under the microscope to be orange-yellow, but the crest glistens lilac or silver in open sunlight (Marshall, 1954).

The best known and most studied combination in sex dimorphism is that involving permanently bright males and sombre hens, as in birds-of-paradise, pea-fowl, pheasants, Brown Leghorns and many other domestic breeds. Owing to the difference in feather-structure, the plumage of male domestic fowl is usually epigamic even where there is little or no difference in colour (*see* Fig. *12.21*).

A curious and extremely rare kind of sexual dimorphism is exhibited by the phalaropes (*Phalaropus*) and Painted Snipe (*Rostratula* spp.) in which the female comes seasonally into display-colour (and exhibits important aspects of the typical male behaviour pattern) whilst the male remains in sombre plumage, incubates the eggs and tends the young.

Sex dimorphism may be absent because both sexes possess dull plumage or display plumage at all times of year. For example, in Sebright bantams, henny Campines and henny game-birds both sexes are " henny-feathered " irrespective of season, while in the European Robin (*Erithacus rubecula*) and the Spotted Bower-bird (*Chlamydera maculata*) both possess display plumage at all seasons. The distinction between the two types, however, is very imprecise and may apply only to plumage. No doubt henny-feathered males stimulate their mates sexually by some kind of display, and conversely, the vivid plumage of the females of brilliant pairs may have a function of some kind.

Further complications are encountered in birds showing seasonal plumage changes. The best-known plumage cycles are those of ducks, notably of the Mallard (*Anus platyrhynchos*). The Mallard drake throughout most of the year retains nuptial display plumage which contrasts strikingly with that of the female. When the mating season ends in May or June, the drake moults and assumes eclipse plumage. This is very similar to that of the female and lasts until the autumn moult. Epigamic plumage and sexual behaviour appear together (Höhn, 1947). The seasonal assumption of nuptial display plumage by the male is also well seen in many finches. The hen Indigo Bunting (*Passerina cyanea*) is light brown in colour throughout the year. During eclipse the cock is very similar, but in the breeding season he becomes brilliantly blue. In the Orange Weaver

(*Xanthophilus aurantius*) a similar change is seen, but in this species the nuptial male is orange in colour. Many other birds show analogous seasonal changes, e.g. the African Pennant-winged Nightjar (Fig. *12*. 1e).

Another interesting type of seasonal change is seen where both sexes undergo the same transformation at the onset of the breeding season. The crest of the Shag (*Phalacrocorax aristolelis*), the black breast of the Golden (*Charadrius apricorius*) and Grey Plovers (*C. squatarola*), the chocolate-brown head of the so-called Black-headed Gull (*Larus ridibundus*), and the black or red throat of the divers (*Colymbus*) are all examples of characters assumed by both sexes only for the breeding season. Other birds in which there is seasonal change but no sex dimorphism include several other waders and certain guillemots (*Uria*), and the Razorbill (*Alca torda*). Such birds may not be directly relevant to the subject of sex dimorphism, but are of great potential endocrinological interest.

Head and neck furnishings

The comb, wattles, and ear lobes of domestic fowl are much better developed in cocks than in hens. In turkeys, the head and upper neck are covered by corunculated skin. This is much more developed and oedematous in the male, which possesses also a special conical fold of the same material. Some ducks have a knob of flesh over the base of the beak which is more highly developed in the male. In the Budgerygah (*Melopsittacus undulatus*) the fold of skin above the nostrils is blue in the male and yellowish-brown in the female. In the male African Wattled Starling (*Creatophora carunculata*) there is a seasonal shedding of feathers and a development and post-nuptial regression of black facial coruncles (Fig. *12*. 1b); in the female these are permanently lacking, but minor feather changes sometimes occur (Roberts, 1951). In the Bell-bird of South America an inflatable tube, which is erected during display, takes the place of a comb (Fig. *12*. 1d). In the Australian Bustard, an enormous gular pouch is inflated and distends the whole of the neck during display (Fig. *12*. 1c).

Beak and spurs

The beak may show sex differences in colour, or shape, or both. Permanent sex dichromism is not uncommon (e.g. the Mallard and Zebra Finch (*Poephila*

Fig. *12*. 1—Epigamic characters, showing some extreme forms of sex dimorphism. (a) Puffin (*Fratercula arctica*), with laterally flattened beak which during the breeding season develops a series of horny flanges and becomes brightly coloured, blue, red and yellow. After reproduction the horny excrescences drop off; the individual components are as follows: superior rim-piece, nasal cuirass, transparent lamella of first flange, inferior rim-piece (of lower mandible), chin cuirass, gape-boundary (stretching to the dotted line during the nuptial period), supra-orbital plaque, infra-orbital plaque (after Grassé). (b) African Wattled Starling (*Creatophora carunculata*) notable for the seasonal development by the male of decorative wattles which regress after each breeding season. The upper figure shows a juvenile male. (From B.M. (N.H.) skins.) (c) The Australian Bustard (*Eupodotus australis*) inflates a relatively enormous gular pouch during display and produces gutteral sounds that precede a noise " not unlike a train blowing off steam " (Chisholm). The pouch opens beneath the tongue and has no direct connection with the respiratory system. *ton*., base of tongue; *oes*., oesophagus and crop; *trach*., trachaea (after Coues). (d) The South American Bell-bird (*Chasmorhynchus niveus*) possesses an inflatable black tube which is erected during song display and contrasts with the white head. The tube is closed distally but opens proximally into the palate at the base of the beak. When not inflated it hangs downwards as shown in the young male (after Romanes). (e) The African Pennant-winged Nightjar in aerial display (*Cosmetornis vexillarius*). The 9th primary of each wing of the male grows into a ribbon-like plume between 18 and 28 inches long at about the time of the pre-nuptial migration (after Bannerman).

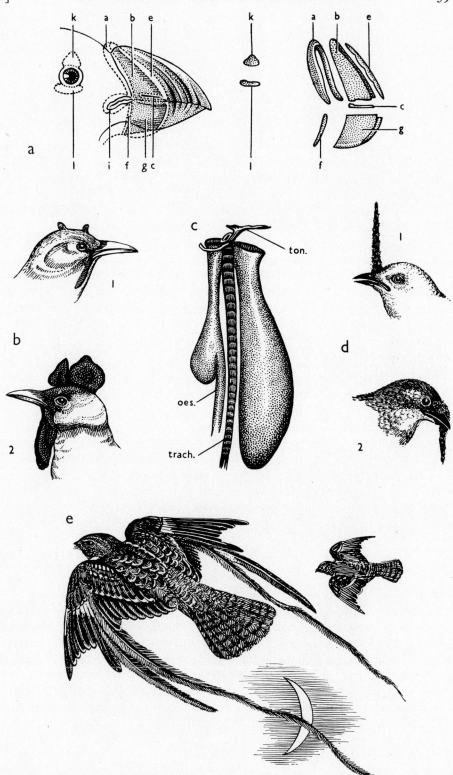

castanotis) and dichromism during the breeding season is frequent in birds that show seasonal changes in beak colour (e.g. House Sparrow, *Passer domesticus*). Usually the male acquires the distinctive colour, as in the Blackbird (*Turdus merula*), but in some instances the female does so (e.g. Red-billed Weaver Finch, *Quelea quelea*). In these species it would seem that one colour is always the neutral pattern, while the other is the sex-dependent one which can be stimulated by either gonad, by ovary only, or by testis only, according to species. Gonadectomy studies (pp. 596, 610) are in agreement with this interpretation. In other species, there is a change in beak colour at the beginning of the sexual season which is the same in both sexes, e.g. Black-headed Gull (*Larus ridibundus*) and Puffin (*Fratercula arctica*). In the latter bird the beak is adorned by a coloured horny sheath which is shed after each breeding season (Fig. *12*. *1a*).

Spurs are present on the males of many species, including all domestic fowl showing display plumage, and only exceptionally on female fowl. They are usually absent in domestic birds in which the male is henny-feathered. In Spur-winged (*Lobibyx*) and certain other plovers a sharp spur is borne on the wing of both sexes. Perhaps the most remarkable of all brachial armoury was possessed by the extinct flightless Solitaire Pigeon (*Pezophaps solitarius*) of Rodriguez in which a rounded mass of bone was borne on the wing of both sexes but was larger in the male.

Eye characters

There is sex dichromism of the iris in many species. In the European Blackbird, the iris of the male is pale yellow and that of the female dark brown. Pézard (1931) has described an ambisexual eye character in fowl : the proportion of red and yellow oil globules in the retina. This is the same in cocks and hens, but is altered in the capon and poulard by reduction in the proportion of red globules by nearly half. According to Champy (1930), the red glow of the eye of the cock fowl is due to the fact that the iris, made hyperaemic by dilation and convolution of capillaries, is reflected from the retina. This character is only slightly developed in the hen. Another example of this is seen in the Satin Bower-bird (*Ptilonorhynchus violaceus*), in which both sexes are blue-eyed, but in which the eyes of the male bulge during display, when a rich anastomotic vascularisation of the iris allows them to be suffused with rose-red of a striking intensity (Marshall, 1954).

Behaviour

Sexual differences in behaviour and temperament are as striking in birds as in other vertebrate groups. Of special interest are the remarkable differences that occur in, say, territorial aggressiveness between closely related species : heredity, as well as hormones, plays an important rôle. It is noteworthy that many relatively powerful birds (e.g. some birds-of-prey of either sex) make no attempt to defend their territory, or even a nest with young, against man, whereas relatively feeble ones (often both sexes) may do so vigorously. Male Australian " magpies " (*Gymnorhina*) sometimes become so savage during the mating season that especially notorious individuals must be shot to protect passing school-children. Male cassowaries (*Casuarius* spp.), when attacked, have been known to kill a man with their specialised claws.

Other forms of behaviour vary enormously between the sexes. Among

bower-birds (Ptilonorhynchidiae) the males play no part in nidification, incubation or feeding the young.   If the nest is menaced the male is generally absent,
whereas the female goes into a paroxism of physical and vocal distraction display
(Marshall, 1954).   On the other hand, the sex rôles in phalaropes (*Phalaropus*) are
reversed.   In the migratory *P. lobatus* the female arrives first on the breeding
territory and subsequently displays to the male.   The eggs are incubated by the
male.

Voice

Remarkable sounds are produced by birds, and many species show sex differences.   Familiar instances of vocalism are the crow and cackle of domestic fowl
and the songs of passerine birds.   In many jungle-dwelling species the song is
interlaced with vocal mimicry of other species (e.g. lyrebirds, *Menura*).   The
performance of the female is often little inferior, but usually much less loud and
sustained.   Many birds develop enhanced vocal powers during the sexual season,
and the male Prairie Chicken (*Tympanunchus cupido*) and other birds " boom "
during courtship.   Such sound is amplified by resonating sacs, analogous to those
of frogs, which hypertrophy during the breeding season, and regress as testis-size
decreases after reproduction (Schwartz, 1945).   In the Australian Whipbird
(*Psophodes olivaceus*) a curious bisexual duet is performed.   The male utters a
long-drawn preliminary call, ending in an explosive " crack," which is immediately followed by a double note generally given by the female.   The hen is not
known to perform the primary or secondary parts of the sequence.

Effects of Castration

Plumage

Castration in the Brown Leghorn cock (taken as a type bird) causes no change in
the plumage except a slight lengthening of certain feathers.   Spur-growth is also
normal or excessive (Pézard, 1911).   It is established, therefore, that the display
plumage in these birds is not dependent on the integrity of the testis ; it is the
neutral or asexual condition.   The results obtained on Leghorns have been extended and confirmed on a number of other domestic fowl, and on turkeys and pea-
fowl (Pézard, 1918 ; Zawadowsky, 1922 ; Scott and Payne, 1934).   The plumes
of the male Ostrich (*Struthio camelus*) are not affected by castration (Duerden,
1919) nor the plumage of the cocks of certain finches (Zawadowsky, 1926).   Some
of the implications of plumage dimorphism of this kind were discussed by Greenwood and Blyth (1938a).

The Satin Bower-bird is here of interest in a different way.   The " immature "
henny-feathered males produce spermatozoa and can breed before they begin to
change to the adult blue-black plumage.   While changing, they are mottled green
and black for at least a year.   Castration either before or during the prolonged
change-over period fails to retard the development of the blue-black epigamic and
threat plumage (Marshall, 1954).   It would seem that this gradual change is
genetically controlled.   Castration of the male House Sparrow (Keck, 1934) and
of the Painted or Nonpareil Bunting (*Passerina ciris*) (Witschi, 1936a) also produces
no effect on the sex dimorphic plumage.   Caution is evidently necessary in defining
plumage types in advance of the necessary evidence.

There seems to be no information about the effect of castration on the plumage of breeds in which both sexes have display plumage (e.g. Robin, *Erithacus rubecula*). Breeds of the other extreme, where both sexes are henny-feathered, provide the now classic case of the Sebright bantam.   Morgan (1919) found that castration of the young male prevented the development of the henny-feathering, and in the adult caused a change-over at the next moult.   After castration, typical display plumage appeared, of a kind which would have been expected in males of such a breed (Fig. *12*. 2a).   Identical results have been obtained in certain Campines and Old English game fowl (Fig. *12*. 2b) in which the cock is henny-feathered (Emmens and Parkes, 1940b).   The fact that removal of the testis prevents the appearance of henny-feathering in these varieties and allows the appearance of display plumage indicates clearly the complete dissociation of " male " feathering and testis activity in domestic fowl.

In other birds in which there is no sex difference in plumage, and in which the male has dull plumage similar to that of the female, e.g. the Dovecot Pigeon (*Columba livia*) and the Guinea-fowl (*Numida meleagris*), the plumage is not affected by castration (Lipschütz and Wilhelm, 1928 ; Finlay, 1925; Krizenecky and Kamenicek, 1933).

A number of investigations have been made on birds in which the male seasonally assumes nuptial display plumage (*see* pp. 589, 592) and it is clear that different endocrine mechanisms may here be at work.   Regarding the Mallard and related ducks, there has been some doubt about the exact effect of castration.   Goodale (1910) showed that castration of the Rouen drake resulted in the display-type plumage becoming permanent, although the annual moult still occurred.   This experiment suggests that the eclipse plumage is conditioned by testis activity.   Benoit (1935a) and Champy (1935) obtained results in keeping with those of Goodale, and concluded that eclipse plumage was always inhibited in completely caponised drakes, contrary results being caused by testis regeneration.   Work by Caridroit and Regnier (1930), by Walton (1937) and Caridroit (1938a) confirmed that the ultimate effect of castration of the mallard is always disappearance of the seasonal plumage cycle, but showed that castration at the beginning of the summer moult does not prevent the change.   Emmens and Parkes (1940b) also showed that castration when an eclipse feather was growing did not cause a sudden change in type, but that castration well in advance of eclipse prevents the change-over. It is possible, as concluded by Walton, that the ultimate effect of castration (and therefore of the testis) is indirect and is due to changes in the pituitary or thyroid glands.

Definite results have been obtained with other birds showing seasonal plumage changes.   Van Oordt and Junge (1934, 1936) found that castration of the Ruff inhibited the appearance of the typical breeding season plumage, which must therefore be a dependent secondary character.   The same authors (1933) castrated Black-headed Gulls and prevented the ambisexual change in the plumage of the head during the breeding season.   In the Indigo Bunting and in both Orange and Red-billed Weavers the seasonal plumage cycle of the male is not affected by castration (Witschi, 1935a).   In this connection Marshall and Disney (1957) found that both sexes of young Red-billed Weavers began to come into breeding plumage while the gonads were still minute, and Marshall and Serventy (1958) reported the same phenomena in the Zebra Finch.   Both species are irregular opportunist breeders that nest quickly after the appearance of green grass in their arid environment. They are usually already in breeding plumage but sexually inactive when

Fig. *12*. *2*—Effects of castration on the plumage of henny-feathered cocks. (a) Sebright bantam—
(1) Normal cock, (2) Capon. (From Morgan, 1919.) (b) Wing-bow feathers of henny
breeds. Henny Campine cock (1) Before castration, (2) After castration; Henny Old English
Game Bantam cock (3) Before castration, (4) After castration. (From Emmens and Parkes,
1940b.)

rain falls. Such an arrangement might be useful since plumage change is necessarily slow, while gonadal change may be very rapid under appropriate external stimuli (p. 667).

Head and neck furnishings

When the young male chick is castrated there is no further growth of the comb, wattles or ear lobes except that associated with growth of the head ; the rudimentary comb and wattles which result are " minces, farineux, et exsangues " (Pézard, 1911, 1912). Goodale (1916a) emphasised that the capon comb is not of a female type but is, in fact, neutral or immature and Huxley (1932) pointed out that whereas the growth of the normal cock's comb is highly allometric, that of the male bird, castrated as a chick, is isometric. Castration of the adult cock leads to hypotrophy of the comb. Shrinkage is fast for the first six weeks, but afterwards much less rapid (Pézard, 1921).

The histology of the normal comb, and the changes occurring after castration, were investigated by Hardesty (1931). She described three layers : (1) a central core of connective tissue carrying large blood vessels, (2) an intermediate layer of loose connective tissue greatly distended with mucoid, and (3) a peripheral layer composed of compact connective tissue carrying an elaborate capillary network. The mucoid layer accounts for the size and erectness of the comb and the superficial capillary network for the colour. A section of a normal comb is shown in Fig. *12*. 32 illustrating the effects of hypophysectomy. Castration prevents the formation or causes the disappearance of the mucoid, and shrinkage of the capillary network, and the comb becomes small and pale.

Less striking, but of equal interest, are the changes that take place in the " sexual skin " on the head and neck of the turkey. Athias (1928a, b), van Oordt and van der Maas (1929) and Scott and Payne (1934) all agreed that the corunculated skin and top-knot of the turkey fail to develop, or hypotrophy, after castration. Van Oordt and Junge (1934) reported that the tubercles of skin which develop round the eye of the Ruff (*Philomachus pugnax*) during the breeding season fail to appear after castration. Champy (1931a) found that complete castration would prevent the development of the red and black facial coruncle of the Barbary drake. In the Ruff, van Oordt and Junge (1936) showed that total castration reduced nuptial adornments and sexual behaviour whereas " partial castration " was compatible with the appearance of breeding plumage, including the ruff, but not of the facial tubercles. The fleshy knob above the beak of the Guinea-fowl, which shows little sex dimorphism, is not apparently affected by castration.

A reciprocal relation between the comb of the domestic cock and the testis has been demonstrated in that removal of the comb is followed by enlargement of the testes (Buckner, Insko and Martin, 1933). Claims to have demonstrated the presence of a testis-inhibiting substance in the comb (Zawadowsky, 1936) were not confirmed (Hoskins and Koch, 1939a), and the mechanism of testicular hypertrophy following removal of the comb is unknown.

Beak and feet

In the castrated House Sparrow, the black of the male beak fades to the brown of the female (Keck, 1934). In the Black-headed Gull (*Larus ridibundus*) the development of the crimson colour of the beak and feet during the breeding season is inhibited by castration (van Oordt and Junge, 1930, 1933). Noble and Wurm (1940a, b) found that the secondary sexual characters in the Black-crowned Night Heron could be abolished by castration and re-established by testosterone propionate and that analogous characters in the Laughing Gull (*Larus atricilla*) were similarly modified. The nuptial sex difference in beak colour in the Red-billed Weaver Finch (*Quelea quelea*) and in the nasal ceres of Budgerygahs is not affected by castration of the male (Witschi, 1935a). In these birds the female beak colour during the breeding season is the dependent secondary sexual character (*see* pp. 610, 637). The Indigo Bunting and the Orange Weaver Finch, on the other hand, resemble the House Sparrow, the change in colour of the cock's beak during the breeding season being prevented by castration (Witschi, 1935a).

Spurs

Castration does not inhibit the development of spurs in domestic fowl. The capon's spurs, like his plumage, are even more luxuriant than those of the cock. In the turkey-cock, however, there seems to be some evidence (reviewed by van Oordt, 1936) that spur development is inhibited by castration.

Voice

Myers (1917) found little evidence of sex dimorphism in the syrinx of domestic fowl, but according to Lewis and Domm (1948) a conspicuous sexual differentiation is evident in the syrinx of domestic ducks from the thirteenth day of incubation and is the " first known sex difference to appear after the differentiation of the gonads." It is not affected by castration (*see* p. 611).

Domestic fowl capons, whether made pre- or post-pubertally, rarely if ever crow. According to Goodale (1916a) the capon may occasionally do so, but this is contrary to the experience of Pézard (1918). The extensive experience of capons gained in the large colonies maintained for hormone testing, indicates that the completely caponised bird does not crow. Crowing in a capon implies gonad regeneration from testicular remnants (Hooker and Cunningham, 1938). Goodale (1916a) failed to observe any lack of development in the syrinx after puberal castration of domestic fowl, and according to Appel (1929a) the adult syrinx is morphologically the same in cocks, hens, capons and poulards. The failure of the capon to crow is therefore not due to lack of development of this apparatus. According to Calvet (1931), however, the syrinx is responsible only for the production of vibrations, the glottis determining the timbre, rhythm and modulation of the voice. He also pointed out that in the capon as compared with the cock the glottis is small and its muscular lips ill-developed.

Van Oordt and van der Maas (1929) and Scott and Payne (1934) declare that the completely castrated turkey loses the characteristic gobble and castration of adult male Satin Bower-birds, besides reducing display, has also a depressing effect on their characteristic song.

Behaviour

In birds, as in mammals, temperament is affected by castration and the difference in temperament between cocks and capons is well attested. All observers note the quietness of capons, their lack of pugnacity, and their unwillingness to fight. This quiescence is, of course, the reason for caponising table poultry. Castrated Satin Bower-birds (*Ptilonorhynchus violaceus*) lose the aggressiveness for which the male is notable (Marshall, 1954).

Birds caponised as chicks fail to develop full sexual behaviour, and castrated cocks rapidly lose it. However, according to Benoit (1929) and others, capons may show modified forms of sexual activity. Goodale (1916a) remarks that the aggressive courtship of the normal cock is entirely missing in the capon, which mates, if at all, only when solicited, and then in an " absent-minded manner ". Finlay (1925) and Carpenter (1933a, b) present evidence concerning the differential degree of inhibition of activity after partial and complete castration.

Since the initial important work by Schjelderup-Ebbe (1935) attention has been paid to the peck-order or social hierarchy that occurs in various species (*see* p. 624). Social status is lowered by castration. Bower-building by male Satin-birds is depressed by castration, as is aggression in this normally very truculent species. It is difficult to separate " combat drive " from aggressive sexual behaviour, and certainly many species show some degree of combativeness while food-gathering during the flocking season when relatively little sexual behaviour is manifest. Goodale (1913) reported reduced combat in castrated fowls. On the other hand, Riddle (1924a, 1925) described " complete and emphatic " masculine activity in pigeons in which testes were congenitally absent. Whether such activity is dictated by innate neural patterns in the absence of steroid hormones, or whether, possibly, some compensatory cortical influences operate, is unknown. Collias' (1944) experiment in which, after hypophysectomy, pigeons sometimes still showed extremely aggressive behaviour, points to the former possibility.

Accessory organs and other structures

An intromittent organ, now retained prominently in only a few avian orders, was probably present in ancestral birds. The genital tubercle persists in male domestic fowl long enough after hatching to allow " sexing " with an accuracy of more than 95 per cent. The tubercle develops embryologically in the domestic duck in the absence of oestrogen (p. 611) and at puberty becomes functional under the influence of testicular androgens (*see* Witschi, 1960). In males it becomes a prominent intromittent organ (penis) ; in females it remains as a vestige (clitoris). In some species seasonal penial changes in the adult male appear to be dependent on the androgenic activity of the testes. Thus, the penis of drakes may be reduced by castration (Goodale, 1916a), and Champy (1931a) has given a detailed description of the changes, including the atrophy of associated cloacal muscles. In the castrated drake the seasonal fluctuation in size does not occur (Domm, 1939a). In Tinamiformes (Tinamous) and " ratites " (Ostrich, Emu, etc.) the size of the penis is also apparently affected by the gonads. During embryonic life the genital tubercle in fowl appears to be under similar endocrine control (Reinbold, 1951). Little work has been carried out on other accessory organs, but the atrophic vas deferens of the Brown Leghorn capon was illustrated by Callow and Parkes (1935). The survival of spermatozoa in the vas deferens, up to 30 days, is not affected by lack of testis hormone (Munro, 1938b).

There is also scope for work on the seminal vesicles. Wolfson (1954) has made the important observation that during the height of the sexual season sperm-storage at a lower temperature may be attained in passerines (e.g. *Junco*, *Zonotrichia*, *Melospiza*) by the descent of the swollen, sperm-laden seminal vesicles into twin node-like cloacal protuberances. The temperature within the projecting cloaca is about 7° F. lower than that of the body. The protuberances may be thermo-

regulatory in function (analogous to the mammalian scrotum) and may also facilitate intromission. At the same season the female cloaca is enlarged and swollen
but it is not extended into a bulbous protuberance. In at least some species
(e.g. domestic fowl) the seminal vesicles do not store spermatozoa and do not
hypertrophy seasonally (Lake, 1957).

It has sometimes been suggested that the activity of the avian thymus is somehow linked with that of the gonads. Höhn (1947, 1956) showed, for example,
that the thymus of adult mallards of both sexes, and of female North American
" Robins " (*Turdus migratorius*), markedly enlarges at the period of post-nuptial
gonad collapse. In male " Robins " the thymus enlarges earlier and almost
synchronously with the testes. At the same time, Höhn failed to produce thymus
hypertrophy in mallards by gonadectomy (or unilateral adrenalectomy) during
the quiescent period. It is possible that thymic changes are related to the moult;
they are probably unconnected with the state of the gonads.

Effects of Grafting and Modifying the Testis

Grafts to castrated males

Hunter's and Berthold's experiments on the transplantation of the testis in
fowl has already been mentioned (p. 583). These classical investigations were
forgotten until 1902, when Foges made what appears to have been an unsuccessful
attempt to repeat them ; his chief evidence for the success of the graft was the full
development of male plumage and spurs. In 1912, Pézard described experiments
confirming and extending Berthold's observations.

Many authors have since carried out such experiments, including Caridroit,
Zawadowsky, Finlay and Domm, and it is certain that a successful testis graft
to the capon will restore the lost male characters, such as the head furnishings, as
well as dependent plumage characters. The androgenic activity of the testis is
well shown by the stimulation of the comb and wattles which occurs in the intact
hen bearing a testis graft (Fig. *12*. 3).

Grafts to ovariectomised females and intact females

Removal of the ovary from the pullet usually leads to regeneration of the
rudimentary right gonad (see pp. 605, 608) which has ambisexual activity. Birds
of this kind, as pointed out by Greenwood and Crew (1926), are clearly unsatisfactory for investigation of the endocrinological properties of the grafted testis.
However, a number of interesting experiments have been carried out. Appel
(1929b) found that regeneration of the right gonad might be suppressed by a testis
graft. Domm (1930) failed to make a sinistrally ovariectomised pullet function as
a male by intragonadal testis grafts, but recorded that the completely gonadectomised hen responds like the capon so that a testis graft causes the appearance of
male characters such as large erect comb and wattles, crowing and stance (Domm,
1929a). The plumage remains of the display type. Effects on behaviour are in
general less emphatic with testis grafts or injected androgens in ovariectomised
females than in capons. However, when Zawadowsky (1922) implanted testicular
tissue into ovariectomised hens they exhibited treading behaviour to compliant
females and Pézard (1922) described two similarly treated birds that still showed
cock feathering and masculine behaviour 5 years after the gonadal exchange.
Profound changes, therefore, are obtained, but not complete reversal of behaviour

(Finlay, 1925).   Much information on this and related topics was later reviewed by Pézard (1928).

(a)

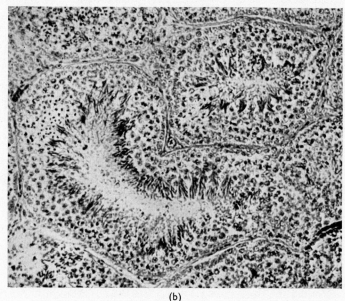

(b)

Fig. *12*. 3—Effect and histology of testis graft.   (a) Brown Leghorn hen with testis graft, showing retention of female plumage and assumption of male comb and wattles.   (b) Section of testis graft from bird in Fig. *12*.3a showing spermatogenesis.   (From the material of Greenwood and Blyth, 1930.)

Histology of the grafted testis

Berthold observed that testis grafts showed a normal histological appearance in parts and contained interstitial tissue and active spermatic tubules.   Later work has revealed the presence of unusual structures in many grafts (Caridroit, 1926), but it is nevertheless clear that intra-peritoneal or subcutaneous testis grafts in the domestic fowl can be histologically and endocrinologically normal. The presence of complete spermatogenesis in grafts agrees with the fact that spermatogenesis in fowl proceeds at full body temperature and can be maintained in the absence of excretory ducts (Fig. *12.* 3b).

Histology of the testis nodule

Small fragments of testis tissue which may remain after castration, and which often apparently arise from among the vasa efferentia, may hypertrophy and form nodules containing interstitial cells and spermatic and syncytial tubules in varying proportions. In some cases these nodules may exist for years without affecting the state of the capon, while others cause a rapid growth of the head furnishings and must therefore be endocrinologically active (Benoit, 1938 ; Benoit, Brard and Assenmacher, 1952). The histology of the nodules was described by Champy (1931a), who records the presence of rudimentary syncytial tubules similar to, but more plentiful than those in the grafted testis tissue. According to Champy, testicular fragments in the drake have remarkable powers of regeneration, and may become tumourous.

Growth of seminomata from testicular remains in capons has been reported by Champy and Lavedan (1938) and by Parkes (1938), who records that even a large seminoma is not necessarily masculinising. Regeneration of testicular tissue in capons from which the original testes were known to have been removed entire has been reported (Hooker and Cunningham, 1938).

Vasectomy

Experiments by Ancel and Bouin on vasectomy in mammals were closely followed by those of Shattock and Seligmann (1904) on the fowl. These authors ligated the vasa deferentia, but failed to obtain total degeneration of the germinal epithelium. Massaglia (1920) secured more positive results, but Nonidez (1924) concluded that vasectomy, as applied to fowl, is of no value in the analysis of the endocrine functions of the component parts of the testis because it does not cause the complete destruction of the germinal elements.

Unilateral castration

Compensatory hypertrophy of the remaining testes has been reported following unilateral castration of young chicks (Benoit, 1923) and even of adult birds (Domm and Juhn, 1927). It is uncertain whether these results indicate some significant difference between birds and mammals (*see* Volume III, Chapter 24).

Hybridisation

Abnormality of the testes has been described in several hybrid males. Thus Guyer (1912) found that the testes of hybrids between Guinea-fowl and domestic fowl showed degenerate seminiferous tubules and large amounts of interstitial tissue, as did those of hybrids between Guinea-fowl and pea-fowl (Poll, 1920). The effects of these testis modifications on plumage and sexual behaviour was uncertain, since the normal condition of the hybrids was difficult to establish.

Hybrids between closely related forms (e.g. geographical races) are of course generally normal sexually, but may exhibit certain traits different from those of their parents. Thus, Leopold (1944) compared the sexual cycles of free-living turkeys (*Meleagris silvestris*) with those of hybrids between *M. silvestris* and a domestic race. The hybrids came into sexual condition and bred earlier each year.

Irradiation

Benoit (1924) was able to effect complete destruction of the spermatogenetic tissue of the testes of Brown Leghorn cocks by exposure to X-rays. The testes were reduced in size but comb-growth was not impaired and Benoit concluded that the androgenic hormone was elaborated by the interstitial tissue or the Sertoli cells. Similar experiments, which gave like results, were carried out subsequently by Mirskaia and Crew (1931), Essenberg and Karrasch (1940) and others. It has been suggested that the collapse of the tubules caused by irradiation, like the seasonal post-nuptial collapse, is associated with an absolute as well as a relative increase in the amount of Leydig tissue.

Source of avian androgen

The experiments discussed above, in which damage to the seminiferous tubules did not impair the androgenic activity of the testis, indicate the interstitial tissue as the probable site of origin of the testicular androgens. A similar conclusion may be drawn from observations on normal birds.

At the height of sexual activity in many species there appear to be few Leydig cells in the interstitium. As a result, an inverse relationship between sexuality and interstitial activity has often been claimed (*see* Oslund, 1928). It must be remembered, however, that at the height of spermatogenesis, the Leydig cells are dispersed by tubule expansion and there are very few in any given section. Moreover, cytological observations show that, as secretion occurs, Leydig cells gradually lose their cholesterol-positive lipids and become non-lipoidal, vacuolated and fuchsinophilic before final disintegration (Fig. *12*. 4). Thus most have disappeared at the period when the effects or their secretion are most evident (Nonidez, 1924; Marshall, 1949, 1951b, 1955) and they become increasingly rare at the end of the sexual season. Other evidence that the lipid Leydig cells are androgenic was provided by Benoit (1922, 1929), Kumaran and Turner (1949a) and Taber (1949). Sluiter and van Oordt (1947) believe they have essentially a storage function. The lipid cells may impart in some birds a yellow hue to the entire organ but this disappears with seasonal gonad expansion (Serventy and Marshall, 1956).

Benoit (1922), concluding that the interstitial cells play an indispensable part in elaborating the testis hormone, suggested that they are the only endocrine elements of the testis. This is now open to doubt (p. 651), and there is some evidence that oestrogen may be secreted by the sudanophilic Sertoli cells of the testis of birds (Teilum, 1950) as it is thought to be in mammals. Further, Siller (1956) has described a distinctly feminised Brown Leghorn capon which was found to be suffering from Sertoli cell tumours that had developed on the site of the gonads (*see* p. 602). It will be remembered, too, that when Greenwood and Blyth (1938b) injected quantities of ground-up testis into a Brown Leghorn cock apparent feminisation effects resulted.

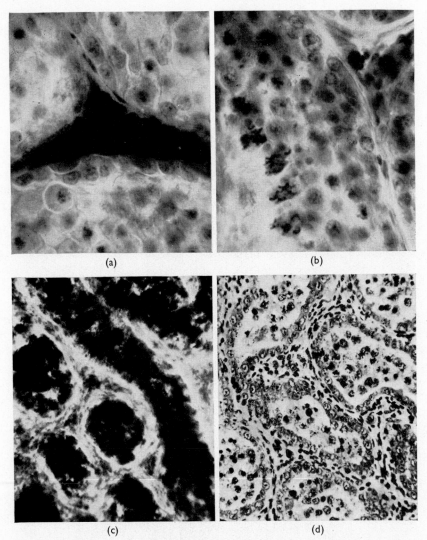

(a)   (b)

(c)   (d)

Fig. *12*. 4—(a) Adult Rook, aged about 11 months, showing typical wedge of heavily lipoidal Leydig cells at a time when the first mature spermatozoa appeared in adjacent tubules. (b) Adult Rook approaching height of spermatogenesis. The great expansion of the seminiferous tubules has dispersed the Leydig cells, which are losing their lipids and cholesterol. (c) Adult Rook testis in post-nuptial phase of tubule metamorphosis and interstitial regeneration, showing collapsed tubule full of cholesterol-positive lipids, and a group of juvenile, lipoidal, cholesterol-positive Leydig cells. (d) Adult Rook testis collapsed during regeneration period. = 400. Note necrotic sperm debris within tubules. (From Marshall, 1951b.)

Effects of Removing and Grafting the Ovary

Bilateral ovariectomy

Investigation of the effects of ovariectomy in birds presents many difficulties. A few species, notably birds-of-prey, normally have equal or unequal paired

(a)

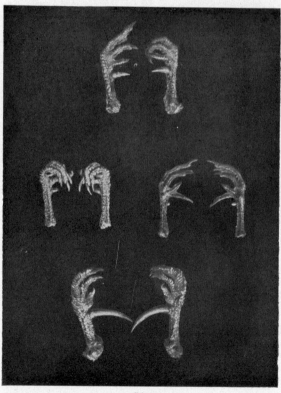

(b)

Fig. *12*. 5—(a) Ovariectomised Brown Leghorn hen. The bird shows male feathering and spurs, but the comb and other erectile structures are not hypertrophied. (From Goodale, 1916a.) (b) Successive stages in the growth of the spurs of a hen after ovarotomy: (left) six months after; (right) one year after; (bottom) two years after; (top) six years after (From Marshall, 1922.)

ovaries (Stanley, 1937; Stanley and Witschi, 1940), while a functional right ovary may occur in other species as an abnormality (*see* review by Riddle, 1925). Usually, however, only the left gonad is developed beyond an embryonic condition (p. 646) and this is a large diffuse body which can only be removed with certainty in the chick. Removal of the rudimentary right gonad presents even greater difficulty, and was not attempted by the early workers. Nevertheless, good descriptions were given of the agonadal hen by Pézard (1915) and Goodale (1916b) (Fig. *12*. 5a, b), presumably of sinistrally ovariectomised birds in which the right gonad had not yet regenerated (*see* below). Domm (1929b) later carried out a long series of operations which provided him with totally gonadectomised birds. He was then able to confirm that the completely agonadal hen is similar to the capon, having

Fig. *12*. 6—Poulard with male comb and male (asexual) plumage, indicating early stages of regeneration of right gonad. (From the material of Greenwood.)

the neutral or asexual type of plumage and atrophic head furnishings. Behaviour is neutral, spurs are present, and the oviduct and Wolffian ducts are rudimentary. A similar condition, with minor exceptions, is seen in cases of congenital agonadism in birds (Greenwood and Crew, 1927).

Sinistral ovariectomy of fowl

The long-term effects of removing only the ovary (sinistral ovariectomy) are very different. Goodale noted that where gonadal tissue was found at autopsy in such birds it was usually on the right side in the region of the right gonad. Pézard, Sand and Caridroit (1925) also reported a number of cases, though they seem to have considered the possibility of spermatic tissue arising from the remains of the ovarian medulla. The tendency in this early work was to emphasise the development of the male head furnishings and the essential masculinisation of the bird which followed sinistral ovariectomy and regeneration of the right gonad. Domm (1927), however, carried out very extensive experiments on the effects of removing the ovary, and described complex plumage conditions associated with the regeneration of the right gonad. His experiments showed that nearly all poulards eventually acquire hen feathering to a greater or less extent. In the early stages the poulard resembles the doubly gonadectomised hen in all respects. Sooner or later, however, the head furnishings begin to grow and ultimately attain a size equal to that in the normal male (Fig. 12. 6). At some stage, female plumage usually begins to appear, though it may be delayed for months or even years after the operation. Greenwood (*see* Punnett, 1937) possessed a sinistrally ovariectomised Brown Leghorn which retained display plumage for more than seven years.

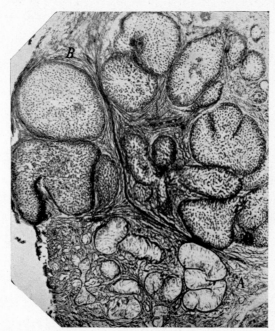

Fig. 12. 7—Section of regenerate right gonad, showing testis tubules. (From Domm, 1929d.)

Some controversy has occurred over the exact condition of the right regenerate gonad, especially concerning the extent to which testicular elements may be present. Goodale, who studied its histology, described the mass found on the right side as nephric tissue rather than as testis or ovary. Benoit (1923) reported two cases and Zawadowsky (1926, 1927) one case of complete spermatogenesis in the seminiferous tubules arising in the hypertrophied right gonad. Greenwood (1925) described one right gonad that was testicular in structure and another resembling an ovotestis. Lillie (1927) emphasised the fact that possibilities for the right gonad extend all the way from spermatogenesis to ovogenesis, and Caridroit (1928) that owing to the mixed state of the regenerate right gonad henny-feathering in the poulard does not imply lack of testicular activity. Domm (1929c, d) studied ninety testis-like right gonads and found spermatogenesis in seven of them, though in no case was the whole gonad composed of spermatogenic tubules (Fig. 12. 7). An attempt to effect artificial fertilisation in the normal hen with spermatozoa from the hypertrophied right gonad of the poulard was unsuccessful (Domm, 1930). However, this is of little significance for Munro (1938a, b) showed that even epididymial spermatozoa were relatively infertile compared with those from the lower vas when inseminated into hens. Further cases of the production of spermatozoa by the regenerate right gonad were recorded by Benoit (1932) and Padoa (1934). Miller (1938) studied the chromosome constitution of the spermatogenic cells and found that the sex chromosome (a V-shaped element, fifth in order of size) was paired in the spermatogonia in the normal testis, but single in those in the regenerated right gonad.

Spontaneous intersexuality

Spontaneous hypotrophy or pathological destruction of the left gonad leading to masculinisation of the hen has been reported by a number of workers, including Zawadowsky and Zubina (1929) and Berner (1925).   In the cases described by Crew (1923) and Arnsdorf (1947), two hens, reputedly a former mother and an egg-layer respectively, underwent changes that allowed them to sire offspring. Riddle (1924b), too, records a Ring Dove that had laid eggs and yet was found, after showing masculine behaviour, to contain testes.   The histological basis of such transformation was described by Fell (1923) and the state of the genitalia by Gatenby and Brambell (1924).

The crowing hen, famous in legend and superstition, arises under natural conditions when the functional left gonad undergoes hypotrophy and the potentially testicular tissue of the opposite organ responds to the endogenous gonadotrophins (pp. 663, 670) by secreting androgens which cause the development of the dependent male characters. Such a bird may continue to lay eggs if the ovary is not completely destroyed. At the next moult deficiency of ovarian hormone may allow the plumage to revert to the male (asexual) type.   Thus arises the so-called " laying cock " which is a genetic hen with changed plumage and characteristic male behaviour, but with sufficient ovarian function occasionally to produce an egg, the chalaza of which sometimes become twisted on the journey down the atrophic oviduct. Up to mediaeval times at least, such intersexual birds were regarded as portents of woeful

Fig. *12*. 8—" I have my wife and daughters to consider."   (From Parkes, 1957.)

events (Forbes, 1947) and there exist records of such birds (and particularly those that laid eggs) being executed with or without the benefit of a formal trial (Cole, 1927).   In modern times, the phenomenon has been regarded as vulgar rather than supernatural (Parkes, 1957) (Fig. *12*. 8).

Such intersexuality is of course of pathological origin, and not to be confused with the genetic condition illustrated by the male pigeons studied by Lahr and Riddle (1945) and Riddle, Hollander and Schooley (1945).   A pathological change from the female condition towards the male has also been recorded in the pheasant (Crew, 1931), in the Common Sandpiper (*Tringa hypoleucos*) and in the Golden Whistler (*Pachycephala pectoralis*) (Marshall, unpublished observations).   A pigeon described by Brambell and Marrian (1929) was in the course of a similar swing from female to male, but there were no signs of ovarian disease.

The rarer condition involving a swing from the genotypic male towards the female condition has been described in the " Magpie ", *Gymnorhina dorsalis*, by Marshall and Serventy (1956).   In this instance the plumage remained male but the peritoneal fat-deposits resembled those of a female.   The right testis appeared to be normal but the left organ was a flattened and irregularly shaped ovotestis. There was a remarkably intimate association of male and female elements of which the latter made up some three-fourths of the total volume.   The numerous oöcytes appeared to be normal, as did the interstitium of the male part with odd mitotic spermatogonia in adjacent tubules.   The female part of the ovotestis was abnormal in that it held vessels of an apparently sinusoidal nature containing erythrocytes and lymphocytes, some of which seemed to be extravasated (Fig. *12. 9*).

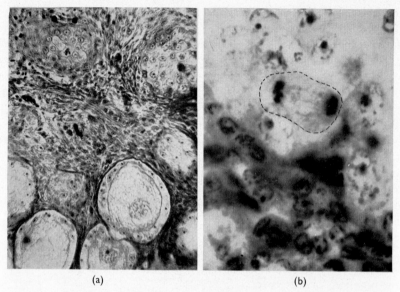

(a)   (b)

Fig. *12. 9*—(a) Portion of ovotestis of *Gymnorhina dorsalis* showing seminiferous tubules and ovarian follicles. (b) A spermatogonium in mitosis in the male portion of the ovotestis. (From Marshall and Serventy, 1956.)

Regeneration of a left testis-like gonad in fowl

In addition to the regeneration of the rudimentary right gonad in the sinistrally ovariectomised domestic hen, it is known that removal of the ovary, with or without removal of the right gonad, may result in the regeneration of a testis-like gonad on the left side.   Several of the earlier workers made observations indicative of such regeneration, but the matter was clarified by Domm (1931a), who examined a series of cases and demonstrated, by the removal of the right gonad, the equipotentiality of the hypertrophied right and left testis-like gonads in ovariectomised fowl (Fig. *12.10*).   Domm found that, in bilaterally gonadectomised hens in which a testis-like left gonad regenerated, there was hypertrophy of the Wolffian ducts, and appearance of masculine characters.   The development of a left ovotestis after complete ovariectomy in a fowl has been described by Benoit (1950).

Effects of ovariectomy in other birds

Some ducks ovariectomised by Goodale (1916a) acquired the brilliant male plumage seen in the normal drake, but it was not subject to seasonal variation; in others Goodale noted the occurrence of a male-female mosaic after ovariectomy.

It is not yet certain whether these results, which have been confirmed by Domm, are complicated by the regeneration of the right gonad in the duck.   Similar experiments carried out by Zawadowsky (1922) and Cavazza (1931, 1932) led to similar results.

A number of experiments have been carried out on the turkey.   Athias (1928a, b) did not at first observe changes in the female turkey's plumage after ovariectomy, though, according to van Oordt (1936), he did so later.   Padoa (1931) also observed no change.   The experiments of Scott and Payne (1934) and of van Oordt (1933) are conclusive and show that the hen assumes male plumage at the first moult after ovariectomy.   There seems to be some difference of opinion, reviewed by van Oordt (1936), as to whether ovariectomised turkey hens develop the " beard " and spurs seen in the normal male.   According to Scott and Payne (1934) the rudimentary right gonad does not develop in the sinistrally ovariecto-

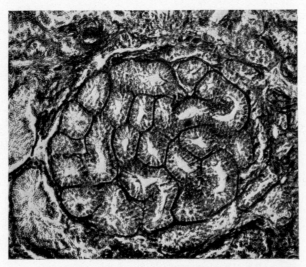

Fig. *12*. 10—Testis tubules in regenerate left ovary of sinistrally
ovariectomised hen.   (From the material of Greenwood.)

mised turkey hen as it commonly does in ovariectomised hens, an observation which makes it difficult to explain Athias' report (1931) that the head furnishing of the ovariectomised turkey may undergo development.

Zawadowsky (1922) performed ovariectomy on a pheasant and noted that male plumage was assumed.   Zawadowsky (1926) and Hachlow (1927) attempted ovariectomy in finches (*Pyrrhula* and *Fringilla*) but with doubtful success.   Duerden (1919) recorded that spaying of female ostriches was practised by farmers because it resulted in the female feathers being replaced by the valuable plumage of the male.   All these birds seem to be of the same type, in that removal of the gonads from the female results in the appearance of the display plumage which is the asexual or neutral type.

Witschi (1935a) revealed a new category of birds in which the opposite effect is found.   Working with the Orange and Red-billed Weaver Finches and Indigo Bunting, he observed that removal of the ovary failed to have any effect on the typical adult plumage of the hen, which was not therefore the result of repression of the display type by the ovary.   On the other hand, the nuptial change of the beak to orange in the Red-billed Weaver Finch was prevented by ovariectomy. He was also able to show that the brilliant plumage of the cock during the breeding season was quite independent of the male gonad and was apparently under the control of the pituitary gland (*see* p. 662).   These experiments, by extending gonadectomy studies to other types of bird, opened up a most interesting field and further exploration of this kind may be expected.   It is noteworthy that the plum- age conditions in the weaver finches are superficially identical with those existing in the mallard, the hen having the permanent dull plumage and the cock a brilliant plumage during the breeding season.   It is remarkable that the two apparently similar types of plumage differentiation should be under entirely different endocrine control.

Ovarian grafts

The feminising effect of ovarian grafts on castrated males can be shown well in birds.   The neutral plumage of the Brown Leghorn capon is converted to the typical female plumage by an ovarian transplantation, as shown by the successful experiments of Goodale (1918), Zawadowsky (1922, 1926) and Pézard, Sand and Caridroit (1923).   Goodale's most emphatic cases showed complete feminisation of plumage and head furnishings, and female behaviour including the care and protection of chicks.   The observations of Domm (1928) are concordant, but he found that capons so treated rarely retained their feminine condition indefinitely. In several instances it has been noticed that, following ovarian grafting, the head furnishings of the capon become male.   It is unlikely that this odd effect is always due to the regeneration of testicular tissue in the capon at the site of the first operation; it is highly probable that the effect is caused by the hypertrophy of medullary elements in the grafted ovary.   Greenwood (1925), Benoit (1926) and Caridroit (1926) all noted that tubules apparently of testicular nature may re- generate in portions of transplanted ovary.

General Observations

Castration and grafting in embryos

Lillie's studies (1917) on the mammalian free-martin aroused great interest in the role of sex hormones in sex differentiation, and experiments were soon started on the readily accessible bird embryo.   Thus, Minoura (1921) made chorioallan- toic grafts of embryonic ovaries into other embryos of either sex, and came to the conclusion that the growth and differentiation of the organs of the homologous sex were stimulated and of the heterologous sex inhibited by the gonad grafts.   Willier (1927), however, obtained no positive results from the transplantation of undif- ferentiated or differentiated gonads which he found did not modify the reproduc- tive system of the host and were not themselves modified by being in a host of a different sex.   Later workers (e.g. Bradley, 1941) obtained what they called a free- martin effect, and Wolff (1947) in extensive experiments found that the host, but not the donor, tissues were modified in the heterosexual graft combinations. Where an ovary was grafted to the left side of a male host, the left testis was con- verted to an ovary or ovotestis; where it was grafted to the right side, the right testis was inhibited.   The right testis was not affected from grafts on the left side.

Mintz and Wolff (1954) investigated the development of the ovarian medulla of embryonic chicks and its feminising effects after intracoelomic grafting into sexually indifferent hosts some two or three days old. The gonadal tissue was obtained from embryonic White Leghorns ranging from 8 to 13 days of incubation and implanted into recipients at very early stages. Autopsies were performed after 13 to 14 days' incubation and in no instance were female hosts found to have responded to the implants, an expected result in view of the female origin of the grafts and the fact that no grafts in female hosts showed any substantial redifferentiation in the male direction. On the other hand, male hosts were all feminised to some, often considerable, degree. The most striking effects appeared in the left male gonad, giving evidence of the capacity of embryonic implants to produce oestrogen.

The surgical difficulties of gonadectomy of the bird embryo were overcome by Dantschakoff (1933), who destroyed the gonads by generalised X-irradiation. Wolff and Wolff (1949, 1951a) improved on the technique by using directional irradiation and destroyed the gonads of embryonic chicks and ducks between the 3rd and 5th days of incubation, large doses from 3300 to 7000 r being used. They assessed the endocrinological results by reference to the syrinx and genital tubercle in ducks, and the development of the Müllerian duct in chicks, all of which characters show early sexual dimorphism. Definite castration effects could be produced by this method, though intersexual conditions might also occur (Wolff and Salzgeber, 1949). In the absence of the gonads the Müllerian ducts in the male embryo continue to develop (Wolff, 1949).

Lewis and Domm (1948) found that in ducks the syrinx shows sex dimorphism by the 13th day of incubation, being symmetrical and little developed in the female and large and highly asymmetrical in the male. Castration by irradiation was observed by Wolff and Wolff (1949) and Wolff (1950) to cause a male-type organ to develop in both sexes, showing that the male type is the asexual form and the female type dependent upon ovarian activity. The observation by Lewis and Domm that the injection of oestrogen between the 4th and 10th days of incubation suppressed the development of the organ in the male is in keeping with this deduction. It is evident, therefore, that the ovary of the embryonic duckling has produced effective quantities of oestrogen before the 13th day of incubation. The genital tubercle in ducks follows the same type of hormone response, the larger organ in the male being initially of the asexual type and susceptible to inhibition by oestrogen (Wolff and Wolff, 1947) and the rudimentary organ in the female being rudimentary because of ovarian activity (Wolff and Wolff, 1951b). After removal of the left gonad in female embryos, the right gonad secretes enough oestrogen to feminise the genital tubercle and syrinx of ducks (Wolff and Wolff, 1951b).

Relationship between the gonads and juvenile behaviour

In the present state of knowledge, it is impossible to say whether certain reactions are hormone induced or not. This applies particularly to the naturally occurring behaviour of young birds of various species, but many observations suggest that the effects of endogenous steroid hormones become manifest at a very early age. Hudson (1892) declared that nestling Oven-birds (*Furnarius rufus*) sometimes sing, an activity usually associated with androgen secretion. Again, a

21-day-old Ring Dove is reputed to have covered eggs (Craig, 1909). White (1941) and Williamson (1941) reported that Swallows (*Hirundo rustica*) of the first brood assist in the feeding of those of the second one. Bullough (1942) showed that juvenile Starlings had for a short period relatively large and active gonads after they left the nest at the age of about 3 weeks. Breneman (1945, 1950) stated that the domestic chick secretes considerable quantities of androgen before the age of 10 days and that there is a marked increase at about 30 days. Marshall and Coombs (1957) found cholesterol-positive lipid Leydig cells in the interstitium of nestling Rooks and, in nestling females, lipoidal atresias (p. 651). Glandular stromal cells were found to be common at the age of 3 months. On the other hand, Boss (1943) caused juvenile male Herring-gulls to assume adult plumage, bill colour and voice by androgen administration, but failed to produce similar effects with gonado-trophins, suggesting that in this species the testes are unresponsive until a certain maturity is attained. Kumaran and Turner (1949b) reported birefringent material (indicative of steroids) in the Leydig cells first at the relatively late age of 12 to 16 weeks at the period of initial comb-growth.

It is of much interest that imprinting (Lorenz, 1935, 1937), as distinct from associative learning, is confined in some species to a very definite and early period of life which is often extremely short. Such imprinting is irreversible once it has been established and involves the learning of species, rather than individual, characteristics (Hinde, Thorpe and Vince, 1956). Experiments are needed to determine whether imprinting is related to endocrine secretion.

Little information is available as to whether hormones concerned with behaviour act directly on central or peripheral neural elements. Further, certain reactions that might be attributed to hormonal influences are possibly a reflex behavioural reaction to a situation stimulus (*see* Tinbergen, 1951).

Endocrine basis of henny-feathering

The experiments described above show that in the normal Leghorn female the plumage type is determined by ovarian activity. The results of transplantation of ovarian tissue into the capon, and of testicular tissue into the completely ovariec-tomised poulard, further show that the sensitivity of the plumage in the two sexes is qualitatively the same towards either gonad. It is uncertain whether the sensi-tivity of the plumage to feminisation is quantitatively the same in the capon as in the agonadal poulard.

It has already been said that castration of the henny-feathered Sebright cock results in the appearance, at the next moult, of typical display-plumage. Removal of the gonad of the Sebright hen has the same effect. It was already known to Darwin (1868) that atrophy of the ovary of the Sebright hen would result in the appearance of male feathering, and Pézard and Caridroit (1927) and Eliot (1928) showed that the Sebright hen developed cock feathering after sinistral ovari-ectomy. It was evident, therefore, that the testis had the same effect as the ovary on the plumage of the Sebright. Nevertheless, the testes of the Sebright and of other henny-feathered breeds are the same, endocrinologically, as those of any other bird, because Roxas (1926) and Greenwood (1928) found that cross-grafting of the testis between henny-feathered and normal males does not result in change of plumage types. Roxas cross-grafted between Sebright and Leghorn, and Green-wood between Leghorn and Campine. It is clear therefore that the peculiarity of Sebrights and Campines lies in the plumage, not in the testes, and takes the form of abnormal sensitivity of the plumage to the small amount of oestrogen produced by the testis, or to the slight gynaecogenic action of testosterone (Callow and Parkes, 1936; Deanesly and Parkes, 1937b; Greenwood and Blyth, 1938b). This conclusion was beautifully confirmed by Danforth (1930), who carried out skin transplantations between a Campine cock and a White Leghorn cock. The henny plumage remained henny in the " display " environment, and the display plumage remained " display " in the henny environment. On the other hand, the plumage on skin transplants into the opposite sex of the same breed took on the character of the host. These results show that a different plumage sensitivity exists in the henny breed, but it is uncertain whether the difference is qualitative or quantitative; experiments on the injection of hormones (p. 616) suggest the former.

Gonadectomy of hybrids

Caridroit (1938b) called attention to the curious results which may be obtained by the gonadectomy of certain interbreed crosses in fowl. Thus if a silver Sebright hen is crossed with a golden Sebright cock the first generation consists of silver cocks and golden hens. Ovariectomy of the hybrids does not alter the plumage colour. By contrast, castration of the silver male hybrid produces a white and golden bird which can be transformed to the condition of the silver hen by the administration of ovarian hormone. As another example, Caridroit quotes the cross between the golden Ardenne hen and silver Ardenne cock, which gives golden cocks and black hens. Gonadectomy results in golden capons and silver poulards. Feminisation of the capon produces black plumage as seen in the female hybrid. A detailed genetic study of the relation of ovarian hormones to racial plumage types was made by Régnier (1937).

Plumage gynandromorphism

The term gynandromorphism might well be applied to any mixture of male and female characters in the same individual, but among vertebrates the term is usually used in a more restricted sense and only mixtures of plumage characters will be considered here.

Plumage gynandromorphism may be of various types: (a) Individual feathers may show male and female characters simultaneously. In this case the line of division may be longitudinal, median, or transverse. (b) Typical male and female feathers may both occur in the same feather tract. (c) One tract may contain only female feathers and another only male. (d) A bird may be completely female on one side and completely male on the other. The fact that female plumage types in fowl are determined by endocrine influences implies that feathers in all parts of the body develop under identical stimulation, and abnormalities such as those listed above must be reconciled with this conception. Where the two sides of a single feather are different it is possible that they had different sensitivities to the circulating gynaecogen, perhaps connected with differential growth rates (Lillie, 1931). Where the line of transformation is transverse it is likely that the threshold requirements of the feathers, or else the available supply of hormone, changed during the course of growth. Both of these causative factors, asymmetrical sensitivity of a feather or change in hormone content of the body, can easily be imagined as occurring in nature.   Similarly, it is easy to explain the occurrence of separate tracts of male or female feathers at the same time in the same bird, because it is known that different tracts have different hormone threshold requirements. The occurrence of mixtures of male and female feathers in the same tract, and particularly of lateral gynandromorphism, is much more difficult to explain.   Pézard, Sand and Caridroit (1926a, b) showed that it is easily possible to produce lateral plumage gynandromorphism experimentally by depluming a cock or capon unilaterally and grafting an ovary so that the new feathers regenerating on the deplumed side become female in pattern.   Such an experiment, however, for obvious reasons throws little light upon the origin of natural lateral gynandromorphism. Crew and Munro (1938) concluded that the condition always results from an aberrant chromosome distribution, which may or may not require hormone action for its expression.

The classic cases of lateral gynandromorphism described in a Chaffinch (*Fringilla coelebs*) by Weber (1890) and in a Ring-necked Pheasant (*Phasianus torquatus*) by Bond (1913) showed a more fundamental derangement because of the presence of a testis and an ovary in the former and of an ovo-testis in the latter. Also, in the chaffinch the female plumage and the female gonad occurred on the same side. If, as seems likely, the male and female feathers grew under identical endocrine stimulation, the cause of the gynandromorphism must have been a different sensitivity of the plumage on the two sides to hormone stimulation.   The association in the chaffinch of female plumage with female gonad, and *vice versa*, could suggest that the oestrogen sensitivity of the plumage normally associated with the ovary in the hen is greater than that of the plumage normally associated with the testis in the cock (*see also* p. 612).

Support for the genetic interpretation of plumage gynandromorphism is found in the fact that body size and skeletal structure have sometimes been observed to be different on the two sides (Witschi, 1960).   It seems probable that gynandromorphs have on one side a male and on the other a female chromosome constitution.   For a consideration of the genetics of gynandromorphism, Hollander (1949) and Witschi (1960) should be consulted.

IV. Biological Action of Androgens
General Characters

Certain general characters of birds are affected by castration (*see* p. 585), but there is little sound evidence of the modification of such characters by exogenous male hormones.   The administration of androgen has been claimed to increase growth in fowls and turkeys, but the data are conflicting (*see* Wilkins and Fleischmann, 1946; Turner, 1948; Fraps, Olsen and Marsden, 1951).   In capons, the injection of testosterone increases the erythrocyte count in females and capons (Domm, Taber and Davis, 1943) so that the higher count in the cock (Table II) is presumably a positive male characteristic.

Sexual Characters of Capons

The effects of androgens on the secondary sexual characters of birds are, of course, profound but different sexual characters may have very different androgen thresholds.   Thus, in a Pheasant capon implanted with 50 mg. testosterone the facial wattles enlarged and reddened long before the animal crowed (Collias, 1950), and it has been shown that a greater amount of testosterone is required to stimulate treading than crowing (Roussel, 1936 ; Davis and Domm, 1943).

Head furnishings

Pézard (1911) injected a capon twice weekly for some months with extracts of cryptorchid pig testis, believed, because of the high proportion of Leydig cells, to be especially rich in male hormone.   The bird showed some enlargement and reddening of the comb, as compared with a control capon, and signs of male behaviour.   The results of this enterprising and far-sighted experiment can hardly be regarded as conclusive, and 17 years elapsed before the Chicago workers produced massive enlargement of the comb of an injected capon to give the first

(a)   (b)

Fig. *12*. 11—Restoration of comb of Brown Leghorn capon by administration of androsterone.   (a) Before treatment; (b) Same bird after
22 daily doses of androsterone.   (From Callow and Parkes, 1935.)

unequivocal demonstration of the presence of androgenic activity in extracts of testis.   Much of the later work suggested that the comb and wattles of the capon could be induced to grow by all extracts or crystalline substances which could be shown, by any test, to have the property of stimulating male characters, but exceptions to this rule were implied by the work of Discherl, Kraus and Voss (1936) and by that on progesterone discussed in Volume III.   For assay work a rather small degree of growth is usually preferred (*see* p. 626), though even in the early work a number of observations of complete, or almost complete, restoration were made (McGee, Juhn and Domm, 1928 ; Moore, Gallagher and Koch, 1929).   Koch (1932), for instance, showed an illustration of a capon in which prolonged administration of testis extract had produced a comb of almost full size.   Freud, Laqueur and Pompen (1932) and Schoeller and Gehrke (1931) also recorded complete restoration of the capon's head furnishings by the prolonged injection of androgenic extracts.   When crystalline androgens became available, Callow and

Parkes (1935) found that daily administration of 2·5 mg. rising to 5·0 mg. of androsterone into the pectoral muscle of a Leghorn capon produced a comb which was almost normal in size after 3 weeks, and indistinguishable from the comb of a normal cock after 5 weeks (Fig. *12*. 11).   Tablets of testosterone propionate, averaging 11 mg. in weight, were found by Emmens (1938) to cause a very rapid and extensive growth of the combs of Leghorn capons, all of which, within 5 weeks of implantation, became indistinguishable from those of normal cocks.   The wattles and ear-lobes are restored about as easily as the comb.   The normality of the histological response of the comb to testosterone and androsterone was shown by Dessau (1935).   Genetic differences exist in sensitivity of the comb to androgen.   Callow and Parkes (1935), for instance, found that the comb of the Rhode Island Red capon was much less sensitive than that of the Brown Leghorn.

Plumage

In most breeds of fowl the colour and structure of the plumage is unaltered by castration (p. 593), so that the injection of androgenic substances would not be expected to have any striking effect.   In practice, androgenic substances seem to

Fig. *12*. 12—Effect of oestrone and androgens on the saddle hackles of the Sebright Bantam capon.   (a) Normal capon saddle hackle.   (b), (c), (d), (e) Saddle hackles regenerating during the injection of (b) 5 μg. oestrone daily, (c) 5 mg. androsterone daily, (d) 1 mg. dehydroepiandrosterone daily, and (e) 1 mg. testosterone daily.   (b), (d) and (e) are indistinguishable from the saddle hackles found in the normal Sebright cock.   (From Deanesly and Parkes, 1937b.)

impede only two minor post-castration changes, i.e. the tendency for the feathers to grow to extreme length and the capacity of the bird to regenerate abundant feathers at any time.   Otherwise, the only changes produced ordinarily in cock-feathered breeds are similar to those caused by slight temporary depression of thyroid activity and may be due to this cause (Emmens and Parkes, 1940a). Massive dosage of testosterone has, however, been reported to bring about some feminisation of the plumage of the Golden Pheasant capon (Champy, 1936).

Obvious and direct feminisation is produced by androgens in the plumage of capons of breeds such as Sebright bantam, in which the cock is normally henny-feathered and in which typical male feathering is acquired only after castration. Several of the androgens—for instance, testosterone, dehydroepiandosterone, and epiandrostenediol—have the power to cause the plumage of the Sebright capon to revert to the female pattern seen in the normal male (Fig. *12*. 12) (Deanesly and Parkes, 1937b). Testosterone has the same effect in feminising the plumage of capons of other breeds, such as some varieties of Campine and Old English game-cock, in which the cock is normally henny-feathered. It must be supposed, there-fore, that the plumage in the henny-feathered cocks has an especial sensitivity to androgens which is not found in the normal breeds, and it may be that the positive results obtained by Gallagher, Domm and Koch (1933) with testis extracts injected into Sebright capons were due to the androgen content of the extracts rather than to any residual oestrogenic activity. Thus, there is an alternative explanation to the suggestion of Callow and Parkes (1936) that the peculiarity of the plumage of henny-feathered cocks is due to a greater sensitivity to oestrogens, and a conse-quent power to respond to the slight oestrogenic activity which may be exerted by the testis. It is difficult to know how far this conclusion may throw light on conditions in other species, but it seems doubtful whether the onset of eclipse plumage in ducks is due to any activity of known androgens since testosterone is quite unable to affect the feathers of the drake capon in that direction (Chu, 1940).

Beak colour

The mechanisms controlling beak colour have been studied in detail by Witschi and his associates. Beak pigments are essentially of two types, brown and black melanins (produced by melanophores) and yellowish or red carotenoids which are apparently obtained from the food and stored in liver and yolk (Kritzler, 1943). Melanins are taken up by epidermal cells that migrate outwards to become part of the beak sheath (Witschi and Woods, 1936). In Weaver Finches (*Pyrolmelana*) (Witschi, 1935a) androgen injection re-establishes the beak pigmentation depleted by castration. In the House Sparrow Keck (1934) and Witschi (1936) found that administration of androgenic extracts to the anoestrous or castrated male bird caused the assumption of the typical black male colour within 10 days. The amounts of androgen required to give this response are about the same as are required by intramuscular injection to cause obvious growth of the capon comb.

The mechanisms by which carotenoids are selectively taken up by some struc-tures (e.g. beaks, legs) and not others is not fully understood. In both sexes of the common Starling the beak changes from black during the eclipse season to bright yellow during the breeding season. Experimentally this change can be brought about by androgens (Witschi and Miller, 1938). Witschi (1945) says that the change of bill colour from black to yellow in the common Starling is one of the most delicate indicators for androgens : it " heralds the start of the breeding season at a time when testicular changes are barely observable under the microscope and the deferent ducts still remain in the eclipse condition." The colour reaction occurs about 2 weeks earlier in the males than in the females. The beaks of the gulls *Larus ridibundus* (van Oordt and Junge, 1933) and *L. argentatus* (Boss, 1943) behave similarly at puberty and, subsequently, seasonally.

x*

Behaviour

Crowing and sexual behaviour can be induced in capons by the administration of androgenic extracts of testis or urine, or of crystalline androgenic substances. Pézard (1911) observed the reappearance of apparently normal combat and mating behaviour in capons after the intraperitoneal injection of an extract of cryptorchid boar's testis. McGee, Juhn and Domm (1928) recorded that testis extracts induced lusty crowing and aggressive behaviour in capons. Callow and Parkes (1935) found that ten daily injections of 5 mg. of androsterone induced vigorous sexual behaviour in a previously inert capon. Roussel (1936) observed a gradient of sensitivity in the reinstatement of sexual behaviour; on a constant daily dose of 1 mg. of testosterone acetate crowing occurred after 16 days, while pugnacity and sexual behaviour developed only after about 40 days, when the comb was almost back to normal size. Noble and Wurm (1940a) found that administration of testosterone propionate led to the re-establishment of breeding calls and other sexual behaviour in the gull *Larus atricilla*, and Boss (1943) obtained similar results with *L. argentatus*.

Accessory organs

There are few accessory reproductive organs in the birds used for experimental work, except the vasa deferentia and the penis of the drake. The latter is not very sensitive to castration (p. 598), though in the adult drake capon it responds to some extent to injected androgens (Witschi, 1960). Callow and Parkes (1935) found that heavy dosage with androsterone caused a considerable increase in size and in epithelial development of the vas deferens in a Leghorn capon (Fig. *12*. 13),

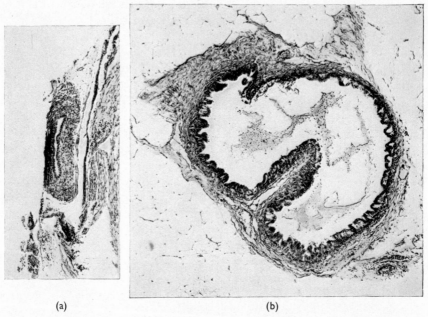

(a)   (b)

Fig. *12*. 13—Effect of androsterone on the atrophic vas deferens of the capon. (a) Vas deferens of untreated capon. (b) Vas deferens of capon receiving 22 daily injections of 5 mg. of androsterone, showing restoration of epithelium and partial restoration of size. (From Callow and Parkes, 1935.)

and Dessau and Freud (1936) obtained a like result with testosterone, but considered that other substances were necessary for the full functional activity of the duct.

Effect on Embryos

The first successful experiments on bird embryos were carried out by injection of hormones into eggs during incubation (Wolff, 1935a, b). Wolff and Wolff (1936, 1937) injected androsterone into fowls' eggs before the 10th day of incubation and found that increasing the dosage decreased the number of normal chicks hatched. With a dose of 1 mg. of androsterone, only a few males and a large proportion of intersexes were produced. The condition of the intersexes showed that

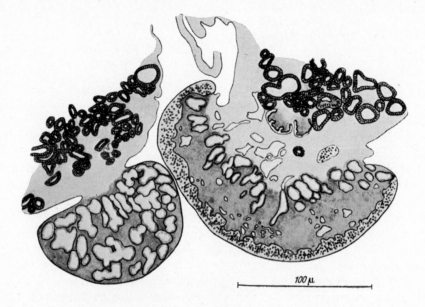

100 μ

Fig. *12*. 14—Diagramatic section through gonads of a male chick embryo, treated with dehydroandrosterone: (left) a normal testis; (right) an ovotestis, with mesonephros above each. In the ovotestis, the ovarian tissue is contained in the well developed cortical area. (From van Oordt and Rinkel, 1940.)

some of them were derived from genetic males. Androsterone exerts both an androgenic and gynaecogenic action on the male embryo (Wolff, 1936c). The left testis develops an ovarian cortex, and ultimately becomes an ovotestis. There is a general hypertrophy of the right testis. Oviducts are formed from the proximal segments of the ovarian ducts. In Leghorn chicks a greater amount of hormone was required to affect genetic males than genetic females. When chicks of a cross between Light Sussex and Rhode Island Red were used the reverse seemed to be true. Methyldihydrotestosterone had the same general effect as androsterone, Wolff (1938a), and so had dehydroandrosterone (van Oordt and Rinkel, 1940) (Fig. *12*. 14). The effects of testosterone are different in being largely androgenic. Thus, the gonads of the male embryos are little affected by testosterone, while the left gonad of the female becomes intersexual by the inhibition of cortical development and the stimulation of the medulla (Dantchakoff, 1938). Dantchakoff

(1937a, d) emphasises that the mesonephric elements and the Wolffian ducts undergo great hypertrophy in embryos of both sexes under the influence of testosterone propionate, while the comb is found to be considerably developed at the time of hatching (Dantchakoff and Kinderis, 1937a) and there may be premature attempts to crow within a few days of hatching (Dantchakoff, 1937b). Domm (1955) reviewing the effects of androgens administered during early embryonic development calls attention to the extent to which different substances produce different results.

Herring-gull embryos, too, were found by Boss and Witschi (1941, 1942) to react to injected testosterone propionate. Chicks from treated eggs assumed adult plumage when between 27 and 90 days old and the adult voice at an age of 45 days instead of, as normally, in the third year of life. For the effects of androgens on the embryonic reproductive system of ducks, *see* Lewis (1946).

Effects on Chicks

Rapid development of the comb and wattles of newly hatched cockerels can be caused by administration of androgenic extracts (Juhn, Gustavson and Gallagher 1932) or by injection or inunction of crystalline androgens. The quantitative side of the comb reaction is considered on p. 627, but it may be noted here that, as early as 1930, Juhn and Gustavson, and later Juhn, Gustavson and Gallagher (1932), showed that the comb of the female chick responds as well as that of the male to injections of androgenic extracts. Breneman (1937) injected androstanediol benzoate and testosterone into White Leghorn chicks, and found that the administration of 0·1 mg. daily of either substance into 5- or 10-day-old chicks caused an immediate cessation of testicular growth, which, however, lasted only during the period of injection. Indeed, at a month old the testes of chicks which had been temporarily retarded were appreciably heavier than those of normals. This effect of androgens could be prevented by the simultaneous injection of gonadotrophic pituitary extracts, and was presumably due to depression of the gonadotrophic activity of the pituitary gland. There was, of course, very considerable comb growth in Breneman's birds.

Other experiments (Breneman, 1938) showed that extensive growth of the comb continued for several weeks after the end of injections, a phenomenon which the author considered to be due to stimulation of the secretion of endogenous androgens rather than to slow absorption of the injected hormone. His conclusion was based on the fact that continued growth did not occur in injected capon chicks. Many others (e.g. Noble and Zitrin, 1942 ; Heistand and Stullken, 1943) have obtained precocious comb-growth by means of androgen administration, and Hamilton and Golden (1939) made interesting observations on the different responses in comb-growth and behaviour in male and female chicks. Implanted androgen pellets elicited comb-growth, together with crowing, within a few days. Crowing stopped in all birds after from 1 to 9 weeks, whereas the combs continued to develop. Juvenile male Herring Gulls (*Larus argentatus*) were similarly caused prematurely to assume adult plumage, bill-colour and mature vocalisation, but after cessation of treatment the birds reverted to the juvenile condition (Boss, 1943).

With somewhat older birds, Morató-Manaro, Albrieux and Buño (1938) found that inunction of androsterone doubled the area of the comb of a 3-month-old cockerel.   Some 12·5 mg. was applied and a considerable amount of the hormone must have been absorbed into the general circulation because inhibition of gonado-trophin output was indicated by atrophy of the testes and cessation of spermato-genesis.   The tubules had only a few rows of cells and their lumina were filled with debris.

Analogous results on the female were described by Herrick and Lockhart (1940), who found a decrease in ovarian weight in androgenised pullets.   Experi-ments on young drakes were carried out by Bulliard and Ravina (1938), who injected 10 mg. of testosterone propionate thrice weekly into 2-month-old birds. At the end of 3 weeks the penis attained adult proportions but the testes were abnormally small.   Plumage was not affected except that growth and keratinisation were accelerated.

Precocious sexual behaviour has also been produced in chicks by androgen administration.   Thus, Noble and Zitrin (1942) observed crowing at 4 days and treading behaviour at 15 days when testosterone propionate was injected from the time of hatching.   Pugnacity and crowing in 10-day-old chicks, together with inhibition of body growth, have also been recorded after injections of testosterone propionate (see Hamilton, 1938 ;   Breneman, 1939).   Month-old Black-crowned Herons developed gutteral adult voices, territory consciousness, and nest-building, copulatory and broody behaviour after treatment with testosterone propionate (Noble and Wurm, 1938, 1940b).   It must be remembered, however, that the young of many species sometimes naturally exhibit sexual behaviour at a very early age (see p. 611).

Effect on Intact Adults

Gonad and sexual characters of the male

The production of excessive growth in the comb of the adult cock, either by androgenic extracts or crystalline androgens, may be difficult or impossible, even by direct injection into the comb (Greenwood and Blyth, 1935).   Implantation of a 6 mg. tablet of testosterone propionate, however, was found by Parkes and Emmens (1944) to stimulate considerable comb-growth in an adult Black Rock cock, and there seems no doubt that under certain circumstances the normal genetic limit of the breed can be exceeded by the administration of exogenous hormone.

Leopold (1944) showed that the seasonal development of wattles in the male Wild Turkey (Meleagris) is under the control of testicular androgens.   Facial tuber-cles and breeding plumage in the male Ruff (Philomachus pugnax) respond to androgen treatment (van Oordt and Junge, 1936).   Salomonsen (1939) likewise demonstrated that the seasonal development of facial " roses " in the Rock Ptar-migan (Lagopus mutus) and the prominent " eyebrows " of the Hungarian Partridge (Pardix perdix) and Prairie Chicken (Tympanunchus cupido) are controlled by testi-cular hormones.   The sexual accessory organs (paired rete testes, vasa efferentia, epididymides, deferent ducts and seminal vesicles) of fringillid finches respond only to androgenic substances (Bailey, 1953).   Testosterone stimulates enlargement of the oviduct in female Starlings as well as of the male ducts, (Witschi and Fugo, 1940).

Androgen administration leads to decrease of testis-size and depression of spermatogenesis, caused apparently by reduction of adenohypophysial activity

(Kumaran and Turner, 1949b ; Nalbandov and Baum, 1948).   Again, Breneman (1951) found that androgen injected into the capon inhibited the enlargement of the hypophysis which usually follows castration and at the same time suppressed basophilia, the anterior lobe becoming composed mainly of chromophobes (*see* p. 670).   On the other hand, Burger (1949) reported that exogenous testosterone neither depressed the active testes in the Starling, nor blocked the effects of photo-stimulation.

Beach (1942) recorded the interesting observation that testosterone propionate revived courtship and mating behaviour in male pigeons which had lost such behaviour after brain injury and induced intense behaviour of this kind in an intact, though sexually inactive, Canada Goose (*Branta canadensis*).

Androgen and oestrogen tend to inhibit post-nuptial moulting which is claimed to be associated closely with cyclical activity of the thyroid (*see* Collias, 1950).

Effects on the adult female

Androgenicity of the normal ovary.   The ovary is androgenic but the precise site of androgen production has not been established.   Domm (1929b, 1933), Uotila (1939), Pfeiffer and Kirschbaum (1943), Taber (1948, 1951) and others have demonstrated the presence of apparently secretory cells in the ovarian medulla, possibly homologous with male Leydig cells and productive of ovarian androgens. Marshall and Coombs (1957) further distinguished two kinds of such stromal cells in the ovary of the Rook (*Corvus frugilegus*), the ex-follicular cell arising from atretic follicles, and a true female interstitial cell developing from stromal connective tissue cells like the androgenic Leydig cell in the male.   Each type appears in considerable numbers during the spring and autumn periods of sexual excitement (*see* below).   In this connection it is relevant that the pullet's comb increases in size, vascularity and turgidity before laying starts, and that Taber (1951) reported that the withdrawal of exogenous gonadotrophic stimulation resulted in comb regression (indicating decreased androgen production) and the " reappearance of foamy, lipoid-filled interstitial cells in the testes and in the medulla of the ovaries."

Breneman (1951), reviewing the evidence that a large portion of the ovary secretes androgen, as well as oestrogen, suggested that a high level of these steroids does not inhibit the production of pituitary gonadotrophin.   Low doses of oestradiol and testosterone may stimulate ovarian growth in hens and augment the action of PMS.   This author further describes work suggesting that testosterone propionate increases pituitary secretion of FSH and thence follicle growth and that the ovarian steroids have various influences on the organ producing them. Certainly, in wild birds both types of the stromal gland cells, mentioned above, become increasingly prolific and active as sexual activity heightens (Marshall and Coombs, 1957).

Comb.   Champy (1931b) implied that he was able to produce growth in the comb of the female fowl by the injection of testis extracts at any time except during the laying season.   Callow and Parkes (1935), by the injection of androsterone caused substantial growth in the comb of a Brown Leghorn hen and a Rhode Island Red hen, both of which were then laying, but the increase in size was much less than that seen in the capon's comb on the same dosage.   Greenwood and Blyth (1935) confirmed these experiments and obtained an increase in comb size in birds in full lay.   Egg production, which averaged 10–13 eggs per fortnight, was not significantly affected.   A striking effect of testosterone propionate on the growth of the pullet comb was noted by Bolton (1953), and further emphasised by Breneman (1955), who showed that 100 mg. daily " produced combs comparable with those in 40-day-old cockerels which received 50 mg. TP daily for 30 days." By contrast, Brard and Benoit (1957) reported that the daily injection of 0·2 mg. of testosterone plus 0·2 mg. of oestradiol benzoate produced pullet-type combs in cockerels and capons.

Behaviour.   Manifestations of masculine behaviour occur in many female birds at certain times and this behaviour is probably an effect of endogenous androgens (Collias, 1943; Davis and Domm, 1943).   In the sedentary British Robin the females establish autumn territories which are relinquished in December and January when pairing occurs (Lack, 1939) and when the sexual organs of both sexes begin their spring modification (Marshall, 1952c).   Likewise the female of the migratory continental Robin establishes territory and becomes aggressive after arriving in southern Italy in the autumn (Alexander, 1917).   Further, the females of many passerine species sing like males during the autumn.   Bullough and Carrick (1940) state that some female starlings sing in the autumn, and that the female beak turns yellow—a sex character of the male (Witschi and Miller, 1938). Spasmodic male responses in untreated wild females are of common occurrence. Thus the Crested Grebe (*Colymbus cristatus*), Water-hen (*Gallinula chloropus*) (Selous, 1901), Tern (*Sterna hirundo*) (Tinbergen, 1931), Adelé Penguin (*Pygoscelis adeliae*) in which the courtship rôles appear to be interchangeable early in the season (Roberts, 1940) and the Rook (Marshall and Coombs, 1957) all show occasional deviation from female to male behaviour.

Androgen administration will produce emphatic masculine behaviour in female birds.   Domestic hens injected with testosterone propionate by Allee, Collias and Lutherman (1939) developed courtship display and lost it at the end of treatment. Domm, Davis and Blivaiss (1942) describe circling, waltzing and crowing, but not treading, in young domestic hens stimulated by testosterone, and Zitrin (1942) also recorded waltzing, crowing and treading behaviour in a testosterone-implanted hen, the effect lasting several months, after which fertile eggs were laid.

Domm and Blivaiss (1943) in further experiments implanted testosterone propionate pellets into domestic hens and observed crowing, walking, circling and " masculine copulation " with other hens.   Nevertheless, the treated hens sometimes adopted the female stance, received cocks and in one instance laid an egg. Similar striking results were obtained by the implantation of pellets of androgen by Domm and Blivaiss (1947).   Davis and Domm (1941) caused crowing and waltzing, but not treading, in bilaterally ovariectomised hens.   Zitrin (1942) and Davis and Domm (1943), however, obtained a full male response.   Beach (1948) concludes that the most reasonable explanation is that the hen possesses neuromuscular mechanisms capable of mediating all of the courtship and mating responses of the cock and that, in the female, as in the male, the reactivity of such mechanisms is increased by androgen, and finally " that the masculine mechanisms in the genetic female are extremely refractory and difficult to activate even under the most optimistic conditions."   Among non-galliforme species, female Ring-Doves exhibited courtship and copulation behaviour after treatment with testosterone propionate (Bennett, 1940) and adult female Herons (*Nycticorax nycticorax*) responded to testosterone propionate injection with masculine behaviour (Noble and Wurm, 1940b). Again, when Emlen and Lorenz (1942) implanted crystalline androgen into free-living female Valley Quail (*Lophortyx californica*) there was a tendency for them to adopt a masculine rôle in courtship.

Typical male song has also been stimulated by androgens. Thus Leonard (1939), Shoemaker (1939a, b) and Voss (1940) each induced male song in female Canaries (*Serinus canarius*) by injections of androgens, and Shoemaker in addition noted the induction of other male traits in courtship behaviour and peck dominance over untreated females, and a change to male-type in the cloacal region. Four of five female Canaries given from two to four injections of 5 mg. testosterone propionate by Leonard sang like males, and Baldwin, Goldin and Metfessel (1940) produced " masculine " song in isolated female Canaries by androgen treatment. Androgen administration inhibited nest-building and other characteristic sexual behaviour in female Canaries which began to sing and court like males, but did not attempt copulation.

Accessory organs. Bailey (1953) found that rudimentary male structures (deferent duct, seminal vesicle) of female fringillid finches hypertrophy during the breeding season. Experimentally these responded only to androgenic substances.

Witschi and Fugo (1940) state that the oviduct of the Common Starling responds to both male and female sex hormones, and that in the spring the two " co-operate in the stimulation of the oviduct." It will be recalled that the male sex hormone causes the beak of the female to become yellow during the same period (p. 617). Brandt and Nalbandov (1956) say that, when injected alone, androgen (like oestrogen and progesterone) leads to increased oviducal weight. However, neither androgen nor progesterone alone causes proliferation of the oviducal albumen-secreting glands whereas oestrogen does so. Combinations of oestrogen with androgen or progesterone are required to make such glands secrete and discharge.

The peck order

Birds in confinement or otherwise associating together soon establish a social hierarchy or peck order. Among half a dozen domestic fowl in a pen there will be No. 1 bird, which pecks all the others and is not itself pecked, No. 2 bird, which is pecked by No. 1 bird, but itself pecks the other four, and so on, down to No. 6 bird, which is pecked by all the other birds and itself does not peck any bird. A dominant position in the hierarchy has high selective value; for example some domestic cocks may fertilise many more eggs than others in the same pen (Guhl and Warren, 1956). Socially dominant blue Satin Bower-birds enjoy a similar advantage over younger green males even though the latter sometimes achieve full spermatogenesis. Species differences in the social hierarchy are remarkable. Thus, in the Silver Pheasant (*Gennaeus mycthemerus*) and the Turkey (*Meleagris gallopavo*) the male is dominant, while in other species the opposite is the case. Allee (1936) and Masure and Allee (1934) reported that the male Budgerygah (*Melopsittacus undulatus*) is dominant during the breeding season but that the rôles become reversed at other times. Shoemaker (1939a) found that during the nonsexual season there was little suggestion of a peck order but that during the reproductive period the female Budgerygah became distinctly dominant. He was unable to improve the status of ovariectomised or non-breeding females by injections of oestrogen.

Androgens, by contrast, have a notable effect on the peck-order, and relevant studies have been made on the intact adults of several species. Bennett's results (1940) suggest that in the Ring Dove (*Streptopelia decaocto*) testosterone propionate injections caused low-ranking males and females to advance in social status with increased vigour and aggression. In agreement with Bennett's findings, Allee, Collias and Lutherman (1939) showed that testosterone propionate tended to elevate the social status of domestic hens (Table III). If the androgen was given

TABLE III

THE SOCIAL ORDER IN A FLOCK OF HENS

BIRD YY RECEIVED 1·25 MG. TESTOSTERONE PROPIONATE DAILY FROM APRIL 22 TO JULY 9

(From Allee, Collias and Lutherman, 1939.)

A (April 22)		B (June 26)		
Individual	Number pecked	Individual	Number pecked	Formerly pecked †
BW	9	YY	8	0
RW	6	BW	7	8
BY	6	BR	4	5
GY *	5	RW	4	5
BR	5	BY	4	5
GG *	4	GG *	3	3
RG	4	GY *	3	5
RY	3	RG	2	3
BG *	2	BG *	1	2
YY	1			

* Poulards; GG is well masculinized.
† RY died on June 13 and is not included.

before the establishment of a social hierarchy the treated individuals generally became dominant. Hamilton and Golden (1939) showed that male and female chicks of the domestic fowl became more aggressive after the administration of testosterone propionate or androsterone, and Heistand and Stullken (1943) found that chicks treated with testosterone propionate became dominant over control birds of the same brood. Shoemaker (1939a) determined the peck order of six female Canaries and then injected the three lowest-ranking birds with male sex hormone. These rose to the top of the group, and also developed typically male song (*see* above). Davis (1957), on the other hand, obtained evidence that among male Common Starlings aggressiveness, song, and former social rank were maintained for at least 5 weeks after castration. Subsequent injections of testosterone at various dosages were reported to be without effect on rank.

Assay and Relative Activity on Birds

Growth of the capon comb

Induction of growth in the atrophic comb of the capon was the first test used successfully for the detection of androgenic activity and for many years it remained the easiest one to use quantitatively. In 1929, Gallagher and Koch described a method for assaying androgenic extracts, and defined a " capon unit " in terms of the average response of the comb in a group of birds. They also established a characteristic dose-response curve for extracts. Possible variables in this test were examined by Gallagher and Koch (1930), Womack, Koch, Domm and Juhn (1931), Koch and Gallagher (1934) and especially by Gallagher and Koch (1935) who used the extract from one ton of bull testes and found that the response of the capon comb was influenced by its initial length and by the intensity of the light during the test, but not by the weight and age of the birds. With the advent of crystalline androgens work on the capon test was intensified, and Greenwood, Blyth and Callow (1935) found a linear relation between response and dose plotted logarithmically. Koch (1937) obtained the same type of dose-response curve for androsterone, dehydroepiandrosterone, androstenedione and androstanedione as for testis extract. Significant studies followed by McCullagh and Cuyler (1939) and by Emmens (1939a) who found a linear relation between response and dose of androsterone given by intramuscular injection, the slope being steeper with a 5-day than with a 3-day period of injection (Fig. *12*. 15).

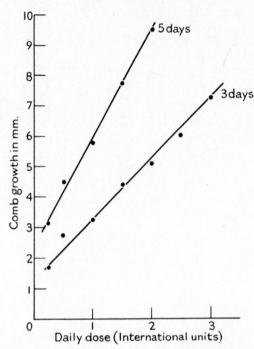

Fig. *12*. 15—Dose-response curves for International Standard androsterone, tested by increase in length plus height of the combs of adult Brown Leghorn capons. The upper curve is for the total dose given by injection over 5 days. The lower curve is for the total dose given by injection over 3 days. (From Emmens, 1939a). (From *M.R.C. Spec. Rep. Ser.* No. 234, by permission of the Controller of H.M. Stationery Office.)

The early authors, and many subsequent ones, expressed comb growth in terms of the increase in length plus height. Several more complicated methods, however, were introduced including planimetric and photo-electric measurement of the area of the comb (Freud, 1931 ; Gradstein, 1935), determination of comb volume (Engel, 1939) and measurement of the electrical resistance of the comb (Caridroit and Tauc, 1948).

Many variables have been described, e.g. season (David, 1938), and the use of a chemically pure reference substance, e.g. androsterone or testosterone, is necessary for assay purposes. There is little delay in the appearance of the maximum effect when non-esterified preparations are used, and measurements are usually made on the day after the last injection. The presence of impurities or X-substance is comparatively unimportant (Dessau and Freud, 1936) ; the volume and nature of the solvent also has little influence (Greenwood, Blyth and Callow, 1935). The capon test, therefore, has the great advantage that many of the variables, which are apt seriously to disturb tests on mammals, hardly influence the result with birds. Capons of light breeds such as the Brown and White Leghorn are usually used for assay purposes. Heavy breeds such as the Barred Rock are much less sensitive (Callow and Parkes, 1935). Bantams, though easier to handle and house, are also of low sensitivity (Parkes, 1936). Intramuscular injection is the usual route of administration and was prescribed for tests involving comparison with the International Standard, but Greenwood, Blyth and Callow (1935) found that sub-cutaneous injection gave similar results.

Local administration to the comb has a remarkable effect in increasing the efficiency of the administered material. Fussgänger (1934) found that direct application of the hormone solution to the surface of the comb caused a much greater response than could be evoked by systemic injection of the same amount of hormone. Ruzicka and Tschopp (1934) and Greenwood and Blyth (1935) obtained a similar increase in effectiveness by injecting the hormone solution into the central core of the comb. Emmens (1939b) found that about 3·5 μg. of androsterone applied by inunction produced a comb growth equivalent to that caused by 500 μg. injected intramuscularly. Androgens administered orally or intravenously have little effect on capons.

Growth of the chick comb

The long delays involved in the use of the adult capon led to a search for a more convenient test bird, and the choice fell on the young chick. Burrows, Byerly and Evans (1936) investigated the effect of androsterone and testosterone given by subcutaneous and intra-comb injections to White Leghorn and Rhode Island Red chicks up to ten days old. They found that the test was particularly sensitive when injections were made into the comb. Frank and Klempner (1937) applied androsterone by inunction, and other observations on the method and on comparative results were made by Dorfman and Greulich (1937), Danby (1938) and Breneman (1938).

Emmens (1939a) used an

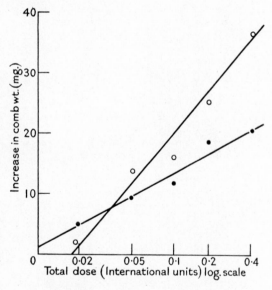

Fig. *12*. 16—Dose-response curves for International Standard androsterone tested by the increase in weight of the combs of 10-day-old chicks, following inunctions on the 1st and 5th days. ○ = males; ● = females. (Modified from Emmens, 1939a.) (From *M.R.C. Spec. Rep. Ser.* No. 234, by permission of the Controller of H.M. Stationery Office.)

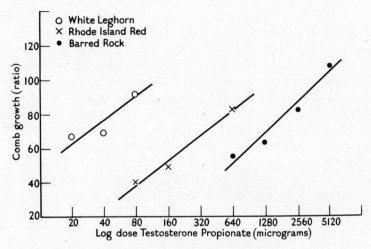

Fig. *12. 17*—Comb responses of three breeds of female chicks to testosterone propionate. (Plotted from Dorfman, 1948b.)

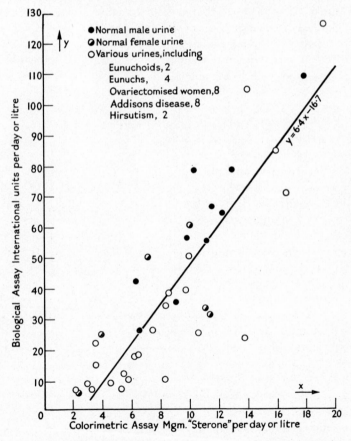

Fig. *12. 18*—Relation between capon assay and colorimetric assay for
urine extracts from various sources. (From Callow, 1938.) (By
courtesy of the Honorary Editors of the *Proceedings of the Royal
Society of Medicine*.)

inunction technique of two applications with a 5-day interval, and found that the two sexes in day-old Brown Leghorn chicks gave dose-response curves differing in slope and standard error (Fig. *12*. 16).   Significant studies were also made by Frank, Klempner and Hollander (1938), Klempner, Frank and Hollander (1940), Breneman (1942a) and Dorfman (1948a, b), and many variables such as age of chick, method of administration, duration of treatment, method of assessing comb growth, etc., have been investigated.   Particularly interesting results were obtained on differences in breed sensitivity (Fig. *12*. 17). Other papers which may be consulted for data relating to the assay of androgens on the chick comb include Jaap and Robertson (1953), Breneman (1939) and Danby (1940).   Since large batches of chicks of the same age can be obtained the chick-comb test is evidently the method of choice.

International Standard for androgenic activity

In 1935, an International Standard Preparation for androgenic activity was established consisting of crystalline androsterone (*see also* Volume III, Chapter 29). The International Unit was defined as the specific biological activity in 100 μg. of the preparation.   This standard preparation greatly facilitated comparative work in the next few years, but it was abandoned in 1950 when androsterone and other androgens had become common chemical substances.

Biological in relation to biochemical assay

With extracts of human urine there is a close relation between colorimetric tests for 17-ketosteroids and androgenic activity on capons (Fig. *12*. 18).   Biological assay has, therefore, largely been abandoned for clinical purposes.   The situation may be more complicated in cattle in which the urine contains quantities of pseudo-ketosterids (Holtz, 1957).

Relative activity of androgens in birds

The chemistry of the androgens is dealt with fully in Volume III, Chapter 31. Most of the androgens which have been assayed on birds belong to the regular androstane series (Table IV).   Well-known modifications include the introduction of a 17-methyl or a 17-ethyl group and the switching of the double bond in the unsaturated compounds from 4–5 to 5–6 or *vice versa*.   Much work has been carried out on the relative activity of these various compounds.

Table V has been compiled from data given by Dannenbaum (1936), Koch (1937), Tschopp (1936), Deanesly and Parkes (1936), Bomskov (1939), Parkes and Emmens (1944), Selye (1943), Dorfman and Shipley (1956) and Fieser and Fieser (1959).   Compounds are listed in descending order of activity and grouped according to the amount in μg. equivalent to 100 μg. (1 i.u.) of androsterone.

Relation between chemical configuration and biological activity

Some generalisations can be made concerning the relation between biological activity and chemical configuration in the androsterone series, as tested by the induction of growth in the capon comb.   When administration is by intramuscular injection, compounds having a ketone or an α-hydroxy group in position 3 are superior to those with a 3-β-hydroxy group.   The following groups of compounds illustrate this relationship : androstanedione and androsterone compared with

epiandrosterone ; androstanolone and androstanediol compared with epi-
androstanediol. This superiority is found both in the unsaturated and in the
saturated series, but it seems to be more evident in the latter. A corresponding
generalisation can be made about the 17 position in which a β-hydroxy group is
clearly superior to a ketone group, which, in turn, is superior to an α-hydroxy
group. This relationship is illustrated by testosterone, androstenedione and

TABLE IV—COMPOUNDS OF THE ANDROSTERONE-TESTOSTERONE SERIES

		17-one	17β-ol	17α-ol
3α-ol	Saturated	I androsterone	II androstanediol	III androstane-3α, 17α-diol
	Δ⁵	IV dehydro- androsterone	V androstenediol	VI androstene-3α, 17α-diol
3β-ol	Saturated	VII epiandrosterone	VIII epiandrostanediol	IX androstane-3β, 17α-diol
	Δ⁵	X dehydroepi- androsterone	XI epiandrostenediol	XII androstene-3β, 17α-diol
3-one	Saturated	XIII androstanedione	XIV androstanolone (dihydro- testosterone)	XV epiandrostanolone
	Δ⁴	XVI androstenedione	XVII testosterone	XVIII epitestosterone

epitestosterone. The seriation is evident both in the saturated and unsaturated
series. Biological activity on capons does not seem to be affected regularly by
desaturation in the normal 4–5 or 5–6 position. The same generalisation applies
when the double bond is switched from 4–5 to 5–6 or *vice versa*. Δ⁴-dehydroepi-
androsterone and Δ⁴-epiandrostenediol are equally active or more active than
the corresponding Δ⁵ or saturated compounds. The abnormal Δ⁵-androstene-
dione is less active than Δ⁴-androstenedione or the corresponding saturated
compound (Tables IV and V).

TABLE V

ACTIVITY OF VARIOUS ANDROGENS AS DETERMINED BY TESTS ON COMB GROWTH

Compound	Compound number Table IV	Amount required to equal 0·1 mg. of androsterone (μg.)
Testosterone . . .	XVII	
Methylandrostanolone .	—	
Androstanediol . .	II	<30
Dihydrotestosterone . .	XIV	
Methyltestosterone . .	—	
Methylandrostanediol .	—	
Androstenediol . .	V	<60
Ethylandrostanediol . .	—	
Androsterone . . .	I	100
Dehydroandrosterone .	IV	
Androstenedione . .	XVI	<120
Androstanedione . .	XIII	
Δ^4-Epiandrostenediol .	—	
Methylepiandrostenediol .	—	<250
Dehydroepiandrosterone .	X	
Δ^4-Dehydroepiandrosterone	—	
Δ^5-Androstenedione .	—	
Dihydroepitestosterone .	XV	
Epiandrostenediol . .	XI	
Epitestosterone . .	XVIII	<500
Androstane-3β, 17α-diol .	IX	
Methylandrostanediol .	—	
Ethylandrostanediol . .	—	
Androstane-3α, 17α-diol .	III	
Epiandrostanediol . .	VIII	
Epiandrosterone . .	VII	<1000
Androstene-3β, 17α-diol .	XII	

Effect of method of administration on absolute and relative activity

The data and conclusions recorded in the two preceding paragraphs are based on tests carried out by intramuscular or subcutaneous injection. When the compounds are given orally, or by direct inunction onto the comb, very different values may be obtained. Testosterone, for instance, is only slightly more active than androsterone when tested by the inunction method; androstenedione, androstanedione and androstanediol are about equally active, and dehydroandrosterone only slightly less so (Voss, 1937; Dessau, 1935, 1937).

Emmens (1938) investigated the relative activity of certain androgens tested by injection, inunction and oral administration. He found that with androsterone, more than 150 times as much was required by injection as by inunction, and 9 times as much again by mouth. The extreme ratios were given by androstanediol, in which more than 10,000 times as much was required by mouth as by inunction (Table VI). A more detailed consideration of this problem has been made by Dorfman and Shipley (1956), who give figures showing that the ratio minimum-dose-by-local-test/minimum-dose-by-systemic-test varied from 1/38 for testosterone to 1/240 for androstenedione.

TABLE VI

Approximate Amounts (µg,) of Various Androgens Required to Produce a 5-mm. Increase in Length Plus Height of the Combs of Brown Leghorn Capons When Given in Oil Solution by Different Routes

(From Emmens, 1938.)

Substance	Assay Method			Dose by mouth / Dose by injection
	Inunction	Injection	By mouth	
Androsterone . . .	3·0	500	4500	9
Testosterone . . .	2·1	85	2500	30
Androstanediol . .	2·4	165	25000	150
Dehydroepiandrosterone .	6·0	1500	22500	15
Methyltestosterone . .	4·5	330	3300	10

Prolongation of effect on birds

The androgens are apparently absorbed rapidly after subcutaneous or intramuscular injection and are quickly used or destroyed, so that a single injection has only a transient effect. Certain esters, however, have a prolonged action. This was observed first of androsterone acetate and androsterone benzoate. More extensive work was carried out by Miescher, Wettstein and Tschopp (1936) when they tested a long series of aliphatic esters of testosterone. Their results in the capon test indicated that the prolongation of effect is, roughly speaking, proportional to the length of the acid chain, but it follows, of course, that where a standard dose is given the intensity of the response will be much reduced as the duration becomes greater.

The di-esters of the enolic form of testosterone, subsequently prepared by Miescher, Fischer and Tschopp (1937), have, in general, a more prolonged but slightly less intense action than the mono-esters. Other work on testosterone esters was carried out by Roussel, Gley and Paulin (1937), who found that the combs of capons injected with the propionic ester showed growth both faster and more prolonged than those of birds receiving other derivatives. Aliphatic esters of androsterone and of androstanediol were also studied in some detail by Schoeller and Gehrke (1938). The mechanism whereby esterification causes prolongation of action is well understood. There is no such effect following intravenous injection, and the prolongation is certainly due to delayed absorption from the site of injection, intramuscular or subcutaneous. With some of the esters, particularly

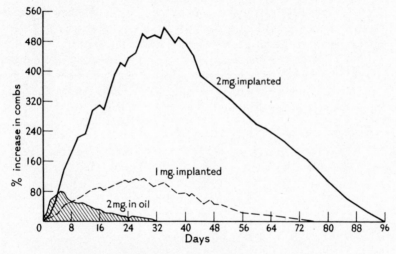

Fig. *12*. 19—Relative effectiveness of testosterone propionate in restoring the atrophic comb of the capon, given by injection in oil solution and by pellet implantation. (From Schoeller and Gehrke, 1938.)

testosterone palmitate and stearate, androstenediol benzoate and androstanediol benzoate, the effect is so prolonged and the intensity so low that effects are barely detectable.

The importance of rate of absorption is well shown by the fact that high effectiveness and long duration of action are obtained in capons when androgens are administered in the form of solid crystals, or compressed pellets of pure hormone implanted intramuscularly. Schoeller and Gehrke (1938) showed that 2 mg. of testosterone thus administered caused a maximum increase of 480 per cent in comb size 16–21 days after implantation of the pellet. The same amount of testosterone administered in oil solution gave a negligible response of 15 per cent very shortly after injection. These authors obtained even more striking results with testosterone propionate (Fig. *12*. 19) and similar ones with crystals of the less active androsterone, androstanediol and androstenediol. Emmens (1938), using pellets of between 5 and 16 mg. per bird, investigated the maximum growth rate of the capon comb by the implantation method. The peak response occurred at 40–50 days after implantation, when the combs had increased up to 10 times in length × height, and were the same size as in the normal cock. In the chick test, also, a very prolonged response is obtained by the implantation of solid crystals (Hamilton and Dorfman, 1939).

Specificity of androgenic activity in birds

Androgenic activity in birds, as in mammals, is remarkably specific and no active compounds have been found outside the steroid group. Among the steroids, only the androstane derivatives are substantially active. Certain of the C_{21} steroids of the progesterone series show some activity of the kind characteristic of the recognised androgens. In tests on the capon comb, Caridroit (1944), Benoit *et al.* (1945) and Parkes (1945) found that progesterone itself had slight activity when given by inunction in massive dosage. According to Pfiffner and North (1940, 1941) 17α-hydroxyprogesterone is about one-half as active as androsterone by intramuscular injection to capons. Dorfman (1950) obtained no consistent effect with this compound, but found that $\triangle^{10}$-dehydroprogesterone had significant activity about 6 per cent that of androsterone. Other C_{21} steroids appeared to be inhibitory in the chick test, possibly because of local competitive antagonism with the endogenous androgens. It is uncertain whether such androgenic activity as is shown by the C_{21} steroids is direct, or whether it depends on some modification of the compounds in the body (*see also* Volume III, Chapter 30).

TABLE VII

COMPARISON OF RELATIVE ACTIVITIES OF ANDROGENS ON THE SEMINAL VESICLES OF IMMATURE MALE RATS AND THE CAPON'S COMB (Testosterone = 100 per cent)

(From Dorfman and Shipley, 1956. Names of compounds abbreviated as in Tables IV and V.)

Compound	Relative activity (per cent)	
	Seminal vesicles	Capon's comb
Testosterone	100	100
Androstanolone	200	75
Methylandrostanediol . · . .	50	50
Androstanediol	33	75
Androstenedione	20	12
Androstanedione	14	12
Epiandrostenediol	14	3
Epiandrostanediol	10	2
Androsterone	10	10
Δ^5-Androstenedione	7	12
Methylepiandrostenediol . . .	5	3
Dehydroepiandrosterone . . .	3	16
Epiandrosterone	3	2

Relative activity in mammals and birds

No strict comparison can be made of the relative activity of the various androgens in mammals and birds. The efficiency of any particular compound, especially in mammals, depends greatly on the method of administration and the test object used, and comparison between activity in mammals and birds is inevitably influenced by the conditions of test. Some of the factors involved were considered by Deanesly and Parkes (1936), who found that testosterone was 6 times as active on capons as androsterone, but 2 to 5 times as active on the prostate, and 10 times as active on the seminal vesicles of the castrated rat. Methylandrostanolone was slightly less active than testosterone on capons, much more so on rats.

Table VII, taken from Dorfman and Shipley (1956), shows a better correspondence than might be expected. With the compounds of low activity the comparisons may mean little; among the others, two comparisons stand out. Androstanolone is much more active than testosterone in the rat test, less active in the capon test. By contrast, androstanediol is much less active on rats, but nearly as active on capons.

V. BIOLOGICAL ACTION OF OESTROGENS

General Characters

Growth of the young fowl may be prevented by chronic treatment with oestrogens, as shown by Zondek (1937), who produced pituitary dwarf fowl. Associated effects are due primarily to depression of the growth-promoting activity of the hypophysis (*see* Volume III). There are few observations of the direct effects of oestrogens on general bodily characters, but metabolic effects are well recognised. Zondek and Marx (1939) found that a pronounced lipaemia, the intensity of which depended on dosage, was induced within 48 hours by the injection of oestrogen to cocks. Thus 2–4 mg. of oestradiol benzoate caused a three- to fourfold increase in blood fat; chronic treatment over a period caused advanced lipaemia and extreme adiposity of various organs. The effects could not be produced by other steroid hormones, and were, therefore, specific to the oestrogens. This curious reaction of fowl to oestrogens has been used to improve the performance of birds being fattened for the table (Lorenz, 1938, 1945; Jaap and Thayer, 1944), but the method, while highly effective, has aroused some controversy because of the faint possibility that effective amounts of oestrogen might be eaten with the bird.

Zondek and Marx also found that a severe calcaemia appeared in the cock after administration of oestrogenic hormones, the increase in the blood calcium being roughly parallel to that in the blood fat. The authors homologise this metabolic change in the oestrogen-injected cock with that seen in the laying hen, in which there is a rise in the concentration of blood fat and calcium. Oestrogen is especially concerned in the deposition of calcium in the narrow cavities of the long bones just before shell-formation. If the ovaries of pigeons contain follicles 10 mm. or more in diameter the marrow cavities contain spicules of bone (Kyes and Potter, 1934). Seasonal hyper-ossification of the endoskeletal system of pigeons and house sparrows can be directly correlated with periodic ovarian activity (Pfeiffer and

Gardner, 1938 ; Kirschbaum *et al.*, 1939). The formation of such medullary bone can be stimulated both in male and non-ovulatory female pigeons by the injection of oestrogen. In the North American Bobwhite Quail (*Collinus virginianus*) seasonal ossification has been enhanced by the same means (Ringoen, 1945). Although most of the calcium needed for shell formation comes from currently ingested material, this is nevertheless insufficient to meet entirely the heavy seasonal requirements and perhaps 35 to 40 per cent is withdrawn from body deposits (Driggers and Comar, 1949 ; Comar and Driggers, 1949). Calcium is not stored in the reproductive tract; that accumulated as medullary bone is probably sufficient for the formation of about six eggs in the domestic hen. The fall in the erythrocyte count which follows oestrogen administration (Taber, Davis and Domm, 1943) may be associated with the formation of medullary bone described by Bloom, Bloom, Domm and McLean (1940). Such tissue is said to hold a greater ratio of calcium to phosphorus than ordinary bone (Common, 1938). In pigeons, hens and ducks a rise in blood calcium and phosphorus is associated with the period of ovulation (McDonald and Riddle, 1945; Fleischmann and Fried, 1945; Common, Bolton and Rutledge, 1948). Oestrogen injections raise the blood calcium level in pigeons even after excision of the parathyroids (Riddle, Rauch and Smith, 1945; Riddle and McDonald, 1945).

The effects of oestrogens on serum vitamin A, serum and liver nucleic acid, liver iron, and on other metabolic indices, have been extensively studied by Chapman *et al.* (1949, 1950) and Common *et al.* (1948, 1951). Oestrogen (like androgen, p. 588) possibly increases the amount of depot fat (p. 587) laid down in circumscribed subcutaneous and infra-peritoneal areas (Thayer, Jaap and Penquite, 1945). Maze-performance is another general character possibly modifiable by oestrogens, because there is evidence that this faculty in Budgerygahs (*Melopsittacus undulatus*) is lowered during the sexual season (Allee, 1936). Both oestrogen and androgen tend to eliminate moult which is said to be closely associated with thyroid activity (Collias, 1950). Exogenous oestrogen leads to adrenal hypertrophy in fowls and pigeons (Breneman, 1942b; Stamler, *et al.*, 1950; Miller and Riddle, 1939), whereas androgen has no appreciable effect (Kar, 1947b; Kumaran and Turner, 1949b).

Direct Effects on Secondary Sexual Characters

A valuable review of the general effects of oestrogens on birds and their commercial applications is given by Lorenz (1954).

Head furnishings

Most observers agree that oestrogenic substances do not stimulate the comb of the capon, the hen or the chick. Large amounts of oestrone, oestradiol, oestriol, equilin and stilboestrol (Parkes, 1937 ; Dorfman and Greulich, 1937 ; Mühlbock, 1938), even when applied directly to the surface of the comb itself, produce no detectable growth. Mühlbock (1938) and Hoskins and Koch (1939b) noted that prolonged administration of large doses of oestrogens caused further atrophy of the comb of the capon, as well as inhibiting the effect of testosterone (Fig. *12.* 20). Breneman (1946), however, has suggested that in White Leghorn pullets comb-growth is, in fact, partly controlled during the first 45 days by oestrogen stored in the egg-yolk and later by endogenous oestrogen.

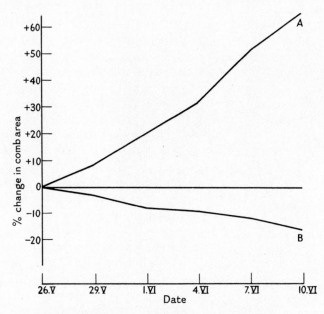

Fig. *12*.20—Inhibition of the effect of androsterone on the capon comb by the simultaneous administration of oestradiol benzoate. (A) After 100 μg. of androsterone per day. (B) After 100 μg. of androsterone plus 5 mg. oestradiol benzoate per day. (From Mühlbock, 1938.)

Beak colour

In certain birds sex dichromism of the beak is under ovarian influence. The beak of the Red-billed Weaver Finch, red in both sexes during the non-breeding season, but yellow in the female during the sexual season (p. 592), can be changed to yellow in either sex during the non-breeding season or after gonadectomy by the administration of oestrone (Witschi, 1935b). In the same way, the typical brown colour at the base of the beak of female Budgerygahs (*Melopsittacus undulatus*) in the breeding season can be produced in males and castrated male and anoestrous females, in all of which the colour is blue, by injection of oestrone.

Plumage

The effects of castration and ovariectomy on cocks and hens suggest that the black breast feathers of the Brown Leghorn cock or capon regenerating under the influence of exogenous oestrogen should be of the female type. This theoretical expectation was realised by Freud, de Jongh and Laqueur (1929, 1930) and by Juhn and Gustavson (1930), and their work was confirmed and extended by a mass of investigations carried out on the feminisation of plumage of the cock or capon (particularly of Brown Leghorns) by the injection of oestrogens. The physiological basis of the change was investigated in detail by Juhn, Faulkner and Gustavson (1931), Greenwood and Blyth (1931), and Champy and Demay (1933), Champy (1934), Caridroit (1936) and many others. It was found that differences in the growth rates of different feathers and various parts of the same feather greatly influenced the response. This particular aspect of the problem was considered very fully by the Chicago school, including Lillie and Juhn (1932). Their most important conclusions about the physiology of feather response to oestrogenic hormones may be summarised as follows.

The feathers in various feather tracts grow at different rates and this is associated with difference in sensitivity to oestrogens. Thus, the breast feather grows much more rapidly than the saddle hackle, which has a greater sensitivity to oestrogen and responds by both colour and structure changes (Fig. 12. 21). The growth gradients found in individual feathers further modify the response. In the breast feather the apical-basal growth rate is approximately constant ; i.e. the bottom of the feather grows at much the same rate as the tip, and has a similar sensitivity to oestrogen. The barbs, however, have a sharp growth gradient, the tip growing faster than the bases, which are therefore more sensitive to oestrogen and can be feminised with a dose which does not affect the tip. Moreover, the response to stimulation is rapid, and the cessation of response when the stimulation falls below the threshold is similarly sharp. It is thus possible to obtain a great variety of response patterns (Fig. 12. 22) which are important in the quantitative use of the feather test for studying the duration and intensity of oestrogenic action (Parkes, 1937).

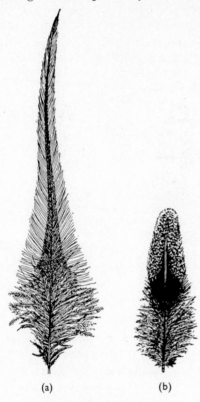

Fig. 12. 21—Effect of oestrone on the structure of the saddle hackle of the Brown Leghorn capon. (a) Normal saddle hackle. (b) Saddle hackle regenerating in oestrogenised bird, showing feminine structure. (From Parkes and Emmens, 1944.)

Another quantitative aspect of the response was studied by Greenwood and Blyth (1935) who found that older birds responded more vigorously, but that neither the body weight of the bird nor the season of the year affected the result. These authors also made the interesting observation that the response could be evoked by the intradermal injection of very small doses, though the result might only be local. The mechanism whereby oestrogenic hormone affects melanogenesis has been considered by many authors ('Espinasse, 1939; Wang, 1946, 1948; Trinkaus, 1948; Markert, 1948).

Brown Leghorns have mainly been used for work of this kind, but many other breeds, including some Old English game bantams, in which the cock has plumage of the red/black Leghorn type, show exactly the same kind of response, although their threshold requirement may be much greater. More remarkable is the fact that the laced, double-laced, barred, or tipped patterns characteristic of the female plumage in such breeds as the Sebright, Partridge Wyandotte, Campine, and Redcap, can be produced in the cocks by methods of oestrogen administration giving continuous unbroken stimulation (Emmens and Parkes, 1940b).   In Mallard ducks the brilliant nuptial plumage of the drake can be suppressed, and the sombre plumage of the duck induced, by the administration of oestrogen (Emmens and Parkes, 1940b).   The same is true for pheasants (Freud, de Jongh and Laqueur, 1930), and certain other breeds. Sensitivity, however, may vary greatly from species to species and even between breeds. Except in breeds where the cock is henny-feathered, males respond to oestrogens in the same way as do capons. Complex results can be obtained by the injection of oestrogens into hybrids between certain breeds of domestic fowl, since the response to oestrogens may reveal differences in superficially identical plumage (Danforth, 1933; Caridroit, 1938b; Régnier, 1934, 1935).   Sex dimorphism in plumage of a type entirely different from that seen in Brown Leghorns, pheasants, etc., may also be dependent on ovarian activity.   In

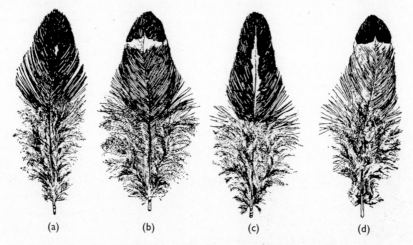

(a)   (b)   (c)   (d)

Fig. 12. 22—Types of response of breast feather of Brown Leghorn capon to oestrogenic stimulation.   (a) Rachis spot, indicating brief weak stimulus. (b) Narrow bar, indicating brief intense stimulus.   (c) Rachis stripe, indicating prolonged weak stimulus.   (d) Broad bar, indicating prolonged intense stimulus.   (From Parkes, 1937.)

the Quail (*Coturnix coturnix*), for instance, female plumage, including the white throat and spotted breast, can be induced in the male by injection of oestrogenic extracts (Agostini, 1935).   The plumage of the domestic pigeon is not influenced by the administration of oestrogens (Lipschütz, 1931 ; Vinals, 1932).

A more complicated control of plumage by oestrogen was found by Witschi (1935a) in the Orange Weaver. In this species the female feathering is the neutral condition and the nuptial plumage of the cock appears to be under the direct influence of the gonadotrophic hormones of the anterior pituitary (pp. 594, 662). The administration of oestrone, oestradiol or oestriol to the male suppresses the incipient nuptial plumage. It seems, therefore, that the female plumage of the hen during the breeding season is caused by the endogenous ovarian hormone suppressing the effect of the gonadotrophic hormone in producing display plumage; the plumage of the anoestrous bird of either sex is female in type and presumably indicates lack of gonadotrophic hormone secretion by the quiescent pituitary gland.

All naturally occurring oestrogens seem to have qualitatively similar effects in feminising plumage, though oestriol (Parkes, 1936) is probably the least effective. Synthetic oestrogens, including those of the diethylstilboestrol series and the oestrogenic carcinogens, are also active (Cook, Dodds and Greenwood, 1934; Caridroit, 1948).

In some species, plumage changes are under the control of androgens (pp. 594, 617). Oestrogens do not cause Herring-gulls or Black-crowned or Laughing gulls to come into adult plumage (Boss and Witschi, 1941, 1942; Noble and Wurm, 1940a, b).

Quantitative use of the plumage response. The response of plumage to oestrogens, though not of much value for the quantitative study of intensity of reaction, can very simply be adapted to the study of the duration of effective stimulation. It is easy to calculate the rate of feather growth; and measurement of the width of the bar or length of the stripe resulting from oestrogenic stimulation will show accurately the time for which a concentration of oestrogen above threshold value was present in the circulation. The breast feathers of the Brown Leghorn capons used by Parkes (1937) grew at the rate of about 2 mm. per day. It was found that 0·1 mg. of oestrone, given as a single injection, caused only a faint response, while 0·25 mg. and 1·0 mg. produced a width of bar averaging about 2 mm. and 4 mm. respectively, indicating an effective duration of oestrogenic stimulation of about 1 and 2 days. Little further increase in duration of

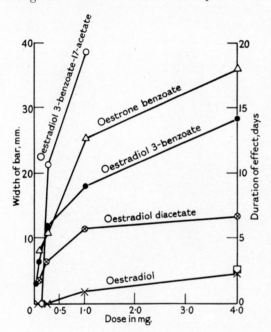

Fig. *12.* 23—Dose-response curve for the duration of action, in the feather test, of various esters of oestrone and oestradiol. (From Parkes, 1937.)

response was produced by increase of the dose. Oestradiol gave almost identical results, while oestriol, used as free hormone, failed to produce a response in the dosage used.

The maximum effect of free hormone given by a single intramuscular injection to capons is therefore transient, unlike the esters of these substances (Parkes, 1937). As in mammalian tests (Volume III), the aliphatic esters show an increasing duration of effect with increasing length of the acid chain, though with the higher esters the minimum dose required to evoke a response is much increased (Figs. *12.* 23; *12.* 24).

The mechanism of this effect of esterification was clearly demonstrated by Deanesly and Parkes (1937a), who studied the influence of route of administration on the relative effectiveness of free oestradiol and its esters. The free hormone was found to be almost as effective by intravenous, as by intramuscular injection, showing that absorption from the muscles is very rapid (Fig. *12*. 25a). The monobenzoate of oestradiol, on the other hand, was much less effective when given intravenously than when given intramuscularly, and lost most of its superiority over the free hormone (Fig. *12*. 25b). Even the dibenzoate, injected intravenously, produced only a transient effect, while the threshold dose became almost as low as for the free hormone. These results show that, as with mammals, the prolongation of action in birds by esterification is due to delay in absorption from the site of injection. It was further shown by Deanesly and Parkes that the direct application of free hormone in oil solution to the skin of the fowl, just before emergence of the growing feathers, caused an effect nearly as prolonged as that of the monobenzoate similarly administered. The most conclusive experiment in this series, however, consisted in the single implantation of a 3 mg. crystal of oestrone into each of a group of three capons. This procedure feminised successive sets

(a)   (b)   (c)

Fig. *12*. 24—Effect of 1 mg. oestradiol on the breast feathers of the Brown Leghorn capon. (a) As acetate, (b) As benzoate, (c) As 3-benzoate 17-acetate. (From Parkes, 1937.)

of growing plumage for a period of nearly 3 months (Fig. *12*. 25c) and gave rise to the technique of administering steroid hormones by pellet implantation.

Behaviour

Oestrogen stops broodiness when injected into hens, probably through inhibition of the anterior pituitary gland (Godfrey and Jaap, 1950) and eliminates crowing and other sexual activity in domestic cockerels (Ceni, 1927; Davis and Domm, 1941). Castrated males sometimes continue to exhibit masculine behaviour patterns after oestrogen injections (Goodale, 1916a, 1918; Davis and Domm, 1941, 1943) but such treatment generally evokes female behaviour. When bilaterally ovariectomised pigeons were injected with oestrogen they adopted a squatting reflex and received the male (Davis and Domm, 1941, 1943). Some individuals, however, did not do so in an experiment carried out by Allee and Collias (1940), who also showed that in domestic hens oestrogen administration tended to reduce social status (*see* p. 624). The gull *Larus atricilla*, when similarly

treated, adopts the food-begging and stooping activities characteristic of the female while mating.   In castrated males injected with oestrogen, as well as in ovariectomised females injected with testosterone, innate mechanisms will sometimes express themselves (Davis and Domm, 1941, 1943).   Lehrman (1958a) has evidence that oestrogen secretion, stimulated by courtship activity, itself induces nest-building behaviour which in turn " encourages progesterone secretion, leading to incubation ".   Oestrogen injections are reported to inhibit the autumn migration from the breeding ground of the female redstart (Schildmacher, 1933).

Direct Effects on Accessory Organs

Riddle and Tange (1928) studied the effects of injecting oestrogenic preparations in immature doves, but were comparatively unsuccessful in promoting premature development of the reproductive organs, even of the reproductive tract. They record, however, that in some birds the oviducts showed the characteristic hyperplasia and hyperaemia associated with the laying period.   The administration of oestrogenic substances to the immature female fowl results in speedy development of the oviduct, which may then show complete morphological and physiological maturity in comparatively young pullets.   This was first shown by Juhn and Gustavson (1930), who injected oestrogenic extracts of placenta into immature female Brown Leghorns and produced a ten-fold enlargement of the oviducts in 10 days.   Moreover, there was development of muscle tissue as well as of the glands of the oviducts, both these structures being rudimentary in the controls.   Juhn and Gustavson (1932) also showed that prolonged injection of a cockerel caused the rudimentary duct to assume the characters of the oviduct of the immature pullet.   In chicks injected with oestrogen Munro and Kosin (1943) noted a 100-fold response in the oviducts within 10 days.   There can be no doubt, therefore, that oestrogens can stimulate development of the Müllerian duct in fowls, a property analogous to their metrotrophic power in mammals, and it may confidently be assumed that endogenous oestrogens are necessary for the development of the oviduct and its functional activity in normal birds.   However, a progestogen, too, may be involved after hatching (p. 652).

Wolff (1936a) injected large doses of oestrogen into chicks of cross-bred Rhode Island fowl (Red cocks × Light Sussex hens), using males and females as well as intersexes obtained by treatment with oestrogen during embryonic life.   All received a total dose of 1·2 mg. to 2·5 mg. of oestradiol benzoate in 2 days.   After 4–6 days males, females and intersexes all showed a similar reaction, the cloaca and margins of the vent becoming hyperaemic and oedematous.   The mucosa of the cloaca became everted in normal birds, whereas in the intersexes there was a

Fig. *12*. 25—Response of the breast feathers of the Brown Leghorn capon to various oestrogens administered in different ways. (a) Oestradiol, (b) Oestradiol monobenzoate; (1) 0·25 mg. in oil solution given intramuscularly, (2) 4 mg. in oil solution given intramuscularly, (3) 5 mg. in propylene glycol solution given intramuscularly, (4) 0·25 mg. in oil solution given by inunction on to the skin of the feather tract. (c) Oestrone (1) 4 mg. given in one injection in oil solution; (2), (3) and (4) 3 mg. given by implantation of a solid crystal of pure hormone; (2) Feather which had begun to grow at the time implantation was made, (3) Feather which grew following a plucking 29 days after implantation, (4) Feather which grew following a plucking 62 days after implantation. Reversion to the male type had begun at the base of the feather, so the total effect of the implantation of oestrone lasted for nearly 3 months. (From Deanesly and Parkes, 1937a.) (*Proc. Roy. Soc.*, B, 1937, **124**, 279.)

marked invagination. Wolff compares the general nature of the effect with that seen in the circumanal region of the male or female monkey injected with oestrogen. There was a great hypertrophy of the left oviduct, and of the rudimentary right duct in females and intersexes, together with a premature and abundant secretion of albumen from the oviducal glands.

Riddle and Lahr (1944a) made a large-scale attempt, involving 255 birds, to use the thread-like undeveloped oviducts of young Ring Doves (*Streptopelia decaocto*)

(a)

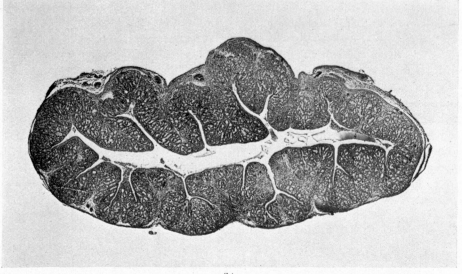

(b)

Fig. *12*. 26—Effect of hormones on oviduct of immature fowl. Oviduct of (a) untreated bird, (b) bird receiving 30 mg. of diethylstilboestrol over 2 weeks. (From Parkes and Emmens, 1944.)

for the study of (a) the relative gynaecogenic potencies of some of the common steroid hormones, including androgens; (b) the effect on the growth response of the oviduct of varying the volume of fluid injected; and (c) the synergism or antagonism of simultaneously injected oestrone and progesterone. Oestrogenic agents had the following relative efficiency in promoting oviducal growth : diethylstilboestrol, 100 ; oestradiol benzoate, 35 ; oestradiol, 8 ; oestrone, 6 + ; the injection of progesterone enhanced the growth-promoting effect of oestrone by 60 to 70 per cent. On the other hand, Brandt and Nalbandov (1956) have evidence that suggests that progesterone (p. 652), too, may be required before the oviducal glands become functional. The effect of diethylstilboestrol is shown in Fig. *12*. 26.

The response of the oviduct to oestrogens is greatly reduced in chicks maintained on a diet deficient in folic acid (Hertz, 1945) or receiving a folic acid antagonist (Hertz and Tullner, 1949). The oviducal production of the biotin antagonist avidin is apparently controlled by oestrogen (Fraps, Hertz and Sebrell, 1943).

Effects on Embryos

Much work has been done on the modification of sex differentiation in the developing embryo by the injection of oestrogens into the egg during incubation. Wolff and Ginglinger (1935) administered oestrone in oil solution by a single injection into the chorioallantoic membrane of the embryo on or after the 5th day of incubation. A proportion of treated males underwent some degree of feminisation, resulting in intersexuality. The dose necessary to modify all genetic males towards intersexuality was 0·01 mg., while the strongest degree of feminisation was obtained with a dose of 0·05 mg. These effects could be produced only if the hormone was injected before the 8th day of incubation. The weakest degree of intersexuality was characterised by asymmetry of the gonads, the right organ remaining as a testis, while the left became an ovo-testis possessing an ovarian cortex peripheral to a core of testis tissue (Fig. *12*. 27). In the embryos showing the strongest degree of intersexuality the right testis was much reduced and in the place of the left testis there was an apparently normal ovary. The Müllerian ducts showed progressive development with increasing degrees of intersexuality. Wolff (1936b) found oestradiol benzoate apparently less effective, weight for weight, than oestrone. Full intersexuality, however, was produced in doses of 0·125 mg. Synthetic oestrogens such as diethylstilboestrol produce a qualitatively similar reaction (Wolff, 1939 ; Wolff and Wolff, 1948). A water-soluble oestrogen, the sodium salt of dehydrodoisynolic acid, which allows of heavy and rapid dosage of the embryo, administered before the 4th day of incubation, caused the appearance of a right ovary in both sexes. A general review of his work on the effects of gonadal hormones on the development of the bird embryo was given by Wolff (1938b).

Similar experiments were carried out by Willier, Gallagher and Koch (1937), who administered single doses of up to 2·0 mg. of oestrone or oestriol 2 days after the beginning of incubaton. In extreme cases the left gonad was entirely ovarian, while the right gonad also possessed ovarian tissue and was reduced in size, though its testicular character was never entirely lost. Gaarenstroom (1937), too, found that 0·1 mg. of oestrone administered up to the 6th day interfered with the developing male embryo and resulted in the occurrence of intersexes, so that the number of normal males at hatching was less than one-quarter of the total. Dantchakoff (1935) observed, like Wolff and Ginglinger, that the effect of oestrogens was greatest if injection was on the 4th day of incubation. It was less on the 6th to 8th days, and slight on the 10th. She found (1937c) that incubation was accelerated by oestrogenisation, treated chicks of both sexes being hatched some 24 hours earlier than is normal. The feminisation of the male is accompanied by persistence of the left or both Müllerian ducts according to the dosage of oestrogen (Gaarenstroom, 1939).

Changes in the genetically female gonad are much less dramatic. Wolff and Wolff (1949) showed that oestrogen administration maintains the germinal epithelium of the right embryonic ovary and that an ovarian cortex arises if injection is carried out before the 4th day.   There appears to be an innate difference in the developmental capacity of the germinal epithelium of right and left organs.   That of the left develops in both sexes until the 8th day.   It then degenerates in the

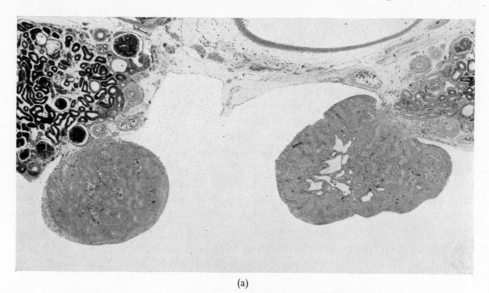

(a)

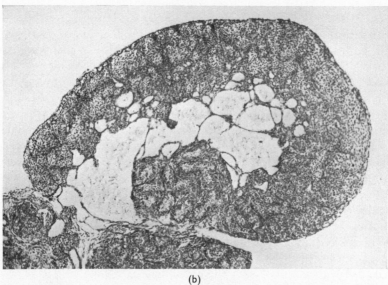

(b)

Fig. *12. 27*—Effect of oestrone on sexual differentiation in the chick.   (a) Gonads, at hatching, of a male chick which received 27 i.u. oestrone on the 5th day of incubation.   The right gonad is a normal testis, the left an ovotestis having embryonic testis tubules in the medulla with a cortex of ovarian tissue.   (b) Higher magnification of a different section of the left gonad of the same chick.   (From the material of Wolff and Ginglinger, 1935.)

male, but until the 12th day of incubation it can respond to oestrogens with the formation of a meagre and abnormal cortex.   The germinal epithelium of the right ovary (which is generally relatively undeveloped) begins to degenerate at the 5th day, and by the end of the 6th day has usually become insensitive to hormones. Such differential regression of the germinal elements of right and left organs probably explains the necessity for early hormone administration if the right ovary is to be affected. Domm (1955) concluded that administration of oestrogens to the fowl embryo can provoke " a supplementary sexual differentiation (i.e. a right ovary) which is only sporadically encountered arising spontaneously."

The subsequent history of modified chicks has been studied by several workers. Wolff (1936b) found that modified males gradually lost the appearance of intersexuality and came to resemble normal males externally. Histological examination showed that the left gonad also developed a more or less normal appearance. Domm (1955) concluded that oestrogen-induced transformation of the embryonic left testis is not stable and that the altered organs revert towards the typical male structure as the animal matures. Dantchakoff (1937a) confirmed Wolff's observation and found that although the oviduct, and the ovary-like appearance of the left testis, might persist to some extent, typical male plumage and head furnishings were nevertheless assumed. Gaarenstroom (1940) found that the proportion of apparent females decreased as the birds became older, so that the sex-ratio had returned to normal 9 months after hatching. Greenwood and Blyth (1938c) investigated the subsequent history of female chicks which had been subjected to the action of oestrone during embryonic stages. Of six females, only one laid normal eggs when sexually mature, the remainder producing eggs devoid of shell, or of shell and egg membrane. Greenwood and Blyth ascribed the phenomenon to abnormality of the oviduct. At autopsy the birds were found to have two oviducts, each showing incomplete development of the whole and of individual parts. The total weight of the two ducts was similar to that of the single left duct of the normal hen.

Interesting observations were made by Domm (1939b, c) on the characteristics of male chicks hatched from eggs injected with oestrogen from the 3rd to 5th day of incubation. Some cockerels grew up exhibiting a marked intersexuality and reduction in male behaviour. Later Domm and Davis (1941) concluded that " the behaviour of intersexual male domestic fowl shows gradations from essentially normal masculine copulatory patterns to neutral or inactive behaviour coinciding in general with the degree of feminisation of plumage. The position of intersexual males in the peck order also follows closely the plumage characteristics (Domm and Davis, 1948).

After the injection of oestrogens into laying female pigeons Riddle and Dunham (1942) reported a modification of the incipient cortex of the left testis of male chicks that hatched from the eggs of treated hens. They considered that the artificially introduced hormone became deposited in the yolk.

In the Herring-gull (Boss, 1943) injection of diethylstilboestrol into genetically male embryos altered the shape and structure of the left gonad. Even 22 months later it might retain the characters of an ovo-testis, containing oöcytes and spermatozoa. The right testis was more normal.

Effects on Adults

Testis and sexual characters of the male

Prolonged dosage of oestrogen to the adult male bird causes hypotrophy of the testes, presumably as in the mammal, by depression of hypophysial activity. The

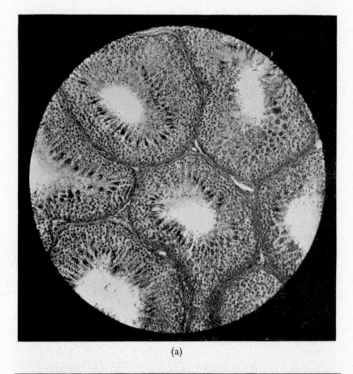

(a)

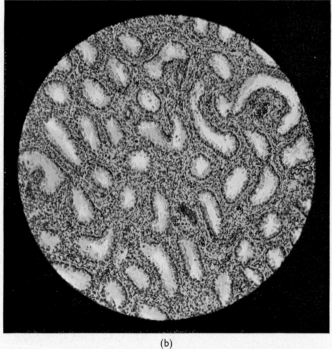

(b)

Fig. *12*. 28—Effect of oestrogen on the testis of the Brown Leghorn
cock. (a) Normal testis, (b) Testis after prolonged treatment
with oestradiol monobenzoate. (From the material of Emmens,
1939b.)

response is a sensitive one, as shown by Morató-Manaro, Albrieux and Buño 1938), who obtained effects on the testis by local application of oestrogen to the comb or by the injection over a week of 5 mg. of oestrone in oil. The testes of Zondek's dwarf cockerels, mentioned above (p. 635) were less than 4 per cent of the normal weight, and the combs were atrophic. Emmens (1939b) injected oestradiol benzoate or implanted pellets of oestrone and also caused testicular hypotrophy similar to that seen after hyprophysectomy (*see* Fig. *12*. 28). There was secondary hypotrophy of the comb (Fig. *12*. 29). Analogous results were obtained by Hoskins and Koch (1939b) and Régnier (1938), and ample confirmation

(a)   (b)

Fig. *12*. 29—Effect of oestrogen on the comb of the Brown Leghorn cock. (a) Before treatment, (b) Same bird 37 days after implantation of a 65 mg. tablet of oestrone. (From Emmens, 1939b.)

has been obtained of the principle involved. It should be noted that where oestrogen is applied locally to the comb of an intact cock the effect on the comb is a combination of (a) decreased testicular activity caused by the pituitary-depressing action of oestrogen absorbed into the circulation, (b) local inhibition by the oestrogen of the effect of endogenous testosterone on the comb, and (c) the comb-shrinking property of oestrogen seen even in the capon. These can partially be disassociated by the ingenious comb dividing technique of Morató-Manaro and Albrieux (1939). According to Skaller and Grigg (1950), the sensitivity of cockerels and capons to oestrogen in the form of orally administered hexoestrol varies with breed and age, but the reaction, as in mammals, consists of a short period of stimulation followed by a prolonged period of hypophysial depression.

Y*

Effects on plumage in normal breeds of fowl are not different from those in capons, but they may be more difficult to show because of the irregularity of feather regeneration except at the annual moult.

The oestrogen effects are not limited to domestic fowl.   Lahr and Riddle (1944) found that 10 daily injections of oestrone, oestradiol benzoate and diethylstil-boestrol reduced the testes of Ring Doves to 20 per cent or less of their normal weight.

Effects on the female

Dunham and Riddle (1942) reported that in the Ring Dove oestradiol benzoate not infrequently retarded ovulation of the second egg of the clutch by some 24 hours.   Fraps (1955) likewise found that oestradiol benzoate delayed ovulation in domestic fowl.   Fraps presented evidence suggesting that a nervous mechanism may be involved in the release of an ovulation-inducing hormone from the anterior pituitary and that the ovarian hormone normally exciting the nervous apparatus causing the release of ovulation-inducing hormone is probably not an oestrogen. It was suggested that it may be a progestagen (p. 652).

Régnier and Caridroit (1938) found that weekly injections of oestradiol ben-zoate into growing hens caused regression of the comb, but the effect was not seen in laying hens and only slightly in adults at other times.   According to Breneman (1942c), the effect of diethylstilboestrol in causing hypotrophy of the comb is mediated in the same way in the hen as in the cock.

VI. BIOLOGICAL ACTION OF PROGESTERONE

Occurrence of Progestagens in Birds

Early reports that persistent post-ovulatory corpora lutea arise in birds proved to be unfounded, (see Fell 1924 ; Harrison, 1948 ; Matthews, 1955), but there is evidence that a third sex steroid, analogous in physiological activity with mam-malian progesterone, is elaborated in both sexes of domestic fowl.

By means of the method of Hooker and Forbes (1947), progesterone (or other progestagen) was demonstrated in the blood plasma of laying hens by Fraps, Hooker and Forbes, (1948).   Concentrations equivalent to at least 5 μg. proges-terone per ml. plasma were found in subsequent tests (Fraps, 1955).   Progestagen was also demonstrated in the plasma of non-laying hens as well as cocks, but not in the plasma of capons (Fraps, Hooker and Forbes, 1949).   It is likely, therefore, that the gonad is the source of the active substance, which may or may not be identical with mammalian progesterone.   Butt et al. (1951) and Edgar (1953) have raised the question of whether the method of Hooker and Forbes measures pro-gesterone or some related substance.   Fraps (1955) has emphasised that although desoxycortiscosterone and testosterone act similarly to progesterone in the hen neither of these substances reproduces the effects of progesterone in the mouse assay of Hooker and Forbes (1947, 1949).   Thus, although androgen may occur in the laying hen (Greenwood and Chu, 1939 ; Nalbandov, 1953), testosterone, at least, is not the progestagen found in the blood-stream of the hen.

Fraps and associates report that a high level of progestagen occurs at the period of ovulation, and Fraps (1955) believes that the maturing follicle is the probable source.   The precise ovarian site of formation remains in doubt, but Marshall and Coombs (1957) have suggested that atretic follicles are involved.   In wild birds (e.g. Rook) lipoidal areas, heavily positive for cholesterol, appear in the ovary while the young are still nestlings.   Such atresias continue throughout life.   During the peaks of sexual activity in spring and autumn the metamorphosis of successive follicles builds up a very considerable reservoir of ovarian cholesterol.   It is unlikely that such cholesterol, rhythmically produced in large amounts is without significance.   Marshall and Coombs (1957) consider that, in the absence of persistent, post-ovulatory luteal bodies, progesterone is produced in atretic follicles and that the associated cholesterol may be concerned with its biosynthesis. Marshall and Serventy (1956) have suggested that the lipids produced during follicular atresia may have their counterpart in the male in the apparently similar substance produced during the post-nuptial metamorphosis of the testis tubules (p. 603).   In wild species tubule luteinisation and cholesterol production occur only after the discharge of spermatozoa and the assumption, in most species, of parental responsibilities.   In the male Satin Bower-bird (which continues to display and does not tend the nest or young) such metamorphosis is delayed (Marshall, 1954).   The Short-tailed Shearwater (*Puffinus tenuirostris*) is in direct contrast.   In this species the male takes the first incubation shift while the female goes to sea.   Post-nuptial tubule luteinisation has begun in the males even before they start to sit (Marshall and Serventy, 1956).

Lofts and Marshall (1959) analysed the lipid and other material of the tubules in two groups of pigeons.   The first group consisted of birds photostimulated to near the height of sexual activity when the testes were of maximum size and contained cholesterol-free seminiferous tubules full of spermatozoa but a densely lipoidal and cholesterol-positive interstitium (as Fig. *12*. 4b).   The second group consisted of similar birds that had been hypophysectomised and possessed small testes containing collapsed tubules full of dense, cholesterol-positive lipid material, and an interstitium which had only moderate quantities of lipid in the Leydig cytoplasm (Fig. *12*. 4c and p. 602).   The gonads in both groups were dissected out and their lipid content extracted with acetone and re-extracted with chloroform. Several steroid hormones were identified by paper chromatography.   The spermatogenetically active pre-nuptial gonads contained only androsterone and androstenediol.   On the other hand, the lipid extracts of the tubules of the hypophysectomised post-nuptial birds contained progesterone and its metabolite pregnanedione and, in addition, androstadienedione.   Since the progestagens appeared only in chromatograms of extracts of post-nuptial testes, and were absent from those of testes containing only interstitial lipids, they may be derived from the intratubular lipid.

The gradual depletion of cholesterol-positive lipids in the Leydig cytoplasm towards the height of the breeding season is almost certainly an indication of androgenic hormone secretion by the interstitium (Marshall, 1949, 1951b).   It now seems possible that the post-nuptial metamorphosis of the tubule contents, and the gradual depletion of the newly arisen cholesterol-positive lipids, is similarly indicative of a post-nuptial secretion of progestagen.

A comparable, though less prolific, post-nuptial manufacture of tubule cholesterol occurs also in at least some fishes (Lofts and Marshall, 1957) and reptiles (Marshall and Woolf, 1957).   It is of phylogenetic interest that the mechanism, as far as is known, has been suppressed in mammals, although it occurs in rats after hypophysectomy (Coombs and Marshall, 1956) or experimental irradiation (Lacy and Rotblat, 1960).

Effects of Progesterone in Birds

Reproductive organs

Fraps and his associates reported a high level of progestagen in the blood at the time of ovulation in hens, and showed also that the experimental administration of progesterone forces ovulation in intact, but not in hypophysectomised birds (Fraps and Dury, 1943; Rothchild and Fraps, 1949a; Fraps, 1955). They believe that oestrogen is probably not influential in stimulating the release of LH from the adenohypophysis of the ovulating hen but that avian progestagen may, in fact, do so. There is evidence, too, that progestagen as well as oestrogen may be involved in the seasonal hypertrophy of the oviduct (Hertz, Larsen and Tullner, 1947 ; Mason, 1952 ; Brandt and Nalbandov, 1952).

The reaction of the oviducal glands in response to progesterone and other sex hormones was investigated by Brandt and Nalbandov (1956). Immature pullets 60 and 70 days of age were injected with varying amounts of oestrogen alone, progesterone alone or androgen alone, and with combinations of oestrogen and progesterone or oestrogen and androgen. Each of the three hormones when injected alone caused increased oviducal weight, but neither progesterone nor androgen alone was able to cause differentiation or proliferation of the albumen-secreting glands. Moreover, when given alone, none of the hormones used was able to induce formation of secretion granules within the glands, or the secretion of albumen into the lumen. Combinations of oestrogen and progesterone or oestrogen and androgen were required to obtain this effect. There was no evidence of antagonism between oestrogen and progesterone but the combination of oestrogen with high doses of androgen resulted in diminished morphological and physiological effectiveness. The oestrogen-progesterone combination was more efficient in " inducing morphological and physiological development " but whether progesterone plays the same rôle in nature is unknown. Lehrman and Brody (1957) believe that the normal sexual cycle in the Ring Dove involves oestrogen secretion " concurrent with nest-building " followed by that of progesterone "associated with egg-laying, maximal oviduct growth, and incubation behaviour ".

Behaviour

Possible behavioural implications of the presence of progestagen in both male and female have been stressed by Marshall and Serventy (1956) and Marshall and Coombs (1957). Some behaviour patterns (e.g. broodiness) often believed to be controlled by prolactin may, in fact, be essentially mediated by progestagen. At the same time very great caution is needed in any consideration of progestagen function in male behaviour. Progestagen is perhaps formed as a result of tubule metamorphosis and luteinisation. Yet in several—perhaps many—plural-brooded species the males incubate, feed, and sometimes defend the young even though tubule luteinisation will probably not occur until after the eggs of the final clutch have been fertilised. Lehrman (1958b) believes that progesterone is involved in the incubation behaviour of experimental Ring Doves.

Plumage

Progesterone has no effect on the plumage of the capon Leghorn, or Sebright bantam (Mühlbock, 1939).

VII. The Effects of Hypophysectomy and of Gonadotrophins in Birds

Technique of Hypophysectomy, and Survival Time

Hypophysectomy appears first to have been carried out on birds by Mitchell (1929). He used the transpharyngeal route in young Brown Leghorn fowl but found that when the anterior lobe was completely removed the bird died within 10 days. Sub-total hypophysectomy was not necessarily fatal but often led to stunting of the bird and delay in the appearance of sexual maturity, as shown by plumage and gonadal changes. An operation on pigeons by an orbital route (involving removal of the eye-ball) was described by Ogata and Nishimura (1927) and Martins (1933). These authors do not appear to have described the subsequent condition of the reproductive organs. Hill and Parkes (1934a, b) used the transpharyngeal route on fowl and turkeys and reported the effects of the operation on the general condition, gonads, accessory organs, and plumage. They observed that totally hypophysectomised birds usually died within a few days of the operation. Of 30 birds which received no post-operative treatment, 80 per cent died within 48 hours. Only one survived more than 14 days. The symptoms preceding death included sluggishness increasing to semi-coma, as well as a rise in body temperature and a fall in blood sugar. In several fowl mild convulsions were observed. Hill and Parkes attributed death to metabolic disturbance and found that it was often avoidable if anterior lobe therapy or injection of adrenal cortex extract was started at the time of operation and continued for the following week. Of 27 birds given adrenal cortical or anterior lobe extract for 46 days after operation, 14 survived more than a fortnight, and showed a gradual recovery of the blood-sugar level during the time of injections (Hill, Corkill and Parkes, 1934).

Schooley (1939) employed a parapharyngeal approach on pigeons, avoiding the Eustachian tubes and giving access to both " lobes," either of which could be removed (without injury to the brain) by aspiration with a fine canula. Schooley reported an operative mortality of less than 2 per cent, and survival for up to a year or more. The operation was followed by a decrease in food and fluid consumption, a marked weight loss, and, sometimes, convulsions resembling hypoglycaemic shock. Although post-operative mortality was low, some birds became sick and were best treated with an injection of whole anterior pituitary extract. Force-feeding was very effective in maintaining body weight and condition, but did not prevent hypotrophy of the testes (Schooley, Riddle and Bates, 1941). Nalbandov and Card (1942, 1943) hypophysectomised young Brown Leghorns and observed a decreased BMR which they ascribed to reduced food consumption rather than to hypopituitarism. They found that young birds survived the operation much better than old ones and Shirley and Nalbandov (1956) record that in the latter the fatal drop in blood sugar can be prevented by the raised food intake brought about by additional illumination. This observation that the post-operative mortality could be avoided by nocturnal illumination is a classic example of the value of the simple approach to an apparently complex problem.

Effects of Hypophysectomy

Male reproductive organs and sexual characters

Hill and Parkes (1934b) found that hypophysectomised cocks suffered rapid atrophy of the testes, the main drop in weight occurring by the end of the 5th week. Within 2 weeks the tubules lacked spermatozoa, and by the end of 5 weeks contained only spermatogonia and a few Sertoli cells. These changes were accompanied by an apparent increase in the amount of intertubular tissue (Fig. *12.* 30). Coincidentally there was a decrease in the size of the accessory reproductive organs and in the dependent secondary sexual characters. Thus, the vasa deferentia were atrophic 5 weeks after the operation and the comb and wattles showed a continuous decline that started within a few days and continued until the comb was similar to that of the caponised adult. Comparison of the rate of comb atrophy after castration and after hypophysectomy suggested that the endocrine activity of the testis stopped immediately on removal of the pituitary (Fig. *12.* 31). Similar results were observed in the turkey and Sebright bantam. The histological appearance of the comb of the hypophysectomised Sebright bantam was found to be similar to that of the capon (Fig. *12.* 32).

As castration does not affect the plumage of Leghorn cocks, feather changes taking place after hypophysectomy could not be ascribed to modifications within the testis. However, a typical castration effect was obtained in a Sebright bantam in which the characteristic henny feathers of the breed were moulted out after hypophysectomy and replaced by essentially male-type plumage.

Benoit (1936) found that the presence of the anterior lobe is indispensable to spermatogenic and endocrine activity in the drake. After hypophysectomy both functions became quiescent, though the threshold requirement of the interstitial cells seemed to be lower than that of the tubules. Complete, or nearly complete removal of the gland caused the dimensions of both elements to decrease by about one-third to one-half in the course of 2 months. Benoit (1935b, 1937) showed also that removal of the pituitary prevented the customary response to artificial illumination. Various other authors have described the gross effects of hypophysectomy on gonad weight and gametogenesis. Changes also occur in the adrenal cortex (Mather and Riddle, 1942).

It is of particular interest that hypophysectomy in the first instance abruptly provokes a testicular decline similar to that occurring naturally at the end of the spermatogenetic cycle of seasonally breeding birds. Thus, the removal from the cockerel or pigeon (Coombs and Marshall, 1956 ; Lofts and Marshall, 1958) of the adenohypophysis leads to a testicular metamorphosis, including tubular steatogenesis and cholesterol production, comparable with that occurring naturally and sharply at the conclusion of the breeding season in wild birds (Fig. *12.* 33a–d). The same phenomenon also occurs, but more slowly, in birds that are prevented from undergoing their full sexual cycle by abnormal environmental conditions (Marshall, 1952b). The most likely explanation—in either case—is the cessation of gonadotrophic activity from the adenohypophysis.

Although the function of this temporary store of cholesterol in the post-nuptial tubules is still uncertain (p. 652) it is at least known that until it is cleared away (at different rates in different species) the next spermatogenetic cycle, and hence the

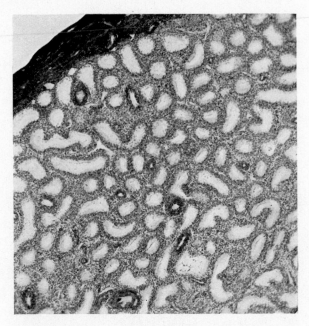

Fig. *12*. 30—Testis of a Brown Leghorn cock 35 days after hypophysectomy, showing shrinkage of tubules, concentration of intertubular tissue and thickening of the tunica by contraction (cf. Fig. *12*. 28b, showing effects of oestrogenisation). (From Hill and Parkes, 1934b.) (*Proc. Roy. Soc.*, B, 1934, **116**, 221.)

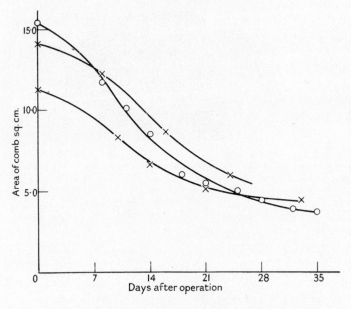

Fig. *12*. 31—Comparative rate of shrinkage of the comb of the Sebright Bantam cock after (×) castration and (o) hypophysectomy. (From Hill and Parkes, 1934b.) (*Proc. Roy. Soc.*, B, 1934, **116**, 221.)

next breeding season, does not begin.   While the tubules are metamorphosing at the end of each spermatogenesis in seasonal birds the exhausted interstitium regenerates itself and the new Leydig cells rapidly become lipoidal.   The testis tunic, too, is renewed (Marshall, 1955; Marshall and Serventy, 1957).   After the complete removal of the adenohypophysis the new interstitium arises as part of the intrinsic rhythm of the testis, but there is no suggestion that the new interstitium can secrete in the absence of gonadotrophin.   On the other hand, the

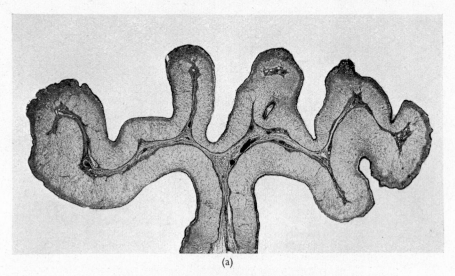

(a)

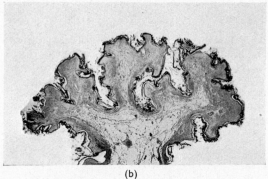

(b)

Fig. *12*. 32—Histological changes in the rose-comb of the Sebright Bantam after hypophysectomy.   Cross-section of the comb of (a) normal adult cock, (b) cock 39 days after hypophysectomy.   (From Hill and Parkes, 1934b.)   (*Proc. Roy. Soc.*, B, 1934, **116**, 221.)

cholesterol-positive tubule lipids are gradually expended after hypophysectomy. Thus, at about 60 days after the operation the " post-nuptial " cholesterol has begun to disappear from the tubules of hypophysectomised cockerels, a process that is hastened by the administration of FSH (Lofts and Marshall, 1958).

Although removal of the anterior pituitary reduces behavioural reactions associated with androgen and oestrogen secretion, Collias (1944) has reported that hypophysectomised pigeons sometimes remain extremely aggressive.   It will be recalled, too, that combat occurs between male pigeons congenitally devoid of testes (p. 598).

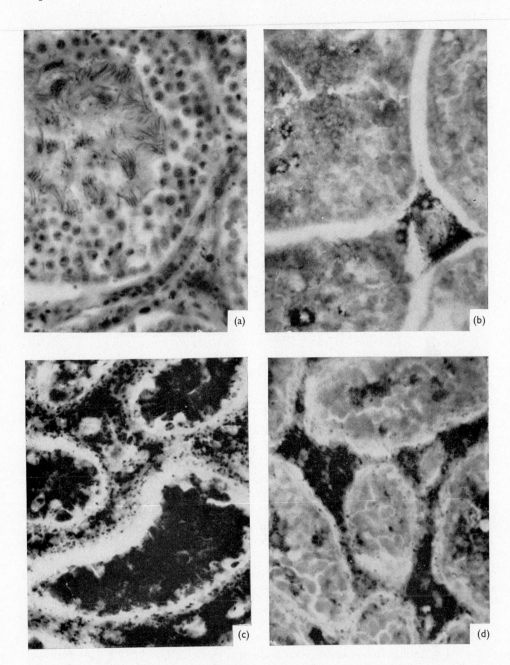

Fig. *12*. 33—Steatogenesis in the testis of the hypophysectomised cock. (a) Remaining testis of unilaterally castrated cockerel, showing bunched spermatozoa and absence of tubular lipids. (b) Testis of cockerel 17 days after hypophysectomy and before reduction in comb-size was apparent. The black mottling indicates the beginning of tubular steatogenesis. (c) Testis of cockerel 62 days after hypophysectomy, showing tubular collapse and massive steatogenesis. A fresh generation of interstitial cells has arisen in the absence of the adenohypophysis. (d) Testis of cockerel 59 days after hypophysectomy. A new interstitium has arisen, and the tubular lipids seem to be disappearing in the absence of the adenohypophysis. (From Coombs and Marshall, 1956.)

Female reproductive organs

Hill and Parkes (1934b) found that hypophysectomised hens stopped laying. The ovary, oviduct and comb hypotrophied to a condition similar to that found in non-laying birds (Fig. *12*. 34). It was concluded that the changes associated with hypophysectomy, i.e. moulting, loss of fertility, comb regression, loss of body weight, etc., were similar to those seen at the end of the laying season, and that the annual moult is due to a temporary pituitary deficiency.

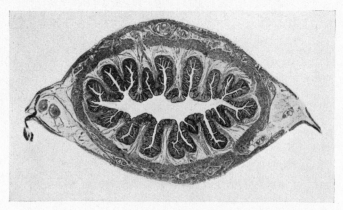

Fig. *12*. 34—Cross-section of the oviduct 44 days after hypophysectomy of a laying hen, showing atrophy of the albumen
secreting tissue. (From Hill and Parkes, 1934b.) (*Proc. Roy.
Soc.*, B, 1934, **116,** 221.)

Hypophysectomy was used by Rothchild and Fraps (1949b) to determine the time of release of the ovulation-producing hormone, in experiments analogous to those on mammals (*see* Volume III). These authors hypophysectomised laying domestic hens at times varying from 2 hours to 10 hours before an expected ovulation. The percentage of birds ovulating decreased as the interval increased, and it was concluded that the ovulation-producing hormone was most frequently released 4 to 6 hours before the time of ovulation.

Indirect effects on sexual characters

Hypophysectomy causes atrophy not only of the gonad, but also of the thyroid, and thyroidectomy leads to profound changes in the plumage of certain breeds (notably the Brown Leghorn). The hypophysectomised fowl, therefore, should have plumage similar to that of the thyroidectomised gonadectomised bird. Hill and Parkes (1935) observed changes in the plumage of the hypophysectomised Brown Leghorn cock in accord with this expectation. The black breast feathers were moulted and fringed brown feathers regenerated after hypophysectomy as after thyroidectomy. All over the body black pigment gave way to brown and the amount of fringing increased (Fig. *12*. 35). In the hen less definite colour changes were produced probably because the effects produced by ovarian deficiency are to some extent reversed by thyroid deficiency. Nevertheless, all over the body fringing increased and the speckling characteristic of the dorsal feathers disappeared.

Fig. *12*. 35—Effect of hypophysectomy on the breast feather of the Brown Leghorn cock. (a) Feather of normal bird, black and compact. (b) Feather regenerated after hypophysectomy, brown and fringed. The effect is typical of thyroid deficiency. (From Hill and Parkes, 1935.) (*Proc. Roy. Soc.*, B, 1935, **117**, 202.)

Sexual development of the embryo

Fugo (1940) developed a method of removing the hypophysis from chick embryos 33–38 hours old, and studied the subsequent development of the soma and various organs including the gonads. He found that the differentiation of the testes was normal but that the intertubular tissue failed to develop. In the hypophysectomised female embryo, the left gonad showed defective cortical development, there being a much reduced number of cortical cords. The right gonad was normal. Fugo's observations on the male embryo correlate well with those of Domm (*see* p. 663) on the effect of hypophysial gonadotrophins administered during incubation; those on the female are less concordant because Domm found that hypophysial gonadotrophins produced medullary rather than cortical growth in the ovary and rudimentary right gonad.

Avian Gonadotrophins

Gonadotrophin content of the avian hypophysis

The occurrence of gonadotrophic substances in the pituitary of birds was demonstrated soon after Smith and Engel, and Aschheim and Zondek, had shown their presence in mammalian pituitaries. Riddle and Flemion (1928), using a stock of 500 fresh glands, found that the implantation of pituitary glands from mature Ring Doves hastened sexual maturity in immature doves. These and similar experiments (e.g. Domm, 1931b, c) established that the pituitary was a gonadotrophic organ in birds as well as in mammals, and many assays of potency have been carried out.   Riley and Fraps (1942a, b) found that the pituitaries of adult males were 7 to 11 times as active as those of females, and that the glands of non-laying hens were less active than those of layers.   Phillips (1943) made

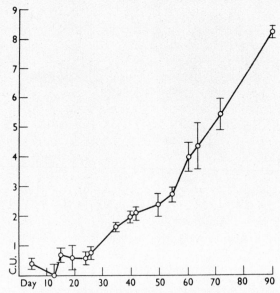

Fig. *12*. 36—Potency of cockerel pituitary in chick units.
Vertical lines represent standard errors.   A total of
864 pituitaries was used.   (From Breneman, 1945.)

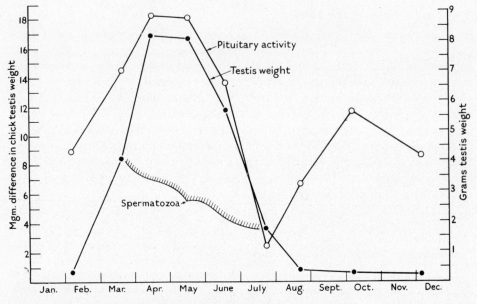

Fig. *12*. 37—Activity of testis and pituitary in pheasants.   (From Greeley and Meyer, 1953.)

similar observations.   Breneman (1945), using a test based on stimulation of the testes of the chick, assayed the gonadotrophic potency of the hypophysis of young cockerels.   The results (Fig. *12*. 36) showed a steady increase in activity up to

3 months of age. Seasonal variation occurs in the gonadotrophic potency of the hypophysis, as shown by Burger (1949) and Greeley and Meyer (1953). The latter authors, working on pheasants, showed, as did Breneman in the young cockerels, that the gonadotrophin content correlated positively with testis size (Fig. *12*. 37).

It should be emphasised, however, as with similar observations on mammals, that the gonadotrophin content of the hypophysis at any particular time represents the excess of elaboration over release, so that a high content does not necessarily imply a functionally active gland.

The separate existence of avian FSH and LH has been demonstrated by many workers. Fractionation can be achieved by the same extraction methods as are used for mammalian pituitaries (Fraps, Fevold and Neher, 1947; Nalbandov, Meyer and McShan, 1951), and LH can be demonstrated in bird pituitaries by specialised biological tests (Witschi, 1935a, 1937; Witschi and Riley, 1940). Benoit (1937), Leonard (1937) and Gorbman (1941), also produced evidence for the presence of distinct FSH and LH in avian pituitaries. An FSH/LH ratio of about 10 : 1 was estimated by Riley and Fraps (1942b) for the domestic fowl.

The identification of the separate mammalian hypophysial gonadotrophins (FSH, LH = ICSH, LTH = prolactin) and nature of the gonadotrophic substances in pregnant mare serum (PMS) and human pregnancy urine (chorionic gonadotrophin = CG) are discussed in Volume III, Chapter 25.

Similarity of avian and mammalian hypophysial gonadotrophins

A general similarity between avian and mammalian gonadotrophins was also demonstrated. Witschi, Stanley and Riley (1937) assayed the gonadotrophin content of 6000 desiccated turkey hypophyses on immature mice and anoestrous birds and found the material to be qualitatively similar to that obtained from the glands of cattle, sheep and rats. Again, Lipschütz, Kallas and Wilckens (1929) induced sexual maturity in immature mice by the implantation of anterior pituitary lobes from pigeons. These various experiments, together with those indicating that mammalian gonadotrophins are active in birds (e.g. Domm and Van Dyke, 1932a, b) and with analogous information for other vertebrates, suggest a lack of species, family, or even class specificity in gonadotrophic activity. This conclusion is of importance because the difficulty of obtaining bulk supplies of avian hypophyses has meant that most of the investigations on birds have involved the use of gonadotrophins of mammalian origin.

There is, however, some evidence that mammalian and avian gonadotrophins are not entirely interchangeable, and Nalbandov, Meyer and McShan (1951) have suggested that avian ICSH (or LH) is appreciably different from its mammalian homologue or that an additional " avian ICSH " occurs in chicks. In their experiments the atrophic combs of hypophysectomised males grew for 10 to 12 days in response to mammalian LH, but regression to pre-injection size then followed despite continued injections. By contrast, continuous comb-growth in such birds was achieved by the injection of fowl pituitary powder. Testes that failed to secrete androgen in response to mammalian LH-containing preparations were caused to do so continuously if fowl pituitary powder was substituted. The implication is that avian LH may possess properties not shared by its mammalian homologue. In other experiments Das and Nalbandov (1955) compared the capacity of avian and mammalian gonadotrophins to stimulate the ovaries of pre-puberal and hypophysectomised fowl. With the avian preparation follicles were transformed to a size involving yolk formation, but in neither intact nor hypophysectomised young fowl did exogenous mammalian gonadotrophins produce an effect. In intact and more mature birds, however, mammalian gonadotrophins induced follicular hypertrophy, presumably because the recipient's own adenohypophysis was already secreting " the factor essential for follicular maturation." On the other hand, gonadotrophins from both sources acted on the ovarian medulla and caused an increase both of total ovarian weight and of comb-growth. The evidence suggested a qualitative inability of the mammalian homologue to induce maturation of the cortical elements (follicles).

There is, however, one important consideration relevant to the continued administration of mammalian gonadotrophins into birds. The mammalian gonadotrophins are antigenically different from the avian ones (Parkes and Rowlands, 1937) and there is little doubt that a bird may become immunised against preparations of mammalian origin. Apparent failure of mammalian gonadotrophins in long-term experiments does not, therefore, necessarily imply that the preparations are hormonally inadequate.

Effects of Exogenous Gonadotrophins

Effects on general and special characters

Gonadotrophins are said to raise blood calcium level in pigeons (Riddle and Dotti, 1936), an effect mainly associated with oestrogen secretion (p. 635). Schildmacher and Steubing (1952) injected migratory Bramblings with PMS and reported the accumulation of depot fat, but this result, like many others obtained after photostimulation, may ultimately be attributable to gonad stimulation and the effect of sex hormones. There is some evidence that pre-migratory restlessness (*Zugunruhe*) can be induced by photostimulation in the absence of testes (p. 587).

Witschi (1935a) demonstrated the direct hypophysial control of the breeding plumage of Weaver-Finches, and in one species, of beak colour as well. It was shown that at least some castrated individuals regularly showed seasonal plumage changes for three years. In *Euplectes pyromelana* and *Quelea quelea* males, females and castrated birds wear the henny plumage during the season of sexual inactivity. During the sexual season the males, and gonadectomised males and females, wear the cock plumage. Only the intact females retain the henny plumage and regenerate henny feathers at this period of the year. Injection experiments indicate that the cock plumage is mediated by gonadotrophin but that the effect in the female is prevented by the ovarian hormone produced as a result of hypophysial stimulation of the ovary. Injection of oestrogens into intact or castrated males during the breeding season prevents the plumage reaction to the hypophysial hormones.

Witschi (1936c, 1955) reports that as little as 1 r.u. of PMS produces cock plumage in *E. pyromelana*, ruling out any suggestion of control by thyrotrophin. Of the constituents of PMS, Witschi believes that LH, generally considered also to induce ovulation, is responsible. Segal and Witschi (1955) conclude that " the weaver feather reacts positively to about 0·1 to 0·01 r.u. of most hypophysial preparations, to 10 r.u. of pregnant mare serum, and to 60 r.u. of human chorionic gonadotrophin. Probably these differences reflect the dependence of the rat unit on the FSH content of the various preparations. Injection of PMS gonadotrophins into non-breeding females stimulated ovarian development, and indirectly the enlargement of oviducts (p. 669). The plumage reaction, however, depended on the amount injected. If small, henny feathers regenerated due to released ovarian hormone; if large, the feathers were of the cock type. Females can thus be induced to lay eggs while they are actually regenerating cock feathers.

Marlow (1950) has suggested that a hypophysial hormone may act directly on the comb of chicks.

Effect on embryos

Highly significant experiments were recorded by Domm (1937) on fowl embryos injected with sheep hypophysial gonadotrophin from day 5 to day 9 of

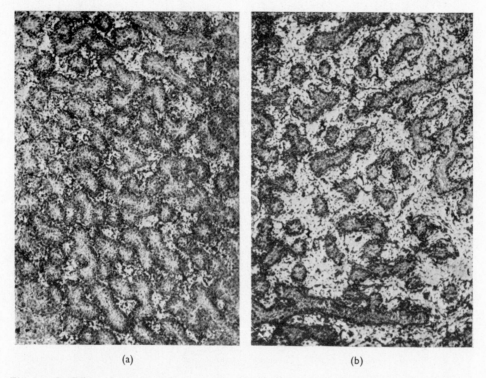

(a)   (b)

Fig. *12*. 38—Effect of gonadotrophin on testis of chick embryo. (a) Testis of untreated chick at 18th day of incubation. (b) Testis of chick receiving sheep hypophysial gonadotrophin on days 5 to 9 of incubation. Note increase in inter-tubular tissue. (From Domm, 1937.)

incubation and examined on day 18 or 19. In the male embryo there was enlargement of the two testes which histologically showed increase in the intertubular tissue but little change in the tubules (Fig. *12*. 38). Other sexual characters were normal. In the female embryo, there was some enlargement of the left ovary, but very great enlargement of the rudimentary right gonad (Fig. *12*. 39). The Müllerian and Wolffian ducts were normal. Histological examination of the gonads showed that the enlargement was almost entirely in the medullary zone, which in extreme cases had a vacuolated appearance owing to distention of medullary tubules.

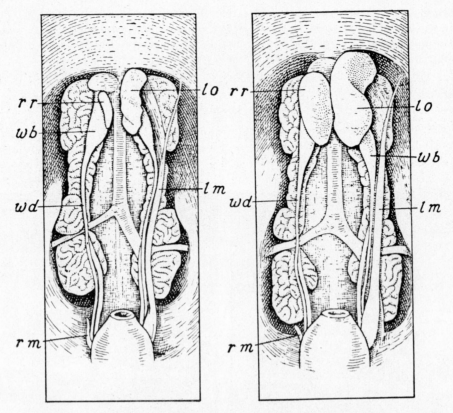

Fig. *12.* 39—Effect of sheep hypophysial gonadotrophin on the urogenital system of the female chick embryo. (a) Control female, 18th day of incubation. (b) Female embryo of the same age which had received daily injections of sheep gonadotrophin from the 5th to 9th days. l.o. = left ovary; r.r. = rudimentary right gonad; w.b. = Wolffian body; w.d. = Wolffian duct; l.m. = left Müllerian duct; r.m. = rudiment of right Müllerian duct. (From Domm, 1937.)

Effect on young fowl

Domm (1931b) found that implantation of homologous pituitary tissue into male Brown Leghorn chicks caused a pronounced hypertrophy of the testes associated with increase in size and colouring of the rudimentary comb. Domm and Van Dyke (1932a) were able to obtain similar results with extracts prepared from sheep pituitary glands, which in 3 weeks caused the testis weight to increase from 0·176 g. to 0·669 g. Domm (1931c) was initially less successful with experiments on female chicks, but Domm and Van Dyke (1932b) produced a five-fold increase in the weight of the ovary and a fifteen-fold increase in the weight of the oviduct in Brown Leghorn chicks by administration of gonadotrophic extract of sheep pituitary. This work was considered in more detail by Domm (1937), who reviewed and integrated results obtained on newly hatched chicks injected for 2 or 3 weeks from the second day after hatching. In both sexes the treatment caused a notable growth of the comb, and in the male attempts to crow and tread were observed within 2 weeks of the start of injection. On dissection at the end of the period of treatment, marked changes were seen in the gonads. In the male, the testes were some ten times heavier in the treated chicks than in the controls, and the vasa deferentia were hypertrophied. Histological examination of the testis tubules showed them to be greatly enlarged and to contain advanced stages of spermatogenesis, though no spermatozoa (Fig. *12*. 40). The interstitial cells

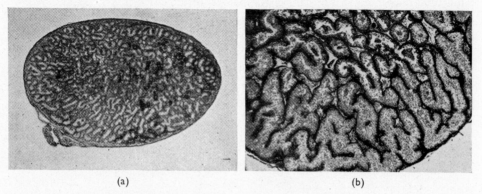

(a) (b)

Fig. *12*. 40—Testes of chicks 24 days after hatching. (a) Untreated. (b) Receiving 21 daily injections of sheep hypophysial gonadotrophin, starting on the 2nd day after hatching. Same magnification. Note great hypertrophy of tubules. (From Domm, 1937.)

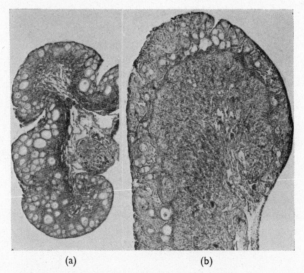

(a) (b)

Fig. *12*. 41—Ovaries of chicks 22 days after hatching. (a) Untreated. (b) Received 15 daily injections of sheep gonadotrophin starting on the 4th day after hatching. Same magnification. Note hypertrophy of medullary layer. (From Domm, 1937.)

appeared to be more abundant. In the female, there was gross enlargement of the ovary and oviduct, but not of the right gonad. Histological examination of the ovary showed enormous enlargement of the medullary tissue around which cortex similar to that seen in the normal ovary was stretched as a cap (Fig. *12*.41). Two points of difference from Domm's results with chick embryos may be noticed:

(a) the lack of effect on the right gonad in the female chick, and (b) the occurrence of tubular enlargement in the testis of the male chick.

Work of this kind was continued with different extracts. Breneman (1936) found that maximum stimulation of the gonads of the chick followed the injection of FSH or of PMS.   Luteinising extracts of horse, sheep or pig pituitaries increased the weight of both ovary and testis.   Breneman concluded that at 5 and 15 days after hatching the ovary of the chick is easily stimulated.   In the experiments of

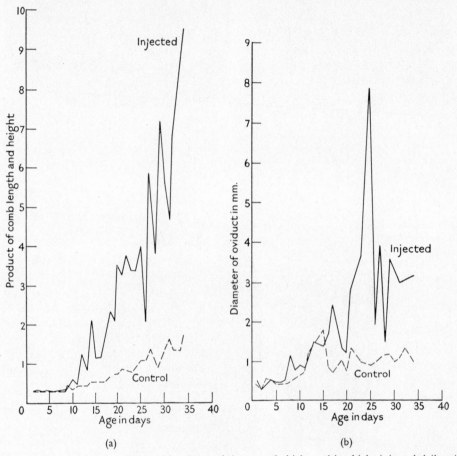

(a)   (b)

Fig. *12*. 42—(a) Comb and (b) oviducal growth in normal chicks and in chicks injected daily with 140 i.u. of PMS. (From Taber, 1948.) (By permission of the publisher from *J. exp. Zool.*, 1948, **107,** 70 and 73.)

Asmundson, Gunn and Klose (1937), the ovaries of birds injected for 10 days with PMS, and killed when 10 or 15 days old, showed an increase in interstitial tissue but no apparent effect on the follicles.   The ovaries of the older females injected for 5 to 42 days and killed when 30 to 100 days old were hyperaemic, and had increased interstitial tissue and enlarged follicles.   Nalbandov and Card (1946) injected female chicks with FSH followed by LH at various stages between 30 and 180 days of age.   There was some increase in the size of the ovaries and oviducts but follicles of ovulating size were produced only 8 to 22 days before uninjected controls began to lay.   Sluiter and van Oordt (1947) obtained a marked increase in male hormone production in cockerels treated with PMS and noted that lipid vacuoles were practically lacking in the interstitial cells of treated birds. Taber (1948) injected young female Leghorns, aged 1 day to $5\frac{1}{2}$ months, with PMS, FSH and LH. All the preparations caused growth of the comb, indicating androgen production, LH being the most effective. PMS and FSH, but not LH, caused oviducal growth indicating oestrogen production (Fig. *12*. 42). None of the preparations caused follicular growth. On the basis of the work reviewed above, it appears that the cortical elements of the ovary of the immature bird are comparatively resistant to gonadotrophins, at least to those of mammalian origin.

In work on male chicks, Byerly and Burrows (1938) showed that under certain conditions the testis is readily stimulated by PMS and Taber (1949) provided interesting information that the Leydig cells of chicks injected with PMS, FSH and LH developed a granular cytoplasm while controls, during the first month, retained cells " filled primarily with large lipoidal droplets " (p. 651). Leydig hyperplasia was accompanied by comb-growth which was not primarily correlated with testis weight or the degree of tubule stimulation. Of the principles injected, LH had the least effect on the tubules and testicular weight. Comb growth was stimulated to a less degree in FSH-treated chicks than in those treated with LH and PMS.

Effect on other young and sexually quiescent birds

Work on immature birds of other species has not been extensive. Schockaert (1931) obtained premature spermatogenesis in young drakes by the injection of saline extract of fresh cattle pituitary. The results of Benoit and Aron (1934) were comparable but indicated that maximum sensitivity occurred at a later stage. Riddle and Polhemus (1931) found that the testes of immature doves and pigeons were extremely sensitive to alkaline extracts of mammalian pituitary, the ovary being much less so. Evans and Simpson (1934) found that the testes of immature pigeons responded to gonadotrophic preparations of pituitary origin, but were insensitive to the gonadotrophic substance of human pregnancy urine. They considered, however, that this was not conclusive differentiation between the hormones of pituitary and chorionic origin, since material obtained from the urine of a man with a testis tumour produced a large response in the testis of the squab (Evans, Simpson, Austin and Ferguson, 1933). These authors failed to obtain growth of the pigeon testis with extracts of pregnant mare serum and they also found that the pigeon testis, unlike the ovary, did not show augmentation or synergism between anterior pituitary extracts and pregnancy urine extracts. Leblond (1938) investigated the effects of FSH and LH, separated by the method of Fevold, on the immature pigeon. FSH caused rapid growth of the testes, ovaries and oviduct, while LH caused regression of the gonads, but development of the crop gland. Lahr, Riddle and Bates (1941) gave daily injections of gonadotrophic pituitary injections to immature pigeons for 4 to 16 days and produced hypertrophy of all testicular tissues for the first 4 to 6 days, and of tubular tissue thereafter. PMS was also found to be effective, and contrary to Riddle's previous results (1931b), chorionic gonadotrophin.

Several most instructive experiments have been carried out on the House Sparrow. Juvenile female House Sparrows injected with 2·5 r.u. PMS by Kirschbaum *et al.* (1939) variously showed follicles with yolk and darkening of bill indicating the production of male hormone, eggs in the oviduct, and medullary bone (p. 635). Such effects were greater in spring. Fledgling males similarly treated developed enlarged testes and black beaks. Again, Pfeiffer and Kirschbaum (1941, 1943) observed that in the House Sparrow PMS caused the advancement of

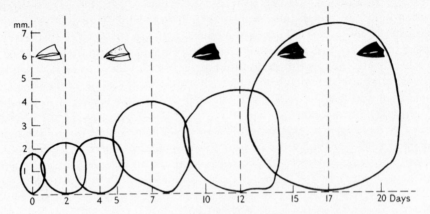

Fig. 12. 43—Effect of horse hypophysial gonadotrophin on testis size and beak colour of anoestrous sparrow. (Beaks are not to scale.) (From Witschi and Keck, 1935.)

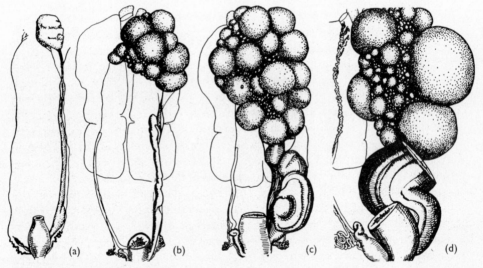

Fig. 12. 44—Sex organs of female sparrow during non-breeding season. (a) Untreated control. (b) Injected with purified FSH. (c) Injected with preparation of human hypophysis, showing excessive number of half-sized follicles and inadequately developed oviduct. (d) Injected with PMS, showing normal appearance of ovary, with a few large follicles and many small ones, and well-developed oviduct. (From Witschi, 1955.)

both tubule and interstitial elements of the testis, as well as ovarian changes. Bill colour gave evidence of androgen secretion by female sparrows. Witschi and Keck (1935) failed to cause any effect in quiescent males by injection of chorionic gonadotrophin, but obtained dramatic results with hypophysial FSH, which included great hypertrophy of the testis and blackening of the beak (Fig. 12. 43). Analogous results, stimulation of the ovary and enlargement of the oviduct, were obtained by similar means in the quiescent female. Extensions of these experiments were recorded by Witschi (1955) and his illustrations showing the comparative effects on the anoestrous female Sparrow of various mammalian gonadotrophic preparations are reproduced in Fig. 12.44. These observations may be compared with those made on fowl by Bates, Lahr and Riddle (1935). Vaugien (1956) found that injections of PMS stimulated vigorously the ovary of the anoestrous Goldfinch (*Carduelis carduelis*), so that egg-laying was induced in winter or early spring. He found that the ovarian changes were about as rapid as those occurring spontaneously at the beginning of the breeding season. Vaugien (1955) obtained similar results with PMS in the Sparrow and other birds. Nalbandov, Meyer and McShan (1946) carried out instructive experiments on hypophysectomised cocks with purified preparations of FSH and LH. They found that FSH alone caused enlargement of the testis but not of the atrophic comb of the hypophysectomised bird. LH alone caused both testicular hypertrophy and comb growth, as did FSH contaminated with LH. Chorionic gonadotrophin had no measurable biological effect on either the intact chick or the hypophysectomised cockerel.

There have been conflicting opinions concerning the capacity of PMS to stimulate the inactive testis, but Miller (1949) showed that the tubules of intact *Zonotrichia coronata* (believed to be in a refractory condition) produced primary spermatocytes after daily injections of 50 i.u. of PMS. Precise evidence was obtained by Lofts and Marshall (1958) by the use of FSH. They showed that, in hypophysectomised pigeons, the daily administration of as little as 0·6 i.u. of FSH caused the clearance of dense masses of recently formed " postnuptial " lipids and the production of spermatocytes. Larger doses resulted in the appearance of spermatozoa. Thus the lingering tubule lipids do not antagonise even very small amounts of FSH and the testis has only a brief refractory period while the new post-nuptial Leydig cells are achieving maturity.

Effect on adult birds

One of the earliest experiments, if not the very earliest, on the effects of gonadotrophic extracts on fowl was carried out by Walker (1925), who, in continuation of Long and Evans' experiments on rats, inhibited ovulation in the hen by injection of a saline extract

Fig. 12.45—Spontaneous hypertrophy of the ovary in a domestic hen. The condition is similar to that produced experimentally by the administration of FSH. (From the material of Greenwood.)

of ox anterior lobe. In laying hens, Fraps and Riley (1942) produced super-ovulation on the mammalian pattern (Volume III) by the intravenous injection of LH after pretreatment with PMS. In non-pretreated laying hens, ovulation can be induced in 6 to 9 hours by the injection of LH (Fraps, Riley and Olsen, 1942), as much as 17 hours before the expected time (Fraps, Olsen and Neher, 1942). The effect is most marked with the first ovulation of the clutch (Fraps and Dury, 1942; Fraps, 1946). Bates, Lahr and Riddle (1935) found that in the non-laying hen, administration of FSH resulted in the production of a mass of medium-sized follicles and increased the weight of the ovary tenfold. A similar condition occurring spontaneously in an adult hen has been recorded by Greenwood (personal communication) as shown in Fig. *12. 45*. Nalbandov and Card (1946) caused superovulation in non-laying hens and increased production in low-grade hens by the injection of FSH followed by LH.

Domm (1933) failed to stimulate the right gonad of sinistrally ovariectomised Leghorns by administration of sheep pituitary extract, and Kornfield and Nalbandov (1954) were unable to accelerate the growth of compensatory gonads or to maintain them in hypophysectomised poulards by the injection of mammalian gonadotrophins.

VIII. The Structure and Reactivity of the Avian Adenohypophysis

General and Cytological Structure of the Adenohypophysis

The avian anterior pituitary contains a bipartite anterior "lobe" and a posterior " lobe " but no pars intermedia. Rahn and Painter (1941) stated that the two distinct areas of the avian adenohypophysis were demonstrable in eighteen different species and their work was confirmed by Wingstrand (1951) and others. The posterior lobe possesses both pressor and oxytocic substances and is influential in the process of ovulation. The anterior lobe, in addition to elaborating the well-known trophic hormones, including the gonadotrophins and prolactin, produces an intermedin-like substance capable of causing melanophore-expansion in the hypophysectomised lizard *Anolis* (Kleinholtz and Rahn, 1940).

Detailed cytological information is available only for the domestic fowl, pigeon and dove, the glands of which are closely similar. Like the mammalian gland, the avian pituitary contains chromophobic cells and chromophilic acidophils and basiphils. It seems well established that the basiphils secrete gonadotrophins (Schooley and Riddle, 1938). To Payne (1940 and subsequently) we are indebted for much painstaking fundamental work on pituitary cytology. Payne (1946) has described two sorts of acidophils (α_1 and α_2). Another type with basiphilic properties is the T cell of Payne (1944) which is possibly concerned with thyroid function. During the period of broodiness there is a striking reduction in acidophils and basiphils together with an extraordinary upsurge of another type, the " broody cell " (Payne, 1943) which is distinct from both basiphils and acidophils. It is still uncertain which cell type elaborates prolactin (*see* p. 676). Of the two principal acidophils, α_1 cells occupy the caudal part of the lobe and α_2 cells the cephalic region. The former are said to resemble the α cells of mammals.

The embryonic pituitary is reported to contain acidophils as early as 10 to 17 days. According to Payne, basiphils, too, develop in birds as young as 10 days, but

Rahn is of the opinion that they are not found in the fully differentiated condition until sexual maturity is reached. Payne further suggests that between the ages of 10 to 30 days the gland in the male more than doubles its weight with the accompanying metamorphosis of chromophobes into chromophils of both principal kinds. An increase in the number and size of basiphils occurs from 30 days of age onwards when there is also a considerable increase in testis size. At 90 days the adenohypophysis appears to be fully functional. Breneman (1944) has shown that in fowls the gland increases by more than 9 times and the testis by more than 80 times in weight between hatching and 90 days of age. He concluded that pituitary secretion is initiated perhaps as early as the 5th day and certainly by the 15th day after hatching. It would seem that at a very early age there arises in fowl the potential for gonadotrophic stimulation, a conclusion which agrees with various reports of sexual precocity in young birds of widely unrelated groups (p. 612).

Moskowska (1949) presented data suggesting that FSH and perhaps LH are present in the chick embryo after 18 days of development. On the other hand, the work of Riddle and Schooley (1935) makes it likely that until the age of about 10 weeks the pituitary of pigeons and doves is without gonadotrophins ; subsequently, the testis comes under the control of the anterior lobe. Riddle (1947) has evidence that the age at which mating occurs in female pigeons is affected markedly by the season of hatching as well as by genetic factors which perhaps act through the basiphilic elements of the anterior pituitary. The selective implications of such variation cannot be discussed here but it will be recalled that xerophilous Red-billed Weavers are able to reproduce at the age of 9 months (Marshall and Disney, 1957). The Zebra Finch, another " opportunist " breeder, can produce bunched spermatozoa at an age of 50 days (Marshall and Serventy, 1958), and Vaugien (1953) has reported the same of the xerophilous Budgerygah. At the other extreme, the Short-tailed Shearwater (*Puffinus tenuirostris*) does not breed until it is 5 years old (Marshall and Serventy, 1956).

Interesting work by Hays (1945) has suggested a possible correlation between ageing and the degree of environmental stimulation necessary to achieve reproductive condition in the testes. Hays has evidence that older cocks are less fertile than young ones early in spring but that injections of chorionic gonadotrophins increase capacity, possibly indicating that like the central nervous system the anterior lobe deteriorates with advancing age.

Activation

The review by Benoit and Assenmacher (1953) summarises much early work on the activation of the adenohypophysis through the central nervous system. Shirley and Nalbandov (1956) transected completely the hypophysial stalk of laying hens and caused an immediate and permanent loss of body weight, and complete atrophy of the ovary, oviduct and comb. Thus, as regards gonadal function, they produced a condition closely resembling that seen after hypophysectomy. Stalk section did not significantly alter the secretion of thyrotrophic or adrenotrophic hormones as judged by the histology and weight of their target organs, the moulting pattern of hens or their ability to withstand sudden temperature changes and prolonged nocturnal fasts, all of which are drastically affected by hypophysectomy.   The data of Shirley and Nalbandov tend to support the theory (*see* Volume III) that the rate of secretion and release of gonadotrophins in birds is governed by a hypothalamic neurohumor transported through the hypophysial portal system (*see also* Assenmacher, 1958).

The extent to which the release of gonadotrophins (and the hypothetical ovulation-inducing hormone) is controlled by neural and hormonal influences is uncertain.   In the hen, ovulation is reflexly inhibited for as long as an egg is retained in the oviduct.   Huston and Nalbandov (1953) demonstrated that the presence of an irritant, such as a loop of thread, in the oviduct of laying hens completely suppressed ovulation in the great majority of the treated birds : yet there was no reduction in ovarian, oviducal, or comb dimensions for as long as 25 days.   When progesterone, or gonadotrophin containing LH was injected into such hens ovulations occurred during the period of treatment.   Huston and Nalbandov suggest that the presence of the described irritant prevents the secretion of amounts of LH sufficient to cause ovulation (" ovulatory peaks "), but does not depress secretion of LH sufficiently to impair normal androgen secretion (*see* p. 667).   Further, since the ovary maintains its normal size, they suggest that the presence of the loop does not prevent the secretion of normal amounts of FSH.   For approximately 25 days the ovary contained follicles of ovulatory size (30 mm. or over) in the same numbers as would be expected in intact hens.   These follicles continued to secrete oestrogen in normal amounts : the oviduct in operated hens did not decrease in size and remained capable of secreting albumen.   The neurogenic system indicated by these experiments no doubt serves to synchronise ovulation with the other events of the laying cycle.   Fraps (1954) concluded that " the neural mechanism believed to control the release of OIH from the anterior pituitary body exhibits diurnal periodicity in its threshold of response to excitation hormones ".

Fraps (1955) reviewed the varying effects of sex hormones in birds and suggested that the neural apparatus concerned, presumably over neurohumoral pathways, with the release of " ovulation inducing hormone " is stimulated by the secretion of an " excitation " hormone from the follicle next due to ovulate.   He concluded that oestrogen probably does not serve in the hen (as it apparently does in the rat) to excite the neural mechanism of OIH release.   Fraps further concluded that progesterone, or a physiologically equivalent progestagen (*see* p. 650), might satisfy the requirements of the postulated excitation hormone.   He described experiments giving at least presumptive evidence that the secretion of excitation hormone by the maturing follicle is dependent upon neurohumoral control of hypophysial secretions.   Thus, the maturation of the ovarian follicle may require " (1) an abrupt or episodic release of LH (or of LH + FSH) for preovulatory luteinisation, and (2) the continuing secretion of gonadotrophins including possibly luteotrophin, for maintenance of follicular function and production of the progestin which in turn elicits the ovulatory release of LH (OIH)."

In the House Sparrow, Kirschbaum *et al.* (1939) suggested that greater gonadotrophic stimulation is required for the ovaries than for the testes.   Under a photoperiod at which ovaries remained comparatively inactive, immature testes implanted into the same birds produced spermatozoa within a couple of weeks while the oöcytes remained relatively small.   Under natural conditions male birds quickly outstrip females in gametogenetic development, even though both sexes of at least some species begin their seasonal cycle at the same time (Marshall, 1955).   In the

Ring-necked Pheasant, the seasonal development of the ovary lagged more than a month behind that of the testis (Kirkpatrick, 1944).

There has been much discussion about the concept that the production or secretion of hypophysial gonadotrophins in birds is inhibited by gonadal hormones. In their assays of fowl pituitaries Riley and Fraps (1942a, b) reported that non-laying birds had the greatest gonadotrophic potential and ovulating individuals the least. Consequently it has been suggested that a high oestrogen level inhibits the secretion of gonadotrophin or, conversely, that there is a constant discharge and little storage of gonadotrophins in the ovulating bird. Breneman (1955) suggested that the modern domestic hen needs a high oestrogen production over a considerable part of the year, but it is arguable that the domestic fowl does not behave " naturally " in regard to reproduction. Thus, many conclusions reached from its study may not be relevant to the class Aves as a whole, of which most members reach an annual peak of reproductive activity followed by prolonged periods of sexual quiescence. Breneman (1950) considered the suggestion that the increase in gonadotrophins after castration is due to lack of utilisation by the usual target organ and consequent accumulation in the adenohypophysis. After an extensive study he concluded that this idea affords a plausible explanation of the observed variation of pituitary sizes in unilaterally castrated chicks, but seemed much less applicable to his data for capons and cockerels. Breneman (1955) summarised further work suggesting that either oestradiol or testosterone propionate given alone exerts little effect on the pituitary gland but that when oestrogen and androgen are administered simultaneously " maximum stimulation " of the reproductive system and hypophysis occurs. According to Kumeran and Turner (1949a) and Nalbandov and Baum (1948), both androgens and oestrogens reduce the secretion of hypophysial gonadotrophins in birds.

The Regeneration (Refractory) Period

A refractory period occurs during the post-nuptial regeneration of the seasonal sexual potential. There is much evidence that the adenohypophysis is unable indefinitely to sustain spermatogenetic activity in seasonal birds (Bissonnette and Wadlund, 1932; and many others). After the last series of parental duties has begun (or after a certain degree of experimental photostimulation) testis metamorphosis occurs (p. 652) and at the same time the bird becomes " refractory " to further external stimuli (see p. 763). In the female, Riley and Witschi (1938) concluded that the ovary of the House Sparrow is refractory to gonadotrophins in the autumn, improves in responsiveness during the winter and becomes fully functional in the subsequent spring.

The refractory period, intervening in the internal rhythm of reproduction, has received much attention in recent years because of its probable importance in the timing mechanism of breeding seasons and migration (Burger, 1949 ; Marshall, 1951a, b, 1954). The refractory period begins at the time of interstitial exhaustion and post-nuptial testis metamorphosis when the spermatogenetic material is converted into an amorphous mass of cholesterol-positive lipids (Marshall, 1949). These events are experimentally produced by hypophysectomy, which in fowls (Coombs and Marshall, 1956) and pigeons (Lofts and Marshall, 1958) causes changes identical with those observed at the termination of the sexual season. In fowls the new generation of interstitial cells arises rhythmically in the absence of the hypophysis, and in both fowls and pigeons the tubules clear slowly but without, of course, undergoing another spermatogenesis.   Observations on Arctic and xerophilous birds (Marshall, 1952b; Keast and Marshall, 1954; Serventy and Marshall, 1957), which undergo premature tubule metamorphosis if their environment is unsuitable for nesting, also suggest that the cessation of gonadotrophic influence is the essential factor involved in tubule metamorphosis.

Greeley and Meyer (1953) produced evidence suggesting that the anterior pituitary becomes refractory to external stimuli. They assayed on day-old male chicks extracts of dried glands collected over a year from sexually mature farm pheasants, and related the testis weight of the pheasants to hypophysial gonadotrophic activity as revealed in the chick tests (Fig. *12*. 37). The two indices ran together until after July when gonadotrophic activity rose without a corresponding enlargement of the testis in the donors. This, significantly, is exactly what happens in wild birds as the result of the post-nuptial regenerative growth in the interstitium (Marshall, 1952c). It is reflected in the typical autumnal recrudescence of sexual behaviour without, generally, the spermatogenesis that would cause testis enlargement. The winter depression before the spring rise in gonadotrophic activity seen in the pheasants also appears to happen in wild birds, but conclusions based on estimation of the gonadotrophic effect of the hypophysis do not of course distinguish between failure of the gland to elaborate and failure to secrete gonadotrophin. The work of Greeley and Meyer, however, certainly suggests that the anterior pituitary body becomes refractory in some way irrespective of day length. It suggests, too, that a regular late-summer recovery of the gland promotes the interstitial stimulation and secretion leading to the autumnal sexual activity that is widespread among birds. If the avian display continues, and the bird is not inhibited by winter conditions, the tubules will clear and the seasonal spermatogenesis begin.

Various experiments carried out by Benoit, Assenmacher and Walter (1950) suggest strongly that the anterior pituitary, in domestic drakes at least, has a refractory phase that may be independent of the gonads; bilateral castration during anoestrus did not induce pituitary hypertrophy nor unilateral castration compensatory hypertrophy of the remaining testis.

There is, then, evidence suggesting that a seasonal inhibition of gonadotrophin output causes the characteristic post-nuptial changes in the testes and that such inhibition can be caused by the lack of appropriate external stimuli or by gross photostimulation (Bissonnette and Wadlund, 1932). Prolactin (p. 677) is produced in both sexes of diverse species at the period of metamorphosis, and exogenous prolactin is known to inhibit hypophysial function (p. 682).   Therefore it might be thought that its seasonal liberation is responsible for the onset of the refractory period.   There remains, however, the fact that the males of plural-brooded species (e.g. House Sparrow), which also incubate and feed the young and therefore probably produce prolactin, are able to fertilise the eggs of successive clutches and do not undergo metamorphosis until the last clutch is hatched (p. 652). It is possible that the onset of the refractory period of the adenohypophysis is essentially under neural control with external stimuli, including behaviour, usually involved.

It would seem that the refractory period of the sexual cycle (taken to be the annual interlude during which individuals are unresponsive to photostimulation) ends with the seasonal recovery of hypophysial function and the time at which this happens is known with some degree of precision in certain species that have been much used in photostimulation studies.   Thus, House Sparrows of a stock acclimatised in North America will not respond to photostimulation in September, whereas young birds that have not reproduced (and therefore not become post-nuptially refractory) will do so (Riley, 1936, 1937).   Again, the North American White-crowned " Sparrow " (*Zonotrichia leucophrys*) ends its refractory period after 11th October (Wolfson, 1945; Farner and Mewaldt, 1955), and *Z. coronata* between 11th October and 20th November (Miller, 1948).   Burger (1947) and Wolfson (1952) have evidence that the refractory period of caged passerines is prematurely dissipated by reduced day lengths.

It now seems that post-nuptial refractoriness, possibly of the anterior pituitary, is the principal factor preventing reproduction for some months after each breeding season, and that the seasonal recovery of gonadotrophic function is an important regulator in the avian sexual cycle.   Thus, the Sooty Tern (*Sterna fusca*) of equatorial Ascension Island breeds about every 9·6 months (Chapin, 1950). It is probable that each breeding rhythm follows closely upon the recovery of gonadotrophic function after the preceding one, the vast flocks being synchronised by sexual display.   Transequatorial migrants likewise probably come spontaneously into seasonal reproductive condition and, after a period of display and resultant sexual synchronisation, reach a condition that will send them towards their breeding ground at about the same time each year.   Such an endogenous rhythm could not be expected to remain perpetually in step with the seasons, so that an external regulator must operate somewhere; but there is now evidence that at least some avian species possess an internal rhythm of remarkable regularity (Marshall, 1959, and *see* Chapter 13).

IX. BIOLOGICAL ACTION OF PROLACTIN

General Characters

Much attention has been paid to the hypophysial hormone prolactin, since the pioneer researches of Riddle and his associates.   In addition to the varied responses concerned directly with reproduction, administration of prolactin causes an increase in total body weight (Riddle and Braucher, 1934) and length of intestine (Bates, Riddle, Lahr and Schooley, 1937).   Riddle and Dotti (1934) reported that prolactin injection in pigeons leads also to hyperglycaemia and suggested that the hormone has an important diabetogenic function in birds.   Prolactin further causes an increase in both carbohydrate and general metabolism (Riddle, 1937a), but it is probable that such effects are associated with the production of crop milk in pigeons and doves which is under prolactin control.

In hypophysectomised pigeons prolactin administration produces a generalised trophic response (Schooley, Riddle and Bates, 1941 ; Riddle, 1947).   Removal of the anterior pituitary gland stops the growth of young pigeons and injections of purified prolactin produce body weights 20 to 35 per cent above normal.   A specific somatotrophic hormone has not been proved to exist in birds.

Schooley and Riddle (1938) showed that a rapid increase in body weight occurred in pigeons at a time when pituitary eosinophils are differentiated and seemingly active, but before basiphils mature (p. 671).   The eosinophils, believed to produce prolactin, differentiate during the last part of embryonic life, whereas basiphils, believed to secrete gonadotrophin, did not mature in Schooley and Riddle's pigeons until the second month after hatching.   According to this work, prolactin is probably present in the anterior lobe at an age when gonadotrophins can still not be detected by implantation techniques.   Payne (1943), however, has shown that in the female chick apparently functional basiphils occur at 10 days, and that in males they are even more abundant at the same age.

Payne (1943) appeared to have localised eosinophilic " broody cells " as the source of prolactin.   When hens periodically become broody, basiphils almost disappear and large numbers of small acidophilic cells arise.   Yasuda (1953), however, later claimed that prolactin is elaborated by carminophilic eosinophils and that the broody cells of Payne are chromophobes (p. 670) and unconnected with the elaboration of the hormone.

Special Characters

Brood-patches

There is convincing evidence that prolactin is partly responsible for the production of the naked, vascular, brood-spots or incubation patches that develop periodically on the ventral surface in one or both sexes of most avian species and facilitate the transference of parental warmth to eggs and young.   Brood-patches were described in 1826 by Faber, who saw that they allowed a closer contact between the body and the eggs.   Faber believed that the female plucked her own breast, or that depluming was caused by abrasion and heat.   The idea that the sitting bird removed the ventral down with its bill persisted for a century, but Lange (1928) showed that in the case of a non-breeding, immature gull, *Larus ridibundus*, depluming was caused by a special moult.

Bailey (1952) has shown that prolactin operates synergistically with oestrogen in the seasonal appearance of brood-spots of which the first depluming stage occurs " several days before the first egg is laid."   Bailey studied the incubation patch of passerine birds in both field and laboratory and found in " over 125 specimens from 12 families " no significant variations in structure in the single large passerine brood-spots located in, and the same size as, the ventral apterium.   He reported in detail the successive events in the formation and regression of the incubation patch and correlated the various stages with phases of the nesting cycle as follows :

1. *Defeatherisation stage:* This involves the loss of all the down from the ventral apterium several days before egg-laying.

2. *Vascularisation stage :* Immediately after depluming, the size and number of dermal blood vessels increases.   The skin becomes slightly thickened by dermal oedema and the feather papillae disappear.   The epidermis undergoes rapid cell division.   This phase lasts until the start of incubation.

3. *Oedematous stage :* The brood-patch becomes increasingly oedematous and vascular and the dermal muscles disappear.   This phase lasts throughout incubation and during the initial care of the young.

4. *Recovery stage :* The oedema and vascularity gradually subside and by the time the young fly the skin has returned to normal unless another clutch is laid, whereupon the cycle is repeated.   The patch is refeathered during the post-nuptial moult.

Bailey produced experimentally an incubation patch in non-breeding birds by continuous treatment with oestradiol. In hypophysectomised individuals, however, oestradiol led only to vascularity. When both oestradiol and prolactin were given to hypophysectomised birds, a complete patch developed. Prolactin alone had no effect. Nor was testosterone effective, either alone or in combination with other hormones. The fact that androgen was ineffective in producing the initial stages of brood-patch formation has interesting implications. It may be that testicular or cortical oestrogens are involved in the species in which males produce such patches.

In the Fringillidae (finches), prolactin plus oestrogen produced a brood-patch in males of species in which one normally arises only in females, a probable indication that the apparatus is a very primitive character. It should be noted also that there appears, at least within the " advanced " order of passerines, to be little correlation between the practice of incubation by the male and his possession of a brood-patch. The incubating males of some species lack it, whereas the non-incubating males of others possess it (Skutch, 1957). This further suggests that the brood-patch is a primitive passerine character which has sometimes survived in the male whether or not he now undertakes incubation duty.

It was concluded by Bailey (1952) that because oestrogen alone was fully effective in intact but not in hypophysectomised birds, it stimulated prolactin secretion. He cites, however, Riddle's suggestion (1935) that the elaboration of prolactin " may occur as the result of psychic stimulation." It is possible that " oestrogen brings about environmental or internal relationships . . . that initiate the necessary psychic stimulations " (see Chapter 13).

Assays of the prolactin content of the pituitary of California gulls (*Larus californicus*) by the pigeon crop-sac method (p. 681) indicated that gulls of both sexes with incubation patches possessed more prolactin than those without, so that a single implanted pituitary gave a recognisable crop-sac response. This work is in agreement with that of Byerly and Burrows (1936) on hens.

Broodiness

Great differences exist between sexes and species in regard to broodiness and parental care. Species extremes are exemplified by the Emperor Penguin (*Aptenodytes forsteri*) and some of the Megapodilidae ("incubator birds"). The Emperor Penguin ovulates in the depths of the Antarctic winter and male and female take turns in incubating the single egg and carrying the young one on their feet, warmed under a protective fold of feathered skin (Fig. *12*. 46). During blizzards the birds aggregate *en masse* with backs to the storm, the outer ring changing position with warmer birds inside. Levick (1914) has reported that stray young are liable to be killed by kindness, so over-solicitous are the adults. In fact, young sometimes crawl under ice ledges to avoid being looked after, and dead chicks may be carried about until the down is rubbed off their bodies. This exaggerated maternalism has obvious survival value because of the unparalleled severity of the environment, but to what extent it is initiated by prolactin or progesterone is unknown. The other extreme is represented by certain incubator birds (*Megapodius* and allies) which bury their numerous eggs in hot beach sand, volcanic mud, or, more often, in a deep pile of mixed earth and rotten vegetation that produces a fairly high and even temperature. After incubator-building and egg-laying, at least some species appear never to see their eggs, or young.   In other species (e.g. *Leipoa ocellata*), both parents regulate the heat of the incubator by removing and adding soil (Frith, 1955).

The production of broodiness in both sexes of some species, and the inhibition of ovulation, are probably under both neural and hormone control.   For many years it has been known that some mechanism exists to control clutch size by stopping ovulation once the traditional number of eggs has been laid.   Thus Phillips (1887) showed that a Flicker (*Colaptes duratus*) could be made to lay 71 eggs in 72 days by removing an egg each day and preventing the completion of the normal clutch.   Wenzel (1908) reported that a House Sparrow could lay as many as 51 eggs in a season.   Similar records are cited by Marshall (1936).   On the other hand, some species (e.g. Herring Gull) will not continue to lay if one egg is

Fig. *12*. 46—Nursing penguins.   (From Marshall, 1960.)

removed.   Conversely, the female gull will not restrict her natural production if her clutch is completed artificially (Davis, 1942).

After the usual clutch has been completed and appreciated, most birds reflexly stop laying.   The importance of tactile impressions was emphasised by Taibel (1928) who fastened a turkey cock to a clutch of eggs and established broodiness. Afterwards the turkey cock could scarcely be kept off the nest.   Schjelderup-Ebbe (1924), too, reported that turkeys, but not fowls, can be made broody by forcing them to sit on eggs.   It is a commonplace, of course, that many birds, both domestic and wild, will far exceed the normal incubation period when sitting on artificial or infertile eggs.   One domestic hen is reported to have remained broody on pot eggs for four months, meanwhile suffering a 40 per cent weight-loss.   The modification of the neuro-endocrine system is well seen in that egg-laying machine, the modern domestic hen.   "A modern 300-egg hen represents a remarkable evolution from the ancestral Jungle-fowl, which lays one clutch, of about 13 to 15 eggs at a time " (Romanoff and Romanoff, 1949). It would be of interest to remove daily an egg of the Jungle-fowl (*Gallus bankiva*) in order to prevent the completion of the clutch and to discover the maximum number of eggs the species can lay in its natural state.

It was believed for many years that prolactin is directly responsible for broodiness but the question is now in dispute. Riddle, Bates and Lahr (1935) reported that prolactin induced broodiness and maternal behaviour only in the actively laying hen, although incomplete maternalism can be stimulated in sexually quiescent females and cocks. Collias (1946, 1950) has shown that if domestic hens are put with *chicks* they become broody, but only if they themselves have already ovulated or have been injected with sex hormones. On the other hand, Ceni (1927) long ago reported that broodiness and parental care are retained after ovariectomy, yet eliminated in the capon by the implantation of an ovary with large follicles. Broodiness can be elicited in cocks, but the response is less than that seen in naturally broody hens (Riddle, Bates and Lahr, 1935). Nalbandov (1945) discovered maternal tendencies, including broodiness, in cocks injected with prolactin, but not in those injected with prolactin plus androgen.

According to Riddle and Bates (1939) different genetic races of the same species of pigeon differ in their response to prolactin. Similarly, to provoke broodiness, one breed of domestic fowl required from four to five times the amount of prolactin that was effective in another (Nalbandov and Card, 1942).

The relation of other hormones to broodiness has been studied extensively. It has been shown that broodiness in fowls cannot be induced by injection of gonadotrophins or thyrotrophins (Riddle, Bates and Lahr, 1935) or by the implantation of pellets of oestrone (Riddle and Lahr, 1944b). Prolactin-induced broodiness can be prevented by androgen (Nalbandov, 1945) and suppressed by oestrogen (Collias, 1946). On the other hand, Riddle and Lahr found that birds treated with progesterone (p. 652), desoxycorticosterone acetate and testosterone propionate became broody in 43 out of 62 tests. Such treatment had no effect in young, isolated and unpaired birds. The suggestion was made that the implants induced a release of prolactin from the bird's own anterior pituitary, but the result does not necessarily imply that any of these hormones do so in nature. It may be recalled that when Asplin and Boyland (1947) administered sulphonamide to chicks, spermatogenic activity with precocious comb-growth and sexual behaviour occurred, probably as the result of pituitary stimulation. It seems possible that when prolactin secretion occurs under natural conditions the release of FSH and thence gonad activity, are temporarily suppressed (*see* p. 682).

Doubt has recently been expressed as to whether prolactin does in fact induce broodiness. Nalbandov, Hochhauser and Dugas (1945) believe that broodiness in cockerels results from the withdrawal of sex hormones, such as occurs after the release of prolactin, and the presence of external stimuli (i.e. eggs or chicks). As regards females, Nalbandov (1953) suggests that broodiness is secondarily produced by preventing ovarian secretion. It may be recalled that in the classical experiments of Riddle, Bates and Lahr (1935) it was reported that the " incubation instinct " in hens was fully expressed only with dosage " sufficient to repress the ovary." Nalbandov (1953) cites the finding by Godfrey and Jaap (1950) that the administration of oestrogen abolishes broodiness, as well as Payne's report of a maximum development of " broody cells " in White Leghorn fowls which, in fact, rarely become broody. Collias (1946) showed that broodiness could develop in the absence of prolactin. A hypophysectomised male pigeon treated for 26 days with oestradiol benzoate paired with a female and helped her incubate the eggs for more than a month. The male, however, did not produce crop-milk, which is under hypophysial control. Lehrman (1956), too, doubts whether prolactin has any more than an indirect effect on inducing broodiness.

Crop gland and pigeon's milk

Associated with broodiness during the second half of the incubation period in pigeons and doves is the production of pigeon's " milk," the proteinous (13·3

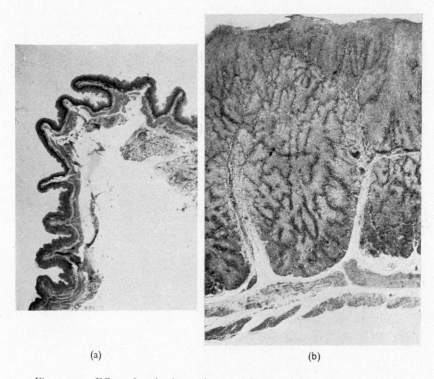

(a)   (b)

Fig. *12*. 47—Effect of prolactin on the crop gland of the pigeon. (a) Control. Adult. Age unknown. (b) Treated. 2 i.u. prolactin per day for 6 days. (From the material of Folley.)

to 18·8 per cent) and fatty (6·9 to 12·7 per cent) material on which the squabs are fed (*see* Needham, 1950). During the second half of the incubation period the crops of both sexes enlarge so that crop-milk and desquamated epithelial cells are ready to be discharged by the time of hatching. The female dove is said to spend about three times as long as the male in incubation and brooding, and to produce more " milk " than the male (Meites and Turner, 1947 ; Lehrman, 1955).

Hypophysectomy prevents the development of the crop-gland, and sex hormones do not stimulate it to activity (Collias, 1946). Remarkable evidence of neural and hormonal co-ordination in the production of pigeon's milk, as with the onset of broodiness, was presented by Cole (1933) and Patel (1936), who showed that male doves separated from females can produce " milk " only if they are allowed to see brooding females.   If the cock is prevented from looking at the hen his crop regresses and broodiness disappears after 2 days.   Prolactin has an important rôle in the proliferation of the mucosa that produces pigeon's milk, as shown by Riddle and Braucher (1931), Riddle, Bates and Dykshorn (1932, 1933) and others (Fig. *12*. 47).   The development of bioassay methods involving the crop-sac of pigeons and doves is reviewed by Riddle (1937b).   If as little as 0·01 mg. of prolactin is injected intracutaneously into the crop-sac area of pigeons a pronounced reaction is achieved within 48 hours (Lyons, 1937).   Subsequently, Bates and Riddle (1936) showed that in young birds of the same age and race the response of the crop-glands to prolactin differed widely according to the route by which it was administered.   Subcutaneous and intracutaneous injections are about 11 times, 5 times and 8 times as effective as intravenous, intramuscular and intra-peritoneal injections respectively.

Burrows and Byerly (1936) found that the implantation of single fowl pituitaries over the crop-glands of 8- to 10-week-old pigeons led in many cases to a prolactin-like reaction.   Pituitaries from broody hens caused a greater reaction than those of laying hens, which in turn were more effective than those of males.   There was some evidence that in a few cases the pituitaries of hens just becoming broody gave a greater reaction than those of birds nearing the end of their broody period. Byerly and Burrows (1936) found also that the pituitary of the male was about equal in crop-stimulating potency to that of the genetically non-broody female.   It appears likely that the glands of males with a genetically broody constitution have a higher prolactin content than those in non-broody strains.

Regurgitation feeding

Regurgitation feeding in pigeons and doves is yet another pattern of behaviour partly under the control of prolactin.   It has been studied by Lehrman (1955), who reports that when North American Ring Doves (*Streptopelia decaocto*) of either sex were each injected subcutaneously with 450 i.u. of prolactin (divided into 7 daily doses) only birds that had previous breeding experience fed squabs presented to them.   Birds with their crops anaesthetised fed squabs " significantly less " than others anaesthetised elsewhere.   Lehrman discounts the suggestion that the regurgitation-feeding response is elicited by the action of prolactin on a brain centre.   After the eggs hatch, the first parental regurgitation by inexperienced birds always follows tactile stimulation of their ventral surface by the squab's head.   In birds that have previously reproduced, regurgitation often occurs in the absence of such stimulation.   Lehrman's final conclusion is that prolactin fails to elicit the parental-regurgitation feeding response " primarily because it causes engorgement of the crop and suppression of sexual behaviour rather than through an effect on central nervous mechanisms specific for parental behaviour." The engorgement of the crop " makes it sensitive to emetic stimuli provided by movements of the squab's head and acts as a drive stimulus through which the dove learns to respond to the sight and/or sound of the squab."   These conclusions do not accord with earlier views of this and comparable activities (*see* Riddle, 1935; Tinbergen, 1951).

z*

Gonads

The injection of prolactin is followed by the appearance of some behaviour patterns and the suppression of others. For example, cooing (an aspect of court-ship behaviour) is inhibited in doves (Lehrman, 1955) and possibly singing in passerines (Bailey, 1950). In this respect the effects of prolactin are similar to those of castration and are probably caused by suppression of pituitary secretion rather than by direct action. Riddle (1935) reported that prolactin also inhibited egg-laying.

The injection of prolactin likewise retards spermatogenesis and leads to testis collapse in pigeons (Riddle and Bates, 1933; Bates, Riddle and Lahr, 1937). Breneman (1942b) observed the same effect in domestic cockerels. Again, it is known that certain secondary sexual characters, such as the hen's comb, which are influenced by gonad hormones, become less prominent during broodiness (Collins, 1940, 1946). Lehrman (1955, 1956), too, has interesting evidence on this point. Injections of prolactin suppressed sexual behaviour and pugnacity in male pigeons, whereas untreated controls showed great violence to squabs exposed to them. Conversely, the male Satin Bower-bird, which continues to display and takes no part in nidification, incubation or parental care, does not suffer testis collapse until the young have left the nest and the post-nuptial family party assembles. It could be thought that the continued production of gonadotrophin is incompatible with that of prolactin. Bailey (1950) inhibited the light-induced testis response of American passerine White-crowned " Sparrows " (*Zonotrichia leucophrys*) by pro-lactin administration.

The " regression " effects described by various authors were studied in detail by Lofts and Marshall (1956), who showed them to be identical with the changes that accompany the normal post-nuptial metamorphosis of the testis in seasonal passerine birds (Fig. *12*. 48). Bates, Lahr and Riddle (1935) showed that pro-lactin likewise inhibits ovarian activity. There has been discussion as to whether prolactin affects the ovaries and testes directly, or whether it acts indirectly by inhibiting the production of gonadotrophin by the hypophysis. Bates, Riddle and Lahr (1937) injected FSH and prolactin simultaneously and found that the customary effects of the latter did not occur. Lofts and Marshall (1958), in a relatively comprehensive study, concluded that prolactin almost certainly had no direct effect on the testis.

Although comparatively large, non-physiological, doses of exogenous prolactin demonstrably lead to tubule metamorphosis, it would not be justifiable to conclude that the endogenous hormone does more than partially and temporarily depress adenohypophysial function. Proof that the regular post-nuptial steatogenesis and testis collapse is not due solely to the action of prolactin seems to be inherent in the capacity of plural-brooded species to produce successive clutches, the eggs of which are fertilised without intervening testis metamorphosis. The alternative would be to assume that the males of double- or treble-brooded passerines (e.g. House Sparrow, *Passer domesticus*) do not produce prolactin, even though they brood and share other parental duties (Summers-Smith, personal communication). The principal cause in nature of pituitary refractoriness, leading to steatogenesis, is probably not hormonal but neural, with external stimuli including behaviour directly involved.

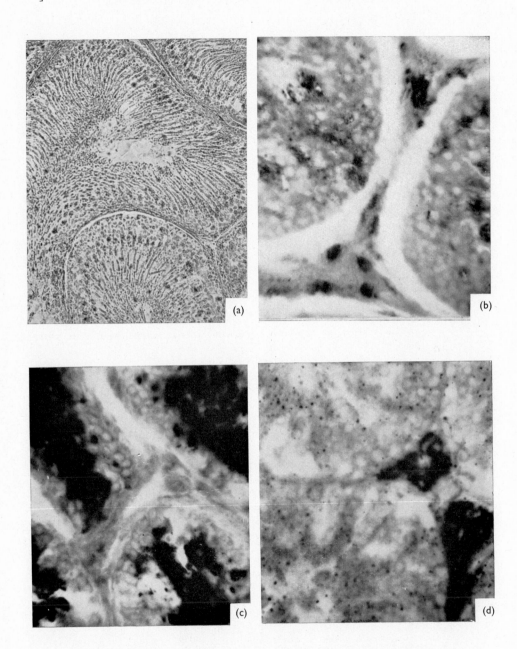

Fig. *12*. 48—Effect of prolactin on testis of Chaffinch.   (a) Testis of photostimulated control showing bunches of spermatozoa and absence of tubular lipids.   (b) Testis of photostimulated and prolactin-treated bird, showing partial tubular steatogenesis in region of sperm bunches. (c) Progressive degree of tubular steatogenesis.   (d) Testis of mouse after prolonged treatment with prolactin, showing absence of tubular steatogenesis.   (From Lofts and Marshall, 1956.)

Bibliography

AGOSTINI, A. (1935). Analisi sperimentale del dimorfiso sessuale del piumaggio della quaglia (*Coturnix coturnix coturnic L.*).   *Arch. zool. (ital.), Napoli*, **22**, 123.

ALEXANDER, C. J. (1917).   Observations on birds singing in their winter quarters and on migration.   *Brit. Birds*, **11**, 98.

ALLEE, W. C. (1936).   Analytical studies of group behaviour in birds.   *Wilson Bull.*, **48**, 143.

—— & COLLIAS, N. (1940).   The influence of estradiol on the social organization of flocks of hens.   *Endocrinology*, **27**, 827.

—— —— & LUTHERMAN, C. Z. (1939).   Modification of the social order in flocks of hens by the injection of testosterone propionate.   *Physiol. Zoöl.*, **12**, 412.

APPEL, F. W. (1929a).   Sex dimorphism in the syrinx of the fowl.   *J. Morph.*, **47**, 497.

—— (1929b).   Testis grafts in ovariotomized fowls.   *J. exp. Zool.*, **53**, 77.

ARNSDORF, R. E. (1947).   Hen into rooster.   *J. Hered.*, **38**, 320.

ASCHOFF, J. (1955).   Jahresperiodik der 11 Fortpflanzung bei Warmblutern.   *Studium gen.*, **8**, 741.

ASMUNDSON, V. S., GUNN, C. A., & KLOSE, A. A. (1937).   Response of the immature female fowl to injections of mare gonadotropic hormone and oestrin.   *Poult. Sci.*, **16**, 194.

ASPLIN, F. D., & BOYLAND, E. (1947).   The effects of pyrimidine sulphonamide derivatives upon the blood clotting system and testes of chicks and the breeding capacity of adult fowls.   *Brit. J. Pharmacol.*, **2**, 79.

ASSENMACHER, I. (1958).   Recherches sur le contrôle hypothalamique de la fonction gonadotrope préhypophysaire chez le canard.   *Arch. Anat. micr. Morph. exp.*, **47**, 447.

ATHIAS, M. (1928a).   Influence de la castration chez le dindon.   *C. R. Soc. Biol., Paris*, **98**, 1606.

—— (1928b).   Les effets de la castration chez le dindon.   *C. R. Soc. Biol., Paris*, **100**, 513.

—— (1931).   Les caractères sexuels somatiques chez le dindon et leur conditionnement physiologique.   *Proc. 2nd. int. Congr. Sex Res.*, 1930.

AUBER, L. (1957).   The structures producing "non-iridiscent" blue colour in bird feathers.   *Proc. zool. Soc. Lond.*, **129**, 455.

BAILEY, R. E. (1950).   Inhibition with prolactin of light-induced gonad increase in white-crowned sparrows.   *Condor*, **52**, 247.

—— (1952).   The incubation patch of passerine birds.   *Condor*, **54**, 121.

—— (1953).   Accessory reproduction organs of male fringillid birds.   Seasonal variations and response to various sex hormones.   *Anat. Rec.*, **115**, 1.

BALDWIN, F. M., GOLDIN, H. S., & METFESSEL, M. (1940).   Effects of testosterone propionate on female roller canaries under complete song isolation.   *Proc. Soc. exp. Biol., N.Y.*, **44**, 373.

BATES, R. W., LAHR, E. L., & RIDDLE, O. (1935).   The gross action of prolactin and follicle-stimulating hormone on the mature ovary and sex accessories of fowl.   *Amer. J. Physiol.*, **111**, 361.

—— & RIDDLE, O. (1936).   Effect of route of administration on the biossay of prolactin.   *Proc. Soc. exp. Biol., N.Y.*, **34**, 847.

—— —— & LAHR, E. L. (1937).   The mechanism of the anti-gonad action of prolactin in adult pigeons.   *Amer. J. Physiol.*, **119**, 610.

—— —— —— & SCHOOLEY, J. P. (1937).   Aspects of splanchnomegaly associated with the action of prolactin.   *Amer. J. Physiol.*, **119**, 603.

BEACH, F. A. (1942).   Analysis of factors involved in the arousal, maintenance and manifestation of sexual excitement in male animals.   *Psychosom. Med.*, **4**, 173.

—— (1948).   *Hormones and Behavior.*   New York.

BENNETT, M. A. (1940).   The social hierarchy in ring doves.   II. The effect of treatment with testosterone propionate.   *Ecology*, **21**, 149.

BENOIT, J. (1922).   Sur les conditions physiologiques rélatives à la parure nuptiale périodique chez les oiseaux.   *C. R. Acad. Sci., Paris*, **174**, 701.

—— (1923).   Transformation expérimentale du sexe par ovariotomie précoce chez la poule domestique.   *C. R. Acad. Sci., Paris*, **177**, 1074.

Benoit, J. (1924). Action des rayons X sur le testicule du coq. *C. R. Soc. Biol.*, *Paris*, **90**, 802.

——— (1926.) Origine des cordons sexuels d'aspect mâle apparus dans des régénérats et des greffons ovariens chez la poule. *C. R. Soc. Biol.*, *Paris*, **94**, 875.

——— (1929). Structure, origine et fonction des cellules interstitielles du testicule chez le coq domestique. *Arch. Anat. micr.*, **25**, 173.

——— (1932). Étude physiologique, histologique et histophysiologique de l'inversion sexuelle de la poule déterminée par l'ablation de l'ovaire gauche. *Arch. Zool. exp. gén.*, **73**, 1.

——— (1935a). A propos du dimorphisme sexuel saisonnier du plumage chez le canard Rouen. *Trans. Dynam. Developm.*, **10**, 49.

——— (1935b). Hypophysectomie et éclairement artificial chez le canard mâle. *C. R. Soc. Biol.*, *Paris*, **120**, 1326.

——— (1936). Rôle de la préhypophyse dans le conditionnement de l'activité génitale du canard, démontré par l'hypophysectomie. *Arch. portug. Sci. biol.*, **5**, 279.

——— (1937). Facteurs externes et internes de l'activité sexuelle. II. Étude du mécanisme de la stimulation par le lumière de l'activité testiculaire chez le canard domestique. Rôle de l'hypophyse. *Bull. biol.*, **71**, 393.

——— (1938). Quelques cas d'eunuchoïdisme par hypoplasie ou absence de tissue interstitiel glandulaire chez le coq domestique. *C. R. Soc. Biol.*, *Paris*, **129**, 234.

——— (1950). Différenciation sexuelle chez les oiseaux au cours du développement normal et de l'intersexualité expérimentale par ovariectomie. *Arch. Anat. micr. Morph. exp.*, **39**, 395.

——— & Aron, M. (1934). Sur le conditionnement hormonique du développement testiculaire, chez les oiseaux. Injections d'extrait préhypophysaire chez le canard. Remarques sur divers éléments d'interprétation des expériences. Influence de l'âge. *C. R. Soc. Biol.*, *Paris*, **116**, 215.

——— & Assenmacher, I. (1953). Rapport entre la stimulation sexuelle préhypophysaire et la neurosécretion chez l'oiseau. *Arch. Anat. micr. Morph. exp.*, **42**, 4, 334.

——— ——— & Walter, F. X. (1950). Réponses du mécanisme gonado-stimulant à l'éclairement artificiel et de la préhypophyse aux castrations bilatérale et unilatérale, chez le canard domestique mâle, au cours de la période de régression testiculaire saisonnière. *C. R. Soc. Biol.*, *Paris*, **144**, 573.

——— Brard, E., & Assenmacher, I. (1952). Régénérats testiculaires et caractères sexuels secondaires chez le coq domestique. Eunuchoïdisme par hypoplasie interstitielle glandulaire. *C. R. Acad. Sci.*, *Paris*, **234**, 2487.

——— Gros, G., Paris, R., & Kehl, R. (1945). Action masculinisante de l'acétate de désoxycorticostérone et de la progestérone (purissimes) sur la crête du chapon. *C. R. Soc. Biol.*, *Paris*, **139**, 725.

Berner, O. (1925). Masculinisation d'une poule chez laquelle fut trouvée une tumeur de l'ovaire. *Arch. Biol.*, *Paris*, **35**, 295.

Berthold, A. A. (1849). Transplantation der Hoden. *Arch. Anat. Physiol.*, *Lpz.*, **16**, 42.

Bissonnette, T. H., & Wadlund, A. P. R. (1932). Duration of testis activity of *Sturnus vulgaris* in relation to type of illumination. *J. exp. Biol.*, **9**, 339.

Blacher, L. J. (1926). L'influence des hormones sexuels sur le nombre des globules rouges et le pourcentage de l'hémoglobine dans les sang des gallinacés. *Biol. gen.*, **2**, 543.

Bloom, M. A., Bloom, W., Domm, L. V., & McLean, F. C. (1940). Changes in avian bone due to injected estrogen and during the reproductive cycle. *Anat. Rec.*, **78**, Suppl. p. 143.

Bloom, W. B., Bloom, M. A., & McLean, F. C. (1941). Calcification and ossification. Medullary bone changes in the reproductive cycle of female pigeons. *Anat. Rec.*, **81**, 443.

Bolton, W. (1953). The effect of sex hormones on comb growth in immature pullets. *J. Endocrin.*, **9**, 440.

Bomskov, C. (1939). *Methodik der Hormonforschung.* Leipzig.

Bond, C. J. (1913). On a case of unilateral development of secondary male characters in a pheasant, with remarks on the influence of hormones in the production of secondary sex characters. *J. Genet.*, **3**, 205.

Boss, W. R. (1943). Hormonal determination of adult characters and sex behaviour in Herring Gulls (*Larus argentatus*). *J. exp. Zool.*, **94**, 181.

—— & Witschi, E. (1941). Male sex hormones inducing adult characters in juvenile Herring Gulls (*Larus argentatus*). *Anat. Rec.*, **81**, Suppl. p. 27.

—— —— (1942). Hormonal determination of sex behaviour in normal and castrate second year juvenile Herring Gulls (*Larus argentatus*). *Anat. Rec.*, **84**, 517.

Bradley, E. M. (1941). Sex differentiation of chick and duck gonads as studied in homoplastic and heteroplastic host graft combinations. *Anat. Rec.*, **79**, 507.

Brambell, F. W. R., & Marrian, G. F. (1929). Sex-reversal in a pigeon (*Columbia livia*). *Proc. Roy. Soc.*, B, **104**, 459.

Brandt, J. W. A., & Nalbandov, A. V. (1952). Role of sex hormones in the secretory activity of the oviducts of hens. *Poult. Sci.*, **31**, 908.

—— —— (1956). Role of sex hormones in albumen secretion by the oviduct of chickens. *Poult. Sci.*, **35**, 692.

Brard, E., & Benoit, J. (1957). Contribution à l'étude du déterminisme de la crête de la poule (*Gallus domesticus*). *C. R. Acad. Sci., Paris*, **244**, 1066.

Breneman, W. R. (1936). The effect on the chick of some gonadotropic hormones. *Anat. Rec.*, **64**, 211.

—— (1937). Male hormone and the testis-comb relationship in the chick. *Endocrinology*, **21**, 503.

—— (1938). Relative effectiveness of testosterone-propionate and dihydroandrosterone-benzoate in the chick as indicated by comb growth. *Endocrinology*, **23**, 44.

—— (1939). Variations in the reaction of chicks to different methods of administering hormones. *Endocrinology*, **24**, 55.

—— (1942a). The chick comb for androgen assay. *Endocrinology*, **30**, 277.

—— (1942b). Action of prolactin and estrone on weights of reproductive organs and viscera of the cockerel. *Endocrinology*, **30**, 609.

—— (1942c). Action of diethylstilbestrol in the chick. *Endocrinology*, **31**, 179.

—— (1944). The growth of the anterior lobe of the pituitary and the testes in the cockerel. *Endocrinology*, **35**, 456.

—— (1945). The gonadotropic activity of the anterior pituitary of cockerels. *Endocrinology*, **36**, 190.

—— (1946). The growth of the anterior lobe of the pituitary, the comb, and the ovary in the pullet. *Anat. Rec.*, **96**, 459.

—— (1950). A study of the pituitary-gonad-comb relationship in normal, unilateral-castrated, and caponized chicks. *J. exp. Zool.*, **114**, 115.

—— (1951). A factorial analysis of pituitary-gonad-comb relationships in the chick. 2. Action of P.M.S. and T.P. on the growth of the pituitary and gonad. *Poult. Sci.*, **30**, 399.

—— (1955). Reproduction in birds: the female. *Mem. Soc. Endocrin.*, **4**, 94.

Buckner, G. D., Insko, W. M. Jr., & Martin, J. H. (1933). Sex characters of battery brooder and colony-raised White Leghorns. *Poult. Sci.*, **12**, 392.

Bulliard, H., & Ravina, A. (1938). Effets de la testostérone chez *Cairina*. *C. R. Soc. Biol., Paris*, **127**, 525.

Bullough, W. S. (1942). The reproductive cycles of the British and Continental races of the starling. *Phil. Trans.*, **231**, 165.

—— (1945). Endocrinological aspects of bird behaviour. *Biol. Rev.*, **20**, 89.

—— & Carrick, R. (1940). Male behaviour of the female starling (*Sturnus v. vulgaris* L.) in autumn. *Nature, Lond.*, **145**, 629.

Burger, J. W. (1947). On the relation of day-length to the phases of testicular involution and inactivity of the spermatogenetic cycle of the starling. *J. exp. Zool.*, **105**, 259.

—— (1949). A review of experimental investigations on seasonal reproduction in birds. *Wilson Bull.*, **61**, 211.

Burrows, W. H., & Byerly, T. C. (1936). Studies of prolactin in the fowl pituitary. I. Broody hens compared with laying hens and males. *Proc. Soc. exp. Biol., N.Y.*, **34**, 841.

—— —— & Evans, E. I. (1936). Sensitivity of the baby-chick comb to male sex hormone. *Proc. Soc. exp. Biol., N.Y.*, **35**, 50.

BUTT, W. R., MORRIS, P., MORRIS, C. J. O. R., & WILLIAMS, D. C. (1951). The polarographic estimation of steroid hormones. *Biochem. J.*, **49**, 434.

BYERLY, T. C., & BURROWS, W. H. (1936). Studies of prolactin in the fowl pituitary. II. Effects of genetic constitution on prolactin content. *Proc. Soc. exp. Biol.*, *N.Y.*, **34**, 844.

—— —— (1938). Chick testis weight response to gonadotropic hormone. *Endocrinology*, **22**, 366.

CALLOW, R. K. (1938). The significance of the excretion of sex hormones in the urine. *Proc. Roy. Soc. Med.*, **31**, 841.

—— & PARKES, A. S. (1935). Growth and maintenance of the fowl's comb by administration of androsterone. *Biochem. J.*, **29**, 1414.

—— —— (1936). Production of oestrogenic substance by the bird testis. *J. exp. Biol.*, **13**, 7.

CALVET, J. (1931). Étude des modifications sexuelles de l'appareil phonateur du coq. *C. R. Soc. Biol., Paris*, **107**, 132.

CARIDROIT, F. (1926). Étude histo-physiologique de la transplantation testiculaire et ovarienne chez les Gallinacés. *Bull. biol.*, **60**, 135.

—— (1928). Le testicule peut-il féminiser le plumage d'une poule ordinaire ovariectomisée? *C. R. Soc. Biol., Paris*, **99**, 1632.

—— (1936). La féminisation du coq domestique par le benzoate de folliculine. *Arch. portug. Sci. biol.*, **5**, 212.

—— (1938a). Recherches expérimentales sur les rapports entre testicules, plumage d'éclipse et mues chez le canard sauvage. *Trav. Sta. zool. Wimereux*, **13**, 47.

—— (1938b). Le rôle des hormones sexuelles dans l'extériorisation des caractères raciaux du plumage de la poule domestique. *Les Hormones Sexuelles*, Paris, Ed. L. Brouha, p. 55.

—— (1944). Masculinisation du chapon par la progestérone purifiée. *C. R. Soc. Biol., Paris*, **138**, 259.

—— (1948). Féminisation du plumage du chapon par un oestrogène (hexoestrol) et par des oestrogènes naturels administrés par voie orale. *C. R. Soc. Biol., Paris*, **142**, 578.

—— & RÉGNIER, V. (1930). Mue et castration du canard de Rouen. *C. R. Soc. Biol., Paris*, **105**, 435.

—— & TAUC, L. (1948). Modifications de la résistance électrique de la crête du chapon sous l'influence de l'hormone mâle. *C. R. Acad. Sci., Paris*, **226**, 1476.

CARPENTER, C. R. (1933a). Psychobiological studies of social behaviour in Aves. I. *J. comp. Psychol.*, **16**, 25.

—— (1933b). Psychobiological studies of social behaviour in Aves. II. *J. comp. Psychol.*, **16**, 59.

CAVAZZA, F. (1931). Alcuni fatti particolari osservati in esperimenti di gonadectomia in Anas boschas L. e alcune riflessioni sul dimorfiso sessuale del piumaggio. *Boll. Zool.*, **2**, 238.

—— (1932). Prima nota su esperimenti di castrazione in rapporto ai caratteri sessuali secondari in alcune specie di ucceli e nei loro ibridi. *Arch. Zool. exp. gén.*, **74**, 111.

CENI, C. (1927). Die endokrinen Faktoren der Mutterliebe und die psychische Feminierung von Männchen. *Schweiz. Arch. Neurol. Psychiat.*, **21**, 131.

CHAMPY, Ch. (1930). Corrélation entre organes sensoriels et caractères sensibles liés aux phénomènes sexuels. *Arch. int. Pharmacodyn.*, **38**, 577.

—— (1931a). Étude du mécanisme de développement de quelques caractères sexuels des oiseau. *Arch. Anat. micr.*, **27**, 301.

—— (1931b). Injections d'extraits testiculaires. *C. R. Soc. Biol., Paris*, **108**, 367.

—— (1934). Nouvelles expériences et considérations sur la chalone des glandes génitales. *C. R. Soc. Biol., Paris*, **115**, 358.

—— (1935). La sensibilité du plumage et la chalone. *Bull. biol.*, **69**, 439.

—— (1936). Action chalonique de l'hormone mâle. *C. R. Soc. Biol., Paris*, **122**, 631.

—— & DEMAY, M. (1933). Étude du mécanisme de l'influence de la chalone ovarienne sur les plumes. *C. R. Soc. Biol., Paris*, **112**, 865.

—— & LAVEDAN, J. (1938). Séminomes par régénération chez les oiseaux. *C. R. Soc. Biol., Paris*, **127**, 1197.

CHAPIN, J. P. (1950). The calendar of Wideawake Fair. *Auk*, **71,** 1.

CHAPMAN, D. G., GLUCK, M., COMMON, R. H., & MAW, W. A. (1949). The influence of gonadal hormones on the serum vitamin A of the immature pullet. *Canad. J. Res.*, D, **27,** 37.

—— HANSON, A. A., COMMON, R. H., & MAW, W. A. (1949). The effect of gonadal hormones on liver nucleic acids in the immature pullet. *Canad. J. Res.*, D, **27,** 200.

—— MAW, W. A., & COMMON, R. H. (1950). Effects of estrogen and androgen on liver iron of the immature pullet. *Sci. Agric.*, **30,** 194.

CHU, J. P. (1940). The endocrine system and plumage types. V. The production of eclipse plumage in the mallard by injection of anterior pituitary extract and dehydroandrosterone. *J. Genet.*, **39,** 517.

COLE, L. J. (1927). The lay of the "rooster". *J. Hered.*, **18,** 97.

—— (1933). The relation of light periodicity to the reproductive cycle, migration and distribution of the Mourning Dove (*Zenaidura macroura carolinensis*). *Auk*, **50,** 284.

COLLIAS, N. (1943). Statistical analysis of factors which make for success in initial encounters between hens. *Amer. Nat.*, **77,** 519.

—— (1944). Aggressive behaviour among vertebrate animals. *Physiol. Zoöl.*, **17,** 83.

—— (1946). Some experiments on broody behaviour in fowl and pigeon. *Anat. Rec.*, **96,** Suppl. p. 572.

—— (1950). Hormones and behaviour with special reference to birds and the mechanisms of hormone action. *A symposium on steroid hormones*. Ed. Edgar S. Gordon. Madison.

COLLINS, N. E. (1940). Some effects of sex hormones on broodiness in fowl and pigeon. *Anat. Rec.*, **78,** Suppl. p. 146.

—— (1946). Some experiments on broody behaviour in fowl and pigeon. *Anat. Rec.*, **96,** 572.

COMAR, C. L., & DRIGGERS, J. C. (1949). Secretion of radioactive Ca in the hen's egg. *Science*, **109,** 282.

COMMON, R. H. (1938). Observations on the mineral metabolism of pullets. *J. agric. Sci.*, **28,** 347.

—— BOLTON, W., & RUTLEDGE, W. A. (1948). The influence of gonadal hormones on the composition of the blood and liver of the domestic fowl. *J. Endocrin.*, **5,** 263.

—— CHAMPY, D. G., & MAW, W. A. (1951). The effect of gonadal hormones on the nucleic acid content of liver and serum in the immature pullet, and the difference between the nucleic acid content of the livers of sexually mature pullets and cockerels. *Canad. J. Zool.*, **29,** 265.

COOK, J. W., DODDS, E. C., & GREENWOOD, A. W. (1934). Sex change in the plumage of Brown Leghorn capons following the injection of certain synthetic oestrus-producing compounds. *Proc. Roy. Soc.*, B, **114,** 286.

COOMBS, C. J. F., & MARSHALL, A. J. (1956). The effects of hypophysectomy on the internal testis rhythm in birds and mammals. *J. Endocrin.*, **13,** 107.

CRAIG, W. (1909). The expression of emotion in the pigeons. I. The blond Ring Dove (*Turtur risorius*). *J. comp. Neurol.*, **19,** 29.

CREW, F. A. E. (1923). Studies in intersexuality. II. Sex reversal in the fowl. *Proc. Roy. Soc.*, B, **95,** 256.

—— (1931). The assumption of the male plumage by the hen pheasant. *Vet. Rec.*, May 9.

—— & MUNRO, S. S. (1938). Gynadromorphism and lateral asymmetry in birds. *Proc. Roy. Soc. Edinb.*, **58,** 114.

DANBY, M. (1938). The assay of male hormones by the "chicken-test". *Acta brev. neerl. Physiol.*, **8,** 90.

—— (1940). Further experiments on the assay of male hormones with the "chicken-test". *Acta brev. neerl. Physiol.*, **10,** 56.

DANFORTH, C. H. (1930). The nature of racial and sexual dimorphism in the plumage of Campines and Leghorns. *Biol. gen.*, **6,** 99.

—— (1933). Genetic factors in the response of feather follicles to thyroxin and theelin. *J. exp. Zool.*, **65,** 183.

DANNENBAUM, H. (1936).   Die Wirkstoffe der männlichen Keimdrüse.   *Ergebn. Physiol.*, **38**, 796.

DANTCHAKOFF, V. (1935).   Sur les différences de sensibilité des récepteurs tissulaires envers la folliculine, à divers stades embryonnaires.   *C. R. Acad. Sci., Paris*, **201**, 161.

—— (1937a).   Sur le sort des femelles génétiques du poulet traitées par de l'hormone mâle dès le stade embryonnaire.   *C. R. Soc. Biol., Paris*, **126**, 275.

—— (1937b).   Sur les facteurs directs de la *pubertas praecox* plus particulièrement sur l'action de l'hormone mâle sur le système nerveux de jeunes poussins.   *C. R. Soc. Biol., Paris*, **126**, 174.

—— (1937c).   Quelques particularités dans les effets des hormones sexuelles sur l'embryon du poulet.   *C. R. Soc. Biol., Paris*, **126**, 177.

—— (1937d).   Effets du testostéron-propionate sur les ébauches sexuelles de l'oiseau.   *C. R. Soc. Biol., Paris*, **124**, 235.

—— (1938).   Réalisation du sexe a volonté par inductions hormonales.   III.   Inversions, et déviations dans l'histogénèse sexuelle chez l'embryon du poulet traité par l'hormone mâle.   *Bull. biol.*, **72**, 187.

—— & KINDERIS, A. (1937).   Sur la croissance de la crête embryonnaire à la suite de l'action de l'hormone mâle.   *C. R. Soc. Biol., Paris*, **124**, 308.

DANTSCHAKOFF, W. (1933).   Keimzelle und Gonade; Sterilizierung der Gonaden im Embryo mittels Röntgenstrahlen.   *Z. Zellforsch.*, **18**, 56.

DARWIN, C. (1868).   *Variation of animals and plants under domestication.* London.

DAS, B. C., & NALBANDOV, A. V. (1955).   Response of ovaries of immature chickens to avian and mammalian gonadotrophins.   *Endocrinology*, **57**, 705.

DAVID, K. (1938).   Über den Einfluss der Saison auf die Empfindlichkeit des Hahnenkammes.   *Acta brev. neerl. Physiol.*, **8**, 133.

DAVIS, D. E. (1942).   Number of eggs laid by herring gulls.   *Auk*, **59**, 549.

—— (1957).   Aggressive behaviour in castrated starlings.   *Science*, **126**, 253.

—— & DOMM, L. V. (1941).   The sexual behaviour of hormonally treated domestic fowl.   *Proc. Soc. exp. Biol., N.Y.*, **48**, 667.

—— —— (1943).   The influence of hormones on the sexual behaviour of domestic fowl.   In *Essays in biology.*   In honor of Herbert M. Evans.   Berkeley, California.

DEANESLY, R., & PARKES, A. S. (1936).   Comparative activities of compounds of the androsterone-testosterone series.   *Biochem. J.*, **30**, 291.

—— —— (1937a).   Factors influencing the effectiveness of administered hormones.   *Proc. Roy. Soc.*, B, **124**, 279.

—— —— (1937b).   Multiple activities of androgenic compounds.   *Quart. J. exp. Physiol.*, **26**, 393.

DESSAU, F. (1935).   Effect of pure crystalline male hormones on the histological structure of the comb of capons.   *Acta brev. neerl. Physiol.*, **5**, 94.

—— (1937).   Weitere Untersuchungen über die Wirksamkeit von Kammwachstunsstoffen im Schmierversuch.   *Acta brev. neerl. Physiol.*, **7**, 126.

—— & FREUD, J. (1936).   Effects of pure crystalline male hormones upon the comb of the capon and the ductus deferens.   *Acta brev. neerl. Physiol.*, **6**, 9.

DISCHERL, W., KRAUS, J., & VOSS, H. E. (1936).   Neue Stoffe mit starker Wirkung auf die Vesikulardrüsen der Kastrierten männlichen Maus. 9. Mitteilung über Sexualhormone und verwandte Stoffe.   *Hoppe-Sely. Z.*, **241**, 1.

DOMM, L. V. (1927).   New experiments on ovariotomy and the problem of sex inversion in the fowl.   *J. exp. Zool.*, **48**, 31.

—— (1928).   The transplantation of ovary into capons.   *Anat. Rec.*, **41**, 43.

—— (1929a).   Testis grafts in the bilaterally ovariotomized fowl.   *Anat. Rec.*, **44**, 204.

—— (1929b).   The effects of bilateral ovariotomy in the Brown Leghorn fowl.   *Biol. Bull.*, **56**, 459.

—— (1929c).   Spermatogenesis following early ovariotomy in the Brown Leghorn fowl.   *Proc. Soc. exp. Biol., N.Y.*, **26**, 338.

—— (1929d).   Spermatogenesis following early ovariotomy in the Brown Leghorn fowl.   *Arch. EntwMech. Org.*, **119**, 171.

—— (1930).   Artificial insemination with motile sperm from ovariotomized fowl   *Proc. Soc. exp. Biol., N.Y.*, **28**, 316.

DOMM, L. V. (1931a).   A demonstration of equivalent potencies of right and left testis-like gonads in the ovariotomized fowl.   *Anat. Rec.*, **49**, 211.

—— (1931b).   Precocious development of sexual characters in the fowl by homeoplastic hypophyseal implants.   I. The male.   *Proc. Soc. exp. Biol., N.Y.*, **29**, 308.

—— (1931c).   Precocious development of sexual characters in the fowl by homeoplastic hypophyseal implants.   II. The female.   *Proc. Soc. exp. Biol., N.Y.*, **29**, 310.

—— (1933).   Response in sinistrally ovariotomized Leghorns to daily injections of hebin.   *Proc. Soc. exp. Biol., N.Y.*, **31**, 356.

—— (1937).   Observations concerning anterior pituitary-gonadal interrelations in the fowl.   *Cold Spr. Harb. Sym. quant. Biol.*, **5**, 241.

—— (1939a).   Modifications in sex and secondary sexual characters in birds.   Chap. 5 in *Sex and internal secretions*, 2nd Edn.   Ed. Edgar Allen.   Baltimore.

—— (1939b).   The effects of embryonic estrogenic treatment upon sexual characters of adult Brown Leghorn cock.   *Anat. Rec.*, **75**, Suppl. p. 57.

—— (1939c).   Intersexuality in adult Brown Leghorn male as a result of estrogenic treatment during early embryonic life.   *Proc. Soc. exp. Biol., N.Y.*, **42**, 310.

—— (1955).   Recent advances in knowledge concerning the role of hormones in the sex differentiation of birds.   In *Recent Studies in Avian Biology*.   Ed. A. Wolfson.   Urbana, Illinois.

—— & BLIVAISS, B. B. (1943).   Male copulatory behaviour in Brown Leghorn hens following implantation of testosterone propionate pellets.   *Anat. Rec.*, **87**, 438.

—— —— (1947).   Induction of male copulatory behaviour in the Brown Leghorn hen.   *Proc. Soc. exp. Biol., N.Y.*, **66**, 418.

—— & DAVIS, D. E. (1941).   Sexual behavior of intersexual domestic fowl.   *Proc. Soc. exp. Biol., N.Y.*, **48**, 665.

—— —— (1948).   The sexual behaviour of intersexual domestic fowl.   *Physiol. Zoöl.*, **21**, 14.

—— —— & BLIVAISS, B. B., (1942).   Observations on the sexual behaviour of hormonally treated Brown Leghorn fowl.   *Anat. Rec.*, **84**, 481.

—— & JUHN, M. (1927).   Compensatory hypertrophy of the testes in Brown Leghorns.   *Biol. Bull.*, **52**, 458.

—— & TABER, E. (1946).   Endocrine factors controlling erythrocyte concentration in the blood of the domestic fowl.   *Physiol. Zoöl.*, **19**, 258.

—— —— & DAVIS, D. E. (1943).   Comparison of erythrocyte numbers in normal and hormone-treated Brown Leghorn fowl.   *Proc. Soc. exp. Biol., N.Y.*, **52**, 49.

—— & VAN DYKE, H. B. (1932a).   Precocious development of sexual characters in the fowl by daily injections of hebin.   I. The male.   *Proc. Soc. exp. Biol., N.Y.*, **30**, 349.

—— —— (1932b).   Precocious development of sexual characters in the fowl by daily injections of hebin.   II. The female.   *Proc. Soc. exp. Biol., N.Y.*, **30**, 351.

DORFMAN, R. I. (1948a).   Studies on the bioassay of hormones: The assay of testosterone propionate and androsterone by a chick comb inunction method.   *Endocrinology*, **42**, 1.

—— (1948b).   Studies on the bioassay of hormones: The relative reactivity of the comb of various breeds of chicks to androgens.   *Endocrinology*, **42**, 7.

—— (1950).   Androgenic activity of C21 steroids.   *Proc. Soc. exp. Biol., N.Y.*, **73**, 223.

—— & GREULICH, W. W. (1937).   The response of the chick's comb to naturally occurring androgens and estrogens.   *Yale J. Biol. Med.*, **10**, 79.

—— & SHIPLEY, R. A. (1956).   *Androgens. Biochemistry, physiology, and clinical significance*.   New York.

DRIGGERS, J. C., & COMAR, C. L. (1949).   The secretion of radioactive calcium (Ca 45) in the hen's egg.   *Poult. Sci.*, **28**, 420.

DUERDEN, J. E. (1919).   Crossing the North African and South African ostrich.   *J. Genet.*, **8**, 155.

DUNHAM, H. H., & RIDDLE, O. (1942).   Effects of a series of steroids on ovulation and reproduction in pigeons.   *Physiol. Zoöl.*, **15**, 383.

EDGAR, D. G. (1953).   The progesterone content of body fluids and tissues.   *J. Endocrin.*, **10**, 54.

ELIOT, T. S. (1928). Influence of gonads on plumage of Sebright bantams. *Physiol. Zoöl.*, **1**, 286.

EMLEN, J. T. Jr., & LORENZ, F. W. (1942). Pairing responses of free-living Valley Quail to sex-hormone pellet implants. *Auk*, **59**, 369.

EMMENS, C. W. (1938). Maximum growth rate of capon comb. *J. Physiol.*, **93**, 413.

—— (1939a). Reports on biological standards—V. Variables affecting the estimation of androgenic and oestrogenic activity. *M.R.C. Spec. Rep. Ser.*, No. 234.

—— (1939b). The effect of prolonged dosage with oestrogens on the adult Brown Leghorn cock. *J. Physiol.*, **95**, 379.

—— & PARKES, A. S. (1940a). The endocrine system and plumage types. II. The effects of thyroxin injections to normal caponized and thyroidectomized caponized birds. *J. Genet.*, **39**, 485.

—— —— (1940b). The endocrine system and plumage types. IV. Feminization of plumage with especial reference to henny cocks and eclipse drakes. *J. Genet.*, **39**, 503.

ENGEL, P. (1939). Cock's comb assay of male hormone. *Arch. int. Pharmacodyn.*, **61**, 354.

'ESPINASSE, P. G. (1939). The developmental anatomy of the Brown Leghorn breast feather, and its reactions to oestrone. *Proc. zool. Soc. Lond.*, A, **109**, 247.

ESSENBERG, J. M., & KARRASCH, R. J. (1940). Experimental study of effects of roentgen rays on gonads of sexually mature domestic fowl. *Radiology*, **34**, 358.

EVANS, H. M., & SIMPSON, M. E. (1934). The response of the gonads of immature pigeons to various gonadotropic hormones. *Anat. Rec.*, **60**, 405.

—— —— AUSTIN, P. R. & FERGUSON, R. S. (1933). Peculiarities of the prolan-like substance in urine in a case of embryonal carcinoma of the testis. *Proc. Soc. exp. Biol., N.Y.*, **31**, 21.

FABER, F. (1826). *Ueber das Leben der hochnordischen Vogel.* Leipzig.

FARNER, D. S. (1950). The annual stimulus for migration. *Condor*, **52**, 104.

—— (1955). The annual stimulus for migration: experimental and physiologic aspects. Chap. 7 in *Recent studies in avian biology.* Edited by Albert Wolfson. Illinois.

—— & MEWALDT, L. R. (1955). Is increased activity of wakefulness an essential element in the mechanism of the periodic responses of avian gonads? *Northw. Sci.*, **29**, 53.

FELL, H. B. (1923). Histological studies on the gonads of the fowl. I. The histological basis of sex reversal. *Brit. J. exp., Biol.* **1**, 97.

—— (1924). Histological studies on the gonads of the fowl. 2. The histogenesis of the so-called "luteal" cells of the ovary. *Brit. J. exp. Biol.*, **1**, 293.

FIESER, L. F., & FIESER, M. (1959). *Steroids.* New York.

FINLAY, G. F. (1925). Studies on sex differentiation in fowls. *Brit. J. exp. Biol.*, **2**, 439.

FLEISCHMANN, W., & FRIED, I. A. (1945). Studies on the mechanism of the hypercholesterolemia and hypercalcemia induced by estrogen in immature chicks. *Endocrinology*, **36**, 406.

FOGES, A. (1902). Zur Lehre von den sekundären Geschlechtscharakteren. *Pflüg. Arch. ges. Physiol.*, **93**, 39.

FORBES, T. R. (1947). Testis transplantations performed by John Hunter. *Endocrinology*, **41**, 329.

—— (1949). A. A. Berthold and the first endocrine experiment: some speculation as to its origin. *Bull. Hist. Med.*, **23**, 263.

FRANK, R. T., & KLEMPNER, E. (1937). The comb of the baby chick as a test for the male sex hormones. *Proc. Soc. exp. Biol., N.Y.*, **36**, 763.

—— —— & HOLLANDER, F. (1938). The comb of the baby chick as a test for the male sex hormone. *Proc. Soc. exp. Biol., N.Y.*, **38**, 853.

FRAPS, R. M. (1946). Differential ovulatory reaction of first and subsequent follicles of the hen's clutch. *Anat. Rec.*, **96**, 573.

—— (1954). Neural basis of diurnal periodicity in release of ovulation-inducing hormone in fowl. *Proc. Nat. Acad. Sci.*, **40**, 348.

—— (1955). The varying effects of sex hormones in birds. *Mem. Soc. Endocrin.*, **4**, 205.

—— & DURY, A. (1942). Relative sensitivity to certain ovulation inducing agents of first and subsequent follicles of clutch sequences in the hen. *Anat. Rec.*, **84**, 453.

Fraps, R. M. & Dury, A. (1943). Occurrence of premature ovulation in the domestic fowl following administration of progesterone. *Proc. Soc. exp. Biol.*, *N.Y.*, **52**, 346.

—— Fevold, H. L., & Neher, B. H. (1947). Ovulatory response of the hen to presumptive luteinizing and other fractions from fowl anterior pituitary tissue. *Anat. Rec.*, **99**, 571.

—— Hertz, R., & Sebrell, W. H. (1943). Relation between ovarian function and avidin content in the oviduct of the hen. *Proc. Soc. exp. Biol.*, *N.Y.*, **52**, 140.

—— Hooker, C. W., & Forbes, C. W. (1948). Progesterone in the blood plasma of the ovulating hen. *Science*, **108**, 86.

—— —— & Forbes, T. R. (1949). Progesterone in blood plasma of cocks and non-ovulating hens. *Science*, **109**, 493.

—— Olsen, M. W., & Marsden, S. J. (1951). Augmentation by PMS of body weight response of male turkeys to testosterone propionate. *Proc. Soc. exp. Biol.*, *N.Y.*, **77**, 356.

—— —— & Neher, B. H. (1942). Forced ovulation of normal ovarian follicles in the domestic fowl. *Proc. Soc. exp. Biol.*, *N.Y.*, **50**, 308.

—— & Riley, G. M. (1942). Hormone-induced ovulation in domestic fowl. *Proc. Soc. exp. Biol.*, *N.Y.*, **49**, 253.

—— —— & Olsen, M. W. (1942). Time required for induction of ovulation following intravenous injection of hormone preparations in fowl. *Proc. Soc. exp. Biol.*, *N.Y.*, **50**, 313.

Freud, J. (1931). Über die männlichen Geschlechtsmerkmale der Leghornhühner, besonders über den Kamm, als Grundlage eines Testobjektes für die Eichung des männlichen Hormons. *Pflüg. Arch. ges. Physiol.*, **228**, 1.

—— de Jongh, S. E., & Laqueur, E. (1929). Over de verandering van het Veerenkleed bij Hoenders door Menformon. *Proc. Acad. Sci. Amst.*, **32**, 1054.

—— —— —— (1930). Über den Einfluss des weiblichen (Sexual-) Hormons Menformon auf das Federkleid der Vögel. *Pflüg. Arch. ges. Physiol.*, **225**, 742.

—— Laqueur, E., & Pompen, A. W. M. (1932). Vollständige Restitution der männlichen sekundären Geschlechtsmarkmale beim Kapaun durch Behandlung mit männlichem Hormon. *Endokrinologie*, **10**, 1.

Frith, H. J. (1955). Incubation in the Mallee Fowl (*Leipoa ocellata*, Megapodiidae). *Acta XI Cong. Orn., Basel*, p.570.

Fugo, N. W. (1940). Effects of hypophysectomy in the chick embryo. *J. exp. Zool.*, **85**, 271.

Fussgänger, R. (1934). Mechanism of the action of male hormone. *Med. Chem. Abh. med. chem Forschungsstätten I.G. Farbenind.*, **2**, 194.

Gaarenstroom, J. H. (1937). Influence of oestrone (menformon) on the sex of chicken embryos. *Acta brev. neerl. Physiol.*, **7**, 156.

—— (1939). Action of sex hormones on the development of the Müllerian duct of the chick embryo. *J. exp. Zool.*, **82**, 31.

—— (1940). Sexual development of fowls derived from eggs treated with oestradiol benzoate. *J. Endocrin.*, **2**, 47.

Gallagher, T. F., Domm, L. V., & Koch, F. C. (1933). The problem of hen-feathering in Sebright cocks. *J. biol. Chem.*, **100**, 47.

—— & Koch, F. C. (1929). The testicular hormone. *J. biol. Chem.*, **84**, 495.

—— —— (1930). The quantitative assay for the testicular hormone by the comb growth reaction. *J. Pharmacol.*, **40**, 327.

—— —— (1935). The quantitative assay for the testicular hormone by the comb-growth reaction. (Second communication). *J. Pharmacol.*, **55**, 97.

Gatenby, J. B., & Brambell, F. W. R. (1924). Notes on the genitalia of a crowing hen. *J. Genet.*, **14**, 173.

Godfrey, E. F., & Jaap, R. G. (1950). Oestrogenic interruption of broodiness in the domestic fowl. *Poult. Sci.*, **29**, 356.

Goodale, H. D. (1910). Some results in castration in ducks. *Biol. Bull., Wood's Hole*, **20**, 35.

—— (1913). Castration in relation to the secondary sexual characters of Brown Leghorns. *Amer. Nat.*, **47**, 159.

GOODALE, H. D. (1916a).   Gonadectomy in relation to the secondary sexual characters of some domestic birds.   *Publ. Carneg. Instn.*, No. 243.

—— (1916b).   Further developments in ovariotomized fowl.   *Biol. Bull., Wood's Hole*, **30,** 286.

—— (1918).   Feminized male birds.   *Genetics*, **3,** 276.

GORBMAN, A. (1941).   Comparative anatomy and physiology of the anterior pituitary. *Quart. Rev. Biol.*, **16,** 294.

GRADSTEIN, S. (1935).   A photo-electric method of measuring the comb of capons in the assay of male hormone.   *Arch. int. Pharmacodyn.*, **51,** 113.

GREELEY, F., & MEYER, R. K. (1953).   Seasonal variation in testis-stimulating activity of male pheasant pituitary glands.   *Auk*, **70,** 350.

GREENWOOD, A. W. (1925).   Gonad grafts in the fowl.   *Brit. J. exp. Biol.*, **2,** 469.

—— (1928).   Studies on the relation of gonadic structure to plumage characterisation in the domestic fowl. IV.—Gonad cross-transplantation in Leghorn and Campine. *Proc. Roy. Soc.*, B, **103,** 73.

—— & BLYTH, J. S. S. (1930).   The results of testicular transplantation in Brown Leghorn hens.   *Proc. Roy. Soc.*, B, **106,** 189.

—— —— (1931).   On significant modifications of feather type induced by injections of female sex hormone (oestrin) to capons.   *Vet. J.*, **87,** 42.

—— —— (1935).   On the relation between the site of injection of androsterone and the comb response in the fowl.   *Quart. J. exp. Physiol.*, **25,** 267.

—— —— (1938a).   Sex dimorphism in the plumage of the domestic fowl.   *J. Genet.*, **36,** 53.

—— —— (1938b).   The influence of testis on sexual plumage in the domestic fowl. *J. Genet.*, **36,** 501.

—— —— (1938c).   Experimental modification of the accessory sexual apparatus in the hen.   *Quart. J. exp. Physiol.*, **28,** 61.

—— —— & CALLOW, R. K. (1935).   Quantitative studies on the response of the capon's comb to androsterone.   *Biochem. J.*, **29,** 1400.

—— & CHU, J. P. (1939).   On the relation between thyroid and sex gland functioning in the Brown Leghorn fowl.   *Quart. J. exp. Physiol.*, **29,** 111.

—— & CREW, F. A E. (1926).   Studies on the relation of gonadic structure to plumage characterization in the domestic fowl.   I.   Henny-feathering in an ovariotomized hen with active testis grafts.   *Proc. Roy. Soc.*, B, **99,** 232.

—— —— (1927).   Studies on the relation of gonadic structure to plumage characterisation in the domestic fowl.   II.   The developmental capon and poularde.   *Proc. Roy. Soc.*, B, **101,** 450.

GUHL, A. M., & WARREN, D. C. (1956).   Number of offspring sired by cockerels related to social dominance in chickens.   *Poult. Sci.*, **25,** 460.

GUYER, M. F. (1912).   Modification in the testes of hybrids from the guinea and common fowl.   *J. Morph.*, **23,** 45.

HACHLOW, V. A. (1927).   Kastrationversuche an Dompfaffen (Pyrrhula).   *Arch. Entw-Mech. Org.*, **110,** 279.

HAMILTON, J. B. (1938).   Precocious masculine behaviour following administration of synthetic male hormone substance.   *Endocrinology*, **23,** 53.

—— & DORFMAN, R. I. (1939).   Influence of the vehicle upon the length and strength of action of male hormone substance, testosterone propionate.   *Endocrinology*, **24,** 711.

—— & GOLDEN, W. R. C. (1939).   Responses of the female to male hormone substances. *Endocrinology*, **25,** 737.

HARDESTY, M. (1931).   The structural basis for the response of the comb of the Brown Leghorn fowl to the sex hormones.   *Amer. J. Anat.*, **47,** 277.

HARRISON, R. J. (1948).   The development and fate of the corpus luteum in the vertebrate series.   *Biol. Rev.*, **23,** 296.

HAYS, F. A. (1945).   Male sex hormones and artificial light as activators of spermatogenesis of adult males.   *Poult. Sci.*, **24,** 66.

HEISTAND, W. A., & STULLKEN, D. E. (1943).   Some observations on androgen-treated baby chicks.   *Anat. Rec.*, **87,** 448.

HERRICK, E. H., & LOCKHART, C. H. (1940). Effect of male sex hormone on developing ovaries of young fowls. *Endocrinology*, **26**, 508.

HERTZ, R. (1945). The quantitative relationship between stilbestrol response and dietary "folic acid" in the chick. *Endocrinology*, **37**, 1.

—— LARSEN, C. P., & TULLNER, W. W. (1947). Inhibition of estrogen-induced tissue growth with progesterone. *J. nat. Cancer Inst.*, **8**, 123.

—— & TULLNER, W. W. (1949). Quantitative interference with estrogen-induced tissue growth by folic acid antagonists. *Endocrinology*, **44**, 278.

HILL, R. T., CORKILL, A. B., & PARKES, A. S. (1934). Hypophysectomy of birds. II. General effects of hypophysectomy of fowl. *Proc. Roy. Soc.*, B, **116**, 208.

—— & PARKES, A. S. (1934a). Hypophysectomy of birds. I-Technique with a note on results. *Proc. Roy. Soc.*, B, **115**, 402.

—— —— (1934b). Hypophysectomy of birds. III. Effect on gonads, accessory organs and head furnishings. *Proc. Roy. Soc.*, B, **116**, 221.

—— —— (1935). Hypophysectomy of birds. IV. Plumage changes in hypophysecto-mised fowls. V. Effect of replacement therapy on the gonads, accessory organs and secondary sexual characters of hypophysectomised fowls. *Proc. Roy. Soc.*, B, **117**, 202.

HINDE, R. A., THORPE, W. H., & VINCE, M. A. (1956). The following response of young coots and moorhens. *Behaviour*, **9**, 213.

HÖHN, E. O. (1947). Sexual behaviour and seasonal changes in the gonads and adrenals of the mallard. *Proc. zool. Soc. Lond.*, A, **117**, 281.

—— (1956). Seasonal recrudescence of the thymus in adult birds. *Canad. J. Biochem.* **34**, 90.

HOLLANDER, W. F. (1949). Bipaternity in pigeons. *J. Hered.*, **40**, 271.

HOLTZ, A. H. (1957). 17-ketosteroids and pseudoketosteroids in the urine of cattle. *Acta endocr., Copenhagen*, **26**, 75.

HOOKER, C. W., & CUNNINGHAM, B. (1938). Regeneration of testis in the fowl, and its bearing on germ-cell theory. *Anat. Rec.*, **72**, 371.

—— & FORBES, T. R. (1947). A biossay for minute amounts of progesterone. *Endocrinology*, **41**, 158.

—— —— (1949). Specificity of the intrauterine test for progesterone. *Endocrinology*, **145**, 71.

HOROWITZ, R. (1934). Über morphologische Folgen der Kastration bei Hähnen. *Biol. gen.*, **10**, 569.

HOSKINS, W. H., & KOCH, F. C. (1939a). The reciprocal nature of the testis-comb relationship. *Endocrinology*, **25**, 257.

—— —— (1939b). The inhibition of comb growth in cockerels and capons by estrone. *Endocrinology*, **25**, 266.

HUDSON, W. H. (1892). *The naturalist in La Plata*. London.

HUNTER, J. (1771). *The natural history of the human teeth:* Pt. I. London.

HUSTON, T. M., & NALBANDOV, A. V. (1953). Neurohumoral control of the pituitary in the fowl. *Endocrinology*, **52**, 149.

HUTT, F. B. (1929). Sex dimorphism and variability in the appendicular skeleton of the Leghorn fowl. *Poult. Sci.*, **8**, 202.

HUXLEY, J. S. (1932. *Problems of relative growth*. London.

JAAP, R. G., & ROBERTSON, H. (1953). The chick comb response to androgen in inbred Brown Leghorns. *Endocrinology*, **53**, 512.

—— & THAYER, R. H. (1944). Oral administration of oestrogens in poultry. *Poult. Sci.*, **23**, 249.

JENNER, E. (1824). Some observations on the migrations of birds. *Phil. Trans.*, **1824**, 11.

JUHN, M., FAULKNER, G. H., & GUSTAVSON, R. G. (1931). The correlation of rates of growth and hormone threshold in the feathers of fowls. *J. exp. Zool.*, **58**, 69.

—— & GUSTAVSON, R. G. (1930). The production of female genital subsidiary characters and plumage sex characters by injection of human placental hormone in fowls. *J. exp. Zool.*, **56**, 31.

—— —— (1932). The response of a vestigial Müllerian duct to the female hormone and the persistence of such rudiments in the male fowl. *Anat. Rec.*, **52**, 299.

JUHN, M., & GUSTAVSON, R. G. & GALLAGHER, T. F. (1932). The factor of age with reference to reactivity to sex hormones in fowl. *J. exp. Zool.*, **64**, 133.

—— & MITCHELL, J. B., Jr. (1929). On endocrine weights in Brown Leghorns. *Amer. J Physiol.*, **88**, 177.

KAR, A. B. (1947a). The action of male and female sex hormones on the adrenals in the fowl. *Anat. Rec.*, **97**, 551.

—— (1947b). The adrenal cortex testicular relations in the fowl: the effect of castration and replacement therapy on the adrenal cortex. *Anat. Rec.*, **99**, 177.

KEAST, J. A. & MARSHALL, A. J. (1954). The influence of drought and rainfall on reproduction in Australian desert birds. *Proc. zool. Soc. Lond.*, **124**, 493.

KECK, W. N. (1934). The control of the secondary sex characters in the English Sparrow, *Passer domesticus* (Linnaeus). *J. exp. Zool.*, **67**, 315.

KING, J. R., & FARNER, D. F. (1956. Bioenergetic basis of light induced for deposition in the White-crowned Sparrow. *Proc. Soc. exp. Biol.*, N.Y., **93**, 354.

KIRKPATRICK, C. M. (1944). Body weights and organ measurements in relation to age and season in ring-necked pheasants. *Anat. Rec.*, **89**, 175.

KIRSCHBAUM, A., PFEIFFER, C. A., VAN HEUVENSWIN, J., & GARDNER, W. U. (1939). Studies on gonad-hypophysial relationship and cyclic osseus changes in the English Sparrow, *Passer domesticus*, L. *Anat. Rec.*, **75**, 249.

KLEINHOLTZ, L. H., & RAHN, H. (1940). The distribution of intermedin: A new biological method of assay and results of tests under normal and experimental conditions. *Anat. Rec.*, **76**, 157.

KLEMPNER, E., FRANK, R. T., & HOLLANDER, F. (1940). Improvement in chick comb response to androsterone obtained with alcohol as vehicle. *Proc. Soc. exp. Biol.*, N.Y., **44**, 633.

KOCH, F. C. (1932). The biochemistry and assay of testis hormones. Chap. 8 in *Sex and internal secretions*. Baltimore.

—— (1937). The male sex hormones. *Physiol. Rev.*, **17**, 153.

—— (1939). Chapter 12 in *Sex and internal secretions*. Ed. E. Allen. 2nd Edn. Baltimore.

—— & GALLAGHER, T. F. (1934). The effect of light on the comb response of capons to testicular hormone. *Proc. Amer. Soc. biol. Chem.*, **8**, xliv.

KORNFIELD, W., & NALBANDOV, A. V. (1954). Endocrine influences on the development of the rudimentary gonad of fowl. *Endocrinology*, **55**, 751.

KRITZLER, H. (1943). Carotenoids in the display and eclipse plumages of bishop birds. *Physiol. Zoöl.*, **16**, 241.

KRIZENECKY, J., & KAMENICEK, L. F. (1933). Die Wirkung der Kastration bei männlichen und weiblichen Perlhühnern. *Arch. Tierernähr. Tierz.*, **9**, 504.

KUMERAN, J. D. S., & TURNER, C. W. (1949a). The endocrinology of spermatogenesis in birds. I. Effect of estrogen and androgen. *Poult. Sci.*, **28**, 593.

—— —— (1949b). The endocrinology of spermatogenesis in birds. II. The effect of androgens. *Poult. Sci.*, **28**, 739.

KYES, P., & POTTER. T. S. (1934). Physiological marrow ossification in female pigeons. *Anat. Rec.*, **60**, 377.

LACK, D. (1939). The behaviour of the robin. *Proc. zool. Soc. Lond.*, A, **109**, 169.

LACY, D., & ROTBLAT, J. (1960). Effects of ionising irradiation on the testes of the rat with some observations on its normal morphology. *Proc. Int. Congr. Electron Microscopy*, Berlin.

LAHR, E. L., & RIDDLE, O. (1944). The action of steroid hormones on the mature dove testis. *Endocrinology*, **35**, 261.

—— —— (1945). Intersexuality in male embryos of pigeons. *Anat. Rec.*, **92**, 425.

—— —— & BATES, R. W. (1941). Response of testes of immature pigeons to gonadotrophins. *Endocrinology*, **28**, 681.

LAKE, P. E. (1957). The male reproductive tract of the fowl. *J. Anat.*, Lond., **91**, 116.

LANDAUER, W. (1937). Studies on the creeper fowl. XI. Castration and length of bones of the appendicular skeleton in normal and creeper fowl. *Anat. Rec.*, **69**, 247.

LANGE, B. (1928). Die Brutflecke der Vogel und die für sie wichtigen Hauteigentümlichkeiten. *Gegenbaurs Jb.*, **59**, 601.

Leblond, C.-P. (1938). Action des gonado-stimulines hypophysaires A et B sur les glandes génitales des pigeons mâles et femelles. *C. R. Soc. Biol., Paris*, **127**, 1248.

Lehrman, D. S. (1955). The physiological basis of parental feeding behaviour in the Ring Dove (*Streptopelia risoria*). *Behaviour*, **7**, 241.

—— (1956). On the organisation of maternal behaviour and the problem of instinct. In *L'instinct dans le comportement des animaux et de l'homme*. Paris.

—— (1958a). Induction of broodiness by participation in court-ship and nest-building in the Ring Dove. *J. comp. physiol. Psychol.*, **51**, 32.

—— (1958b). Effect of female sex hormones on incubation behaviour in the Ring Dove (*Streptopelia risoria*). *J. comp. physiol. Psychol.*, **51**, 142.

—— & Brody, P. (1957). Oviduct response to estrogen and progesterone in the Ring Dove. (*Streptopelia risoria*). *Proc. Soc. exp. Biol., N.Y.*, **95**, 373.

Leonard, S. L. (1937). Luteinising hormone in bird hypophyses. *Proc. Soc. exp. Biol., N.Y.*, **37**, 566.

—— (1939). Induction of singing in female canaries by injections of male hormones. *Proc. Soc. exp. Biol., N.Y.*, **41**, 229.

Leopold, A. S. (1944). The nature of hereditable wildness in turkeys. *Condor*, **46**, 133.

Levick, G. M. (1914). *Antarctic Penguins*. London.

Lewis, L. B. (1946). A study of some effects of sex hormones upon the embryonic reproductive system of the White Pekin duck. *Physiol. Zoöl.*, **19**, 282.

—— & Domm, L. V. (1948). Sexual transformation of the osseus bulla in the duck embryo following administration of oestrogens. *Physiol. Zoöl.*, **31**, 65.

Lillie, F. R., (1917). The free-martin; a study of the action of sex-hormones in the foetal life of cattle. *J. exp. Zool.*, **23**, 371.

—— (1927). The present status of the problem of "sex-inversion" in the hen. *J. exp. Zool.*, **48**, 175.

—— (1931). Bilateral gynandromorphism and lateral hemihypertrophy in birds. *Science*, **74**, 387.

—— & Juhn, M. (1932). The physiology of the development of feathers. I. Growth rate and pattern in the individual feather. *Physiol. Zoöl.*, **5**, 124.

Lipschütz, A. (1931). La folliculine agit-elle sur le plumage du pigeon? *C. R. Soc. Biol., Paris*, **108**, 690.

—— Kallas, H., & Wilckens, E. (1929). Physiologie comparée du lobe antérieur de l'hypophyse. *C. R. Soc. Biol., Paris*, **100**, 28.

—— & Wilhelm, O. (1928). Castration chez le pigeon. *C. R. Soc. Biol., Paris*, **99**, 691.

Lofts, B., & Marshall A. J. (1956). The effects of prolactin administration on the internal rhythm of reproduction in male birds. *J. Endocrin.*, **13**, 101.

—— —— (1957). Cyclical changes in the distribution of the testis lipids of a teleost fish, *Esox lucius*. *Quart. J. micr. Sci.*, **98**, 79.

—— —— (1958). An investigation of the refractory period of reproduction of birds by means of exogenous prolactin and follicle stimulating hormone. *J. Endocrin.*, **17**, 91.

—— —— (1959). The post-nuptial occurrence of progestins in the seminiferous tubules of birds. *J. Endocrin.*, **19**, 16.

Lorenz, F. W. (1938). Effects of estrin in blood lipids of the immature fowl. *J. biol. Chem.*, **126**, 763.

—— (1945). The influence of diethylstilboestrol on fat deposition and meat quality in chickens. *Poult. Sci.*, **24**, 128.

Lorenz, F. W. (1954). Effects of estrogens on domestic fowl and applications in the poultry industry. *Vitamins & Hormones*, **12**, 235.

—— Entenman, C., & Chaikoff, I. L. (1938). The influence of age, sex, and ovarian activity on the blood lipids of the domestic fowl. *J. biol. Chem.*, **122**, 619.

Lorenz, K. (1935). Der Kumpan im der Umwelt des Vogels. *J. Orn., Lpz.*, **83**, 137 & 289.

—— (1937). The companion in the bird's world. *Auk*, **54**, 245.

Lyons, W. R. (1937). The preparation and assay of mammotropin. *Symp. Quant. Biol.*, **5**, 198.

McCreal, R. D., & Farner, D. F. (1956). Premigratory fat deposition in the Gambel White Crowned Sparrow: some morphologic and chemical observations. *Northw. Sci.*, **30**, 12.

McCullagh, D. R., & Cuyler, W. K. (1939). The response of the capon's comb to androsterone. *J. Pharmacol.*, **66**, 379.

McDonald, M. R., & Riddle, O. (1945). The effect of reproduction and estrogen administration on the partition of calcium, phosphorus, and nitrogen in pigeon plasma. *J. biol. Chem.*, **159**, 445.

McGee, L. C., Juhn, M., & Domm, L. V. (1928). The development of secondary sex characters in capons by injections of extracts of bull testes. *Amer. J. Physiol.*, **87**, 406.

McGowan, J. P. (1936). Suprarenal "virilism" in a domestic hen; its possible significance. *J. exp. Biol.*, **13**, 377.

Markert, C. L. (1948). The effects of thyroxine and anti-thyroid compounds on the synthesis of pigment granules in chick melanoblasts cultured *in vitro*. *Physiol. Zoöl.*, **21**, 309.

Marlow, H. W. (1950). Pituitary-comb relationship. *Endocrinology*, **47**, 300.

Marshall, A. J. (1949). On the function of the interstitum of the testis: the sexual cycle of a wild bird, *Fulmarus glacialis* (L.). *Quart. J. micr. Sci.*, **90**, 265.

—— (1951a). Food availability as a timing factor in the sexual cycle of birds. *Emu*, **50**, 267.

—— (1951b). The refractory period of testis rhythm in birds and its possible bearing on breeding and migration. *Wilson Bull.*, **63**, 239.

—— (1952a). Display and sexual cycle in the Spotted Bowerbird (*Chlamydera maculata*, Gould). *Proc. zool. Soc. Lond.*, **122**, 239.

—— (1952b). Non-breeding among Arctic birds. *Ibis*, **94**, 310.

—— (1952c). The interstitial cycle in relation to autumn and winter sexual behaviour in birds. *Proc. zool. Soc. Lond.*, **121**, 727.

—— (1954). *Bower Birds: their displays and breeding cycles*. Oxford.

—— (1955). Reproduction in birds: the male. *Mem. Soc. Endocrin.*, **4**, 75.

—— (1959). Internal and environmental control of breeding. *Ibis*, **101**, 456.

—— (1960). Parker and Haswell's *Text-book of Zoology*. Volume II. 7th Edn. London.

—— & Coombs, C. J. F. (1957). The interaction of environmental, internal and behavioural factors in the Rook, *Corvus f. frugilegus Linnaeus*. *Proc. zool. Soc. Lond.*, **128**, 545.

—— & Disney, H. J. (1957). Experimental induction of the breeding season in a xerophilous bird. *Nature, Lond.*, **180**, 647.

—— & Serventy, D. L. (1956). A case of inter-sexuality in *Gymnorhina dorsalis*. *Emu*, **56**, 207.

—— —— (1957). On the post-nuptial rehabilitatoin of the avian testis tunic. *Emu*, **57**, 59.

—— —— (1958). The internal rhythm of reproduction in xerophilous birds under conditions of illumination and darkness. *J. exp. Biol.*, **35**, 666.

—— & Williams, M. C. (1959). The migration of Yellow Wagtails (*Budytes* spp.) from latitude 0.04'. *Proc. zool. Soc. Lond.*, **132**, 313.

—— & Woolf, F. M. (1957). Second lipid changes in the sexual elements of a male snake. *Vipera berus*. *Quart. J. micr. Sci.*, **98**, 89.

Marshall, F. H. A. (1922). *Physiology of Reproduction*. 2nd Edn. London.

—— (1936). Sexual periodicity and the causes which determine it. *Phil. Trans.*, B, **226**, 423.

Martins, T. (1933). Technique de l'hypophysectomie chez les oiseaux. *C. R. Soc. Biol., Paris*, **114**, 837.

Mason, R. C. (1952). Synergistic and antagonistic effects of progesterone in combination with estrogens on oviduct weight. *Endocrinology*, **51**, 570.

Massaglia, A. C. (1920). The internal secretion of the testis. *Endocrinology*, **4**, 547.

Masure, R. H., & Allee, W. C. (1934). Flock organization of the Shell-parakeet, *Melopsittacus undulatus* Shaw. *Ecology*, **15**, 388.

Mather, R. A., & Riddle, O. (1942). The cytology of the adrenal cortex of normal pigeons and in experimentally induced atrophy and hypotrophy. *Amer. J. Anat.*, **71**, 311.

Matthews, L. H. (1955). The evolution of vivipary invertebrates. *Mem. Soc. Endocrin.*, **4**, 129.

MEITES, J., & TURNER, C. W. (1947).   Effect of sex hormones on pituitary lactogen and crop glands of common pigeons.   *Proc. Soc. exp. Biol., N.Y.*, **64,** 465.

MERKEL, F. W. (1938).   Zûr Physiologie der Zugunruhe bei Vögeln.   *Ber. Ver. Schles. Ornith.*, **25,** 1.

MIESCHER, K., FISCHER, W. H., & TSCHOPP, E. (1937).   The effect of enol-esters of testosterone.   *Nature, Lond.*, **140,** 726.

—— WETTSTEIN, A., & TSCHOPP, E. (1936).   The activation of the male sex hormones. 11.   *Biochem. J.*, **30,** 1977.

MILLER, A. H. (1948).   The refractory period in light-induced reproductive development of golden-crowned sparrows.   *J. exp. Zool.*, **109,** 1.

—— (1949).   Potentiality for testicular recrudescence during the annual refractory period of the Golden-crowned Sparrow.   *Science*, **109,** 546.

MILLER, R. A. (1938).   Spermatogenesis in a sex-reversed female and in normal males of the domestic fowl, *Gallus domesticus*.   *Anat. Rec.*, **70,** 155.

—— & RIDDLE, O. (1939).   Stimulation of adrenal cortex of pigeons by anterior pituitary hormones and by their secondary products.   *Proc. Soc. exp. Biol., N.Y.*, **41,** 518.

MINOURA, T. (1921).   A study of testis and ovary grafts on the hen's egg and their effects on the embryo.   *J. exp. Zool.*, **33,** 1.

MINTZ, B., & WOLFF, E. (1954).   The development of embryonic chick ovarian medulla and its feminizing action in intracoelomic grafts.   *J. exp. Zool.*, **126,** 511.

MIRSKAIA, L., & CREW, F. A. E. (1931).   The effect of destruction of spermatogenic tissue by X-rays upon certain secondary gonadic characters of the cock.   *Quart. J. exp. Physiol.*, **21,** 135.

MITCHELL, H. H., CARD, L. E., & HAINES, W. T. (1927).   Effect of age, sex and castration on basal heat production of chickens.   *J. agric. Res.*, **34,** 945.

MITCHELL, J. B. (1929).   Experimental studies on bird hypophysis; effects of hypophysectomy in Brown Leghorn fowl.   *Physiol. Zoöl.*, **2,** 411.

MOORE, C. R., GALLAGHER, T. F., & KOCH, F. C. (1929).   The effects of extracts of testis in correcting the castrated condition in the fowl and in the mammal.   *Endocrinology*, **13,** 367.

MORATÓ-MANARO, J., & ALBRIEUX, A. (1939).   The effect of sex hormones on the combs of castrated and normal cocks.   *Endocrinology*, **24,** 518.

—— —— & BUÑO, W. (1938).   Wirkung der Sexualhormone auf den Hahnenkamm.   *Klin. Wschr.*, **17,** 784.

MORGAN, T. H. (1919).   The genetic and the operative evidence relating to secondary sexual characters.   *Publ. Carneg. Instn.*, No. 285.

MOSZKOWSKA, A. (1949).   Moyen de mettre en évidence de faibles quantités de gonadotrophines dans les hypophyses de poule.   *C. R. Soc. Biol., Paris*, **143,** 791.

MÜHLBOCK, O. (1938).   Über die weitere Rückbildung des Kapaunenkammes nach oestrogenem Hormon.   *Acta brev. neerl. Physiol.*, **8,** 142.

—— (1939).   Versuche über die hormonale Beeinflussung der Federfarbe bei rebhuhnfarbigen Leghorn-Hähnen.   *Acta brev. neerl. Physiol.*, **9,** 264.

MUNRO, S. S. (1938a).   Functional changes in fowl sperm during their passage through the excurrent ducts of the male.   *J. exp. Zool.*, **79,** 71.

—— (1938b).   The effect of testis hormone on the preservation of sperm life in the vas deferens of the fowl.   *J. exp. Biol.*, **15,** 186.

—— & KOSIN, I. L. (1943).   Dramatic response of the chick oviduct to estrogen.   *Poult. Sci.*, **22,** 330.

MYERS, J. A. (1917).   Studies on the syrinx of *Gallus domesticus*.   *J. Morph.*, **29,** 165.

NALBANDOV, A. V. (1945).   A study of the effect of prolactin on broodiness and on cock testes.   *Endocrinology*, **36,** 251.

—— (1953).   Endocrine control of the physiological functions.   *Poult. Sci.*, **32,** 88.

—— & BAUM, G. J. (1948).   The use of stilboestrol inhibited-males as test animals for gonadotrophic hormones.   *Endocrinology*, **43,** 371.

—— & CARD, L. E. (1942).   Effect of hypophysectomy of growing chicks upon their basal metabolism.   *Proc. Soc. exp. Biol., N.Y.*, **51,** 294.

—— —— (1943).   Effect of hypophysectomy of growing chicks.   *J. exp. Zool.*, **94,** 387.

NALBANDOV, A. V., & CARD, L. E. (1946). Effect of FSH and LH upon the ovaries of immature chicks and low-producing hens. *Endocrinology*, **38**, 71.

—— HOCHHAUSER, M., & DUGAS, M. (1945). A study of the effect of prolactin on broodiness and on cock testes. *Endocrinology*, **36**, 251.

—— MEYER, R. K., & McSHAN, W. H. (1946). Effect of purified gonadotropes on the androgen-secreting ability of testes of hypophysectomized cocks. *Endocrinology*, **39**, 91.

—— —— —— (1951). The rôle of a third gonadotrophic hormone in the mechanism of androgen secretion in chicken testes. *Anat. Rec.*, **110**, 475.

NEEDHAM, J. (1950). *Biochemistry and morphogenesis*. Cambridge.

NICE, M. M. (1946). Weights of resident and winter visitant song sparrows in central Ohio. *Condor*, **48**, 41.

NOBLE, G. K., & WURM, M. (1938). Effect of testosterone propionate on the black-crowned night heron. *Anat. Rec.*, **72**, Suppl. p. 60.

—— —— (1940a). The effect of hormones on the breeding of the laughing gull. *Anat. Rec.*, **78**, Suppl. p. 50.

—— —— (1940b). The effect of testosterone propionate on the black-crowned night heron. *Endocrinology*, **26**, 837.

—— & ZITRIN, A. (1942). Induction of mating behaviour in male and female chicks following injections of sex hormones. *Endocrinology*, **30**, 327.

NONIDEZ, J. F. (1924). Studies on the gonads of the fowl. IV. The intertubular tissues of the testis in normal and hen-feathered cocks. *Amer. J. Anat.*, **34**, 359.

OGATA, D., & NISHIMURA, H. (1927). A new (orbital) method for extirpation of the hypophysis in the pigeon. *Endocrinology*, **11**, 451.

OSLUND, R. M. (1928). Seasonal modification in testes of vertebrates. *Quart. Rev. Biol.*, **3**, 254.

PADOA, E. (1931). La gonadectomia nei tacchini. *Boll. Soc. ital. Biol. sper.*, **6**, 689.

—— (1934). Richerche sperimentale sulla sessualeta nei polle. *Arch. ital. Anat. Embriol.*, **33**, 242.

PARKES, A. S., (1936). The use of bantam capons for the assay of male hormone preparations. *Quart. J. Pharm.*, **9**, 669.

—— (1937). Relative duration of action of various esters of oestrone, oestradiol and oestriol. *Biochem.*, *J.*, **31**, 579.

—— (1938). Ambisexual activity of the gonads. *Les Hormones Sexuelles*. Paris. Ed., L. Brouha. p. 67.

—— (1945). The androgenic activity of progesterone. *Arch. int. Pharmacodyn.*, **70**, 316.

—— (1957). The dilemma of medical science. Chap. 4 in *The human sum*, Wm. Heinemann Ltd., London.

—— & EMMENS, C. W. (1944). Effect of androgens and estrogens on birds. *Vitamins and Hormones*, **2**, 361.

—— & ROWLANDS, I. W. (1937). Ineffectiveness in birds of antisera for mammalian gonadotropic and thyrotropic substances. *J. Physiol.*, **90**, 100.

PATEL, M. D. (1936). The physiology of the formation of "pigeon's milk". *Physiol. Zoöl.*, **9**, 129.

PAYNE, F. (1940). Signet-ring or castration cells in the chick pituitary. *Anat. Rec.*, **76**, 29.

—— (1942). The cytology of the anterior pituitary of the fowl. *Biol. Bull.*, **82**, 79.

—— (1943). The cytology of the anterior pituitary of broody fowls. *Anat. Rec.*, **86**, 1.

—— (1944). Pituitary changes in aging capons. *Anat. Rec.*, **89**, 563.

—— (1946). The cellular picture in the anterior pituitary of normal fowls from embryo to old age. *Anat. Rec.*, **96**, 77.

—— (1947). The effects of gonad removal on the anterior pituitary of the fowl from ten days to six years. *Anat. Rec.*, **97**, 507.

PÉZARD, A. (1911). Sur la détermination des caractères sexuels secondaires chez les Gallinacés. *C. R. Acad. Sci.*, Paris, **153**, 1027.

—— (1912). Sur la détermination des caractères sexuels secondaires chez les Gallinacés. *C. R. Acad. Sci.*, Paris, **154**, 1183.

Pézard, A. (1915). Transformation expérimentale des caractères sexuels secondaires chez les Gallinacés. *C. R. Acad. Sci., Paris,* **160,** 260.

—— (1918). Le conditionnement physiologique des caractères sexuels secondaires chez les oiseaux. Du rôle endocrine des glandes génitales. *Bull. biol.,* **52,** 1.

—— (1921). Numerical law of regression of certain secondary sex characters. *J. gen. Physiol.,* **3,** 271.

—— (1922). Modifications périodiques ou définitives des caractères sexuels secondaires et du comportement chez les Gallinacés. *Ann. Sci. nat.,* **5,** 83.

—— (1928). Die Bestimmung der Geschlechtsfunktion bei den Hühnern. *Ergebn. Physiol.,* **27,** 552.

—— (1931). Influence de sexe, de la maturité et de la castration sur la rétine des oiseaux. Variation de la proportion des boules colorées. *C. R. Soc. Biol., Paris,* **108,** 722.

—— & Caridroit, F. (1927). Forme neutre, changement de sexe de l'ovaire et valeur de C° chez les poules de race Sebright normale, variété dorée. *C. R. Soc. Biol., Paris,* **96,** 1101.

—— Sand, K., & Caridroit, F. (1923). Féminisation d'un coq adulte de race Leghorn doré. *C. R. Soc. Biol., Paris,* **89,** 947.

—— —— —— (1925). L'évolution des potentialités chez la poulette. *C. R. Soc. Biol., Paris,* **92,** 495.

—— —— —— (1926a). La bipartition longitudinale de la plume. Faits nouveaux concernant le gynandromorphisme élémentaire. *C. R. Soc. Biol., Paris,* **94,** 1074.

—— —— —— (1926b). Les hormones sexuelles et le gynandromorphisme chez les Gallinacés. *Arch. Biol., Paris,* **36,** 541.

Pfeiffer, C. A. & Gardner, W. U. (1938). Skeletal changes and blood serum calcium level in pigeons receiving estrogens. *Endocrinology,* **23,** 485.

—— & Kirschbaum, A. (1941). Secretion of androgen by the sparrow ovary following stimulation with pregnant mare serum. *Yale J. Biol. Med.,* **13,** 315.

—— —— (1943). Relation of interstitial cell hyperplasia to secretion of male hormone in the sparrow. *Anat. Rec.,* **85,** 211.

Pfiffner, J. J., & North, H. B. (1940). 17-β-Hydroxyprogesterone. *J. biol. Chem.,* **132,** 459.

—— —— (1941). The isolation of 17-Hydroxyprogesterone from the adrenal gland. *J. biol. Chem.,* **139,** 855.

Phillips, C. L. (1887). Egg-laying extraordinary in *Colaptes autantus. Auk,* **4,** 346.

Phillips, R. E. (1943). Ovarian response of hens and pullets to injections of Ambinon. *Poult. Sci.,* **22,** 368.

Pirsche, E. (1902). L'influence de la castration sur le développement du squelette. (Thése de Lyons.)

Poll, H. (1920). Pfaumischlinge nebst einem Beitrag zur Kern-Erbträger-Lehre. *Arch. mikr. Anat.,* **94,** 364.

Punnett, R. C. (1937). Henny feathering in the fowl: a fresh interpretation. *J. Genet.,* **35,** 129.

Rahn, H., & Painter, R. T. (1941). The comparative histology of the bird pituitary. *Anat. Rec.,* **79,** 297.

Régnier, V. (1934). Note sur un nouveau cas de récessivité commandé par l'hormone ovarienne, dans un croisement de poules domestiques. *C. R. Soc. Biol., Paris,* **116,** 286.

—— (1935). Étude d'un nouveau cas de transmission héréditaire du caractère de sensibilité pigmentaire du plumage à l'hormone ovarienne, dans un croisement de poules domestiques. *C. R. Soc. Biol., Paris,* **118,** 848.

—— (1937). Hormone ovarienne et caractères raciaux de plumage chez le coq et la poule domestiques. *Bull. biol.,* **22.**

—— (1938). Action of folliculin on normal cocks' combs. *C. R. Soc. Biol., Paris,* **127,** 519.

—— & Caridroit, F. (1938). Action of oestradiol benzoate on the hen's comb. *C. R. Soc. Biol., Paris,* **128,** 404.

Reinbold, R. (1951). Le rudiment de tubercule génital du poulet: Développement embryonnaire et sensibilité aux hormones sexuelles. *Bull. biol.,* **85,** 347.

RIDDLE, O. (1924a).   Birds without gonads.   *J. exp. Biol.*, **2**, 211.

—— (1924b).   A case of complete sex-reversal in the adult pigeon.   *Amer. Nat.*, **58**, 167.

—— (1925).   On the sexuality of the right ovary of birds.   *Anat. Rec.*, **30**, 365.

—— (1931a).   Factors in the development of sex and secondary sexual characteristics. *Physiol. Rev.*, **11**, 63.

—— (1931b).   Studies on pituitary function.   *Endocrinology*, **15**, 307.

—— (1932).   Metabolism and sex.   Chap. 6 in *Sex and internal secretions*.   Baltimore.

—— (1935).   Aspects and implications of the hormonal control of the maternal instinct. *Proc. Amer. Phil. Soc.*, **75**, 521.

—— (1937a).   Carbohydrate metabolism in pigeons.   *Cold Spr. Harb. Symp. quant. Biol.*, **5**, 362.

—— (1937b).   Physiological responses to prolactin.   *Cold Spr. Harb. Symp. quant. Biol.*, **5**, 218.

—— (1947).   Endocrines and constitutions in doves and pigeons.   *Publ. Carneg. Instn.*, No. 572.

—— & BATES, R. W. (1933).   Concerning anterior pituitary hormones.   *Endocrinology*, **17**, 689.

—— —— (1939).   The preparation, assay and actions of lactogenic hormones.   In *Sex and internal secretions*.   2nd Edn.   Ed. Edgar Allen.   Baltimore.

—— & DYKSHORN, S. W. (1932).   A new hormone of the anterior pituitary.   *Proc. Soc. exp. Biol., N.Y.*, **29**, 1211.

—— —— (1933).   The preparation, identification and assay of prolactin—a hormone of the anterior pituitary.   *Amer. J. Physiol.*, **105**, 191.

—— —— & LAHR, E. L. (1935).   Prolactin induces broodiness in the fowl.   *Amer. J. Physiol.*, **111**, 352.

—— & BRAUCHER, P. F. (1931).   Studies on the physiology of reproduction in birds. XXX. Control of the special secretion of the crop-gland in pigeons by an anterior pituitary hormone.   *Amer. J. Physiol.*, **97**, 617.

—— —— (1934).   Body size changes in doves and pigeons incident to stages of the reproductive cycle.   *Amer. J. Physiol.*, **107**, 343.

—— & DOTTI, L. B. (1934).   Action of parathyroid hormone in normal and hypophysectomised pigeons.   *Proc. Soc. exp. Biol., N.Y.*, **32**, 507.

—— —— (1936).   Blood calcium in relation to anterior pituitary and sex hormones. *Science*, **84**, 557.

—— & DUNHAM, H. H. (1942).   Transformation of males to intersexes by oestrogen passed from blood of Ring Doves to their ovarian eggs.   *Endocrinology*, **30**, 959.

—— & FLEMION, F. (1928).   Studies on the physiology of reproduction in birds.   XXVI. The role of the anterior pituitary in hastening sexual maturity in ring doves. *Amer. J. Physiol.*, **87**, 110.

—— HOLLANDER, W. F., & SCHOOLEY, J. P. (1945).   A race of hermaphrodite-producing pigeons.   *Anat. Rec.*, **92**, 401.

—— & LAHR, E. L. (1944a).   Relative ability of various steroid hormones to promote growth in oviducts of immature ring-doves.   *Yale J. Biol. Med.*, **17**, 259.

—— —— (1944b).   On broodiness of Ring Doves following implants of certain steroid hormones.   *Endocrinology*, **35**, 255.

—— & McDONALD, M. R. (1945).   The partition of plasma calcium and inorganic phosphorus in estrogen-treated, normal and parathyroidectomised pigeons.   *Endocrinology*, **36**, 48.

—— & POLHEMUS, I. (1931).   Studies on the physiology of reproduction in birds.   XXXI. Effects of anterior pituitary hormones on gonads and other organ weights in the pigeon.   *Amer. J. Physiol.*, **98**, 121.

—— RAUCH, V. M., & SMITH, G. C. (1945).   Action of estrogen on plasma calcium and endosteal bone formation in parathyroidectomized pigeons.   *Endocrinology*, **36**, 41.

—— & SCHOOLEY, J. P. (1935).   Absence of follicle-stimulating hormone in pituitaries of young pigeons.   *Proc. Soc. exp. Biol., N.Y.*, **32**, 1610.

—— & TANGE, M. (1928).   Studies on the physiology of reproduction in birds.   XXV. The action of the ovarian and placental hormone in the pigeon.   *Amer. J. Physiol.*, **87**, 97.

Riley, G. M. (1936). Light regulation of sexual activity in the male Sparrow (*Passer domesticus*). *Proc. Soc. exp. Biol., N.Y.*, **34**, 331.

—— (1937). Experimental studies on spermatogenesis in the House Sparrow. *P. domesticus* (Linn.). *Anat. Rec.*, **67**, 327.

—— & Fraps, R. M. (1942a). Relationship of gonad-stimulating activity of female domestic fowl anterior pituitaries to reproductive activity. *Endocrinology*, **30**, 537.

—— —— (1942b). Biological assays of the male chicken pituitary for gonadotrophic potency. *Endocrinology*, **30**, 529.

—— & Witschi, E. (1938). Comparative effects of light stimulation and administration of gonadotrophic hormones in female sparrows. *Endocrinology*, **23**, 618.

Ringoen, A. R. (1945). Deposition of medullary bone in the female English Sparrow, *Passer domesticus* L. and the Bobwhite Quail, *Colinus virginianus*. *J. Morph.*, **77**, 265.

Roberts, A. (1951). *The birds of South Africa*. 8th impression. London.

Roberts, B. L. (1940). The breeding behaviour of penguins. *Brit. Polar Land Exped. Sci. Rep.*, **1**, 195.

Romanoff, A. C., & Romanoff, A. J. (1949). *The avian egg*. New York.

Rothchild, I., & Fraps, R. M. (1949a). The induction of ovulating hormone release from the pituitary of the domestic hen by means of progesterone. *Endocrinology*, **44**, 141.

—— —— (1949b). The interval between normal release of ovulating hormone and ovulation in the domestic hen. *Endocrinology*, **44**, 134.

Roussel, G. (1936). L'acétate de testostérone hormone testiculaire synthétique. *Bull. Acad. Méd., Paris*, **115**, 458.

—— Gley, P., & Paulin, G. (1937). Étude comparative de l'action de la testostérone et de certains de ses esters sur les caractères sexuels secondaires. *Bull. Acad. Méd., Paris*, **117**, 197.

Rowan, W., & Batrawi, A. M. (1939). Comments on the gonads of some European migrants collected in East Africa immediately before their spring departure. *Ibis*, **3**, 58.

Roxas, H. A. (1926). Gonad cross-transplantation in Sebright and Leghorn fowls. *J. exp. Zool.*, **46**, 63.

Ruzicka, L., & Tschopp, E. (1934). Ueber die künstliche Herstellung und die physiologischen Wirkungen des männlichen Sexualhormons. *Schweiz. med. Wschr.*, **64**, 1118.

Salomonsen, F. (1939). Moults and sequences of plumages in the Rock Ptarmigan (*Lagopus mutus*). *Vidensk. Medd. dansk. Naturh. Foren. Kbh.*, **103**, 1.

Schildmacher, H. (1933). Zur Physiologie des Zugtriebes. I. Versuche mit weiblichem Sexualhormon. *Vogelzug*, **4**, 21.

—— (1934a). Zur Physiologie des Zugtriebes. II. Weitere Versuche mit weiblichem Sexualhormon. *Vogelzug*, **5**, 1.

—— (1934b). Reply to H. Desselberger and G. Steinbacher, Weiblicher Sexualhormon und Vogelzug. *Vogelzug*, **5**, 171.

—— & Steubing, L. (1952). Untersuchungen zur hormanalen Regulierung des Fettwerdens der Zugvogel im Frühjahr. *Biol. Zbl.*, **71**, 272.

Schjelderup-Ebbe, T. (1924). Fortgesetzte biologische Beobachtungen des *Gallus domesticus*. *Psychol. Forsch.*, **5**, 343.

—— (1935). *A handbook of social psychology*. Mass.

Schneider, M., & Dunn, L. C. (1924). On the length and variability of the bones of the White Leghorn fowl. *Anat. Rec.*, **27**, 229.

Schockaert, J. A. (1931). Response of the male genital system of the immature domestic duck to injections of anterior-pituitary substances. *Anat. Rec.*, **50**, 381.

Schoeller, W., & Gehrke, M. (1931). Zur Standardisierung des männlichen Sexualhormons. *Wien Arch. Med.*, **21**, 329.

—— —— (1938). Tierphysiologische Versuche über die Wirkung männlicher Keimdrüsenhormone. I. Versuche an Kapaunen. *Klin. Wschr.*, **17**, 694.

Schooley, J. P., (1939). Technic for hypophysectomy of pigeons. *Endocrinology*, **25**, 372.

SCHOOLEY, J. P. & RIDDLE, O. (1938). The morphological basis of pituitary function in pigeons. *Amer. J. Anat.*, **62**, 314.

—— —— BATES, R. W. (1941). Replacement therapy in hypophysectomized juvenile pigeons. *Amer. J. Anat.*, **69**, 123.

SCHWARTZ, C. W. (1945). The ecology of the prairie chicken in Missouri. *St. Univ. Mont. Stud.*, **20**, 1.

SCOTT, H. M., & PAYNE, L. F. (1934). The effect of gonadectomy on the secondary sexual characters of the Bronze Turkey (*M. gallopavo*). *J. exp. Zool.*, **69**, 123.

SEGAL, S. J., & WITSCHI, E. (1955). The specificity of the weaver-finch-test for the luteinizing gonadotrophins (LH and CGH). *J. clin. Endocrin.*, **15**, 880.

SELOUS, E. (1901). An observational diary of the habits—mostly domestic—of the Great Crested Grebe (*Podicips custatus*). *Zoologist*, **5**, 180.

SELYE, H. (1943). *Encyclopedia of Endocrinology*. Vol. 4. Montreal.

SERVENTY, D. L., & MARSHALL, A. J. (1956). Factors influencing testis colouration in birds. *Emu*, **56**, 219.

—— —— (1957). Breeding periodicity in Western Australian birds. *Emu*, **57**, 99.

SHATTOCK, S. G., & SELIGMANN, C. G. (1904). Observations upon the acquirement of secondary sexual characters, indicating the formation of an internal secretion by the testicle. *Proc. Roy. Soc.*, **73**, 49.

SHIRLEY, H. V., Jr., & NALBANDOV, A. V. (1956). Effects of transecting hypophyseal stalks in laying hens. *Endocrinology*, **58**, 694.

SHOEMAKER, H. H. (1939a). Social hierarchy in flocks of the canary. *Auk*, **56**, 381.

—— (1939b). Effect of testosterone propionate on behavior of the female canary. *Proc. Soc. exp. Biol., N.Y.*, **41**, 299.

SILLER, W. G. (1956). A Sertoli cell tumour causing feminization in a Brown Leghorn capon. *J. Endocrin.*, **14**, 197.

SKALLER, F., & GRIGG, G. W. (1950). The effect of orally administered synthetic oestrogen (hexoestrol) on the male fowl. *Aust. J. agric. Res.*, **1**, 496.

SKUTCH, A. E. (1957). The incubation patterns of birds. *Ibis*, **99**, 69.

SLUITER, J. W., & VAN OORDT, G. J. (1947). Experimental data on the function of the interstitium of the gonads: experiments with cockerels. *Quart. J. micr. Sci.*, **88**, 135.

STAMLER, J., BOLENE, C., DUDLEY, M., & LEVINSON, E. (1950). Effect of prolonged exhibition of diethylstilbestrol on plasma and tissue lipids in the chick. *Endocrinology*, **46**, 375.

STANLEY, A. J. (1937). Sexual dimorphism in North American hawks. 1. Sex organs. *J. Morph.*, **61**, 321.

—— & WITSCHI, E. (1940). Germ cell migration in relation to asymmetry in the sex glands of hawks. *Anat. Rec.*, **76**, 329.

STONOR, C. R. (1940). *Courtship and display among birds*. London.

TABER, E. (1948). The relation between ovarian growth and sexual characters in Brown Leghorn chicks treated with gonadotrophins. *J. exp. Zool.*, **107**, 65.

—— (1949). The source and effects of androgen in the male chick treated with gonadotrophins. *Amer. J. Anat.*, **85**, 231.

—— (1951). Androgen secretion in the fowl. *Endrocrinology*, **48**, 6.

—— DAVIS, D. E., & DOMM, L. V. (1943). Effect of sex hormones on the erythrocyte number in the blood of the domestic fowl. *Amer. J. Physiol.*, **138**, 479.

TAIBEL, A. (1928). Risveglio artificiale di instinti tipicanente femminili nei maschi di taluni uccelli. *Atti Soc. Nat. Mat. Modena*, **59**, 93.

TEILUM, G. (1950). Oestrogen production by Sertoli cells in the etiology of benign senile hypertrophy of the human prostate. Testicular "Lipoid cell ratio" and oestrogen-androgen quotient in human male. *Acta endocr., Copenhagen*, **4**, 43.

THAYER, R. H., JAAP, R. G., & PENQUITE, R. (1945). Fattening chickens by feeding androgens. *Poult. Sci.*, **24**, 483.

TINBERGEN, N. (1931). Zur Paarungsbiologie der Fluss-seeschwalbe (*Sterna h. hirundo* L.). *Ardea*, **20**, 1.

—— (1951). *The study of instinct*. Oxford.

Trinkaus, J. P. (1948).   Factors concerned in the response of melanoblasts to estrogen in the Brown Leghorn fowl.   *J. exp. Zool.*, **109**, 135.

Tschopp, E. (1936).   Untersuchungen über die Wirkung der männlichen Sexualhormone und ihrer Derivate.   *Arch. int. Pharmacodyn.*, **52**, 381.

Turner, C. W. (1948).   Oral effectiveness of androgens in fowls.   *Poult. Sci.*, **27**, 789.

Uotila, U. U. (1939).   The masculinizing effect of some gonadotropic hormones on pullets compared with spontaneous ovariogenic virilism in hens.   *Anat. Rec.*, **74**, 165.

van Oordt, G. J. (1933).   Weitere Untersuchungen über den Einfluss der Geschlechtshormone auf die sekundären Geschlechtsmerkmale des Truthuhns.   Ovariektomie der Truthenne.   *Arch. EntwMech. Org.*, **130**, 11.

—— (1936).   The effect of gonadectomy on the secondary sexual characters of the turkey.   *Arch. portug. Sci. biol.*, **5**, 205.

—— (1949).   *Vogeltrek.*   3rd Edition.   Brill, Leyden.

—— & Junge, G. C. A. (1930).   Die hormonale Wirkung des Hodens auf Federkleid und Farbe des Schnabels und der Füsse bei der Lachmöwe (*Larus ridibundus* L.).   *Zool. Anz.*, **91**, 1.

—— —— (1933).   The influence of the testis hormone on the development of ambosexual characters in the Blackheaded Gull (*Larus ridibundus*).   *Acta brev. neerl. Physiol.*, **3**, 15.

—— —— (1934).   The relation between the gonads and the secondary sexual characters in the Ruff (*Philomachus pugnax*).   *Bull. Soc. Biol. Lett.*, **4**, 141.

—— —— (1936).   Die hormonale Wirkung der Gonaden auf Sommer- und Prachtkleid.   III. Der Einfluss der Kastration auf männliche Kampfläufer (*Philomachus pugnax*).   *Arch. EntwMech. Org.*, **134**, 112.

—— & Rinkel, G. L. (1940).   Der Einfluss von Geschlechtshormonen, insbesondere von Dehydroandrosteron, auf die Gonadenentwicklung von Hühnerembryonen.   *Arch. EntwMech. Org.*, **140**, 59.

—— & van der Maas, C. J. J. (1929).   Kastrationsversuche am Truthahn.   *Arch. EntwMech. Org.*, **115**, 651.

Vaugien, L. (1953).   Sur l'apparition de la maturité sexuelle des jeunes perruches ondulées mâles soumises à diverses conditions d'éclairement : Le développement testiculaire est plus rapide dans l'obscurité complète.   *Bull. biol.*, **37**, 274.

—— (1955).   Sur les réactions ovariennes du moineau domestique soumis, durant le repos sexuel, à des injections de gonadotrophine sérique de jument gravide.   *Bull. biol.*, **89**, 1.

—— (1956).   Ponte du Chardonneret induite, en toutes saisons, par l'injection de gonadotrophine équine.   *C. R. Acad. Sci., Paris*, **243**, 444.

Vinals, E. (1932).   Influence de la folliculine sur le plumage du pigeon.   *C. R. Soc. Biol., Paris*, **109**, 1332.

Voss, H. E. (1937).   Die örtliche Wirkung von Sexualhormonen.   *Klin. Wschr.*, **16**, 769.

—— (1940).   Causation of singing in female canaries by male sex hormone.   *Endokrinologie*, **22**, 399.

Waite, R. H. (1920).   Capons vs. cockerels.   *Bull. Md. agric. Exp. Sta.*, **235**, 1.

Walker, A. T. (1925).   An inhibition in ovulation in the fowl by the intraperitoneal administration of fresh anterior hypophyseal substance.   *Amer. J. Physiol.*, **74**, 249.

Walton, A. (1937).   On the eclipse plumage of the Mallard (*Anas platyrhyncha platyrhyncha*).   *J. exp. Biol.*, **14**, 440.

Wang, H. (1946).   The reaction to female hormone of the breast-saddle chimaeric feathers in Brown Leghorn capons.   *Anat. Rec.*, **94**, 399.

—— (1948).   Modulation of tract specificity by estrogenic hormone in experimentally produced feather-chimaerae of Brown Leghorn capons.   *J. exp. Zool.*, **109**, 451.

Weber, M. (1890).   Über einen Fall von Hermaphroditismus bei *Fringilla coelebs*.   *Zool. Anz.*, **13**, 1.

Wenzel, K. (1908).   Zur Naturgeschichte des Kuckucks und seiner Brutpfleger.   *Orn. Mschr.*, **33**, 462, 475.

WHITE, W. W. (1941). Bird of first brood of swallow assisting to feed second brood. *Brit. Birds*, **34,** 179.

WILKINS, L., & FLEISCHMANN, W. (1946). The influence of various androgenic steroids on nitrogen balance and growth. *J. clin. Endocrin.*, **6,** 383.

WILLIAMSON, K. (1941). First brood of swallow assisting to feed second brood. *Brit. Birds*, **34,** 179.

WILLIER, B. H. (1927). The specificity of sex, of organization, and of differentiation of embryonic chick gonads as shown by grafting experiments. *J. exp. Zool.*, **46,** 409.

—— GALLAGHER, T. F., & KOCH, F. C. (1937). The modification of sex development in the chick embryo by male and female sex hormones. *Physiol. Zoöl.*, **10,** 101.

WINGSTRAND, K. G. (1951). *The structure and development of the avian pituitary.* Lund.

WITSCHI, E. (1935). Seasonal sex characters in birds and their hormonal control. *Wilson Bull.*, **47,** 177.

—— (1936a). Secondary sex characters in birds and their bearing on the theory of evolution. *Scientia*, **60,** 263.

—— (1936b). The bill of the sparrow as an indicator for the male sex hormone. I. Sensitivity. *Proc. Soc. exp. Biol., N.Y.*, **33,** 484.

—— (1936c). Effect of gonadotropic and estrogenic hormones on regenerating feathers of Weaver Finches (*Pyromelana franciscana*). *Proc. Soc. exp. Biol., N.Y.*, **35,** 484.

—— (1937). Comparative physiology of the vertebrate hypophysis (anterior and intermediate lobes). *Cold Spr. Harb. Symp. quant. Biol.*, **5,** 180.

—— (1945). Quantitative studies on the seasonal development of the deferent ducts in passerine birds. *J. exp. Zool.*, **100,** 549.

—— (1955). Vertebrate gonadotrophins. *Mem. Soc. Endocrin.*, **4,** 149.

—— (1960). Sex and secondary sexual characters. In *The Biology and Physiology of Birds*, Ed. A. J. Marshall. New York. (In press).

—— & FUGO, N. W. (1940). Response of sex characters of the adult female starling to synthetic hormones. *Proc. Soc. exp. Biol., N.Y.*, **45,** 10.

—— & KECK, W. N. (1935). Differential effect of some gonadotropic substances on development of cyclical sex characters in the English sparrow. *Proc. Soc. exp. Biol., N.Y.*, **32,** 598.

—— & MILLER, R. A. (1938). Ambisexuality in the female starling. *J. exp. Zool.*, **79,** 475.

—— & RILEY, G. M. (1940). Quantitative studies on the hormones of human pituitaries. *Endocrinology*, **26,** 565.

—— STANLEY, A. J. & RILEY, G. M. (1937). Gonadotropic hormones of the hypophysis of the turkey. *Proc. Soc. exp. Biol., N.Y.*, **36,** 647.

—— & WOODS, R. P. (1936). The bill of the sparrow as indicator of the male sex hormone. *J. exp. Zool.*, **73,** 445.

WOLFF, EM. (1950). La différenciation sexuelle normale et le conditionnement hormonal des caractères sexuels somatiques précoces: tubercule génital et syrinx, chez l'embryon de canard. *Bull. biol.*, **84,** 119.

WOLFF, ET. (1935a). Sur l'action de l'hormone mâle (androstérone) injectée à l'embryon de poulet. Production expérimentale d'intersexués. *C. R. Soc. Biol., Paris*, **120,** 1312.

—— (1935b). Interprétation des résultats obtenus au cours des expériences d'injection d'androstérone synthétique aux embryons de poulet. *C. R. Soc. Biol., Paris*, **120,** 1314.

—— (1936a). L'action de l'oestrone sur l'oviducte et le cloaque des poussins femelles, intersexués et mâles. *C. R. Soc. Biol., Paris*, **123,** 235.

—— (1936b). L'évolution, apres l'éclosion, des poulets mâles transformés en intersexués par l'hormone femelle injectée aux jeunes embryons. *Arch. Anat., Strasbourg*, **23,** 1.

—— (1936c). La double action—masculinisante et féminisante—de l'androstérone sur le tractus génital des embryons de poulet. *C. R. Soc. Biol., Paris.* **121,** 1474.

—— (1938a). Sur l'existence d'hormones intermédiaires susceptibles de masculiniser les femelles et de féminiser les mâles chez l'embryon de poulet. *C. R. Soc. Biol., Paris*, **128,** 420.

WOLFF, ET. (1938b). L'action des hormones sexuelles sur les voies génitales femelles des embryons de poulet. *Trav. Sta. zool. Wimereux*, **13,** 825.

—— (1939). L'action du diéthylstilboestrol sur les organes génitaux de l'embryon de poulet. *C. R. Acad. Sci., Paris*, **208,** 1532.

—— (1947). Récherches sur l'intersexualité expérimentelle produite par la méthode des greffes de gonades à l'embryon de poulet. *Arch. Anat. micr. Morph. exp.*, **36,** 69.

—— (1949). L'évolution des canaux de Müller de l'embryon d'oiseau après castration précoce. *C. R. Soc. Biol., Paris*, **143,** 1239.

—— & GINGLINGER, A. (1935). Sur la transformation des poulets mâles en intersexués par injection d'hormone femelle (folliculine) aux embryons. *Arch. Anat., Strasbourg*, **20,** 219.

—— & SALZGEBER, B. (1949). Sur un nouveau procédé permettant d'obtenir l'inter-sexualité expérimentale chez l'embryon d'oiseau: L'irradiation des gonades embryonnaires à l'aide des rayons X. *C. R. Soc. Biol., Paris*, **143,** 532.

—— & WOLFF, EM. (1936). Sur les différences de sensibilité des embryons femelles de deux races de poules à une hormone sexuelle: l'androstérone. *C. R. Soc. Biol., Paris*, **123,** 1191.

—— —— (1937). L'action de différentes substances du groupe de l'androstérone sur les organes génitaux de l'embryon de poulet. *C. R. Soc. Biol., Paris*, **124,** 367.

—— —— (1947). La différenciation sexuelle du tubercule génital et son déterminisme chez le canard. *C. R. Soc. Biol., Paris*, **141,** 916.

—— —— (1948). Action d'une substance oestrogène artificielle, l'acide N-bisdéhydro-doisynolique (sel de sodium) racémique, sur l'appareil génital mâle et femelle de l'embryon de poulet. *C. R. Soc. Biol., Paris*, **142,** 700.

—— —— (1949). Application de la méthode de castration a l'embryon de canard: sur deux tests de l'activité précoce des gonades embryonnaires, le syrinx et le tubercule génital. *C. R. Soc. Biol., Paris*, **143,** 529.

—— —— (1951a). The effects of castration on bird embryos. *J. exp. Zool.*, **116,** 59.

—— —— (1951b). Mise en évidence d'une action féminisante de la gonade droite chez l'embryon femelle des oiseaux par les expériences d'hémicastration. *C. R. Soc. Biol., Paris*, **145,** 1218.

WOLFSON, A. (1945). The role of the pituitary, fat deposition, and body weight in bird migration. *Condor*, **47,** 95.

—— (1952). The occurrence and regulation of the refractory period in the gonadal and fat cycles of the Junco. *J. exp. Zool.*, **121,** 311.

—— (1954). Notes on the cloacal protuberance, seminal vesicles, and possible copulatory organ in male passerine birds. *Bull. Chicago Acad. Sci.*, **10,** 1.

WOMACK, E. B., KOCH, F. C., DOMM, L. V., & JUHN, M. (1931). Some factors affecting the comb growth response in the Brown Leghorn capons. *J. Pharmacol.*, **41,** 173.

YASUDA, M. (1953). Catological studies of the anterior pituitary in the broody fowl. *Proc. imp. Acad., Japan*, **29,** 586.

ZAWADOWSKY, M. M. (1922). *Das Geschlect und die Entwickelung der Geschlectsmerkmale.* Moscow.

—— (1926). Materiale zur Analyse des Gynandromorphismus. I. Kastration der Finken und Gimpel. *Arch. EntwMech. Org.*, **108,** 563.

—— (1927). Bisexual nature of the hen and experimental hermaphroditism in hens. *Biol. gen.*, **3,** 129.

—— (1936). On the reciprocal action of organs in the animal body. *Bull. Biol. Méd. exp. URSS.* **1,** 196.

—— & ZUBINA, E. M. (1929). Cock-crowing hens. *Trans. Lab. exp. Biol., Zoopark, Moscow*, **5,** 177.

ZITRIN, A. (1942). Induction of male copulatory behaviour in a hen following adminis-tration of male hormone. *Endocrinology*, **31,** 690.

ZONDEK, B. (1937). Impairment of anterior pituitary functions by follicular hormone. *Folia clin. orient.*, **1,** 1.

—— & MARX, L. (1939). The induction of lipemia and calcemia in the cock by means of oestrogenic hormone. *Arch. int. Pharmacodyn.*, **61,** 77.

CHAPTER 13

EXTERNAL FACTORS IN SEXUAL PERIODICITY

By E. C. Amoroso and F. H. A. Marshall

I. Introduction

It is well known that the complex phenomena attendant upon the initiation of the sexual cycle of vertebrates include changes in the endocrine balance and involve several very specific hormonal effects. Indeed, the reproductive rhythms of the female can well be regarded as constituting one general category of behaviour that is perhaps more clearly influenced by endocrine substances than any other aspect of animal life. Nevertheless, it would be a mistake to assume that reproductive behaviour is unaffected by, or is completely independent of, ecological and neurological phenomena. On the contrary, there is good evidence that the secretion of certain of the interacting hormones is mediated, at least in part, by the nervous system and that the whole mechanism may be influenced or inhibited by nutritional and environmental factors. Marshall (1936, 1942) was the first to emphasise the dependence of the breeding season, in many species, on environmental or " exteroceptive factors " and he suggested that such factors exert their effects by nervous and reflex stimulation of the secretion of gonadotrophic hormones, primarily FSH, from the anterior pituitary.[1]

A number of facts about animals suggest the intervention of various agencies tending to adjust their reproductive activities to a special season of the year, thus ensuring that the young are born at the most propitious time. Moreover, analysis of breeding records of many species has established that sexual periodicity is influenced by many extrinsic and intrinsic factors ; and of the environmental factors that influence reproduction and " anchor " the breeding-cycle, light, temperature and food supply are the most important. However, there does seem to be some evidence that environmental experiences derived from association of the sexes may also stimulate the seasonal cycle in photoperiodically regulated animals. Thus, ovulation in many mammals and birds follows upon a more or less complicated train of courtship behaviour and probably would not occur in the absence of such sexual stimuli.

Within the body, on the other hand, it has been shown that the changes in the reproductive organs that regulate the physiological and psychological aspects of the breeding behaviour of mammals, birds and the three classes of cold-blooded vertebrates are conditioned by the internal secretions of the gonads ; and that the activity of the gonad is, in turn, predominantly under the control of the anterior pituitary. It has been shown, moreover, that in the female mammal there may be

---

[1] The term " exteroceptive " was first used by Hartridge (1936) to describe " external local factors " affecting the pituitary.

secondary or dioestrous cycles within the major cycle and that these also are usually dependent upon the ovarian hormones which are successively produced. Furthermore, the duration of the corpus luteum depends partly, at any rate, on the anterior pituitary, as shown especially in such species as the rat. It would thus appear that the pituitary gland is a mediating structure through which the organism adjusts its reproductive life to environmental change. As to whether the ovarian hormones react upon the anterior pituitary at certain stages in the cycle, we have no completely satisfactory proof, but it is almost certain that such an influence exists (*see also* Mixner, Lewis and Turner, 1940; Leonard and Reece, 1942; Burrows, 1949).

Variation in reproductive processes is revealed not only in their normal external manifestations but also in the influence which environmental factors have upon the sensitivity of tissues to different forms of hormonal stimulation. Yet, howsoever favourable the environment, one cannot but agree wholeheartedly with Beach's insistence (1948) that the development of flexibility in the control of sexual behaviour and the consequent reduction of control by stereotyped anatomical and hormonal mechanisms, has been a pre-eminent evolutionary process in the progress from lower animals, through those of intermediate phyletic status, to man. It is apparent, nevertheless, that at least three types of controlling factors have to be considered in any explanation of the processes which take place in sexual cycles, namely hormonal, neurological and ecological. But in view of the extent to which the effects of all these factors are integrated, any sharp segregation of them can be justified only as an expedient in the explanatory consideration of a subject which, despite many recent advances, must still be treated tentatively.

We may now proceed to consider the evidence as to the parts played by external or other stimuli which regulate the gonadotrophic activities of the anterior pituitary; but before dealing with the experimental researches bearing upon this subject, it will be convenient to summarise the general evidence relating to breeding periodicity derived from the observational study of the higher animals living under natural conditions as well as those in a state of domestication or in confinement.

Spontaneous and Post-copulatory Ovulation

The dominant event in the oestrous cycle is ovulation. It is a phenomenon which is initiated in the gonads through the action of the gonadotrophic hormones and its time of occurrence is usually regarded as the most important reference point in the cycle from which such things as changes in the ovary, uterus, vagina and sexual behaviour may be dated and correlated. In many species of mammals— for example, cow, sheep, goat, mare, sow and bitch—ovulation occurs spontaneously and is ushered in by a short period of very rapid follicular growth, commonly referred to as the " pre-ovulatory swelling." In others—the induced ovulators— the final enlargement of the follicle, the secretion of liquor in quantity and ovulation require an additional stimulus, either actual coitus or simulation of the coital stimulus by mechanical irritation of the cervix.

Post-copulatory ovulation is normal in the rabbit (Hammond and Marshall, 1925), thirteen-lined ground squirrel (Foster, 1934), cat (Greulich, 1934; Gros, 1935; Dawson and Friedgood, 1940; Amoroso, 1952), ferret (Hammond and

Marshall, 1930), mink (Enders, 1939; Hansson, 1947), raccoon (Llewellyn and Enders, 1954) and short-tailed shrew (Pearson, 1944), and it may be taken as established for the rabbit, and as a strong possibility for the other forms, that sexual excitement affects LH secretion by nervous reflex activation of the anterior pituitary (Marshall and Verney, 1936; Deanesly, Fee and Parkes, 1930). There are thus at least seven species in which post-copulatory ovulation is known to occur. That this represents a phylogenetic series may be questioned, but from the reproductive behaviour of allied species we should not be surprised if, as more individuals from different families are investigated, the condition is found to be more widespread than is known at present (*soricidae, sciuridae, mustelidae* and *felidae*). It was long believed to exist in man as well, until finally disproved comparatively recently (Eckstein, 1949). In many fishes, amphibia, reptiles and birds also, ovulation occurs after a more or less complicated series of courtship encounters, and it is quite possible that these sexual displays have a direct bearing upon ovulation.

Rabbits ovulate about 10 hours after coition (Heape, 1905), but the processes start earlier. Ferrets also normally ovulate only after coition (Marshall, 1905b; Hammond and Marshall, 1930) and usually about 30 hours later (Hammond and Walton, 1934). The 13-lined ground squirrel ovulates 8 to 12 hours after coition (Foster, 1934). Enders (1939, 1941) states that in the mink also, ovulation occurs as a result of the stimulus of mating, taking place from 42 to 50 hours afterwards, but in the earlier periods it may not do so owing to the absence of ripe ova (cf. Hansson, 1947, who found that ovulation occurred 36 or 37 hours after coition). Post-copulatory ovulation has been shown to occur normally in the raccoon (Llewellyn and Enders, 1954). In the cat, Longley (1911), Gros (1935), Liche (1939), Dawson and Friedgood (1940), Dawson (1950), and Amoroso (1952) found that ovulation takes place 24–36 hours after mating but there is good evidence that occasionally it may occur spontaneously (Amoroso, unpublished data).

The stimulus necessary for ovulation may vary a good deal. For example, although ovulation is ordinarily post-coital in the rabbit, Hammond and Marshall (1925) found that oestrous females occasionally ovulate after mounting other females in masculine fashion, and since the same response may be obtained by manual stimulation of the vulva, cervical contact is regarded as unnecessary. Similar findings in the mink have been reported by Enders (1939). He states that in this species ovulation may follow a prolonged struggle with the male although no intromission has occurred. In the cat also, mechanical stimulation of the cervix can simulate the coital stimulus, as was first shown by Greulich (1934).

The intensity of the necessary stimulus for ovulation, as indicated by the duration of sexual congress, is also variable. It is comparatively brief in the rabbit, squirrel and cat, protracted, rough and violent in the ferret and mink, while in the short-tailed shrew ovulation occurs only if a relatively high number of copulations have occurred; one or two copulations a day do not induce release of the ovum, and the least effective number of matings recorded is nineteen (Pearson, 1944); the process of discharge occurring from 55 to 70 hours after the first copulation.

But, even in species in which ovulation is generally considered to be independent of mating, there is reason to believe that secretory function of the pituitary is influenced by stimuli derived from copulatory activity and is dependent on a chronologically limited neurohumoral stimulus to the hypophysis that is qualitatively similar to that in the rabbit and cat. Thus, Everett, Sawyer and Markee (1949) demonstrated that in cyclic rats ovulation can be blocked either by intravenous injection of dibenamine or by subcutaneous injection of atropine before 2 p.m. on the day of pro-oestrus (4-day cycle). Similar treatment at 4 p.m. does not usually interfere with ovulation. Identical results, with similar time relationships, have been obtained with intravenous SKF. 501 (Sawyer, Markee and Everett, 1950), subcutaneous banthine and the barbiturates (Everett and Sawyer, 1950). In the cow also, Quinlan, Bisschop and Adelaar (1941) report that infertile coitus shortens the oestrous cycle, while copulation is said to hasten the occurrence of ovulation (Marion, Smith, Wiley and Barrett, 1950).

There is also good reason to believe that the secretion of the luteotrophic hormone (LTH) or prolactin with consequent prolongation of life of the corpus luteum and the secretion of progesterone is involved in the copulatory activities of the rat. In females of this species, ovulation is followed by the formation of numerous large corpora lutea, but if no mating has occurred these structures are non-functional and do not secrete progesterone. If, on the other hand, the oestrous female is mated to a sterile male, the ensuing corpora lutea are functionally active and pseudopregnancy results. It is evident, therefore, that stimulation of the cervix in the rat is necessary to start the chain of reactions and determines whether the oestrous cycle shall consist merely of a succession of waves of ripening follicles, or whether the dioestrous interval in which the corpora lutea are active shall separate these waves (Asdell, 1946a, b). This is, as Asdell suggests, obviously a mechanism which economises hormone synthesis and results in greater opportunity for fertilisation and implantation. It should of course, be recorded that it is more than a quarter of a century ago since Long and Evans (1922) reported that pseudopregnancy may be induced in the female rat by mechanical stimulation of the vagina and cervix with a glass rod, as well as by infertile copulation. The mouse also requires a sterile copulation or stimulation of the cervix uteri to activate the corpus luteum in the absence of fertile copulation, and then she displays the phenomenon of pseudopregnancy which lasts for 10 to 12 days (Parkes, 1926). Similarly, sterile coition in the rabbit and ferret is followed by pseudopregnancy with mammary development and secretion. The stimulus therefore causes a switch-over from the oestrous or follicular phase to the luteal phase. Moreover, the switch cannot be effected in the absence of the pituitary, whereas, on the other hand, it can be brought about by the injection of anterior pituitary or anterior pituitary-like extracts (Fee and Parkes, 1929). The presumption is that ovulation is due normally to a nerve reflex but the stimulus may be carried by several nervous paths. Thus, it is not necessarily started from the vagina and vulva, since Fee and Parkes (1929) have shown that local anaesthesia of these parts does not inhibit ovulation after coition, neither does injection of atropine (Makepeace, 1938). *See*, however, Everett, Sawyer and Markee (1949); Sawyer, Markee and Townsend (1949); and Sawyer, Markee and Everett (1949a, b). Ovulation can likewise occur after complete thoraco-sympathectomy (Cannon, Newton, Bright, Menkin and Moore, 1929), and in the absence of any nerve pathway to the ovaries (Hinsey and Markee, 1932a); also after ovarian transplantation to an abnormal position (Asdell, 1926; Friedman, 1929a). It can likewise occur in the rabbit after cervical sympathectomy—pregnancy (Hinsey and Markee, 1933; Hinsey, 1937), or pseudo-pregnancy following—(Vogt, 1933; Haterius, 1933), after avulsion of the facial nerve and geniculate ganglion (Hair and Merzen, 1939), and after bilateral destruction of the greater superficial petrosal nerve (Vogt, 1942).

Collin (1937, 1938) has described the morphology and the physiology of the nervous factors in pituitary activity, giving a complete bibliography. He states that there are two affectory centres, one hypothalamic and the other sympathetic. He discusses the sensory reflexes with pituitary relay, including those starting from olfactory sensations and those starting from the retina, as well as " interoceptive " reflexes with pituitary relay (factors determining milk secretion, etc.). He states that double superior cervical ganglionectomy is followed by profound structural modification of the pituitary such as (in the rabbit) cyanophilic changes in the anterior lobe and excretion of colloid, the organs then becoming chromophilic and showing endocrine modifications. On the other hand, Donovan and van der Werff ten Bosch (1956c) found that cervical sympathectomy, delays but does not abolish the oestrous response to light, apparently by diminishing the amount of light impinging on the retina. *See also* Brooks (1938), who found what appeared to be nerve fibres entering the anterior pituitary from the stalk. Nerve fibres have, likewise, been found in the pars intermedia by Croll (1928), but their source and origin have not been traced. The papers by Clark, McKeown and Zuckerman (1937, 1939); Vasquez-Lopez (1942, 1949); Metuzals (1952, 1954, 1955); Vasquez-Lopez and Williams (1952); and Vasquez-Lopez (1953) are referred to below (p. 748).

Loewi (1935), in his Ferrier lecture to the Royal Society, remarked that the anterior pituitary appears to receive its messages humorally and transmits them in the same way, but the former of these statements is only partially true.

In the rat, unlike the rabbit, ovulation takes place spontaneously, but, as previously mentioned, a prolongation of the life of the corpora lutea with consequent pseudopregnancy can be induced by sterile coition or on artificially stimulating the cervix uteri by mechanical or electrical means (Long and Evans, 1922 ; Shelesnyak, 1931). Meyer, Leonard and Hisaw (1929) found that general and spinal anaesthesia inhibited the occurrence of the pseudopregnancy which otherwise follows electrical stimulation of the cervix. Bacq and Brouha (1932) found that sympathectomy had no effect on the cycle in the female rat and they do not mention the occurrence of pseudopregnancy. Haterius (1933) and Friedgood and Bevin (1938) have shown, however, that sympathectomy in the rat may interfere with the pseudopregnancy that normally follows some forms of artificial stimulation. Friedgood and Bevin (1941) also showed that the operation of sympathectomy itself may be followed by a period of pseudopregnancy, whilst Britt (1941) found that psychic stimuli, which normally produce an oestrogenic effect in rats, are ineffective after sympathectomy.

Brouha (1938) states that sympathetic denervation makes no change in the genital physiology of the guinea-pig. Harris (1936, 1950b), on the other hand, found that electrical stimulation through the brain of the oestrous rat, after the manner of Marshall and Verney (1936) for the rabbit, caused definite pseudopregnancy, and deciduomata could be induced to form in response to a mechanical stimulus introduced in the uterus. These observations seem to indicate that the switch-over from the oestrous to the pseudopregnant condition in the rat must be due to a change in the anterior pituitary and not merely to the corpus luteum, which is formed in any case, whether a stimulus is applied or not. Selye and

McKeown (1934) have shown that mechanical stimulation of the nipple without the withdrawal of milk (as after the removal of the galactophores), in both rats and mice, also produces a prolongation in the duration of the corpora lutea, but the stimulus must be continued if this effect is to be produced. The well-known fact that suckling is normally essential for the continuance of lactation in mammals is similarly to be accounted for on the assumption that external stimuli are conveyed from the nipples to the anterior pituitary by nervous paths. In this connection, the fact must be mentioned that, according to Desclin (1938), the nervous stimulus resulting from suckling is capable of modifying the structure of the anterior lobe, since in rats whose ovaries are removed immediately after parturition, the castration effects upon the hypophysis (which normally occur after removal) are arrested if the animals are allowed to continue suckling their young. The further fact that menstruation in women in about 60 per cent of cases is inhibited by suckling is perhaps also relevant.

A closely similar situation has been observed in the cat. Friedgood and Dawson (1942) find that post-coital ovulation in this species may be prevented by surgical shock—such as that attendant upon any type of abdominal operation—provided the insult occurs within fifteen to fifty-five minutes after mating. Operations performed six hours after copulation have no effect upon discharge of the ovum. Early operations which prevent ovulation also result in a marked modification of the carmine cell reactions in the anterior pituitary, which the authors believe are concerned with the production and release of luteinizing hormone.

II. Observations on Sexual Periodicity in Mammals

Reproductive Periodicity in the Female

The seasonal release of eggs or embryos from the ovary is the common reproductive pattern among the fishes. As a general rule, copulation and the birth of young occur most actively during the spring and summer, while the female reproductive tract is relatively quiescent in autumn and winter. A seasonal wave of reproductive activity is also typical of many amphibia, and the same is, in general, true of reptiles and birds, though certain tropical reptiles and some domestic species of birds breed rather continuously throughout the year without any indication of a seasonal rhythm.

In the non-pregnant, post-pubertal, female mammal, reproductive capacity manifests itself by the cyclical occurrence of structural changes in the reproductive organs and in the cyclical repetition of periods of sexual receptivity or " heat " during which the animals are said to be in " oestrus." Monoestrous animals complete a single oestrous cycle annually, while polyoestrous forms complete two or more cycles each year if not interrupted by pregnancy (Heape, 1901). In some (spring breeders, e.g. horse, donkey, insectivores and some carnivores, and autumn or winter breeders, e.g. goat, sheep and deer) these recurring cycles may be limited to a part of the year ; in others (e.g. cow, guinea-pig and many rodents) they may occur uninterruptedly throughout the year. Many wild mammals exhibit monoestrous cycles. Correspondingly, the duration of the cycle itself varies considerably, but in all species the cycle ceases after the ovaries are removed. On the other hand, even the reproductive organs of ovariectomised animals may continue, for a time at least, to undergo rhythmical changes, e.g. in rats (Kostitch and Teleba-kovitch, 1929 ; Mandl, 1951).

In the bitch, the oestrous cycle is repeated twice each year (Evans and Cole, 1931 ; Griffiths and Amoroso, 1939 ; Amoroso, 1949 ; Hancock and Rowlands, 1949 ; Rowlands, 1950). In cats prevented from becoming pregnant, recurrent oestrous cycles appear only during a portion of the year, usually from January to July or August. There is a possibility that confinement is responsible for some modification of the reproductive cycle, since, in animals kept under laboratory conditions, heat periods may not occur at regular intervals, though occasional females may maintain a regular 2- or 3-week cycle during spring and summer. In the cat also, the duration of oestrus varies greatly from individual to individual and even in the same individual from time to time. Each cycle may require as little as 3 days for completion after the first copulation (van der Stricht, 1911), while in the absence of the male the period of sexual receptivity will often continue for a week or even longer (Liche, 1939 ; Mellen, 1946).

In the cat, pseudopregnancy occurs after any non-fertile ovulation whether brought about by a sterile mating (Gros, 1935 ; Liche, 1939), by mechanical stimulation of the cervix (Dawson and Kosters, 1944 ; Amoroso, 1952) or by hormonal treatment (Foster and Hisaw, 1935 ; Rowlands and McPhail, 1936 ; van Dyke and Li, 1938, and others). When so induced the uterine changes which follow parallel, with some slight retardation, those found at the time of implanta-tion of fertilised ova. The duration of this pseudopregnancy is, however, very variable. Thus, Gros (1935) finds that after sterile copulation with a vasectomised male, the active phase of pseudopregnancy lasts about 23 days after ovulation, and the regressive phase about 10 days ; the female is in oestrus again by the fortieth day. These data are in general agreement with our own (Amoroso, 1952) and with those of Liche (1939), who states that pseudopregnancy lasts 36 days. On the other hand, Foster and Hisaw (1935) report an active phase of 30 days in a pseudopregnancy induced by the injection of FSH and LH, while, according to Van Dyke and Li (1938), pseudopregnancy is no longer present 20 days after hormonal induction of ovulation. These data on hormonally induced pseudo-pregnancy in the cat are thus much more variable than those derived from sterile mating or from mechanical stimulation of the cervix. (*See also* Deanesly, 1943b).

In the bitch, Evans and Cole (1931) state that glandular regression appears to begin about the twentieth day of metoestrus with the uterus usually in repose on the ninetieth metoestrous day. Probably, as Asdell (1946a) states, it is too gradual to set any definite limits. No obvious differences in the cellular content of smears taken during pregnancy and pseudopregnancy have been observed (Hancock and Rowlands, 1949). Details of sexual periodicity in farm animals, together with an extensive bibliography, will be found in Laing's (1955) excellent monograph. The rich and varied data on human and comparative mammalian reproduction are summarized by Asdell (1946b) in his book on "Patterns of Mammalian Reproduction."

The Influence of Seasonal Factors on Sexual Periodicity

It has been remarked in the first chapter that whereas there is no month in the year which is not the sexual season of some species of mammals, yet for the species

2A*

in question this season is most regular. Thus, although there is a natural rhythm in the periodicity of the reproductive phenomena depending primarily on an alternation between rest and activity, this rhythm is brought into relation with the seasonal environment more particularly at the times of sexual activity. But, however constant a feature of reproductive processes periodicity may be, the phasing of the changes by which it is manifested is hardly the same in any two species of animal. Yet, as is well known, the majority of animals breed in the spring and presumably in response to some change or changes which occur at that season.

Among mammals, the insectivores, carnivores, rodents and non-ruminating ungulates, with very few exceptions outside the tropical areas, breed in the spring or first half of the year in the northern hemisphere and in the spring or second half of the year in the southern hemisphere. In subtropical areas there may or may not be a breeding season in the mammals inhabiting them, and its occurrence is to some extent related to latitude. Some of the rodents in temperate countries are exceptional in having very extended seasons or in breeding throughout practically the whole year. Amongst carnivores, the badger and the Grey Seal are exceptional in breeding in October (Neal, 1948; Davies, 1949; Amoroso, Goffin, Halley, Matthews and Matthews, 1951; Amoroso and Matthews, 1952) and this may be in some way correlated with their delayed implantation and their unusually long period of gestation (Gibbney, 1953; Fisher, 1954; Backhouse and Hewer, 1956; Neal and Harrison, 1958; Harrison and Neal, 1959; Mayer, 1959b).

With other orders of mammals there would appear to be more variation in the seasonal response of the generative organs. With marsupials nearly every month of the year may be the breeding season of some species, but many of them live under comparatively uniform conditions, at any rate in regard to the incidence of daylight (Wood Jones, 1923–5).

Sexual periodicity in the bat has been discussed and the main facts summarised by Baker and Baker (1936), Baker and Bird (1936) and Marshall (1948). The fruit bats breed in the autumn (or corresponding time even though the environmental conditions are almost uniform over the whole year as in the New Hebrides) in both hemispheres. The insectivorous bats that hibernate, as is well known, copulate in the autumn and ovulate in the spring, but many copulate again in the spring. The insectivorous bat *Miniopterus australis* in the New Hebrides has a sexual season in the Southern " spring " (*see also* Baker, 1947).

For the primates, the evidence as to sexual periodicity has been summarised by Zuckerman (1932a). Although some species are described as having restricted seasons, Zuckerman concludes that, speaking generally, " monkeys and apes, like man, experience a smooth and uninterrupted sexual and reproductive life." This conclusion, however, must be accepted with reservation, and there is evidence that primitive man had an annual breeding season in spring.

The ruminating ungulates, with a few possible exceptions, stand out in marked contrast to the majority of mammals in breeding in the late summer or autumn or when the daylight is diminishing, and this applies to species both in the northern and in the southern hemispheres (*see below*, p. 716). Teleologically, this may be interpreted as a device to secure that the young shall be born at the most favourable season for their development, that is to say, usually in the spring, and indeed a similar explanation may be made for the sexual seasons of birds. This, however, is no solution of the physiological problems as to the causes of seasonal activity in the individual animal but is merely an expression of the fact that the physiological processes of animals are adapted to their particular way of life, and, as implied already, these causes must differ in passing from group to group, or even from species to species or from breed to breed.

It has been pointed out that for animals living under tropical or sub-tropical conditions, where the seasons are less marked or non-existent, there is often a much less pronounced sexual periodicity, but even in these regions the rhythm of reproduction may be closely related to annual occurrences and it is probable that ecological factors play a part in determining the time of breeding. It is well known that several, at least, of the domestic mammals have partially or entirely freed themselves from the influence of the seasonal changes upon their sexual activity, their oestrous cycles being accelerated. This has happened almost completely in domestic cattle and is perhaps partly the result of artificial selection, but warmth, plenteous nutrition and comparatively uniform conditions are probably contributory causes. In " Wild " White cattle, however, there is a tendency to mate about July (Wallace, 1907). In the domestic cow, oestrous phenomena are much less prominent in the winter months and often may be absent altogether, although the ovarian cycle may still continue (silent heat). Moreover, winter sterility or subfertility is very common in cattle. Folley (1955) has expressed his belief that in the wild state the winter may have been an anoestrous season, and that the ability to breed all the year round has arisen through the process of artificial selection in the course of domestication. It may be relevant in this connection that Roberts (1928) has shown that with advancing age domestic cows show a greater disposition to conceive in June, July and August, since more calves are born in March, April and May. As with cattle, there are certain breeds of British sheep in which the mating season is more extended than in others. Of these the Dorset Horn is well known, but according to Marshall and Hammond (1937) the Derbyshire Gritstone has the same habit. The Merino too, in some parts of the world, but not in all (Roux, 1936; Kelly and Shaw, 1939), will take the ram at practically any season of the year and the same is also true of the Russian Romanov (Polovtzeva, 1937), the Polish Wryosowka (Ozaja, 1937) and the Punjab Bikaner (Smith and Singh, 1938) breeds among European and Asiatic sheep.

The domestic bitch may experience oestrus at any time of the year though maintaining a definite internal rhythm (Amoroso, 1949; Hancock and Rowlands, 1949). Heape (1901), however, states that in Danish Greenland the dogs have only one annual breeding season (instead of two) and resemble the wolf and jackal, which in their wild state breed in the first part of the year. The dingo of Australia, which is believed to be descended from some dog- or wolf-like animal, usually breeds in August and September in the southern spring (Wood Jones, 1923–5). The wild cat in Britain usually breeds only in the spring (Millais, 1904–6), and the allied African wild cat in South Africa has its sexual season in the southern spring (Fitzsimons, 1919–20). The domestic cat, on the other hand, has two (sometimes three) sexual seasons in the year, breeding at any time, though perhaps oftener in the spring. Similarly, many wild species, e.g. elephants (Perry, 1953), baboons (Zuckerman, 1931; Gillman and Gilbert, 1946), giraffes (Hediger, 1952) and the axis deer (Zuckerman, 1953), may have young at any time. On the other hand, the polar bear is an arctic animal and almost invariably has its young in

November and December, usually in the latter half of November (Hediger, 1952; Zuckerman, 1953), at the only time of the year when they have a chance of survival.

Differences of this magnitude in the periodicity of reproduction apply not only to distantly related animals. They also exist between some which can be presumed to be closely related phylogenetically. Within the same family of lemurs (Lorisidae,) the galago (*Galago garnetii*) breeds for only a restricted part of the year, but the slow loris (*Nycticebus concang*) does so continuously (Zuckerman, 1932b). Similarly, the red squirrel (*Sciurus vulgaris*) breeds during a period of at least 6 months (Rowlands, 1938), whereas the thirteen-lined ground squirrel (*Citellus tridecemlineatus*), which belongs to the same sub-family, has a breeding season that lasts no more than 2 weeks (Foster, 1934). Furthermore, the periodicity of reproduction can even vary within the same species, as is shown by the fact that the field mouse (*Microtus agrestis*) breeds earlier in the south than in the north of England (Baker and Ranson, 1933). The same is also true of the common mole (*Talpa europea*), which breeds earlier in Nottinghamshire than in Caernarvonshire (Morris, 1958). *See also* Rottensten (1954).

The Relationship between Latitude and Breeding Seasons

While the foregoing illustrations suggest that an animal's pattern of reproduction is merely a part of its genetic make-up, and is to a certain extent autonomous, it can be modulated by environmental factors to a degree which varies according to the species. One such way is the ease with which animals adjust their reproductive habits to a trans-equatorial shift. Some immediately switch their season of breeding in the northern hemisphere to that of the southern. Others, which have a restricted breeding season, may become continuous breeders when transported to the opposite side of the equator. But in a few cases it seems that the animal goes on breeding at the same calendar time regardless of its position relative to the equator. (*See* Marshall and Corbet, 1959).

The wild rabbit in England breeds usually from February to May but may breed again about harvest-time in August. The domesticated rabbit, if kept warm and well fed, may breed all the year round. Mr. W. Weatherly informs us that in Victoria the sexual season of the introduced rabbits is from August to October, but that there may be a less pronounced season after the rains in April. In Central Australia in favourable seasons the rabbits may breed all the year round. It is said also that in New Zealand, where the rabbit has likewise been introduced, it breeds in some localities all the year (Watson, 1954). Other introduced mammals in New Zealand, excepting the ruminants, are said to breed in the southern spring, and a similar statement may be made about acclimatised species in the southern hemisphere generally. Domestic sheep and goats, however, like other ruminants, breed in the first part of the year (summer and autumn) in the southern hemisphere. Similarly, the red deer, the fallow-deer, the moose, the wapiti, the Virginian deer, and the chamois have reversed their times for breeding in New Zealand (Donne, 1924 ; Marshall, 1937). The thar (*Hemitragus jemlahicus*) in New Zealand ruts, not at the reverse of the time for this species in India (where it breeds in September–October), but at the reverse of its present rutting time in the Zoological Society's Gardens in London, where it breeds in early November. Zuckerman (1953) states that the thar, on first being introduced into London, tended to rut in September but that the season gradually became later.   The thar now ruts in New Zealand at the end of April or beginning of May, the reverse of the acquired English time.   According to Donne (1924) the sambar in New Zealand ruts in March and April.   This is an Indian species, and it is to be noted that tropical and subtropical deer, like many other mammals, tend to have extended sexual seasons and may breed at any time of the year.   According to the Duke of Bedford (Marshall, 1936), however, no tropical deer adapt themselves to European seasons, but spring- and summer-bred fawns do better than winter-bred ones and have more chance of survival.   Thus, the Indian axis deer, the hog deer and the Reeve's muntjac breed at all seasons in the wild state, and after these species have been kept for 40 years in the deer park at Woburn Abbey or at complete liberty in the woods outside they still do the same.   Tropical deer with a regular breeding season appear as unadaptable as those which breed at all times of the year.   The Javan rusa deer, also after 40 years in the Woburn deer park, still produce their young in very late autumn, and Eld's deer (thamin) as long as they were kept at Woburn Park continued to drop their fawns in winter.   A large antelope, the Indian nylghai, likewise showed no disposition to abandon winter breeding.   Pére David's deer at Woburn breed in late spring (cf. Bedford, Duke of, and Marshall 1942).   It would appear, therefore, that tropical deer do not have the capacity to respond to seasonal external factors, natural selection not having developed such a capacity amid the comparatively uniform conditions of the countries they inhabit.   In a similar way domestic animals not living under the influence of natural selection (or at any rate only very partially so) might be expected partially to lose the capacity to respond to seasonal environmental change.   The sambar in having acquired a regular autumn breeding season in New Zealand, as recorded by Donne (1924), is apparently exceptional.

The evidence presented above shows that in all species of mammals there is a sexual rhythm which is presumably dependent upon an endocrine cycle but that this is in most cases, at any rate, adjusted to external seasonal change.   That the recurrence of the sexual periods is not due entirely to endocrine factors is shown especially clearly by those individual animals which belong to breeds or species that ordinarily have only one sexual season annually, yet can be induced to have two seasons by transferring them across the equator from one hemisphere to the other.   Such an acceleration in the sexual cycle has been known to occur in sheep, as well as in red deer, for both of which exact records are available.   Thus a flock of Southdown ewes which were sent when in lamb from England to South Africa lambed in January and came on heat in May (the South African autumn) so that at the commencement the change-over was very rapid.   But not all of the animals settled down to the conditions typical of the new environment ; other consignments remained barren for a whole year or more.   Nevertheless, in just over two years all ewes became almost or quite adjusted to the Southern hemisphere conditions (Marshall, 1937).   Analysed in terms of the time of year of the transfer and the known reaction time to light changes of the animals concerned, these apparently irreconcilable reports have been satisfactorily explained (Yeates, 1949a, b).   Furthermore, on the basis of an understanding of these considerations, the most opportune time for a breeder in the southern hemisphere to import ewes from Great Britain or other northern hemisphere countries may be predicted.   Similar observations have been recorded for English sheep imported to the Argentine, New Zealand

and Australia.   For red deer shipped from England to New Zealand the complete
adjustment also takes about two years.   The rutting time for England is September–October, and for New Zealand March–April.   Two stags from Warnham
Court Park, England, were sent out in October and had their first rut in New
Zealand in May, about 6 weeks later than the native animals.   Moreover, at this
rut the antlers for the year had not had time to develop fully, being smaller than
the previous year's antlers.   Hinds became adjusted in about the same time as
stags—for instance, hinds imported (in this case) from New Zealand to Warnham
Court, first came on heat in England in April (the New Zealand time), next in
December–January, and then at the normal European time in September-October
(Marshall, 1937).   It is thus clearly seen that both in sheep and deer, whereas
there is undoubtedly an internal rhythm which must depend on endocrine
influences, the cycle may be accelerated by changes in the action of periodic external
factors, and eventually become completely adjusted to new or reversed seasonal
conditions.   A similar reversal occurs in the maximum egg laying period of poultry.

It is now known that ferrets behave similarly.   Thus, ferrets arriving in Pre-
toria, South Africa, in October, 1937, bred immediately after arrival.   Eventually
the ferrets changed over completely so as to be adjusted to the southern hemisphere
seasons and remained so.   Ferrets sent to Kenya, where the conditions remain
very uniform in regard to light, experienced oestrus at the end of the year and some
individuals afterwards bred irregularly (Bedford, Duke of, and Marshall, 1942).
The case of the pony which Cossar Ewart imported from the island of Timor in
the southern hemisphere to Scotland and which first came on heat in the autumn
at a time synchronising with spring in Timor and afterwards adjusted itself and
experienced oestrus in the Scottish spring, is also relevant in this connection.

The Influence of Confinement on Reproductive Rhythms

The varying capacity of animals to adapt autonomous reproductive rhythms
to changed environmental conditions is also revealed by the way breeding habits
are adjusted to captivity (Hediger, 1950).   Thus, Catarrhine monkeys, polar
bears and most ruminants breed readily in Zoological Gardens, whereas gorillas
and cheetahs do not (Hediger, 1950, 1952; Eckstein and Zuckerman, 1955).

Much the same kind of variation in reproductive behaviour emerges from
Zuckerman's (1953) studies of the records of the times of breeding of the mammals
at the London Zoological Gardens.   The only southern hemisphere species which
appeared to maintain its original reproductive rhythm was the Patagonian hare
(*Dolichotis magellanica*) of South America.   It is possible, however, that this may
have been due to the animals being kept under abnormal conditions in regard to
temperature and light, and so being comparatively uninfluenced by seasonal
changes in England.   The analysis showed, moreover, that the breeding behaviour
of a whole species can be correctly inferred from even a few births.   In a particular
comparison, the African collared fruit bat (*Rousettus leachi*), which breeds fairly
evenly throughout the year, was compared with both the Barbary sheep (*Ammotragus lervia*), which is apparently able to breed in all months but gives birth mostly
between March and May, and the thar (*Hemitragus jemlahicus*), which delivers its
young only between May and September.   Thirty birth records were sufficient
to establish the existence of these differences in breeding habits.

Likewise, the annual peaks of intense breeding have been recorded in a number of polyoestrous antelopes from tropical regions living in captivity at the Giza Zoological Gardens in Cairo, e.g. *Gazella dorcas*, *G. leptoceros*, *G. arabica*, *G. Soemmeringi* and *G. rufricollis* (Flower, 1932).   Bodenheimer (1938) points out that these sundry kinds of gazelle retain the breeding seasons of their various native countries and that the rhythm maintained by these captive creatures bears a relation to the rainy seasons in their natural habitat, although in Cairo there is no rainy season or variation of food supply.   These animals, however, had not crossed the equator, so there was presumably nothing that might be expected to disturb any " inherent " rhythm that they may have possessed.

Although the causes of reproductive failure under conditions of captivity are probably quite complex in some cases, in others it appears that relatively simple distortions of the natural environment may be responsible for infertility.   Thus, Woitkewitsch (1945) found that by gradually increasing the amount of light per 24 hours, it was possible to induce fertile matings in squirrels, *Sciurus vulgaris*, which had failed to breed during several years of captivity.

Any discussion of the influence of external factors on sexual periodicity would be incomplete without at least a brief reference to the adaptations of domesticated animals brought about by their symbiotic association with man.   Since certain external factors obviously are important to the timing of reproductive activity, it is not surprising that domestication, which often imposes marked environmental changes, has sometimes resulted in detectable alterations in mating functions and fertility.   Rice (1942) points out that domestication of certain farm animals has led to " almost complete obliteration of seasonal manifestations."   For example, the cow and sow breed all the year round, and some breeds of ewes reproduce in late spring, summer and autumn.   Hammond (1939) also has observed that domestication has, in some instances, included extension of the normal breeding season.   In many instances attempts to domesticate various species have failed because of cessation of reproductive activity under conditions of captivity.   Hence, it can be no accident that human history over the past 10,000 years is also the history of the horse, of the ox, of sheep and goats and of cats and dogs ; whereas other animals—for example, the eland—have consistently refused to be tamed, or to adjust themselves to a life of relative restraint.   The creatures that man has succeeded in domesticating must have been marked at the start by an unusual capacity for physiological adaptation (*see* Eckstein and Zuckerman, 1955).   Many other factors are doubtless involved in the reproductive changes accompanying domestication, but the subject is too complex to be pursued here.   For further details the reader may consult the excellent book on "A history of domesticated animals," by Zeuner (1960.)

Psychological Factors Associated with Courtship and Mating

It now seems likely that, in addition to physical stimuli, many psychological factors have profound effects upon the breeding cycle in birds and mammals. There is overwhelming evidence that many species of birds and mammals, although perfectly healthy and in an apparent state of complete physiological well-being, fail to exhibit seasonal periodicity and never breed in captivity.   Something appears to be lacking in the psychological climate that either inhibits or fails to stimulate the regular seasonal gametogenesis associated with breeding activities (Amoroso and Matthews, 1955).

Little is known about the importance of psychological stimuli in the breeding cycles of mammals, though they probably play as large a part in regulating the cycle in many species of mammals as they do in birds. In many species of seal there is a characteristic harem system on the breeding grounds (Amoroso and Matthews, 1952 ; Davies, 1953), whereby a dominant male becomes the proprietor of a number of females which he guards against the attention of rival males. In all these species there is a post-partum oestrus during which sexual congress is permitted, and it is possible that such colonial enterprises are highly important to the achievement of normal reproductive function in these carnivores. A harem

Fig. *13.1*—Roe-deer. A figure-of-eight play ring. These appear to go out of use around the end of June. (This figure kindly supplied by Mr. Taylor-Page).

system is also employed by some ungulates, and it has been suggested, but not proved, that the stag of the red deer herding his harem of hinds, and challenging or even sparring with rival stags, provides the necessary pituitary stimulation to induce oestrus in his hinds.

In the roe, which is not polygamous, but usually goes in small parties consisting of a buck, a doe and her fawns, there is a peculiar " courtship " habit that may well provide a psychological stimulus. In many places, particular parts of the territory of the roe are centres for the activities of the animals during the rut ; these are the " racing rings," more or less circular tracks trodden out by the bucks chasing the does among the trees, round one of which the ring is often centred. Some observers (Millais, 1906) report that the doe allows the buck to chase her round and round the ring, the play sometimes lasting so long that both partners become temporarily exhausted. At the end of the chase pairing takes place, and then racing is resumed, and the whole process may be repeated many times. Buxton

(1948, 1949), has reported a rather different pattern of behaviour. Roe deer watched by this observer in Scotland did not race, they walked, and only occasionally did the buck break into a " slight trot " when he fell behind the doe. His activity appeared to be directed to preventing the doe from leaving the area in which the ring lay, for not only did he follow her but he dodged round in front beneath her nose as if to head her off or stop her. He also shouldered her from side to side so that she was guided into a more or less circular course, and it is suggested that the ring is formed by the action of the buck in thus herding the doe on a circular tract. The doe evidently enjoys this play as much as the buck for she does not attempt to break away ; while a pair were watched walking the ring for half an hour, the buck served the doe nine times. According to Taylor-Page

Fig. *13*.2—Roe-deer. A rutting ring. These are usually much smaller than play rings; here the focal point is some more scrubby bushes. (This figure kindly supplied by Mr. Taylor-Page.)

(1958), courtship display in a circle has also been noted in a herd of hartebeest; in the bush antelope (*Antilope madoqua*) ; in the impala ; in a small bird of the Kenya highlands called Jackson's Whydah (*Drepenoplectes jacksoni*) ; in hares and in goats. Even a small spider (*Saitis pulex*) and moths of the genus *Crambus* circle in rings. "Movement in a circle is a very normal method of progression, enabling an animal to see what is going on behind. The anti-clockwise tendency is a natural one. Horses are trained by running them left-handed, and in both horse and greyhound racing, as well as in circus rings, the course is anticlockwise."

Taylor-Page (1958), speaking of the roe deer's ring, states that "the behaviour pattern produces for the animal a familiar setting in which its activities can be localised and in which synchronisation of sexual rhythms can be given a better chance of success than would occur by fortuitous encounter. Roe, having no strong herd instinct as in red and fallow deer, appear to have developed this activity as an alternative." (Figs. *13*.1, *13*.2).

Heape's (1901) observations on captive animals in zoos led him to suggest that in various species the presence of the male stimulated the female to oestrus ; while that of the female stimulates the male to rut. Similarly, the stimulating action of " teasing " or " heckling " by the male mink as a factor contributing to early breeding each season is emphasised by Beach (1948).

Without going into a detailed discussion of observations and experiments of the same kind (in domesticated species), it is safe to say that evidence is accumulating which indicates that among British breeds of sheep the presence of the ram may influence the times the ewes come on heat. One such study is that of Underwood, Shier and Davenport (1944) who made the observation that when the ram was turned into a flock of Border Leicester × Merino cross ewes, a peak number of ewes came into heat some 18–20 days later. These authors suggested that the presence of the ram had stimulated the occurrence of oestrus in the ewes. Robinson (1951) also regards it as " . . . not unlikely that in those breeds in which the anoestrum is not very deep, introduction of the ram towards the end of anoestrum may stimulate the pituitary to exceed the threshold for ovulation and advance the onset of the season ". Along similar lines, Hafez (1952a, b) has suggested that the introduction of rams or teasers to a flock of ewes may hasten the breeding season by converting silent heat (ovulation without oestrus) into true heat (ovulation plus oestrus). Supporting evidence of the stimulating effect of the ram's introduction, with or without preliminary teasing by vasectomised males, may be found in the reports of Coleman (1950, 1951), Schinkel (1954) and Riches and Watson (1954).

The foregoing considerations make it clear that the environment exercises a profound effect on the physiological functions of the reproductive glands, but the exact manner by which changes in environmental temperature, light, food supply and social impact affect gonadal development is not surely known. Surgical removal of the pituitary gland abolishes the normal seasonal cycle in many mammals and birds and renders the gonads unable to respond to environmental factors which normally activate them. This indicates that the hypophysis is a necessary link in the chain of reactions which leads to sexual activation. There is little doubt also that the gonad-stimulating potency of the hypophysis increases during the period of normal or artificial reactivation of the gonad. Thus, it appears that the seasonal cycle is conditioned by certain external environmental factors which excite or inhibit the secretion of gonadotrophins by the anterior pituitary and make it possible for reproduction to occur at the appropriate breeding season. It must be admitted, however, that there is a serious gap in our knowledge regarding the effects of environmental conditions on the neuro-endocrinological systems of farm animals.

III. Observations on Sexual Periodicity in Birds

The Influence of Seasonal Factors on Sexual Periodicity

The subject of seasonal periodicity in the reproductive system of birds, already dealt with in Chapter I, has been well treated by Rowan (1926), whose experimental investigations are referred to below, and more recently by A. J. Marshall and his associates in several important papers. As is well known, most birds breed in the spring when the daylight is increasing, yet, as Baker (1939) has remarked, the general evidence shows that light can be only one of the factors concerned. There is little evidence that warmth is a factor in the seasonal recrudescence of the generative organs but it may sometimes be a contributory influence.   It has been suggested that the increase in the size of the gonads and the greater quantity of hormones presumably secreted in correlation with this increase may be the source of the migratory stimulus in certain species; the most widely quoted experiments and observations in this connection are those of Rowan (1929), whose original experiments dealt chiefly with the junco, as well as those of Heape (1931) and Bullough (1942, 1943).   Likewise, migratory behaviour is known to occur in many invertebrates, and it is often stated that increase or decrease of hormone secretions is one source of the migratory impulse (Yakhontov, 1945).   *See also* Baggerman (1959).

There are, however, several investigators who disagree with the extreme view as to the primary importance of secretions from reproductive glands for the initiation of migratory movements.   Various studies appear to show that the physiological conditions essential to migration involve much more than change in the secretory activity of a single type of tissue.   Thus, northward migration may occur despite complete castration (Hann, 1939; Emlen, cited by Wolfson, 1942) and is regularly accomplished by juvenile birds in which gonad development is incomplete (Shafer, 1907; Woodbury, 1941); such features as the extent of fat deposition are regarded as factors contributing heavily to migratory behaviour (Thomson, 1936). In the case of those species which migrate in the first part of the year from the southern to the northern hemisphere, the gonadal increase is said to commence before the migration starts and in such cases it must be supposed mainly to be the result of a gonadal rhythm.   At any rate, it is not due to increase of daylight. Rowan and Batrawi (1939) have reported on eight species of European birds (shrikes and warblers) wintering in Africa, south of the equator.   The spring recrudescence had begun in all the samples as far as the testes were concerned, and also as regards the ovaries except in *Lanius collurio*.   This had occurred under conditions of light decrease and not increase.   That decreasing day-lengths can affect gametogenesis has also been established for the short-tailed shearwater, *Puffinus tenuirostris* (Marshall and Serventy, 1957).

The Relationship between Latitude and Breeding Seasons

The duration and intensity of light, though important, are not the only factors involved in the seasonal activities in birds.   We have no precise information on the responses of equatorial birds to light increments, but it would seem reasonable to suppose that on the equator, where the days and nights are approximately of equal length throughout the year, the fluctuations are too small to be the sole effective factor.   Moreover, the observation that certain trans-equatorial migrants move northward from regions where the days are increasing in length is sufficient to suggest that factors other than light increments are involved in tropical and equatorial species.   With non-migratory tropical birds which live where there is little or no variation in daylight, seasonal breeding may still occur (Baker, 1929 ; cf. Bannerman, 1930–39) and it is suggested that the recurrence of the rains and various ecological factors may play a part. In the tropical areas of India, where heat and light during the year vary but little, many birds (and also mammals) may breed at any time, and with those species which do not have definite seasons the cause may usually be traced to food supply (Stuart-Baker, personal communication). In the unvarying climate of the northern New Hebrides the passerine bird *Pachycephala pectoralis* is as seasonal in its reproduction as are the birds of temperate climates and the environmental change controlling the breeding season is unknown (Baker, Marshall and Harrison, 1940). Moreau (1936, 1951), from his observations in East Africa, has adduced further evidence bearing on this subject. In this connection, it is of interest to note that, according to Baker (1937), although the length of daylight does not alter appreciably, and only rises to a maximum once annually in the tropics, the intensity of illumination (both visible and ultraviolet) has, at least in certain tropical regions, two maxima in the year.

Murphy (1936), in his book on the oceanic birds of South America, states that in the Atlantic equatorial isles of Fernando de Noronha and St. Paul Rocks, the majority of the fowl apparently have no breeding season, for eggs and young may be found in any month of the twelve, but that the sooty tern is an exception. With this species there is evidence that the nesting season on Ascension begins a little earlier in each successive year, and that the change in time is sufficient to make the birds breed on the average four times within three years. In order to account for the reproductive behaviour of such tropical birds as the sooty tern, it may be necessary to postulate some degree of inherent sexual rhythm unaffected by seasonal environmental factors. On the other hand, although there are facts pointing to an inherent seasonal cycle in photoperiodically regulated animals, there seems to be evidence of the cycle being re-set by factors other than light, since Fraps, Neher and Rothchild (1947) showed that under constant light the rhythm of egg-laying in the domestic fowl could be re-set by changing the times of feeding.

Murphy (1936) also records some facts about the periodic breeding of certain species of penguins which are in striking contrast to the great majority of birds. The Peruvian and African penguins, that is, the two members of the genus *Spheniscus* which, coming presumably from the south, have invaded warm, temperate and tropical environments, may have two broods of young, nearly the whole of the year being occupied in breeding operations. Kearton (1930) says that the African penguins have mating seasons in February and in September. According to Levick (1914), the black-footed penguins in the Zoological Gardens can breed several times a year. Thus it would appear that the penguins are almost unique among birds in having freed themselves from external seasonal influence. In this respect they are comparable to the domestic dog among mammals. Murphy also gives many instances of sea-birds of various kinds which seem to have a " continuous breeding season " under uniform conditions.

Speaking generally, however, in the southern hemisphere most native birds breed in the southern spring, and this is true also for birds imported from the northern hemisphere. Thus, in New Zealand, Hutton (1901) records that the starling, linnet, redpoll, robin and hedge-sparrow conform to the seasonal cycle of that country. Thomson (1922) records a similar fact for the thrush and the domestic sparrow. The two breeding seasons which occur with certain species of birds in Ceylon and probably in other tropical countries may be accounted for by the greater intensity of irradiation (visible and ultra-violet) which is believed to exist at the two maxima in the year when the sun passes overhead.   Again, as Betts (1952) has shown, the majority of the species of birds in South India have a breeding season which is little more extended than that of birds in temperate climates, although the country is well within the tropics and the climate is presumably favourable to breeding throughout the greater part of the year.   Seasonal breeding in tropical birds has also been studied by Bannerman (1930–39), who suggests that it is determined by the recurrence of rains and other ecological factors which may also act, through the nervous system, upon the anterior pituitary.   For further details *see* Voous (1950).

Of migratory birds which breed in the southern hemisphere the mutton bird of New Zealand and certain other species of shearwaters (*Puffinus*) are examples. They breed in the south (South America, Australia and New Zealand) in the second half of the year and migrate across the equator to the north (where they do not breed) in the first part of the year (Murphy, 1936).   Marshall and Serventy (1957) suggest that the reproductive rhythm and the journey south, which is so dramatically rigid and constant, may be stimulated by decreasing photo-periods.   But, how the light factor is able to achieve the very precise timing necessary simultaneously to activate birds apparently scattered over a wide area of northern seas remains unknown.   The cessation of parental responsibility, they believe, may be a major factor in the stimulus for contra-nuptial migration.

Birds which have been transported from the southern to the northern hemisphere and kept in captivity or in a state of domestication or semi-domestication, generally adapt themselves to the northern seasons in a short time, and this applies not merely to the species but to the individual birds.   There are, however, exceptions.   Thus, the Duke of Bedford found that parakeets (the hooded parakeet and Brown's parakeet) from North Australia retain their original breeding season, which is October (Marshall, 1936, 1937).   Witschi (1935) states that tropical weaver finches from Africa retain their original cycles in America.   Other birds, such as the black swan, the Cereospis goose and the emu, have been said to keep their southern hemisphere seasons in Europe, but the statements to this effect appear to have been based on mistaken knowledge as to their times for breeding in Australia.

Baker and Ranson (1938) have made an extended study of this question, citing all the available records (with full references), which shows that whereas most birds adjust their sexual cycles to their new environment, with some the original oestrous rhythm is still a stronger factor since they maintain their original cyclical periodicity (*see also* Baker, 1938a, b).   Fisher (1939), who has also briefly discussed this question, remarks that in birds which keep their rhythm in a new country the " offspring on the whole seem to lose it."   He mentions further the case of the birds in the semi-desert, thorn, bush country (as described to him by L S. V. Venables).   The birds breed in the " short rains " in November and their gonads come up in anticipation of this and without any palpable environmental stimulus. If the rains fall, the birds do not breed and their gonads regress (cf. Marshall, 1951 ; also Keast and Marshall, 1954).

The case of the European white storks in Peru recorded by Murphy (1925) is one of exceptional interest, for the stork is a migratory bird which crosses the equator and migrates far south annually. Yet, Murphy found that the storks kept in captivity at Lima bred at the appropriate season for the southern hemisphere, laying eggs in October, thus reversing their sexual cycle.

As evidence that some birds breed in response to ecological factors the Arctic terns on Bear Island, as recorded by Lack (1933), may be cited. This observer found that the time for ovulation and egg-laying was apparently controlled by the condition of the nesting site. If this is not in a fit state, as in a late season, breeding may be postponed or not take place at all. Lack concludes that with this species breeding is regulated by the nervous system (cf. Bles's experiments with amphibians, Chapter I, p. 21). Baker (1938a, b) has also given instances of this type of phenomenon among different kinds of birds (*see* Chapter I, p. 25).

In a later paper, Baker (1939) has reverted to the question as to the relation between latitude and breeding seasons in birds and his conclusions may be summarised as follows :

" As one goes north from the temperate latitudes one finds a general tendency for the egg-laying seasons of birds of all kinds to start later and later at the rate of some 20 or 30 days per 10° of latitude. Conversely, as one goes south from the temperate latitudes into the northern tropical and equatorial zones one finds a general tendency for the *Accipitres, Coraciiformes* and, to a less extent, the *Passeres* to start their egg-laying earlier and earlier. The *Charadriformes, Grallae, Heriodiones* and *Anseres* behave differently. In the northern hemisphere they tend to breed later in the tropical and equatorial zones than in the subtropical and temperate. There is a general tendency for birds in the tropics to reach the height of their main breeding seasons somewhat before the sun passes overhead. Two breeding seasons in the year are quite common, but birds which breed only once select either the northward (*Accipitres*, etc.) or southward (*Grallae*, etc.) swing of the sun." " . . . It is thinkable that the stimulus provided by the sun is its light (visible and ultra-violet) which is at maximum intensity when it passes overhead ". (Baker, 1937). " The main proximate causes of the breeding seasons of birds in nature are thought to be temperature and length of day in the boreal and temperate zones, and rain and/or intensity of isolation near the equator. The time of arrival from migration is often an important factor. Much egg-laying occurs when days are getting shorter, and indeed, it often proceeds rapidly while they are decreasing in length and only between eleven and twelve hours long. There is, however, little egg-laying when the day is shorter than eleven hours, and almost none when it is less than ten " (Baker, 1939. For tabulated list of latitude and egg-seasons in old-world birds, *see* Baker, 1938a.)

That there is a general relation between the breeding migration of birds, the spawning migrations of fishes and the migratory movements of sea animals on the one hand, and external stimuli dependent on seasonal change on the other, has been made evident in an introductory paragraph (Heape, 1931) ; yet there is a good deal of variation in passing from species to species among all kinds of animals. The internal stimuli no doubt generally come from the gonads and it is known that sterile birds sometimes do not migrate. Nevertheless, as with juvenile individuals, there may be a stimulus resulting from association with others. It is to be presumed, however, that as a general rule external factors acting through the intermediation of the nervous system are what regulate the migratory movements which are correlated with reproductive change. (Wolfson, 1959).

IV. Observations on Sexual Periodicity in Lower Vertebrates

Fish

Under normal conditions marked seasonal rhythms are characteristic of breed-ing activity in fishes. One annual reproduction occurs in some teleosts, while others produce several broods at regular intervals for a period of several months. In some species, on the other hand, the period of sexual inactivity is either non-existent or very brief, and ovulation is almost as continuous as spermatogenesis. Under normal diurnal illumination *Ozyrias latipes* ovulates and spawns every 24 hours for prolonged periods, but even this regularity disappears under con-tinuous illumination (Robinson and Rugh, 1943). At the other extreme there are species such as the members of the genus *Oncorhynchus*, in which the gonads mature only once and death inevitably follows spawning. Cyclical changes have, likewise, been described in the testes of several seasonally spawning species. In general, a short period of quiescence after the spring spawning is followed by a wave of activity during the late summer and autumn.

Although there is considerable variation in detail, fish which spawn in the spring or summer show a marked production of oöcytes and enlargement of the gonads during the summer and autumn after spawning. In several fish—*Cottus* (Hann, 1927); *Gasterosteus* (Craig-Bennett, 1931); *Merluccius* (Hickling, 1935); *Phoxinus* (Bullough, 1939)—these events have been carefully correlated with the season. Although environmental variables such as temperature and light are important in the timing of these changes, Bullough (1940) finds an internal rhythm in the reproduction of *Phoxinus* which is reinforced and rendered more precise by seasonal changes, but appears even under very constant laboratory conditions. Seasonal changes in the rate of oöcyte formation have been observed in the ovaries of juvenile hake (Hickling, 1935), indicating that completion of the maturation processes is not an essential part of the seasonal rhythm observed.

Virgin female *Lebistes*, likewise, show an ill-defined cyclical production of eggs (Rosenthal, 1952), again indicating that ovulation or gestation is not a necessary feature of these rhythmic occurrences. Pituitary control is an obvious possibility, but has not been established. It is stated by Mendoza (1939) that the viviparous teleost, *Neotoca bilineata*, exhibits a regular breeding cycle, which he believes is controlled by an internal mechanism exhibiting inherent periodicity. He finds, moreover, that the mating behaviour of the female is closely correlated with periodic activation of the ovaries. Mendoza regards this female fish's reproductive cycle as comparable to the oestrous cycle of female mammals and advances the suggestion that certain endocrine products of the ovary may be responsible for the female's sexual receptivity.

Amphibia

The spawning dates of the spring-breeding Anura are subject to considerable annual variation, and it might be expected that identification of the environmental factors which initiate the release of pituitary gonadotrophins would be possible. Savage (1935) made extensive field observations on the spawning dates of *Rana temporaria*, and investigated the degree of correlation with various climatic factors.

The average spawning date was apparently more dependent on the weather over a long period preceding, than on that obtaining at the time of spawning. The two most important factors in the pre-spawning period were rainfall and temperature. According to Savage, the actual migration of the frogs to their breeding ponds seemed to be due to specific olfactory stimuli emanating from the spring outburst of algal growth. Spawning does not begin until a further change in the algal cycle again changes the chemical constitution of the water. This change, Savage suggests, is perceived by the animals through skin receptors and acts on the gonads via the pituitary. Noble and Noble (1923) discussed the relation of the breeding season to external factors in several North American Anura. They divided them into explosive and protracted breeders, suggesting that the gonads mature either uniformly or irregularly in all individuals of a given species in a particular area. Within each group the spawning date of some species was temperature-controlled, while in others it was rain-controlled. Berk (1938) attempted to correlate ovarian changes in *Xenopus laevis* living under natural conditions with climatic factors. The onset of pairing in the ponds corresponded in time with a sharp rise in temperature and a high rainfall, while ovarian regeneration in February began during a period of increasing rainfall and decreasing temperature. Alexander and Bellerby (1938), on the other hand, found that the annual cessation of ovarian activity occurred when the ponds inhabited by the toads dry up at the end of the breeding season. Bellerby (1938) has shown, moreover, that the sexual cycle is not influenced by seasonal variation in light intensity or wave-length. Therefore, he concluded that the sexual cycle of *Xenopus* is related to changes in water volume and to the effects of temperature and nutrition. Along similar lines are the observations of Weisman and Coates (1944a, b), who believe that a similar combination of environmental factors, including amount of rainfall, mean temperature, and food supply, affects the pituitary cycle of *Xenopus*, and thus controls the cycle of seasonal breeding. In *Rana pipiens*, Zahl (1937) considered various external factors which might act on the pituitary. He concluded that while cold had a delaying action on spawning, the converse did not seem to be true. Thus it would seem that a complex pattern of external stimuli is necessary to induce breeding behaviour in amphibia, and that, although no single stimulus alone is adequate, rainfall and temperature are two important factors. There is as yet little or no evidence to show how rainfall and pituitary activation might be related.

Reptiles

According to Reynolds (1943), the spring mating season of the lizard *Eumeces fasciatus* is correlated with the functional state of the reproductive organs. Testis secretion is high at this time and affects sexual activity as well as the growth of the accessories. In *E. latiscutatus* spermatozoa are absent from the seminiferous tubules between April and the beginning of June. Primary and secondary spermatocytes and the maturation stages appear in July and August, followed by spermiogenesis in November and December (Kidata, 1951). Evans (1935a, b) has observed that during the winter, when sexual activity is lacking, the testis and ovaries of the American chameleon, *Anolis carolinensis*, are in a state of regression; and with the approach of the breeding season gonadal and accessory development is marked. Hamlett (1952) observes that the period of reproduction lasts from April to August. Taken together these studies offer presumptive evidence for the conclusion that gonadal hormones affect sexual behaviour in these reptiles.

Seasonal changes in the reproductive organs of *Vipera berus* have been described by Volsoe (1944) and by Marshall and Woolf (1957).

V. Experiments with Light and Ultra-violet Irradiation

Photostimulation and Sexual Periodicity in Birds

There now seems to be overwhelming evidence that sexual periodicity in numerous species of temperate zone birds is somehow controlled by light and dark fluctuations (Amoroso and Matthews, 1955). Encouraging egg production by subjecting hens to artificial lighting by night, now an established practice in poultry husbandry, seems to have been employed by the Spaniards for at least 120 years (Rowan, 1938b). But it was not until Rowan's investigations (1925, 1926, 1929, 1930, 1931, 1932, 1936, 1938b) on migration in the junco, in some finches and in the American crow, and those of Bissonnette (1930a, b, c; 1931a, b; 1932a, b; 1933) on the European starling, showed that the coincidence of gonadal recrudescence with increasing hours of daylight and northward migration was no accident, that photo-experimentation became a subject of major scientific interest. Even so, it is only during the last fifteen or twenty years that the study of photo-periodicity in farm livestock has been redeveloped and expanded, notably by F. H. A. Marshall, Hammond, Yeates, Robinson, Hendricks and others. The mechanism by which the gonads may be influenced by environmental light changes has been studied mainly in birds and small mammals.

By exposing juncos in mid-winter in Canada to ordinary electric light, Rowan (1926, 1930) obtained an increase in the size of the gonads comparable to what occurs with the increase of daylight in spring. Warmth was not a factor in the process since the birds were kept at the temperature of the outside environment, which was very cold. It was not so clear, however, that the more prolonged exercise undergone by the birds, as a consequence of the illumination, may not have induced the gonadal growth. Rowan's original results with the junco finch were subsequently confirmed by him for canaries and crows, and experiments with the junco showed that, while food supply, weather conditions and temperature may be contributory factors in determining the sexual and migratory activities of this bird, it is the recurring periods of light and darkness that act as the proximate environmental stimulus for migration ; both sexes are equally dependent on variation in exposure to light for the seasonal changes of activity in the sex glands.

Later experiments in which Rowan made use of mechanical devices producing forced exercise or causing disturbance have supported the view that exercise may play a part. Moreover, observations on the London starlings which roost above Trafalgar Square, where they are subject to traffic disturbances at night-time while receiving but a dim illumination, have tended to confirm the suggestion as to exercise being a contributory factor in the growth of the gonads (Rowan, 1937; 1938a, b; 1946). Rowan believed that the extra illumination induced gonadal differentiation during periods of sexual quiescence by permitting the birds to indulge in increased exercise. This view, subsequently modified by substituting "wakefulness" for physical activity, retains certain adherents (Wolfson, 1949a, b), but subsequent studies by others (Bissonnette, 1931a, b; 1936a, b, c; Benoit, 1935a, b, c, d, e, 1937; Riley, 1936, 1937, 1940; Burger, Bissonnette and Doolittle, 1942

Burger, 1949) did not give such importance to increased exercise, but considered light *per se* as the causal agency of the seasonal sexual cycle. According to Rowan the additional period of wakefulness imposed nightly on the London starlings is the crucial factor. Furthermore, he states (1938b) that sparrows and juncos subjected to increasing periods of mechanically induced wakefulness in total darkness for 4 weeks, following a faint and diminishing light for 2 weeks, attained full breeding condition and highly developed reproductive organs. It seems quite possible, nevertheless, that such results may be actually brought about by other external stimuli of various kinds (cf. ferrets, *see* below). Here it may be mentioned that Riley (1940) found that in the sparrow activity in complete darkness in a revolving drum did not affect the gonads (cf. Wolfson, 1941, 1945, who criticises the results), and Burger (1949) was able to write that "no experiment thus far devised has proven that any external stimulus, operating in darkness, produced precocious gametogenesis."

Wolfson (1941) has attempted to reconcile these contrasting hypotheses by suggesting that increased daily illumination causes recrudescence of the gonads under both experimental and natural conditions because the birds are awake, and presumably active, for longer periods of time under longer lighting schedules. But, notwithstanding the importance of these factors in regulating seasonal gonadal development, it has been suggested that photo-periodicity is not a necessary factor in regulating the time of lay in certain birds (cf. Fraps, Neher, and Rothchild, 1947; Fraps, 1954a, b). Moreover, the problem as to gonadal recrudescence is further complicated by the fact observed by Bullough and Carrick (1939) that the organs in immigrant starlings from the Continent mature later in the season than in most of the British birds.

In the meantime, Kirschbaum's (1933) experiments on the sparrow showed that artificial lengthening of the day brings about a precocious development of the sex glands, especially in the male in winter, and Witschi (1935), repeating the experiments, obtained the same effects. Later experiments by Ringoen and Kirschbaum (1937), in which the birds had their eyes covered, showed that there was no such development of the gonads. Other researches upon birds, showing gonadal increase or activity after illumination, have been carried out on mourning doves (Cole, 1933), mejiros (*Zosterops*) (Miyazaki, 1934), sparrows (Kech, 1934; Riley, 1937), pheasants (Martins, 1935; Clark, Leonard and Bump, 1937b; Clark and Bump, 1939; Bissonnette and Csech, 1941), turkeys (Scott and Payne, 1937), quail, ruffed grouse, etc. (Clark, Leonard and Bump, 1937a), and blue jays (Bissonnette, 1939), and Bissonnette and Csech (1937b) have succeeded in getting pheasants' eggs in November and hatching chicks on Christmas Day. (For further references, *see* Bissonnette, 1935c, 1937.)

Van Oordt and Damsté (1939) have shown that greenfinches, if placed in the dark in May and kept there until August, undergo gonadal regression in regard to both size and functional activity, and in both sexes, but when brought to the light begin to sing and come into breeding condition again, the testes and ovaries showing increased and renewed activity (*see also* Damsté, 1946). Burger (1939a, b, c) found that to effect spermatogenesis in the starling, light duration must be for 9 hours with periodic increases (*see also* Burger, Bissonnette and Doolittle, 1942). Ringoen and Kirschbaum (1939) found that with the sparrow gonadal precocity could occur chiefly in the male in spring and autumn as a result of artificially increased light rations.　In experiments by Walton and Marshall on ducks, artificial lighting in the spring accelerated the cyclical change, as was shown by the birds displaying courtship phenomena, the drakes fighting, and the occurrence of the seasonal eclipse in April instead of at the usual time in July (Walton, 1938).　But in these experiments, probably as a result of otherwise unsuitable conditions, the birds did not lay.　Riley (1937) has found that young sparrows in their first autumn respond more readily to increased lighting in early October than adult males that have recently completed the active phase of the cycle and since regressed (cf. Riley and Witschi, 1937, 1938).

Benoit (1934) also has shown that light has a pronounced effect in stimulating the testis of the drake, both immature and mature birds being affected.　When a hood was used to cover the eyes the effects did not supervene.　Benoit, therefore, at first concluded that the stimulus must pass through the eyes and optic nerves and brain and thence to the anterior pituitary, but in his later experiments (Benoit, 1935a) he severed the optic nerves or removed the eyeballs.　Under these conditions the effect of lighting still led to acceleration (unlike the ferrets referred to below), yet hooding of the eyes and the region around them had an inhibitory effect.　Benoit concluded that there may be some other receptor organs in this region, or that the rays acted on the pituitary itself, for if an artificial light were directed through a thin glass tube into the eye socket on to the gland it was effective as a stimulating agent (Benoit, 1935–1938); *see also* Damsté, 1947, who gives further references).

Few data are available concerning the environmental factors involved in the timing of the reproductive cycles of equatorial birds and attempts to photostimulate tropical birds have been rare.　On the equator the annual fluctuation of daylength is only about 2 minutes and it is unlikely that the breeding seasons of truly equatorial birds (or even mammals) are controlled photoperiodically.　Scott and Payne (1942) exposed guinea-fowl to additional illumination in the United States and ascribed the lack of response in this species to its tropical origin.　On the other hand, Brown and Rollo (1940) and Rollo and Domm (1943) showed that the cycles of a variety of tropical whydahs and weavers (purchased in California) were modifiable by photoperiodicity.　Similarly, Morel and Bourliere (1955, 1956) and Marshall and Disney (1956) have shown that at 16° N. (Senegal) and even at 3·20° S. (Tanganyika), respectively, the sexual cycle of the males of the equatorial weaver finch (*Quelea quelea*) has been advanced by artificial illumination of 5 hours daily, whereas birds which received an additional 5 minutes of light per day showed no significant gonad modification, even though they received an additional grand total of 275 minutes (Marshall and Disney, 1956).　These results give no support to Wolfson's (1952a, 1953) hypothesis that summation of day-lengths or the daily dose of light, rather than increasing day-lengths as such, might be the critical environmental factor in determining the periods of migration and breeding of equatorial, as well as other, species.　On the contrary, Marshall (1949b, 1955) and Marshall and Disney (1956) have demonstrated experimentally that it is the environmental conditions arising after rainfall, operating in conjunction with the internal sexual rhythm, that constitute the critical factors regulating the time of reproduction.　They have shown, moreover, that successful nest-building cannot take place until the environment provides green grass with stems and blades sufficiently long to be used by the males for weaving.　Whether the male weaver finch's predilection for green grass is the result of free choice or an automatic selection due to the anatomical composition of its retinae remains unknown. Summarising, it appears that, notwithstanding the fact that the cycles of a variety of tropical birds are modifiable by photic stimuli, these creatures present a strong argument against the overall control of the breeding cycle in the natural state by light fluctuations (Moreau, Wilk and Rowan, 1947).

According to Ivanova (1935), plucking the feathers of irradiated sparrows resulted in a greater augmentation of testicular growth than in birds with feathers, but the latter also underwent an increase with additional illumination. There is probably considerable species variation, and though the eyes normally receive stimuli which are transmitted through nervous paths to the anterior pituitary, the effects in some animals are conveyed by alternative paths. Moreover, as already stated, external stimuli of various kinds may be effective in certain cases.

Photostimulation and Sexual Periodicity in Mammals

As with birds, some seasonally breeding mammals are known to show the same sensitivity to waxing and waning of daylight hours. Thus the ferret has a long autumn–winter period of sexual quiescence or anoestrus, from August or September until March. Without artificial manipulation of lighting cycles or hormone treatments, ferrets have not been known to breed during that period in the northern hemisphere. However, Bissonnette (1932a, b), as a result of researches in Cambridge, made the important discovery that with increased illumination by electric light (200-watt bulbs) in mid-winter, and therefore at the time of normal anoestrum, ferrets came into full oestrus with typical vulval swelling in 38 to 64 days. In the male ferret the response in the earlier experiments was less complete, but by modifying the method of increasing the length of day to a more gradual one, complete spermatogenesis and copulation were brought about, and pregnancy in the female with parturition in January was obtained (Bissonnette and Bailey, 1936). At the same time, Baker and Ranson (1932a, 1933), in Oxford, showed that the oestrous cycle in the vole *Microtus agrestis* could be modified by varying the rations of artificial light, though food and probably latitude might alter the response (winter type of food being best ; earlier activity further north). In the Orkney vole (*Microtus orcadensis*), on the other hand, Marshall and Wilkinson (1956) could find no significant difference between the breeding rates of animals exposed to a mere 6 hours of day-length (slightly less than that of the Orkney mid-winter) and those living under the full day-length of the London summer. These results do not, of course, suggest that day-length fluctuations are unimportant. On the contrary, they appear to indicate that in at least some mammals, as in birds, external factors other than photoperiodicity are effective in the control of the sexual cycle.

The effect of illumination with ordinary electric light in producing oestrus in the ferret was fully confirmed by Hill and Parkes (1933) and later by Marshall and Bowden (1934, 1935), Clark *et al.* (1939), Marshall (1940), Jefferson (1940), Thomson (1951, 1954), Thomson and Zuckerman (1953, 1954, 1955) and Donovan and Harris (1954, 1955, 1956). Hill and Parkes (1933) showed, moreover, that the anterior pituitary is bound up with the sexual photoperiodicity since hypophysectomised animals are unaffected by artificial lighting and go into permanent anoestrum unless injected with pituitary extracts. This is in conformity with what we know about the function of the pituitary in other animals and with the experimental results of pituitary implants and the injection of extracts. On the other hand, the experiments of Thomson and Zuckerman (1953) and Zuckerman (1954a, b) suggest that light is effective after abolition of the portal blood supply to the *pars distalis* following stalk section. This is denied by Donovan and Harris (1954, 1955, 1956), who insist that the hypophysial portal vessels form a necessary part of the pathway of the light-induced oestrous response in the ferret. They have shown that ferrets in which the pituitary stalk is transected become reproductively active in winter when subjected to artificially lengthened periods of light only when vascular connections are re-established between the median eminence of the tuber cinereum and the anterior pituitary gland.

Other experiments upon irradiated mammals are those of Whitaker (1936, 1940) on the white-footed mouse (*Peromyscus leucopus noveboracensis*) which showed a similar gonadal reaction to illumination, and those by Bissonnette and Csech (1937a) on the raccoon, in which the results have been more striking, for these investigators have succeeded, not merely in accelerating the oestrous cycle by inducing the animals to breed in December instead of February, but in obtaining two litters in one year and thereby increasing the fecundity. These results were obtained by luminous irradiation (*see also* Bissonnette and Csech, 1939a, b). In the hedgehog (Allanson and Deanesly, 1934) and in the mink (Hansson, 1947; and Hronopulo, 1955), sexual activation was induced by extra illumination and also by increases in temperature and other factors. Likewise, Burkhardt (1947) and Nishikawa, Sugie and Harada (1952) have shown in a series of controlled experiments that pony mares (Shetland and Korean, respectively) in a state of deep anoestrum may be made to undergo sexual rhythm by general irradiation with strong artificial light. In this way oestrus and ovulation, followed by pregnancy, could be induced. Moreover, Burkhardt (1947) showed that there was a close connection between the shedding of the coat and ovarian activity; the mares were not allowed out of their boxes during the period of irradiation, so exercise could not have been a factor. Following the same type of treatment, out-of-season improvement in semen quality and in the total volume of semen has been recorded for the Korean stallion (Nishikawa and Horie, 1952; Sakanouje, 1940).

In the latitude of Cambridge, Mass., domestic cats usually breed from the middle of January until the middle of July; but Dawson (1941) and Farris (1950) have elicited oestrus during November and December, by increasing the amount of illumination for each 24 hours. In rats also (Fiske, 1939, 1941) it appears that light caused a greater output of follicle-stimulating hormone than luteinising hormone, since females receiving additional rations of light remain in an oestrous condition for several weeks instead of the normal period of 14 hours. Whereas, in animals kept in constant darkness, the metoestrous phase is the most protracted portion of the sexual cycle. Moreover, immature females kept in the light from birth or from the twenty-first day of life come into sexual maturity about 6 days earlier than the controls and 16 days earlier than those kept in the dark. Fiske's results are confirmed in part by Truscott's (1944) report that the attainment of sexual maturity in rats is accelerated by constant lighting. In addition, if the optic nerve is cut, maturation is delayed beyond the normal period, despite constant lighting conditions. Similarly, Meyer and Meyer (1944) have shown that cotton rats, raised in constant darkness, display retarded development of the reproductive tract and delayed attainment of sexual maturity whereas, constant lighting has no perceptible effect. On the other hand, Browman (1936, 1943) working on the albino rat, found that oestrous rhythm was not affected by blindness or continuous darkness. Furthermore, Hemmingsen and Krarup (1937) have shown that in the rat there is a correlation between the oestrous phenomena and the ordinary daylight diurnal rhythm. Heat and also muscular activity (as recorded by " activity cages ") are at their maximum in the dark. All the phenomena (mating instincts, cyclical anatomical changes in the vagina, and the correlated increase in activity) are shifted 12 hours if an artificial day–night rhythm is established by exposing the animals to light in the night and to darkness in the daytime. An 8-hour alternating rhythm of light and darkness, however, was not followed by adjustment. Constant light was found to stimulate vaginal cornification and to induce heat. It is to be presumed that the results were brought about through nervous action on the pituitary. Likewise, Gresson (1940), investigating the effect of electrical illumination on the mouse, found that long day conditions accelerated oestrus and induced copulation in mid-winter. (*See also* Enders, 1940; Logan, 1954a, b.)

The facts presented thus far show a curious discrepancy when compared with the findings of Chase (1941). This investigator, who studied reproductive phenomena in a strain of mice displaying congenital anophthalmia, reported that females from the eyeless strain showed vaginal opening somewhat earlier than eyed mice and exhibited first vaginal cornification considerably earlier. The eyeless males likewise matured and showed spermatogenesis at about the same age as males from an eyed strain. Nevertheless, it is, as Beach (1948) points out (p. 170), unsafe to compare these results directly with those of other workers who studied only eyed animals, since it is obvious that the genetic factors responsible for eyelessness may well have been accompanied by other hereditary abnormalities affecting the reproductive cycle.

Hart (1951) investigated the effects of a fixed dark–light rhythm without the necessity of a gradual reduction in the amount of light and found that, in ferrets, oestrus could be induced by the unusual treatment of subjecting them to an additional hour of light in the middle of each night. The onset of reproductive activity was greatly accelerated in the experimental female ferrets, and the rapidity with which the response was elicited indicates that this method of stimulation may be particularly potent. It emphasises, moreover, the importance of the dark periods in the photoperiod responses (Kirkpatrick and Leopold, 1953) and implies that one way in which the pituitary may be activated is through such a contrast-sensitive mechanism which is stimulated by light–dark sequences. This suggestion is supported by experimental evidence with birds, Kirkpatrick and Leopold (1952) having demonstrated that a daily quota of 10 hours of light including a one hour light interruption of the night causes development of the reproductive organs of the bobwhite quail, whereas the same light ration, applied as a single daily exposure, failed to cause development (*see,* however, Dempsey, Myers, Young and Dennison, 1934; Hammond, Jnr. 1953a; Kirkpatrick and Leopold, 1953). Applying the principle of light-dark contrast sequences to sheep, by providing a sequence of 4 hours light, 2 hours dark, 4 hours light, 14 hours dark, every 24-hour period, Hart (1950) was unable to obtain out-of-season lambs.

The treatment induced oestrus, but despite many matings pregnancy did not ensue. Failure to conceive was probably due to infertility of the rams, each of which apparently received a mixture of three different light treatments. (For a comprehensive account of the subject, *see* De Francescantonio, 1956).

It should be emphasised that increases in light have no effect on animals if the pituitary be removed (as first shown by Hill and Parkes, 1933, for the ferret), and further, that the same effects as those produced by light can be evoked at any season of the year by the injection of the gonad-stimulating principles. Similarly, hypophysectomy of the ferret (Bissonnette, 1938a, b) and the duck (Benoit and Ott, 1944) prevented gonad development under favourable photo-periodic cycles, again demonstrating the intermediary action of the pituitary hormones. Removal of the gonads of the varying hare (Lyman, 1943), on the other hand, did not stop the change in coat colour, nor did similar treatment of crows interfere with their southward migration in autumn (Rowan, 1946). The effects of stimulation, however, are not permanent, for the animals eventually go into a state of sexual rest in spite of the continuance of the stimulating agents used. The existence of this refractory period and its significance in relation to the sexual cycle have been emphasised by Bissonnette (1937) and are discussed below.

Bissonnette and Bailey (1936) have commented upon the frequency of luteinisation in unruptured follicles of ferrets which have been stimulated by light, and they attribute this phenomenon to the liberation of luteinising hormones in excess, as a result of repeated coition acting upon the pituitary. The possibility must always be borne in mind, however, that light may sometimes act by producing chemical changes in the skin and not through receptor organs. Again, Bissonnette (1936b) has shown that the pituitaries of stimulated ferrets undergo histological changes similar to those of castrated animals, large clear cells being produced.[1]

It must, of course, be freely admitted that all animals do not show the same sensitivity to waxing and waning of daylight hours ; there are exceptions both among mammals and among birds. Thus, while in many species—the so-called "Long-day" animals—an artificially lengthened day advances the breeding season, in others—for example, the guinea-pig (Dempsey, Meyers, Young and Dennison, 1934), the ground-squirrel (Moore, Simmons, Wells, Zalesky and Nelson, 1934; Wells, 1935) the cow (Laing, 1955), rabbit (Smelser, Walton and Whetham, 1934) and a fish, the brook trout (Hoover and Hubbard, 1937)—such treatment has so far failed to show any definite effects, suggesting that these species seem to have freed themselves wholly or partly from this particular environmental influence. This is particularly true of guinea-pigs, which are natives of the tropics and so have probably failed to acquire the capacity to respond to seasonal changes of daylight which in their natural state do not exist. Similarly, guinea-fowls, which also come from the tropics, fail to respond to increase of light (Scott and Payne, 1937).

Furthermore, Bissonnette (1941) reported that the breeding cycle of certain breeds of goats is controlled by light in such a way that increasing daily light periods from 25th January to 5th April, followed by decreasing light until July, resulted in the cessation of oestrous cycles in February instead of March and the resumption

---

[1] Denniston (1942) found that Röntgen-ray treatment of the hypophysis had little or no effect on the reproductive systems of the ground squirrel and rat.

of oestrus in May and June instead of September. We may conclude, therefore, that in the same animal light can have double effects : promoting gonadal activity, or bringing the season to a close and blocking further stimulation. Moreover, many mammals, such as the horse, donkey, ferret, cat, etc., have " long-day " breeding seasons in the spring, whereas others, like the sheep, goat, and deer, breed during the autumn or "short-day" season. Thus, if light be regarded as stimulatory to the former, then it is inhibitory to the latter (cf. Johnson and Gann, 1933). Long-day animals include a great number of birds. Bissonnette (1936b) listed junco, crow, canary, starling, mejiro, turkey, chicken, sparrow, mourning dove, duck, pheasant, quail and grouse. Long-day mammals include ferrets (Bissonnette, 1932a), field mice (Baker and Ranson, 1932a), hedgehogs (Allanson and Deanesly, 1934), raccoons (Bissonnette and Csech, 1937a), cats (Dawson, 1941) and many others (cf. Everett, 1942).

In contrast to the results of Bissonnette (1941), alluded to above, are certain findings of Yoshioka, Awasawa and Suzuki (1952), also in goats, concerning the effectiveness of short-day treatment in inducing oestrus. Working in Japan, these investigators found that a gradual shortening of the daylight hours in spring and summer, led to the same effect as maintaining a constant day-length corresponding to that of mid-October. With both treatments the majority of the animals came into oestrus 70–80 days after the commencement of treatment. These results were virtually independent of temperature. However, the fact that a few of the untreated animals came into oestrus during the non-breeding season in July and August suggests that reproductive periodicity in this species may be tied to a number of factors other than short-day. Similar results have been reported by Eaton and Simmons (1953) in sheep and goats.

Comparable out-of-season sexual behaviour and reproduction have been produced in sheep by Sykes and Cole (1944) as a result of experimental modification of the amount of light per 24 hours. Likewise, Yeates (1947, 1948, 1949a, 1954) found that by decreasing the length of daylight for Suffolk Border Leicester-Cheviot ewes, by placing them for appropriate times in a blacked-out pen, they were brought on heat in spring and had lambs, in some cases twins and triplets, in autumn, and that, conversely, an increase of light sent them into anoestrum. It would seem often to be less the absolute amount of light than the changes in extent of the exposure to light which governs the onset of reproductive activity (Hammond, 1944). In a long-term experiment—also with sheep—Yeates (1949a) successfully reversed the breeding season of ewes by gradually altering the daily rations of light each week, thus simulating fairly closely the slow but continuous changes which occur naturally. This treatment was effective for both males and females. Yeates (1949a, b) states that in grade Suffolk ewes the onset of the sexual season is a response to decreasing daily amounts of light and occurs 13 to 16 weeks after the change from increasing to decreasing length of day ; and that the cessation of the sexual season is a response to increasing daily amounts of light and occurs 14 to 19 weeks after change from decreasing to increasing length of day. Moreover, these responses took place irrespective of the level at which the change-over in trend of daily lighting occurs, and are also unrelated to " specific " thresholds of light. It is to be noted that while Anderson (1944) found that additional light at night had no effect on the oestrous cycle in zebras and grade cattle, Mercier and Salisbury (1947) showed that there was a statistical correlation of day-length with fertility in dairy cattle (*see* however Hafez, 1951a, b, c; Laing, 1955; Watson and Radford, 1955).

Finally, the case of the nocturnal animal in the wild state, which is compelled to spend daylight hours in the darkness of the burrow, should not be overlooked. The polecat, the wild ancestor of the domestic ferret, for example, usually emerges only at twilight and consequently its ration of light must be considerably reduced yet there is no reason to suppose that the broad pattern of the photoperiodic phenomenon differs in the wild and domestic races (Amoroso and Matthews, 1955). Similarly, in the ground squirrel, *Citellus tridecemlineatus*, full spermato-genesis occurs naturally in the darkness of the hibernation burrow (Wells and Zalesky, 1940). Whether darkness is stimulating in these cases may be debatable, but it can scarcely be inhibiting.

Smelser, Walton and Whetham (1934) found that rabbits showed equal mating response, ovulation and pseudopregnancy whether they were subjected to intense illumination or to total darkness. It must, however, be remembered that domestic rabbits if kept warm and well fed may breed all the year and have no sexual periodicity. That there is variation in passing from species to species is shown, too, in birds, for whereas the Adelie penguin in the Antarctic breeds in the warmest and lightest time of the year, the emperor penguin lays its eggs in the dark. Nubling (1941) states that the Australian Satin Bower-bird builds its bowers in May and June, whilst courtship and nidification also occur at a time of decreasing light. Nevertheless, Marshall (1954) holds that increasing light may be a factor in the breeding of these birds.

Animals, like plants are adapted in growth to the seasons, even at the equator, and a feature of the adaptation is the sensing of a favourable or an unfavourable season before it comes. In some species of mammals the gonads begin their annual development in winter before the days begin to lengthen, and in birds which migrate from the southern hemisphere to the northern the periodic enlarge-ment does not commence until shortly before the migration starts, the gonads remaining small during the long period of residence in the south when the daylight is very long (Rowan, 1938b). The periodic enlargement must be correlated with a reproductive rhythm which, nevertheless, is probably brought into some relation with seasonal changes by the influence of daylight—more especially just before breeding. That there may be inherent differences in the reproductive rhythm even in closely allied races is shown, for example, in the starling (Bullough, 1942). Thus, the gonads of adult British starlings begin to increase in early autumn; but those of the Continental race do not grow until January, and there are other variations. There are, however, undoubtedly some birds which breed in the autumn. Thus, Rooke (1935) describes the Newfoundland red crossbill, the white-winged crossbill and the Newfoundland grosbeak as having well-developed gonads in August, and probably breeding in Newfoundland in September.

Delayed Implantation of the Blastocyst

Seasonal changes in the duration of illumination not only affect the attainment of breeding condition, but may also control subsequent phases of the reproductive process. In many species of mammals the total length of gestation may be con-siderably longer than the period of embryonic development, and in the great majority the prolongation of pregnancy is due to the interpolation of a period of quiescence of the blastocyst which varies from a few weeks to over several months. This phenomenon of delayed implantation (*see* Table I) seems to be quite wide-spread among members of the *Mustelidae* and an interesting series of observations based on experiments on the pine marten and mink suggests that artificial illumination at the end of hours of daylight can hasten implantation, and so reduce the total

TABLE I

Distribution of Delayed Implantation in Mammals

Orders or Sub-orders	Families or Species	Authors
	Wallabies.	
Marsupialia	*Setonix brachyurus* *Protemnodon eugenii.*	Sharman (1955).
Xenarthra	Armadillo (*Dasypus*)	Patterson (1912, 1913); Hamlett (1932b, 1935); Talmage and Buchanan (1954); Talmage, Buchanan, Kraintz, Lazo-Wasem and Zarrow (1954); Buchanan, Enders and Talmage (1956).
Artiodactyla	Roe deer (*Capreolus*)	Harvey (1651); Ziegler (1843); Bischoff (1854); Retzius (1900); Keibel (1902); Prell (1938).
	Mustelids.	
Carnivora	European badger (*Meles meles*)	Fries (1880); Fischer (1931); Neal (1948); Harrison and Neal (1956, 1959); Neal and Harrison (1958); Mayer (1959a, b).
	American badger (*Taxidea americana*)	Hamlett (1932a).
	Marten (*Martes pinea*)	Prell (1927, 1931, 1938).
	Pine marten (*Martes americana*)	Wright (1942b).
	Western pine marten (*Martes caurina caurina*)	Marshall and Enders (1942).
	Siberian sable (*Martes Zibellina*)	Hamlett (1935).
	Stoat (*Mustela mustela*)	Watzka (1940); Deanesly (1943a).
	Long-tailed weasel (*Mustela frenata*)	Wright (1942a, b).
	Short-tailed weasel (*Mustela cicognani*)	Wright (1942a, b)
	Mink (*Mustela vison*)	Hansson (1947).

Orders or Sub-orders	Families or Species	Authors
Carnivora	*Seals.*	
	Fur seal	Enders, Pearson and Pearson (1946).
	(*Callorhinus ursinus*)	
	Elephant seal	Gibbney (1953).
	(*Mirounga Leopina*)	
	Harbour seal	Fisher (1954).
	(*Phoca vitulina*)	
	Grey seal	Backhouse and Hewer (1956, 1957).
	(*Halichoerus grypus*)	
	Bears.	
	Black bear	Hamlett (1935).
	(*Euarctos americanus*)	
	European brown bear	Hamlett (1935).
	(*Ursus arctos*)	Hamlett (1935).
	Grizzly bear	Hamlett (1935).
	(*Ursus horribilis*)	
	Polar bear	Hamlett (1935).
	(*Thalarctos maritinum*)	

duration of pregnancy (Enders and Pearson, 1943; Pearson and Enders, 1944; Hansson, 1947; Enders, 1952, 1956). *See also*, Eckstein, Shelesnyak and Amoroso, (1959).

The American marten, *Martes americana*, breeds in July and August and produces its young the following spring. Enders and Pearson (1943) have shown that by gradually increasing the light rations from September onwards, early implantation could be induced, the animals whelping in December instead of April. Similarly, the long-tailed weasel (Wright, 1942b) mates in summer and normally implants about March, but extra light in winter has reduced gestation by upwards of 100 days. Similarly, in the mink which mates in March, irradiation with ultra violet light in February led to a marked curtailment of gestation (Hansson, 1947). Pearson and Enders (1944), Hansson (1947) and Enders (1956) suggest that increasing day-length stimulates the pituitary to secrete hormones which in turn evoke the elaboration of ovarian substances essential to implantation. There seems little reason to doubt that the light effect is through the pituitary on the corpus luteum and that the uterus requires conditioning in some special way, not yet understood, before implantation may proceed (Mayer, 1959a). If we assume this much, the question remains as to the hormone responsible. Hammond (1951b) has shown that, in the mink at any rate, implantation is not simply a matter of the supply of progesterone. Accompanying implantation in this species, he postulates the presence of an extra-ovarian factor acting upon the uterus, and, clearly enough, its production or activity seems to be regulated by light. According to Yeates (1954) the existence of some such special uterotrophic hormone is suggested by, and probably accounts for, the fact that whereas implantation is satisfactory in ewes whose sexual season has been reversed by light treatment (Yeates, 1949a), it is also disappointing in those in which ovulation and oestrus have been induced by gonadotrophin injections during the anoestrum (Robinson, 1951).

TABLE II

Month in which due (336 days) to foal	Duration of the pregnancy (days)								
	Average −			Average	Average +				
	11 to 15	6 to 10	1 to 5	336	1 to 5	6 to 10	11 to 15	16 to 20	21 to 25
March 16–31								X	X
April 1–15									
April 16–30							X	X	
May 1–15				X	X	X X			
May 16–31									
June 1–15			X		X				
June 16–30	X	X	X						

This effect of light on the implantation has also been presumed in the horse, Hammond (1935) having found in England that mares due to foal early in the season (March) exceeded the average duration of pregnancy by 20 days, whereas those due to foal late (June) did so about 10 days under the average time. More recently, Howell and Rollins (1951) have analysed environmental sources of such variation in Arab mares and found that season of breeding accounted for 44 per cent of the total variance and level of nutrition for only 5 per cent. The implication is that some important environmental influence other than condition of the pasture is operating to produce the observed seasonal variation. Howell and Rollins (1951) suggest light as a cause, and, as with the mustelids, it is believed to exert its influence by regulating the time taken for the zygote to implant. (Table II). For further accounts of this and other related problems the interested reader should consult the papers by Lintvareva (1955a, b).

Gonadal and Antler Cycles

It is probable that the gonadal and antler cycles in deer are subject to regulation by light operating through the anterior pituitary. In the Virginia deer (*Odocoileus virginianus borealis*) in the latitude of New England, the testes are active in the autumn but the antlers, normally only developed by the male, start to grow in the spring (April) provided the rudiment has been previously sensitised by testis secretion. During late summer the antlers stop growing, they ripen, lose their velvet covering and become essentially dead organs. The shedding of the velvet depends upon the recrudescence of gonad activity and, thereafter, the antlers become dependent on the gonads (Wislocki, 1943; Wislocki, Aub and Waldo, 1947). After the fall rutting season is over, the antlers are shed, as a rule in mid-winter, at a period when the testes are regressing.

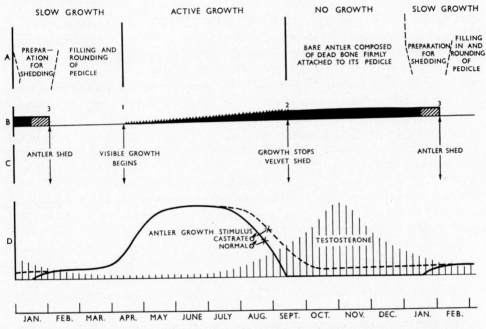

Fig. *13.3*—Diagrams relating the phases of the antler cycle to seasonal changes in hormone levels in male Virginia deer kept in captivity. (A) divides the cycle into three major phases consisting of periods of slow growth, active growth and inhibition of growth. The phase of slow growth is sub-divided to indicate the changes which occur prior to shedding of the antlers (preparation for shedding) and the growth which takes place following shedding and preceding the phase of grossly visible active growth. (B) represents the relative physical size of the antlers during each phase of the cycle. The numbers 1, 2 and 3 indicate the principal events of the cycle as designated below in (C). The thickness of the black bar indicates relative size of the antlers, the serrated upper border the presence of the velvet, and the shaded portion the occurrence of changes at the antler base in preparation for shedding. (D) illustrates our concept of the seasonal variations of the "antler-growth stimulus" (for normal males and castrates) and of testosterone. (From Waldo and Wislocki, 1951.)

From the observed relationships of the antler and gonadal cycles, Wislocki and his associates concluded that the maximal influence of the pituitary (spring and early summer) precedes the maximal influence of the testes (fall) by a number of months, so that as the pituitary influence is declining (late summer), the testicular stimulus is rising. In this predicated cycle, the pituitary gland presumably stimulates antler growth (late spring) and testicular growth (early summer), whereas the rising testosterone inhibits pituitary function (late summer and fall). The relationship of some of these seasonal phenomena are illustrated diagrammatically (Fig. *13.3*).

Statistical Studies

The general conclusion that light or ultra-violet irradiation is very generally a factor in breeding periodicity is reinforced by statistical studies of the times of breeding of the domestic animals. In view of the practice adopted by poultry-keepers of using artificial light to increase and extend the time of egg production, Whetham (1933) undertook a statistical investigation based on available records to ascertain if there were any relation between egg production and variation in daylight in different latitudes, and found that there was a correspondence which, though not absolute, was nevertheless definite, the stimulus for increased egg production in poultry being provided by the difference in the light ration and not by any particular amount of light. Similarly, in the case of horses (although in the more domestic breeds, i.e. in the "better bred" or more improved types, the dioestrous cycle may recur for a great part of the year) there is a definite tendency for foaling to occur in the spring. From the records obtained from the stud books of different countries, Hammond (1935) has constructed frequency curves with peaks showing when foaling was most common. In Canada, as with Britain, there is a very pronounced peak in May. In the United States, which extends far down towards the tropics, where the seasonal differences are less, there is for the whole country a definite peak also in May, but not so pronounced as in Canada. In Australia and New Zealand there are very marked peaks in October and November respectively, in the spring of these countries. In South Africa there are only slight peaks in September and again in November. In India, where, comparatively speaking, conditions are much more uniform, there is only a slight peak in March. The gestation period being eleven months, the service peaks are in all cases a month later than the foaling peaks. The results as a whole undoubtedly suggest a correlation between the sexual season and the incidence of daylight. Hammond noted that with the Shetland pony, which is comparatively primitive, the service and foaling peaks were more pronounced than with the more improved breeds, and this again is in conformity with the experience that the domestic animals tend to free themselves from external influences in regard to periodicity of breeding (cf. Hammond, 1940; also Moule, 1950).

In view of the facts recorded above it is clear that all animals have their own characteristic sexual rhythm but that this is probably, as a general rule, brought into relation with the seasons by the pituitary, which is played upon by external influences acting through the intermediation of the nervous system. One of the most important of these influences is the increase of daylight, while experiments have shown that ultra-violet irradiation in its prolonged effects may be even more potent than luminous rays. The ruminants (and some other animals) present a difficulty since they usually have their sexual season when daylight is decreasing. In view of the experiments on ferrets recorded above, it would seem possible, however, that this autumn season for reproductive activity is due partly at any rate to the protracted effects of ultra-violet irradiation experienced in the preceding summer. Further, the fact that the sexual season in sheep is later in the more northerly and southerly regions of the world (e.g. North Scotland, Iceland and Patagonia) is also suggestive of this cause, for the animals living in these areas might be expected to require a more extended interval from the time of the initial stimulus earlier in the year, before the cumulative effects of irradiation upon the pituitary were sufficient to stimulate the organ to full gonadotrophic activity. It is true, nevertheless, that some of Bissonnette's observations on the goat (1941), referred to above, do not apparently support this view.

An admirable review of the subject of seasonal rhythm in growth and metabolism, with a number of references, is given by Brody (1945) in his recent book on growth.

Quality and Quantity of Light

Other workers have confirmed and extended Rowan's observations on the stimulating action on the gonads of increasing periods of light. Thus, Bissonnette (1930a, 1931a, 1932b, 1933) and Bissonnette and Wadlund (1932), studying the European starling, and Benoit (1936, 1937 ; Benoit and Ott, 1944) the domestic duck, found that light of long wavelength was most effective for supplanting natural daylight and that green light exerted a definite inhibitory effect upon the gonads. In addition they found that intensity and wavelength as well as daily periods of light were important factors, and that although increased lighting induced sexual activity it would not maintain it indefinitely. An important aspect of Benoit's experiments is that he showed that there is a quantitative relation between the gonadal response of drakes and the duration and intensity of illumination, but that neither hypophysectomy nor shielding the eyes of normal birds prevented a response. According to Benoit, Walter and Assenmacher (1950), testis development was induced in immature male ducks by orange and red lights directed to the orbital region and by indigo, blue and yellow lights directed to the hypothalamus. In each treatment other colours were ineffective. However its effect is transmitted, light to produce an effect must first be absorbed. Consequently, this most astonishing result suggests the rather widespread presence of either receptors or of some light-sensitive pigment or pigments ; and in either case, a differential reaction to wavelength according to the locality of interaction.

In poultry, birds illuminated for 13 hours each day during the winter months responded equally well when irradiated with white, red, or white plus ultra violet light (Dobie, Carver and Roberts, 1946). Wolfson (1953) found, likewise, that in the white-throated sparrow there was increased reproductive response in the ovary and oviduct when the birds were subjected to a 6-hour cycle of light and darkness. This response was greater than in birds exposed continuously to 20 hours of illumination a day. It appears that in birds a light intensity of a certain rather feeble standard is essential for the full photoperiodic response ; increase beyond that point has no additive effect (Rowan, 1938b), but below that point the degree of gonadal development varies with the intensity used (Bissonnette, 1931b). Thus, starlings show progressive acceleration in the rate of testicular activation when irradiated from the same distance by bulbs of 10, 15, and 25 watts, but with bulbs of 40 watts and upwards, the progressive effects cease. Similar results have been obtained with poultry (Nicholas, Callenbach and Murphy, 1944 ; Dobie, Carver and Roberts, 1946). Furthermore, Baker (1937) has pointed out that the two breeding seasons which occur with certain species of birds in Ceylon and probably in other tropical countries may be accounted for by the greater intensity of irradiation (visible and ultra-violet) which is believed to exist at the two maxima in the year when the sun passes overhead (*see* p. 724).

The question as to whether the acceleration of the recurrence of the cycle in the ferret is brought about by general light and heat radiation or whether the effect is due to stimulation by definite portions of the spectrum was investigated by Marshall and Bowden (1934). It was found that for the ferret, heat rays and near infra-red were inactive. The effect began with the red radiation and extended throughout the visible to the near ultra-violet. Thus ferrets differ in their responses from starlings (*see* p. 743, and cf. Bissonnette, 1932b). Pairs of ferrets were subjected further to the same total quantity of radiation from incandescent lamps, but in one case it was concentrated into 2 hours, and in the other spread over 16 hours. The results were similar in each. The ferrets which were subjected to ultra-violet irradiation remained on heat for a longer period than the others, although the irradiation had for some months been discontinued; that is, they remained on heat into the autumn and for four or five months after irradiation ceased. This result occurred in 100 per cent of cases extending over 4 years. Thus, although irradiation with luminous rays in a few instances was followed by a prolonged oestrus, speaking generally ultra-violet irradiation caused a far more decided and prolonged effect which must be interpreted as one of increased activity on the part of the pituitary. In this connection it should be recalled that Bissonnette (1936b) found that the anterior pituitaries of stimulated ferrets underwent histological changes comparable to those of castrated animals, a condition which is usually regarded as an indication of hyperpituitarism. The excessive fertility of the marmosets at the Lister Institute, which were subjected to ultra-violet treatment as described by Lucas, Hume and Smith (1937) is also suggestive of hyperpituitarism. Similarly, Barbanti (1932) working with the field mouse, *Microtus agrestis*, found that red and yellow radiation stimulated sexual activity and the same is also true of Romney Marsh ewes in Portugal (Mies Filho and Ramos, 1954).

In all the experiments on ferrets, warmth may be ruled out as a factor in the periodicity—the controls as well as the results of infra-red radiation show this— while food may also be excluded since the irradiated ferrets ate no more than the normal animals. Moreover, increased movement (following upon the irradiation), of which there was little or no evidence, could not have been a factor, since ferrets kept under more natural conditions, as when employed for "rabbiting," do not come on heat before the usual season. A later investigation (Marshall, 1940) showed that with female ferrets subjected to different degrees of intensity of light irradiation, as measured by placing them at different distances from a 1000-watt lamp, the acceleration of the oestrous cycle was roughly correlated with the degree of intensity. Moreover, feeding vitamin D to anoestrous ferrets did not result in accelerating the cycle, the ferrets coming on heat at the normal time.

Photostimulation and Sexual Periodicity in lower Animals

Fishes

By methods of light control, breeding outside of the ordinary season has been induced in both fish and amphibians. With sticklebacks, by gradually increasing increments of artificial light, mating and nest-building with normally developing eggs have been brought about in January and February (long before the normal season) (Tinbergen, quoted by Rowan, 1938b). Hoover and Hubbard (1937) have induced spawning in the rainbow trout in December instead of March. Moreover, in the brook trout, which normally spawns in October–December, by first augmenting the light ration (in February) and later decreasing it, Hoover, has caused egg production in August.   Bullough (1939, 1941), working on the minnow (*Phoxinus laevis*), found that experimental darkness caused delay in ovarian development and slight retardation in testicular development.   He concludes that the breeding cycle, although governed by an internal rhythm, is regulated by external factors, especially light.

A photoperiodic control of pituitary function is indicated in experiments in which precocious sexual maturity has been achieved in a variety of fish by control of illumination (van den Eeckhoudt, 1947 ; Harrington, 1950 ; Hazard and Eddy, 1951).   There is, moreover, ample morphological evidence for direct nervous connections between the different peripheral sense organs and the pituitary (Bretschneider and Duyvene de Wit, 1947 ; Metuzals, 1952).   Craig-Bennett (1931) did not find that light or food had any effect on the reproductive cycle of *Gasterosteus*.   However, it has been shown subsequently that appropriate changes in illumination may induce rapid development of eggs and the appearance of male secondary sex characters at a season when the gonads are normally quiescent (van den Eeckhoudt, 1947), and it seems probable that a photoperiodic control exists here as in many other vertebrates.

Illumination is by no means the only seasonal variable controlling reproduction of fish.   In *Fundulus* (Matthews, 1938) and *Gambusia* (Medlen, 1951) light was found to play a minor role, while temperature dominated the sexual cycle.   Precipitation (von Ihering, 1935) and chemicals (Bretschneider and Duyvene de Wit, 1947) may likewise induce sexual development and spawning, but it is not known whether these effects are mediated through the pituitary or whether the environmental variables act directly by releasing behaviour patterns.

Amphibia

March (1937) has shown that augmented lighting can induce breeding in frogs (cf. Zwarenstein and Shapiro, 1933, for Cape clawed toad).   Berk (1938), however, states that rainfall and more especially temperature are the chief determining factors for breeding in *Xenopus laevis*.   He describes three phases in the normal cycle, the incidence of which is correlated with these factors.   Berk expresses the view that the anterior pituitary controls the cycle, the external factors acting on the pituitary.   Alexander and Bellerby (1935, 1938), however, obtained evidence that ovarian growth and regression in *Xenopus* depends upon fluctuations in food supply or water.   Bellerby (1938) found that light, or, alternatively, darkness had no effect and that eyeless toads developed their gonads and bred normally.   The fact that such animals can have a breeding periodicity with alternating periods of rest and activity is not contrary to the view that the periodicity is normally brought into relation to the environment by external stimuli acting through the pituitary. It must be mentioned, however, that Parhon and Coban (1935) state that four blinded drakes attained sexual maturity more rapidly than the controls.   This is contrary to the result of comparable experiments of Benoit (1935a).

Maxwell Savage (1935) concludes that the environmental change which controls the breeding behaviour of the common frog is mainly rainfall which influences the phosphate content of the water, and this in turn influences the algal cycle,

2B*

which provides the definitive stimuli. On the other hand, Spaul (quoted from Rowan, 1938b) induced breeding in common frogs, newts and salamanders by long-continued illumination (as contrasted with controls), as well as in minnows during the autumn and winter. Spaul (1930) and Kerr (1940), as a result of their histological investigations of the pituitaries of lower vertebrates, state that they justify the view that the gland has responsibilities in the adjustment between internal and external environments.

Tuchmann-Duplessis (1945) found increased development of the secondary sexual characters and weak stimulation of the testes when male *Triturus* were artificially illuminated from 2 to 4 hours daily in January. However, he pointed out that these results required cautious interpretation, as any increase in environmental temperature caused by the light source would have led to a similar result.

Reptiles

The reproductive responses to light by the various kinds of reptiles which have been studied are by no means uniform. For a review of the literature on photoperiodism in cold-blooded vertebrates, see Merriman and Schedl (1941).

In the horned lizard, *Phrynosoma cornutum*, Mellish (1936) reported that exposure to continuous light and a temperature of 35°C for approximately 2 months during the winter caused only slightly greater testicular development than normally occurred during hibernation in the same season. On the other hand, Bartholomew (1950) who investigated the effects of light and temperature on the reproductive cycle of a small viviparous lizard, *Xanthusia vigilis*, found that neither males nor females exposed to normal day length showed significant gonadal acceleration whether kept at 19°–23°C or 30°–32°C. But both males and females kept at 19°–23°C and exposed to 16 hours light, alternating with 8 hours darkness, showed marked unseasonal gonadal development; maintenance for 2 to 5 months on a day length reduced to 8 hours light alternating with 16 hour darkness, did not inhibit the testicular cycle of animals kept at 19°–23°C. Bartholomew suggests that light may reinforce the internally controlled reproductive rhythm rather than act as the primary controller of the season of reproduction.

Burger (1937) reported that in the turtle, *Pseudemys elegans*, an artificial increase of day length started during the middle of November inhibited the spermatogenic cycle already in progress and induced the initiation of a new cycle. Similarly, Clausen and Poris (1937) found that the daily addition of 6 hours of light starting on 25th November, and continuing for 50 days, had a marked stimulatory effect on spermatogenesis in the American chameleon, *Anolis carolinensis*. Pearse (1939) also describes the action of light in accelerating or controlling breeding in *Anolis*, as well as in other reptiles, fish and invertebrates, and Evans and Clapp (1940) concur, stating that active spermatogenesis occurs in response to stimulation by light.

Finally, Baker (1947) reported that on the island of Espiritu Santo in the New Hebrides, where seasonal changes in temperature and rainfall are remarkably small and the difference between the longest and the shortest days of the year is only 1 hour 48 minutes, the season of maximal reproductive activity of two species of lizards of the genus *Emoia* coincides with the period of longest days, while the season of minimal reproductive activity coincides with the period of shortest days.

It remains, therefore, an outstanding fact that in nearly all animals with a sexual periodicity, breeding phenomena occur in response to seasonal change, and in the majority of these (but not in all), as shown by observations under both natural and experimental conditions, the principal stimulus is increase of light. Changes in temperature and food are generally eliminated by control observations, though in some cases these factors not merely condition the phenomena, but play a part in determining the sexual cycle.

The Mode of Action of Light

It is now generally recognised that the pituitary gland is a mediating structure in the light-gonad response (Hill and Parkes, 1933 ; Marshall, 1936, 1937 ; Rowan, 1938b ; Donovan and Harris, 1954, 1955, 1956) ; but the means by which light stimuli are transmitted to the pituitary remains controversial. Certain experiments made with the ferret indicate that the eyes are the avenues of reception of light (Bissonnette, 1932a, 1935a, b, 1938a, b); that after hypophysectomy, female ferrets do not come on heat even though they are artificially irradiated (Hill and Parkes, 1933) ; and that the initial mechanism in the transference of light stimuli from the eye to the hypophysis is a nervous one (Thomson, 1951). In birds, on the other hand, Benoit and his associates (Benoit, 1935a, b, c, d, e ; Benoit and Ott, 1944, and Benoit, Assenmacher and Walter, 1950a, b, 1952, 1953; and Benoit, Assenmacher and Manuel, 1953) advance evidence that the eyes are dispensable. By ingenious experimentation they have shown that the hypothalamus, as well as the retina, can be influenced by direct lighting. Light, they believe, stimulates the retina, which stimulates the hypothalamus; light may also stimulate the hypothalamus directly by penetration through the tissues of the orbit. When the hypothalamus is excited in these two ways, it stimulates the pars distalis of the hypophysis, probably through a neuro-humoral mechanism. It was shown, moreover, that whereas light would normally reach the brain *in vivo*, it was not a necessary stimulus for the complete development of the duck's gonads ; but when present, light enhances this development.

Unlike the duck, the ferret does not respond to light after the optic nerves have been cut, the animal still displaying an inherent sexual cycle which is independent of light and hence does not progress in accordance with seasonal changes. Marshall and Bowden (1934) found that ferrets subjected to incomplete darkness did not come on heat, but individuals which had already begun to come on heat entered into full oestrus and remained in that state for a normal period. A blind ferret (with cataract) did not come on heat at all, although kept under observation for 2 years, during which time it was apparently healthy and fed well. Hill and Parkes (1934), however, found that in ferrets subjected to darkness there was, on the average, some lag in the times of onset of oestrus but this was slight. Bissonnette (1935b), on the other hand, found that by employing hoods or curtains or otherwise reducing the light received, there was a definite arrest of the cycle ; that with ferrets already on light, treatment by darkness led to regression ; and that in general the onset and duration of oestrus could be regulated artificially by changes in the duration and intensity of the light to which the ferrets were exposed. Further, Bissonnette (1936a, b) found that severing the optic nerves of ferrets frees the cycle from the influence of the seasons and sexual activity can occur at abnormal times (June to November or July to December instead of March to August). Clark,

McKeown and Zuckerman (1937, 1939) also found that ferrets whose optic nerves had been divided did not come on heat at all, or did so much later than the control animals. Burkhardt (1947), also, observed that mares, if hooded, were unresponsive to additional lighting in winter and blind white-footed mice apparently do not exhibit any seasonal cyclic tendency to breeding activity.

Since the integrity of the optic nerves appears to be essential to the response of the ferret's gonad to light, the problem has been to discover whether nerve fibres from the optic pathway enter the anterior lobe of the pituitary. The experiments of Clark, McKeown and Zuckerman (1939) failed to provide the answer to this specific question, but led to the conclusion that although the integrity of the optic nerve is necessary, neither the visual cortex nor the mid-brain is essential to the gonadal-light response in the ferret.

These investigators say that (unless a few isolated normal cells in the dorsal nucleus of the lateral geniculate body provide the basis for adequate cortical stimulation) a normal response can occur in the combined absence of the visual cortex and the superior colliculi, while another experiment strongly suggested that it can occur even after the interruption of retinal impulses passing to the dorsal nucleus of the lateral geniculate body, visual cortex, superior colliculi and pretectal area. This being so, the conclusion is suggested that the visual response depends on impulses either to the ventral nucleus of the lateral geniculate body, or to the subthalamus by way of the accessory optic tracts. However, Jefferson (1940) could find no histological evidence for the presence of the accessory optic tracts in the ferret, or for fibre connections between the optic tracts and the ventral nucleus of the lateral geniculate body. Jefferson suggested that the gonadal stimulation by extra light rations in the ferret might be an indirect response dependent on changes in the total bodily activity. However, as already stated, this is unlikely. From time to time reports appear describing optic nerve fibres terminating in the hypothalamus. Thus, Frey (1951) has described a hypothalamic optic root in the dog and other forms, but such an account requires confirmation in the ferret.

There is some doubt as to whether the axons of hypothalamic neurons actually innervate the anterior lobe of the pituitary as has been suggested by Bretschneider and Duyvene de Wit (1947), Metuzals (1952, 1954, 1955), Vasquez-Lopez and Williams (1952), and Vasquez-Lopez (1953). On the other hand, there is little doubt that the visual stimuli are conveyed to the anterior pituitary through the central nervous system and that a close physiological relationship exists between the hypothalamus and the pars distalis of the pituitary. Since the discovery of the relationship of the hypophysial-portal system to the hypothalamus (Popa and Fielding, 1930, 1933 ; Houssay, Biasotti and Sammartino, 1935 ; Wislocki, 1937 ; Green and Harris, 1947 ; Harris, 1948a ; Green, 1952), Harris and his collaborators, in several publications (Harris, 1948b, 1950b, 1952, 1955a; Harris and Jacobsohn 1952; Donovan and Harris, 1954, 1955, 1956), have advanced the view that in mammals the proximate stimulus for the specific activation of the secretory cells of the pituitary gland is a chemical substance which is discharged from certain hypothalamic neurons that constitute a specific "sex centre" (Markee, Everett and Sawyer, 1952). This chemo-transmitter substance passes down the axons and diffuses into the capillary loops of the hypophysial portal vessels (Green and Harris, 1947), whence it passes into the sinusoids of the anterior lobe (Harris and

Jacobsohn, 1952; Worthington, 1955; Engelhardt, 1956; Long, 1956). A great deal of most stimulating work by Benoit and his collaborators and others on the duck (Benoit and Assenmacher, 1953 ; Wingstrand, 1951) seems directly to support the hypothesis of Green and Harris (1947). It must be pointed out, however, that Zuckerman and his co-workers (Zuckerman, 1954a, b; 1955a, b; Thomson and Zuckerman, 1954, 1955) are unyielding in their views that the timing mechanism which regulates the phasing of the gonadotrophic action of the anterior lobe is independent of the integrity of the hypophysial portal circulation, and " these vessels are neither a sufficient explanation of, nor necessary for, certain of the responses in question " (Zuckerman, 1955b).

Regardless of these considerations the neuro-humoral-pituitary portal system hypothesis is widely accepted. However, the possibility that the hypothalamus may exert an inhibitory influence over the adenohypophysis must not be overlooked. Thus, it has been observed that bilateral lesions placed in the anterior region of the hypothalamus of female ferrets may be followed by the development of oestrus in the winter months of the year ; that is, at a time of the year when animals would normally be in anoestrus (Donovan and van der Werff ten Bosch, 1956a, b). The possibility that this is a result of some stimulating effect of the lesion is unlikely since prolonged electrical stimulation of this area of the hypothalamus in other animals did not result in oestrus. Consequently, the possibility that the lesion has abolished some inhibitory influence, with consequent release of some excitatory mechanism, must be presumed. (*See also* Donovan and van der Werff ten Bosch 1959a, b.)

If we concede that, in the domestic duck, light pinpointed through a glass rod on various brain regions produced effects in the hypothalamus, but not on the supposed visual area of the cortex, leading to an acceleration of gonadal recrudescence (Benoit and Kehl, 1939 ; Benoit, Walter and Assenmacher, 1950 ; Benoit, Assenmacher and Walter, 1953), it is tempting to surmise that the acceleration of the gonadal recrudescence might be related to the presence in nervous tissue of characteristic porphyrins (Parker, Hendricks, Borthwick and Jenner, 1952). These porphyrins, it is suggested, might be concerned—by virtue of their supposed photochemical reactivity to particular radiations—with light activation of the pituitary. In any case, we must surely believe that between the afferent pathways from various exteroceptors (visual, auditory, tactile, thermic and possibly olfactory organs in some sea-birds (Wood Jones, 1937)), and proprioceptors (e.g. in regard to hunger and other influences) and the median eminence, there are also analysing and correlating centres, which, in conditions normal for the wild bird, receive, integrate and act upon the effects of such stimuli.

The foregoing discussion has been based on the assumption that light, received by the eye or possibly some region close to it, regulates the seasonal activity of the pituitary of photoperiodically regulated animals. However, an action of darkness, as well as light, is suggested by the work of Hammond (1951a), who found that ferrets exposed to 14 hours constant light daily come into oestrus sooner than those exposed to 24 hours light daily. The latter group were in fact little ahead of what would have been expected in daylight. The studies of Hart (1951) in the ferret, alluded to previously, also indicate that the total daily quantity of light is not the controlling factor in accelerating oestrus during the winter months, but that a long-light–short-dark sequence each day produces the maximum acceleration.

It would thus appear that to induce an out-of-season oestrous state in female ferrets extra light is essential but not to the extent of eliminating darkness altogether; a light–dark sequence is of importance (*see also* Yeates, 1949a, b).

The view that light acts only indirectly by modifying the activity of birds is advanced by Rowan (1928, 1938a, b). He supposes that light is concerned only in so far as it provides a means of keeping the animals awake, and that stimulation of the pituitary is effected by changes in metabolism induced by lengthening the period of diurnal activity. Thus he states that gonadal development has been induced in birds submitted to enforced wakefulness in light below the intensity required to induce sexual development. He suggests, moreover, that failure of hooded and blinded animals to respond to light is simply due to their failure to be wakeful for long enough. On the other hand, if such blinded or hooded animals are kept in the same enclosures as unblinded individuals the gonads of all develop at the same rate. This, Rowan suggests, is because the blinded animals have wakefulness enforced on them by their unblinded companions. It has been pointed out by several investigators that the onset of sexual activity cannot be due simply to increased physical exercise and movement (Marshall and Bowden, 1934; Bissonnette, 1936a, b; Burkhardt, 1947). Indeed, Benoit (1935b) has shown that birds trussed so that free movement was impossible, reacted just as quickly to increased lighting as did birds receiving similar light but permitted complete freedom. Nevertheless, Rowan (1938b) insists that although muscular activity might be reduced to a minimum under these circumstances, it does not affect his argument that wakefulness, rather than light as such, might be the important factor.

It has sometimes been suggested—particularly in the case of poultry—that the changes induced by increasing the photoperiods are due to the longer day available for feeding (Fairbanks and Rice, 1924). However, Callenbach, Nicholas and Murphy (1943), who investigated the effect of light and feeding on egg production, state that whereas increased exposure to light during the period of decreasing day-length resulted in superior production, availability of food had no observable influence. Likewise, it has been stated that in light experiments with farm animals, food supply could have had no bearing on the observed differences in reproductive activity, since the quantity of feed supplied to control and experimental animals has generally been stated to be the same (Yeates, 1954, p. 384). On the other hand, it has been shown, in the laboratory, that quality, not merely bulk, in food is necessary for photostimulated starlings to produce spermatozoa (Bissonnette, 1933), and Breneman (1942) seems to have shown that limitation of food led to a diminution of basophil cells in the pituitary. It is of interest in this connection that the effect of an inadequate diet on the reproductive capacity of the rat may be compensated by extra lighting or, conversely, that rats may breed efficiently under conditions of shortened illumination provided that the diet is adequate (Alexander and Frazer, 1952), suggesting that the effects of certain dietary variations on the reproductive system may, as in the case of light, be mediated through the central nervous system and the pituitary gland. This view receives further support from the fact that the ovarian atrophy which follows starvation in female rats may be repaired by administration of anterior pituitary extract or PMSG (Werner, 1939). For a fuller discussion of the relationship of nutrition to endocrine-reproductive functions (*see* Stroink, 1947; Meites, 1953).

In drawing conclusions regarding the mode of action of light it may be said in summary that at the moment it seems likely that light acts by way of the optic-nerve fibres, which transmit a stimulus in some way to the hypothalamus, trans-mission to the pituitary being completed in both birds and mammals by a humoral relay involving the hypophysial portal blood-vessels (Harris, 1955a, b, c, 1956; Benoit and Assenmacher, 1955). This view is strengthened by the recent finding of Thomson (1954), which is in agreement with that of previous investigators, that the gonadal response to light in ferrets depends on the integrity of the ganglion-cell layer of the retina and by his conclusion that the initial mechanism in the transference of light stimuli from the eye to the hypophysis is a nervous one. Harris (1955a), however, criticises Thomson's experimental data on the ground that the techniques employed to blind the animals are unsatisfactory. He points out, moreover, that from a consideration of the neuro-anatomy of the visual path-way there is no reason to believe that animals subjected to either midline sagittal section through the optic chiasma, or incision between the posterior margin of the optic chiasma and the anterior limit of the hypothalamus, would be blinded. On the other hand, Donovan and Harris (1954, 1955, 1956) report perfect correlation between regeneration of portal vessels and light-induced oestrus in the ferret. Nevertheless, there are sceptics (Thomson and Zuckerman, 1955; Zuckerman, 1955a, b; Eckstein and Zuckerman, 1955, 1956; Gaupp and Spatz, 1955), and the theory of direct innervation of anterior lobe gland cells still has a champion in Metuzals (1952, 1954, 1955).

Evidence that light is really able to penetrate through the tissues and stimulate specific deep photoreceptors in the hypothalamus is strengthened by the demon-stration by Benoit and his associates that (i) a fiftieth of the externally applied amount of red rays (as measured by photographic and photocell methods) penetrate the hypothalamus and that the sensitivity to light of the hypothalamus itself is higher than that of the retina, and (ii) that in normal conditions, light may stimu-late simultaneously two photoreceptors, the retina and the nervous centres located in the hypothalamus (Benoit, 1955a).

The view that light provides a means of keeping birds awake and that stimu-lation of the pituitary is effected by changes in metabolism induced by lengthen-ing the period of diurnal activity has gained few adherents. On the other hand, further evidence for the view that the beneficial effects of increased illumination in poultry might be brought about by increasing the opportunity for increased food uptake, is provided by the shepherd's practice of " flushing " ewes pre-paratory to tupping. This practice consists in supplying the ewes with extra food which is thought to hasten forward the sexual season and to increase the crop of lambs (Heape, 1899 ; Marshall, 1905a) ; " not only the level of nutrition at and before the time of mating but also changes in this level may have a considerable effect on the frequency of twins " (Reeve and Robertson, 1953).

Absence of Light and Its Effects

Most of the experimental work considered thus far focuses attention almost entirely on the light period. This is not surprising for this feature of the environ-ment is most evident to man and there is, in consequence, a predilection for supposing that photoperiodic responses are determined by the length of the light period. On the other hand, there is good reason for believing that the length of the dark period, too, has an effect as is indicated by the results of Hammond, Jnr. (1951a) who found that ferrets, subjected to 14 hours of constant light daily and 10 hours of darkness, came into breeding condition sooner than those subjected to 24 hours of light daily. The experiment was useful, too, in showing that the latter treatment was only slightly more effective in inducing oestrus than would have been the case with daylight.

The effectiveness of the dark period is best shown by its interruption with short light periods. One such quantitative study is that of Jenner (1951) who reported that the pulmonate snail, *Limnaea palustris*, shows a well-defined photoperiodic response in regard to ovulation. In this animal the gonad apparently contains fully formed eggs at all times, once the snail has attained a certain size. On a 13·5 hour photo-period or longer, egg laying was initiated and egg production was maintained over an extended period of time, but on a cycle of 11-hour light, alternating with 13-hour dark periods, it was long delayed. If, however, to a short-day (9-hour photoperiods), was added an interval of 1 hour illumination to break up the accompanying 15-hour dark period, it stimulated egg laying, showing that the time dependent phase of the photoperiodic response occurs during the dark.

Interruption of dark periods by short periods of light has also been shown to be effective in controlling the photoperiodic responses of some mammals (including the ferret) and birds. Thus, Hart (1951) found that reproductive activity could be greatly accelerated in female ferrets by subjecting them to an additional hour of light in the middle of long dark periods thus emphasizing the importance of the light-dark contrast sequences in producing the maximum acceleration of gonadal responses. Interruptions of long nights have likewise promoted sexual activity in bobwhite quail (Kirkpatrick and Leopold, 1952) and sparrows (Burger, Bissonnette and Doolittle, 1942; Farner, Mewaldt and Irving, 1953a, b) but delayed that in sheep (Hart, 1950), for although the treatment induced oestrus in the ewes, Hart was unable to obtain out-of-season lambs. It must be realized, however, that a great number of combinations of light–dark sequences was not possible because of the difficulty in having large numbers of animals.

In the male starling, *Sturnus vulgaris*, Burger, Bissonnette and Doolittle (1942), observed that flashing lights (of 0·9 sec. or greater duration) interrupting the evening dark period, led to sexual development of the testes. Similarly, Kirkpatrick and Leopold (1952) and Jenner and Engels (1952) working with bobwhite quails found that the breaking-up of the dark period with light led to a greater spermatogenic response than that obtained with the same amount of uninterrupted light. These authors believe that the dark period is an important regulatory factor. Farner, Mewaldt and Irving (1953a, b) have, likewise, broken the dark period in a variety of ways and obtained differential gonad responses. They, however, share Hammond's, (1953a) and Marshall's (1955) scepticism that darkness has an active role.

An action of darkness is further suggested by results from experiments of Vaugien (cited by Benoit and Assenmacher, 1953) who found that total darkness for several weeks allowed a more rapid maturation of the gonads of immature budgerigars (*Melopsittacus*) than those of illuminated controls. Furthermore, the testes of controls became bigger when the birds were put in the dark. An active role is, however, denied by Marshall (1955) who points out that the only reliable evidence concerning its natural breeding habits suggests that in its arid, inland environment of spasmodic rainfall, the budgerigar delays reproduction until the growth of grass after rain (Serventy and Whittell, 1951). Thus, it breeds irrespective of the differential length of day and night.

Although the data do not belong strictly in the category now under consideration, it is interesting to note, in passing, that certain observations made by Shull (1929) show clearly that in certain aphids, the production of winged offspring from wingless females required a period of darkness, the optimum being 12–14 hours. On the other hand, dark periods shorter than 12 hours, rather than long light periods, were required for further parthenogenetic reproduction as wingless forms.

In the case of plants it is well known that a very long night either stimulates or inhibits reproduction when applied to short-day or long-day species, respectively. Plant photoperiodism is reviewed by Leopold (1951) and by Borthwick, Hendricks and Parker (1956).

VI. The Influence of Temperature and Rainfall on Sexual Rhythms

Temperature

It has long been assumed that high environmental temperatures are deleterious to both physiological and mental activity, and there is little doubt that, in many captive or domesticated mammals, reproductive efficiency is impaired and that fertility is minimal during the summer months. On the other hand, Farner and Mewaldt (1952) and Farner, Mewaldt and Irving (1953a) have shown that high environmental temperature results in considerable nocturnal activity of the white-crowned sparrow, such warmth augmenting the gonad-stimulating effect of artificially long days. Birds receiving extra illumination in the cold, however, showed far greater gonadal (testicular) development than did others on warmth and diminished rations of light, although the total duration of activity in the latter group was far greater than in the former. The possible influence of external temperature on the reproductive cycle in birds is emphasized by Kendeigh (1934). He regards this climatological factor as particularly important in causing the extensive metabolic change which is believed to be responsible for migratory behaviour in birds. For an account of thermo-regulation of sexual cycles in vertebrates, *see* Galgano and Mazzi (1951).

Similarly, Marshall (1949b) compared the state of the gonads and breeding activities of several species of passerine birds after the severe British winter of 1946–7, with that after the very mild one of 1947–8. He found that, despite the arrested development at the primary spermatocyte stage in mid-March 1947, at least three species bred at about the normal time, following a sharp rise in temperature and an increase of sunshine in April. Following the abnormally warm winter of 1947–8, three, and probably four, species bred abnormally early. He concludes that proximate factors, other than the number of hours of daylight and resultant activity, are significant in timing the breeding seasons of birds, and that temperature and sunshine may play an important part in some species. The same author (1952a) finds that the post-nuptial display of the robin and the rook is partly or almost wholly extinguished in normally severe December weather, but the pre-nuptial display following this is governed by the week-to-week environmental experiences, including the behaviour reactions of the pair. Sunshine, as opposed to mere lengthening days, is a potent stimulus; excessively dull cold weather and hunger are inhibitors. Marshall (1952b) also found that the gonads of migratory passerine birds showed considerable activity on the arrival of the birds in England, and he ascribed to this activity the singing of these birds while on passage. The stomach contents showed that the birds had paused to feed on their journey north, yet, despite the advanced condition of their gonads, they had continued their flight instead of taking up territory and breeding at some suitable locality on the way. Marshall (1952c) concluded that, among non-breeding birds of the Arctic, in the summer the gonad cycle of non-breeders of both sexes does not develop to its full extent because the environment does not present to the exteroceptors the appropriate stimuli, including behaviour, reactions to which each species has evolved its own neuro-endocrine response.

Temperature may affect the endocrine activity and, therefore, behaviour of constant breeders (Steinach and Kammerer, 1920) and in some animals it seems to be more important than light. In the male ground-squirrel investigated by Wells (1935, 1936) and Wells and Zalesky (1940), gonadal development is not modified under laboratory conditions by extra illumination, and animals maintained at laboratory temperatures experience practically the same seasonal cycle as those under field conditions. In the wild state, testicular regression is associated with rising summer temperatures, whereas seasonal activation coincides with the diminishing temperatures of autumn and winter. Further proof that temperature does have a marked effect on testicular rehabilitation is given by the observation that breeding males kept at 40° F.($t°$F. $= \frac{5}{9}(t-32)$ C)° for one year remain in breeding condition throughout this period, the sexually quiescent phase of the cycle failing to appear (cf. Zalesky and Wells, 1940). In the experimental squirrels the adrenals showed a highly developed cortex as in normal squirrels at the breeding season. Also Erb and Waldo (1952), reviewing the evidence relating to dairy cattle, concluded that in areas where high environmental temperatures are common during a portion of the year, breeding efficiency declines in summer. The summer depression in the production of both milk and butter fat has, likewise, been known for a long time.

Similarly observation on the low birth-weight of lambs following a summer gestation (made possible by light treatment), has led to the recent finding (Yeates, 1953) that high environmental temperature, though having no effect on the incidence of oestrus, may be inimical to satisfactory gestation in the ewe.

Although in the great majority of British breeds, ewes come into heat only in autumn and winter, it is very generally agreed that rams do not have the definite rutting season of the stag. Nevertheless, it has been shown that rams possess better semen, and are, therefore, presumably of higher potential fertility at certain times of the year than at others. Thus, McKenzie and Berliner (1937), in their study of Shropshire and Hampshire rams observed distinct periods of increased spermatogenesis in both breeds, that for the Shropshire being from October to January, and of the Hampshire from August to January, both under American conditions. Similarly, Gunn, Sanders and Granger (1942) in Australia, recorded seasonal changes in the semen of Merino and British breeds corresponding to changes in atmospheric temperature; hot weather (90°–100°F) caused seminal degeneration, and cooler weather favoured recovery. So striking indeed were the changes that Gunn believes it probable that in the hotter districts of Australia rams may become temporarily impotent simply because of the heat. (*See also* Mercier and Salisbury, 1946.)

It is of interest that a low environmental temperature may affect gonadal activity in several ways. Thus, Rice (1942) observes that Shropshire and Hampshire rams show regular waves of libido which are more closely related to cooler seasonal periods than to spermatogenic cycles. Similarly, for red deer there is a well-attested belief that a fall of temperature is essential to bring the animals into their full autumn rut (Marshall, 1937), and Dutt and Bush (1955) have shown that artificially maintained low environmental temperatures in summer advanced oestrus some 8 weeks in ewes. On this point, however, McKenzie and Phillips (1933) found that experimental lowering of the surrounding temperature had no effect in bringing ewes on heat. Likewise, Parkes (1924–5) states that mice subjected to normal outdoor temperatures do not breed from November to February, whereas, when the same individuals are kept in heated laboratories, they reproduce 12 months of the year. On the other hand, according to Lee (1926) and Denison and Zarrow (1955) the effect of a low environmental temperature under controlled lighting conditions, is to lengthen the oestrous cycle in the rat by prolonging the proestrous and oestrous stages, and this probably indicates a state of lowered gonadal activity. This is denied by Soliman and Abd-el-Malek (1959).

In general, however, environmental temperature seems to play only a minor role in sexual reproduction in warm-blooded vertebrates. The striking response of egg laying at temperatures far below $0°C$ on artificially lengthened winter days in Rowan's earliest experiments (1926), as well as the later investigations with pheasants (Bissonnette and Csech, 1941), emphasised dark period rather than temperature as a controlling factor (cf. Blanchard, 1941).

In the killifish (*Fundulus heteroclitus*) the testes normally involute at the close of the breeding season, but Burger (1939c) finds that if the water temperature is artificially lowered the process of gonadal regression is markedly retarded. Again, the female African salamandrid, *Pleurodeles waltl*, can be induced to lay eggs, under laboratory conditions, if she is placed in an ice-box overnight and transferred to a breeding tank at room temperature the following morning (Noble, 1931). Similarly, by maintaining a constant temperature throughout the year, Branin (1935) found that spermatogenesis could be made to continue in the four-toed salamander for twelve months. In the toad *Bufo cognatus*, Bragg (1940) found that breeding only occurred if the temperature was above $12°$ C., and then only in rain. In contrast, males of *Bufo woodhousii woodhousii* may become sexually active in dry weather, and will " seek the females," provided—and this is interesting —the toad can find water from which to call.

There is as yet little or no evidence to show how rainfall may induce pituitary activation, but it is of interest to consider the possible role of temperature more closely. Houssay (1947) states that ovulation was obtained in *Bufo arenarum* by pituitary injection when the temperature was between $16°$ and $35°$ C. but did not occur at $0°$, $4°$ and $10°$ C. This would imply that gonadotrophins are ineffective at low temperatures. On the other hand, Rugh (1935) investigated the effect of varying temperature on induced ovulation in *Rana pipiens* in some detail. The total number of eggs leaving the ovary at $5·5°$ C. was the same as at $22°$ C. after injection with equal amounts of anterior-pituitary extract, but eggs reached the uterus only after approximately 200 hours at the lower, instead of 24 hours at the higher temperature. If temperature is a controlling factor in the occurrence of natural ovulation in *B. arenarum*, it must be due to an inhibitory effect of low temperature on the release of gonadotrophins from the anterior pituitary.

Apart from some of Rowan's observations there is little indication that increased exercise accelerates gonadal activity and with mammals there is no such evidence. It is certain, however, that sexual activity and oestrus may be modified by external stimuli of various kinds, and in some cases may be increased.[1] Thus, Britt (1941) states that air blast and noise might modify and increase the number of oestrous cycles in the rat, and Farris and Yeakel (1944) found that air blasted daily for 5 minutes for five days increased the pregnancies by 30 per cent, but depressed the maternal behaviour of the rats at parturition.

Among birds, the deterrent effect of song on other males is shown by Lack's (1939b) notes on a robin:

" Song advertises ownership of territory, as propounded by Howard, and, like posturing, often replaces fighting. For instance, on May 27th, 1936, an unringed newcomer started to sing in the corner of a territory owned by male 44. Male 44, then in the opposite corner, promptly sang, the newcomer (which could not yet be aware that it was in occupied territory) sang again, the owner replied from nearer, the newcomer again sang, and this procedure was repeated twice more, the owner finally answering from only about fifteen yards away, still hidden in thick bushes. At this the newcomer fled, from an opponent it never saw, and did not appear again."

Rainfall and Drought

Many authors have considered alternative factors which might initiate breeding cycles in various parts of the world, where the light hypothesis appeared either inadequate or unsatisfactory. Thus, Ingram (1907), Hill (1913), Barnard (1914), White (1921), Alexander (1923), Whitlock (1924) and Fisher (1939) suggest that in deserts, or even in relatively well-watered areas, the sexual cycles of vertebrates may be inhibited by drought and stimulated to sudden activity by rainfall (or its effects) irrespective of season and the movement of the sun. Likewise, Baker (1929, 1938a, b) and Marshall and Disney (1956) emphasised the importance of rain as one such regulating factor of nesting seasons in non-migratory tropical birds (e.g. *Quelea quelea*), and Bannerman (1930–1939) and Moreau (1951) have shown how closely the breeding seasons in tropical birds appears to be determined by the recurrence of rains and not only in the semi-arid regions in Africa. Lack (1950) has demonstrated the same fact for several Galapagos birds (*Geopspize*) many of which breed from mid-December to April during the wet season when in a wild state near the equator. Serventy and Whittell (1948) and Serventy and Marshall (1957), too, showed that although most South-Western and Western Australian birds nested in the spring, and hence might appear to be stimulated by

---

[1] There can be no doubt that periodicity in migration, as in reproduction, with which it is correlated, varies with different species of migrants, the periodicity being " linked with different factors in the environment according to circumstances " (Thomson, 1936 ; cf. Moreau, 1931, and Bissonnette, 1937, who express essentially the same ideas ; *see also* Shuel, 1938).

increasing light, that was probably coincidental. The critical stimuli to reproduction are, in their view, probably environmental conditions that arise after rainfall
and the relatively high temperatures that accompany the lengthening photoperiods.

In this connection, evidence concerning spring-nesting Western Australian
birds is of importance. Thus, the dusky wood-swallow (*Artemus cyanopterus*) will
reproduce in autumn (when light is declining) if rain falls, and again in mid-
winter if rain falls once more (Robinson, 1933). Similarly, data presented by
Keast and Marshall (1954) show that two groups of Australian desert birds taken
at the same locality (Ayer's Rock) before and after the breaking of a drought
showed markedly different breeding development. The reproductive organs of
the birds taken during the drought were minute and inactive, whereas, after the
breaking of the drought, many species of birds had reached spermatogenesis and
others had eggs or young. It thus appears that this differential sexual development was caused by unseasonal falls of rain and the resultant creation of an environmental pattern which, irrespective of day-length or light increment, stimulated the
male neuro-hormonal apparatus to reproductive activity. Likewise, another group
of birds taken in drought-stricken country (Alexandria Downs) exhibited radically
different gonadal states from those of a second group collected a few days later in a
similar nearby locality, where 1·5 inches of chance rain had previously fallen.
Following this rain and a resultant meagre alleviation of drought, a considerable
male recrudescence, including spermatogenesis, occurred, yet the females remained
relatively inactive and breeding did not take place. This failure of the females to
respond led to a disturbance of the normal sequence of events in the male gonads,
and abnormal conditions similar to those found in Arctic, zoo and other non-
breeders were observed in the undischarged testis. No precise endocrinological
explanation for this peculiar disturbance of the internal sequence of events in the
testes can yet be given.

This capacity of animals to react to changes in climatically unstable regions
in which they have evolved is seen as a physiological aspect of drought adaptation,
since most xerophilous species that did not respond to rainfall or its effects would
be eliminated by natural selection (Marshall, 1951). But there is at present no
evidence that rainfall *per se* causes the initiation of gametogenesis. Neither is
there any proof that actual precipitation stimulates mating. There seems, nevertheless, little reason to doubt that some xerophilous and other species of birds, which
have of necessity evolved a neuro-endocrinological response to rain or its effects,
will breed in all manner of habitats quite independently of the movements of the
sun *per se*. The possible importance of rainfall in controlling the sexual cycle of
amphibia has already been alluded to (*see*, however, Chapter 1, and Noble and
Noble, 1923 ; Maxwell Savage, 1935 ; Zahl, 1937 ; Berk, 1938).

VII. INHERENT RHYTHM OF REPRODUCTION AND THE REFRACTORY PERIOD

Internal Rhythm

The only experimental evidence, so far as we are aware, that there may be an
"inherent" pituitary rhythm is that supplied by Witschi (1937), Lyman (1943) and
Rowan (1946). Witschi found that in certain finches, the seasonal moulting and
regeneration of the feathers still continued after castration. The changes were,

however, somewhat irregular and the male birds sometimes adopted an intermediate plumage in the quiescent season instead of the typical hen plumage. In
such cases the rhythm was primitively a gonadal one, and having been instituted
by the reproductive organs, continued somewhat erratically after their removal.
Likewise, removal of the gonads of the varying hare, *Lepus americanus*, did not
stop the change in coat colour (Lyman, 1943), nor did similar treatment of crows
interfere with their southward migration in autumn (Rowan, 1946). It is known,
however, that in rats castration completely obliterates the pituitary rhythm
(Wolfson, 1941, 1945). *See*, however, Kostitch and Telebakovitch (1929); Mandl
(1951); and Beach and Levinson (1949).

Until comparatively recently some have held that it was simply the rising temperature of spring that induced breeding. But, from time to time, the idea has
been postulated that each animal has within it a mechanism which, quite independently of external influences, operates annually to enable a given species to
breed at a certain precise time every year. Thus, it was suggested (Bissonnette
and Wadlund, 1932) that the breeding cycle and migration in some birds might be
governed by " inherent rhythms of the anterior pituitary more or less fixed in the
absence of, or without responsiveness to external, usually stimulating factors."
Marshall (1936, 1937), Baker and Baker (1936) and Baker and Ranson (1938)
were probably the first to stress the importance of internal rhythm in reproduction, and Marshall (1936, 1937) used it to account for " antagonistic " tendencies in the reproductive performance of some animals, when first transferred
to a new latitude. It was shown that annual breeders which reproduce regularly
in the spring (or autumn) in one hemisphere may, when transferred across the
equator, at first conform to their original reproduction time in obedience to internal
rhythm and then later approximately reverse their sexual season. The case of the
Timor pony which Cossar Ewart imported into Scotland is relevant in this connection and there is evidence that many other species of birds and mammals
behave in a broadly similar fashion.

Baker and Baker (1936), pointed out, however, that internal rhythm could not
alone regulate breeding periodicity since in the absence of external stimuli the
cycle would get out of step with seasons. Thus in time the animal would inevitably
come into sexual condition at precisely the " wrong " period of the year, i.e. a
spring-breeding species might attempt to reproduce in autumn. Baker (1938a,
1947), nevertheless, suggested that the return trans-equatorial breeding journey
from South Africa in such species as the European swallow (*Hirundo rustica*) might
be governed by internal rhythm. He did not, however, suggest internal or external means by which the rhythm of such species might be regulated in order that,
over the ages, the northern pre-nuptial journey would continue to be made at the
appropriate period of the year. From what is known of the time factor in biological reactions, any such exactitude is inconceivable. It is certain, then, that
each annually breeding organism must be influenced from time to time by external
factors that act as a regulating " finger " to keep the " clock " in step with the
seasons. If this were not true, breeding could occur at unpropitious times of the
year and the young would freeze or starve.

The presence of an internal rhythm is also suggested by the eventual spontaneous regression of the gonads of male ferrets (Bissonnette, 1935b) and ducks
(Benoit, 1938), when light treatment is prolonged. Likewise, Bullough (1951)

makes special mention of experiments with ferrets in which the imposition of almost continual darkness, at a time when the days have only just commenced to lengthen, does not invariably prevent the maturation of the gonad. Similarly, he states that with minnows the same type of treatment does no more than delay gonad growth, whilst in the golden crown sparrow the gonads are resistant to the stimulus of an experimentally increasing day-length until after the month of November in the northern hemisphere.

Another type of observation which is frequently cited to prove the existence of an internal rhythm, is that concerning certain early spring breeders which become quiescent sexually before the days stop lengthening in midsummer. The implication is that the animals concerned are stimulated entirely by increasing light, when in fact they may owe stimulation to a mixed pattern of decreasing, followed by increasing day-length. Strong evidence for inherent rhythmicity is, likewise, provided by the occurrence of full oestrus—though with some delay—in ferrets kept in light-proof cupboards (Hill and Parkes, 1933), as well as in animals in which the optic nerves had been sectioned previously—assuming that the operation removed all influence of light. This is recorded by Bissonnette (1935b) in two of three animals ; by Clark, McKeown and Zuckerman (1939) in two of four ; and by Thomson (1951) in thirty-two of forty-three (see, however, Harris (1955a), who criticises some of the experimental data).

In contradiction to the foregoing results are those of Marshall and Bowden (1934), who found that a blind ferret with cataract showed no oestrus in two years, although it was apparently healthy and well fed. Similarly, females with optic nerves sectioned did not come on heat in 500 days after operation (Clark et al., 1937), and a female with double cataract and nerves sectioned showed no ovarian activity for 2 years after the operation, but had a breeding season of approximately normal onset and duration during the third year. There is evidence then, from the histories of these few animals, which considerably weakens the case for an inherent rhythm based on oestrus occurring after optic nerve section.

During the past decade considerable attention has been paid to the problem of internal rhythm in birds by A. J. Marshall and co-workers. Marshall (1949a, b, 1951) showed that at the termination of the avian breeding season the interstitium becomes exhausted and the spermatogenetic material of the tubules metamorphoses into a mass of cholesterol-positive lipids (see p. 603, Chapter 12). Thus, both endocrine- and sperm-producing elements of the testis are put temporarily out of action. During this post-nuptial period of metamorphosis, birds fall into a refractory period during which they cannot respond to artificial photostimulation (Bissonnette and Wadlund, 1932). The study of periodically non-breeding Arctic species gave evidence that the events were connected with the state of the environment and its effect on the anterior pituitary (Marshall, 1952a, b, c).

Marshall (1951) suggested that the internal rhythm of reproduction, involving a demonstrable phase of testis metamorphosis and regeneration, is the most important single factor in the timing of avian breeding seasons since it is only after the end of such a period that the bird again becomes responsive to environmental stimuli. He pointed out that the hitherto inexplicable cycle of the sooty tern (*Sterna fusca*) of equatorial Ascension Island (which breeds four times every three years in equable conditions) could probably be explained on the grounds that, after the ending of its post-nuptial refractory period, it began its succeeding sexual cycle.   Marshall at the same time extended Baker's (1938a) hypothesis, pointing out that equatorially " wintering " birds, having emerged aphasically from their refractory period, could be brought into pre-migratory sexual synchronisation by display.

The work of Emlen and Lorenz (1942), who implanted pellets of testosterone in free-living Valley Quail (*Lophortyx californica*) and observed accelerated sexual behaviour in neighbouring untreated birds as well, was cited as a compelling illustration of how such synchronisation could be achieved.   It was suggested, moreover, that the cycles of young birds could be similarly brought into phase once a certain maturity was reached.   Further evidence was adduced that trans-equatorial migrant waders do in fact display before departure north to their breeding grounds.   It was shown, too, that many passerine migrants already possessed bunched spermatozoa before reaching their northern breeding stations (Marshall, 1952b).   It was further stated that birds " wintering " on the equator, and migrating northward as a response to internal rhythm and sexual synchronisation, could, nevertheless, have their cycles " timed " by the traditional stimuli controlling nidification and ovulation on the habitual breeding ground.   In all species yet investigated the male cycle outstrips the female ; and in both Arctic and desert birds reproduction does not take place unless the external environment presents conditions satisfactory to the female (Marshall, 1951).

Meanwhile, Miller (1948, 1949), Benoit, Assenmacher and Walter (1950a, b), Greeley and Meyer (1953), Coombs and Marshall (1956) and Lofts and Marshall (1956) provided evidence that appears conclusively to establish that the anterior pituitary becomes refractory in birds.   Lofts and Marshall (1958) subsequently concluded that, probably in conjunction with neural factors, the anterior pituitary possesses the primary role in internal rhythm and that the testis can be refractory for only a very brief period during interstitial regeneration (*see* p. 673, Chapter 12). Coombs and Marshall (1956) showed that even in hypophysectomised birds the interstitium regenerated itself as part of the internal gonad rhythm!   That the post-nuptial tubule lipids could be dispersed and a new spermatogenesis started after the injections of minute quantities of FSH was proved by Lofts and Marshall (1958).

Thus, the existence of an internal rhythm of reproduction based on pituitary refractoriness, interstitial regeneration, and pituitary recovery (after which individuals are once more susceptible to external stimuli) seems now well established in birds.   Höhn (1947) with the mallard (*Anas platyrhynchos*), Bullough (1942) with the starling (*Sternus vulgaris*) and Marshall (1952c) with the European robin (*Erithacus rubecula*) and rook (*Corvus frugilegus*), have shown that the characteristic autumnal display of birds occurs only after the rhythmical recovery of gonad (and no doubt pituitary) function.   Marshall and Coombs (1957) state that such is the case in both sexes of the rook.   Such species are potentially capable of winter reproduction, but breeding activity is almost always extinguished by unfavourable external conditions.   During unusually clement autumns there is widespread sexual activity among the birds, and successful winter reproduction occasionally occurs.

We have seen that in some species living in localities in which exist conditions for reproduction throughout the year, one rhythm of reproduction probably follows closely upon the last (e.g. sooty tern of Ascension Island).   At the other extreme are " opportunist " xerophilous species, the sexual cycles of which may remain dormant, or almost so, for several years (Marshall, 1955); then they may be abruptly stimulated to productivity after heavy rainfall. Keast and Marshall (1954) and Serventy and Marshall (1957) studied Australian desert birds collected in various localities during, and soon after, severe droughts. It was revealed that comparatively meagre rainfall and the resultant creation of relatively beneficial conditions have a more stimulating effect on the male than on the female cycle (*see* above). There was evidence that the females do not respond until the advent of conditions appropriate for actual reproduction. It was made clear that such desert birds have evolved an unusually high degree of nomadic mobility to defeat droughts and that they exhibit a further vital physiological aspect of drought adaptation in that their sexual cycles can respond with unusual rapidity to external stimuli. Thus, nidification may begin very soon after heavy precipitation and the appearance of verdure, irrespective of photofluctuations.

That an internal rhythm of reproduction exists in the xerophilous African Red-billed Weaver Finch (*Quelea quelea*) was shown in an experimental study carried out in Tanganyika by Disney and Marshall (1956) and Marshall and Disney (1956, 1957). This rhythm controls the assumption of sexual colouration of the beak, soft parts, plumage and, in the male, the onset of sexual display that leads to copulation. *Q. quelea* breeds only after heavy rainfall and the appearance of long grass. Even before rainfall, however, the birds are already brightly coloured even though their gonads are still small. This rhythm is very slightly modifiable by external conditions, including possibly rainfall and other external effects (for example, social stimulation). Many birds of both sexes came into breeding dress when only $5\frac{1}{2}$ months old. Thus the breeding which occurs in this highly nomadic pest in southern Kenya in December and January—or anywhere else where rain falls—could be by birds themselves hatched as recently as the previous March or April in Tanganyika.

Convincing evidence of the existence of an internal rhythm has been further provided by Vaugien (1953) and Marshall and Serventy (1957, 1959) with xerophilous Australian budgerigars (*Melopsittacus undulatus*) and zebra finches (*Poephila castanotis*) respectively. Vaugien reported that young budgerigars kept in " complete darkness " produced spermatozoa (as did those under natural illumination) within 52 days. Because un-illuminated budgerigars developed spermatozoa, and those kept under *continuous* photostimulation were found to possess only primary spermatocytes, Vaugien claimed that darkness seems to favour spermatogenesis and light to jeopardise it. Marshall and Serventy (1957), working with zebra finches, confirmed Vaugien's discovery that some xerophilous birds can achieve spermatogenesis in the almost complete absence of light. At the same time, however, they showed that Vaugien's own photographs revealed that, far from retarding spermatogenesis, the continuous light treatment had driven his budgerigars right through one sexual cycle into the next, thus explaining the lack of spermatozoa in his continuously illuminated birds.

The operation of an internal rhythm in migratory passerine yellow wagtails (*Motacilla*) is suggested by work carried out by Marshall and Williams (1959). These wagtails breed in Central Europe and winter above, on and below the equator in Africa. Birds were taken almost precisely on the equator, where, on the northern shores of Lake Victoria, the climate is equable (and light fluctuations, of course, negligible).   These came rhythmically into nuptial plumage while the gonads were still minute and months before the start of the northern breeding journey.   Later, before their departure north, the birds began to pair and gonads of both sexes began to enlarge slightly.   Again it must be assumed that such phenomena are under the control of an internal rhythm involving the anterior pituitary.   The timing of the rhythm is probably governed by the factors allowing the culmination of the sexual cycle on the distant European breeding ground.

The most convincing demonstration of internal rhythm yet shown in birds is that in the shearwater, *Puffinus tenuirostris*.   This species migrates between Southern Australia and the southern Arctic with remarkable regularity.   It leaves its Australian and Tasmanian breeding islands in April, and returns to them during the same 21 days of the following spring (in September).   Marshall and Serventy (1957), although paying due regard to the possibility that the movements may be essentially the expression of internal rhythm, concluded that the extraordinary regularity of the return journey suggests that an astronomical constant (i.e. decreasing day-length in the northern hemisphere) is probably involved.   A second consideration leading to this conclusion was that although the cycle must be " anchored " in time at *some* period of the sexual cycle, there did not at first sight seem to be any seasonally changing, yet constant, external factor on the breeding ground.

The possibility that decreasing day-lengths operate to " time " the internal rhythm of reproduction was next tested experimentally (Marshall and Serventy, 1957).   One group of petrels was kept under natural Australian day-lengths, and another under a telescoped sequence of those experienced on the vast journey to the southern Arctic and back.   Samples from each group were periodically killed but no difference in gonad condition was found.   Yet four birds (two of each sex) allowed to survive the experiment came into reproductive condition at the same time as the wild population that flew to the Aleutians and back !

It is inconceivable that any animal could continue to " time " its cycle indefinitely within such narrow and accurate limits in the absence of external regulators, but it has yet to be discovered where and what external factors are operable.

The bitch is generally supposed to provide an instance of inherent rhythm in having about two heat periods annually with no particular seasonal restriction (Amoroso, 1949; Hancock and Rowlands, 1949).   An influence of light might nevertheless be suspected from relationship with light regulated carnivores, from a reported spring season in Greenland (Heape, 1901) and from an observation on hair growth in the Antarctic (Captain R. F. Scott, quoted by Bissonnette, 1935a).   According to Hammond (1954), however, we may attribute the first oestrus in the bitch "to the ageing process which normally brings the pituitary to full gonadotrophic activity.   The corpus luteum thus formed, presumably by its secretion, depresses pituitary activity as it does in other animals; but the state that follows corpus luteum regression is considered to be one of rest (until the next cycle begins), and this rest one must suppose to be due to a condition of fatigue or inhibition set up by the previous cycle.   The site of this fatigue and the manner of its dispersal are the unknowns of the inherent rhythm."

Finally, it should be recalled that as early as 1933, Hill and Parkes were already pointing out that the ferret in domestication has a well-marked breeding season from April to August, and were finding it "difficult to imagine what environmental changes take place during April in an artificially heated animal house not particularly accessible to direct sunlight." Later (Hill and Parkes, 1934), following their discovery that ferrets did not experience infertility after a reduction of day-length in winter and early spring, they concluded that the onset of the breeding season is not dependent on the increasing length of day. Indeed, they even went so far as to suggest that the provision of extra light in winter is an artificial laboratory technique the results of which do not reflect conditions in nature, and that the breeding cycle is solely dependent on an internal physiological rhythm. The unlikelihood of such a rhythm being the sole factor in control of breeding seasons has since been recognized (Baker and Baker, 1936).

Notwithstanding these considerations, Yeates (1949a, b, 1954) argues the case against the existence of internal rhythm. He suggests that some of the apparently irreconcilable cases alluded to above can be explained without the necessity of invoking any such mechanism. For example, in the case of animals transported across the equator, although it is no doubt true that for a time there may be two antagonistic tendencies, both of them result from the influence of the light environment, one stimulus or influence having been received in the old environment and requiring a particular time (depending on the species or breed) to die out; and the other in the new. Furthermore, he states (1954, p. 385) that the case against any inherent rhythm is strengthened by experiments in which various groups of ewes were brought into oestrus by suitable light treatment at different times of the year with equal ease, i.e. after approximately the same time interval following change-over from increasing to decreasing light exposure (Yeates, 1949a). It is argued from this that no inherent rhythm exists, for if it did, the difficulty or delay with which activity could be induced would vary from time to time according to whether the internal effect was being assisted or opposed.

Summarising the conclusions to be drawn from the evidence detailed above, one may say that the final timing of the breeding season of many species each spring, or at an otherwise appropriate time as determined by natural selection, is controlled not by a single factor such as photoperiodicity, but by a combination of external stimuli (including, specially, behavioural interactions) which, varying from species to species, operate through the exteroceptors, the central nervous system, and the anterior pituitary of the female when the environment becomes seasonally appropriate for reproduction. Any theory of avian breeding seasons based primarily on internal rhythm and secondarily on *various* environmental changes has the advantage of possible application to all seasonal species whether they breed in the spring, in the depth of winter (as does the emperor penguin), or on the equator where light fluctuations (about 2 minutes difference between " winter " and " summer ") are almost certainly too small to command serious consideration !

The Refractory Period

Emphasis upon the major effects of seasonal changes in light, temperature, rainfall and similar environmental factors upon the reproductive cycle of seasonal breeding animals should not preclude recognition of the fact that, however favourable the environment for reproduction, there is a period which follows breeding in which it is impossible for another sexual cycle to be restarted. This has been called the " refractory period " (Bissonnette and Wadlund, 1932). In birds refractoriness has been detected by Riley (1936, 1937), who found that treatment with light stimulated both adult and immature male sparrows in November ; if, however, treatment was started 7 weeks earlier, adults failed to respond, though males hatched in the same season could do so. In the pheasant (*Phasianus*) a seasonal period of refractoriness intervenes in the pars distalis of the pituitary as well as in the testes (Greeley and Meyer, 1953). Refractoriness has also been studied in the starling (Burger, 1947), duck (Benoit, Assenmacher and Walter, 1950a), golden-crowned sparrow (Miller, 1948, 1951, 1954), the junco finch (Wolfson, 1952b), and in the bower-bird (Marshall, 1954, 1955), and in mammals its existence in the mink has been claimed by Hammond, Jnr. (1951a, 1953a, b, 1954).

We do not know with certainty what specific factors, either external or internal, operate in bringing about the refractory state, but, starting with the idea that naturally long days stimulate and short ones do not, so that only days beyond a threshold length are stimulating, one view would hold that the stimulus itself was withdrawn, because the essential feature was not length, but increase of length of day or even rate of increase (Wolfson, 1952b). An alternative view would hold that the stimulus was not withdrawn but that a process of accommodation or relative refractory state occurred, requiring an increased stimulus to elicit response (Bissonnette, 1935a, 1936a). On the basis of further evidence, Bissonnette (1938a) concluded that " females, like males, became refractory to photic sexual stimulation after a time and required greater stimulus to induce estrus." A third view would make refractoriness absolute, a fatigue occurring in the gonad or its control mechanism. (*See also* Bissonnette, 1937; Riley and Witschi, 1937.)

In an excellent critical review of numerous investigations on light regulation of hormone secretion, Hammond, Jnr. (1954) points out the serious weaknesses of the various experiments purporting to show that refractoriness is purely inherent. He admits that some of these reports are compatible with refractoriness being an inherent phenomenon, but asserts that his own findings, as well as those of Burger (1947), Miller (1951) and Wolfson (1952b), show that it is not, as its duration depends on the duration of long-day exposure. In Hammond's opinion there does not appear to be any good reason why this inhibitory effect of light on reproduction should be supposed to be brought about in a different manner from the stimulating effect. The results, he states, are in fact all compatible with the hypothesis of a cumulative inhibitory action more slowly produced and less readily dispersed than the stimulating effect.

The view of refractoriness proposed by Marshall (1950, 1951, 1954) is based upon histological changes in the avian testis under natural lighting. This author believes that refractoriness is due to the end of the life-cycle of one generation of Leydig cells, and that its duration is determined by the time required for the next generation to mature. It is, however, possible that the gonads merely reflect pituitary activity. To illustrate—the oestrous female rabbit is sexually receptive, and stimuli associated with mating lead eventually to the discharge of luteinising hormone from the pituitary and then to ovulation. Pregnant and pseudopregnant females also mate, but in such cases ovulation does not follow copulation. Analysed in terms of refractoriness, these seemingly anomalous results are now capable of straightforward explanation. In pseudopregnant and pregnant rabbits in which the chorio-allantoic placenta has been established, the pituitary contains ample supplies of gonadotrophin to produce ovulation, and the ovarian follicle is quite sensitive to the ovulation-producing hormone (Makepeace, Weinstein and Friedman, 1938). Bioassays reveal that in the oestrous female the gonadotrophic content of the pituitary is rapidly depleted after copulation, whereas, in the pregnant or pseudopregnant animal, no such post-copulatory reduction in pituitary potency occurs. There is evidence, then, that absence of post-copulatory ovulation in pregnancy and pseudopregnancy is due to refractoriness of the mechanism which normally causes discharge of gonadotrophic materials from the anterior pituitary. Whether the corpus luteum and/or the placenta are implicated remains an open question.

Along similar lines are the findings of Benoit, Assenmacher and Walter (1950a). They observe that castration of the duck with active testes causes marked pituitary hypertrophy, but very little if the operation is performed during the refractory period. Assay of duck pituitaries (Benoit *et al.*, 1950b) showed greater hormone content in the refractory condition than when the testes were active, and they conclude that refractoriness causes depression of the rate of hormone release, followed by that of hormone formation. It is clear, therefore, that refractoriness does not operate by shifting of the fulcrum of the gonad-pituitary balance, because, whatever its position, the effect on this mechanism of removing the negative feed-back would be the same. Whether refractoriness acts specifically through one component of the hormone complex that governs the gonads remains unknown (Hammond, 1954).

VIII. External Stimuli of a Sexual Kind Controlling the Cycle in Birds

In Chapter 27 instances have been given from among mammals showing that the succession of the phases of the cycle in some species may be modified by external stimuli acting through the intermediation of the nervous system upon the anterior pituitary gland. Cases of the same kind of phenomena are also very common among birds. There is no luteal stage in birds, but nevertheless there occurs from the beginning of the season of reproductive activity a succession of phases which manifest themselves in the bird's behaviour, and which often grade into one another and to a certain extent overlap. There is, of course, much species variation, but, speaking generally, the order is as follows : movement to the breeding area, which may consist of migration over long distances, this occurring more or less contemporaneously with the periodic development of the gonads, the taking up of territories (where this is done), pairing, sexual display, coition, nest-building (during which display and coition are usually repeated), and in the female ovulation and egg-laying, and then, sometimes for one and sometimes for both sexes, incubation, and the feeding and rearing of the young. Jourdain and Tucker (1938–1941) state that birds differ as to the time when incubation begins. It may start after the laying of the first or second egg, or it may be postponed until the complete clutch has been laid. Here we may quote Eliot Howard (1935) :

" No one doubts that the generative organs determine sexual activity, though all may not agree that pro-oestrum and oestrus in a bird depend upon ovarian processes comparable with the uterine changes in a female mammal, or, indeed, that these phases are really there ; what some may doubt is the wider view that behaviour which custom thinks a matter of mind is in some way determined by changes in the body. True, no change in testis or ovary, or hormone in the blood stream, has yet been found to correspond with territory, with building shells, or with care of young. But from point to point, consider the events. In the spring a male shuns his own kind and makes himself public ; singing if a song bird ; drumming on a dead branch, if a pied woodpecker, wandering in air like a butterfly or dancing in it like a moth, sparrow-hawk ; gowit, curlew, with slow flapping flight ; redshank and dunlin with vibrating wings, each after his kind ; moreover, he defies intruders, threatens, attacks, fights until one or other yields ; and before a mate finds him he builds a nest, if a whitethroat ; or a platform, if a waterhen, and broods upon it ; or, like a lapwing, bores hollows in the ground to enjoy it, or merely carries stuff in its beak to drop it anywhere."

In each species there is a characteristic succession of phases in both sexes, and this, as Howard supposes, must be related to internal change. The study of bird behaviour has already become a large subject as a result of intensive watching of birds in a state of nature. Howard (1907–14, 1929, 1935, 1940), Huxley (1914, 1923), Selous (1901, 1927) and many others in recent years have made important observations upon the relations of the sexes. But concerning the physiological causes which are responsible for the successive phases we have little knowledge beyond those endocrine factors which have been alluded to above. Here we confine ourselves to some further matters where there is direct evidence as to the effects of external stimuli in altering the succession of the physiological processes which constitute the cycle (cf. Marshall, 1929, 1936 ; and *see also* Landsborough Thomson, 1940).

The Effect of Stimuli Associated with the Presence of Eggs

The first point we wish to refer to is one which is now well known to all orni- thologists. For any one species the number of eggs in the clutch is generally constant within narrow limits, that is to say, there is a tendency to lay a definite number of eggs and then to brood over them. If, however, the eggs are with- drawn shortly after being laid, many birds will go on laying, making an attempt so to speak, to lay up to the right number, and the incubation phase in the cycle is postponed in correlation with the repeated ovulations. This was first pointed out in the seventeenth century by John Ray (*see* Raven, 1942), who recorded that a swallow, by having one of her eggs taken from her daily, was induced to lay nineteen eggs. A well-known example of the same phenomenon was afforded by a wryneck, a bird that normally lays seven or eight eggs, but which, in this instance, laid forty-two eggs as a result of the daily withdrawal of the egg deposited. The incident was repeated in the next year, when the wryneck again laid forty-two eggs before its ovary was exhausted (Yarrell, 1882 ; Kirkman, 1911–13). Jesse (1935) mentions similar observations upon the blackbird, the lark and the long-tailed tit. About the lark, he says : " If only one or two eggs are allowed to remain in the nest, the bird will go on to lay for a time indefinite, but if there are three she will sit. The usual number of eggs in a lark's nest is five." Davie (1889) describes how a flicker was induced to lay seventy-one eggs in 73 days by withdrawing an egg every day. Witschi (1935) found that for the house sparrow, whereas the normal number of eggs is 4 or 5 in a clutch, by removing the eggs daily, the bird may lay up to 50 eggs in succession and often 12 to 14 on consecutive days. On the other hand, if the full clutch is allowed to remain, the ovary rapidly regresses during incubation through degeneration of the larger eggs, a result which occurs, according to Riddle (1937), through the secretion of the anterior pituitary hormone, prolactin. (*See also* Walmesley-White, 1931 and p. 775.)

The pheasant and the partridge are said to be similar and may be induced to lay over 100 eggs. In the case of the common fowl, as is well known, as a result of domestication and prolonged artificial selection, the maternal habit of broodiness may be bred out, while the bird has become a veritable factory of egg production. Since in the fowl, and, therefore, presumably in most birds, there is an interval of only about a day between ovulation and the laying of the egg, it follows that in the cases just cited the repetition of ovulation must be the result of external stimuli, though whether these are derived from perception by the eye, or through tactile perception by the ventral surface of the body, is uncertain. In any case, presumably, the stimulus must pass through the intermediation of the nervous system to the pituitary and so interfere with the normal course of succession in the sexual cycle, the incubation phase being postponed for a long period or indefinitely. Moreover, if the nest of the birds is removed along with the clutch, the nest-building may be repeated and the succeeding egg-laying and incubation periods are deferred accordingly, ovulation being resumed in due course (Chance, 1936). By removing the complete clutch, Chance obtained " repeat layings " in the blackcap, carrion crow, raven, dunlin, and golden plover. Further, the house sparrow, garden warbler, kestrel and merlin could be induced to lay three complete clutches, and the red-backed shrike four clutches, but there was some reduction in the normal number of eggs in the fourth clutch. Walmesley-White (1931) states that with the night-jar, when all the eggs are taken, though there is no nest to make, the bird will wait 3 weeks before starting to lay again. As evidence that the stimulus to incubate may be tactile, Taibell (1928) has shown that broodiness may be induced in the turkey by fastening the bird down on to a nest of eggs ; when released the turkey immediately proceeded to lay again.

Lastly, Lack (1933) records a case of a Sarus crane in which ovulation was apparently inhibited when extra eggs were supplied. The succession of the phases, therefore, is not merely a matter of cyclical endocrine control. In some birds, however, the number of eggs is apparently determined by the character of the ovaries, this being fixed by heredity. Friedman (1929) has attempted to divide birds into two categories in this respect, determinate and indeterminate, according to whether they lay a fixed or an indefinite number of eggs. Some birds can only lay one egg, which if taken away is not replaced. This is the case with Wilson's petrel in the Antarctic and nearly all the *Tubinares*, e.g. shearwaters (Roberts, 1940b). The tropic birds lay only one irreplaceable egg (Gibson-Hall 1941), and there are probably many other species which are similar. Moreover, with the social nesting cuckoos (*Crotophaginae*) in which several birds tend to lay into one nest, the hypophysial-ovarian mechanism is seemingly determined to produce a fixed number of laid eggs, no matter how many may be in the nest. So also Davis (1942b), describing an experiment on the herring gull, says that the birds were not induced to lay more than three eggs by the removal of eggs nor restrained from laying more by the addition of eggs (*see also* Davis, 1942a, c, and Emlen, 1941). In such cases, external stimuli would appear to play a comparatively small part in regulating the ovarian processes.

The Synchronisation of the Mating Cycles of the two Sexes

So far we have been considering the factors causing the continuance of ovulation in birds after it has once started and those responsible for the cessation of the process. The question as to the initiation of the first seasonal ovulation, which we have reserved for longer consideration, is another matter. Like mammals, birds in respect of ovulation fall into two categories : (i) those that ovulate spontaneously when the ovaries are in the appropriate condition, and (ii) those that require an additional stimulus which is usually provided by the male. The common fowl and the pheasant are examples of the first kind : the pigeon is an example of the second. Concerning the pigeon, Harper, in a paper published in 1904, writes as follows :

"When a pair ready for mating is put together, egg-laying ordinarily ensues at the end of a rather definite period, at the least, eight days. The female functions are held in abeyance till the proper stimulus is received from the mate. The maturing of the egg is so exclusively a female function that it seems odd at first thought that an apparent exception should occur to the rule. Of course, we know that the final maturation of the egg, or the giving off of the polar bodies, awaits in most animals the act of fertilisation. But here the effect is produced upon the egg by the entrance of the sperms. How mating and the act of copulation (which is repeated at frequent intervals every day at this time) could influence the ripening of the egg in the ovary is another problem. In this connection the curious fact must be mentioned that two female pigeons placed in confinement may both take to laying eggs. The function of ovulation is in a state of tension, so to speak, that requires only a slight stimulus, ' mental ' apparently in this case, to set the mechanism to working. At any rate, it is impossible to regard the presence of sperm in the oviduct as an essential element of the stimulus to ovulation, although it may have an important influence in the normal case. Our attention is directed to the various and complex instincts of the male which come under the head of courtship, both before and after mating is effected, as furnishing a part of the stimulus to the female reproductive organs."

Harper proceeds to describe a curious habit which is common among pigeons before copulating. The male bird regurgitates some secretion in its throat, presumably from the crop gland, and this is taken up by the bill of the female in much the same manner as the young take their food. " It is easy to see that here may be one of the sources of indirect stimulation to the female reproductive organs." Here it may be mentioned that William Harvey, 300 years ago (*see* Willis's translation, 1847), was apparently aware of some of the effects of sexual stimuli in influencing the reproductive processes of female birds, but it has only been in recent years that any considerable data bearing on this subject have been obtained and their physiological significance realised.

Robinson (1892), in an article on ticklishness, writes as follows : " Harvey records that by stroking the back of a favourite parrot (which he possessed for years and supposed to be a male) he not only gave the bird gratification—which was the sole intention of the illustrious physiologist—but also caused it to reveal its sex by laying an egg." Harvey himself says : " Birds are sometimes so lustful that if you stroke their beaks gently with your hand they will immediately lie down and expose and obtrude their uterine orifices and if you touch this they proclaim their satisfaction and they may lay eggs " (blackbird, thrush and others) (Harvey, Willis's translation, 1847 ; cf. Aristotle, *Historia Animalium*, D'A. Thompson's

translation, 1910).   Harvey also says that a cassowary was stimulated to lay by
seeing ostriches displaying.   Most birds, he says, only lay if the male has access,
but, with some exceptions, they must be stimulated.

" These and other instances induce me to believe that the common fowl and pheasant
do not only solace their females with their crowing but further give them the faculty to
produce eggs by its means ; for when the cock crows in the night some of the hens
perched near him bestir themselves, clapping their wings and shaking their heads,
shuddering and gesticulating as they are wont to do after intercourse."

With many birds—" the more salacious they are, the more fruitful they are."

Craig (1911) has shown that with six collared turtle-doves (*Turtur risorius*)
egg-laying was induced by the courtship behaviour of male doves.   Moreover, a
dove which was used to human companionship was caused to lay an egg by having
her head and neck preened.   Craig (1913) states further, quoting an observation
by Whitman on the pigeon, that even if a male is present other stimuli may be
essential for laying (e.g. nesting-box and other nesting conveniences).   This is in
accordance with what has been described above concerning egg-laying.   Craig
quotes a remark by Aristotle (*Historia Animalium*) that pigeons may retain their
eggs if disturbed in the process of laying, but oviposition is not identical with
ovulation, though the two are normally correlated.   Craig concludes by saying
that the great transformation towards the states of matehood (under which egg-
laying occurs) is determined in the dove by the " entire social situation and not by
any one factor, mechanical or other."

As not irrelevant to the subject, Hartman (1939), quoting from " the current
Science news letter," states that Australian parrots in the Missouri Zoological Park
have been persistently sterile.   On being presented with a hollow branch
resembling the ancestral nesting site, mating, nest-building and egg-laying began
as if by magic.   As also bearing on the question as to stimuli for initiating certain
sexual phases the following observations of the Duke of Bedford may be quoted.
He found :

" that two unmated males of the little Japanese Monra finch, the *Bengalese*, if provided
with a nest and some eggs will within a few days, start to incubate and will hatch the eggs
and rear the young as well, or better, than a true pair.   A female Amboina parakeet
(*Alistennus ambionensis*) in my collection, kept alone, was excited by the presence of a
male Australian King (*A. scapulatus*) in the next aviary and laid two infertile eggs which
she did not incubate.   A few weeks later, she laid two more and the day after the second
egg was laid I gave her a day-old hybrid chick of *Polytelis swainsoni* × *Ptistes erythrop-
terus*.   This chick she fed and reared, only failing to adapt herself entirely to the abnormal
conditions by brooding the young bird until it left the nest instead of ceasing to brood
it as soon as it was well feathered, but some days before it actually flew.   Thus she
incubated the full normal time but she was not so much the slave of sequence that she
could not feed young hatched on the first day of the incubation."   (Letter to F. H. A.
Marshall.)

Other observations on the pigeon were made likewise by Whitman (1919),
who speaks of posturing as self-stimulating.   Confirmatory observations have also
been made more recently by Martins (1935).   Matthews (1939) has shown that
the mere sight of another bird or of a mirror image may produce a visual stimulation which leads to ovulation.   That the display is accompanied by a high degree
of emotional disturbance in all birds that show, is very apparent.

The late Duke of Bedford, to whom we are much indebted for giving us the benefit of his extensive experience of birds of all kinds in a state of captivity, states that apart from gallinaceous birds he has very seldom known egg-laying to occur in any species excepting in the presence of the male.[1] Spontaneous ovulation, in his experience, is non-existent or most rare in species which normally mate for life. It may occur, however, in unmated swans and with various kinds of cranes when two females live in abnormally close association. Otherwise, the Duke informs us, these birds never lay unless mated. The conditions are clearly comparable to those seen in the pigeon. The mere presence of another individual provides an external stimulus which acts on the pituitary and starts the nest-building and ovulating stage of the cycle. Allen (1934), as a result of his observations and experiments on the ruffed grouse (in which he put together males and females in different stages of sexual activity), likewise concludes that the behaviour of the birds is to be explained on the basis of a necessity for synchronisation of the mating cycles of the two sexes. He does not, however, put forward any definite physiological theory as to how the synchronisation is effected, but concludes that the critical stage of the cycle is somehow determined by the vigour of the bird and its metabolism and also its mental state. The latter is influenced by the results of conflicts, and defeat may be followed by an " inferiority " which keeps the bird from arriving at a mating period. Successful conflicts, on the other hand, are supposed to stimulate the development of the gonads which, with most birds, are not fully functional until the time of arrival at the nesting ground Allen describes also the behaviour of two female Canada geese which behaved like a mated pair. During March and April one would lay eggs while the other stood over the ground like a gander. Later they would reverse their roles. The case was clearly one of mutual stimulation comparable to those of the pigeons, swans and cranes cited above.

Hudson (1920) states that with the Argentine cow-bird, which like the cuckoo has the parasitic habit of laying in other birds' nests, the males may be seen wooing the females from the beginning of September until the end of January, and in correlation with this extended period of courtship without nest-building or incubation, the number of eggs produced is phenomenally large (probably from 60 to 100), many of the eggs being dropped on the ground and wasted. Friedman (1929), however, disputes this, stating that in his experiences *Molothrus bonariensis* only lays from six to ten eggs and that the breeding season is about three months. And Davis (1942a) says that this and other species of cow-birds lay in clutches of probably not more than five. That there are other external factors on which ovulation depends besides strictly sexual ones, is shown by the necessity for satisfactory nesting conditions for egg-laying (cf. Lack, 1933, and *see below*, p. 771). This is true for penguins (Roberts, 1940a) as for many other birds. Chance (1940) has shown that the cuckoo will not lay in the absence of a suitable nest. But if the egg is already in the oviduct it may be laid in an unusual fosterer's nest (cf. Stuart Baker, 1930, 1932–1935).

External stimuli of a suitable kind may initiate other processes or phases in the sexual cycle of birds but only provided that they are in an appropriate gonadal condition. Thus a cock bishop-bird with developed testes may feed

---

[1] Spontaneous ovulation occurs normally in domestic ducks and geese and has been noted occasionally in parrots, as recorded above, owls and some other birds in captivity. (Cf. Whitman's American robin which laid, without a mate, in a nest built by himself.)

young canaries in response to their appeals and even remove their faeces. This case, kindly supplied to us by Mr. K. B. Rooke, is only one example out of many. Lodge (1946), referring to an observation by Percy Lowe, says that the drumming of woodpeckers is sex-stimulating in function. Goethe (1937), in a memoir on the biology of the herring gull on the Bird Island of Mmertsand, describes at length the elaborate stimulatory practices adopted by the male, such as pretending to feed the hen and attempting to copulate with her.

External Factors of Various Kinds

Apart from Rowan's (1928, 1938a, b) observations on birds there is little indication that increased exercise accelerates gonadal activity and with mammals there is no such evidence. It is certain, however, that sexual activity and oestrus may be modified by external stimuli of various kinds, and in some cases may be increased. Furthermore, there can be no doubt that periodicity in migration, as in reproduction with which it is correlated, varies with different species of migrants, the periodicity being "linked with different factors in the environment according to circumstances" (Thomson, 1936; cf. Moreau, 1931; 1936; and Bissonnette, 1937, who express essentially the same idea; see also Shuel, 1938; Rowan, 1946.)

To our list of proximate causes which may influence sexual periodicity must be added such factors as auditory stimuli, food supply, the phases of the moon and inheritance. Thus, Britt (1941) states that air blast and noise might modify and increase the number of oestrous cycles in the rat, and Farris and Yeakel (1944) found that air blasted daily for 5 minutes for 5 days increased the pregnancies by 30 per cent, but depressed the maternal behaviour of the rats at parturition.

In the case of birds, Thornton and Cummings (1946) record that the spermatogenic cycle of the English sparrow is unaffected by auditory stimulation. On the other hand, Benoit (1955b, p. 218) writes as follows:

"Psychical and auditory stimuli (singing) may play a part in the regulation or synchronization of sexual activity in birds. Vaugien placed male and female green parakeets in different cages in different rooms and connected the two rooms by telephone only, so that the females could hear the males' song; in some cases the results were positive. Assenmacher and myself have placed male immature drakes in a dark room and had the wireless switched on for 12 hours a day for several weeks (all types of programmes) but observed no effect whatever on sexual activity. Evidently the mere presence of noise caused no stimulation, or perhaps we provided the wrong kind of noise!"

The only other factor that seems likely to inhibit testicular resurgence in these birds is the long dark period. This is, however, extremely improbable, since Assenmacher and Benoit (cited by Benoit, 1955b) have shown that light is not a necessary stimulus for the complete development of the duck's testis although, when present, light enhances this development.

It has long been known that when food is abundant and other factors are favourable, sheep may breed twice a year (Marshall, 1905a). Presumably its effect may be exerted through the growth of the reproductive tract, the activity of the ovaries in producing ova (perhaps both quantitatively and qualitatively), and the uterine environment (Heape, 1899). Similarly, Baker (1938a) has suggested that food supply may act as a proximate cause in determining the times of the breeding seasons in many kinds of animals. He has pointed, for example, to the possible effect in an equatorial rain-forest (where the physical environment is so constant), of the seasonal production of fruits which so many animals eat.

Food supply may also act as a trigger mechanism in determining the times of the breeding season in the lizard, *Agama agama* (Marshall and Hook, 1959). This equatorial reptile possesses a distinct breeding period which occurs during the peak of the seasonal harvest of proteinous animal food that follows the so-called "long rains." The males contain bunches of spermatozoa throughout the year, whereas, in the females, ovulation is widespread during 4 months of the year (June–September inclusive), the peak occurring in July and early in August. As the proportion of ingested animal food increases the sexual condition of the animals heightens and there is a concurrent growth of large leaf-shaped abdominal fat bodies. Since any possibility of photoperiodic control of reproduction is eliminated by the choice of the collecting locality (almost on the equator), it is suggested that the sexual cycle of *Agama agama* is timed not by rainfall but by the seasonal appearance of proteinous insect food.

The effect of underfeeding on rats is of interest in this connection, in that malnutrition in this animal may produce a condition similar to that following hypophysectomy and therefore termed pseudohypophysectomy (Mulinos and Pomerantz, 1940, 1941). On the other hand, the effect of an inadequate diet on the reproductive capacity of the rat may be compensated by extra lighting, or conversely, the rats may breed as efficiently under conditions of shortened illumination provided that the diet is adequate (Alexander and Frazer, 1952). Similarly, if the field mouse, *Microtus agrestis*, be fed wholly on its usual foodstuff, grass, its reproduction in the laboratory can be controlled by extra illumination (Baker and Ranson, 1932b); if, however, it be fed on the optimum food for rapid reproduction, its breeding activity cannot be influenced by darkness. Conversely, starlings will not respond fully to light if kept on a poor diet (Bissonnette, 1933). These experiments are useful, too, in showing that breeding seasons are probably often controlled by the interaction of two or more separate proximate causes.

Among invertebrates too, there seems to be no doubt that the growth and development of the larvae of certain hymenopterous parasites are governed by the quality of food. For example, in the eulophid *Mellitobia chalybii*, a gregarious external parasite of the wasp, *Tryphoxylon*, it has been shown that the rate of larval development and the form of the imago are determined by the parts of the dead host which are available as food for the larvae (Schmieder, 1933). The first sixteen or twenty parasite larvae to hatch ingest all the blood of the fresh host and proceed to develop in about 14 days into brachypterous adults. The remainder, often numbering several hundred, consume the remaining tissues of the host and develop slowly in about 90 days into macropterous individuals.

It has long been known that there is a connection between the phases of the moon and breeding seasons in certain organisms. Among birds there are indications that ovulation in the nightjar, a crepuscular species, is controlled by the moon (Wynne-Edwards, 1930). This worker has described how the two eggs are laid during the last quarter of the lunar cycle so that the chicks are reared during the next full moon when hunting can continue all night. Similarly, it has been shown (Walmesley-White, 1931) that when the eggs of a nightjar are taken, though there is no nest to make, a period of three weeks must elapse before the bird can lay again.

Another example of a regularly timed reproductive rhythm, in a vertebrate, which is quite possibly controlled by external events is the spawning behaviour of the Californian grunnion or sand smelt, *Lauresthes tenuis*, described by Thompson (1919). During the annual breeding season the mating and oviposition responses of this fish are synchronized with high tides. Clark (1925) is of the opinion that the periodicity depends upon a definite ovarian cycle which leads to the maturation of a fresh batch of eggs every 14 to 15 days. At the height of each spring tide the males and females swim in with the highest waves and partially bury themselves in the wet sand where the eggs are deposited and fertilised. There the eggs remain until the next "springs" 2 weeks later, when they are washed back into the ocean by the recurring high tides; and at the same time spawning occurs again and fresh eggs are buried. Clark (1925) and Russell (1937) suggest that the tidal rhythm gives timing to the ovarian cycle of the female, whereas Thompson (1919) suspects that the stage of the moon is influential. (*See also* Mayer, 1909).

But for still greater precision in the timing of reproductive cycles, it is necessary to turn to the invertebrates. The pearl oyster on the Great Barrier Reef breeds in May and again in November, on both occasions at the full moon (Stephenson, 1933). The coral, *Pocillopora bulbosa*, on the contrary, appears to choose the time of the full moon at one, and the new moon at the other, of its two breeding seasons in the year (Marshall and Stephenson, 1933). Similarly, in the palolo worm, *Eunice viridis*, which lives in the seas around Samoa and which spends the whole year hidden in crevices in the rocks, spawning occurs at dawn on the day before and the day on which the moon enters its last quarter in each of the months of October and November (Russell and Yonge, 1928). So striking is this act of spawning, and so precise is it in its timing, that the natives of Fiji have included it in their calendar.

An interesting case in which breeding appears to be determined by the availability of somewhere to breed is afforded by the white-throated Cormorant (*Phalacrocorax carbo lugubris* Rupp) and the Reed or Pigmy Cormorant (*P. africanus* Gmelin), which exist on the Victoria Nyanza (Marshall and Roberts, 1959). In these birds of Northern Lake Victoria (lat. 0° 20′ N), a totally synchronized, regular and rhythmical reproduction, such as occurs in the sooty tern (*Sterna fuscata*) of Ascension Island (lat. 7° 55′ S) (Murphy, 1936; Chapin, 1954), seems to be prevented by two important external inhibitors: (1) the relatively squally December–April period, and (2) the availability of very few safe nesting sites which in turn governs the number of birds that can nest at any given period. During this period groups of the cormorants are in reproductive phase; but the population as a whole is not. Accordingly, it is not yet known how often a given pair is able to reproduce.

Long known to exist in plants (Allard, 1919), the inheritance of photoperiodic response has been little studied in mammals. A report possibly bearing on this subject is that of Hafez (1950) on variation in the sexual season of three breeds of sheep. Hafez found that the duration of the breeding season of sheep is related to their origin, breeds from the Scottish Highlands having a considerably shorter season than those from Southern England and the latter a shorter season than breeds of Spanish origin. Furthermore, the breeding season of ewes originating in Scotland was in the period when the nights were 11·5–12·5 hours or more in duration. Night lengths during the breeding season for a breed originating in southern England varied from 10·5–12 hours and were shorter still for breeds from Spain having Merino blood.

Another instance of the importance of the external stimulus situation is to be found in the reports of Lee and Boot (1956) that the incidence of "spontaneous" pseudopregnancy in mice is elevated by some social factor attendant upon grouping several previously solitary females together. See, however, Bruce (1960), Cristian (1959), Dewar (1959), Lamond (1959) and Whitten (1959) who provide good evidence that a true anoestrus may occur.

Psychological Factors Associated with Courtship and Mating

It now seems likely that, in addition to physical stimuli, many psychological factors have profound effects upon the breeding cycle in birds and mammals. There is overwhelming evidence that many species of birds and mammals, although perfectly healthy and in an apparent state of complete physiological well-being, fail to exhibit seasonal periodicity and never breed in captivity. Something appears to be lacking in the psychological climate that either inhibits or fails to stimulate the regular seasonal gametogenesis associated with breeding activities (Amoroso and Matthews, 1955).

The elaborate courtship rituals of many species of vertebrates are a striking example of psychological stimuli that affect the breeding cycle. In many birds the cycle-pairing, nest-building, copulation, ovulation, incubation and the rearing of young—fails to occur unless the traditional ritual is adhered to. This condition for the success of the breeding cycle is practically universal throughout the birds, and in many species there is a very complicated sequence of activities forming the nuptial display that is essential to the successful production and rearing of off-spring. Indeed, so stereotyped are these sequences of events that, if they are interrupted, it is necessary for the participants to restart the ritual in all its detail for successful breeding to occur. Examples may be found in all the families of birds from passerines to tubinares—the displays in some of the birds of paradise and the bower-birds being perhaps the most spectacular.

Darling (1938) and Tinbergen (1951) have studied the effect that the total numbers of individuals have on the efficiency of the breeding activity of sea-birds that nest in colonies. Darling has shown that within limits the larger the colony the higher the percentage of successful hatchings, and that there is a minimum density of numbers in the colony below which there is little or no success in breed-ing. He further suggests that in some sea-birds that nest gregariously, the period of egg-laying is more protracted in small colonies than in large ones, since the necessary stimulus to breeding is weaker in the small colony. In a small colony, the nidifugous young appear in smaller numbers over a much longer period of time, and consequently have poorer chances of surviving attacks from predators than the greater number in the large colony, whose appearance is more concen-trated in time round the peak of the breeding season. Darling studied chiefly the herring-gull, but also extended his observations to the fulmar, which, as Fisher (1952) has shown, is gradually extending its breeding range in the British Isles It is usual for this species to appear in numbers at new nesting sites on the margins of its breeding range, and for the birds to show every apparent intention of breeding ; but no eggs are laid or young reared until the colony has built up in numbers to the necessary minimum, a process which may extend over several years. Accordingly, it is suggested that an essential stimulus is lacking until the number of birds in the colony attains a specific minimum size. The importance of numbers in influencing the breeding cycle through psychological stimuli is very great in those species in which there are communal nuptial displays, such as the blackcock, fulmar, ruff and some species of albatross. It has been suggested that the widespread reduction in numbers of the blackcock throughout the British Isles in recent years, although it is due primarily to coccidiosis, is in part brought about by a secondary consequence of the disease, which has left a population too thinly spread to allow the necessary psychological stimuli to be built up through concentration of birds on their breeding grounds (Amoroso and Matthews, 1955).

Similar psychological stimuli necessary to successful mating and breeding are found in all families of birds ; for example, the sexual displays and song of the passerine birds, the nuptial dances of the waders, ducks, tubinarine and ratite birds. Throughout the group, successful breeding cannot be accomplished unless the correct psychological atmosphere is produced by the presence of birds in sufficient numbers or by the stereotyped courtship displays that lead up to and release the appropriate innate responses.

It is well known that in many species of birds the display is not confined to the breeding season, and consequently the psychological stimuli that it produces do not then immediately lead to breeding. Moreover, in many species, and particularly in those showing display activities outside the breeding season, the birds pair for life. Marshall (1936, 1942) suggests that display in such species serves not only for promoting an effective synchronisation of the male and female sexual processes, but also for keeping the pairs together and thus securing a " marriage bond." Display outside the breeding seasons does not necessarily occur in species that pair for life, as is shown by some of the oceanic birds that nest in burrows. The birds are dispersed over thousands of square miles [1] of sea while they are not breeding, but the birds of each pair return to the same burrow for nesting year after year, although it is believed that the birds of a pair do not remain in company throughout the year. In this example, the restricted territory of the breeding burrow may be the bond that reunites the pair every breeding season.

It is probable that the route by which the psychological stimuli act upon the gonads is via the hypothalamus and the hypophysis. In many female birds, ovulation is not spontaneous, but depends upon the appropriate releasers being presented by the sexual partner. Thus, Harper (1904), Craig (1913) and Matthews (1939) have shown that visually isolated female pigeons with auditory and olfactory access to other birds do not lay eggs ; whereas females with mirrors in their cages, or those placed so that they can see other pigeons, do oviposit. Similarly, Roberts (1940a), who studied the breeding behaviour of various species of penguins, concluded that visual stimulation provided by other individuals contributes materially to regulation of the reproductive cycle in these birds. This author suggests that stimulation arising from the male's courtship display contributes to the induction of secretion of ovarian hormones essential to the female's sexual activities.

Also directly related to the problems under immediate consideration are

[1] 1 mile = 1·609 km.

observations which indicate that some birds (e.g. sparrows and flickers) which normally lay a relatively small number of eggs and then become broody, may be induced to produce ten times the normal complement if the newly laid eggs are removed promptly (Witschi, 1935). Similarly, Roberts (1940a) found that the female penguin lays new eggs to replace those that are removed ; but if small stones are substituted for the plundered eggs the replacement interval is prolonged.

The possible importance of such stimuli appears to extend even to the male. Thus Witschi (1935) reports that the male pigeon exhibits crop gland secretion if he is able to see an incubating female; and, as mentioned previously, Taibell (1928) states that a turkey cock which was tied down on a nest of eggs quickly became broody and returned to incubate the eggs after being released!

IX. EXTERNAL STIMULI OF A SEXUAL KIND CONTROLLING THE CYCLE IN LOWER ANIMALS

It is recorded above that both with some mammals and many birds ovulation cannot take place in the absence of appropriate external stimuli which normally come from the male. It is not generally known that with some lower vertebrates also, ovulation and oviposition may be similarly dependent on the presence of the male. Ovulation and oviposition are, of course, different processes, but the latter depends on the former and there is usually a time relation between them.

Reptiles and Amphibia

Hartman (1939) remarks that whereas some species of snakes can ovulate in the absence of the male, lizards seem to require the stimulus of sex play (cf. Evans, 1936). Among amphibians, amplexus seems essential in some frogs and toads, but not in all. Thus, in *Gastrotheca marsupiatum*, the actual extrusion of eggs is initiated while the male and female are in amplexus, but once oviposition has begun it may continue in the absence of the male (Amoroso, 1956). Waring, Landgrebe and Neill (1941) express the view that in the anuran *Xenopus* the ovaries are close to the threshold of ovulation at all times. Oviposition in this animal immediately succeeds ovulation, but in *Rana* the eggs accumulate in the lower third of the oviduct and are expelled in bulk. This expulsion is probably under nervous control for it cannot occur in pithed frogs. Smith (1940) states that in the Pacific coast tree-toad, *Hyla regilla*, the females produce 500 to 750 eggs, but only if mated, for isolated toads produce very few. With urodeles there appears to be an indication that courtship plays a part in the stimulus for the deposition of the spermatheca and its appropriation by the female (Noble, 1931).

Fishes

Among fish it is obvious that the females, probably in the majority of species, will ovulate apart from the male, and Hartman (1939) remarks that viviparous pœcilids will lay six to eight batches of eggs after a single mating. The male may, however, initiate the processes. Nevertheless, there are some species which normally require the presence of the male in order that any eggs may be produced. Thus Hamlyn-Harris (1931) states that the Australian trout-gudgeon will not ovulate unless the male in nuptial condition engages the female in sex play and kneads her body with his mouth. Again, Hobbs (1937), writing of the quinnat salmon and the brown trout of New Zealand, states that whereas the females choose the sites and make the redds (or areas excavated by the fish for the deposition of the ova in the stream bed), they can only deposit the ova if the male is in attendance. Similarly, in the case of the brown trout, Hobbs says that " the presence of a male is not necessary to stimulate the female into preparing a redd but is necessary to excite oviposition." It is very probable that other Salmonidae act similarly, and it has been suggested that the baggots (or baggits)—that is, mature fish whose discharge of ova is delayed or does not take place and are found months after spawning time with ovaries full of ripe ova—are individuals which failed to ovulate owing to the absence of the male. In such fish the ova subsequently atrophy *in situ* (the aged ova being opaque and straw-coloured) and new, healthy, pink-coloured ova like those in fish ascending the rivers appear in the ovaries (Neill, 1939).

An instance of mutual stimulation is supplied by the grunion, *Leuresthes tenuis*. The males closely attend the females, and when the females agitate the wet sand the males extrude the milt and fertilisation takes place in the water (Green, 1926).

Evidence as to the part played by the nervous system in controlling another phase of the cycle has been obtained experimentally by Noble (1937), who found that lesions in the corpus striatum, but not in other parts of the brain, in chalcid fishes caused an inhibition of brooding behaviour.

Invertebrates

The influence of external stimuli of a sexual nature in regulating the sequence of reproductive processes in invertebrate animals has not so far been dealt with systematically in any work on animal physiology. Certain relevant facts, however, relating to reproduction in insects are recorded by Wigglesworth (1942) and some of these may be briefly mentioned. In many species, e.g. of Lepidoptera, the eggs are set free rapidly as soon as formed without external stimulus. But in *Glossina* ovulation appears to depend upon coition, the nervous system probably controlling the process, three or four eggs being discharged at a time. Speaking generally, sexual behaviour in insects is probably not affected by the gonads. Females of Aleurodidae copulate before the ovaries are fully developed. Castrated individuals of *Lymantria* and *Gryllus* copulate normally. Stimuli of many kinds are the causes of mating—sounds (e.g. chirping of crickets), luminous organs and ceremonial love-play, scents from a distance (as with some Lepidoptera and the trypetid flies), these probably being aphrodisiac. With *Rhizopertha dominica*, a coleopteran, in the absence of the appropriate pattern involving both olfactory and tactile stimuli, oviposition does not usually occur (Crombie, 1941). Other examples of external stimuli of a sexual nature in invertebrates might be given, but the subject, speaking generally, is outside the scope of this work. Those interested should consult the book by Lees (1955).

X. Hypothalamic-Hypophysial Interrelationships

The Relationship of the Nervous System to the Release of Gonadotrophins

More than 20 years ago Marshall and Verney (1936) obtained the first direct evidence that the central nervous system might be involved in the neuro-humoral control of reproduction, when they found that strong electrical stimulation through the head might be followed by ovulation and pseudo-pregnancy. Previously, Hinsey and Markee (1933) had suggested that a neuro-humoral substance might

2 C*

intervene between the hypothalamus and the anterior pituitary and so be involved in the liberation of gonadotrophic hormones necessary for ovulation. Since that time these possibilities have been considered in more detail and it has now been shown that more localized stimuli applied to various regions of the hypothalamus result in ovulation in the rat (Harris, 1936, 1950b) and in the rabbit (Harris, 1937, 1944, 1948a, 1955a, b; Markee, Sawyer and Hollinshead, 1946a, b), whereas more localised lesions disturb gonadotrophic secretion (Brooks, 1940; Hillarp, 1949; Harris, 1955a, b, c; 1956). *See also* Dempsey (1939) and Dey (1943) for effects in the guinea-pig. Furthermore, it has been suggested that a humoral stimulus to the anterior pituitary (Markee, Sawyer and Hollinshead, 1947, 1948) might be carried by hypophysial portal vessels (Harris, 1948a, b, 1952, 1955a, b, c, 1956; Hume and Wittenstein, 1950; Assenmacher and Benoit, 1958) and the latter are, in consequence, believed to be intimately related to the maintenance and control of anterior pituitary activity.

Marshall and Verney (1936) found, moreover, that the stimulus was equally effective whether applied through the brain or through the lumbo-sacral part of the cord. In a few animals, however, haemorrhagic follicles were produced instead of corpora lutea, but it is to be observed that this also often happens after injecting anterior pituitary-like principles. Further, ovulation did not supervene until 17 to 24 hours later instead of the usual interval of 10 hours, and pseudo-pregnancy might be a day or two shorter than usual. It is clear, therefore, that an electrical stimulus could switch the cycle over from the oestrous to the luteal phase. Ball and Hartman (Hartman, 1939) have confirmed these results.

Likewise, Friedgood and Pincus (1935) found that ovulation could supervene after stimulation of the cervical sympathetic ganglia, but, as in the experiments of Marshall and Verney (1936), there was a delay of 12 to 14 hours beyond the normal interval. In a later statement, however, Friedgood and Pincus express some doubt as to the correct interpretation of their results since the excitation may have been due to "spread" to some other organ or to the pituitary itself. In this connection it is perhaps worth while pointing out that Haterius (1934) could not produce ovulation in the rabbit after cervical sympathetic stimulation, whereas Abrams, Marshall and Thomson (1954) have reported that cervical sympathectomy was effective in preventing the light-induced oestrous response in ferrets. But this is denied by Donovan and van der Werff ten Bosch (1956c), and Harris (1956). Harris (1937, 1948a, b) and Markee, Sawyer and Hollinshead (1946a, b) found that discharge of gonadotrophic hormone in conscious female rabbits could be elicited by stimulation of the hypothalamus both in the tuber cinereum and in the posterior hypothalamus, but not by stimulation of the pituitary gland directly. Previously, Haterius and Derbyshire (1937) had shown that ovulation could be produced in the rabbit by stimulation of an area above and anterior to the optic chiasma.

The question of the pathways of nervous impulses to the anterior pituitary has been fully discussed by Harris (1944, 1947, 1948a, c, 1955a), Benoit and Assenmacher (1955), Cleghorn (1955), Green (1956) and Donovan and Harris (1960).

Effects of Hypophysial Stalk Section on Gonadal Function.

The effects of pituitary stalk section have been frequently studied but with divergent results, gonadal atrophy having been both affirmed and denied. For accounts of techniques of operations on the hypothalamo-hypophysial region, *see* Harris and Popa, (1938) and Harris (1955a), as well as Holmes, Brodie Hughes and Zuckerman (1959).

Harris (1948a, b; 1955a, b, c) and Donovan and Harris (1954, 1955, 1956) have given an account of their own experiments on rabbits and ferrets in which pituitary activity was studied following section or damage of the pituitary stalk. They show that lesions of the stalk of the pituitary caused gonadal atrophy in both male and female rabbits and suppressed oestrus in female ferrets in which all vascular connections between the median eminence of the tuber cinereum and the anterior pituitary gland had been interrupted; the appearance of oestrus, when it occurred, could be correlated with the presence of such vascular links. Gonadal atrophy following stalk section in the rabbit has also been described by Hinsey (1937) and by Westman and Jacobsohn (1937, 1940). In addition, the latter workers (1937) found that if the pituitary stalk is first cauterised ovulation does not occur after stimulation through the brain. If, however the stalk was cut 2 hours after stimulation, ovulation could occur, followed by short-lived corpora lutea.

Brooks (1938, 1939, 1940) has confirmed Harris as to the failure of rabbits to ovulate after transection of the stalk, but found that the operation did not necessarily cause gonadal atrophy or inhibit desire (*see below*). The ovaries showed no marked regressive changes, and follicles could usually be made to discharge by injecting appropriate chemical substances; in the male, effects upon the testes and upon capacity for coition were not apparent or were only slight. Degenerative changes in the pituitary were also slight and the capacity for hormone production was very little reduced in rabbits of both sexes.

In experiments on male and female rats, Westman and Jacobsohn (1938), Brolin (1946) and Harris (1950b) reported that transection of the infundibular stalk resulted in gonadal atrophy, whereas Greep and Barrnett (1951) and Barrnett and Greep (1951) observed hypo-activity rather than total loss of gonadal function. These observations are not, however, in agreement with those of Uotila (1940) who reported that the ovaries of stalk-sectioned rats were normal, nor with those of Dempsey and Uotila (1940) and Dempsey and Searles (1943) who concluded that the basic sexual rhythm of rats was unaltered by stalk section. Dempsey and Searles (1943) showed, moreover, that constant-light caused follicular development without ovulation, but that both ovulation and pseudo-pregnancy could be produced by sterile mating. Furthermore, simultaneous exposure to cold and light also produced constant oestrus as well as adrenal and thyroid stimulation. All these reactions, with the exception of thyroid stimulation by cold, were produced after stalk section. Previously, Richter (1933) had found that transection of the stalk in rats caused prolonged dioestrus or pseudo-pregnancy periods, the cycles extending to 12 to 16 days.

The results following stalk-section in the guinea-pig, bitch, ferret and monkey are in no better agreement. Uncomplicated oestrous cycles have been reported by Dempsey (1939) in the guinea-pig after stalk transection, whereas irregular or absent vaginal cycles were sometimes observed by Leininger and Ranson (1943). In a more recent study Tang and Patton (1951) noted no alteration in structure or function of the testes or other genital organs. Gonadal atrophy was observed in dogs by Mahoney and Sheehan (1936) after application of a silver clip to the stalk and by Dott (1923) after stalk-section, but normal sex activity was reported by Keller and Hamilton (1937). Subsequently, however, Breckenridge and Keller (1948) reported that 3 of 9 dogs showed pronounced uterine and gonadal atrophy. On the contrary, in the experiments on ferrets carried out by Thomson and Zuckerman (1953, 1954, 1955) and reviewed by Zuckerman (1955b), as well as those of Holmes, Brodie Hughes and Zuckerman (1959) on monkeys, evidence has been presented which purports to show that apparently normal cyclical ovarian activity is possible in females despite complete structural and vascular separation of the pituitary from the hypothalamus and the same would appear to be true for the monkey (Holmes, Brodie Hughes and Zuckerman, 1959). This is vigorously denied by Donovan and Harris (1954, 1955, 1956) and Harris (1955a, 1956) who maintain that the post-operative return of ovarian activity in their ferrets could be correlated with the regeneration of the portal vessels (*see below*); the anoestrous animals having few, if any, such vascular connections between the tuber cinereum of the median eminence and the anterior pituitary glands.

In the duck where the anterior and posterior lobes of the pituitary gland are separated by a septum, discrete lesions may be made in either the portal vessels of the stalk or the nerve fibres of the stalk. In this animal Benoit and Assenmacher (1953, 1955) showed that section of the pituitary stalk did not prevent the development of the testes, whereas, after section of the median eminence near the optic chiasma, or after section of the anterior part of the portal vessels the gonads remained small. Accordingly the conclusion drawn by these investigators was that section of the median eminence or of the anterior portal vein stops the gonadotrophic activity of the pars distalis, probably by preventing the arrival in it of a substance which should have flowed from the special region of the median eminence and passed through into the blood vessels which subsequently enter the cephalic lobe of the hypophysis. This substance, they state, may be related to the neurosecretory substance found in the median eminence and in some hypothalamic nuclei. For further details, *see* Scharrer (1928), Bargmann (1949), Scharrer and Scharrer (1954), Hild (1956), Benoit (1955a), Benoit and Assenmacher (1955) and Assenmacher and Benoit (1958).

Hypophysial Portal Vessels.

In view of the relative scarcity of nerve fibres in the anterior pituitary (Rasmussen, 1938; Drager, 1944; and others), the suggestion has been made (Harris, 1944, 1955a, b, c, 1956; Green and Harris, 1947) that the anterior pituitary is brought under hypothalamic control by means of the hypophysial portal vessels. These vessels were first described by Popa and Fielding (1930, 1933), and their presence confirmed by Wislocki and King (1936). Drager (1944) states that in the porpoise and the bird no hypothalamico-hypophysial nerve fibres could be found in the pars distalis, but the prominent sinusoidal vascular channels between the distalis and the tuberalis suggested a humoral rather than a nervous control of the anterior lobe. That the blood stream was involved, forming a vascular link between the brain and the pituitary, was previously suggested by Hinsey and Markee (1933) and Hinsey (1937) and by Harris (1937). Green (1946), who summarised the evidence, concluded that such a connection reaching the gland by means of the hypophysial stalk probably exists. Later investigations have shown them to be widely distributed amongst the vertebrates (Green and Harris, 1947;

Harris, 1947, 1950a, 1955a; Green, 1947, 1948, 1951a, b, 1956; Assenmacher and Benoit, 1958).

The hypothesis that nerve fibres in the hypothalamus cause the liberation of some humoral mediator which is carried by the vessels to regulate the activity of the anterior pituitary has received considerable support in recent years (Markee, Sawyer and Hollinshead, 1946a, b; Sawyer, Markee and Hollinshead, 1947; Everett, Sawyer and Markee, 1949; Sawyer, Markee and Everett, 1950; Markee, Everett and Sawyer, 1952; Harris, 1955a, b, 1956; Assenmacher and Benoit, 1958). And in the opinion of Harris and his co-workers Donovan and van der Werff ten Bosch (1956c) offers a possible explanation for the persistence of normal genital organs in some of the animals with alleged stalk-transection. According to this neuro-vascular concept, interruption of the stalk and, thereby, the portal vessels, effectively blocks transport of the neuro-humor to the pituitary and alters the function of the gland. Once such a vascular connection is re-established, normal function of the pars distalis is possible, the extent of which is dependent on the varying degrees of regeneration of the portal vessels. That such regeneration may occur has been observed by Harris (1948a, 1950b), Harris and Johnson (1950), Thomson and Zuckerman (1954, 1955) and by Holmes, Brodie Hughes and Zuckerman (1959).

In view of such considerations the results of Dempsey (1939), Dey (1943) and Leininger and Ranson (1943), Brookhart, Dey and Ranson (1941) and others, indicating that a greater disturbance of the oestrous cycle of the guinea-pig may follow damage to the median eminence than section of the pituitary stalk, may be explained by the former producing an irreparable nerve lesion, and the latter a reparable vascular lesion. Again, recent repetition of experiments, whereby the ovulatory mechanism of the rabbit is excited by electrical stimulation, has demonstrated that it is easier to elicit ovulation by stimulating the hypothalamus rather than the pituitary gland directly (Markee, Sawyer and Hollinshead, 1946a, b; Harris, 1948b; Critchlow, 1957; Bodemer, Remery and Blandau, 1959). It may be argued, therefore, that the hypothalamic stimulation is exciting nerve fibres, and that the anterior pituitary, linked to the hypothalamus by the portal vessels, lacks a secreto-motor nerve supply and so is inexcitable to electrical stimuli.

On the contrary, there are those who, like Greep and Barrnett (1951) believe that the hypo-pituitary state which follows complete stalk section is due to ischemia as a result of interruption of that part of the vascular supply of the anterior lobe of the pituitary which traverses the stalk. Thus, it is the interference with the total blood supply to the pituitary gland, and not necessarily interference with a hypophysial portal blood supply, that is responsible for the initial damage to the pituitary gland, and thus the subsequent activity of the pituitary depends on the severity of the vascular damage and the later extent of revascularization. But notwithstanding the attractiveness of these hypotheses, Zuckerman (1954a, 1955a, b), Thomson and Zuckerman (1955) and Holmes, Brodie Hughes and Zuckerman (1959) insist that the integrity of the pituitary portal vessels is not essential for the reflex activation of the anterior pituitary, nor is it necessary to suppose that chemotransmitters are involved in the process.

The evidence relating to the nature of the hypothetical humoral substance transmitted by the portal vessels is contradictory. The work of Taubenhaus and Soskin (1941) would indicate an acetylcholine substance, whereas Markee, Sawyer and Hollinshead (1946a, b), Sawyer, Markee and Hollinshead (1947), Everett, Sawyer and Markee (1949), Sawyer, Markee and Everett (1949b, 1950) and Markee, Everett and Sawyer (1952) suggest that the pituitary is stimulated by an adrenergic mechanism. The fact that dibenamine, an adrenergic-blocking agent, may inhibit ovulation following coitus in the rabbit (Sawyer, 1947; Sawyer, Markee and Everett, 1949a) and may also block progesterone-induced ovulation in the hen (Fraps and Dury, 1943; van Tienhoven, Nalbandov and Norton, 1954) appears to support the latter view.[1] Adrenergic substances have also been shown to exert a stimulatory action on the metabolism of the posterior hypothalamus and the adenohypophysis directly (Shirley and Nalbandov, 1956). A criticism against adrenaline as the possible transmitter involved was, however, raised by Donovan and Harris (1956) who observed that whereas the injection of acid solutions of adrenaline into the pituitary gland gave ovulatory responses in some rabbits, adrenaline in neutral solutions did not induce ovulation in any of the animals injected; rabbits treated with noradrenaline showed no sign of ovarian activation.

Recently attention has been drawn to a possible relationship between the hormonal polypeptides stored in the posterior lobe of the pituitary gland and the secretion of anterior pituitary hormones. It has been suggested that gonadotrophin secretion (Shibusawa, Saito, Fukuda, Kawai, Yamada and Tomizawa, 1955; Armstrong and Hansel, 1958; Martini, Mira, Pecile and Saito, 1959), as well as the secretion of the luteotrophic hormone prolactin (Desclin, 1956; Benson and Folley, 1956; McCunn, Mack and Gale, 1958) may be triggered by oxytocin. On the other hand, from the results of experiments employing morphine as a blocking agent (Briggs and Munson, 1955; Sawyer, Critchlow and Baraclough, 1955), Briggs and Munson (1955) conclude that the postulated hypothalamic neuro-hormone activating the adenohypophysis is not histamine, epinephrine or vaso-pressin. Jöchle's (1956) hypothesis that intermedin might act as an activator of gonadotrophin release in rats needs further investigation. But, regardless of the nature of the transmitter substances, the neuro-pituitary portal system hypothesis is widely accepted.

Pharmacological Activation of the Hypothalamus.

It has long been known that various substances of animal or vegetable origin (yeast, etc.) as well as copper salts, zinc sulphate and iron salts promoted ovulation (Friedman, 1929a, b; Friedman and Friedman, 1934; Maxwell, 1934; Fevold, Hisaw and Greep, 1936), but it was usually supposed that these had an augmentor effect on the pituitary hormones, although according to Fevold *et al.* (1936) their action was supposed to be catalytic on the synergism between the follicle-stimulating and lutealising hormones. Emmens (1940) also found that copper and cadmium salts will cause ovulation (with the usual delay as in other experiments) in oestrous rabbits, but not salts of barium, cobalt, gold, iron, manganese, nickel, silver or zinc. He suggested that the effect is a stimulating one on the pituitary. The action in all the experiments was delayed as in the other experiments described above. (*See also* Deanesly, 1939.) Brooks, Beadenkopf and Bojar (1940) have also described ovulation in the rabbit following upon the injection of copper acetate,

---

[1] The time of administration of morphine has been shown to be an important consideration in studies on its inhibiting effect on the release of pituitary gonadotrophin in rodents (Baraclough and Sawyer, 1955).

picrotoxin and metrazol, but transection of the hypophysial stalk before or shortly after the injection was found to inhibit the result. Nevertheless, the follicles showed no marked retrogressive changes and they could usually discharge after injection of pregnancy urine or PMSG. The corpora lutea were normal and the uterus was one of pseudo-pregnancy (Brooks and Lambert, 1939). Harris (1941) found that copper acetate injected into the third ventricle of oestrous rabbits caused ovulation, probably by stimulating the nervous pathway to the pituitary. Dury and Bradbury (1942), likewise induced pseudo-pregnancy in oestrous rats by intravenous administration of copper solutions as well as by pituitary extracts, but since it has recently been shown that a wide variety of injected substances will also result in the same reaction (Swingle, Seay, Perlmutt, Collins, Barlow Jnr., and Fedor, 1951) this response does not seem to be of a very specific nature.

Ovulation has also been induced in the rabbit by injection of picrotoxin, a stimulating drug acting on the central nervous system (Marshall, Verney and Vogt, 1939). The reaction was delayed as in the electrical experiments and the follicles might not rupture until 48 hours after the injection. In some experiments also, enlarged cystic or haemorrhagic follicles were produced. There is a presumption that the stimulus acted upon the hypothalamus. Other convulsive drugs such as strychnine, apomorphine and coriomyrtin, as well as pilocarpine, eserine, acetylcholine and adrenaline (Marshall and Verney, 1936) had no effect on the ovaries so that it would appear that picrotoxin has a selective influence. Recently, however, Sawyer and Markee (1950) have adduced evidence which indicates that picrotoxin acts on some neural structure, whereas copper acetate may act directly on pituitary cells. These investigators found that rabbits previously given atropine or dibenamine failed to ovulate when subsequently treated with picrotoxin, and that nembutal in anaesthetic doses likewise blocked its action. On the other hand, neither atropine, nembutal nor dibenamine was effective in preventing ovulation in animals given intravenous copper acetate subsequently. Furthermore, copper acetate injected directly into the substance of the pituitary gland produced ovulation in 6 out of 8 animals. Markee, Sawyer and Hollinshead (1948) also reported that injection of adrenaline into the pituitary gland by a para-pharyngeal approach resulted in ovulation in a proportion of cases.

Following the observations of Harris (1941), alluded to above, that copper acetate was effective in causing ovulation in oestrous rabbits when injected into the third ventricle, Sawyer and Markee (1950) suggested that these results were due to the substance being carried by the hypophysial portal vessels to act on the anterior pituitary gland. On the other hand, the results of Brooks, Beadenkopf and Bojar (1940), also referred to above, are difficult to understand if the copper salts act directly on anterior pituitary gland cells. But, as Harris (1955a) points out, it is possible that a toxic substance, such as copper acetate, in sufficient concentration, may activate both nerve cells and gland cells.

Blockage of Ovulation.

Reflexogenic stimulation of the rabbit adenohypophysis leading to ovulation is apparently a rapid process which is completed within a short time after copulation. Fee and Parkes (1929) showed that, while hypophysectomy of the female rabbit (by decerebration) one hour after coitus would prevent ovulation, the same operation performed later than this had no such effect. The final link in the reflex was thought to involve an adrenergic neuro-humor (Markee, Sawyer and Hollinshead, 1948; Sawyer, Markee and Everett, 1950), which is brought to the gland from the median eminence by the hypophysial portal veins alluded to above (Harris, 1948a). The reflex can be blocked by the anti-adrenergic agent dibenamine or its cogener SKF.501, when intravenous injection is completed within a minute after coitus (Sawyer, Markee and Hollinshead, 1947; Sawyer, Markee and Townsend, 1949; Sawyer, Markee and Everett, 1950). A cholinergic mechanism preceding the adrenergic one is assumed from the finding that intravenous injection of atropine will also usually prevent ovulation when injection begins within 15 seconds and ends 30 seconds *post coitum*. These observations have been extended to the cow by Hansel and Trimberger (1951); administration of atropine at the beginning of oestrus delayed ovulation for from 24 to 76 hours in four of five animals. It will be recalled, however, that notwithstanding its attractiveness, the evidence in favour of an adrenergic transmitter being involved in the hypophysial portal vessels as an excitant to pituitary activity has been questioned (Harris, 1955a; Donovan and Harris, 1956; Briggs and Munson, 1955).

The question of pharmacological control of LH release and ovulation has likewise been studied by Hough, Bearden and Hansel (1955). They found that progesterone advancement of ovulation in the cow is blocked by atropine, thus confirming earlier findings in the rat (Everett, Sawyer and Markee, 1949). Similarly, Baraclough and Sawyer (1955) and Baraclough (1956) have shown that morphine and chlorpromazine respectively, both of which upset reproductive cycles in the human (Whitelaw, 1956) block the release of ovulatory hormone in the rat if injected before 2.0 p.m. on the day of pro-oestrus. They believe that these agents, like atropine which earlier had been shown to interfere with ovulation in a similar way (Everett, Sawyer and Markee, 1949), raise thresholds in the reticular formation of the brain stem and the results suggest that afferent nerve pathways to the hypothalamus may include these multisynaptic extra-lemniscal routes (Sawyer, Critchlow and Baraclough, 1955).

Evidence from several sources (Fraps and Case, 1953; Huston and Nalbandov, 1953; Fraps, 1954a, b; van Tienhoven, Nalbandov and Norton, 1954), supports the view that the discharge of ovulation-inducing hormone from the hypophysis of the domestic fowl is mediated by a nervous mechanism, as in the rat (Everett, 1952). The interval from "excitation" for the release of the hormone to ovulation has been estimated to be of the order of 8 to 14 hours (Rothchild and Fraps, 1949a, b; Fraps, 1954a, b). As in mammals, ovulation in the hen may be suppressed by the interruption, long before the estimated hour of release of the ovulation-inducing hormone, of processes presumably associated with maturation of the ovarian follicle (Fraps and Conner, 1954). The suppressing agents included phenobarbital sodium, diallyl-barbituric acid ("Dial"), pentobarbital sodium ("Nembutal"), the adrenergic blocking agents SKF-501 and "dibenamine" and the anti-cholinergic drug atropine sulphate. It should of course be remembered that more than fifteen years ago Dunham and Riddle (1942) reported that oestradiol benzoate fairly frequently delayed ovulation of the second of the ring-dove's usual clutch of two eggs by 24 hours and that pituitary gonadotrophins may likewise "block" the release of ovulating hormone in the hen if they are injected several hours prior to release (Fraps and Fevold, 1955, *see also* Fraps, 1955).

Other Neuro-humoral Mechanisms.

The fact that the endocrine functions of the ovary dominate the uterus and vagina is well known to many biologists. What is not so generally known, nor so fully understood, is that the uterus exercises an influence on the ovary through the corpus luteum. The evidence from hysterectomy is, however, equivocal.

It is highly probable that the uterus may affect the anterior pituitary gland by nervous reflex paths, for it has been shown that hysterectomy in the pseudo-pregnant rabbit (Asdell and Hammond, 1933), guinea-pig (Loeb, 1923, 1927; Loeb and Smith, 1936) or rat (Bradbury, 1937) will prolong the life-span of corpora lutea in the ovaries. On the other hand, even partial hysterectomy in women may sometimes be followed by a premature menopause. In the pregnant guinea-pig (as in most mammals), removal of the products of conception is followed by regression of the corpus luteum; whereas, the removal of the uterus, as well as its contents, lengthens the life-span for two months or longer (Desclin, 1932; Klein, 1939). It has been suggested (Heckel, 1942) that hysterectomy exerts a sparing effect on endogenous oestrogen, which then becomes available in quantity and is utilised for prolonging the life-span of the corpora lutea (Robson, 1937, 1947). Selye and McKeown (1934) showed in rats that removal of the foetuses by caesarean section initiates lactation and the recurrence of oestrous cycles, though this does not occur if the uterus is afterwards distended with wax. Shelesnyak and Rosen (1938) found that various reagents applied to the nasal mucous membrane in rats affected the oestrous cycle; thus, mustard oil made the cycles irregular, tannic acid or dichloroacetic acid caused prolongation of dioestrus and anaesthetisation with nupercaine caused pseudo-pregnancy. (*See also* Rosen, Shelesnyak and Zacharius, 1940.)

The role of the uterus and its innervation in the regulation of cyclic reproductive phenomena and in the maintenance of corpora lutea has been little studied. Dickinson and Smith (1913) showed that local distension of the cervical portion of the uterus stimulated the ovaries of women with involuted and infantile uteri. Again, Selye (1934) was able to maintain corpora lutea of pregnancy and prolong gestation in rats by substituting paraffin for the products of conception. The link between the stimulus arising in the uterus and the anterior lobe of the pituitary gland was assumed to be neural.

Attempts by Bradbury (1941) and Green (1941) to confirm the foregoing results of Selye failed. However, Moore and Nalbandov (1953) and Nalbandov, Moore and Norton (1955) showed that the insertion of an 8 mm. bead into the uterus of the ewe on the third day of the cycle caused a significant shortening of the cycle and a luteolytic effect, while the introduction of this foreign body on the eighth day caused a significant prolongation of the cycle and a luteotrophic effect. No change in mean cycle length or in the life-span of the corpus luteum occurred when the foreign body was inserted on the thirteenth day. They demonstrate, moreover, that the rhythm once altered, remained shifted to the new period in subsequent cycles, the short cycles remaining short, and the long ones long and that both shortening and lengthening could be prevented by denervating the uterine segment containing the bead. These authors suggest, therefore, that the mechanism involved is neural or neuro-humoral. And since Sawyer, Everett and Markee (1949), Everett and Sawyer (1949) and Sawyer and Markee (1950) showed that the varying sensitivity of the "hypothalamic centre" may be altered by varying the level of either circulating oestrogens or progesterone, Nalbandov and his co-workers advance the view that in their experiments, the endocrine environment being different at the different times during the cycle, the inherent rhythm of the hypothalamic centre is being altered by the presence of the foreign body in the uterus. It might thus be said that there is considerable evidence of neural mediation in the production of luteotrophic substances by the anterior pituitary in mammals.

Such factors cannot be excluded as contributory, but that they are not fundamental is evident from the work of Eleftheriou (1937), who showed that fragments of the gravid uterine horn when grafted on the ear of a rabbit could maintain the corpora lutea in the absence of all reflex pathways. Moreover, since pregnancy continues in the hypophysectomised rats (Pencharz and Long, 1933) it is unlikely that the pituitary plays any considerable role as a reflex central pathway responsible for maintaining the corpora lutea during gestation in this species. The probability that the placenta is implicated should not be overlooked.

In the domestic fowl approximately 23–28 hours elapse between ovulation and the laying of the finished egg (oviposition), and in hens laying daily ovulation takes place 30 to 60 minutes after oviposition, but never while there is an egg in the oviduct. This suggests that an intricate timing mechanism is involved in the synchronisation of the events of the laying cycle. The timing mechanism may, however, be altered. Thus, Huston and Nalbandov (1953) have shown that the presence of an irritant, such as a loop of thread, in the magnum portion of the oviduct of laying hens completely suppresses ovulation, while the injection of progesterone or of gonadotrophins containing LH into such hens causes ovulation, but only so long as the injections are continued. Accordingly, the mechanism whereby a loop of thread in the uterus of the laying hen suppresses ovulation is regarded as neural or neuro-humoral (Huston and Nalbandov, 1953). Moreover, bearing in mind the fact that ovulation in the hen does not occur while there is an egg in any portion of the oviduct (Warren and Scott, 1936) the conclusion is drawn that such a neuro-humoral mechanism may be of physiological importance in the normal hen, in that it may serve to synchronise ovulation with the other events of the laying cycles.

General evidence of a functional correlation between the hypothalamus and the gonads is furnished by the described effects of hypothalamic lesions in inducing the symptoms of dystrophia adiposo-genitalis. Smith (1930) has included genital atrophy among the results of injury to the tuber cinereum in the rat, but according to Cushing (1932) the gonadal effect may be an instance of interference with the hypophysial blood supply or with its nerve supply. Cushing, however, after a discussion of the clinical and other evidence, strongly emphasises the essential unity of the diencephalo-hypophysial mechanism.

Theobald (1936) has collected evidence showing that drugs such as morphine as well as psychical factors (suggestion, etc.) may affect the rhythm of the menstrual cycle in women and he suggests the results are transmitted through a centre in the hypothalamus, but further evidence is required before such a conclusion can be established. Zuckerman (1938) considers that there is little definite evidence of the existence of a hypothalamic centre for menstruation. Though the menstrual rhythm is readily disturbed by neuro-vascular change it is soon restored and can continue in regular cycles in spite of extensive and severe neuro-vascular lesions. The ovaries and uterus, however, may become smaller. Post-operative "menstruation" is only a temporary phenomenon affecting one cycle. It may occur after transection of the spinal cord in the thoracic region or after bilateral division of two, three or more pairs of adjacent spinal roots in the thoracic, lumbar or sacral regions. More recently, Gilbert and Gillman (1956) have reported that bleeding occurs 2 to 8 days after hypophysectomy or on stalk-section in baboons.

Zuckerman's main conclusion is that the uterine bleeding is a result of vaso-motor paralysis. There can be little or no doubt, however, that menstrual periodicity can be altered by suggestion, and amenorrhoea and other disorders improved or even cured by hypnotic treatment (in certain special instances) as the cases cited by Forel (1907), Bramwell (1913) and Hoch and McCurdy (1921) apparently demonstrate. The latter authors attribute the results to alterations in the influences of the endocrine or involuntary nervous systems. *See also* Reynolds (1949) whose book contains many references to this and cognate subjects.

The late Sir Flinders Petrie suggested to one of us (F. H. A. Marshall) that the lunar cycle in women may have become "fixed" in primitive peoples by the custom of promiscuous dancing, etc. at the full moon, the idea being that these influences may have acted exteroceptively (cf. Havelock Ellis, 1900, who has made similar suggestions). It must be mentioned, however (as perhaps against this idea), that some of the lower Primates have a lunar menstrual cycle. Also Gunn, Jenkins and Gunn (1937) as a result of studying the data of over 10,000 menstruations could detect no connection whatever between menstruation and the moon. In the chimpanzee the cycle is 35 days (Elder and Yerkes, 1936). In the baboon, accord-ing to Gillman (1935), it varies from 29 to 63 days, the variation being produced partly by seasonal variation and partly by emotional disturbances. Here we have a suggestion of the cycle in a lower primate being modified by external factors. (*See* Beach's very important summaries of the subject 1947 and 1948. These papers give further references. For analyses of the factors involved in arousing and main-taining the sexual instinct of male animals, *see also* Beach, 1942a, b.)

Brain Functions in Mating Behaviour.

Just over 80 years ago, Goetz (1874) reported that bitches deprived of both cerebral hemispheres are capable of fertile coition and the same has been shown to be true of female cats (Bard, 1936, 1939). Among rodents, too, copulatory reactions have been shown to survive after decortication in female guinea-pigs (Dempsey and Rioch, 1939) and in female rats (Beach, 1943, 1944, 1947a, b, 1952). Beach's analysis has been the most extensive and in what follows some of his main conclusions are summarised.

One index to sexual receptivity in the rat is the ease with which the female can be induced to display the lordosis response which is essential to the male's achieve-ment of intromission. The "copulatory quotient" is a score based upon the number of times the female responds with lordosis when she is mounted by an aggressive male. This measure, Beach (1943, 1952) found to be unaffected after partial or total loss of the cerebral cortex. It was otherwise with the males. After removal of various amounts of the neo-cortex, male rats became sexually less active. In cats also, the coital performance of the male is greatly impaired in the absence of this part of the central nervous system. However, unlike the male rat, the partially decorticated tom cat may evince marked sexual arousal even though he is unable to carry out the necessary reactions involved in coitus. This latter point undoubtedly reflects the increased corticalisation of sensory and motor functions in which the carnivore differs from the rodent.

These observations suggest that the role of the cerebral cortex in masculine and feminine sexual activities may not be the same and this is confirmed by studying male and female coital reactions shown by the same individual animal (Beach, 1943, 1952). Female rats, like female rabbits and cows, often exhibit male-like copulatory responses when placed with a second female that is in oestrus; females showing this behaviour are in no way abnormal, and when in oestrus respond in accepted fashion to the approach of the male.

We have already seen that in the female rat feminine responses do not diminish following removal of all the cortex. However, partial destruction of this region of the brain tends to reduce masculine responses in female rats and total destruction completely eliminates the tendency altogether. It is thus evident that, within the same individual, the masculine and feminine patterns are separately mediated, and by decortication the one can be eliminated without materially affecting the other.

Experiments in rabbits, by Bard (1935), Bard and Rioch (1937) and by Brooks (1937, 1938) indicate that if there is a controlling "sex centre" in the nervous system it lies in the sub-cortical region of the brain, for removal of the whole neopallium leaves the doe capable of copulating and ovulating even when in addition the genital organs are denervated, the abdominal sympathetics removed and the cord severed. Brooks (1937) found that three completely decorticated female rabbits mated; one ovulated. Moreover, destruction of the labyrinths and auditory apparatus, enucleation of the eyes and removal of the olfactory bulbs did not inhibit sexual activity in either male or female. The view is expressed that ovulation in the rabbit depends normally upon sexual excitement which may be induced by a variety of stimuli. (See also Collin (1937, 1938) and Brooks (1938) who describe apparent nerve fibres entering the anterior pituitary gland from the stalk). For further information with accounts of experiments, see Hinsey (1937), Haterius (1937), Bard (1940), Brouha (1938) and Brooks and Gersh (1941). The latter authors have found that nerve fibres of the posterior pituitary originate in the hypothalamus and that many of these continue into the anterior lobe.

Dempsey (1939), working on the guinea-pig, found that after brain lesions in the septal and pre-optic regions, and in the pre-tectal area, normal reproductive cycles occurred. It must be remembered however, that ovulation is normally spontaneous in the guinea-pig. Lesions destroying the inferior colliculi while abolishing mating behaviour and the "evading response" to sexual stimuli did not interfere with ovulation. Dey, Fisher, Berry and Ranson (1940) and Dey (1943), also working on the guinea-pig, and Hillarp (1949) and Greer (1953) working on rats found that lesions between the optic chiasma and the attachment of the infundibulum caused sterility. The lesions may have disturbed the cyclical sexual phenomena but to varying degrees; some animals showed constant or prolonged oestrus and some did not, and some had large follicles and others none. In the male guinea-pig, Brookhart and Dey (1941) state that experimental lesions in the hypothalamus of male guinea-pigs, abolish or much reduce sexual activity but spermatogenesis and the condition of the seminal vesicles remain normal.

More recently, Donovan and van der Werff ten Bosch (1956a, 1959a) have found that lesions placed in the hypothalamus, immediately behind the optic chiasma of infantile rats 10 or 14 days postpartum, advanced puberty by 5 and 7 days respectively; lesions in the pre-optic region were ineffective. Likewise, they have shown (Donovan and van der Werff ten Bosch, 1956b, 1959b) that similarly placed lesions in female ferrets during the winter anoestrus advanced the onset of oestrus to within 4 weeks of operation whereas control lesions in the posterior hypothalamus, thalamus and amygdaloid region failed to hasten the onset of oestrus.

The mechanisms underlying the gonadal response to hypothalamic damage are, as yet, imperfectly understood. However, it is possible, as suggested by Donovan and van der Werff ten Bosch (1959a, b), that lesions in the anterior hypothalamus hastened the onset of puberty in infantile rats and advanced oestrus in anoestrous ferrets by destruction of, or interference with, an area which normally inhibits the secretion of pituitary gonadotrophin, thus permitting the discharge of pituitary hormones.

Rosen, Shelesnyak and Zacharius (1940) have found evidence of a naso-genital relationship in the rat, for after extirpation of the sphenopalatine ganglion there was a luteal or pseudo-pregnancy phase of 13 days, similar to that which may be caused by anaesthetisation of the nasal mucosa; no such result followed removal of the olfactory bulbs (cf. Shelesnyak and Rosen, 1938).

XI. The Meaning of Sexual Display

Synchronisation

In view of such facts as these it is easy to see that sexual display and courtship phenomena generally, probably serve an important function in producing the necessary synchronisation of the male and female reproductive processes without which procreation cannot be accomplished. Such a view was put forward by Eliot Howard (1907–14) and adopted by Pycraft (1913), and also by Huxley (1914), who had studied sexual posturing in the great crested grebe and other birds. Howard says that the purpose of posturing is the provocation of sexual reaction by mutual stimulation, Huxley (1914) and Marshall (1954) refer to it as having an aphrodisiac action, and Beebe (1931), who has also discussed the meaning of display, supposes that it has "a slow indirect effect upon the nerves." In his Croonian lecture, one of us (Marshall, 1936) has suggested for it a more precise physiological signification.

It has been shown that the gonad-stimulating hormone of the pituitary will cause ovarian development and ovulation, and that sexual posturing or even the mere association of two individual birds will initiate nest-building and ovulation. It would seem, therefore, that such behaviour patterns are largely or wholly inherent and controlled in their expressions by internal environmental stimuli, including those from the opposite sex and from other members of the community. There is a presumption, therefore, that sexual posturing produces external stimuli which act upon the anterior pituitary gland through the hypothalamus, and so effects the necessary synchronisation between the sexual processes of the male and female birds. Herein then, in all probability, lies the biological or race-survival value of sexual display and of the adornment which in many species is taken advantage of to render the display more effective. Those birds which have brighter colours, more elaborate ornamentation, and a greater power of display must be supposed to possess a superior capacity for effecting by pituitary stimulation a close degree of physiological adjustment between the two sexes, so as to bring about ovulation and the related processes at the most appropriate times. Upon the basis of this theory we may construct an hypothesis as to the evolutionary development of the display and the acquirement of adornment and of the aesthetic sense, comparable to Darwin's theory of sexual selection, and without encountering the main objections to which that theory is open. For an admirable review of the " present standing of the theory of sexual selection " with an analysis of the different kinds of displays and the characters evolved in relation thereto, *see* Huxley (1938a). This author designates the various kinds of characters which exert an effect upon other organisms via the (distant) receptors as allaesthetic characters. They include many different types of characters besides those concerned with display (e.g. cryptic, warning, threat, recognitional, etc.). *See also* Huxley (1938b).

Mutual Stimulation

Darwin (1871) applied his theory generally to all cases of sifting in relation to pairing and more especially to those involving the preferential, but not necessarily conscious, choice by the female of that particular male which by his superior beauty and more effective posturing was most attractive to her. Moreover, Darwin made use of the argument that unless the female is influenced by the male so as to select him, the display of the males before her is meaningless. In the light of the theory of mutual stimulation postulated here, the display is not meaningless at all but subserves a definite purpose. According to this theory, it is not the female which selects the male ; it is the pair which have the highest capacity for mutual stimulation which are, so to speak, selected by Nature for the perpetuation of the race. Nevertheless, that sexual selection occurs in some species, such as the ruff and the blackcock, would seem probable in view of the observations of Selous (1927), and it also appears to take place on occasion with various species of duck. There is evidence, also, that sexual selection may operate with the budgerigar. Yet as a generalisation of wide application the theory fails. Wallace (1889), on various grounds, rejected it, and Morgan (1903) advanced no fewer than twenty reasons as to why it cannot be true. Some of the objections are supported by Eliot Howard (1907–14) as a result of his researches on the warblers, and by Beebe (1931) from his observations on the pheasants. But we do not wish to go into the objections here except to refer to a further reason, which appears to us outstanding, namely, that many birds are already paired before they begin their display.

Thus, the rook undergoes considerable sexual posturing every breeding season, although the evidence shows that the male and female pair for years together, if not for life (Yeates, 1934). The male stormy petrel, as observed by Lockley (1936) displays before the female, after the birds, already paired, come to land at Skokholm Island in April. The male nightjar undergoes a curious courting behaviour, shooting high up in the air, before its mate, and this happens as late as mid-July before the second laying (Walmesley-White, 1931). In the case of the black skimmer at Cardwell Island, Virginia, courtship of the paired female by the male was observed when the nest already had two eggs in it (Pettingill, 1937). The male was seen to pick up sticks and offer them to the female, and just afterwards they copulated.   Two days later there were three eggs in the nest.   The behaviour of the flicker, a small American woodpecker, was cited by Darwin in support of his theory of sexual selection, but Noble (1936) says there is no female choice exercised at the time of the display and in his view the bright colours are used for intimidation.

Eliot Howard (1907–14) gives descriptions of courtship phenomena in the lesser-spotted woodpecker which make it clear that it occurs after the birds have paired. Similarly, Stuart Baker (1930) has given an account of the elaborate posturing of the Burmese peacock-pheasant as taking place when there was only one pair of birds present.   So also, from the account given by Rickman (1931),

Fig. *13.4*—Wandering albatross (*Diomedia exulius*).   Male faces camera and spreads wings before female with back to camera and upraised bill. This photograph, as well as the following two, were taken by Dr. Harrison Matthews in the island of South Georgia.

it would appear that woodcock court one another after they have already mated. And Matthews (1929) has given a full account of the very elaborate displays of the wandering and black-browed albatrosses which may occur during and after nesting (Fig. *13.4*).   Twomey (1934) has described courting by Bonaparte's gulls when the birds were apparently already paired.   Professor Raven, to whom we are indebted for much relevant information, tells us that at the herring-gull colony on Godrevy Island, off St. Ives, the birds may remain paired for years.   His informant was Mr. J. W. Lewis, one of the lighthouse-keepers, who kept careful watch for eight years and reported on the birds, many of which he knew individually.   And herring-gulls undoubtedly show display.

The gannet displays elaborately, as shown in Huxley's remarkable film (1935) ; yet Kirkman (1911–13) states that the gannet pairs for life.   So also, grey-lag geese are known to be paired before the breeding season, and other species of geese are said to pair for life (Pycraft, 1911–13). Many shearwaters likewise mate for life (Lockley, 1942). There are, as is well known, many other birds which do this, and Hudson (1919) has shown that even in gregarious species like the starling,

Fig. *13*.5—Sooty Albatross (*Phoebetia pulpilrata*). Male with uplifted head calling and displaying to female who was on a ledge above just out of the picture. (Elephant seal on the beach in background.)

Fig. *13*.6—Black-browed Albatross (*Diomedia melanophrys*). Sexes indistinguishable. Bird on the nest is bowing head, the other paying attention to it.

there is evidence that the birds pair for life ; yet most species, if not all, show some sort of display.   Hingston (1933) states that ducks pair off within the flock during the winter, whereas they may be seen displaying in the spring.

Colyer (1936) has described a pair of goosanders courting and copulating in January, the duck often taking the initiative.   Mallard may be seen copulating early in January and occasionally in November and December, and display goes on in the first months of the year, whereas they do not lay eggs until March. Domestic pigeons, also (fantails, etc.), may copulate in early February long before they commence laying.   Redshank are recorded by Taylor (1938) as courting and copulating in November (cf. deer among mammals, and *see* Chapter 1, p. 30).   It would seem very probable that these are stimulating performances.

In the warblers, buntings and other passerine birds which form territories in the spring, the male takes up his position and then the female follows him, and it is not until the birds have already associated in pairs that posturing begins and it often takes place during the time of nest-building.   Sometimes, as the Duke of Bedford has found with passerine birds in captivity, coition precedes nest-building, and it is probable that in such cases also, where the process takes place so long before the laying of eggs, its significance lies in stimulation rather than in fertilisation, for it is repeated later and often more than once while nest-building is proceeding.   It is interesting to note that Jourdain and Tucker (1938–41) take the same view.   They say :

" The larger number of ' courtship ' displays amongst birds occur after pairs have settled down for the season and are, in fact, primarily stimulating performances whose biological function is to induce (more particularly in the female) the requisite nervous and physiological conditions for successful coition."

They give throughout the work numerous instances which illustrate this point.

Noble and Wurm (1942) have described the courtship pattern in the night herons, *Nycticorax*.   This case, unlike most of those cited, might be interpreted as one of Darwinian selection.   Unmated males attract females by a " snap-hiss " ceremony, but the females only stay if the male overtures and displays.   The male's plumes emphasise the ceremony and assist the nuptial bond.   When the male's plumes were experimentally removed, the response of the female was weaker and the pair synchronised less well in every case.

A further matter of interest is that sexual stimulation by display is often mutual, as seen in the simultaneous bobbing up and down of the head by both the drake and the duck, and in the far more elaborate display by both male and female during the courtship of the great-crested grebe and the red-throated diver, as described by Huxley (1914, 1923).   Indeed, Fisher (1939) remarks that :

" Some of the most beautiful displays of birds are mutual.   Guillemots, and better, Louisiana herons, may twine their necks together.   Bateleur eagles may bow and arch their wings to each other, while gannets, fulmars, and albatrosses (Figs. *13*.4, 5, 6) bow and posture, and go through the curious action known as " scissoring " when they clash their mandibles together like the sharpening of a carving knife.   Grebes present each other with nest material, while many birds make apparently purposeless journeys closely side by side or following one another."

Hollom (1937) has observed a ceremony in the smew of mutual false drinking, and false preening is found among grebes, swans and many ducks.   The sexual display of the little grebes has been admirably described by Hartley (1937), who shows that the birds manifest a special behaviour pattern after they have paired, both sexes playing a part ; it leads to nest-building as well as to coition.

For further accounts of courtship phenomena pointing to the stimulating nature of display and illustrating similar points, *see* Bent (1921, 1922), Huxley and Montague (1925), Winterbottom (1929), Boase (1931), Marshall (1934), Ryves and Ryves (1934), Hollom (1937), Parmenter (1937), Keith (1937, 1938), Bletchley (1938), Southern (1938), Tucker (1938), Buddle (1939), Gunn (1939), Hosking (1939), Lack (1939b, 1940a, b, 1943), Netherson-Thompson (1939), Perry (1939, 1940), Stonor (1939, 1944), Roberts (1940a, b), Hartley (1941), Buxton (1938, 1945), Hillstead (1945), Skutch (1945), Vincent (1945), Mason (1945) and Richdale (1945a, b).   For a discussion as to the purpose and value of sexual fighting, *see* Tinbergen (1936).   Writing of the blackcock, Lack (1939a) says that mature male birds visit the "leks" and display in October but this autumn display is aggressive and not sexual, and the same is probably true of other birds which display at such a time.   The sections on display and posturing by Jourdain and Tucker in Witherby's *Handbook of British Birds* (1938–41) are very full and of great value. *See also* Tinbergen (1940).

Buxton (1938) has given an interesting account of post-nuptial mutual " leap-frog " display in the green sandpiper.

Nubling (1941), after describing a remarkable series of field observations on the satin bower-bird, concludes by saying :

" The sexual stimulation the male receives from posturing in the ceremonial in her presence no doubt reacts on her in a similar way.   Mutual stimulation is thus not only important psychologically but must exercise a decisive influence on her reproductive organs.   It would seem probable that the construction of the bowers and the elaborate ornamentation which often characterises them (and in more than one kind of bower bird (Fig. *13.7*)) must react on the sexual system and conduce to mutual stimulation in the pair of birds " (cf. Marshall, 1944).

Marshall (1954) sees the origins of bower-building as some form of displacement activity that is fundamentally allied to nest-building.   In short, nest-building is of a bisexual nature and this has made bower-construction possible in the form of a displaced building drive, the new product of which has become valuably ritualised and permanent in the course of the evolution of the species.   The bowers, display grounds, and the activities that take place near them are primarily connected with sexual reproduction.   These complex and remarkable phenomena are probably expressions of innate behaviour patterns that are annually called into play by the secretion of sex hormones during the period of pre-nuptial testis modification which begins at approximately the same time each year except in birds that inhabit dry areas of spasmodic and uncertain rainfall.   At his display-ground, increasingly as the sexual season heightens, the male displays energetically and noisily, each according to his kind.   The display-ground is the focal point of his territory, and to it is drawn a female which, in some species, watches intently but impassively as he performs.   The display, which may continue for months, attracts and retains the female's interest, keeps off rivals and helps synchronise the male and female reproductive processes until the female goes off to build her nest and to rear her young without masculine assistance.   The male (in at least one species studied in detail) continues to display at the bower.

Lack (1938a) describes the display of a single green sandpiper, the apparent stimulus in this case being a pair of greenshanks. This author (Lack, 1938b) remarks elsewhere that the term courtship display has been applied extremely loosely in bird behaviour. Many displays serve a threat function, and displays which are directed at the female may occur in three different phases of the breeding cycle : (i) by the unmated male before pairing up ; (ii) by one or both sexes after the pair has associated and leading up to copulation ; (iii) by both sexes during the post-nuptial period. Lack points out that sexual selection in Darwin's sense typically has reference only to the first phase.

Fig. *13.7*—Nest of Spotted Bower Bird (*Chlamydara mocelata*) at bower. Note bleached bones in front of the bower, presumably for ornamentation. (Photograph by J. S. P. Ramsay.)

Communal Display

Fraser Darling (1938), as a result of much observational study on Priest Island, Western Ross, Scotland, has found that gulls forming considerable colonies begin to breed earlier than those which live in small groups, and he concludes that the communal mode of life conduces to more potent external stimuli due to the display occurring on a greater scale and that this is the explanation of the earlier sexual season in the large colonies. Fraser Darling noticed this phenomenon both in the herring-gull and in the lesser black-backed gull, although the colonies in the latter were scattered, and the birds came together for social display in a special area of the breeding ground. As further evidence of the effectiveness of communal display, Huxley (1938a, b), on the evidence of Seth-Smith, states that budgerigars breed more easily when a considerable number are kept together ; and

Perry (1938), from his own observations on roseate terns, has adduced confirmatory evidence as to the greater stimulating effects of sexual display among birds living in communities as contrasted with single pairs, the former being ahead of the latter in egg-laying and incubation.   Similarly, Lockley (1945) says that a colonial mode of life is conducive to earlier breeding in gulls, guillemots and razor-bills. Lack (1939a), also, in describing the communal display of the blackcock, expresses the opinion that courtship and copulation may be more efficient at the larger than at the smaller " leks " or breeding grounds.

Höhn (1943) describes courtship in the common pochard as being a collective affair which takes place before the birds are paired.   As possibly relevant to this matter it has been pointed out that, with the human species, living in communities is conducive to earlier menstruation.   Thus, town-dwellers are said to menstruate earlier than country people.   This is referred to in the Talmud.   Mental surroundings, education and nerve stimulation rather than nutrition are suggested as the main factors in alleged American precocity (Ellis, 1934).   Conversely, inanition during war is often blamed for the amenorrhoea and menstrual irregularities that are seen at such times, but Bass (1947), who reported that amenorrhoea occurred in 54 per cent of women in a concentration camp, stated that the loss of cycles occurred within four weeks of the beginning of internment, which makes it unlikely that nutritional factors were involved.   Stroink (1947) reported similar cases during the occupation of Holland and concluded that the main cause was psychic.

Emlen and Lorenz (1942) described an experiment with the valley quail in which they implanted tablets of sex hormone (testosterone) under the skin.   Three males and two females pursued and paired with birds of the opposite sex much earlier in the year than the normal time for the species.   The most striking result, however, was that eight out of ten *untouched* males showed contagious behaviour and formed pairs abnormally early.

Bird display is the subject matter of recent books by Stonor (1940), Armstrong (1942, 1947) and Marshall (1954), the latter two giving accounts of the recent literature.   All these authors stress the importance of sexual display as promoting an effective synchronisation of the reproductive states of the male and female ; Stonor illustrates this more particularly in the case of gallinaceous and paradise birds, while Marshall focuses attention on bower-birds.   Armstrong says that various birds (king penguins, Arctic terns, kittiwakes, guillemots, razor-bills, etc.) synchronise well in their groups but not in the breeding station as a whole.   Similarly, Lack and Emlen (1939) state that with tricoloured redwings in California, the members of each colony showed a marked simultaneity in breeding but that neighbouring colonies might be in different phases of the cycle.

Armstrong (1942), in view of such facts and considerations as these, accepts the conclusion that sexual behaviour, initiated by gonadal endocrine activity, itself stimulates gonadal development in its final states.   The presence of a suitable environment in which courtship and nest-building can occur, the stimulating presence of a male and, in colonially nesting species, the psychological interaction of the whole group of birds, are all necessary and play a part before the eggs are discharged from the ovary (cf. Bullough, 1941 ; 1945).

Marshall (1954) points out that the same is also true of bower-birds.   He considers that the display habits of these birds, however bizarre they appear on casual considerations, are in fact no more than the extraordinary elaboration of the territorial and display impulses that are found in other, quite commonplace birds. Avian display—visual, auditory, or a combination of both—is, he states, usually associated with conflict and the establishment of territorial domination (including often the spacing out of the population), the formation of the pair-bond, and the development and synchronisation of the sexual processes of the pair until the environment becomes seasonally appropriate for the female to build her nest and to rear her brood. Not before will she accept the male, however ardently and energetically he postures beforehand. It is the same with the bower-birds in so far as they are known.

Display in Lower Animals

Among amphibians courtship is shown in the active movement of male newts in front of the females, which they often scrape up against, at the same time vibrating their tails. This takes place *after* the males have dropped their sperma-tophores (or packets containing the sperms), which the females are apparently stimulated to pick up, for if the males do not perform, the females do not pick up the packets (Huxley, 1941). As Huxley has remarked, there can hardly be any possibility of Darwinian sexual selection since a female cannot know that a par-ticular packet has been dropped by a particular male.

As has been shown above, there is clear evidence that courtship behaviour and even the mere presence of the male may aid in effecting synchronisation of the sexual stages of fish. Courtship of the female fish by a male may consist merely of the male swimming round in the vicinity of the female, or may take the form of a more elaborate display comparable to the nuptial antics of some birds. It usually only lasts for one season (Norman, 1936). Norman describes the fighting fish of Siam (*Batt*) as extending its fins to the utmost and displaying its bright-red gills and iridescent colours and quivering with intense excitement. Innumerable examples of the same kind of phenomena might be cited of other species. Among the marine fish, where the number of eggs spawned is usually very large, courtship is rare. As a general rule, in those fish in which courtship and pairing takes place at the breeding season the number of eggs produced by the female is small or moderate (Norman, 1936). This is clearly suggestive of the importance of a functional synchronisation of the generative processes in facilitating fertilisation in such cases.

Noble (1938, 1939) also refers to the importance of courtship and display in favouring a synchronisation of the active sexual phases in fish. But, he remarks, there are other factors to consider :

" The elaborate courtship of nest-building fish differs from the simple display of most viviparous species, roughly, in the same degree that courtship of birds differs from that of mammals. It is the nest-building habit of birds and the need for the formation of bonds in species which rely chiefly on visual and auditory cues that have been respon-sible for the elaborate display of birds. Where the courtship is short but brilliant, the display may be a threat essential to induce female posturing but not producing a marriage bond. Where the courtship is long and with many symbolic components, bonds are formed which will hold the pair together for life " (Noble, 1939).

The Significance of Display

The precise nature of the stimuli which produce the cumulative effect of display is undoubtedly very variable, and it may well be that a condition such as that implied in the " Gestalt " conception of Köhler (1930) plays a part in transmitting the necessary impulses to the pituitary and thence to the gonads. According to such a conception, response does not succeed stimulus after the automatic manner of a reflex, but the results of a succession of stimuli become organised in mass in the central nervous system, and the response of the regions and parts eventually affected is a consequence of the organised whole.

The biological advantages of securing an effective synchronisation of the male and female reproductive processes, and more particularly in relation to the time of ovulation, becomes very apparent when one considers the high degree of temporary infertility which animals may show in cases where the correlation concerned is imperfect. It is known that in some mammals ovulation is not always coincident with oestrus. Thus, Deanesly (1935) has shown that in the stoat ovulation cycles may precede oestrous cycles, that is to say, that outside of, or early in, the sexual season, the female stoat may ovulate on successive occasions before the oestrous periods commence. The same lack of correlation occurs also in sheep and cattle (silent heat), as has been shown by Grant (1933), Hammond (1927) and others, but in both these species at the later periods of the sexual season ovulation takes place within the phase of oestrus. These are instances of " disharmony " in functional adaptation, of which the reproductive system affords other examples. Moreover, at the end of the sexual season in the sheep, it sometimes happens that oestrus occurs without ovulation, as though the stimulating power of the ewe were insufficient to induce the process in the absence of the ram. Nevertheless, the degree of sterility in the sheep from all causes is estimated by Heape (1899, 1906) at not more than 6·76 per cent. (This percentage figure includes abortion.) In the horse, on the other hand, there is an exceptionally high degree of sterility, the reports of the Royal Commission on Horse Breeding in the last century showing that in any one year as many as 40 per cent of mares in England fail to have foals. Statistical information subsequently obtained points to the percentage of sterility being at least as great in recent years (according to Sanders (1926), 50 per cent). What is almost certainly the explanation of this unduly high percentage of temporarily or permanently sterile mares has been supplied by Hammond (1935) as the outcome of his studies on the oestrous cycle. Unlike the sheep, which has an oestrous period of a day or less, the mare often remains in a condition to receive the stallion for fully a week and sometimes even longer (Day, 1940). Ovulation generally occurs towards the end of the period, and most commonly about 24 hours before the end. Since, assuming that the released gametes of the horse are capable of conjugating for approximately the same duration of time as with the rabbit (in which the times have been ascertained experimentally), that is, for about 30 hours for the spermatozoa and 6 hours for the ova, it follows that service (which may take place at any time within the limits of oestrus) is often sterile, owing to the gametes losing their power of conjugation before it is possible for them to meet. This most frequently happens to the spermatozoa when the mare is served early in oestrus and many hours or even days before ovulation.

Thus, the importance of an effective synchronisation between certain of the sexual processes is illustrated negatively by the condition which we find in an animal under domestication and not subject to the influence of natural selection. And we may conclude that in birds, and probably also in other animals, the significance of sexual adornment and display lies in their race-survival value, the pair which is more effective in mutual stimulation having an advantage over the others in the perpetuation of the species or variety ; that is to say, we are dealing with a special case of natural selection.

XII. Summary and General Conclusions

In attempting to assess the significance of the foregoing data we are embarrassed by the existence of much scattered, but suggestive evidence and the lack of a unifying principle. We know, as did the ancients, that breeding seasons occur, but, as yet, we are still ignorant of the precise combination of factors that initiates the sexual rhythms of even a single London sparrow. Nevertheless, speaking generally, there is an internal rhythm of reproduction which is primitive and depends primarily upon the alternation of periods of rest and activity as shown in nearly all animals (not to mention plants) ; in correlation with this rhythm hormones are periodically elaborated by the gonads and act upon the accessory organs and secondary sexual characters where these exist. But in the higher animals the internal rhythm is brought into special relation with seasonal changes and other external environmental phenomena, these not merely conditioning the metabolic processes (as they do also in all or most of the lower animals, as well as in plants), but, in part at any rate, acting exteroceptively through the nervous system and probably through the hypothalamus upon the anterior pituitary and thence upon the testis or ovary. In the bird and in the male mammal the hypophysial and gonadal levels of activity tend to rise and fall together, but in the female mammal the matter is complicated by the occurrence of pregnancy (or pseudopregnancy) and in polyoestrous species by the repetition of short dioestrous cycles within the sexual season. In these female cycles there are two main phases, the oestrous or follicular and the luteal, and their repetition in the absence of pregnancy is probably controlled by the pituitary and ovary acting and reacting upon each other. The condition of pregnancy causes the anterior pituitary to react differently and to prolong the duration of the corpus luteum. Apart from pregnancy, however, both the longer and the shorter cycles are liable to considerable modification by external stimuli which play upon the pituitary through the nervous system. The sequence in the female bird's cycle is also frequently interfered with by various kinds of external stimuli which control ovulation and the related processes.

The importance of environmental factors is indicated by the close correlation of reproductive function in many animals with the seasons of the year. The length of day and night, the exposure to artificial light and darkness, and temperature are known to have an important influence on the regularity of the oestrous cycle and sexual behaviour. If the environment is too dark, too cold or too hot, if there is lack of water, food, a mate or of any appropriate stimuli, the neural mechanism that governs the anterior pituitary gland will not operate, or will operate only partially, with resultant failure of gametogenesis and reproduction. Likewise, surgical removal of the pituitary gland abolishes the normal seasonal cycle in many mammals and birds and renders the gonads unable to respond to environmental factors which normally activate them.

The influence of light on gonadal development appears to depend on retinal stimulation and the effects of such stimulation upon the pituitary. The response elicited by light does not occur after hypophysectomy, and division of the optic nerves or removal of the eyes either prevents or greatly retards the reaction in mammals. Such observations suggest the existence of nervous connections between the eye and the pituitary, but the final common path within the organism remains controversial.

The sexual cycles are also under the influence of the higher centres, and it is possible on this basis to divide animals roughly into two groups, those in which the central nervous system exerts a marked measure of control, and others where this is not apparent. In the former group, ovulation follows copulation or any intense nervous stimulation resembling coitus in its results ; in the latter it occurs spontaneously. This control by the higher centres is also mediated through the pituitary and there is ample evidence that the nervous stimulus causes a sudden release of anterior pituitary hormones. This is shown by the fact that it can be artificially reproduced by the judicious use of gonadotrophic hormones. It is also noteworthy that whereas female copulatory responses do not diminish following decortication in the rat, cat, guinea-pig and bitch, the male's coital performance depends heavily upon the cortex of the brain and cannot be carried out in the absence of this part of the central nervous system (Marshall, 1938).

In view of the evidence set forth here, it seems certain that the hypophysis— " the conductor of the endocrine orchestra " (Langdon-Brown, 1935)—is an essential link in the chain of reactions which leads to sexual activation, and that it does this as a result of the external stimuli which it receives through the intermediation of the nervous system. Thus, the hypothalamo-hypophysial mechanism brings the cycle into appropriate relation with the seasonal and other environmental changes, and by securing an effective synchronisation between the generative processes of the male and female promotes the successful procreation of the race. Nevertheless, it must be emphasised that our understanding of the modes of action of the mechanisms by which changes in environmental temperature, light, food supply and social impact affect gonadal development remains an outstanding issue on which further research is urgently needed.

Bibliography

ABRAMS, M. E., MARSHALL, W. A., & THOMSON, A. P. D. (1954). Effect of cervical sympathectomy on the onset of oestrus in ferrets. *Nature, Lond.*, **174,** 311.

ALEXANDER, W. B. (1923). A week on the Upper Barcoo, Central Queensland. *Emu*, **28,** 82.

ALEXANDER, D. P., & FRAZER, J. F. D. (1952). Interchangeability of diet and light in rat breeding. *J. Physiol.*, **116,** 50P.

ALEXANDER, S. S., & BELLERBY, C. W. (1935). The effect of captivity upon the reproductive cycle in the South African clawed toad (*Xenopus laevis*). *J. exp. Biol.*, **12,** 306.

—— —— (1938). Experimental studies on the sexual cycle of the South African clawed toad (*Xenopus laevis*). *J. exp. Biol.*, **15,** 74.

ALLANSON, M., & DEANESLY, R. (1934). The reaction of anoestrous hedgehogs to experimental conditions. *Proc. roy. Soc.* B, **116,** 170.

ALLARD, H. A. (1919).   Gigantism in *Nicotiana tabacum* and its alternative inheritance. *Amer. Naturalist*, **53,** 218.

ALLEN, A. A. (1934).   Sex rhythm in the ruffed grouse (*Bonasa umbellus*) and other birds. *Aük*, **51,** 180.

AMOROSO, E. C. (1949).   Reproduction in the bitch. *Vet. Rec.*, **61,** 177.

—— (1952).   Chapter 15: Placentation. In: A. S. Parkes, Ed. *Marshall's Physiology of Reproduction*, 3rd ed., Vol. 2, p. 127. London.

—— (1956).   The mating behaviour of *Gastrotheca marsupiatum*. Film.

—— GOFFIN, A., HALLEY, G., MATTHEWS, L. H., & MATTHEWS, D. J. (1951).   Lactation in the Grey Seal. *J. Physiol.*, **113,** 4P.

—— & MATTHEWS, L. H. (1952).   Reproduction and lactation in the seal. *Rep. II Intern. Congr. Anim. Repr., Copenhagen*, **11,** 193.

—— —— (1955).   The effect of external stimuli on the breeding-cycle of birds and mammals. *Brit. med. Bull.*, **11,** 87.

ANDERSON, J. (1944).   The periodicity and duration of oestrus in zebras and grade cattle. *J. agric. Sci.*, **34,** 57.

ARISTOTLE (1910).   *Historia animalium*. English translation. Edited by D'Arcy Thompson, Oxford.

ARMSTRONG, E. A. (1942).   *Bird display, an introduction to bird psychology*. London.

—— (1947).   *Bird display and behaviour*. London.

ARMSTRONG, D. T., & HANSEL, W. (1958).   Alteration of the bovine oestrous cycle with oxytocin. *Fed. Proc.*, **17,** 6.

ASDELL, S. A. (1926).   *Studies in the physiology of lactation*. Ph.D. Thesis, Cambridge.

—— (1946a).   Patterns of estrous cycles. In: E. T. Engle, Ed. *The problem of fertility*. Princeton, New Jersey.

—— (1946b).   *Patterns of mammalian reproduction*. London.

—— & HAMMOND, J. (1933).   The effects of prolonging the life of the corpus luteum in the rabbit by hysterectomy. *Amer. J. Physiol.*, **103,** 600.

ASSENMACHER, I., & BENOIT, J. (1958).   In: *Pathophysiologia diencephalica*, p. 401.   Ed. S. B. Curri and L. Martini. Wien.

BACKHOUSE, K. M., & HEWER, H. R. (1956).   Delayed implantation in the Grey seal, *Halichoerus grypus* (Fab.). *Nature, Lond.*, **178,** 550.

—— & HEWER, H. T. (1957).   A note on spring pupping in the Grey Seal. *Proc. zool. Soc. Lond.*, **128,** 593.

BACQ, Z. M., & BROUHA, L. (1932).   Récherches sur la physiologie du système nerveux autonome. 2. Le comportement, des organes génitaux après dénervation sympathique. *Arch. Int. Physiol.*, **35,** 250.

BAGGERMAN, B. (1959).   The role of external factors and hormones in migration of sticklebacks and juvenile salmon. In: *Comparative Endocrinology*, A Gorbman, Ed., p. 24, New York and London.

BAINBRIDGE, F. A., & MENZIES, J. A. (1936).   *Essentials of Physiology*. Edited by Hartridge, H., London.

BAKER, E. C. S. (1930).   *The game birds of India, Burma and Ceylon*. London.

—— (1932–1935).   *The nidification of the birds of the Indian Empire*. 4 vols., London.

BAKER, J. R. (1929).   *Man and animals in the New Hebrides*. London.

—— (1937).   Light and breeding season. *Nature, Lond.*, **139,** 414.

—— 1938a).   The evolution of breeding seasons. *Evolution. Essays on aspects of evolutionary biology*. G. R. de Beer, Ed., Oxford.

—— (1938b).   Latitude and breeding seasons in old-world birds. *Tabul. biol. Berl.*, **15,** 333.

—— (1939).   The relation between latitude and breeding seasons in birds. *Proc. zool. Soc. Lond.*, A, **108,** 557.

—— (1947).   The seasons in a tropical rain-forest (New Hebrides). Summary and general conclusions. *J. linn. Soc. (Zool.)*, **41,** 248.

—— & BAKER, Z. (1936).   The seasons in a tropical rain-forest (New Hebrides). 3. Fruit-bats (*Pteropidae*). *J. linn. Soc. (Zool.)*, **40,** 123.

—— & BIRD, T. F. (1936).   The seasons in a tropical rain-forest (New Hebrides). 4. Insectivorous bats (*Vespertillionidae* and *Rhinolophidae*). *J. linn. Soc. (Zool.)*, **40,** 143.

BAKER, J. R., MARSHALL, A. J., & HARRISON, T. (1940). The seasons in a tropical rain-forest (New Hebrides). 5. Birds (*Pachycephala*). *J. linn. Soc. (Zool.)*, **41,** 50.

—— & RANSON, R. M. (1932a). Factors affecting the breeding of the field mouse (*Microtus agrestis*). Part 1. Light. *Proc. roy. Soc.* B, **110,** 313.

—— —— (1932b). Factors affecting the breeding of the field mouse (*Microtus agrestis*). Part 2. Temperature and food. *Proc. roy. Soc.* B, **112,** 39.

—— —— (1933). Factors affecting the breeding of the field mouse (*Microtus agrestis*). Part 3. Locality. *Proc. roy. Soc.* B, **113,** 486.

—— —— (1938). The breeding seasons of northern hemisphere birds in the northern hemisphere. *Proc. zool. Soc. Lond.*, **108,** 101.

BANNERMAN, D. A. (1930–1939). *The birds of tropical West Africa.* Vols. 1–5, London.

BARACLOUGH, C. A. (1956). Blockade of the release of pituitary gonadotrophin by chlorpromazine. *Anat. Rec.*, **124,** 255.

—— & SAWYER, C. H. (1955). Inhibition after release of pituitary ovulatory hormone in the rat by morphine. *Endocrinology*, **57,** 329.

BARBANTI, S. E. (1932). Influenza di alcune luci colorati sulli funzioni della riproduzione e dell' accrescimento. *Monit. ostet-ginecol.*, **4,** 145.

BARD, P. (1935). The effects of denervation of the genitalia on the oestrual behaviour of cats. *Amer. J. Physiol.*, **113,** 5.

—— (1936). Oestrual behaviour in surviving decorticate cats. *Amer. J. Physiol.*, **116,** 4.

—— (1939). Central nervous mechanisms for emotional behaviour patterns in animals. *Proc. Ass. Res. nerv. Dis.*, **19,** 190.

—— (1940). The hypothalamus and sexual behaviour: The hypothalamus and central levels of anatomic function. *Res. Publ. Ass. nerv. ment. Dis.*, **20,** 551.

—— & RIOCH, M. M. (1937). A study of four cats deprived of neo-cortex and additional portions of the forebrain. *Johns Hopk. Hosp. Bull.*, **60,** 73.

BARNARD, H. G. (1914). Birds of the Brunnette Downs (Northern Territory). *Emu*, **13,** 205.

BARGMANN, W. (1949). Ueber die neurosekrotorische Verknüpfung von Hypothalamus und Neurohypophyse. *Ztschr. Zellforsch. u. mikr. Anat.*, **34,** 610.

BARRNETT, R. J., & GREEP, R. O. (1951). The pituitary gonadotropic activity of stalk-sectioned male rats. *Endocrinology*, **49,** 337.

BARTHOLOMEW, G. A. (1950). The effect of artificially controlled temperature and day length on gonadal development in a lizard (*Xantusia vigilis*). *Anat. Rec.*, **106,** 49.

BASS, F. (1947). L'amenorrhée au camp de concentration de Terezin (The resienstadt). *Gynaecologia*, **123,** 211.

BEACH, F. A. (1942a). Analysis of the stimuli adequate to elicit mating behaviour in the sexually inexperienced male rat. *J. comp. Psychol.*, **33,** 163.

—— (1942b). Analysis of factors involved in the arousal, maintenance and manifestation of sexual excitement in male animals. *Psychosomat. Med.*, **4,** 173.

—— (1943). Effects of injury to the cerebral cortex upon the display of masculine and feminine mating behaviour by female rats. *J. comp. Psychol.*, **36,** 169.

—— (1944). Effects of injury to cerebral cortex upon sexually receptive behaviour in the female rat. *Psychosomat. Med.*, **6,** 40.

—— (1947a). Hormones and mating behaviour in vertebrates. Recent progress in hormone research. *Proc. Laurentian Conference*, **1,** 29.

—— (1947b). A review of physiological and psychological studies of sexual behaviour in mammals. *Physiol. Rev.*, **27,** 240.

—— (1948). *Hormones and Behaviour:* A survey of inter-relationships between endocrine secretions and patterns of overt response. New York.

—— (1952). Sex and species differences in the behavioural effects of gonadal hormones. In G. E. W. Wolstenholme, Ed. *Hormones, psychology and behaviour. Ciba Foundation Colloquia on Endocrinology*, Vol. III, p. 3. London.

—— & LEVINSON, G. (1949). Diurnal variations in the mating behaviour of male rats. *Proc. Soc. exp. Biol. N.Y.*, **72,** 78.

BEDFORD, DUKE OF, & MARSHALL, F. H. A. (1942). On the incidence of the breeding season in mammals after transference to a new latitude. *Proc. roy. Soc.* B, **132,** 306.

BEEBE, W. (1931). *Pheasants, their lives and homes.* New York.

BELLERBY, C. W. (1938). Experimental studies on the sexual cycle of the South African clawed toad (*Xenopus laevis*). *J. exp. Biol.*, **15**, 82.

BENOIT, J. (1934). Activation séxuelle obtenue chez le canard par l'éclairement artificiel pendent la période de repos génital. *C. R. Acad. Sci., Paris*, **199**, 1671.

—— (1935a). Nouvelles expériences rélatives à la stimulation par la lumière du développement testiculaire chez le canard. *C. R. Acad. Sci., Paris*, **201**, 359.

—— (1935b). Stimulation de dévelopment testiculaire par l'éclairement artificiel (avec demonstrations). *C. R. Soc. Biol., Paris*, **118**, 664.

—— (1935c). Rôle des yeux dans l'action stimulante de la lumière sur le développement testiculaire chez le canard (avec demonstrations). *C. R. Soc. Biol., Paris*, **118**, 669.

—— (1935d). Sur la croissance du testicule du canard immature déclenchée par l'éclairement artificiel. Étude histologique. *C. R. Soc. Biol., Paris*, **120**, 1323.

—— (1935e). Hypophysectomie et éclairement artificiel chez le canard mâle. *C. R. Soc. Biol., Paris*, **120**, 1326.

—— (1936). Facteurs externes et internes de l'activité sexuelle. I. Stimulation par la lumière de l'activité sexuelle chez le canard et la cane domestiques. *Bull. biol.*, **70**, 487.

—— (1937). Étude du méchanisme de la stimulation par la lumière de l'activité testiculaire chez le canard domestique. Rôle de l'hypophyse. *Bull. biol.*, **71**, 393.

—— (1938). Action des facteurs externes sur l'hypophyse et les glandes génitales chez les oiseaux. In: *Les hormones sexuelles*. Edited by L. Brouha. p. 255. Paris.

—— (1955a). Discussion on reproduction in male birds. In: I. C. Jones & P. Eckstein. Eds. *The comparative endocrinology of vertebrates*. Part 1. The comparative physiology of reproduction and the effects of sex hormones in vertebrates. *Mem. Soc. Endocrin.* No. 4, p. 89.

—— (1955b). Discussion on the varying effects of sex hormones in birds. In: I. C. Jones & P. Eckstein. Eds. *The comparative endocrinology of vertebrates*. Part 1. The comparative physiology of reproduction and the effects of sex hormones in vertebrates. *Mem. Soc. Endocrin.* No. 4, p. 214.

—— & ASSENMACHER, I. (1953). Rapport contre la stimulation sexuelle préhypophysaire et la neurosecretion chez l'oiseau. *Arch. Anat. micr.*, **42**, 334.

—— —— (1955). Le contrôle hypothalamique de l'activité préhypophysaire gonadotrope. *J. Physiol. (Paris)*, **47**, 427.

—— —— & MANUEL, S. (1953). Pénétration des radiations visibles jusqu'à l'encéphale à travers la région orbitaire, chez le canard. Sa mesure par un procédo photographique. *C. R. Soc. Biol., Paris*, **147**, 40.

—— —— & WALTER, F. X. (1950a). Résponse du méchanisme gonado-stimulant à l'éclairement artificiel et de la préhypophyse aux castrations bilatérale et unilatérale, chez le canard domestique mâle, au cours de la période de régression testiculaire saisonnière. *C. R. Soc. Biol., Paris*, **144**, 573.

—— —— —— (1950b). Activité gonadotrope de l'hypophyse du canard domestique, au cours de la régression testiculaire saisonniére et de la prépuberté. *C. R. Soc. Biol., Paris*, **144**, 1403.

—— —— —— (1952). Différences de sensibilité de la rétina du canard aux radiations calorées dans le réflexe pupillair et dans la réflexe opto-sexuel. *C. R. Soc. Biol., Paris*, **146**, 1027.

—— —— —— (1953). Dissociation expérimentale des rôles des récepteurs superficiel et profond dans la lumière chez le canard. *C. R. Soc. Biol., Paris*, **147**, 186.

—— & KEHL, R. (1939). Nouvelles récherches sur les voies nerveuses photoréceptrices et hypophysostimulantes chez le canard domestique. *C. R. Soc. Biol., Paris*, **131**, 89.

—— & OTT, L. (1944). External and internal factors in sexual activity. Effect of irradiation with different wave-lengths on the mechanism of photostimulation of the hypophysis and on testicular growth in the immature duck. *Yale J. Biol. Med.*, **17**, 27.

—— WALTER, F. X., & ASSENMACHER, I. (1950). Contribution à l'étude du réflexe optohypophysaire gonadostimulant chez le canard soumis à des radiations lumineureux de diverses longueurs d'onde. *J. Physiol. Paris*, **42**, 537.

BENSON, G. K., & FOLLEY, S. J. (1956). Oxytocin as stimulator for the release of prolactin from the anterior pituitary. *Nature, Lond.*, **177**, 700.

Bent, A. C. (1921). Life histories of North American gulls and terns. *Bull. U.S. nat. Mus.*, 113.

—— (1922). Life histories of North American petrels and pelicans and their allies. *Bull. U.S. nat. Mus.*, 121.

Berk, L. (1938). Studies on the reproduction in *Xenopus laevis*. I. The relation of external environmental factors to the sexual cycle. *S. Afr. J. med. Sci.*, **3**, 72.

Betts, F. N. (1952). The breeding season of birds in the hills of South India. *Ibis*, **94**, 621.

Bischoff, T. L. W. (1854). *Entwicklungsgeschichte des Rehes*. Giessen.

Bissonnette, T. H. (1930a). Studies on the sexual cycle in birds. 1. Sexual maturity, its modification and possible control in the European starling (*Sturnus vulgaris*). *Amer. J. Anat.*, **45**, 289.

—— (1930b). Studies on the sexual cycle in birds. 2. The normal progressive changes in the testes from November to May in the European starling (*Sturnus vulgaris*). *Amer. J. Anat.*, **45**, 307.

—— (1930c). Studies on the sexual cycle in birds. 3. The normal regressive changes in the testes of the European starling (*Sturnus vulgaris*). *Amer. J. Anat.*, **46**, 477.

—— (1931a). Studies on the sexual cycle in birds. 4. Experimental modification of the sexual cycle in males of the European starling (*Sturnus vulgaris*) by changes in the daily period of illumination and muscular work. *J. exp. Zoöl.*, **58**, 281.

—— (1931b). Studies on the sexual cycle in birds. V. Effect of light of different intensities upon the testis activity of the European starling (*Sturnus vulgaris*). *Physiol. Zool.*, **4**, 542.

—— (1932a). Modification of mammalian sexual cycles: Reactions of ferrets (*Putorius vulgaris*) of both sexes to electric light added after dark in November and December. *Proc. roy. Soc.* B, **110**, 322.

—— (1932b). Studies on the sexual cycle in birds. VI. Effects of white, green and red lights of equal luminous intensity on the testis activity of the European starling (*Sturnus vulgaris*). *Physiol. Zool.*, **5**, 92.

—— (1933). Light and sexual cycles in starlings and ferrets. *Quart. Rev. Biol.*, **8**, 201.

—— (1935a). Modification of mammalian sexual cycles. III. Reversal of the cycle in male ferrets (*Putorious vulgaris*) by increasing periods of exposure to light between October second and March thirtieth. *J. exp. Zool.*, **71**, 341.

—— (1935b). Modification of mammalian sexual cycles. IV. Delay of oestrus and induction of anoestrus in female ferrets by reduction of intensity and duration of daily light periods in the normal oestrous season. *J. exp. Biol.*, **12**, 315.

—— (1935c). Sexual periodicity. *Collecting Net*, **10**, 149, 152.

—— (1936a). Sexual photoperiodicity. *Quart. Rev. Biol.*, **11**, 371.

—— (1936b). Sexual photoperiodicity. Influence of varying quantities and qualities of light on sexual activity in plants and animals: an example of the interaction of genetic and environmental factors in conditioning the expression of characters. *J. Hered.*, **27**, 171.

—— (1936c). Modification of mammalian sexual cycles. V. The avenue of reception of sexually stimulating light. *J. comp. Psychol.*, **22**, 93.

—— (1937). Photoperiodicity in birds. *Wilson Bull.*, **49**, 241.

—— (1938a). Influence of light on the hypophysis. Effects of long-continued "night-lighting" on hypophysectomised female ferrets and those with optic nerves cut. *Endocrinology*, **22**, 92.

—— (1938b). The influence of light upon pituitary activity. In: *The pituitary gland*. Baltimore, p. 361.

—— (1939). Sexual periodicity in the blue jay (*Cyanocitta cristata*). *Wilson Bull.*, **51**, 227.

—— (1941). Experimental modification of breeding cycles in goats. *Physiol. Zoöl.*, **14**, 379. *See* also *U.S. Dept. Agric. Rep.* 1950.

—— & Bailey, E. E. (1936). Litters from ferrets in January induced by increased exposures to light after nightfall. *Amer. Nat.*, **70**, 454.

—— & Csech, A. G. (1937a). Modification of mammalian sexual cycles. VII. Fertile matings of raccoons in December instead of February induced by increasing daily periods of light. *Proc. roy. Soc.* B, **122**, 246.

—— —— (1937b). Hatching pheasant chicks on Christmas Day. *Amer. Nat.*, **71**, 525.

BISSONNETTE, T. H. & CSECH, A. G. (1939a). A third year of modified breeding behaviour with raccoons. *Ecology* **20,** 156.

—— —— (1939b). Modified sexual photoperiodicity in cotton-tail rabbits. *Biol. Bull. Woods Hole*, **77,** 364.

—— —— (1941). Light-induced egg production in large pens followed by normal nesting in pheasants. *J. Wild Life Management*, **5,** 383.

—— & WADLUND, A. P. R. (1932). Duration of testis activity of *Sturnus vulgaris* in relation to type of illumination. *J. exp. Biol.*, **9,** 339.

BLANCHARD, B. D. (1941). The white crowned sparrows (*Zonotrichia leucophrys*) of the Pacific seaboard: Environmental and annual cycle. *Univ. Calif. Pubs. Zool.*, **46,** 1.

BLETCHLEY, J. D. (1938). Some observations in the breeding habits of birds. *Brit. Birds*, **32,** 8.

BOASE, H. (1931). Display of the mallard. *Brit. Birds*, **25,** 12.

BODEMER, C. W., REMERY, R. E., & BLANDAU, R. J. (1959). Studies on induced ovulation in the intact immature hamster. *Fertility and Sterility*, **10,** 350.

BODENHEIMER, F. S. (1938). *Problems of animal ecology.* Oxford.

BORTHWICK, H. A., HENDRICKS, S. B., & PARKER, M. W. (1956). Chapter 10, Photoperiodism. In: A. Hollaender, Ed. *Radiation Biology.* Vol. 3, p. 479. New York.

BRADBURY, J. T. (1937). Prolongation of the life of the corpus luteum by hysterectomy in the rat. *Anat. Rec.*, **70,** Suppl. p. 51.

—— (1941). Uterine distention and lactation. *Endocrinology*, **29,** 393.

BRAGG, A. N. (1940). Observations on the ecology and natural history of *Bufo cognatus*. 1. Habit, habitat and breeding. *Amer. Nat.*, **74,** 424.

BRAMWELL, J. M. (1913). *Hypnotism.* London.

BRANIN, M. L. (1935). Courtship activities and extra-seasonal ovulation in the four-toed salamander (*Hemidactylium scutatum*). *Copeia*, **4,** 172.

BRECKENRIDGE, C. G., & KELLER, A. D. (1948). Retention of sex functions after isolation of the pars anterior by extirpation of the hypophysial stalk. *Amer. J. Physiol.*, **152,** 591.

BRENEMAN, W. R. (1942). Action of prolactin and estrone on weights of reproductive organs and viscera of the cockerel. *Endocrinology*, **30,** 609.

BRETSCHNEIDER, L. H., & WIT, J. J. D. DE (1947). *Sexual endocrinology of non-mammalian vertebrates.* (*Monographs on the progress of research in Holland during the war*, No. 11.) Amsterdam.

BRIGGS, F. N., & MUNSON, P. L. (1955). Studies on the mechanism of stimulation of ACTH secretion with the aid of morphine as a blocking agent. *Endocrinology*, **57,** 205.

BRITT, L. P. (1941). Effects of autonomic stimulation on the oestrous cycle of the rat. *Amer. J. Physiol.*, **133,** 223.

BRODY, S. (1945). *Bioenergetics and growth.* New York.

BROLIN, S. E. (1946). A study of the structural and hormonal reactions of the pituitary body of rats exposed to cold. *Acta Anat.* (Suppl. 3), 165.

BROOKHART, S. M., & DEY, F. L. (1941). Reduction of sexual behaviour in male guinea-pigs by hypothalamic lesions. *Amer. J. Physiol.*, **133,** 551.

BROOKHART, J. M., DEY, F. L., & RANSON, S. W. (1941). Failure of ovarian hormones to cause mating reactions in spayed guinea-pigs with hypothalamic lesions. *Proc. Soc. exp. Biol. N.Y.*, **44,** 61.

BROOKS, C. McC. (1937). The rôle of the cerebral cortex and of various sense organs in the excitation and execution of mating activity in the rabbit. *Amer. J. Physiol.*, **120,** 544.

—— (1938). A study of the mechanism whereby coitus excites the ovulation-producing activity of the rabbit's pituitary. *Amer. J. Physiol.*, **121,** 157.

—— (1939). The effect of hypophysial stalk transection upon the gonadotrophic functions of the rabbit's hypophysis. *Amer. J. Physiol.*, **128,** 57.

—— (1940). Relation of the hypothalamus to gonadotrophic functions of the hypophysis. The hypothalamus and central levels of autonomic function. *Res. Publ. Assn. nerv. ment. Dis.*, **20,** 525.

BROOKS, C. McC., BEADENKOPF, W. G., & BOJAR, S. (1940). A study of the mechanisms whereby copper acetate and certain drugs can produce ovulation in the rabbit. *Amer. J. Physiol.*, **129**, 320.

—— & GERSH, I. (1941). Innervation of the hypophysis of the rabbit and rat. *Endocrinology*, **28**, 1.

—— & LAMBERT, E. F. (1939). The effect of hypophysial stalk transection upon the gonadotrophic functions of rabbit's hypophysis. *Amer. J. Physiol.*, **128**, 57.

BROUHA, L. (1938). La fonction génitale après enervation sympathique. In: *Les hormones sexuelles*. Edited by L. Brouha. Paris.

BROWMAN, L. G. (1936). Light in its relation to activity and oestrous rhythm in the albino rat. *Anat. Rec.*, **67**, (Suppl.), 107.

—— (1943). The effect of controlled temperatures upon the spontaneous activity rhythms of the albino rat. *J. exp. Zool.*, **94**, 477.

BROWN, F. A. Jr., & ROLLO, M. (1940). Light and molt in weaver finches. *Auk*, **57**, 485.

BRUCE, H. M. (1960). A block to pregnancy in the mouse caused by proximity of strange males. *J. Reprod. Fert.*, **1**, 96.

BUCHANAN, G. D., ENDERS, A. C., & TALMAGE, R. V. (1956). Implantation in armadillos ovariectomized during the period of delayed implantation. *J. Endocrin.*, **14**, 121.

BUDDLE, G. A. (1939). Some notes on the breeding habits of the dabchick. *Emu*, **39**, 77.

BULLOUGH, W. S. (1939). A study of the reproductive cycle of the minnow in relation to the environment. *Proc. zool. Soc. Lond.* A, **109**, 79.

—— (1940). The effect of the reduction of light in spring on the breeding season of the minnow (*Phoxinus laevis*). *Proc. zool. Soc. Lond.* A, **110**, 149.

—— (1941). The effect of the reduction of light in spring on the breeding season of the minnow (*Phoxinus laevis*). *Proc. zool. Soc. Lond.* A, **110**, 149.

—— (1942). The reproductive cycles of the British and Continental races of the starling. *Phil. Trans.* B, **231**, 165.

—— (1943). Autumn sexual behaviour and the resident habit of many British birds. *Nature, Lond.*, **151**, 531.

—— (1945). Endocrinological aspects of bird behaviour. *Biol. Rev.*, **20**, 89.

—— (1951). *Vertebrate sexual cycles*. London.

—— & CARRICK, R. (1939). Spring development of the gonads of the starling. *Nature, Lond.*, **144**, 33.

BURGER, J. W. (1937). Experimental photoperiodicity in the male turtle, *Pseudemys elegans* (Wied). *Amer. Nat.*, **71**, 481.

—— (1939a). On the relative rôles of increased and constant periods of illumination in the sexual photoperiodic activation of the male starling. *J. exp. Zool.*, **80**, 249.

—— (1939b). Some aspects of the rôles of light intensity and the daily length of exposure to light in the sexual photoperiodic activation of the male starling. *J. exp. Zool.*, **81**, 333.

—— (1939c). Some further experiments on the relation of the external environment to the spermatogenic cycle of *Fundulus Heteroclitus*. *Anat. Rec.*, **75**, Suppl. 138.

—— (1947). The relation of the day-length to the testicular involution and inactivity of the spermatogenic cycle of the starling. *J. exp. Zool.*, **105**, 259.

—— (1949). A review of experimental investigations on seasonal reproduction in birds. *Wilson Bull.*, **61**, 211.

—— BISSONNETTE, T. H., & DOOLITTLE, H. D. (1942). Some effects of flashing light on testicular activation in the male starling (*Sturnus vulgaris*, L.). *J. exp. Zool.*, **90**, 73.

BURKHARDT, J. (1947). Transition from anoestrus in the mare and effects of artificial lighting. *J. agric. Sci.*, **37**, 64.

BURROWS, H. (1949). *Biological actions of the sex hormones*. 2nd Ed. London.

BUXTON, A. (1948). Roe deer and their fairy rings. *Ctry. Life, Lond.*, **104**, 1266.

—— (1949). Roe deer and their fairy rings: a sequel. *Ctry. Life, Lond.*, **106**, 1367.

BUXTON, E. J. M. (1938). Display of green sandpiper. *Brit. Birds*, **32**, 119.

—— (1945). Display of redstart. *Brit. Birds*, **38**, 282.

CALLENBACH, E. W., NICHOLAS, J. E., & MURPHY, R. R. (1943). Effect of light and availability of feed on egg production. *Bull. Pa. agric. Exp.*, No. 455.

CANNON, W. B., NEWTON, H. F., BRIGHT, E. M., MENKIN, V., & MOORE, R. M. (1929). Some aspects of the physiology of animals surviving complete exclusion of sympathetic nerve impulses. *Amer. J. Physiol.*, **89,** 84.

CHANCE, E. P. (1936). Some observations on egg collecting. Privately printed. London.

—— (1940). The truth about the cuckoo. *Ctry. Life*, Lond.

CHANG, M. C., & FERNANDEZ-CANO, L. (1959). Effects of short changes of environmental temperature and low atmospheric pressure on the ovulation of rats. *Amer. J. Physiol.*, **196,** 653.

CHAPIN, J. P. (1954). The calendar of Wideawake Fair. *Auk*, **71,** 1.

CHASE, E. B. (1941). Studies on an anophthalmic strain of mice. II. Effect of congenital eyelessness on reproductive phenomena. *Anat. Rec.*, **80,** Suppl. 33.

CLARK, F. N. (1925). The life history of *Leuresthes tenuis*, an Artherine fish with tide controlled spawning habits. *Fish. Bull. Sacramento*, No. 10.

CLARK, L. B., & BUMP, G. (1939). Light and reproduction in pheasants. 2. Effect of rate of increase of daily illumination on the reproductive cycle. *Anat. Rec.*, **75** (Suppl.), 59–60.

—— LEONARD, S. E., & BUMP, G. (1937a). Light and the sexual cycle of game birds. *Science*, **85,** 339.

—— —— (1937b). Light and reproduction in pheasants. 1. Effect of intensity of artificial illumination on the reproductive cycle. *Anat. Rec.*, **75** (Suppl.), 59.

CLARK, W. E., LE GROS, MCKEOWN, T., & ZUCKERMAN, S. (1937). Visual mechanisms in gonadal stimulation. *J. Anat. Lond.*, **72,** 152.

—— —— (1939). Visual pathways concerned in gonadal stimulation in ferrets. *Proc. roy. Soc.* B, **126,** 449.

CLAUSEN, H. J., & PORIS, E. G. (1937). The effect of light upon sexual activity in the lizard, *Anolis carolinensis*, with special reference to the pineal body. *Anat. Rec.*, **69,** 39.

CLEGHORN, R. A. (1955). Hypothalamic-endocrine system. *Psychosom. Med.*, **17,** 367.

COLE, L. J. (1933). The relation of light periodicity to the reproductive cycle, migration and distribution of the mourning dove (*Zenaidura macroura carolinensis*). *Auk*, **50,** 284.

COLEMAN, J. M. (1950). Teaser ram induces mating. *Agric. Gaz. N.S.W.* (*Austral.*), **61,** 440.

—— (1951). Use of teaser ram again induces earlier lambing. *Agric. Gaz. N.S.W.* (*Austral.*), **62,** 318.

COLLIN, R. (1937). *L'Innervation de la glande pituitaire*. Paris.

—— (1938). Les facteurs nerveux de l'activité hypophysaire. In: *Les hormones sexuelles.* Edited by L. Brouha. p. 265. Paris.

COLYER, W. L. (1936). The courtship and mating of the goosander. *Brit. Birds*, **31,** 199.

COOMBS, C. J. F., & MARSHALL, A. J. (1956). The effects of hypophysectomy on the internal testis rhythm in birds and mammals. *J. Endocrin.*, **13,** 107.

CRAIG, M. (1911). Oviposition induced by the male in pigeons. *J. Morph.*, **22,** 299.

—— (1913). The stimulation and inhibition of ovulation in birds and mammals. *J. Anim. Behav.*, **3,** 215.

CRAIG-BENNETT, A. (1931). The reproductive cycle of the three-spined stickleback. *Phil. Trans.* B, **219,** 197.

CRISTIAN, J. J. (1959). Adrenocortical, splenic and reproductive responses of mice to inanition and grouping. *Endocrinology*, **65,** 189.

CRITCHLOW, B. V. (1957). Ovulation induced by hypothalamic stimulation in the rat. *Anat. Rec.*, **127,** 283.

CROMBIE, A. C. (1941). On oviposition, olfactory conditioning and host selection in *Rhizopertha dominica Fab.* (*Insecta, Coleoptera*). *J. exp. Biol.*, **18,** 62.

CROLL, M. M. (1928). Nerve fibres in the pituitary of a rabbit. *J. Physiol.*, **66,** 316.

CUSHING, H. (1932). *Pituitary body, hypothalamus and parasympathetic nervous system.* Springfield and Baltimore.

DAMSTÉ, P. H. (1946). *Experimentale Verandaring von de Voort-plantingscyclus von der Groenling.* Utrecht.

—— (1947). Experimental modification of the sexual cycle of the green-finch. *J. exp. Biol.*, **24,** 20.

DARLING, F. F. (1938). *Bird flocks and the breeding cycle.* Cambridge.

DARWIN, C. (1871) *The descent of man.* London.

DAVIE, O. (1889). *Nests and eggs of North American birds.* 5th Ed. Columbus.

DAVIES, J. L. (1949). Observations on the grey seal (*Halichoerus grypus*) at Ramsey Island, Pembrokeshire. *Proc. zool. Soc. Lond.*, **119**, 673.

—— (1953). Colony size and reproduction in the grey seal. *Proc. zool. Soc. Lond.*, **123**, 327.

DAVIS, D. E. (1942a). The number of eggs laid by cow birds. *Condor*, **44**, 10.

—— (1942b). Number of eggs laid by herring gulls. *Auk*, **59**, 549.

—— (1942c). The phylogeny of social nesting habits in the *Crotophaginae*. *Quart. Rev. Biol.*, **17**, 115.

DAWSON, A. B. (1941). Early estrus in the cat following increased illumination. *Endocrinology*, **28**, 907.

—— (1950). The domestic cat. In: E. J. Farris, Ed. *The care and breeding of laboratory animals.* London.

—— & FRIEDGOOD, H. B. (1940). The time and sequence of pre-ovulatory changes in the cat ovary after mating or mechanical stimulation of the cervix uteri. *Anat. Rec.*, **76**, 411.

—— & KOSTERS, B. A. (1944). Preimplantation changes in the uterine mucosa of the cat. *Amer. J. Anat.*, **75**, 1.

DAY, F. T. (1940). Clinical and experimental observations on reproduction in the mare. *J. agric. Sci.*, **30**, 144.

DEANESLY, R. (1935). The reproductive processes of certain mammals. 9. Growth and reproduction in the stoat. (*Mustela erminea*). *Phil. Trans. B*, **225**, 459.

—— (1939). Modification of the effectiveness of gonadotrophic extracts. *J. Endocrin.*, **1**, 309.

—— (1943a). Delayed implantation in the stoat (*Mustela mustela*). *Nature, Lond.*, **151**, 365.

—— (1943b). The reproductive cycle of the female weasel. *Proc. zool. Soc. Lond.*, **114**, 339.

—— FEE, A. R., & PARKES, A. S. (1930). Studies in ovulation. II. The effect of hypophysectomy on the formation of the corpus luteum. *J. Physiol.*, **70**, 38.

DE FRANCESCANTONIO, E. (1956). Il Fotoperiodismo negli animali domestici. (Photoperiodicity in domestic animals.) *Riv. Agric. subtrop. trop.*, **50**, 65.

DEMPSEY, E. W. (1939). Relationship between central nervous system and reproductive cycle in female guinea-pig. *Amer. J. Physiol.*, **126**, 758.

—— MYERS, H. I., YOUNG, W. C., & DENNISON, D. B. (1934). Absence of light and the reproductive cycle in the guinea-pig. *Amer. J. Physiol.*, **109**, 307.

—— & RIOCH, D. McK. (1939). The localization in the brain stem of the oestrous responses of the female guinea-pig. *J. Neurophysiol.*, **2**, 9.

—— & SEARLES, H. F. (1943). Environmental modification of certain endocrine phenomena. *Endocrinology*, **32**, 119.

—— & UOTILA, U. U. (1940). The effect of pituitary stalk-section upon reproductive phenomena in the female rat. *Endocrinology*, **27**, 573.

DENISON, M. E., & ZARROW, M. X. (1955). Changes in estrous cycle of rat during prolonged exposure to cold. *Proc. Soc. exp. Biol., N.Y.*, **89**, 632.

DENNISTON, R. H. (1942). The influence of roentgen-ray treatments of the hypophysis on the reproductive systems of ground squirrel and rat. *J. exp. Zool.*, **91**, 237.

DESCLIN, L. (1956). L'Ocytocin peut elle déclancher la libération de lutéotrophine hypophysaire chez le rat. *C. R. Soc. Biol., Paris*, **150**, 1489.

—— (1932). A propos des interactions entre l'uterus et le corps jaune au cours de la grossesse chez le corbaye. *C. R. Soc. Biol., Paris*, **109**, 972.

—— (1938). Quelques observations à propos du rôle du systéme nerveux dans les ripostes du lobe anterieur de l'hypophyse. In: *Les hormones sexuelles.* Edited by L. Brouha. p. 275. Paris.

DEWAR, A. D. (1959). Observations on pseudopregnancy in the mouse. *J. Endocrin.*, **18**, 186.

DEY, F. L. (1943). Evidence of hypothalamic control of hypophyseal gonadotrophic function in the female guinea-pig. *Endocrinology*, **33**, 75.

DEY, F. L., FISHER, C., BERRY, C. M., & RANSON, S. W. (1940). Disturbances in reproductive functions caused by hypothalamic lesions in the female guinea-pig.
Amer. J. Physiol., **129**, 39.

DICKINSON, R. L., & SMITH, W. S. (1913). The treatment of antiflexion, defective function
and sterility by glass or silver stems. *Amer. J. Obst.*, **68**, 686.

DISNEY, H. J. DE S., & MARSHALL, A. J. (1956). A contribution to the breeding biology of
the weaver-finch, *Quelea quelea* (Linnaeus) in East Africa. *Proc. zool. Soc. Lond.*,
127, 379.

DOBIE, J. B., CARVER, J. S., & ROBERTS, J. (1946). Poultry lighting for egg production.
Bull. Wash. St. Agric. Exp. Sta., 471.

DONNE, T. E. (1924). *The game animals of New Zealand* London.

DONOVAN, B. T., & HARRIS, G. W. (1954). Effect of pituitary stalk section on light-induced
oestrus in the ferret. *Nature, Lond.*, **174**, 503.

—— —— (1955). Neuro-humoral mechanisms in reproduction. *Brit. med. Bull.*, **11**, 93.

—— —— (1956). The effect of pituitary stalk section on the light induced oestrus in the
ferret. *J. Physiol.*, **131**, 102.

—— —— (1960). Neuro-humoral mechanisms in reproduction. In: A. S. Parkes, Ed.
Marshall's Physiology of Reproduction, Chap. 27, Vol. III. London.

—— & VAN DER WERFF TEN BOSCH, J. J. (1956a). Adrenergic agents and the release of
gonadotrophic hormone in the rabbit. *J. Physiol.*, **132**, 577.

—— —— (1956b). Regulation of the reproductive cycle of the ferret. *Proc. III Intern.
Congr. Anim. Repr.* (1), 75.

—— —— (1956c). The cervical sympathetic system and light induced oestrus in the
ferret. *J. Physiol.*, **132**, 123.

—— —— (1959a). The hypothalamus and sexual maturation in the rat. *J. Physiol.*, **147**,
78.

—— —— (1959b). The relationship of the hypothalamus to oestrus in the ferret. *J.
Physiol.*, **147**, 93.

DOTT, N. M. (1923). An investigation into the functions of the pituitary and thyroid glands.
Part 1. Technique of their experimental surgery and summary of results. *Quart.
J. exp. Physiol.*, **13**, 241.

DRAGER, G. A. (1944). A comparative study of the innervation of the pars distalis of the
hypophysis cerebri. *Anat. Rec.*, **88**, 428 (Abstract).

DUNHAM, H. H., & RIDDLE, O. (1942). Effects of a series of steroids on ovulation and
reproduction in pigeons. *Physiol. Zool.*, **15**, 383.

DURY, A., & BRADBURY, J. T. (1942). Copper induced pseudo-pregnancy in the adult
oestrous rat. *Amer. J. Physiol.*, **138**, 587.

DUTT, R. H., & BUSH, L. F. (1955). The effect of low environmental temperature on
initiation of the breeding season and fertility in sheep. *J. Anim. Sci.*, **14**, 885.

EATON, C. N., & SIMMONS, V. L. (1953). Inducing extraseasonal breeding in goats and
sheep by controlled lighting. *Circ. U.S. Dep. Agric.*, No. 933.

ECKSTEIN, P. (1949). Patterns of the mammalian sexual cycle. *Acta Anat.*, **7**, 389.

—— SHELESNYAK, M. C., & AMOROSO, E. C. (1959). A survey of the physiology of ovum
implantation in mammals. In: P. Eckstein, Ed. *Implantation of ova. Mem. Soc.
Endocrin.*, No. 6, p. 3.

—— & ZUCKERMAN, S. (1955). Reproduction in mammals. In: I. C. Jones & P. Eckstein,
Eds. *The comparative endocrinology of vertebrates.* Part 1. *The comparative
physiology of reproduction and the effects of sex hormones in vertebrates. Mem. Soc.
Endocrin.*, No. 4, p. 114.

—— —— (1956). Chapter 2. Morphology of the reproductive tract. In: A. S. Parkes, Ed.
Marshall's Physiology of Reproduction. 3rd ed. Volume 1, Part 1, p. 43. London.

EECKHOUDT, J. P. VAN DEN (1947). Récherches sur l'influence de la lumière sur le cycle
sexual de l'epinocho. *Ann. Soc. zool. Belg.*, **77**, 83.

ELDER, J. H., & YERKES, R. M. (1936). Chimpanzee births in captivity: a typical case
history and report of sixteen births. *Proc. roy. Soc. B*, **120**, 409.

ELEFTHERIOU, D. S. (1937). Sur la possibilité d'obtenir un développement foetal dans la
corne uterine transplantée. *Arch. Anat., Strasbourg.*, **24**, 95.

ELLIS, HAVELOCK (1900). *Studies in psychology of sex.* Philadelphia.

2 D*

ELLIS, HAVELOCK (1934). *Men and Women.* 8th Ed. London.

EMLEN, J. T. (1941). An experimental analysis of the breeding cycle of the tricoloured red wing. *Condor*, **43,** 209.

—— & LORENZ, F. W. (1942). Pairing responses of free-living valley quail to sex-hormone pellet implants. *Auk*, **59,** 369.

EMMENS, C. W. (1940). The production of ovulation in the rabbit by the intravenous injection of salts of copper and cadmium. *J. Endocrin.*, **2,** 63.

ENDERS, R. K. (1939). Reproductive phenomena in the mink (*Mustela vison*). *Anat. Rec.*, **75,** Suppl. 122.

—— (1940). A primer for mink breeders. *Black Fox Mag.*, **23,** 5.

—— (1941). Theory and practice in mink breeding. *Amer. Fur Breeder*, **13,** 6.

—— (1952). Reproduction in the Mink. *Proc. Amer. phil. Soc.*, **96,** 691.

—— (1956). Delayed implantation in mammals. C. Ville, Ed. *Trans. Second Conf.*, *Josiah Macy, Jr., Foundation, New York.*

—— & PEARSON, O. P. (1943). Shortening gestation by inducing early implantation with increased light in the marten. *Amer. Fur Breeder*, **15,** 18.

—— —— & PEARSON, A. K. (1946). Certain aspects of reproduction in the fur seal. *Anat. Rec.*, **94,** 213.

ENGELHARDT, T. (1956). Über die Angioarchitektonik der Hypophysar-hypothalamischen system. *Acta Neuroveg.*, **13,** 129.

ERB, R. E., & WALDO, D. R. (1952). Seasonal changes in fertility of dairy bulls in North-western Washington. *J. Dairy Sci.*, **35,** 245.

EVANS, H. M., & COLE, H. H. (1931). An Introduction to the study of the oestrous cycle in the dog. *Mem. Univ. Calif.*, **9,** 66.

EVANS, L. T. (1935a). The effects of pituitary implants and extracts on the genital system of the lizard. *Science*, **81,** 468.

—— (1935b). The effect of antuitrin-S on the male lizard, *Anolis carolinensis.* *Anat. Rec.*, **62,** 213.

—— (1936). Social behaviour of the normal and castrated females of *Anolis carolinensis.* *Science*, **8,** 104.

—— & CLAPP, M. L. (1940). The effect of ovarian hormone and seasons on *Anolis carolinensis.* *Anat. Rec.*, **77,** 47.

EVERETT, J. W. (1942). Certain functional interrelationships between spontaneous persistent estrus, " light " estrus and short-day anestrus in the albino rat. *Anat. Rec.*, **82,** 409.

EVERETT, J. W. (1952). Presumptive hypothalamic control of spontaneous ovulation. In: G. E. W. Wolstenholme, Ed. *Anterior pituitary secretion and hormonal influences in water metabolism. Ciba Foundation Colloquia on Endocrinology.* Vol. V, p. 167. London.

—— & SAWYER, C. H. (1949). A neural timing factor in the mechanism by which progesterone advances ovulation in the cyclic rat. *Endocrinology*, **45,** 581.

—— —— (1950). A 24-hour periodicity in the "LH-release apparatus" of female rats, disclosed by barbiturate sedation. *Endocrinology*, **47,** 198.

—— —— & MARKEE, J. E. (1949). A neurogenic timing factor in control of the ovulatory discharge of luteinizing hormone in the cyclic rat. *Endocrinology*, **44,** 234.

FAIRBANKS, F. L., & HEUSER, G. F. (1940). Artificial illumination of poultry laying house for winter egg production. *Cornell Ext. Bull.*, 411.

—— & RICE, J. E. (1924). Artificial illumination of poultry laying house for winter egg production. *Cornell Ext. Bull.*, 90. (*See also* Fairbanks, F. L., & Heuser, G. F., 1940.)

FARNER, D. S., & MEWALDT, L. R. (1952). The relative rôles of photoperiod and temperature in gonadal recrudescence in male *Zonotrichia leucophrys gambelii.* *Anat. Rec.*, **113,** 612.

—— —— & IRVING, S. D. (1953a). The rôle of darkness and light in the activation of avian gonads. *Science*, **118,** 351.

—— —— —— (1953b). The rôles of darkness and light in the photoperiodic response of the testes of white-crowned sparrows. *Biol. Bull. Wood's Hole*, **105,** 434.

FARRIS, E. J. (1950). *The care and breeding of laboratory animals.* New York; London.

FARRIS, E. J. & YEAKEL, E. H. (1944). Breeding and rearing of young albino rats subjected to auditory stimulation. *Anat. Rec.*, **89,** 325.

FEE, A. R., & PARKES, A. S. (1929). Studies on ovulation. 1. The relation of the anterior pituitary body to ovulation in the rabbit. *J. Physiol.*, **67,** 383.

FEVOLD, H. L., HISAW, F. L., & GREEP, R. (1936). Augmentation of the gonad-stimulating action of pituitary extract by inorganic substances, particularly copper salts. *Amer. J. Physiol.*, **117,** 68.

FISCHER, E. (1931). Die Entwicklungsgeschichte des Dachses und die Frage der Zwillings bildung. *Vehandl. d. anat. Gesellsch.*, **72,** 22.

FISHER, H. D. (1954). Delayed implantation in the harbour seal. *Phoca vitulina L. Nature, Lond.*, **173,** 879.

FISHER, J. (1939). *Birds as animals.* London.

—— (1952). *The fulmar.* London.

FISKE, V. M. (1939). Effects of light and darkness on activity of the pituitary of the rat. *Proc. Soc. exp. Biol. Med.*, **40,** 189.

—— (1941). Effect of light on sexual maturation, estrous cycles, and anterior pituitary of the rat. *Endocrinology*, **29,** 187.

FITZSIMONS, F. W. (1919–1920). *The natural history of South Africa.* Vols. 1–4. London.

FLOWER, S. S. (1932). Notes on the recent mammals of Egypt, with a list of the species recorded in that Kingdom. *Proc. zool. Soc. Lond.*, 369.

FOLLEY, W. J. (1955). Discussion on reproduction in mammals. In: I. C. Jones & P. Eckstein, Eds. *The comparative endocrinology of vertebrates.* Part I. *The comparative physiology of reproduction and the effects of sex hormones in vertebrates. Mem. Soc. Endocrinol.*, No. 4, p. 127.

FOREL, A. (1907). *Hypnotism or suggestion and psychotherapy.* New York.

FOSTER, M. A. (1934). The reproductive cycle in the female ground squirrel, *Citellus tridecemlineatus* (Mitchell). *Amer. J. Anat.*, **54,** 487.

—— & HISAW, F. L. (1935). Experimental ovulation and the resulting pseudo-pregnancy in anoestrus cats. *Anat. Rec.*, **62,** 75.

FRAPS, R. M. (1954a). Natural basis of diurnal periodicity in release of ovulation-inducing hormone in fowl. *Proc. nat. Acad. Sci., Wash.*, **40,** 348.

—— (1954b). Timing functions of a neural component in the mechanism of release of pituitary gonadotrophin for ovulation in the hen. *Tenth World's Poult. Congr., Edinburgh*, p. 170.

—— (1955). The varying effects of sex hormones in birds. In: I. C. Jones & P. Eckstein, Eds. *The comparative endocrinology of vertebrates.* Part 1. *The comparative physiology of reproduction and the effects of sex hormones in vertebrates. Mem. Soc. Endocrin.*, No. 4, p. 205.

—— & CASE, J. R. (1953). Premature ovulation in the domestic fowl following administration of certain barbiturates. *Proc. Soc. exp. Biol., N.Y.*, **82,** 167.

—— & CONNER, M. H. (1954). Neurohypophysial control of follicular maturation in the domestic fowl. *Nature, Lond.*, **174,** 1148.

—— & DURY, A. (1943). Occurrence of premature ovulation in the domestic fowl following administration of progesterone. *Proc. Soc. exp. Biol. Med.*, **52,** 346.

—— & FEVOLD, H. L. (1955). Delaying action of gonadotrophins on ovulation in the hen. *Proc. Soc. exp. Biol. Med.*, **90,** 440.

—— NEHER, B. H., & ROTHCHILD, I. (1947). The imposition of diurnal ovulatory and temperature rhythms by periodic feeding of hens maintained under continuous light. *Endocrinology*, **40,** 241.

FREY, E. (1951). Über die hypothalamische Opticuswurzel des Hundes. *Bull. schweiz. Akad. med. Wiss.*, **7,** 115.

FRIEDGOOD, H. B., & BEVIN, S. (1938). Relation of the cervical sympathetics to pseudo-pregnancy in the rat. *Amer. J. Physiol.*, **123,** 71.

—— —— (1941). Relation of the cervical sympathetics to anterior pituitary gonadotropic activity in the rat. *Amer. J. Physiol.*, **133,** 282.

—— & DAWSON, A. B. (1942). Inhibition of carmine-cell reaction in the pituitaries of cats which mate but do not ovulate. *Endocrinology*, **30,** 252.

Friedgood, H. B. & Pincus, G. (1935). Studies on conditions of activity in endocrine organs. 30. The nervous control of the anterior hypophysis as indicated by maturation of ova and ovulation after stimulation of cervical sympathetics. *Endocrinology*, **19**, 710.

Friedman, H. (1929). *The cowbirds: A study in the biology of social parasitism.* Springfield and Baltimore.

Friedman, M. H. (1929a). The mechanism of ovulation in the rabbit. 1. The demonstration of a humoral mechanism. *Amer. J. Physiol.*, **89**, 438.

—— (1929b). The mechanism of ovulation in the rabbit. II. Ovulation produced by the injection of urine from pregnant women. *Amer. J. Physiol.*, **90**, 617.

—— & Friedman, G. S. (1934). A gonad-stimulating extract from alfalfa meal. *Proc. Soc. exp. Biol., N.Y.*, **31**, 842.

Fries, S. (1880). Über die Fortpflanzung von *Meles taxus. Zool. Anz.*, **3**, 486.

Galgano, M., & Mazzi, V. (1951). Modalita di regolazione dei cicli sessuali foto- e termoperiodici nei vertebrati. (The regulation of the photo- and thermo-periodical sexual cycles in vertebrates.) *Riv. Biol.*, **43**, 21 (B). (English summary.)

Gaupp, V., & Spatz, H. (1955). Hypophysenstieldurchtrennung und Geschlechtsreifung über Regenerationerscheinungen an der suprasellaren Hypophyse. *Acta neuroveg., Wien*, **12**, 285.

Gibbney, L. (1953). Delayed implantation in the elephant seal. *Nature, Lond.*, **172**, 590.

Gibson-Hall, C. A. (1941). The tropic or bosun birds. *Field*, **177**, 304.

Gilbert, C., & Gillman, J. (1956). Role of adrenal and thyroid in promoting bleeding in hypophysectomized baboons (*Papio ursinus*). *Endocrinology*, **58**, 753.

Gillman, J. (1935). The cyclical changes in the external genital organs of the baboon (*Papio porcarius*). *S. Afr. J. Sci.*, **32**, 342.

—— & Gilbert, C. (1946). The reproductive cycle of the Chacma baboon (*Papio ursinus*) with special reference to the problems of menstrual irregularities as assessed by the behaviour of the sex skin. *S. Afr. J. Sci.*, **11** (Biol. Suppl.), 1.

Goethe, F. (1937). Beobachtungen und Untersuchungen zür Biologie der Silbermowe (*Larus argentatius*) auf der Vögelinsel Mmertsand. *J. Orn. Lpz.*, **85**, 1.

Goetz, F. (1874). Über den Einfluss des Nervensystems auf die Vorgänge während der Schwangerschaft und des Gebärakts. *Pflüg. Arch. ges. Physiol.*, **9**, 552.

Grant, R. (1933). Studies on the physiology of reproduction in the ewe. 1. The symptoms, periodicity and duration of oestrus. 2. Changes in the vagina and cervix. 3. Gross changes in the ovaries. *Trans. roy. Soc. Edin.*, **58**, 1.

Greeley, F., & Meyer, R. K. (1953). Seasonal variation in testes-stimulating activity of male pheasant pituitary glands. *Auk*, **70**, 350.

Green, C. W. (1926). The physiology of spawning migrations. *Physiol. Rev.*, **6**, 201.

Green, J. D. (1946). The adenohypophysis and the central nervous system. *Alexander Blain Hospital Bull.* (Detroit), **5**, 186.

—— (1947). Vessels and nerves of amphibian hypophyses: a study of the living circulation and of the histology of the hypophysial vessels and nerves. *Anat. Rec.*, **99**, 21.

—— (1948). The histology of the hypophysial stalk and median eminence in man with special reference to blood vessels, nerve fibres and a peculiar neuro-vascular zone in this region. *Anat. Rec.*, **100**, 373.

—— (1951a). The comparative anatomy of the hypophysis, with special reference to its blood supply and innervation. *Amer. J. Anat.*, **88**, 225.

—— (1951b). Innervation of the pars distalis of the adenohypophysis studied by phase microscopy. *Anat. Rec.*, **109**, 99.

—— (1952). Comparative aspects of the hypophysis especially of blood supply and innervation. In: G. E. W. Wolstenholme, Ed. *Anterior pituitary secretion and hormone influences in water metabolism. Ciba Foundation Colloquia on Endocrinology*, Vol. IV, p. 106. London.

—— (1956). Neural pathways to the hypophysis. In: W. S. Fields, R. Guillemin and C. A. Carton, Eds. *Hypothalamic-hypophysial interrelationships*, p. 1. Springfield, Illinois.

—— & Harris, G. W. (1947). The neurovascular link between the neurohypophysis and adenohypophysis. *J. Endocrin.*, **5**, 136.

GREEN, R. R. (1941). Uterine distention and lactation in the rat. *Endocrinology*, **29**, 1026.

GREEP, R. O., & BARRNETT, R. J. (1951). The effect of pituitary stalk-section on the reproductive organs of female rats. *Endocrinology*, **49**, 172.

GREER, M. A. (1953). The effect of progesterone on persistent vaginal estrus produced by hypothalamic lesions in the rat. *Endocrinology*, **53**, 380.

GRESSON, R. A. R. (1940). The effect of increased daily illumination and of reversed day and night on the oestrous cycle of the mouse. *Proc. roy. Soc. Edin.*, **60**, 333.

GREULICH, W. W. (1934). Artificially induced ovulation in the cat. (*Felis domesticus*). *Anat. Rec.*, **58**, 217.

GRIFFITHS, W. F. B., & AMOROSO, E. C. (1939). Pro-oestrus, oestrus, ovulation and mating in the greyhound bitch. *Vet. Rec.*, **51**, 1279.

GROS, G. (1935). Evolution de la muqueuse uterin chez la chatte. *C. R. Soc. Biol., Paris*, **131**, 172.

GUNN, D. (1939). On the courtship display of the golden-eye. *Brit. Birds*, **33**, 48.

GUNN, D. L., JENKINS, P. M., & GUNN, A. L. (1937). Menstrual periodicity. *J. Obstet. Gynaec.*, **44**, 839.

GUNN, R. M. C., SANDERS, R. N., & GRANGER, W. (1942). Studies in fertility in sheep. 2. Seminal changes affecting fertility in rams. *Bull. Coun. Sci. industr. Res. Aust.*, No. 148.

HAFEZ, E. S. E. (1950). Sexual season of the ewe and daylight environment. *Nature, Lond.*, **166**, 822.

—— (1951a). The influence of environment and heredity on the breeding season of the ewe. *Experientia*, **7**, 353.

—— (1951b). Reproduction in sheep and the response to artificial light. *Experientia*, **7**, 423.

—— (1951c). Inhibitory action of artificial light on the sexual season of the ewe. *Nature, Lond.*, **168**, 336.

—— (1952a). The sexual season and photoperiodicity in the ewe. *Rep. II Intern. Congr. Anim. Repr., Copenhagen*, **1**, 105.

—— (1952b). Studies on the breeding season and reproduction of the ewe. I. The breeding season in different environments. II. The breeding season in one locality. III. The breeding season and artificial light. IV. Studies on the reproduction of the ewe. V. Mating behaviour and pregnancy diagnosis. *J. agric. Sci.*, **42**, 189, 232, 241, 255.

HAIR, G. W., & MERZEN, J. F. (1939). A study of the functional innervation of the hypophysis. *Endocrinology*, **25**, 965.

HAMLETT, G. W. D. (1932a). Observations on the embryology of the badger. *Anat. Rec.*, **53**, 283.

—— (1932b). The reproductive cycle in the Armadillo. *Ztschr. f. wissensch. Zool.*, **141**, 143.

—— (1935). Delayed implantation and discontinuous development in the mammals. *Quart. Rev. Biol.*, **10**, 432.

—— (1952). Notes on breeding and reproduction in the lizard, *Anolis carolinensis*. *Copeia*, **3**, 183.

HAMLYN-HARRIS, R. (1931). A further contribution to the breeding habits of *Morgurnda adspersus*, the trout gudgeon. *Australian Zool.*, **7**, 55.

HAMMOND, J. (1927). *The physiology of reproduction in the cow.* Cambridge University Press, London.

—— (1935). Oestrus and ovulation in the mare. *15th Int. Physiol. congr. Summary of communications*, p. 142. Leningrad and Moscow.

—— (1939). Physiological aspects of bovine sterility. *57th Ann. Congr. Nat. Vet. Med. Assoc. of Great Britain and Ireland.*

—— (1940). *Farm animals: Their breeding, growth and inheritance.* London.

—— (1954). *Progress in the physiology of farm animals.* Hammond, J., Ed., vol. 1. *See* Yeates (1954). London.

—— & MARSHALL, F. H. A. (1925). *Reproduction in the rabbit.* Edinburgh.

—— —— (1930). Oestrus and pseudo-pregnancy in the ferret. *Proc. roy. Soc. B*, **105**, 607.

HAMMOND, J. & WALTON, A. (1934). Notes on ovulation and fertilization in the ferret. *J. exp. Biol.*, **11**, 307.

HAMMOND, J., Jr. (1944). On the breeding season in the sheep. *J. agric. Sci.*, **34**, 97.

—— (1951a). Control by light of reproduction in ferrets and mink. *Nature, Lond.*, **167**, 150.

—— (1951b). Failure of progesterone treatment to affect delayed implantation in mink. *J. Endocrinol.*, **7**, 330.

—— (1953a). Photoperiodicity in animals: the rôle of darkness. *Science*, **117**, 389.

—— (1953b). *Effects of artificial lighting on the reproductive and pelt cycles of mink.* Cambridge.

—— (1954). Light regulation of hormone secretion. *Vitamins and Hormones*, **12**, 157.

HANCOCK, J. L., & ROWLANDS, I. W. (1949). The physiology of reproduction in the dog. *Vet. Rec.*, **61**, 721.

HANN, H. W. (1927). The history of the germ cells of *Cottus Bairdii girard*. *J. Morph.*, **43**, 427.

—— (1939). The relation of castration to migration in birds. *Birdbanding*, **10**, 122.

HANSEL, W., & TRIMBERGER, G. W. (1951). Atropine blockade of ovulation in the cow and its possible significance. *J. Anim. Sci.*, **10**, 710.

HANSSON, A. (1947). *The physiology of reproduction in mink (Mustela vison schreb). With special reference to delayed implantation.* Stockholm.

HARPER, E. H. (1904). The fertilization and early development of the pigeon's egg. *Amer. J. Anat.*, **3**, 349.

HARRINGTON, R. W. (1950). Preseasonal breeding by the bridled shiner, *Notropis bifrenatus*, induced under light-temperature control. *Copeia*, 304.

HARRIS, G. W. (1936). The induction of pseudo-pregnancy in the rat by electrical stimulation through the head. *J. Physiol.*, **88**, 361.

—— (1937). The induction of ovulation in the rabbit by electrical stimulation of the hypo-thalamohypophysial mechanism. *Proc. roy. Soc. B*, **122**, 374.

—— (1941). Further evidence concerning the rôle of the hypothalamus in the induction of ovulation in the rabbit following injections of copper acetate. *J. Physiol.*, **100**, 231.

—— (1944). The secreto-motor innervation and actions of the neurohypophysis; an investigation using the method of remote control stimulation. Thesis for M.D. degree, Cambridge University.

—— (1947). The innervation and actions of the neurohypophysis; an investigation using the method of remote control stimulation. *Phil. Trans. B*, **232**, 385.

—— (1948a). Neural control of the pituitary gland. *Physiol. Rev.*, **28**, 139.

—— (1948b). Electrical stimulation of the hypothalamus and the mechanism of neural control of the adenohypophysis. *J. Physiol.*, **107**, 418.

—— (1948c). The excretion of an antidiuretic substance by the kidney, after electrical stimulation of the neurohypophysis in the unanaesthetized rabbit. *J. Physiol.*, **107**, 430.

—— (1950a). Hypothalamo-hypophysial connexions in the cetacea. *J. Physiol.*, **111**, 361.

—— (1950b). Oestrus rhythm, pseudo-pregnancy and the pituitary stalk in the rat. *J. Physiol.*, **111**, 347.

—— (1952). Hypothalamic control of the anterior pituitary gland. In: G. E. W. Wolstenholme, Ed. *Anterior pituitary secretion and hormone influence in water metabolism. Ciba Foundation Colloquia on Endocrinology*, Vol. IV, p. 106. London.

—— (1955a). *Neural control of the pituitary gland.* Monographs of the Physiological Society, No. 3. Ed.: L. E. Bayliss, W. Felberg, A. L. Hodgkin. London.

—— (1955b). Function of pituitary stalk. *Bull. Johns Hopk. Hosp.*, **97**, 358.

—— (1955c). Pituitary-hypothalamic mechanisms. *Arch. Neurol. Psychiat.*, **73**, 124.

—— (1956). Hypothalamic control of the anterior lobe of the hypophysis. In: W. S. Fields, R. Guillemin and C. A. Carton, Eds. *Hypothalamic-hypophysial interrelationship*, p. 31. Springfield, Illinois.

—— & JACOBSOHN, D. (1952). Functional grafts of the anterior pituitary gland. *Proc. roy. Soc. B*, **139**, 263.

HARRIS, G. W. & JOHNSON, R. T. (1950). Regeneration of the hypophysial portal vessels, after section of the hypophysial stalk in the monkey (*Macacus rhesus*). *Nature, Lond.*, **165**, 819.

—— & POPA, G. T. (1938). A technique for operations on the hypothalamo-hypophysial region of the rabbit. *J. Anat., Lond.*, **72**, 226.

HARRISON, R. J., & NEAL, E. G. (1956). Ovulation during delayed implantation and other reproductive phenomena in the badger (*Melles melles L.*). *Nature, Lond.*, **177**, 977.

—— —— (1959). Delayed implantation in the badger (*Meles meles L.*). In: P. Eckstein, Ed. *Implantation of ova. Mem. Soc. Endocrinol.*, No. 6, p. 19.

HART, D. S. (1950). Photoperiodicity in Suffolk sheep. *J. agric. Sci.*, **40**, 143.

—— (1951). Photoperiodicity in the female ferret. *J. exp. Biol.*, **28**, 1.

HARTLEY, P. H. T. (1937). The sexual display of the little grebe. *Brit. Birds*, **30**, 266.

—— (1941). The sexual display of swallows. *Brit. Birds*, **34**, 256.

HARTMAN, C. G. (1939). Ovulation, fertilisation and viability of eggs and spermatozoa. In: E. Allen, Ed. *Sex and internal secretions*. New York and London.

HARTRIDGE, H. (1936). *See* Bainbridge, F. A., & Menzies, J. A. (1936).

HARVEY, W. (1651). Translated by Willis, R. (1847). *The works of William Harvey*. Sydenham Society, London.

HATERIUS, H. O. (1933). Partial sympathectomy and induction of pseudo-pregnancy. *Amer. J. Physiol.* **103**, 97.

—— (1934). The genital-pituitary pathway. Non-effect of stimulation of superior cervical sympathetic ganglia. *Proc. Soc. exp. Biol., N.Y.*, **31**, 1112.

—— (1937). Studies on a neuro-hypophysial mechanism influencing gonadotropic activity. *Cold Spring Harbor Symposium on Quantitative Biology*, **5**, 280.

—— & DERBYSHIRE, A. (1937). Ovulation in the rabbit following upon stimulation of the hypothalamus. *Amer. J. Physiol.*, **119**, 329.

HAZARD, T. P., & EDDY, R. E. (1951). Modification of the sexual cycle in the brook trout (*Salvelinus fontinalis*) by control of light. *Trans. amer. Fish Soc.*, **80**, 158.

HEAPE, W. (1899). Abortion, barrenness and fertility in sheep. *J. Roy. agric. Soc. of England* (Series 3), **10**, 217.

—— (1901). The "sexual season" of mammals and the relation of the "pro-oestrum" to menstruation. *Quart. J. micr. Sci.*, **44**, 1.

—— (1905). Ovulation and degeneration of ova in the rabbit. *Proc. roy. Soc. B*, **76**, 260.

—— (1906). *The breeding industry*. Cambridge.

—— (1931). *Emigration, migration and nomadism*. Cambridge.

HECKEL, G. P. (1942). The estrogen sparking effect of hysterectomy. *Surg. Gynec. Obstet.*, **75**, 379.

HEDIGER, H. (1950). *Wild animals in captivity*. London.

—— (1952). Observations on reproductive behaviour in zoo animals. In: G. E. W. Wolstenholme, Ed. *Hormones, psychology and behaviour and hormone administration. Ciba Foundation Colloquia on Endocrinology*. Vol. III, p. 74. London.

HEMMINGSEN, A. M., & KRARUP, N. B. (1937). The production of mating instincts in the rat with chemically well defined estrogenic compounds. *Biol. Med. Kbh.*, **13**, 1.

HICKLING, C. F. (1935). Seasonal changes in the ovary of the immature hake, *Merlucius merlucius L. J. Mar. biol. Ass. U.K.*, **20**, 443.

HILD, W. (1956). Neurosecretion in the central nervous system. In: W. S. Fields, R. Guillemin and C. A. Carton, Eds. *Hypothalamic-hypophysial interrelationships*, p. 17. Springfield, Illinois.

HILL, G. F. (1913). Ornithological notes. Barclay expedition. *Emu*, **12**, 238.

HILL, M., & PARKES, A. S. (1933). Studies on the hypophysectomized ferret. V. Effect of hypophysectomy on the response of the female ferret to additional illumination during anoestrus. *Proc. roy. Soc. B*, **113**, 537.

—— —— (1934). Effect of absence of light on the breeding season of the ferret. *Proc. roy. Soc. B*, **115**, 14.

HILLARP, N. A. (1949). Studies on the localization of hypothalamic centres controlling the gonadotrophic function of the hypophysis. *Acta Endocrinol.*, **2**, 11.

HILLSTEAD, A. F. C. (1945). *The blackbird*. London.

Hingston, R. W. G. (1933). *The meaning of animal colour and adornment.* London.

Hinsey, J. C. (1937). The relation of the nervous system to ovulation and other phenomena of the female reproductive tract. *Cold Spr. Harb. Sym. quant. Biol.,* **5,** 269.

—— & Markee, J. E. (1932a). A search for a neurological mechanism in ovulation. *Proc. Soc. exp. Biol., N.Y.,* **30,** 136.

—— —— (1932b). Studies on prolan induced ovulation in mid-brain and mid-brain hypophysectomized rabbits. *Amer. J. Physiol.,* **106,** 48.

—— —— (1933). Pregnancy following bilateral section of the cervical sympathetic trunks in the rabbit. *Proc. Soc. exp. Biol., N.Y.,* **31,** 270.

Hobbs, D. F. (1937). Natural reproduction of quinnat salmon, brown and rainbow trout in certain New Zealand waters. *N.Z. Marine Dept. Fisheries Bull.,* No. 6. Wellington.

Hoch, A., & McCurdy, J. T. (1921). *Benign stupors.* New York.

Höhn, E. O. (1943). Some observations on the common pochard. *Brit. Birds,* **37,** 102.

—— (1947). Sexual behaviour and seasonal changes in the gonads and adrenals of the mallard. *Proc. zool. Soc. Lond.,* A, **117,** 281.

Hollom, P. A. D. (1937). Observations on the courtship and mating of the smew. *Brit. Birds,* **31,** 106.

Holmes, R. L., Brodie Hughes, E., & Zuckerman, S. (1959). Section of the pituitary stalk in monkeys. *J. Endocrin.,* **18,** 305.

Hoover, E. E., & Hubbard, H. F. (1937). Modification of the sexual cycle of trout by control of light. *Copeia,* **4,** 206.

Hosking, E. J. (1939). Courtship and display of the Slavonian grebe. *Brit. Birds,* **33,** 170.

Hough, W. H., Bearden, H. J., & Hansel, W. (1955). Further studies on factors affecting ovulation in the cow. *J. Anim. Sci.,* **14,** 739.

Houssay, B. A. (1947). La funcion sexual del sapo. *An. Acad. nat. Cienc., B. Aires,* **12,** 103.

Houssay, A. G., Biasotti, A., & Sammartino, R. (1935). Modifications functionelles de l'hypophyse après les lesions infundibulo-tuberiennes chez le crapaud. *C. R. Soc. Biol., Paris,* **120,** 725.

Howard, H. E. (1907–1914). *The British warblers.* London.

—— (1929). *Introduction to the study of bird behaviour.* Cambridge.

—— 1935). *The nature of a bird's world.* Cambridge.

—— (1940). *A water hen's world.* Cambridge.

Howell, C. E., & Rollins, W. C. (1951). Environmental sources of variation in the gestation length of the horse. *J. Anim. Sci.,* **10,** 789.

Hronopulo, N. P. (1955). Povysenie mogoplodija norok putem uvelicenija svetovogo dnja. (Increasing multi-foetation in the mink by increasing daylight.) *Karakulevodstvo i Zverovodstvo,* **8** (4), 32.

Hudson, W. H. (1919). *Birds in town and village.* London.

—— (1920). *Birds of La Plata.* London.

Hume, D. M., & Wittenstein, G. J. (1950). The relationship of the hypothalamus to pituitary-adrenocortical function. In: J. R. Mote, Ed. *Proceedings first clinical ACTH conference.* Philadelphia.

Huston, T. M., & Nalbandov, A. V. (1953). Neurohumoral control of the pituitary in the fowl. *Endocrinology,* **52,** 149.

Hutton, F. W. (1901). Our migratory birds. *Trans. Proc. N.Z. Inst.,* **33,** 251.

Huxley, J. S. (1914). The courtship habits of the great crested grebe (*Podiceps cristatus*); with an addition to the theory of sexual selection. *Proc. zool. Soc.,* 491.

—— (1923). Courtship activities in the red-throated diver (*Colymbus stellatus Portopp*); together with a discussion of the evolution of courtship in birds. *J. linn. Soc. (Zool.),* **35,** 253.

—— (1935). *The private life of the gannets.* Film.

—— (1938a). The present standing of the theory of sexual selection. In: G. R. de Beer, Ed. *Evolution. Essays in evolutionary biology presented to Prof. E. S. Goodrich,* p. 11. Oxford.

—— (1938b). Darwin's theory of sexual selection and the data subsumed by it, in the light of recent research. *Amer. Nat.,* **72,** 416.

HUXLEY, J. S (1941). The courtship of animals. In *The uniqueness of man*. London.

—— & MONTAGUE, F. A. (1925). Studies on the courtship and sexual life of birds. V. The oyster catcher. *Ibis*, **1** (Ser. 12), 868.

IHERING, R. VON (1935). Die Wirkung von Hypophyseninjektion auf den Laichakt von fischen Kannibalismus bei Diplopoden. *Zool. Anz.*, **111**, 273.

INGRAM, C. (1907). On the fiords of the Alexandra District, Northern Territory. *Ibis* (9), **1**, 387.

IVANOVA, S. (1935). Über den Mechanismus der Wirkung von Licht auf die Hoden der Vogel (*Passer domesticus*). *Arch. exp. Path. Pharmak.*, **179**, 349.

JEFFERSON, J. M. (1940). A study of the subcortical connexions of the optic tract system of the ferret, with special reference to gonadal activation by retinal stimulation. *J. Anat., Lond.*, **75**, 106.

JENNER, C. E. (1951). The significance of the period of darkness in animal photoperiodic responses. *Anat. Rec.*, **111**, 512.

—— & ENGELS, W. L. (1952). The significance of the dark period in the photoperiodic response of male juncos and white throated sparrows. *Bid. Bull. Wood's Hole*, **103**, 345.

JESSE, E. (1935). *Gleanings in natural history*. London.

JÖCHLE, W. (1956). Uber den Einfluss des Lichtes auf Sexual-entwicklung und Sexual Periodik bei Säugern. *Endokrinologie*, **33**, 129.

JOHNSON, S. E., & GANN, E. L. (1933). Light in relation to the sexual cycle and to hibernation in the thirteen-lined ground squirrel. *Anat. Rec.*, **57** (Abstract), 28.

JONES, F. WOOD (1923–1925). *The mammals of South Australia*. British Science Guild (South Australia Branch), Adelaide.

—— (1937). The olfactory organ of the tubinares. *Emu*, **36**, 281.

JOURDAIN, F. C. R., & TUCKER, B. W. (1938–1941). *The handbook of British Birds*. Ed. H. F. Witherby. Vols. 1–5. London.

KEARTON, C. (1930). *The island of penguins*. New York.

KEAST, J. A., & MARSHALL, A. J. (1954). The influence of drought and rainfall on reproduction in Australian desert birds. *Proc. zool. Soc. Lond.*, **124**, 493.

KECK, W. N. (1934). Control of the secondary sex characters of the English sparrow. *J. exp. Zool.*, **67**, 315.

KEIBEL, F. (1902). Die Entwicklung des Rehes bis zür Anlage des Mesoblast. *Arch. f. Anat. u. Physiol., Anat. Abt.*, **292.**

KEITH, D. B. (1937). The red-throated diver in North-East Land. *Brit. Birds*, **31.** 66.

—— (1938). Observations on the purple sand-piper in North East Land. *Proc. zool. Soc. Lond.* A, **108**, 185.

KELLER, A. D., & HAMILTON, J. W. (1937). Normal sex functions following section of the hypophyseal stalk in the dog. *Amer. J. Physiol.*, **119**, 349.

KELLY, R. B., & SHAW, H. E. B. (1939). Observations on the periodicity of oestrus in certain Australian merino ewes and a half-bred group. Interim report upon the fertility of sheep. *Bull. Counc. sci. indust. Res. Aust.*, **12**, 18.

KENDEIGH, S. C. (1934). The rôle of environment in the life of birds. *Ecol. Monogr.*, **4**, 199.

KERR, T. K. (1940). On the histogenesis of some teleost pituitaries. *Proc. roy. Soc. Edinb.*, **60**, 224.

KIDATA, JIN ICHI (1951). Histological observations on the seasonal changes in the testis of a lizard, *Eumeces Latiscutatus*. *Jap. J. Genet.*, **26**, 195.

KIRKMAN, F. B. (1911–1913). *The British bird book*. London.

KIRKPATRICK, C. M., & LEOPOLD, A. C. (1952). The rôle of darkness in sexual activity of the quail. *Science*, **116**, 280.

—— —— (1953). Photoperiodicity in animals; the rôle of darkness. *Science*, **117**, 390.

KIRSCHBAUM, A. (1933). Experimental modification of the seasonal sexual cycle of the English sparrow (*Passer domesticus*). *Anat. Rec.*, **57** (Suppl.), 62.

KLEIN, M. (1939). Action du placenta sur le corps jaune gravidique et sur le cycle vaginal chez le cobaye. *C. R. Soc. Biol., Paris*, **130**, 1393.

KÖHLER, W. (1930). *Gestalt Psychologie*. London.

Kostitch, A., & Telebakovitch, A. (1929). Sur un rythme vaginal chez les animaux ovariectomisés. *C. R. Soc. Biol., Paris,* **100,** 51.

Lack, D. (1933). Nesting conditions as a factor controlling breeding time in birds. *Proc. zool. Soc. Lond.,* **103,** 231.

—— (1938a). Display of green sandpiper. *Brit. Birds,* **32,** 86.

—— (1938b). Bird courtship and aggressive behaviour. (Abstract.) *Brit. Assoc.,* Cambridge.

—— (1939a). The display of the blackcock. *Brit. Birds,* **32,** 290.

—— (1939b). The behaviour of the robin. *Proc. zool. Soc. Lond.* A, **109,** 169.

—— (1940a). Pair formation in birds. *Condor,* **43,** 169.

—— (1940b). Courtship feeding in birds. *Auck,* **57,** 169.

—— (1943). *The life of the robin.* London.

—— (1950). Breeding seasons in the Galapagos. *Ibis,* **92,** 268.

—— & Emlen, J. T. (1939). Observations on breeding behaviour of tricoloured redwings. *Condor,* **41,** 225.

Laing, J. A. (1955). *Fertility and infertility in the domestic animals.* London.

Lamond, D. R. (1959). Effect of stimulation derived from other animals of the same species on oestrous cycles in mice. *J. Endocrin.,* **18,** 343.

Langdon-Brown, W. (1935). *Horsley Memorial Lecture.* Cambridge.

Lee, M. O. (1926). Studies of the oestrous cycle of the rat. The effect of low environmental temperature. *Amer. J. Physiol.,* **78,** 246.

Lee, van der S., & Boot, L. M. (1956). Brief report on investigations on the occurrence of spontaneous pseudo-pregnancy in mice. *Excerpta Med. Amst. III,* **10,** 551.

Lees, A. D. (1955). *The physiology of diapause in arthropods.* Cambridge.

Leininger, C. R., & Ranson, S. W. (1943). The effect of hypophysial stalk transection upon gonadotrophic function in the guinea-pig. *Anat. Rec.,* **87,** 77.

Leonard, S. L., & Reece, R. P. (1942). Failure of steroid hormones to induce mammary growth in hypophysectomized rats. *Endocrinology,* **30,** 32.

Leopold, A. C. (1951). Photoperiodism in plants. *Quart. Rev. Biol.,* **26,** 247.

Levick, G. M. (1914). *Antarctic penguins.* London.

Liche, H. (1939). Oestrus cycle in the cat. *Nature, Lond.,* **143,** 900.

Lintvareva, N. I. (1955a). *Voprosy fiziologii razmnozenija losadei.* (Problems in the physiology of reproduction in horses.) *Trud. vsesojuz. nauc.-issled. Inst. Konev. Moscow: Seljhozgiz.,* 44–65.

—— (1955b). Vlijanie svetovogo faktora na funkcii razmozenija zivotnyh. (The effect of light on reproduction.) *Trud. vsesojuz. nauc.-issled. Inst. Konev. Moscow: Seljhozgiz.,* 44–65.

Llewellyn, L. M., & Enders, R. K. (1954). Ovulation in the raccoon. *J. Mammal.,* **35,** 550.

Lockley, R. M. (1936). The courtship of the stormy petrel. *Field,* 24 Oct., 1025.

—— (1942). *Shearwaters.* London.

—— (1945). *Birds of the sea.* London.

Lodge, G. E. (1946). *Memoirs of an artist naturalist.* London.

Loeb, L. (1923). The effect of extirpation of the uterus on the life and function of the corpus luteum in the guinea-pig. *Proc. Soc. exp. Biol., N.Y.,* **20,** 44.

—— (1927). The effects of hysterectomy on the system of sex organs and on the periodicity of the sexual cycle in the guinea-pig. *Amer. J. Physiol.,* **83,** 202.

—— & Smith, M. G. (1936). The effect of hysterectomy on the duration of life and retrogression of the corpora lutea and on secondary sex organs in the rabbit. *Amer. J. Anat.,* **58,** 1.

Loewi, O. (1935). The Ferrier lecture: On problems connected with the principle of humoral transmission of nervous impulses. *Proc. roy. Soc.* B, **118,** 299.

Lofts, B., & Marshall, A. J. (1956). The effects of prolactin administration on the internal rhythm in male birds. *J. Endocrin.,* **13,** 101.

—— —— (1958). An investigation of the refractory period of reproduction in male birds by means of exogenous prolactin and follicle stimulating hormone. *J. Endocrin.,* **17,** 91.

LOGAN, R. E. (1954a). Transient response of estrous cycle in the rat to changes in environmental illumination. *Fed. Proc.*, **13,** 91.

—— (1954b). Influence of environmental lighting conditions on the estrous cycle of the rat. *Diss. Abstr.*, **14,** 1781.

LONG, C. N. H. (1956). Pituitary-adrenal relationships. *Ann. Rev. Physiol.*, **18,** 409.

LONG, J. A., & EVANS, H. M. (1922). The oestrous cycle in the rat and its associated phenomena. *Mem. Univ. Calif.*, 6.

LONGLEY, W. H. (1911). The maturation of the egg and ovulation in the domestic cat. *Amer. J. Anat.*, **12,** 139.

LUCAS, N. S., HUME, E. M., & SMITH, H. H. (1937). On the breeding of the common marmoset (*Hapale, jacchus Linn*) in captivity when irradiated with ultra-violet rays. 2. A ten years' family history. *Proc. zool. Soc. Lond.*, **107,** 205.

LYMAN, C. P. (1943). Control of coat colour in the varying hare, *Lepus americanus* Erxleben. *Bull. Museum Comp. Zool., Harvard Univ.*, **93,** 393.

MAHONEY, W., & SHEEHAN, D. (1936). The pituitary-hypothalamic mechanism; experimental occlusion of the pituitary stalk. *Brain*, **59,** 62.

MAKEPEACE, A. W. (1938). Failure of atropine to prevent ovulation following coitus in the rabbit. *Endocrinology*, **23,** 241.

—— WEINSTEIN, G. L., & FRIEDMAN, M. H. (1938). Effect of coitus on gonadotropic content of pituitary glands of pseudo-pregnant rabbits. *Endocrinology*, **22,** 667.

MANDL, A. M. (1951). Cyclical changes in the vaginal smear of adult ovariectomized rats. *J. exp. Biol.*, **28,** 585.

MARCH, F. (1937). Some hormone effects in amphibia. *Proc. zool. Soc. Lond.*, **107,** 603.

MARION, G. G., SMITH, V. R., WILEY, T. E., & BARRETT, G. R. (1950). The effect of sterile copulation on the time of ovulation in dairy cattle. *J. Dairy Sci.*, **33,** 391.

MARKEE, J. E., EVERETT, J. W., & SAWYER, C. H. (1952). The relationship of the nervous system to the release of gonadotrophin and the regulation of the sex cycle. *Recent. Progr. Hormone Res.*, **7,** 139.

—— SAWYER, C. J., & HOLLINSHEAD, W. H. (1946a). Activation of the anterior hypophysis by electrical stimulation in the rabbit. *Endocrinology*, **38,** 345.

—— —— —— (1946b). Electrical stimulation of the ovulatory mechanism in the rabbit. *Anat. Rec.*, **94,** 521.

—— —— —— (1947). An adrenergic link in the ovulatory mechanism of the rabbit. *Anat. Rec.*, **97,** 398.

—— —— —— (1948). Adrenergic control of the release of luteinizing hormone from the hypophysis of the rabbit. *Recent Progr. Hormone Res.*, **2,** 117.

MARSHALL, A. J. (1934). Notes on the satin bower-bird in south-east Queensland. *Emu*, **34,** 57.

—— (1944). Display and bower-building in bower birds. *Nature, Lond.*, **153,** 625.

—— (1948). The breeding cycle of an equatorial bat. *Proc. linn. Soc., Lond.*, **159,** 103.

—— (1949a). On the function of the interstitium of the testis: the sexual cycle of a wild bird, *Fulmarus glacialis* (L.). *Quart. J. micr. Sci.*, **90,** 265.

—— (1949b). Weather factors and spermatogenesis in birds. *Proc. zool. Soc. Lond.*, **119,** 711.

—— (1950). Mechanism and significance of the "refractory period" in the avian testis cycle. *Nature, Lond.*, **166,** 1034.

—— (1951). The refractory period of testis rhythm in birds and its possible bearing on breeding and migration. *Wilson Bull.*, **63,** 238.

—— (1952a). The causes of periodic non-breeding among Arctic birds. *Ibis*, **94,** 310.

—— (1952b). The condition of the interstitial and spermatogenic tissue of migratory birds on arriving in England in April and May. *Proc. zool. Soc. Lond.*, **122,** 287.

—— (1952c). The interstitial cycle in relation to autumn and winter sexual behaviour in birds. *Proc. zool. Soc. Lond.*, **121,** 727.

—— (1954). *Bower birds: Their displays and breeding cycles.* Oxford.

—— (1955). Reproduction in birds: the male. In: I. C. Jones & P. Eckstein, Eds. *The comparative endocrinology of vertebrates.* Part 1. *The comparative physiology of reproduction and the effects of sex hormones in vertebrates. Mem. Soc. Endocrin.*, No. 4, p. 75.

MARSHALL, A. J. & COOMBS, C. J. F. (1957). The interaction of environmental, internal and behavioural factors in the rook, *Corvus frugilegus frugilegus* Linnaeus. *Proc. zool. Soc. Lond.*, **128,** 545.

—— & CORBET, P. S. (1959). The breeding biology of equatorial vertebrates: Reproduction of the bat, *Chaererphon hindei*, Thomas at latitude o°26′ N. *Proc. zool. Soc. Lond.*, **132,** 607.

—— & DISNEY, H. J. DE S. (1956). Photostimulation of an equatorial bird (*Quelea quelea* (Linnaeus)). *Nature, Lond.*, **177,** 143.

—— —— (1957). Experimental induction of the breeding season in a zerophilous bird. *Nature, Lond.*, **180,** 647.

—— & HOOK, R. (1959). The breeding biology of equatorial vertebrates: reproduction of the lizard *Agama agama lionotus* Boulenger at lat. o° o1′ N. *Proc. zool. Soc. Lond.*, **133.**

—— & SERVENTY, D. L. (1957). The breeding cycle of the short-tailed shearwater, *Puffinus tenuirostris* (Temminck) in relation to transequatorial migration and environment. *Proc. zool. Soc. Lond.*, **127,** 489.

—— —— (1959). The experimental determination of an internal rhythm of reproduction in a transequatorial migrant, the short-tailed shearwater, *Puffinus tenuirostris* (Temminck). *Proc. zool. Soc., Lond.*, in press.

—— & ROBERTS, J. D. (1959). The breeding biology of equatorial vertebrates: reproduction of cormorants (*Phalacrocoracidae*) at latitude o°20′ N. *Proc. zool. Soc. Lond.*, **132,** 617.

—— & WILKINSON, O. (1956). Reproduction in the Orkney Vole (*Microtus orcadensis*), under a six-hour day-length and other conditions. *Proc. zool. Soc. Lond.*, **126,** 391.

—— & WILLIAMS, M. C. (1959). The pre-nuptial migration of the yellow wagtail (*Motacilla flava*) from latitude o° o4′ N. *Proc. zool. Soc. Lond.*, **132,** 313.

—— & WOOLF, F. M. (1957). Seasonal lipid changes in the sexual elements of a male snake, *Vipera berus*. *Quart. J. micr. Sci.*, **98,** 89.

MARSHALL, F. H. A. (1905a). Fertility in Scottish sheep. *Proc. roy. Soc.* B, **77,** 58.

—— (1905b). The oestrous cycle in the common ferret. *Quart. J. micr. Sci.*, **48,** 323.

—— (1929). Sexual behaviour in birds. *Nature, Lond.*, **124,** 655.

—— (1936). The Croonian lecture: Sexual periodicity and the causes which determine it. *Philos. Trans.* B, **226,** 423.

—— (1937). On the change over in the oestrous cycle in animals after transference across the equator, with further observations on the incidence of the breeding seasons and the factors controlling sexual periodicity. *Proc. roy. Soc.* B, **122,** 413.

—— (1938). On the hypophysis as the regulator of gonadal rhythm. In: *Les hormones sexuelles*. Edited by L. Brouha. p. 245. Paris.

—— (1940). The experimental modification of the oestrous cycle in the ferret by different intensities of light irradiation and other methods. *J. exp. Biol.*, **17,** 139.

—— (1942). Exteroceptive factors in sexual periodicity. *Biol. Rev.*, **17,** 68.

—— & BOWDEN, F. P. (1934). The effect of irradiation with different wavelengths on the oestrous cycle of the ferret, with remarks on the factors controlling sexual periodicity. *J. exp. Biol.*, **11,** 409.

—— —— (1935). The further effect of irradiation on the oestrous cycle of the ferret. *J. exp. Biol.*, **13,** 383.

—— & HAMMOND, J. (1937). *Fertility and animal breeding*, 4th ed. *Bull. Minist. Agric., Lond.*, No. 39.

—— & VERNEY, E. B. (1936). The occurrence of ovulation and pseudo-pregnancy in the rabbit as a result of central nervous stimulation. *J. Physiol.*, **86,** 327.

—— —— & VOGT, M. (1939). The occurrence of ovulation in the rabbit as a result of stimulation of the central nervous system by drugs. *J. Physiol.*, **97,** 128.

MARSHALL, S. M., & STEPHENSON, T. A. (1933). The breeding of reef animals. Part I. The corals. *Great Barrier Reef Expedition* 1928–1929: *Sci. Rep.*, **3,** 219.

MARSHALL, W. H., & ENDERS, R. K. (1942). The blastocyst in the marten (*Martes*). *Anat. Rec.*, **84,** 307.

MARTINI, L., MIRA, L., PECILE, A., & SAITO, S. (1959). Neurohypophysial hormones and release of gonadotrophins. *J. Endocrin.*, **18**, 245.

MARTINS, T. (1935). The nervous control of the anterior hypophysis. *Transactions on the dynamics of development*, **10**, 181.

MASON, A. G. (1945). The display of the corncrake. *Brit. Birds*, **38**, 351.

MATTHEWS, L. H. (1929). The birds of South Georgia. *Discovery Rep.*, **1**, 561.

—— (1939). Visual stimulation and ovulation in pigeons. *Proc. roy. Soc.* B, **126**, 557.

MATTHEWS, S. A. (1938). The seasonal cycle in the gonads of fundulus. *Biol. Bull. Wood's Hole*, **75**, 66.

MAYER, A. G. (1909). The annual breeding-swarm of the Atlantic palolo. *Publ. Carneg. Instn.*, **102**, 105.

MAYER, G. (1959a). Recent studies on hormonal control of delayed implantation and super-implantation in the rat. In: P. Eckstein, Ed. *Implantation of ova. Mem. Soc. Endocrin.*, No. 6, p. 76.

—— (1959b). Discussion on delayed implantation in the badger (*Meles meles* L.). In: P. Eckstein, Ed. *Implantation of ova. Mem. Soc. Endocrin.*, No. 6, p. 23.

MAXWELL, L. C. (1934). The quantitative and qualitative ovarian response to distributed dosage with gonadotropic extracts. *Amer. J. Physiol.*, **110**, 458.

McCUNN, S. M., MACK, R., & GALE, C. (1958). Neural control of lactation. *Fed. Proc.*, **17**, 107.

McKENZIE, F. F., & BERLINER, V. (1937). The reproductive capacity of rams. *Res. Bull. Mo. agric. Exp. Sta.*, No. 265.

—— & PHILLIPS, R. W. (1933). Studies on the physiology of reproduction. *Res. Bull. Mo. agric. Exp. Sta.*, **328**, 13.

MEDLEN, A. B. (1951). Preliminary observations on the effects of temperature and light upon reproduction in *Gambusia affinis*. *Copeia*, 148.

MEITES, J. (1953). Relation of nutrition to endocrine-reproductive functions. *Iowa St. Coll. J. Sci.*, **28**, 19.

MELLEN, I. M. (1946). *A practical cat book for amateurs and professionals.* New York.

MELLISH, C. H. (1936). The effects of anterior pituitary extract and certain environmental conditions on the genital system of the horned lizard (*Phrynosoma cornutum*, Harlan). *Anat. Rec.*, **67**, 23.

MENDOZA, G. (1939). Reproductive cycle of the viviparous teleost, *Neotoca bilineata*, a member of the family Goodeidae. I. The breeding cycle. *Biol. Bull.* Woods Hole, **76**, 359.

MERCIER, E., & SALISBURY, G. W. (1946). The effects of season on the spermatogenic activity and fertility of dairy bulls used in artificial insemination. *Cornell Vet.*, **36**, 301.

—— —— (1947). Fertility level in artificial breeding associated with season, hours of day-light and the age of cattle. *J. Dairy Sci.*, **30**, 747.

MERRIMAN, D., & SCHEDL, H. P. (1941). The effects of light and temperature on gameto-genesis in the four-spined stickleback, *Apeltes quadracus* (Mitchell). *J. exp. Zool.*, **88**, 413.

METUZALS, J. VON (1952). Über eigenartige Nervenzellen in der Hypophyse des Bitterlings (*Rhodeus amarus Bl.*). *Acta anat.*, **14**, 124.

—— (1954). Neurohistologische Studien über die nervöse Verbindung der Pars distalis der Hypophyse mit den Hypothalamus auf dem Wege des Hypophysenstieles. *Acta anat.*, **20**, 258.

—— (1955). Die Innervation der Drüsenzellen der Pars distalis der Hypophyse bei der Ente. *Z. Zellforsch.*, **43**, 319.

MEYER, B. J., & MEYER, R. K. (1944). Effect of light on maturation and oestrous cycle of cotton rat (*Sigmodon hispidus hispidus*). *Endocrinology*, **34**, 276.

MEYER, R. K., LEONARD, S. L., & HISAW, F. L. (1929). Effect of anaesthesia on artificial production of pseudo-pregnancy in the rat. *Proc. Soc. exp. Biol., N.Y.*, **27**, 340.

MIES FILHO, A., & DE ALMEIDA RAMOS, A. (1954). Fotoperiodicidade e estacao sexual de ovelhas da raca Romney Marsh. (Photo-periodicity and breeding season in Romney Marsh ewes). *Biol. Insem. artif. (Rio de J.)*, **6** (1), 35.

MILLAIS, J. G. (1904–1906). *The mammals of Great Britain and Ireland.* Vols. 1–3. London.

MILLER, A. H. (1948). The refractory period in light-induced reproductive development of golden-crowned sparrows. *J. exp. Zool.*, **109**, 1.

—— (1949). Potentiality for testicular recrudescence during the annual refractory period of the golden-crowned sparrow. *Science*, **109**, 546.

—— (1951). Further evidence on the refractory period in the reproductive cycle of the golden-crowned sparrow. *Auk*, **68**, 380.

—— (1954). Breeding cycles in a constant equatorial environment in Colombia, South America. *Acta XI Congr. Int. Orn.*, 495.

MIXNER, J. P., LEWIS, A. A., & TURNER, C. W. (1940). Evidence for the presence of a second mammogenic (Lobule-Alveolar) factor in the anterior pituitary. *Endocrinology*, **27**, 888.

MIYAZAKI, H. (1934). On the relation of the daily light period to the sexual maturity and to the moulting of *Zosterops palpebrosa japonica*. *Sci. Rep. Toohoka Univ.*, 4th Ser., **9**, 183.

MOORE, C. R., SIMMONS, G. F., WELLS, L. J., ZALESKY, M., & NELSON, W. O. (1934). On the control of reproductive activity in an annual-breeding mammal (*Citellus tridecemlineatus*). *Anat. Rec.*, **60**, 279.

MOORE, W. W., & NALBANDOV, A. V. (1953). Neurogenic effects of uterine distension on the estrous cycle of the ewe. *Endocrinology*, **53**, 1.

MOREAU, R. E. (1931). Equatorial reflection of periodism in birds. *Ibis*, 1 (Ser. 12), 553.

—— (1936). Breeding seasons of birds in East African evergreen forests. *Proc. Zool. Soc. Lond.*, Pt. iii, 631.

—— (1951). The breeding seasons of African birds: I. Land birds. *Ibis*, **92**, 223.

—— WILK, A. L., & ROWAN, W. (1947). The moult and gonad cycles of three species of birds at five degrees south of the equator. *Proc. zool. Soc. Lond.*, **117**, 345.

MOREL, G., & BOURLIERE, F. (1955). Récherches écologique sur *Quelea quelea quelea* K., de la basse vallée du Senegal. *Bull. Inst. franc. Afr. noire*, **17**, 618.

—— —— (1956). Récherches écologiques sur les *Quelea quelea quelea* de la basse vallée du Senégal. II. La reproduction. *Alauda*, **24**, 97.

MORGAN, T. H. (1903). *Evolution and adaptation.* New York and London.

MORLEY, A. (1940). Courtship action of male meadow pipit. *Brit. Birds*, **34**, 65.

MORRIS, B. (1958). The yolk-sac of *Talpa europea*. *Proc. zool. Soc. Lond.*, **131**, 1.

MOULE, G. R. (1950). The influence of a rapid decrease in the hours of daylight on the sexual desire of merino rams. *Aust. vet. J.*, **26**, 84.

MULINOS, M. G., & POMERANTZ, L. (1940). Pseudo-hypophysectomy: a condition resembling hypophysectomy produced by malnutrition. *J. Nutrit.*, **19**, 493.

—— —— (1941). Pituitary replacement therapy in pseudo-hypophysectomy. *Endocrinology*, **29**, 558.

MURPHY, R. C. (1925). *Bird islands of Peru.* New York and London.

—— (1936). *Oceanic birds of South America.* The American Museum of Natural History, New York.

NALBANDOV, A. V., MOORE, W. W., & NORTON, H. W. (1955). Further studies on the neurogenic control of the estrous cycle by uterine distension. *Endocrinology*, **56**, 225.

NEAL, E. (1948). *The badger.* London.

NEAL, E. G., & HARRISON, R. J. (1958). Reproduction in the European badger (*Meles meles, L.*). *Trans. zool. Soc. Lond.*, **29**, 67.

NEILL, R. M. (1939). Reproductive cycle in *Salmo salar* Linn. *Nature, Lond.*, **144**, 332.

NETHERSON-THOMPSON, C. (1939). Some observations on the sexual life, display and breeding of the red grouse as observed in Inverness-shire. *Brit. Birds*, **32.** 24.

NICHOLAS, J. E., CALLENBACH, E. W., & MURPHY, R. R. (1944). Light intensity as a factor in the artificial illumination of pullets. *Bull. Pa. agric. Exp. Sta.*, No. 462.

NISHIKAWA, Y., & HORIE, T. (1952). Studies on the effect of day length on the reproductive function in horses. II. Effect of day length on the function of testes. *Bull. nat. Inst. agric. Sci.* (*Chiba*), Series G (Animal Husbandry), No. 3, 45.

—— SUGIE, T., & HARADA, N. (1952). Studies on the effect of day length on the reproductive function in horses. I. Effect of day length on the function of ovary. *Bull. nat. Inst. agric. Sci.* (*Chiba*), Series G (Animal Husbandry), No. 3, 35.

NOBLE, G. K. (1931).   *The biology of the amphibia.*   New York.

—— (1936).   Courtship and sexual selection of the flicker (*Coloptes auratus luteus*).   *Auk,* **53,** 269.

—— (1937).   Effect of lesions on the corpus striatum on the brooding behaviour of chalcid fishes.   *Anat. Rec.,* **70** (Suppl.), 58.

—— (1938).   Sexual selection among fishes.   *Biol. Rev.,* **13,** 133.

—— (1939).   The rôle of dominance in the social life of birds.   *Auk,* **56,** 263.

—— & NOBLE, R. C. (1923).   The Anderson tree frog.   Observations on its habits and life history.   *Zoologica, N.Y.,* **2,** 417.

—— & WURM, M. (1942).   Further analysis of the social behaviour of the black-crowned night heron.   *Auk,* **59,** 205.

NOBLE, G. R. (1940).   A new species of Brevicipit frog from Madagascar.   *Proc. New Eng. Zool. Cl.,* **18,** 77.

NORMAN, J. R. (1936).   *A history of fishes.*   2nd Ed., London.

NUBLING, E. (1941).   A contribution to the biology of the satin bower-bird.   *Aust. Zool.,* **10,** 95.

OZAJA, M. (1937).   *Studia nad Wryosowka,* Warsozawa.

PARHON, C. L., & COBAN, B. (1935).   Correlations oculoarchitiques.   Nouvelles contributions à l'étude des organes actino-récepteurs.   *C. R. Soc. Biol., Paris,* **119,** 219.

PARKER, M. W., HENDRICKS, S. R., BORTHWICK, H. A., & JENNER, C. E. (1952).   Photoperiodic responses of plants and animals.   *Nature, Lond.,* **169,** 242.

PARKES, A. S. (1924–1925).   Fertility in mice.   *Brit. J. exp. Biol.,* **2,** 21.

—— (1926).   Observations on the oestrus cycle of the albino mouse.   *Proc. roy. Soc. B,* **100,** 151.

PARMENTER, L. (1937).   Notes on the courtship and mating of smew and goosander.   *Brit. Birds,* **31,** 151.

PATTERSON, J. F. (1912).   A preliminary report on the demonstration of polyembryonic development in the armadillo (*Tatusia novemcinctum*).   *Anat. Anz.,* **41,** 369.

—— (1913).   Polyembryonic development in *Tatusia novemcincta.*   *J. Morp.,* **24,** 559.

PEARSE, A. S. (1939).   *Animal ecology.*   New York and London.

PEARSON, O. P. (1944).   Reproduction in the shrew (*Blarina brevicauda* Say.).   *Amer. J. Anat.,* **75,** 39.

—— & ENDERS, R. K. (1944).   Duration of pregnancy in certain mustelids.   *J. exp. Zoöl.,* **95,** 21.

PENCHARZ, R. T., & LONG, J. A. (1933).   Hypophysectomy in the pregnant rat.   *Amer. J. Anat.,* **53,** 117.

PERRY, J. S. (1953).   The reproduction of the African elephant, *Loxodonta africana.*   *Phil. Trans. B,* **237,** 93.

PERRY, R. (1938).   *At the turn of the tide.*   London.

—— (1939).   The significance of display in ducks.   *Naturalist,* 169.

—— (1940).   *Lundy: Isle of puffins.*   London.

PETTINGILL, O. S. (1937).   Behaviour of black skimmers at Cardwell Island, Virginia.   *Auk,* 54.

POLOVTZEVA, V. V. (1937).   Methods of increasing the number of lambings.   *A. B. Abst.,* **5,** 409.

POMERAT, G. R. (1942).   Cell changes in the pituitary and ovary of the white rat following exposure to constant light or darkness.   *Anat. Rec.,* **82,** 531.

POPA, G. T., & FIELDING, U. (1930).   A portal circulation from the pituitary to the hypothalamic region.   *J. Anat., Lond.,* **65,** 88.

—— —— (1933).   Hypophysio-portal vessels and their colloid accompaniment.   *J. Anat., Lond.,* **67,** 227.

PRELL, H. L. (1927).   Über doppelte Brünstzeit und verlängerte Tragezeit bei den einheimischen Arten der Mardergattung, *Martes pinca.*   *Zool. Anz.,* **74,** 128.

—— (1931).   Die Tragezeitverlängerung bei Säugetiere.   *Forsch. u. Fortschr.,* **7,** 187.

—— (1938).   Die Tragezeit des Rehes ein historisches Rückblick.   *Züchtungsk.,* **13,** 325.

PYCRAFT, W. P. (1911–1913).   *See* Kirkman, F. B. (1911–1913).

—— (1913).   *The courtship of animals.*   London.

QUINLAN, J., BISSCHOP, J. H. R., & ADELAAR, T. F. (1941). Bionomic studies on cattle in the semi-arid regions of the Union of South Africa. IV. The ovarian cycle of heifers during summer. *Onderstepoort J. Vet. Sci. & Anim. Indust.*, **16,** 213. (Taken from *Biol. Absts.*, **18,** 4714.)

RASMUSSEN, A. T. (1938). Innervation of the hypophysis. *Endocrinology*, **23,** 263.

RAVEN, C. E. (1942). *John Ray, naturalist. His life and works.* Cambridge.

RAY, J. (1848). *The correspondence of John Ray.* Edited by E. Lankester. London.

REEVE, E. C. R., & ROBERTSON, F. W. (1953). Factors affecting multiple births in sheep. *Anim. Breed. Abstr.*, **21,** 211.

RETZIUS, G. (1900). Zür Kenntnis der Entwicklungsgeschichte des Renntieres und des Rehes. *Biol. Untersuch.*, **9,** 109.

REYNOLDS, A. E. (1943). The normal seasonal reproductive cycle in the male *Eumeces fasciatus* together with some observations on the effects of castration and hormone administration. *J. Morph.*, **32,** 331.

REYNOLDS, S. R. M. (1949). *Physiology of the uterus,* 2nd ed. New York.

RICE, V. A. (1942). *Breeding and improvement in farm animals,* 3rd ed. New York.

RICHDALE, L. E. (1945a). Courtship and allied behaviour in penguins. *Emu,* **44,** 305.

—— (1945b). Courtship and allied behaviour in penguins. *Emu,* **45,** 37.

RICHES, J. H., & WATSON, R. H. (1954). The influence of the introduction of rams on the incidence of oestrus in Merino ewes. *Aust. J. agric. Res.*, **5,** 141.

RICHTER, C. P. (1933). Cyclical phenomena produced in rats by section of the pituitary stalk and their possible relation to pseudo-pregnancy. *Amer. J. Physiol.*, **106,** 80.

RICKMAN, P. (1931). *A bird painter's sketch book.* London.

RIDDLE, O. (1937). Prolactin. *Cold Spr. Harb. Symp. quant. Biol.*, **5,** 218, 321.

RILEY, G. M. (1936). Light regulation of sexual activity in the male sparrow (*Passer domesticus*). *Proc. Soc. exp. Biol., N.Y.*, **34,** 331.

—— (1937). Experimental studies on spermatogenesis in the house sparrow, *Passer domesticus* (Linnaeus). *Anat. Rec.*, **67,** 327.

—— (1940). Light versus activity as a regulator of the sexual cycle in the house sparrow. *Wilson Bull.*, **52,** 73.

—— & WITSCHI, E. (1937). Comparative effects of light stimulation and administration of gonadotropic hormones on female sparrows. *Anat. Rec.*, **70** (Suppl.), 50.

—— —— (1938). Comparative effects of light stimulation and administration of gonadotropic hormones on female sparrows. *Endocrinology*, **23,** 618.

RINGOEN, A. R., & KIRSCHBAUM, A. (1937). Correlation between ocular stimulation and spermatogenesis in the English sparrow (*Passer domesticus*). *Proc. Soc. exp. Biol., N.Y.*, **36,** 111.

—— —— (1939). Factors responsible for the sexual cycle in the English sparrow. *J. exp. Zool.*, **80,** 173.

ROBERTS, B. B. (1940a). The breeding behaviour of penguins with special reference to *Pygoscelis papua, Forster.* British Graham Land Expedition (1934–1937). *Scientific Reports (Brit. Mus. Nat. Hist.),* **1,** 195.

—— (1940b). The life-cycle of Wilson's petrel, *Oceanites oceanicus Kuhl.* British Graham Land Expedition (1934–1937). *Scientific Reports (Brit. Mus. Nat. Hist.),* **1,** 141.

ROBERTS, E. J. (1928). A comparison of milk yields given by heifers in their first lactation with those given by the same animals at later periods. *Int. Dairy Congr. Rep.*, **281.**

ROBINSON, A. (1933). Notes on wood-swallows and swallows of the Barlee Range, W. Australia. *Emu,* **33,** 95.

ROBINSON, E. J., & RUGH, R. (1943). The reproductive processes of the fish, *Oryzias latipes. Biol. Bull. Wood's Hole,* **84,** 115.

ROBINSON, L. (1892). Article on ticklishness in Tuke's *Dictionary of psychological medicine.* London.

ROBINSON, T. J. (1951). Reproduction in the ewe. *Biol. Rev.*, **26,** 121.

ROBSON, J. M. (1937). Maintenance of pregnancy and of the luteal function in the hypophysectomized rabbit. *J. Physiol.*, **90,** 145.

—— (1947). *Recent advances in sex and reproductive physiology,* 3rd ed. London.

ROLLO, M., & DOMM, L. V. (1943). Light requirements of the weaver finch. *Auk,* **60,** 357.

ROOKE, K. B. (1935). Observations on the birds of Newfoundland during the 1934 expedition of the Public Schools Exploring Society. *Ibis*, **5** (Ser. 13), 856.

ROSEN, S., SHELESNYAK, M. C., & ZACHARIAS, W. R. (1940). Naso-genital relationship. II. Pseudo-pregnancy following extirpation of sphenopalatine ganglion in rat. *Endocrinology*, **27**, 463.

ROSENTHAL, H. L. (1952). Observations on the reproduction of the Poeciliid *Lebistes reticulatus* (Peters). *Biol. Bull. Wood's Hole*, **102**, 30.

ROTHCHILD, I., & FRAPS, R. M. (1949a). Interval between normal release of ovulating hormone and ovulation in the domestic hen. *Endocrinology*, **44**.

—— —— (1949b). Induction of ovulating hormone release from the pituitary of the domestic hen by means of progesterone. *Endocrinology*, **44**, 141.

ROTTENSTEN, K. (1954). I. De saesonmaessige svingninger i de ydre brunstsymptomers styrke og regelmaessighed. (I. Seasonal variations in the intensity and regularity of the external symptoms of oestrus.) 274. *Beretn. Forsøgslab. (Kbn.)*, 5–14.

ROUX, L. L. (1936). Sex physiology of sheep. *Onderst. J. Vet. Sci.*, **6**, 465.

ROWAN, W. (1925). Relation of light to bird migration and developmental changes. *Nature, Lond.*, **115**, 494.

—— (1926). On photoperiodism, reproductive periodicity and the annual migration of birds and certain fishes. *Proc. Boston Soc. nat. Hist.*, **38**, 147.

—— (1928). Reproductive rhythm in birds. *Nature, Lond.*, **122**, 11.

—— (1929). Experiments in bird migration. I. Manipulation of the reproductive cycle: seasonal histological changes in the gonads. *Proc. Boston Soc. nat. Hist.*, **39**, 151.

—— (1930). Experiments on bird migration. II. Reversed migration. *Proc. nat. Acad. Sci., Wash.*, **16**, 520.

—— (1931). *The riddle of migration*. Baltimore.

—— (1932). Experiments in bird migration. III. The effects of artificial light, castration and certain extracts on the autumn movements of the American crow (*Corvus brachyrhynchos*). *Proc. nat. Acad. Sci., Wash.*, **18**, 639.

—— (1936). Die Wirkung planmässinger beleuchtung auf die Fortpflanzungstätigkeit der Vögel. *VIth World's Poult. Congr.*, **3**, 112.

—— (1937). Effects of traffic disturbance and night illumination on London starlings. *Nature, Lond.*, **139**, 668.

—— (1938a). London starlings and seasonal reproduction. *Proc. zool. Soc. Lond.* A, **108**, 51.

—— (1938b). Light and seasonal reproduction in animals. *Biol. Rev.*, **12**, 374.

—— (1946). Experiments on bird migration. *Trans. roy. Soc. Can.*, **40**, 123.

—— & BATRAWI, A. M. (1939). Comments on the gonads of some European migrants collected in East Africa immediately before their spring departure. *Ibis*, **3** (Ser. 14), 58.

ROWLANDS, I. W. (1938). Preliminary note on the reproductive cycle of the red squirrel. (*Sciurus vulgaris*). *Proc. zool. Soc. Lond.*, **108**, 441.

—— (1950). Some observations on the breeding of dogs. *Proc. Soc. Stud. Fertil.*, **1**, 40.

—— & McPHAIL, M. K. (1936). The action of progestin on the uterus of the cat. *Quart. J. exp. Physiol.*, **26**, 109.

RUGH, R. (1935). Ovulation in the frog. *J. exp. Zool.*, **71**, 149.

RUSSELL, E. S. (1937). Instinctive behaviour and bodily development. *Folia Biotheoretica*, **2**, 67.

RUSSELL, F. S., & YONGE, C. M. (1928). *The Seas*. London.

RYVES, B. H., & RYVES, MRS. (1934). The breeding habits of the corn bunting. *Brit. Birds*, **28**, 154.

SAKANOUJE, K. (1940). The effect of the visible light upon the biological strength of the follicular hormone. *Jap. J. Obstet. Gynec.*, **23**, 167.

SANDERS, H. G. (1926). On the fertility of stallions. *J. agric. Sci.*, **16**, 466.

SAVAGE, H. MAXWELL (1935). The ecology of young tadpoles with special reference to some adaptations to the habit of mass-spawning in *Rana temporaria temporaria*. *Proc. zool. Soc. Lond.*, Pt. iii, 605.

SAWYER, C. H. (1947). Cholinergic stimulation of the release of melanophore hormone by the hypophysis in salamander larvae. *J. exp. Zool.*, **106**, 145.

—— CRITCHLOW, B. V., & BARACLOUGH, C. A. (1955). Mechanism of blockade of pituitary activation in the rat by morphine, atropine and barbiturates. *Endocrinology*, **57**, 345.

—— EVERETT, J. W., & MARKEE, J. E. (1949). A neural factor in the mechanism by which oestrogen induces the release of luteinizing hormone in the rat. *Endocrinology*, **44**, 218.

—— & MARKEE, J. E. (1950). The differential mechanisms by which picrotoxin and copper acetate induce ovulation in the rabbit. *Endocrinology*, **46**, 177.

—— —— & EVERETT, J. W. (1949a). The mechanisms by which dibenamine blocks pituitary activation in the rabbit and rat. *Proc. Soc. exp. Biol., N.Y.*, **71**, 670.

—— —— —— (1949b). Activation of the adenohypophysis by intravenous injection of epinephrine in the atropinized rabbit. *Endocrinology*, **46**, 536.

—— —— —— (1950). Further experiments on blocking pituitary activation in the rabbit and the rat. *J. exp. Zool.*, **113**, 659.

—— —— & HOLLINSHEAD, W. H. (1947). Inhibition of ovulation in the rabbit by the adrenergic-blocking agent dibenamine. *Endocrinology*, **41**, 395.

—— —— & TOWNSEND, B. F. (1949). Cholinergic and adrenergic components in the neurohumoral control of the release of LH in the rabbit. *Endocrinology*, **44**, 18.

SCHARRER, E. (1928). Ueber die Lichtempfindlichkeit blinder Elritzen. I. Untersuchungen über das Zwischenhirn der Fische. *Ztschr. vergl. Physiol.*, **7**, 1.

—— & SCHARRER, B. (1954). Neurosecretion. In *Mollendorff's Handbuch d. mikrosk. Anat. d. Menschen.* Vol. VI, Chap. 5, p. 953.

SCHINKEL, P. G. (1954). The effect of the presence of the ram on the ovarian activity of the ewe. *Aus. J. agric. Res.*, **5**, 465.

SCHMIEDER, R. G. (1933). The polymorphic forms of *Mellitobia chalybii* Ashmead and the determining factors involved in their production (Hymenoptera: Chalcidoidea, Eulophidae). *Biol. Bull. Wood's Hole*, **65**, 338.

SCOTT, H. M., & PAYNE, L. F. (1937). Light in relation to the experimental modification of the breeding season of turkeys. *Poult. Sci.*, **16**, 90.

—— —— (1942). Cited by Marshall, F. H. A. (1942). *Biol. Rev.*, **17**, 68.

SELOUS, E. (1901). *Bird watching.* London.

—— (1927). *Realities of bird life.* London.

SELYE, H. (1934). Influence of the uterus on ovary and mammary gland. *Proc. Soc. exp. Biol. Med.*, **31**, 488.

—— & MCKEOWN, T. (1934). Further studies on the influence of suckling. *Anat. Rec.*, **60**, 323.

SERVENTY, D. L., & MARSHALL, A. J. (1957). Breeding periodicity in Western Australian birds: With an account of unseasonal nestings in 1953 and 1955. *Emu*, **57**, 99.

—— & WHITTELL, H. M. (1948). *A handbook of the birds of Western Australia.* (With the exception of the Kimberley Division). Perth, W.A.

—— —— (1951). *A handbook of the birds of Western Australia.* Perth, W.A.

SHAFER, E. A. (1907). On the incidence of daylight as a determining factor in bird migration. *Nature, Lond.*, **77**, 159.

SHARMAN, G. B. (1955). Studies on marsupial reproduction. IV. Delayed birth in *Protemnodon eugenii Desmarest. Aust. J. Zool.*, **3**, 156.

SHELESNYAK, M. C. (1931). The induction of pseudo-pregnancy in the rat by means of electrical stimulation. *Anat. Rec.*, **49**, 179.

—— & ROSEN, S. (1938). Naso-genital relationship. Induction of pseudo-pregnancy in rat by nasal treatment. *Endocrinology*, **23**, 58.

SHIBUSAWA, K., SAITO, S., FUKUDA, M., KAWAI, T., YAMADA, H., & TOMIZAWA, K. (1955). Neurosecretion of oxytocin stimulates the release of the pituitary gonadotrophin. *Endocrinol. Japan*, **2**, 183.

SHIRLEY, H. V., Jr., & NALBANDOV, A. V. (1956). Affects of neurohypophysectomy in domestic chickens. *Endocrinology*, **58**, 477.

SHUEL, R. (1938). Further notes on the eggs and nesting habits of birds in N. Nigeria. *Ibis*, **2** (Ser. 14), 463.

SHULL, A. F. (1929). The effect of intensity and duration of light and of duration of dark-ness, partly modified by temperature, upon wing-production in aphids. *Roux Arch. Entw. Mech. Organ.*, **115**, 825.

SKUTCH, A. F. (1945). Incubation and nestling periods of Central American birds. *Auk*, **62**, 8.

SMELSER, G. K., WALTON, A., & WHETHAM, E. O. (1934). The effect of light on the ovarian activity in the rabbit. *J. exp. Biol.*, **11**, 351.

SMITH, L. W., & SINGH, G. (1938). A preliminary note on the study of oestrus in sheep. Dioestrus cycle in Bikaner ewes. *Agric. Live-stock, India*, **8**, 683.

SMITH, P. E. (1930). Hypophysectomy and a replacement therapy in the rat. *Amer. J. Anat.*, **45**, 205.

SMITH, R. E. (1940). Mating and oviposition in the Pacific coast tree toad. *Science*, **92**, 379.

SOLIMAN, F. A., & ABD-EL-MALEK, A. (1959). Influence of temperature and light on reproduction in male rats. *Nature, Lond.*, **183**, 266.

SOUTHERN, H. N. (1938). Posturing and related activities of the common tern. *Proc. zool. Soc. Lond.* A, **108**, 423.

SPAUL, E. A. (1930). On the activity of the anterior lobe of the pituitary. *Brit. J. exp. Biol.*, **7**, 49.

STEINACH, E., & KAMMERER, P. (1920). Klima and Mannbarkeit. *Arch. Entw. Mech. Org.*, **46**, 391.

STEPHENS, G. J. (1952). Mechanisms regulating the reproductive cycle in the crayfish, *Cambarus*. I. Female cycle. *Physiol. Zool.*, **25**, 70.

STEPHENSON, T. A. (1933). Lunar periodicity in reproduction. *Nature, Lond.*, **131**, 622.

STONOR, C. R. (1939). Notes on the breeding habits of the common screamer (*Chauna torquata*). *Ibis*, **3** (Ser. 14), 45.

—— (1940). *Courtship and display among birds.* Country Life, London.

—— (1944). A note on the breeding habits of the Indian zotter, *Coracias benghalensis*. *Ibis*, **86**, 94.

STROINK, J. A. (1947). Kreigsamenorrhoe. *Gynaecologia*, **124**, 160.

SWINGLE, W. W., SEAY, P., PERLMUTT, J., COLLINS, E. J., BARLOW, G. Jr., & FEDOR, E. J. (1951). An experimental study of pseudopregnancy in the rat. *Amer. J. Physiol.* **167**, 586.

SYKES, J. F., & COLE, C. L. (1944). Modification of mating season in sheep by light treat-ment. *Quart. Bull. Mich. agric. Exp. Sta.*, **26**, 250.

TAIBELL, A. (1928). Resveglio artificiale di instint itipicamente femminili nei maschi di taluni ucceli. *Atti. Soc. Nat. Mat. Modena*, **59**, 93.

TALMAGE, R. V., & BUCHANAN, G. D. (1954). The armadillo (*Dasypus novemcinctus*). A review of its natural history, ecology, anatomy and reproductive physiology. *Rice Inst. Pamph.*, **41** (2), 1.

—— BUCHANAN, G. D., KRAINTZ, F. W., LAZO-WASEM, E. A., & ZARROW, M. X. (1954). The presence of a functional corpus luteum during delayed implantation in the armadillo. *J. Endocrin.*, **11**, 44.

TANG, P. C., & PATTON, H. D. (1951). Effect of hypophysial stalk section on adenohypo-physial function. *Endocrinology*, **49**, 86.

TAUBENHAUS, M., & SOSKIN, S. (1941). Release of luteinising hormone from the anterior hypophysis by an acetylcholine-like substance from the hypothalamic region. *Endocrinology*, **29**, 958.

TAYLOR, J. S. (1938). Redshank mating in November. *Brit. Birds*, **31**, 270.

TAYLOR-PAGE, F. J. (1958). The roe deer's ring: circles and figures-of-eight and the part they play in the ceremonials which are part of courtship. *The Field*, **232**, 729.

THEOBALD, G. W. (1936). A centre or centres, in the hypothalamus controlling menstrua-tion, ovulation, pregnancy and parturition. *Brit. med. J.*, **1**, 1038.

THOMPSON, W. F. (1919). The spawning of the grunnion (*Leuresthes tenuis*). *Sacramento Calif. Fish & Game Comm. Fish. Bull.*, **3**, 1–29.

THOMSON, A. L. (1936). Recent progress in the study of bird-migration: A review of the literature, 1926–1935. *Ibis*, **6**, 472.

—— (1940). Some remarks on periodicity in the life of birds. *Bull. Brit. Ornithologists' Club*, No. 427, 31.

THOMSON, A. P. D. (1951). Relation of retinal stimulation to oestrus in the ferret. *J. Physiol.*, **113**, 425.

—— (1954). The onset of oestrus in normal and blinded ferrets. *Proc. roy. Soc.* B, **142**, 126.

—— & ZUCKERMAN, S. (1953). Functional relations of the adenohypophysis and hypothalamus. *Nature, Lond.*, **171**, 970.

—— —— (1954). The effect of pituitary stalk section on light-induced oestrus in ferrets. *Proc. roy. Soc.* B, **142**, 437.

—— —— (1955). Anterior-pituitary hypothalamic relations in the ferret. *Nature, Lond.*, **175**, 74.

THOMSON, G. M. (1922). *The naturalization of animals and plants in New Zealand.* Cambridge.

THORNTON, C. W., & CUMMINGS, S. B. (1946). The effect of auditory stimulation on the spermatogenic cycle of the male English sparrow. *Auk*, **62**, 75.

TINBERGEN, N. (1936). The function of sexual fighting in birds and the problem of the origin of territory. *Bird Boundary*, **7**, 1.

—— (1940). Die Übersprungbewegung. *Z. Tierpsychol.*, **4**, 1.

—— (1951). *The study of instinct.* Oxford.

TRUSCOTT, B. L. (1944). Physiological factors in hypophysial-gonadal interaction. I. Light and the follicular mechanism in the rat. *J. exp. Zool.*, **95**, 291.

TUCHMANN-DUPLESSIS, H. (1945). Correlations hypophyso-endocrines chez le triton. *Actualités sci. industr.*, No. 987. Paris.

TUCKER, B. B. (1938). Display of the bullfinch. *Brit. Birds*, **32**, 25.

TWOMEY, A. C. (1934). Breeding habits of Bonaparte's gull. *Auk*, **51**, 291.

UNDERWOOD, E. J., SHIER, F. L., & DAVENPORT, N. (1944). Studies in sheep husbandry in Western Australia. V. The breeding season of Merino, cross-bred and British breed ewes in the agricultural districts. *J. Dep. Agric. West. Austral.*, **21**, 1.

UOTILA, U. U. (1940). Hypothalamic control of anterior pituitary function. The hypothalamus and central levels of autonomic function. *Res. Publ. Ass. nerv. ment. Dis.*, **20**, 580.

VAN DER STRICHT, O. (1911). Sur le mécanisme de la fixation de l'oeuf de chauve-souris (*V. noctula*) dans l'uterus. *C. R. Ass. Anat.*, **13**, 1.

VAN DYKE, H. B., & LI, R. C. (1938). The secretion of progesterone by the cat's ovary following the formation of corpora lutea due to the injection of anterior pituitary extract or prolan. *Chin. J. Physiol.*, **13**, 213.

VAN OORDT, G. J., & DAMSTÉ, P. H. (1939). Experimental modification of the sexual cycle and moult of the greenfinch. *Acta Brev. neerl. Physiol.*, **9**, 140.

VAN TIENHOVEN, A., NALBANDOV, A. V., & NORTON, H. W. (1954). Effect of dibenamine on progesterone-induced and "spontaneous" ovulation in the hen. *Endocrinology*, **54**, 605.

VASQUEZ-LOPEZ, E. (1942). Structure of the neurohypophysis with special reference to nerve endings. *Brain*, **65**, 1.

—— (1949). Innervation of the rabbit adeno-hypophysis. *J. Endocrin.*, **6**, 158.

—— (1953). The strucutre of the rabbit neurohypophysis. *J. Endocrin.*, **9**, 30.

—— & WILLIAMS, P. C. (1952). Nerve fibres in the adenohypophysis under normal and experimental conditions. In: G. E. W. Wolstenholme, Ed. *Anterior pituitary secretion and hormone influence in water metabolism. Ciba Foundation Colloquia on Endocrinology*, Vol. IV, p. 54. London.

VAUGIEN, L. (1953). Sur l'apparition de la maturité sexuelle des jeunes perruches ondulées mâles sourmises à diverses conditions d'éclairement. *Bull. Biol.*, **87**, 274.

VINCENT, A. W. (1945). On the breeding habits of some South African birds. *Ibis*, **87**, 203.

VOGT, M. (1933). Über den Mechanismus der Auslosüng der Gravidität, und Pseudogravidität. *Arch. exp. Path Pharmak.*, **170**, 72.

—— (1942). Ovulation in the rabbit after destruction of the greater superficial petrosal nerves. *J. Physiol.*, **100**, 410.

VOITKEVIC, A. A. (1947). Izmeneie gonadotropnoi funkeii gipofiza pod vlijaniem tiouracila v uslovijah razlicnogo svetovogo rezima. (The effect of thiouracil on the gonadotropic activity of the pituitary under different light regimes.) *Bjull. eksp. Biol. Med.*, **24**, 253.

VOLSOE, H. (1944). Structure and seasonal variation of the male reproductive organs of *Vipera berus* (Linnæus). *Spolia zool. Mus. Hauniensis*, **5**, 1.

VOOUS, K. K. (1950). The breeding seasons of birds in Indonesia. *Ibis*, **92**, 279.

WALDO, C. M. & WISLOCKI, G. B. (1951). Observations on the shedding of the antlers of Virginia deer (*Odocoileus virginianus borealis*). *Amer. J. Anat.* **88**, 351.

WALLACE, A. R. (1889). *Darwinism.* London.

WALLACE, R. (1907). *Farm livestock of Great Britain.* 4th Ed. London.

WALMESLEY-WHITE, W. (1931). *Bird life in Devon.* London.

WALTON, A. (1938). On the eclipse plumage of the mallard (*Anas platyrhyncha platyrhyncha*). *J. exp. Biol.*, **14**, 440.

WARING, H., LANDGREBE, F. W., & NEILL, R. M. (1941). Ovulation and oviposition in Anura. *J. exp. Biol.*, **18**, 11.

WARREN, D. C. & SCOTT, H. M. (1936). Influence of light on ovulation in the fowl. *J. exp. Zool.*, **74**, 137.

WATSON, J. S. (1954). Breeding season of the wild rabbit in New Zealand. *Nature, Lond.*, **174**, 608.

WATSON, R. H. & RADFORD, H. M. (1955). A note on the hours of daylight associated with the seasonal increase in sexual activity in Merino ewes. *Aust. vet. J.* **31**, 31.

WATZKA, M. (1940). Mikroskopisch-anatomische Untersuchungen über die Ranzzeit und Tragendauer des Hermelins (*Putorius ermineus*). *Ztschr. f. mikr.-anat. Forsch.*, **48**, 359.

WEISMAN, A. I., & COATES, C. W. (1944a). Effect of illumination on the egg-extrusion reaction of *Xenopus laevis* in the frog test for pregnancy. *Endocrinology*, **35**, 68.

—— —— (1944b). The African frog (*Xenopus laevis*) in pregnancy diagnosis. *Res. Bull. N.Y. Biol. Res. Foundation.*

WELLS, L. J. (1935). Seasonal sexual rhythm and its experimental modification in the male of the thirteen-lined ground squirrel (*Citellus tridecemlineatus*). *Anat. Rec.*, **62**, 409.

—— (1936). Prolongation of breeding capacity in males of an annual breeding wild rodent (*Citellus tridecemlineatus*) by constant low temperature. *Anat. Rec.*, **64**, 38.

—— & ZALESKY, M. (1940). Effects of low environmental temperature on the reproductive organs of male mammals with annual aspermia. *Amer. J. Anat.*, **66**, 429.

WERNER, S. C. (1939). Failure of gonadotrophic function of the rat hypophysis during chronic inanition. *Proc. Soc. exp. Biol., N.Y.*, **4**, 101.

WESTMAN, A., & JACOBSOHN, D. (1937). Experimentelle Untersuchungen über die Bedeutung des Hypophysenzwischen-hirnsystems für die Produktion gonadotroper Hormone des Hypophysenvorder-lappens. *Acta obst. gynec. Scand.*, **17**, 235.

—— —— (1938). Endocrinologische Untersuchungen an Ratten mit durchtrenntem Hypophysenstiel, 4. Mitteilung: Die Genitalverhänderungen der Ratten mannchen. *Acta path. microbiol. Scand.*, **15**, 301.

—— —— (1940). Endocrinologische Untersuchungen an Kaninchen mit durchtrennten Hypophysen-stiel. *Acta obstet. gynec. Scand.*, **20**, 392.

WHETHAM, E. O. (1933). Factors modifying egg production with special reference to seasonal changes. *J. agric. Sci.*, **23**, 303.

WHITAKER, W. L. (1936). Effect of light on reproductive cycle of *Peromyscus leucopus noveboracensis. Proc. Soc. exp. Biol., N.Y.*, **34**, 329.

—— (1940). Some effects of artificial illumination on reproduction in the white-footed mouse, *Peromyscus leucopus noveboracensis. J. exper. Zool.*, **83**, 33.

WHITE, S. A. (1921). A central Australian expedition. *Emu*, **21**, 84.

WHITELAW, J. (1956). Delay in ovulation and menstruation induced by chlorpromazine. *J. clin. Endocrin.*, **16**, 972.

WHITLOCK, F. L. (1924). Journey to Central Australia in search of the night parrot. *Emu*, **23**, 248.

WHITMAN, C. O. (1919). *The behaviour of pigeons.* (Posthumous works.) The Carnegie Institution of Washington.

WHITTEN, W. K. (1959). Occurrence of anoestrus in mice caged in groups. *J. Endocrin.*, **18**, 102.

WIGGLESWORTH, V. B. (1942). *The principles of insect physiology.* London.

WINGSTRAND, K. G. (1951). *The structure and development of the avian pituitary.* Lund.

WINTERBOTTOM, J. M. (1929). Studies in sexual phenomena. VI. Communal display in birds. *Proc. zool. Soc. Lond.,* 189.

WISLOCKI, G. B. (1937). The vascular supply of the hypophysis cerebri of the cat. *Anat. Rec.,* **69,** 361.

—— (1943). Studies on growth of deer antlers: II. Seasonal changes in the male reproductive tract of the Virginia deer (*Odocoileus virginianus borealis*); with a discussion of the factors controlling the antler-gonad periodicity. *Essays in Biology,* pp. 629–654. Berkeley and Los Angeles.

—— AUB, J. C., & WALDO, C. M. (1947). The effect of gonadectomy and the administration of testosterone propionate on the growth of antlers, in male and female deer. *Endocrinology,* **40,** 202.

—— & KING, L. S. (1936). The permeability of the hypophysis and hypothalamus to vital dyes, with a study of the hypophysial vascular supply. *Amer. J. Anat.,* **58,** 421.

WITHERBY, H. F. (1938–1941). *The handbook of British birds.* London.

WITSCHI. E. (1935). Seasonal sex characters in birds and their hormonal control. *Wilson Bull.,* **47,** 177.

—— (1937). Comparative physiology of the hypophysis. *Cold Spr. Harb. Symp. quant. Biol.,* **5,** 180.

WOITKEWITSCH, A. A. (1945). Seasonal sexual cycle in *Sciurus Vulgaris* L. stimulated by means of light. *C. R. acad. Sci. URSS.,* **42,** 71.

WOLFSON, A. (1941). Light versus activity in the regulation of the sexual cycles of birds: the role of the hypothalamus. *Condor,* **43,** 125.

—— (1942). Regulation of spring migration in juncos. *Condor,* **44,** 237.

—— (1945). The rôle of pituitary fat deposition and body weight in bird migration. *Condor,* **47,** 95.

—— (1949a). Further studies on the relation between wakefulness and the gonadal cycle in birds. *Anat. Rec.,* **105,** 603.

—— (1949b). The relation of daylength and gonadal regression to post-nuptial moult in the white-throated sparrow and other fringillids. *Anat. Rec.,* **105,** 522.

—— (1952a). Daylength, migration and breeding cycles in birds. *Sci. Mon., N.Y.,* **74,** 191.

—— (1952b). The occurrence and regulation of the refractory period in the gonadal and fat cycles of the Junco. *J. exp. Zool.,* **121,** 311.

—— (1953). Gonadal and fat response to a 5:1 ratio of light to darkness in the white-throated sparrow. *Condor,* **55,** 187.

—— (1959). Ecologic and physiologic factors in the regulation of spring migration and reproductive cycle in birds. In: *Comparative Endocrinology,* A. Gorbman, Ed., p. 38, New York and London.

WOODBURY, A. M. (1941). Animal migration—periodic-response theory. *Auk,* **58,** 463.

WORTHINGTON, W. C., Jr. (1955). Some observations on hypophysial portal system in living mouse. *Bull. Johns Hopk. Hosp.,* **97,** 343.

WRIGHT, P. L. (1942a). A correlation between the spring mult and spring changes in the sexual cycle in the weasel. *J. exp. Zool.,* **91,** 103.

—— (1942b). Delayed implantation in the long-tailed weasel (*Mustela frenata*), the short-tailed weasel (*Mustela cicognani*), and the marten (*Martes Americana*). *Anat. Rec.,* **83,** 341.

WYNNE-EDWARDS, V. C. (1930). On the waking-time of the nightjar (*Caprimulgus europaeus*). *J. exp. Biol.,* **7,** 241.

YAKHONTOV, V. V. (1945). On the internal secretion of insects. *C. R. acad. Sci. URSS.,* **46,** 127.

YARRELL, W. (1882). *British birds.* 4th Ed. London.

YEATES, G. K. (1934). *The life of the rook.* London.

YEATES, N. T. M. (1947). Influence of variation in length of day upon the breeding season in sheep. *Nature, Lond.,* **160,** 429.

—— (1948). Modification of breeding season in the sheep. *Brit. Sci. News,* **1.**

YEATES, N. T. M. (1949a). The breeding season of the sheep with particular reference to its modification by artificial means using light. *J. agric. Sci.*, **39,** 1.

—— (1949b). Vlijanie izmenenii svetovogo rezima ovec na vremja nastuplenija i prodolziteljnostj ih slucnogo sezona. (The influence of variation in length of day upon the breeding season in sheep.) *Agrobiologija*, 1948 (2), 133.

—— (1953). The effect of high air temperature on reproduction in the ewe. *J. agric. Sci.*, **43,** 199.

—— (1954). Daylight changes. In: J. Hammond, Ed. *Progress in the physiology of farm animals.* Vol. 1, Chapter 8., p. 363. London.

YOSHIOKA, Z., AWASAWA, T., & SUZUKI, S. (1952). Effect of the short day treatment on the modification of the breeding season in goats. *Bull. nat. Inst. agric. Sci.* (*Chiba*), Series G (Animal Husbandry), No. 1, 111.

ZAHL, P. A. (1937). Cytologische Untersuchungen über die Hypophysis cerebri des weiblichen Frosches. Unter besonderer Berücksichtigung der Fortpflanzungstätigkeit. *Z. Mikr. -anat. Forsch.*, **41,** 303.

ZALESKY, M., & WELLS, L. S. (1940). Effect of low environmental temperature on the thyroid and adrenal glands of the ground squirrel. *Citellus tridecemlineatus.* *Physiol. Zool.*, **13,** 268.

ZEUNER, F. E. (1960). *A history of domesticated animals.* London.

ZIEGLER, L. (1843). *Beobachtungen über die Brunst und den Embryo der Rehe.* Hanover.

ZUCKERMAN, S. (1931). The menstrual cycle of the primates. Part III. The alleged breeding season of primates with special reference to the Chacma baboon (*Papio porcarius*). *Proc. zool. Soc. Lond.*, 325.

—— (1932a). *The social life of monkeys and apes.* London.

—— (1932b). The menstrual cycle of the primates. VI. Further observations on the breeding of primates, with special reference to the suborders *Lemuroidea* and *Tarsioidea P.* *Proc. zool. Soc. Lond.*, **102,** 1059.

—— (1938). Uterine bleeding after neural lesions. In: *Les Hormones sexuelles.* Edited by L. Brouha. Paris.

—— (1953). The breeding season of animals in captivity. *Proc. zool. Soc. Lond.*, **122,** 827.

—— (1954a). The secretions of the brain: relation of hypothalamus to pituitary gland. *Lancet*, **1,** 789.

—— (1954b). Hypothalamic-anterior pituitary relations. *Pubbl. Staz. zool. Napoli.*, **24,** Suppl., p. 21.

—— (1955a). Biology of the oestrogens. *Brit. med. Bull.*, **11,** 111.

—— (1955b). The possible functional significance of the pituitary portal vessels. In: G. E. W. Wolstenholme, Ed. *Human adrenal cortex. Ciba Foundation Colloquia on Endocrinology*, Vol. VIII, p. 551. London.

ZWARENSTEIN, H., & SHAPIRO, H. A. (1933). Metabolic changes associated with endocrine activity and the reproductive cycle in *Xenopus laevis.* 3. Changes in the calcium content of the serum associated with captivity and the normal reproductive cycle. *J. exp. Biol.*, **10,** 372.

A

B

C

D

E

F

G

H

L

N

O

P

Q

R

S

T

U

V

W

SUBJECT INDEX

female, hypophysectomy in, 503; immature male, hypophysectomy in, 498, 499; implantation and injection of amphibian pituitary gland material in, 503–506; injection of gonadotrophins from vertebrates other than amphibia in, 506–510; interstitial tissue and secondary sex characters of, 510; mature male, hypophysectomy in, 495–498; ovaries of, 483; ovarian hormones in, 519–523; pelvic glands of, 488; photostimulation and sexual periodicity in, 745, 746; pituitary and reproduction in, 495–510; pituitary gland in, 491–495; pregnancy diagnosis tests with, 164, 165; primary sex-differentiation in, 523–529; reproductive hormones of, 480–529; seasonal growth-cycle of oviducts in, 520; secondary sexual characters of, 487–491; sex-determination in, 527, 529; sexual periodicity in, 727, 728; testicular hormones in, 510–519; transplantation of testes in, 513–516; urogenital system in, 482

Amphibian larvae, treatment with steroid hormones, 527

Amphibians: artificial insemination in, 164–166; spermatozoa of, 164–166

Amphimixis, 311

Amphotoky, 384

Amplection, 131

Ampulla, 134

Anaesthetics, as egg-activating agents, 389, 390

Anaphase, 48

Anas platyrhynchos: plumage cycles of, 589; sexual cycle in, 760

Andragamone II, 324, 325

Andragamone III, 326

Androgenesis: effects of various agents on, 382; effect of X-irradiation on, 382; mechanically induced, 381; possible, in rat and mouse, 381

Androgenesis and gynogenesis, 380–383

Androgenic activity, International Standard for, 629

Androgens: activity of, as determined by tests on comb growth, 631; assay and relative activity on birds, 626–635; avian, source of, 602; biological action of, in birds, 614–635; biological, in relation to biochemical assay, 629; effect of method of administration on absolute and relative activity, 632; effect on accessory organs in birds, 624; effects of, in fish, 471–475; effects on ovaries of fish, 472, 473; effect on peck order in birds, 624, 625; effects on secondary sexual characters in fish, 473–475; effects on secondary sexual characters in reptiles, 551, 552; effects on sexual structures in developing reptiles, 547–552; effects on testes of hypophysectomised fish, 471, 472; injection of, in Amphibia, 516–519; injection and implantation of, in elasmobranchii, 439; injection of, in reptiles, 547–552; prolongation of effect on birds, 632–634; relation between chemical configuration and biological activity of, 629–631; relative activity in mammals and birds, 629, 635; secretion, in young birds, 611, 612; specificity of androgenic activity in birds, 634;

Andromerogeny, 381

Androsterone-testosterone series, compounds of, 629–631

Anguilla, implantation of pituitary glands in, 460

Anguilla anguilla: effect of chorionic gonadotrophin in, 465, 466; pituitary of, 453

Anguis: effects of castration in, 543; hermaphroditism in, 547

Anguis fragilis: injection of human pregnancy urine in, 542; injection of pituitary material into, 540; sex dimorphism in, 532, 533

Anhydroxyprogesterone, effect on sex differentiation in *S. caniculus*, 441

Anolis: effects of ovariectomy in, 546; pituitary gland of, 536; sex dimorphism in, 534

Anolis carolinensis: effects of androgen treatment in, 551; effects of castration in, 544; effects of oestrogen treatment in, 554, 556; effects of ovariectomy in, 546; effects of testosterone treatment of, 550; injection of chorionic gonadotrophin in, 542; injection of pituitary material into, 540, 541; pituitary gland of, 535; photostimulation of, 746; sexual cycle in, 728

"Antagglutin" in semen, 325

Anteater, spiny: germinal disc in, 344; pronucleus in, 361; spermatozoa of, 3; syngamy in, 363

Antelope madoqua, courtship display of, 721

Antelopes, breeding habits of, 719

Anterior lobe pituitary extract (ALP), effects of, in fish, 462

Antibodies to spermatozoa, 31, 213–217

Antibiotics: addition to semen, 186, 198, 199; effects on spermatozoa, 294, 295; use in diluents for semen, 294, 295

Antifertilisins, 324, 325

Antigenic incompatibility, of spermatozoa, 42

Antigenic properties of spermatozoa, 213–217

Antigenic specificity of spermatozoa, 30–32

Antigens, spermatozoal, 213–217

Anti-testis reaction, 90, 91

Antler cycles in deer, 740, 741

Anurans: colour dimorphism in, 491; effects of castration in, 512, 513; effects of ovariectomy in, 520; interspecific fertilisation in, 41; male reproductive ducts in, 483; pituitary gland in, 492; secondary sexual characters of, 488–491; testes of, 481, 512; vocal sacs of, 491

Apes, sexual behaviour in, 132

Apis mellifera, polyspermy in, 372

Apoda: pituitary gland in, 492; reproductive physiology of, 480

Apodemus, genus, perforatorium in, 10

Apodemus flavicollis, size of spermatozoon, 6

Apodemus sylvaticus, size of spermatozoon, 6

Aptenodytes forsteri, broodiness and parental care in, 677

Arbacia, oxygen consumption of eggs of, 346

Arginine: content of mammalian spermatozoa, 22, 23; content of spermatozoon nuclei, 21; in abnormal spermatozoa, 35

Armadillo: parthenogenesis in, 385; polar bodies in, 350; pronuclei in, 361

Arrhenotoky, 384

Arsenic, effect on spermatogenesis, 89

Arthroleptella lightfooti, colour dimorphism in, 491

Artificial insemination, in birds, 166–169

Ascaphus, intromittent organ in, 491

Ascaris: fate of spermatozoon components in, 343; fertilisation in, 314; polyspermic eggs of, 362; pronuclei in, 361; syngamy in, 363

Aspermatogenesis, production by spermatozoa and testis tissue, 90, 91

Aster 313; growth of, 361, 362

Asterias: fertilisation in, 329; fertilisation membrane in, 331; polyspermy in, 335